Conversion Factors from BG to SI Units (Continued)

	To Convert from	To	Multiply by
Pressure	lbf/ft^2	Pa	4.7880 E + 1
	lbf/in^2	Pa	6.8948 E + 3
	atm	Pa	1.0133 E + 5
	mm Hg	Pa	1.3332 E + 2
Specific weight	lbf/ft^3	N/m^3	1.5709 E + 2
Specific heat	$ft^2/(s^2 \cdot {}^\circ R)$	$m^2/(s^2 \cdot K)$	1.6723 E − 1
Temperature	$^\circ F$	$^\circ C$	$t_C = \frac{5}{9}(t_F - 32^\circ)$
	$^\circ R$	K	0.5556
Velocity	ft/s	m/s	0.3048
	mi/h	m/s	4.4704 E − 1
	knot	m/s	5.1444 E − 1
Viscosity	$lbf \cdot s/ft^2$	$N \cdot s/m^2$	4.7880 E + 1
	$g/(cm \cdot s)$	$N \cdot s/m^2$	0.1
Volume	ft^3	m^3	2.8317 E − 2
	L	m^3	0.001
	gal (U.S.)	m^3	3.7854 E − 3
	fluid ounce (U.S.)	m^3	2.9574 E − 5
Volume flow	ft^3/s	m^3/s	2.8317 E − 2
	gal/min	m^3/s	6.3090 E − 5

Fluid Mechanics

ALSO AVAILABLE FROM McGRAW-HILL

SCHAUM'S OUTLINE SERIES IN MECHANICAL ENGINEERING

Most outlines include basic theory, definitions, hundreds of example problems solved in step-by-step detail, and supplementary problems with answers.

RELATED TITLES ON THE CURRENT LIST INCLUDE:
Acoustics
Continuum Mechanics
Elementary Statics & Strength of Materials
Engineering Economics
Engineering Mechanics
Engineering Thermodynamics
Fluid Dynamics
Fluid Mechanics & Hydraulics
Heat Transfer
Lagrangian Dynamics
Machine Design
Mathematical Handbook of Formulas & Tables
Mechanical Vibrations
Operations Research
Statics and Mechanics of Materials
Strength of Materials
Theoretical Mechanics
Thermodynamics with Chemical Applications

SCHAUM'S SOLVED PROBLEMS BOOKS

Each title in this series is a complete and expert source of solved problems with solutions worked out in step-by-step detail.

RELATED TITLES ON THE CURRENT LIST INCLUDE:
3000 Solved Problems in Calculus
2500 Solved Problems in Differential Equations
2500 Solved Problems in Fluid Mechanics & Hydraulics
1000 Solved Problems in Heat Transfer
3000 Solved Problems in Linear Algebra
2000 Solved Problems in Mechanical Engineering Thermodynamics
2000 Solved Problems in Numerical Analysis
700 Solved Problems in Vector Mechanics for Engineers: Dynamics
800 Solved Problems in Vector Mechanics for Engineers: Statics

Available at most college bookstores, or for a complete list of titles and prices, write to:

Schaum Division
McGraw-Hill, Inc.
Princeton Road, S-1
Hightstown, NJ 08520

Fluid Mechanics

THIRD EDITION

Frank M. White

UNIVERSITY OF RHODE ISLAND

McGRAW-HILL, INC.

NEW YORK   ST. LOUIS   SAN FRANCISCO   AUCKLAND   BOGOTÁ   CARACAS

LISBON   LONDON   MADRID   MEXICO CITY   MILAN   MONTREAL   NEW DELHI

SAN JUAN   SINGAPORE   SYDNEY   TOKYO   TORONTO

FLUID MECHANICS

Copyright © 1994, 1986, 1979 by McGraw-Hill, Inc. All rights reserved. Printed in the United States of America. Except as permitted under the United States Copyright Act of 1976, no part of this publication may be reproduced or distributed in any form or by any means, or stored in a data base or retrieval system, without the prior written permission of the publisher.

This book is printed on acid-free paper.

1 2 3 4 5 6 7 8 9 0   DOC/DOC   9 9 8 7 6 5

P/N 069714-0
PART OF
ISBN 0-07-911695-7

This book was set in Times Roman by CRWaldman Graphic Communications.
The editors were John J. Corrigan and David A. Damstra;
the designer was Hermann Strohbach;
the production supervisor was Leroy A. Young.
New drawings were done by Fine Line Illustrations, Inc.
R. R. Donnelley & Sons Company was printer and binder.

Cover photo by David Fuciarelli and Helen L. Reed.

Library of Congress Cataloging-in-Publication Data

White, Frank M.
    Fluid mechanics / Frank M. White.—3rd ed.
      p.   cm.
    Includes bibliographical references and index.
    ISBN 0-07-911695-7 (set)
    1. Fluid mechanics.   I. Title.
  TA367.W48   1994
  620.1'06—dc20   93-26501

INTERNATIONAL EDITION

Copyright 1994. Exclusive rights by McGraw-Hill, Inc. for manufacture and export. This book cannot be re-exported from the country to which it is consigned by McGraw-Hill. The International Edition is not available in North America.

When ordering this title, use ISBN 0-07-113765-3.

About the Author

Frank M. White, a native of Augusta, Georgia, went to undergraduate school at Georgia Tech and received a B.M.E. degree in 1954. He then attended the Massachusetts Institute of Technology for an S.M. degree in 1956, returning to Georgia Tech to earn a Ph.D. in mechanical engineering in 1959. He began teaching aerospace engineering at Georgia Tech in 1957 and went to the University of Rhode Island in 1964, where he continues to serve as professor of mechanical and ocean engineering.

At the University of Rhode Island, he became interested in oceanographic and coastal flow problems and in 1966 helped found the first department of ocean engineering in the United States. His research interests have always been in shear layers and convection heat transfer. Known primarily as a teacher and writer, he has received the ASEE Westinghouse Teaching Excellence Award in addition to six University of Rhode Island teaching awards. His research accomplishments include some 80 technical papers and reports and the 1973 ASME Lewis F. Moody Research Award in Fluids Engineering. He has written three undergraduate textbooks: *Fluid Mechanics, Heat Transfer,* and *Heat and Mass Transfer.*

During 1979–1990 he was editor in chief of the ASME *Journal of Fluids Engineering* and now serves as chairman of the ASME Publications Committee. In 1986 he was named a Fellow of ASME and in 1991 received the ASME Fluids Engineering Award. He lives with his wife, Jeanne, in Narragansett, Rhode Island.

To Jeanne

Contents

Preface

The third edition of this textbook sees additions and deletions but no philosophical change. The basic outline of eleven chapters and five appendixes remains the same. The triad of integral, differential, and experimental approaches is retained. The informal, student-oriented style is retained. On the other hand, many problem exercises and some fully worked examples have been changed, and a number of new photographs and figures have been added.

The total number of problem exercises continues to increase, from 1089 in the first edition, to 1169 in the second, to 1392 in this third edition. About 750, or 53 percent, of the present problems are new. Also new to this edition are ninety-one word problems, or ''thought exercises,'' and, also a first, there are nine design projects: more extensive, open-ended exercises which challenge the student to obtain parameter studies and flow optimizations without knowing any obvious exact ''answers.''

There are some revisions in every chapter, with the most extensive being in Chapters 3, 4, 7, 8, and 10. Chapter 1—which is purely introductory and could be assigned as reading—continues to be toned down from earlier editions. I am trying to accept the constant reviewer suggestions that this chapter can do without such detailed discussions.

Chapter 2 is improved by a better discussion of the stability of floating bodies, with a simpler procedure for computing the metacentric height. Coverage is confined to static fluids and rigid-body motions.

Chapter 3 has been rearranged so that Bernoulli's equation comes *last*, after control-volume mass, linear momentum, angular momentum, and energy studies. I know that some texts have an entire chapter on the Bernoulli equation, but it is a dangerously restrictive relation which is often misused by both students and graduate engineers.

Chapter 4 used to be confined solely to the basic partial differential equations of fluid mechanics, but now a few *solutions* are included also, for both potential flow and viscous flow. This meant bringing forward some viscous material from Chapter 6 and some inviscid flow from Chapter 8. Both reviewers and students complained that they wanted to see some applied results right after covering the equations themselves. If you disagree with this, just hold back and treat Sections 4.10 and 4.11 later in your course.

Chapter 5 has been slightly modified to approach dimensional analysis from the point of view of selecting *scaling variables* before using the pi theorem. Students have always complained that the pi theorem is too ambiguous, leading to a multitude of different parameter groups. By deciding in advance how to scale and present the data, the ambiguity is reduced or eliminated. Section 5.6, on ''inventive use of the data,'' has been eliminated, made unnecessary by scaling concepts.

In Chapter 6, Section 6.5 on "alternate forms of the Moody chart" has been dropped and replaced by a standard presentation of the three basic pipe-flow computations: pressure drop, flow rate, and pipe sizing. I liked the "alternate forms," obviously, but no one else did. I have also introduced some newer types of flow meters for further enrichment.

Chapter 8 now picks up from the sample plane potential flows of Section 4.10 and plunges right into inviscid-flow analysis. The method of *boundary elements* is now introduced briefly because it is a simple and powerful technique which is very popular in industry.

In the study of gradually varied open-channel flow, Section 10.6, the older tabular method of computation has been replaced by a direct numerical integration. Students are now quite familiar with numerical techniques such as Runge-Kutta and need not use a table or spreadsheet.

Some additional fluid properties and correlation formulas have been included in the appendixes, which are otherwise much the same.

This text now includes some elegant software, prepared by Password, Inc., of Baltimore, Maryland, to help the student learn fluid mechanics and to illustrate certain topics. A diskette is included in the back of the book and is available for both Macintosh and PC Windows systems. The software is divided into seven numbered sections, or scenarios, as follows:

1. Viscosity and density of gases at various temperatures.
2. Viscosity and density of liquids at various temperatures.
3. Hydrostatic pressure and force on immersed plates.
4. Force required to support a fluid jet turning through an angle.
5. Three types of pipe flow calculations using the Moody chart:
    a. Pressure drop for known flow rate and pipe size.
    b. Flow rate for known pressure drop and pipe size.
    c. Pipe size for known flow rate and pressure drop.
6. Plane potential flow patterns illustrated in detail:
    a. A source near a plane wall.
    b. Two equal vortices of like sense.
    c. Two equal vortices of unlike sense.
    d. The Rankine oval of arbitrary aspect ratio.
7. Compressible flow of an ideal gas:
    a. Isentropic nozzle flow with area changes.
    b. The normal shock wave.
    c. Constant-area duct flow with friction.
    d. Constant-area frictionless duct flow with heat transfer.
    e. Oblique shock waves.
    f. Prandtl-Meyer supersonic expansion waves.

When one of these topics appears in the text, a numbered computer-disk icon will appear in the text margin to key the reader toward the software. I have found this software to be very helpful and educational, and recommend that it be installed and used in your course. It is quite easy to use.

So many people have helped me that I cannot remember or list them all. I would like especially to express my appreciation to the reviewers and correspondents who gave detailed suggestions: A. J. Baker, University of Tennessee; John R. Biddle, California Polytechnic University; David Caughey, Cornell University; John M. Cimbala, Pennsylvania State University; M. E. Clark, University of Illinois; Martin Crawford, University of Alabama at Birmingham; Robert M. Hartman, Widener University; Jacques Lewalle, Syracuse University; George C. Lindauer, University of Louisville; D. E. Richards, Rose-Hulman; Richard F. Salant, Georgia Tech; Alexander J. Smits, Princeton University; and R. J. Sobey, University of California at Berkeley. Finally, I continue to enjoy the support of my wife and family in these writing efforts.

Frank M. White

Fluid Mechanics

Chapter 1
Introduction

Fluid mechanics is the study of fluids either in motion (fluid *dynamics*) or at rest (fluid *statics*) and the subsequent effects of the fluid on the boundaries, which may be either solid surfaces or other fluids. Both gases and liquids are classified as fluids, and the number of fluids engineering applications is enormous: breathing, blood flow, swimming, pumps, fans, turbines, airplanes, ships, rivers, windmills, pipes, missiles, icebergs, engines, filters, jets, and sprinklers, to name a few. When you think about it, almost everything on this planet either is a fluid or moves with respect to a fluid.

The essence of the subject of fluid flow is a judicious compromise between theory and experiment. Since fluid flow is a branch of mechanics, it satisfies a set of well-documented basic conservation laws, and thus a great deal of theoretical treatment is available. The theory is often frustrating, however, because it applies mainly to certain idealized situations which may be invalid in practical problems. The two chief obstacles to a workable theory are geometry and viscosity. The general theory of fluid motion (Chap. 4) is too difficult to enable the user to attack arbitrary geometric configurations, so that most textbooks concentrate on flat plates, circular pipes, and other easy geometries. It is possible to apply numerical techniques to arbitrary geometries, and specialized textbooks are now appearing which explain these digital-computer approximations [1, 2].[1] This book will present many theoretical results while keeping their limitations in mind.

The second obstacle to a workable theory is the action of viscosity, which can be neglected only in certain idealized flows (Chap. 8). First, viscosity increases the difficulty of the basic equations, although the boundary-layer approximation found by Ludwig Prandtl in 1904 (Chap. 7) has greatly simplified viscous-flow analyses. Second, viscosity has a destabilizing effect on all fluids, giving rise, at frustratingly small velocities, to a disorderly, random phenomenon called *turbulence*. The theory of turbulent flow is crude and heavily backed up by experiment (Chap. 6), yet it can be quite serviceable as an engineering estimate. Textbooks are beginning to present digital-computer techniques for turbulent-flow analysis [3], but they are based strictly upon empirical assumptions regarding the time mean of the turbulent stress field.

Thus there is theory available for fluid-flow problems, but in all cases it should be

---

[1] Numbered references appear at the end of each chapter.

backed up by experiment. Often the experimental data provide the main source of information about specific flows, such as the drag and lift of immersed bodies (Chap. 7). Fortunately, fluid mechanics is a highly visual subject, with good instrumentation [4, 5], and the use of dimensional analysis and modeling concepts (Chap. 5) is widespread. Thus experimentation provides a natural and easy complement to the theory. Appendix C lists a variety of interesting films which have been prepared to visualize fluid-flow phenomena. You should keep in mind that theory and experiment should go hand in hand in all studies of fluid mechanics.

1.2 The Concept of a Fluid

From the point of view of fluid mechanics, all matter consists of only two states, fluid and solid. The difference between the two is perfectly obvious to the lay person, and it is an interesting exercise to ask a lay person to put this difference into words. The technical distinction lies with the reaction of the two to an applied shear or tangential stress. *A solid can resist a shear stress by a static deformation; a fluid cannot.* Any shear stress applied to a fluid, no matter how small, will result in motion of that fluid. The fluid moves and deforms continuously as long as the shear stress is applied. As a corollary, we can say that a fluid at rest must be in a state of zero shear stress, a state often called the hydrostatic stress condition in structural analysis. In this condition, Mohr's circle for stress reduces to a point, and there is no shear stress on any plane cut through the element under stress.

Given the definition of a fluid above, every lay person also knows that there are two classes of fluids, *liquids* and *gases*. Again the distinction is a technical one concerning the effect of cohesive forces. A liquid, being composed of relatively close-packed molecules with strong cohesive forces, tends to retain its volume and will form a free surface in a gravitational field if unconfined from above. Free-surface flows are dominated by gravitational effects and are studied in Chaps. 5 and 10. Since gas molecules are widely spaced with negligible cohesive forces, a gas is free to expand until it encounters confining walls. A gas has no definite volume, and when left to itself without confinement, a gas forms an atmosphere which is essentially hydrostatic. The hydrostatic behavior of liquids and gases is taken up in Chap. 2. Gases cannot form a free surface, and thus gas flows are rarely concerned with gravitational effects other than buoyancy.

Figure 1.1 illustrates a solid block resting on a rigid plane and stressed by its own weight. The solid sags into a static deflection, shown as a highly exaggerated dashed line, resisting shear without flow. A free-body diagram of element A on the side of the block shows that there is shear in the block along a plane cut at an angle θ through A. Since the block sides are unsupported, element A has zero stress on the left and right sides and compression stress $\sigma = -p$ on the top and bottom. Mohr's circle does not reduce to a point, and there is nonzero shear stress in the block.

By contrast, the liquid and gas at rest in Fig. 1.1 require the supporting walls in order to eliminate shear stress. The walls exert a compression stress of $-p$ and reduce Mohr's circle to a point with zero shear everywhere, i.e., the hydrostatic condition. The liquid retains its volume and forms a free surface in the container. If the walls are removed, shear develops in the liquid and a big splash results. If the container is tilted, shear again develops, waves form, and the free surface seeks a horizontal configuration, pouring out over the lip if necessary. Meanwhile, the gas is unrestrained and expands out of the container, filling all available space. Element A in the gas is also hydrostatic

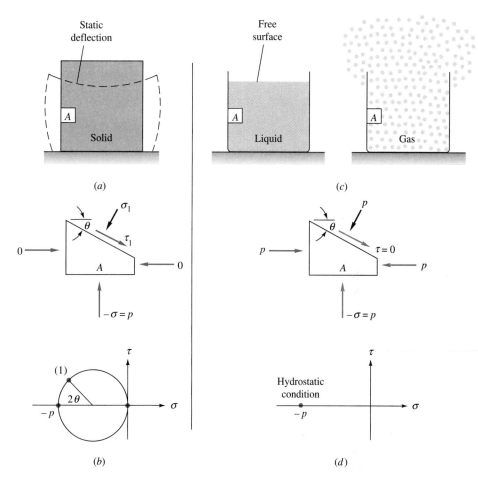

Fig. 1.1 A solid at rest can resist shear. (*a*) Static deflection of the solid; (*b*) equilibrium and Mohr's circle for solid element *A*. A fluid cannot resist shear. (*c*) Containing walls are needed; (*d*) equilibrium and Mohr's circle for fluid element *A*.

and exerts a compression stress $-p$ on the walls.

In the above discussion, clear decisions could be made about solids, liquids, and gases. Most engineering fluid-mechanics problems deal with these clear cases, i.e., the common liquids, such as water, oil, mercury, gasoline, and alcohol, and the common gases, such as air, helium, hydrogen, and steam, in their common temperature and pressure ranges. There are many borderline cases, however, of which you should be aware. Some apparently "solid" substances such as asphalt and lead resist shear stress for short periods but actually deform slowly and exhibit definite fluid behavior over long periods. Other substances, notably colloid and slurry mixtures, resist small shear stresses but "yield" at large stress and begin to flow as fluids do. Specialized textbooks are devoted to this study of more general deformation and flow, a field called *rheology* [6]. Also, liquids and gases can coexist in two-phase mixtures, such as steam-water mixtures or water with entrapped air bubbles. Specialized textbooks present the analysis of such *two-phase flows* [7]. Finally, there are situations where the distinction between a liquid and a gas blurs. This is the case at temperatures and pressures above the so-called *critical point* of a substance, where only a single phase exists, primarily resembling a gas. As pressure increases far above the critical point, the gaslike substance becomes so dense that there is some resemblance to a liquid and the usual thermodynamic approximations like the perfect-gas law become inaccurate. The critical temperature and pressure of water are $T_c = 647$ K and $p_c = 219$ atm,[1] so that typical problems involving water and steam are below the critical point. Air, being a mixture of gases, has no distinct critical point, but its principal component, nitrogen, has $T_c = 126$ K and $p_c = 34$ atm. Thus typical problems involving air are in the range of high temperature and low pressure where air is distinctly and definitely a gas. This text will be concerned solely with clearly identifiable liquids and gases, and the borderline cases discussed above will be beyond our scope.

1.3 The Fluid as a Continuum

We have already used technical terms such as *fluid pressure* and *density* without a rigorous discussion of their definition. As far as we know, fluids are aggregations of molecules, widely spaced for a gas, closely spaced for a liquid. The distance between molecules is very large compared with the molecular diameter. The molecules are not fixed in a lattice but move about freely relative to each other. Thus fluid density, or mass per unit volume, has no precise meaning because the number of molecules occupying a given volume continually changes. This effect becomes unimportant if the unit volume is large compared with, say, the cube of the molecular spacing, when the number of molecules within the volume will remain nearly constant in spite of the enormous interchange of particles across the boundaries. If, however, the chosen unit volume is too large, there could be a noticeable variation in the bulk aggregation of the particles. This situation is illustrated in Fig. 1.2, where the "density" as calculated from molecular mass δm within a given volume δV is plotted versus the size of the unit volume. There is a limiting volume δV^* below which molecular variations may be important and above which aggregate variations may be important. The *density* ρ of a fluid is best defined as

$$\rho = \lim_{\delta V \to \delta V^*} \frac{\delta m}{\delta V} \tag{1.1}$$

The limiting volume δV^* is about 10^{-9} mm³ for all liquids and for gases at atmospheric pressure. For example, 10^{-9} mm³ of air at standard conditions contains approximately

---

[1] One atmosphere equals 2116 lbf/ft² = 101,300 Pa.

Fig. 1.2 The limit definition of continuum fluid density: (*a*) an elemental volume in a fluid region of variable continuum density; (*b*) calculated density versus size of the elemental volume.

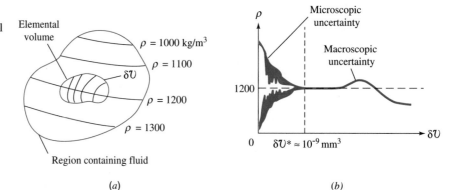

Elemental volume

$\rho = 1000$ kg/m³

$\rho = 1100$

δV

$\rho = 1200$

$\rho = 1300$

Region containing fluid

(*a*)

ρ

Microscopic uncertainty

Macroscopic uncertainty

1200

0    $\delta V^* \approx 10^{-9}$ mm³ δV

(*b*)

3×10^7 molecules, which is sufficient to define a nearly constant density according to Eq. (1.1). Most engineering problems are concerned with physical dimensions much larger than this limiting volume, so that density is essentially a point function and fluid properties can be thought of as varying continually in space, as sketched in Fig. 1.2*a*. Such a fluid is called a *continuum*, which simply means that its variation in properties is so smooth that the differential calculus can be used to analyze the substance. We shall assume that continuum calculus is valid for all the analyses in this book. Again there are borderline cases for gases at such low pressures that molecular spacing and mean free path[1] are comparable to, or larger than, the physical size of the system. This requires that the continuum approximation be dropped in favor of a molecular theory of rarefied-gas flow [8]. In principle, all fluid-mechanics problems can be attacked from the molecular viewpoint, but no such attempt will be made here. Note that the use of continuum calculus does not preclude the possibility of discontinuous jumps in fluid properties across a free surface or fluid interface or across a shock wave in a compressible fluid (Chap. 9). Our calculus in Chap. 4 must be flexible enough to handle discontinuous boundary conditions.

1.4 Dimensions and Units

A *dimension* is the measure by which a physical variable is expressed quantitatively. A *unit* is a particular way of attaching a number to the quantitative dimension. Thus length is a dimension associated with such variables as distance, displacement, width, deflection, and height, while centimeters and inches are both numerical units for expressing length. Dimension is a powerful concept about which a splendid tool called *dimensional analysis* has been developed (Chap. 5), while units are the nitty-gritty, the number which the customer wants as the final answer.

Systems of units have always varied widely from country to country, even after international agreements have been reached. Engineers need numbers and therefore unit systems, and the numbers must be accurate because the safety of the public is at stake. You cannot design and build a piping system whose diameter is *D* and whose length is *L*. And U.S. engineers have persisted too long in clinging to British systems of units. There is too much margin for error in most British systems, and many an engineering student has flunked a test because of a missing or improper conversion factor of 12 or 144 or 32.2 or 60 or 1.8. Practicing engineers can make the same errors. The writer is aware from personal experience of a serious preliminary error in the design of an aircraft due to a missing factor of 32.2 to convert pounds of mass to slugs.

In 1872 an international meeting in France proposed a treaty called the Metric Convention, which was signed in 1875 by 17 countries including the United States. It was an improvement over British systems because its use of base 10 is the foundation of our number system, learned from childhood by all. Problems still remained because even the metric countries differed in their use of kiloponds instead of dynes or newtons, kilograms instead of grams, or calories instead of joules. To standardize the metric system, a General Conference of Weights and Measures attended in 1960 by 40 countries proposed the *International System of Units* (SI). We are now undergoing a painful period of transition to SI, an adjustment which may take the remainder of this century to complete. The professional societies have led the way. Since July 1, 1974, SI units

---

[1] The mean distance traveled by molecules between collisions.

Table 1.1 Primary Dimensions in SI and BG Systems

Primary dimension	SI unit	BG unit	Conversion factor
Mass $\{M\}$	Kilogram (kg)	Slug	1 slug = 14.5939 kg
Length $\{L\}$	Meter (m)	Foot (ft)	1 ft = 0.3048 m
Time $\{T\}$	Second (s)	Second (s)	1 s = 1 s
Temperature $\{\Theta\}$	Kelvin (K)	Rankine (°R)	1 K = 1.8°R

have been required by all papers published by the American Society of Mechanical Engineers, which prepared a useful booklet explaining the SI [9]. The present text will use SI units together with British gravitational (BG) units.

In fluid mechanics there are only four *primary dimensions* from which all other dimensions can be derived: mass, length, time, and temperature.[1] These dimensions and their units in both systems are given in Table 1.1. Note that the kelvin unit uses no degree symbol. The braces around a symbol like $\{M\}$ mean "the dimension" of mass. All other variables in fluid mechanics can be expressed in terms of $\{M\}$, $\{L\}$, $\{T\}$, and $\{\Theta\}$. For example, acceleration has the dimensions $\{LT^{-2}\}$. The most crucial of these secondary dimensions is force, which is directly related to mass, length, and time by Newton's second law

$$\mathbf{F} = m\mathbf{a} \tag{1.2}$$

From this we see that, dimensionally, $\{F\} = \{MLT^{-2}\}$. A constant of proportionality is avoided by defining the force unit exactly in terms of the primary units. Thus we define the newton and the pound of force

$$
\begin{aligned}
1 \text{ newton of force} &= 1 \text{ N} \equiv 1 \text{ kg} \cdot \text{m/s}^2 \\
1 \text{ pound of force} &= 1 \text{ lbf} \equiv 1 \text{ slug} \cdot \text{ft/s}^2 = 4.4482 \text{ N}
\end{aligned} \tag{1.3}
$$

In this book the abbreviation *lbf* is used for pound-force and *lb* for pound-mass. If instead one adopts other force units such as the dyne or the poundal or kilopond or adopts other mass units such as the gram or pound-mass, a constant of proportionality called g_c must be included in Eq. (1.2). We shall not use g_c in this book since it is not necessary in the SI and BG systems.

---

[1] If electromagnetic effects are important, a fifth primary dimension must be included, electric current $\{I\}$, whose SI unit is the ampere (A).

Table 1.2 Secondary Dimensions in Fluid Mechanics

Secondary dimension	SI unit	BG unit	Conversion factor
Area $\{L^2\}$	m^2	ft^2	1 m^2 = 10.764 ft^2
Volume $\{L^3\}$	m^3	ft^3	1 m^3 = 35.315 ft^3
Velocity $\{LT^{-1}\}$	m/s	ft/s	1 ft/s = 0.3048 m/s
Acceleration $\{LT^{-2}\}$	m/s^2	ft/s^2	1 ft/s^2 = 0.3048 m/s^2
Pressure or stress $\{ML^{-1}T^{-2}\}$	Pa = N/m^2	lbf/ft^2	1 lbf/ft^2 = 47.88 Pa
Angular velocity $\{T^{-1}\}$	s^{-1}	s^{-1}	1 s^{-1} = 1 s^{-1}
Energy, heat, work $\{ML^2T^{-2}\}$	J = N · m	ft · lbf	1 ft · lbf = 1.3558 J
Power $\{ML^2T^{-3}\}$	W = J/s	ft · lbf/s	1 ft · lbf/s = 1.3558 W
Density $\{ML^{-3}\}$	kg/m^3	slugs/ft^3	1 slug/ft^3 = 515.4 kg/m^3
Viscosity $\{ML^{-1}T^{-1}\}$	kg/(m · s)	slugs/(ft · s)	1 slug/(ft · s) = 47.88 kg/(m · s)
Specific heat $\{L^2T^{-2}\Theta^{-1}\}$	m^2/(s^2 · K)	ft^2/(s^2 · °R)	1 m^2/(s^2 · K) = 5.980 ft^2/(s^2 · °R)

A list of some important secondary variables in fluid mechanics, with dimensions derived as combinations of the four primary dimensions, is given in Table 1.2. A more complete list of conversion factors is given in App. D.

EXAMPLE 1.1

A body weighs 1000 lbf when exposed to a standard earth gravity $g = 32.174$ ft/s^2. (a) What is its mass in kg? (b) What will the weight of this body be in N if it is exposed to the moon's standard acceleration $g_{moon} = 1.62$ m/s^2? (c) How fast will the body accelerate if a net force of 400 lbf is applied to it on the moon or on the earth?

Solution

Part (a)   Equation (1.2) holds with F = weight and $a = g_{earth}$:

$$F = W = mg = 1000 \text{ lbf} = (m \text{ slugs})(32.174 \text{ ft/s}^2)$$

or

$$m = \frac{1000}{32.174} = (31.08 \text{ slugs})(14.5939 \text{ kg/slug}) = 453.6 \text{ kg} \qquad Ans. (a)$$

The change from 31.08 slugs to 453.6 kg illustrates the proper use of the conversion factor 14.5939 kg/slug.

Part (b)   The mass of the body remains 453.6 kg regardless of its location. Equation (1.2) applies with a new value of a and hence a new force

$$F = W_{moon} = mg_{moon} = (453.6 \text{ kg})(1.62 \text{ m/s}^2) = 735 \text{ N} \qquad Ans. (b)$$

Part (c)   This problem does not involve weight or gravity or position and is simply a direct application of Newton's law with an unbalanced force:

$$F = 400 \text{ lbf} = ma = (31.08 \text{ slugs})(a \text{ ft/s}^2)$$

or

$$a = \frac{400}{31.08} = 12.43 \text{ ft/s}^2 = 3.79 \text{ m/s}^2 \qquad Ans. (c)$$

This acceleration would be the same on the moon or earth or anywhere.

Many data in the literature are reported in inconvenient or arcane units suitable only to some industry or specialty or country. The engineer should convert these data to the SI or BG system before using them. This requires the systematic application of conversion factors, as in the following example.

EXAMPLE 1.2

An early viscosity unit in the cgs system is the poise (abbreviated P), or g/(cm · s), named after J. L. M. Poiseuille, a French physician who performed pioneering experiments in 1840 on water flow in pipes. The viscosity of water (fresh or salt) at 293.16 K = 20°C is approximately $\mu = 0.01$ P. Express this value in (a) SI and (b) BG units.

Solution

Part (a)
$$\mu = [0.01 \text{ g/(cm} \cdot \text{s)}] \frac{1 \text{ kg}}{1000 \text{ g}} (100 \text{ cm/m}) = 0.001 \text{ kg/(m} \cdot \text{s)} \qquad \textit{Ans. (a)}$$

Part (b)
$$\mu = [0.001 \text{ kg/(m} \cdot \text{s)}] \frac{1 \text{ slug}}{14.59 \text{ kg}} (0.3048 \text{ m/ft})$$

$$= 2.09 \times 10^{-5} \text{ slug/(ft} \cdot \text{s)} \qquad \textit{Ans. (b)}$$

Note: Result (b) could have been found directly from (a) by dividing (a) by the viscosity conversion factor 47.88 listed in Table 1.2.

We repeat our advice: Faced with data in unusual units, convert them immediately to either SI or BG units because (1) it is more professional and (2) theoretical equations in fluid mechanics are *dimensionally consistent* and require no further conversion factors when these two fundamental unit systems are used, as the following example shows.

EXAMPLE 1.3

A useful theoretical equation for computing the relation between pressure, velocity, and altitude in a steady flow of a nearly inviscid, nearly incompressible fluid with negligible heat transfer and shaft work[1] is the *Bernoulli relation*, named after Daniel Bernoulli, who published a hydrodynamics textbook in 1738:

$$p_0 = p + \tfrac{1}{2}\rho V^2 + \rho g Z \qquad (1)$$

where p_0 = stagnation pressure
p = pressure in moving fluid
V = velocity
ρ = density
Z = altitude
g = gravitational acceleration

(a) Show that Eq. (1) satisfies the principle of dimensional homogeneity, which states that all additive terms in a physical equation must have the same dimensions. (b) Show that consistent units result without additional conversion factors in SI units. (c) Repeat (b) for BG units.

Solution

Part (a)
We can express Eq. (1) dimensionally, using braces by entering the dimensions of each term from Table 1.2:

$$\{ML^{-1}T^{-2}\} = \{ML^{-1}T^{-2}\} + \{ML^{-3}\}\{L^2T^{-2}\} + \{ML^{-3}\}\{LT^{-2}\}\{L\}$$

$$= \{ML^{-1}T^{-2}\} \qquad \text{for all terms} \qquad \textit{Ans. (a)}$$

Part (b)
Enter the SI units for each quantity from Table 1.2:

[1] That's an awful lot of assumptions, which need further study in Chap. 3.

$$\{N/m^2\} = \{N/m^2\} + \{kg/m^3\}\{m^2/s^2\} + \{kg/m^3\}\{m/s^2\}\{m\}$$

$$= \{N/m^2\} + \{kg/(m \cdot s^2)\}$$

The right-hand side looks bad until we remember from Eq. (1.3) that $1 \text{ kg} = 1 \text{ N} \cdot s^2/m$.

$$\{kg/(m \cdot s^2)\} = \frac{\{N \cdot s^2/m\}}{\{m \cdot s^2\}} = \{N/m^2\} \qquad \textit{Ans. (b)}$$

Thus all terms in Bernoulli's equation will have units of pascals, or newtons per square meter, when SI units are used. No conversion factors are needed, which is true of all theoretical equations in fluid mechanics.

Part (c)   Introducing BG units for each term, we have

$$\{lbf/ft^2\} = \{lbf/ft^2\} + \{slugs/ft^3\}\{ft^2/s^2\} + \{slugs/ft^3\}\{ft/s^2\}\{ft\}$$

$$= \{lbf/ft^2\} + \{slugs/(ft \cdot s^2)\}$$

But, from Eq. (1.3), $1 \text{ slug} = 1 \text{ lbf} \cdot s^2/ft$, so that

$$\{slugs/(ft \cdot s^2)\} = \frac{\{lbf \cdot s^2/ft\}}{\{ft \cdot s^2\}} = \{lbf/ft^2\} \qquad \textit{Ans. (c)}$$

All terms have the unit of pounds-force per square foot. No conversion factors are needed in the BG system either.

There is still a tendency in English-speaking countries to use pound-force per square inch as a pressure unit because the numbers are more manageable. For example, standard atmospheric pressure is $14.7 \text{ lbf/in}^2 = 2116 \text{ lbf/ft}^2 = 101{,}300$ Pa. The pascal is a small unit because the newton is less than $\frac{1}{4}$ lbf and a square meter is a very large area. It is felt nevertheless that the pascal will gradually gain universal acceptance; e.g., repair manuals for U.S. automobiles now specify pressure measurements in pascals.

Homogeneous versus Dimensionally Inconsistent Equations

All thereotical equations in mechanics (and in other physical sciences) are *dimensionally homogeneous*; i.e., each additive term in the equation has the same dimensions. For example, Bernoulli's equation (1) in Example 1.3 is dimensionally homogeneous: Each term has the dimensions of pressure or stress of $\{F/L^2\}$. Another example is the equation from physics for a body falling with negligible air resistance:

$$S = S_0 + V_0 t + \tfrac{1}{2}gt^2$$

where S_0 is initial position, V_0 is initial velocity, and g is the acceleration of gravity. Each term in this relation has dimensions of length $\{L\}$. The factor $\frac{1}{2}$, which arises from integration, is a pure (dimensionless) number, $\{1\}$.

However, the reader should be warned that many empirical formulas in the engineering literature, arising primarily from correlations of data, are dimensionally inconsistent. Their units cannot be reconciled simply, and some terms may contain hidden variables. An example is the formula which pipe valve manufacturers cite for liquid volume flow rate Q (m^3/s) through a partially open valve:

$$Q = C_V \left(\frac{\Delta p}{SG}\right)^{1/2}$$

where Δp is the pressure drop across the valve and SG is the specific gravity of the liquid (the ratio of its density to that of water). The quantity C_V is the *valve flow coefficient*, which manufacturers tabulate in their valve brochures. Since SG is dimensionless $\{1\}$, we see that this formula is totally inconsistent, with one side being a flow rate $\{L^3/T\}$ and the other being the square root of a pressure drop $\{M^{1/2}/L^{1/2}T)\}$. It follows that C_V must have dimensions, and rather odd ones at that: $\{L^{7/2}/M^{1/2}\}$. Nor is the resolution of this discrepancy clear, although one hint is that the values of C_V in the literature increase nearly as the square of the size of the value. The presentation of experimental data in homogeneous form is the subject of *dimensional analysis* (Chap. 5). There we shall learn that a homogeneous form for the valve flow relation is

$$Q = C_d A_{\text{opening}} \left(\frac{\Delta p}{\rho}\right)^{1/2}$$

where ρ is the liquid density and A the area of the valve opening. The *discharge coefficient* C_d is dimensionless and changes only slightly with valve size. Please believe—until we establish the fact in Chap. 5—that this latter is a *much* better formulation of the data.

   Meanwhile, we conclude that dimensionally inconsistent equations, though they abound in engineering practice, are misleading and vague and even dangerous, in the sense that they are often misused outside their range of applicability.

Convenient Prefixes in Powers of 10

Engineering results often are too small or too large for the common units, with two many zeros one way or the other. For example, to write $p = 114,000,000$ Pa is long and awkward. Using the prefix "M" to mean 10^6, we convert this to a concise $p = 114$ MPa (megapascals). Similarly, $t = 0.000000003$ s is a proofreader's nightmare compared to the equivalent $t = 3$ ns (nanoseconds). Such prefixes are common and convenient, in both the SI and BG systems. A complete list is given in Table 1.3.

Table 1.3 Convenient Prefixes for Engineering Units

Multiplicative factor	Prefix	Symbol
10^{12}	tera	T
10^{9}	giga	G
10^{6}	mega	M
10^{3}	kilo	k
10^{2}	hecto	h
10	deka	da
10^{-1}	deci	d
10^{-2}	centi	c
10^{-3}	milli	m
10^{-6}	micro	μ
10^{-9}	nano	n
10^{-12}	pico	p
10^{-15}	femto	f
10^{-18}	atto	a

EXAMPLE 1.4

In 1890 Robert Manning, an Irish engineer, proposed the following empirical formula for the average velocity V in uniform flow due to gravity down an open channel (BG units):

$$V = \frac{1.49}{n} R^{2/3} S^{1/2} \tag{1}$$

where $R =$ hydraulic radius of channel (Chaps. 6 and 10)
  $S =$ channel slope (tangent of angle that bottom makes with horizontal)
  $n =$ Manning's roughness factor (Chap. 10)

and n is a constant for a given surface condition for the walls and bottom of the channel. (*a*) Is Manning's formula dimensionally consistent? (*b*) Equation (1) is commonly taken to be valid in BG units with n taken as dimensionless. Rewrite it in SI form.

Solution

Part (a)   Introduce dimensions for each term. The slope S, being a tangent or ratio, is dimensionless, denoted by {unity} or {1}. Equation (1) in dimensional form is

$$\left\{\frac{L}{T}\right\} = \left\{\frac{1.49}{n}\right\}\{L^{2/3}\}\{1\}$$

This formula cannot be consistent unless $\{1.49/n\} = \{L^{1/3}/T\}$. If n is dimensionless (and it is never listed with units in textbooks), then the numerical value 1.49 must have units. This can be tragic to an engineer working in a different unit system unless the discrepancy is properly documented. In fact, Manning's formula, though popular, is inconsistent both dimensionally and physically and does not properly account for channel-roughness effects except in a narrow range of parameters, for water only.

Part (b)   From part (a), the number 1.49 must have dimensions $\{L^{1/3}/T\}$ and thus in BG units equals 1.49 $ft^{1/3}/s$. By using the SI conversion factor for length we have

$$(1.49 \ ft^{1/3}/s)(0.3048 \ m/ft)^{1/3} = 1.00 \ m^{1/3}/s$$

Therefore Manning's formula in SI becomes

$$V = \frac{1.0}{n} R^{2/3} S^{1/2} \qquad\qquad \textit{Ans. (b)} \quad (2)$$

with R in m and V in m/s. Actually, we misled you: This is the way Manning, a metric user, first proposed the formula. It was later converted to BG units. Such dimensionally inconsistent formulas are dangerous and should either be reanalyzed or treated as having very limited application.

1.5 Properties of the Velocity Field

In a given flow situation, the determination, by experiment or theory, of the properties of the fluid as a function of position and time is considered to be the *solution* to the problem. In almost all cases, the emphasis is on the space-time distribution of the fluid properties. One rarely keeps track of the actual fate of the specific fluid particles.[1] This treatment of properties as continuum-field functions distinguishes fluid mechanics from solid mechanics, where we are more likely to be interested in the trajectories of individual particles or systems.

Eulerian and Lagrangian Descriptions

There are two different points of view in analyzing problems in mechanics. The first view, appropriate to fluid mechanics, is concerned with the field of flow and is called the *eulerian* method of description. In the eulerian method we compute the pressure field $p(x, y, z, t)$ of the flow pattern, not the pressure changes $p(t)$ which a particle experiences as it moves through the field.

The second method, which follows an individual particle moving through the flow, is called the *lagrangian* description. The lagrangian approach, which is more appro-

---

[1] One example where fluid-particle paths are important is in water-quality analysis of the fate of contaminant discharges.

priate to solid mechanics, will not be treated in this book. However, certain numerical analyses of sharply bounded fluid flows, such as the motion of isolated fluid droplets, are very conveniently computed in lagrangian coordinates [1].

Fluid-dynamic measurements are also suited to the eulerian system. For example, when a pressure probe is introduced into a laboratory flow, it is fixed at a specific position (x, y, z). Its output thus contributes to the description of the eulerian pressure field $p(x, y, z, t)$. To simulate a lagrangian measurement, the probe would have to move downstream at the fluid particle speeds; this is sometimes done in oceanographic measurements, where flowmeters drift along with the prevailing currents.

The two different descriptions can be contrasted in the analysis of traffic flow along a freeway. A certain length of freeway may be selected for study and called the field of flow. Obviously, as time passes, various cars will enter and leave the field, and the identity of the specific cars within the field will constantly be changing. The traffic engineer ignores specific cars and concentrates on their average velocity as a function of time and position within the field, plus the flow rate or number of cars per hour passing a given section of the freeway. This engineer is using an eulerian description of the traffic flow. Other investigators, such as the police or social scientists, may be interested in the path or speed or destination of specific cars in the field. By following a specific car as a function of time, they are using a lagrangian description of the flow.

The Velocity Field

Foremost among the properties of a flow is the velocity field $\mathbf{V}(x, y, z, t)$. In fact, determining the velocity is often tantamount to solving a flow problem, since other properties follow directly from the velocity field. Chapter 2 is devoted to the calculation of the pressure field once the velocity field is known. Books on heat transfer [for example, 10] are essentially devoted to finding the temperature field from known velocity fields.

In general, velocity is a vector function of position and time and thus has three components u, v, and w, each a scalar field in itself:

$$\mathbf{V}(x, y, z, t) = \mathbf{i}u(x, y, z, t) + \mathbf{j}v(x, y, z, t) + \mathbf{k}w(x, y, z, t) \tag{1.4}$$

The use of u, v, and w instead of the more logical component notation V_x, V_y, and V_z is the result of an almost unbreakable custom in fluid mechanics.

Several other quantities, called *kinematic properties*, can be derived by mathematically manipulating the velocity field. We list some kinematic properties here and give more details about their use and derivation in later chapters:

1. Displacement vector: $\qquad \mathbf{r} = \displaystyle\int \mathbf{V}\, dt \qquad$ (Sec. 1.9)

2. Acceleration: $\qquad \mathbf{a} = \dfrac{d\mathbf{V}}{dt} \qquad$ (Sec. 4.1)

3. Volume rate of flow: $\qquad Q = \displaystyle\int (\mathbf{V} \cdot \mathbf{n})\, dA \qquad$ (Sec. 3.2)

4. Volume expansion rate: $\qquad \dfrac{1}{\mathcal{V}}\dfrac{d\mathcal{V}}{dt} = \nabla \cdot \mathbf{V} \qquad$ (Sec. 4.2)

5. Local angular velocity: $\boldsymbol{\omega} = \tfrac{1}{2}\boldsymbol{\nabla} \times \mathbf{V}$ (Sec. 4.8)

We will not illustrate any problems regarding these kinematic properties at present. The point of the list is to illustrate the type of vector operations used in fluid mechanics and to make clear the dominance of the velocity field in determining other flow properties. *Note:* The fluid *acceleration*, item 2 above, is not as simple as it looks and actually involves four different terms due to the use of the chain rule in calculus (see Sec. 4.1).

EXAMPLE 1.5

To illustrate the complicated nonlinear form of the fluid acceleration vector, consider an unsteady two-dimensional flow field $\mathbf{V} = \mathbf{i}u(x, y, t) + \mathbf{j}v(x, y, t) + \mathbf{k}(0)$. Find a general expression for vector $\mathbf{a}$ for this case.

Solution

The calculus limit for the derivative of the velocity field is

$$\mathbf{a} = \frac{d\mathbf{V}}{dt} = \lim_{dt=0} \frac{\mathbf{V}(x + dx, y + dy, t + dt) - \mathbf{V}(x, y, t)}{dt}$$

$$= \lim_{dt=0} \frac{\mathbf{i}\left(u + \dfrac{\partial u}{\partial x}dx + \dfrac{\partial u}{\partial y}dy + \dfrac{\partial u}{\partial t}dt\right) + \mathbf{j}\left(v + \dfrac{\partial v}{\partial x}dx + \dfrac{\partial v}{\partial y}dy + \dfrac{\partial v}{\partial t}dt\right) - (\mathbf{i}u + \mathbf{j}v)}{dt}$$

Note the use of partial derivatives: If u and v vary with position and time, their changes during a short interval (dx, dy, dt) are proportional to these derivatives. Simplifying the above limit, we obtain

$$\mathbf{a} = \mathbf{i}\left(\frac{\partial u}{\partial x}\frac{dx}{dt} + \frac{\partial u}{\partial y}\frac{dy}{dt} + \frac{\partial u}{\partial t}\right) + \mathbf{j}\left(\frac{\partial v}{\partial x}\frac{dx}{dt} + \frac{\partial v}{\partial y}\frac{dy}{dt} + \frac{\partial v}{\partial t}\right)$$

But, for a particle moving with the fluid through the field, $dx/dt = u$ and $dy/dt = v$, the local fluid velocities. The above relation is thus rewritten in the standard two-dimensional form:

$$\mathbf{a} = \mathbf{i}\left(u\frac{\partial u}{\partial x} + v\frac{\partial u}{\partial y} + \frac{\partial u}{\partial t}\right) + \mathbf{j}\left(u\frac{\partial v}{\partial x} + v\frac{\partial v}{\partial y} + \frac{\partial v}{\partial t}\right) \qquad Ans.$$

Note the nonlinear products of velocity and the velocity derivative. We extend this expression to three dimensions in Sec. 4.1.

1.6 Thermodynamic Properties of a Fluid

While the velocity field $\mathbf{V}$ is the most important fluid property, it interacts closely with the thermodynamic properties of the fluid. We have already introduced into the discussion the three most common such properties

1. Pressure p
2. Density ρ
3. Temperature T

These three are constant companions of the velocity vector in flow analyses. Four other thermodynamic properties become important when work, heat, and energy balances are treated (Chaps. 3 and 4):

4. Internal energy e
5. Enthalpy $h = û + p/\rho$
6. Entropy s
7. Specific heats c_p and c_v

In addition, friction and heat conduction effects are governed by the two so-called *transport properties*:

8. Coefficient of viscosity μ
9. Thermal conductivity k

All nine of these quantities are true thermodynamic properties which are determined by the thermodynamic condition or *state* of the fluid. For example, for a single-phase substance such as water or oxygen, two basic properties such as pressure and temperature are sufficient to fix the value of all the others:

$$\rho = \rho(p, T) \qquad h = h(p, T) \qquad \mu = \mu(p, T) \qquad (1.5)$$

and so on for every quantity in the list. Note that the specific volume, so important in thermodynamic analyses, is omitted here in favor of its inverse, the density ρ.

Recall that thermodynamic properties describe the state of a *system*, i.e., a collection of matter of fixed identity which interacts with its surroundings. In most cases here the system will be a small fluid element, and all properties will be assumed to be continuum properties of the flow field: $\rho = \rho(x, y, z, t)$, etc.

Recall also that thermodynamics is normally concerned with *static* systems, whereas fluids are usually in variable motion with constantly changing properties. Do the properties retain their meaning in a fluid flow which is technically not in equilibrium? The answer is yes, from a statistical argument. In gases at normal pressure (and even more so for liquids), an enormous number of molecular collisions occur over a very short distance of the order of 1 μm, so that a fluid subjected to sudden changes rapidly adjusts itself toward equilibrium. We therefore assume that all the thermodynamic properties listed above exist as point functions in a flowing fluid and follow all the laws and state relations of ordinary equilibrium thermodynamics. There are, of course, important non-equilibrium effects such as chemical and nuclear reactions in flowing fluids which are not treated in this text.

Pressure

Pressure is the (compression) stress at a point in a static fluid (Fig. 1.1). Next to velocity, the pressure p is the most dynamic variable in fluid mechanics. Differences or *gradients* in pressure often drive a fluid flow, especially in ducts. In low-speed flows, the actual magnitude of the pressure is often not important, unless it drops so low as to cause vapor bubbles to form in a liquid. For convenience, we set many such problem assignments at the level of 1 atm = 2116 lbf/ft^2 = 101,300 Pa. High-speed (compressible) gas flows (Chap. 9), however, are indeed sensitive to the magnitude of pressure.

Temperature

Temperature T is a measure of the internal energy level of a fluid. It may vary considerably during high-speed flow of a gas (Chap. 9). Although engineers often use Celsius or Fahrenheit scales for convenience, many applications in this text require *absolute* (Kelvin or Rankine) temperature scales:

$$°R = °F + 459.69$$

$$K = °C + 273.16$$

If temperature differences are strong, *heat transfer* may be important [10], but our concern here is mainly with dynamic effects. We examine heat-transfer principles briefly in Secs. 4.5 and 9.8.

Density

The density of a fluid, denoted by ρ (lowercase Greek rho), is its mass per unit volume. Density is highly variable in gases and increases nearly proportionally to the pressure level. Density in liquids is nearly constant; the density of water (about 1000 kg/m^3) increases only 1 percent if the pressure is increased by a factor of 220. Thus most liquid flows are treated analytically as nearly "incompressible."

In general, liquids are about three orders of magnitude more dense than gases at atmospheric pressure. The heaviest common liquid is mercury, and the lightest gas is hydrogen. Compare their densities at 20°C and 1 atm:

$$\text{Mercury:} \quad \rho = 13{,}580 \text{ kg/m}^3 \qquad \text{Hydrogen:} \quad \rho = 0.0838 \text{ kg/m}^3$$

They differ by a factor of 162,000! Thus the physical parameters in various liquid and gas flows might vary considerably. The differences are often resolved by the use of *dimensional analysis* (Chap. 5). Other fluid densities are listed in Tables A.3 and A.4 (in App. A).

Specific Weight

The *specific weight* of a fluid, denoted by γ (lowercase Greek gamma), is its weight per unit volume. Just as a mass has a weight $W = mg$, density and specific weight are simply related by gravity:

$$\gamma = \rho g \tag{1.6}$$

The units of γ are weight per unit volume, in lbf/ft^3 or N/m^3. In standard earth gravity, $g = 32.174 \text{ ft/s}^2 = 9.807 \text{ m/s}^2$. Thus, e.g., the specific weights of air and water at 20°C and 1 atm are approximately

$$\gamma_{air} = (1.205 \text{ kg/m}^3)(9.807 \text{ m/s}^2) = 11.8 \text{ N/m}^3 = 0.0752 \text{ lbf/ft}^3$$

$$\gamma_{water} = (998 \text{ kg/m}^3)(9.807 \text{ m/s}^2) = 9790 \text{ N/m}^3 = 62.4 \text{ lbf/ft}^3$$

Specific weight is very useful in the hydrostatic-pressure applications of Chap. 2. Specific weights of other fluids are given in Tables A.3 and A.4.

Specific Gravity

Specific gravity, denoted by SG, is the ratio of a fluid density to a standard reference fluid, water (for liquids), and air (for gases):

$$SG_{gas} = \frac{\rho_{gas}}{\rho_{air}} = \frac{\rho_{gas}}{1.205 \text{ kg/m}^3} \tag{1.7}$$

$$SG_{liquid} = \frac{\rho_{liquid}}{\rho_{water}} = \frac{\rho_{liquid}}{998 \text{ kg/m}^3}$$

For example, the specific gravity of mercury (Hg) is $SG_{Hg} = 13{,}580/998 \approx 13.6$. Engineers find these dimensionless ratios easier to remember than the actual numerical values of density of a variety of fluids.

Potential and Kinetic Energies

In thermostatics the only energy in a substance is that stored in a system by molecular activity and molecular bonding forces. This is commonly denoted as *internal energy û*. A commonly accepted adjustment to this static situation for fluid flow is to add two more energy terms which arise from newtonian mechanics: the potential energy and kinetic energy.

The potential energy equals the work required to move the system of mass m from the origin to a position vector $\mathbf{r} = \mathbf{i}x + \mathbf{j}y + \mathbf{k}z$ against a gravity field $\mathbf{g}$. Its value is $-m\mathbf{g} \cdot \mathbf{r}$, or $-\mathbf{g} \cdot \mathbf{r}$ per unit mass. The kinetic energy equals the work required to change the speed of the mass from zero to velocity V. Its value is $\frac{1}{2}mV^2$ or $\frac{1}{2}V^2$ per unit mass. Then by common convention the total stored energy e per unit mass in fluid mechanics is the sum of three terms:

$$e = \hat{u} + \tfrac{1}{2}V^2 + (-\mathbf{g} \cdot \mathbf{r}) \tag{1.8}$$

Also, throughout this book we shall define z as upward, so that $\mathbf{g} = -g\mathbf{k}$ and $\mathbf{g} \cdot \mathbf{r} = -gz$. Then Eq. (1.8) becomes

$$e = \hat{u} + \tfrac{1}{2}V^2 + gz \tag{1.9}$$

The molecular internal energy $\hat{u}$ is a function of T and p for the single-phase pure substance, whereas the potential and kinetic energies are kinematic properties.

State Relations for Gases

Thermodynamic properties are found both theoretically and experimentally to be related to each other by state relations which differ for each substance. As mentioned, we shall confine ourselves here to single-phase pure substances, e.g., water in its liquid phase. The second most common fluid, air, is a mixture of gases, but since the mixture ratios remain nearly constant between 160 and 2200 K, in this temperature range air can be considered to be a pure substance.

All gases at high temperatures and low pressures (relative to their critical point) are in good agreement with the *perfect-gas law*

$$p = \rho RT \qquad R = c_p - c_v = \text{gas constant} \tag{1.10}$$

Since Eq. (1.10) is dimensionally consistent, R has the same dimensions as specific heat, $\{L^2 T^{-2} \Theta^{-1}\}$, or velocity squared per temperature unit (kelvin or degree Rankine). Each gas has its own constant R, equal to a universal constant Λ divided by the molecular weight

$$R_{gas} = \frac{\Lambda}{M_{gas}} \tag{1.11}$$

where $\Lambda = 49{,}700 \; \text{ft}^2/(\text{s}^2 \cdot {}^\circ\text{R}) = 8314 \; \text{m}^2/(\text{s}^2 \cdot \text{K})$. Most applications in this book are for air, with $M = 28.97$:

$$R_{\text{air}} = 1717 \; \text{ft}^2/(\text{s}^2 \cdot {}^\circ\text{R}) = 287 \; \text{m}^2/(\text{s}^2 \cdot \text{K}) \tag{1.12}$$

Standard atmospheric pressure is 2116 lbf/ft^2, and standard temperature is $60{}^\circ\text{F} = 520{}^\circ\text{R}$. Thus standard air density is

$$\rho_{\text{air}} = \frac{2116}{(1717)(520)} = 0.00237 \; \text{slug}/\text{ft}^3 = 1.22 \; \text{kg}/\text{m}^3 \tag{1.13}$$

This is a nominal value suitable for problems.

One proves in thermodynamics that Eq. (1.10) requires that the internal molecular energy $\hat{u}$ of a perfect gas vary only with temperature: $\hat{u} = \hat{u}(T)$. Therefore the specific heat c_v also varies only with temperature:

$$c_v = \left(\frac{\partial \hat{u}}{\partial T}\right)_\rho = \frac{d\hat{u}}{dT} = c_v(T)$$

or

$$d\hat{u} = c_v(T) \, dT \tag{1.14}$$

In like manner h and c_p of a perfect gas also vary only with temperature:

$$h = \hat{u} + \frac{p}{\rho} = \hat{u} + RT = h(T)$$

$$c_p = \left(\frac{\partial h}{\partial T}\right)_p = \frac{dh}{dT} = c_p(T) \tag{1.15}$$

$$dh = c_p(T) \, dT$$

The ratio of specific heats of a perfect gas is an important dimensionless parameter in compressible-flow analysis (Chap. 9)

$$k = \frac{c_p}{c_v} = k(T) \geq 1 \tag{1.16}$$

As a first approximation in airflow analysis we commonly take c_p, c_v, and k to be constant

$$k_{\text{air}} \approx 1.4$$

$$c_v = \frac{R}{k-1} \approx 4293 \; \text{ft}^2/(\text{s}^2 \cdot {}^\circ\text{R}) = 718 \; \text{m}^2/(\text{s}^2 \cdot \text{K})$$

$$c_p = \frac{kR}{k-1} \approx 6010 \; \text{ft}^2/(\text{s}^2 \cdot {}^\circ\text{R}) = 1005 \; \text{m}^2/(\text{s}^2 \cdot \text{K}) \tag{1.17}$$

Actually, for all gases, c_p and c_v increase gradually with temperature, and k decreases gradually. Experimental values of the specific-heat ratio for eight common gases are shown in Fig. 1.3.

Many flow problems involve steam. Typical steam operating conditions are relatively close to the critical point, so that the perfect-gas approximation is inaccurate. The properties of steam are therefore available in tabular form [13], but the error of using the perfect-gas law is sometimes not great, as the following example shows.

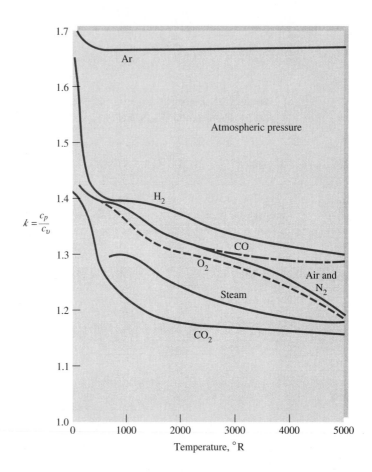

Fig. 1.3 Specific-heat ratio of eight common gases as a function of temperature. (*Data from Ref. 12.*)

Atmospheric pressure

$k = \dfrac{c_p}{c_v}$

Ar

H$_2$

CO

O$_2$

Air and N$_2$

Steam

CO$_2$

Temperature, °R

EXAMPLE 1.6

Estimate ρ and c_p of steam at 100 lbf/in^2 and 400°F (*a*) by a perfect-gas approximation and (*b*) from the ASME steam tables [13].

Solution

Part (a)   First convert to BG units: $p = 100$ lbf/in^2 = 14,400 lb/ft^2, $T = 400$°F = 860°R. From Table A.4 the molecular weight of H$_2$O is $2M_H + M_O = 2(1.008) + 16.0 = 18.016$. Then from Eq. (1.11) the gas constant of steam is approximately

$$R = \frac{49{,}700}{18.016} = 2759 \text{ ft}^2/(\text{s}^2 \cdot {}^\circ\text{R})$$

whence, from the perfect-gas law,

$$\rho \approx \frac{p}{RT} = \frac{14{,}400}{2759(860)} = 0.00607 \text{ slug/ft}^3 \qquad \qquad \textit{Ans. (a)}$$

From Fig. 1.3, k for steam at 860°R is approximately 1.30. Then from Eq. (1.17),

$$c_p \approx \frac{kR}{k-1} = \frac{1.30(2759)}{1.30-1} = 12,000 \text{ ft}^2/(\text{s}^2 \cdot {}^\circ\text{R}) \qquad \textit{Ans. (a)}$$

Part (b)   From Ref. 13, the specific volume v of steam at 100 lbf/in^2 and 400°F is 4.935 ft^3/lbm. Then the density is the inverse of this, converted to slugs:

$$\rho = \frac{1}{v} = \frac{1}{(4.935 \text{ ft}^2/\text{lbm})(32.174 \text{ lbm/slug})} = 0.00630 \text{ slug/ft}^3 \qquad \textit{Ans. (b)}$$

This is about 4 percent higher than our ideal-gas estimate in part (*a*).

Reference 13 lists the value of c_p of steam at 100 lbf/in^2 and 400°F as 0.535 Btu/(lbm · °F). Convert this to BG units:

$$c_p = [0.535 \text{ Btu}/(\text{lbm} \cdot {}^\circ\text{R})](778.2 \text{ ft} \cdot \text{lbf/Btu})(32.174 \text{ lbm/slug})$$

$$= 13,400 \text{ ft} \cdot \text{lbf}/(\text{slug} \cdot {}^\circ\text{R}) = 13,400 \text{ ft}^2/(\text{s}^2 \cdot {}^\circ\text{R}) \qquad \textit{Ans. (b)}$$

This is about 11 percent higher than our ideal-gas estimate in part (*a*). The chief reason for the discrepancy is that this temperature and this pressure are quite close to the critical point and saturation line of steam. At higher temperatures and lower pressures, say, 800°F and 50 lbf/in^2, the perfect-gas law gives ρ and c_p of steam within an accuracy of ± 1 percent.

Note that the use of pound-mass and British thermal units in the traditional steam tables requires continual awkward conversions to BG units. Newer tables and disks are in SI units.

State Relations for Liquids

The writer knows of no "perfect-liquid law" comparable to that for gases. Liquids are nearly incompressible and have a single reasonably constant specific heat. Thus an idealized state relation for a liquid is

$$\rho \approx \text{const} \qquad c_p \approx c_v \approx \text{const} \qquad dh \approx c_p \, dT \qquad (1.18)$$

Most of the flow problems in this book can be attacked with these simple assumptions. Water is normally taken to have a density of 1.94 slugs/ft^3 and a specific heat $c_p = 25,200$ ft^2/(s^2 · °R). The steam tables may be used if more accuracy is required.

The density of a liquid usually decreases slightly with temperature and increases moderately with pressure. If we neglect the temperature effect, an empirical pressure-density relation for a liquid is

$$\frac{p}{p_a} \approx (B+1)\left(\frac{\rho}{\rho_a}\right)^n - B \qquad (1.19)$$

where B and n are dimensionless parameters which vary slightly with temperature and p_a and ρ_a are standard atmospheric values. Water can be fitted approximately to the values $B \approx 3000$ and $n \approx 7$.

Seawater is a variable mixture of water and salt and thus requires three thermodynamic properties to define its state. These are normally taken as pressure, temperature, and the *salinity* $\hat{S}$, defined as the weight of the dissolved salt divided by the weight of the mixture. The average salinity of seawater is 0.035, usually written as 35 parts per 1000, or 35‰. The average density of seawater is 2.00 slugs/ft^3. Strictly speaking, seawater has three specific heats, all approximately equal to the value for pure water of 25,200 ft^2/(s^2 · °R) = 4210 m^2/(s^2 · K).

EXAMPLE 1.7

The pressure at the deepest part of the ocean is approximately 1100 atm. Estimate the density of seawater at this pressure.

Solution

Equation (1.19) holds for either water or seawater. The ratio p/p_a is given as 1100:

$$1100 \approx (3001)\left(\frac{\rho}{\rho_a}\right)^7 - 3000$$

or

$$\frac{\rho}{\rho_a} = \left(\frac{4100}{3001}\right)^{1/7} = 1.046$$

Assuming an average surface seawater density $\rho_a = 2.00$ slugs/ft³, we compute

$$\rho \approx 1.046(2.00) = 2.09 \text{ slugs/ft}^3 \qquad \qquad \textit{Ans.}$$

Even at these immense pressures, the density increase is less than 5 percent, which justifies the treatment of a liquid flow as essentially incompressible.

1.7 Viscosity and Other Secondary Properties

The quantities such as pressure, temperature, and density discussed in the previous section are *primary* thermodynamic variables characteristic of any system. There are also certain secondary variables which characterize specific fluid-mechanical behavior. The most important of these is viscosity, which relates the local stresses in a moving fluid to the strain rate of the fluid element.

Viscosity

When a fluid is sheared, it begins to move at a strain rate inversely proportional to a property called its *coefficient of viscosity* μ. Consider a fluid element sheared in one plane by a single shear stress τ, as in Fig. 1.4a. The shear strain angle $\delta\theta$ will continuously grow with time as long as the stress τ is maintained, the upper surface moving

Fig. 1.4 Shear stress causes continuous shear deformation in a fluid: (*a*) a fluid element straining at a rate $\delta\theta/\delta t$; (*b*) newtonian shear distribution in a shear layer near a wall.

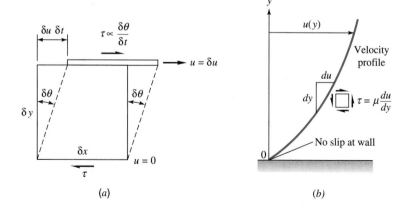

(*a*) (*b*)

at speed δu larger than the lower. Such common fluids as water, oil, and air show a linear relation between applied shear and resulting strain rate

$$\tau \propto \frac{\delta\theta}{\delta t} \tag{1.20}$$

From the geometry of Fig. 1.4a we see that

$$\tan \delta\theta = \frac{\delta u \, \delta t}{\delta y} \tag{1.21}$$

In the limit of infinitesimal changes, this becomes a relation between shear strain rate and velocity gradient

$$\frac{d\theta}{dt} = \frac{du}{dy} \tag{1.22}$$

From Eq. (1.20), then, the applied shear is also proportional to the velocity gradient for the common linear fluids. The constant of proportionality is the viscosity coefficient μ

$$\tau = \mu \frac{d\theta}{dt} = \mu \frac{du}{dy} \tag{1.23}$$

Equation (1.23) is dimensionally consistent; therefore μ has dimensions of stress-time: $\{FT/L^2\}$ or $\{M/(LT)\}$. The BG unit is slugs per foot-second, and the SI unit is kilograms per meter-second. The linear fluids which follow Eq. (1.23) are called *newtonian fluids*, after Sir Isaac Newton, who first postulated this resistance law in 1687.

We do not really care about the strain angle $\theta(t)$ in fluid mechanics, concentrating instead on the velocity distribution $u(y)$, as in Fig. 1.4b. We shall use Eq. (1.23) in Chap. 4 to derive a differential equation for finding the velocity distribution $u(y)$—and, more generally, $V(x, y, z, t)$—in a viscous fluid. Figure 1.4b illustrates a shear layer, or *boundary layer*, near a solid wall. The shear stress is proportional to the slope of the velocity profile and is greatest at the wall. Further, at the wall, the velocity u is zero relative to the wall: This is called the *no-slip condition* and is characteristic of all viscous-fluid flows.

The viscosity of newtonian fluids is a true thermodynamic property and varies with temperature and pressure. At a given state (p, T) there is a vast range of values among the common fluids. Table 1.4 lists the viscosity of eight fluids at standard pressure and temperature. There is a variation of six orders of magnitude from hydrogen up to glyc-

Table 1.4 Viscosity and Kinematic Viscosity of Eight Fluids at 1 atm and 20°C

Fluid	μ, kg/(m · s)[†]	Ratio $\mu/\mu(H_2)$	ρ, kg/m³	ν, m²/s[†]	Ratio $\nu/\nu(Hg)$
Hydrogen	8.8 E–6	1.0	0.084	1.05 E–4	920
Air	1.8 E–5	2.1	1.20	1.51 E–5	130
Gasoline	2.9 E–4	33	680	4.22 E–7	3.7
Water	1.0 E–3	114	998	1.01 E–6	8.7
Ethyl alcohol	1.2 E–3	135	789	1.52 E–6	13
Mercury	1.5 E–3	170	13,580	1.16 E–7	1.0
SAE 30 oil	0.29	33,000	891	3.25 E–4	2,850
Glycerin	1.5	170,000	1,264	1.18 E–3	10,300

[†] 1 kg/(m · s) = 0.0209 slug/(ft · s); 1 m²/s = 10.76 ft²/s.

erin. Thus there will be wide differences between fluids subjected to the same applied stresses.

Generally speaking, the viscosity of a fluid increases only weakly with pressure. For example, increasing p from 1 to 50 atm will increase μ of air only 10 percent. Temperature, however, has a strong effect, with μ increasing with T for gases and decreasing for liquids. Figure A.1 (in App. A) shows this temperature variation for various common fluids. It is customary in most engineering work to neglect the pressure variation.

The variation $\mu(p, T)$ for a typical fluid is nicely shown by Fig. 1.5, from Ref. 14, which normalizes the data with the *critical-point state* (μ_c, p_c, T_c). This behavior, called the *principle of corresponding states*, is characteristic of all fluids, but the actual numerical values are uncertain to ±20 percent for any given fluid. For example, values of $\mu(T)$ for air at 1 atm, from Table A.2, fall about 8 percent low compared to the "low-density limit" in Fig. 1.5. Values of the critical-point constants for various fluids are given in Table A.7.

Note in Fig. 1.5 that changes with temperature occur very rapidly near the critical point. In general, critical-point measurements are extremely difficult and uncertain.

As we shall see in Chaps. 5 and 6, the primary parameter correlating the viscous

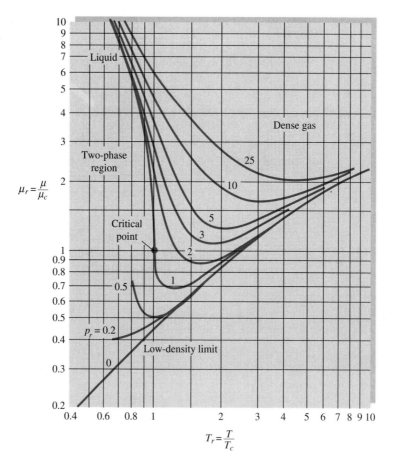

Fig. 1.5 Fluid viscosity nondimensionalized by critical-point properties. This generalized chart is characteristic of all fluids but is only accurate to ±20 percent (from Ref. 14).

behavior of all newtonian fluids is the dimensionless *Reynolds number*, denoted Re:

$$\text{Re} = \frac{\rho VL}{\mu} = \frac{VL}{\nu} \tag{1.24}$$

where V and L are characteristic velocity and length scales of the flow. The second form of Re illustrates that the ratio of μ to ρ has its own name, the *kinematic viscosity*:

$$\nu = \frac{\mu}{\rho} \tag{1.25}$$

The mass units cancel, and ν has units of square meters per second or square feet per second, hence the term *kinematic viscosity*.

Table 1.4 also lists values of ν for the same eight fluids. The pecking order changes considerably, and mercury, the heaviest, has the smallest viscosity relative to its own weight. All gases have high ν relative to thin liquids such as gasoline, water, and alcohol. Oil and glycerin still have the highest ν, but the ratio is smaller. For a given value of V and L in a flow, these fluids exhibit a spread of four orders of magnitude in the Reynolds number.

Flow between Plates

A classic problem is the flow induced between a fixed lower plate and an upper plate moving steadily at velocity **V**, as shown in Fig. 1.6. The clearance between plates is h, and the fluid is newtonian and does not slip at either plate. If the plates are large, this steady shearing motion will set up a velocity distribution $u(y)$, as shown, with $v = w = 0$. The fluid acceleration is zero everywhere.

With zero acceleration and assuming no pressure variation in the flow direction, you should show that a force balance on a small fluid element leads to the result that the shear stress is constant throughout the fluid. Then Eq. (1.23) becomes

$$\frac{du}{dy} = \frac{\tau}{\mu} = \text{const}$$

which we can integrate to obtain

$$u = a + by$$

The velocity distribution is linear, as shown in Fig. 1.6, and the constants a and b can be evaluated from the no-slip condition at the upper and lower walls:

Fig. 1.6 Viscous flow induced by relative motion between two parallel plates.

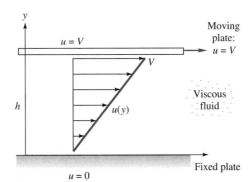

$$u = \begin{cases} 0 = a + b(0) & \text{at } y = 0 \\ V = a + b(h) & \text{at } y = h \end{cases}$$

Hence $a = 0$ and $b = V/h$. Then the velocity profile between the plates is given by

$$u = V\frac{y}{h} \tag{1.26}$$

as indicated in Fig. 1.6. Turbulent flow (Chap. 6) does not have this shape.

Although viscosity has a profound effect on fluid motion, the actual viscous stresses are quite small in magnitude even for oils, as shown in the following example.

EXAMPLE 1.8

Suppose that the fluid being sheared in Fig. 1.6 is SAE 30 oil at 20°C. Compute the shear stress in the oil if $V = 3$ m/s and $h = 2$ cm.

Solution

The shear stress is found from Eq. (1.23) by differentiating Eq. (1.26):

$$\tau = \mu\frac{du}{dy} = \frac{\mu V}{h} \tag{1}$$

From Table 1.4 for SAE 30 oil, $\mu = 0.29$ kg/(m · s). Then, for the given values of V and h, Eq. (1) predicts

$$\tau = \frac{[0.29 \text{ kg/(m · s)}](3 \text{ m/s})}{0.02 \text{ m}} = 43 \text{ kg/(m · s}^2)$$

$$= 43 \text{ N/m}^2 = 43 \text{ Pa} \qquad\qquad Ans.$$

Although oil is very viscous, this is a modest shear stress, about 2400 times less than atmospheric pressure. Viscous stresses in gases and thin liquids are even smaller.

Variation of Viscosity with Temperature

Temperature has a strong effect and pressure a moderate effect on viscosity. The viscosity of gases and most liquids increases slowly with pressure. Water is anomalous in showing a very slight decrease below 30°C. Since the change in viscosity is only a few percent up to 100 atm, we shall neglect pressure effects in this book.

Gas viscosity increases with temperature. Two common approximations are the power law and the Sutherland law:

$$\frac{\mu}{\mu_0} \approx \begin{cases} \left(\dfrac{T}{T_0}\right)^n & \text{power law} \\[2ex] \dfrac{(T/T_0)^{3/2}(T_0 + S)}{T + S} & \text{Sutherland law} \end{cases} \tag{1.27}$$

where μ_0 is a known viscosity at a known absolute temperature T_0 (usually 273 K).

The constants n and S are fit to the data, and both formulas are adequate over a wide range of temperatures. For air, $n \approx 0.7$ and $S \approx 110$ K $= 199°$R. Other values are given in Ref. 3.

Liquid viscosity decreases with temperature and is roughly exponential, $\mu \approx ae^{-bT}$; but a better fit is the empirical result that $\ln \mu$ is quadratic in $1/T$, where T is absolute temperature

$$\ln \frac{\mu}{\mu_0} \approx a + b\left(\frac{T_0}{T}\right) + c\left(\frac{T_0}{T}\right)^2 \tag{1.28}$$

For water, with $T_0 = 273.16$ K, $\mu_0 = 0.001792$ kg/(m $\cdot$ s), suggested values are $a = -1.94$, $b = -4.80$, and $c = 6.74$, with accuracy about ± 1 percent. The viscosity of water is tabulated in Table A.1.

Thermal Conductivity

Just as viscosity relates applied stress to resulting strain rate, there is a property called *thermal conductivity* k which relates the vector rate of heat flow per unit area $\mathbf{q}$ to the vector gradient of temperature ∇T. This proportionality, observed experimentally for fluids and solids, is known as *Fourier's law of heat conduction*

$$\mathbf{q} = -k\nabla T \tag{1.29a}$$

which can also be written as three scalar equations

$$q_x = -k\frac{\partial T}{\partial x} \qquad q_y = -k\frac{\partial T}{\partial y} \qquad q_z = -k\frac{\partial T}{\partial z} \tag{1.29b}$$

The minus sign satisfies the convention that heat flux is positive in the direction of decreasing temperature. Fourier's law is dimensionally consistent, and k has SI units of joules per second-meter-kelvin. Thermal conductivity k is a thermodynamic property and varies with temperature and pressure in much the same way as viscosity. The ratio k/k_0 can be correlated with T/T_0 in the same manner as Eqs. (1.27) and (1.28) for gases and liquids, respectively.

Further data on viscosity and thermal-conductivity variations can be found in Ref. 11.

Nonnewtonian Fluids

Fluids which do not follow the linear law of Eq. (1.23) are called *nonnewtonian* and are treated in books on rheology [6]. Figure 1.7a compares four examples with a newtonian fluid. A *dilatant*, or shear-thickening, fluid increases resistance with increasing applied stress. Alternately, a *pseudoplastic*, or shear-thinning, fluid decreases resistance with increasing stress. If the thinning effect is very strong, as with the dashed-line curve, the fluid is termed *plastic*. The limiting case of a plastic substance is one which requires a finite yield stress before it begins to flow. The linear-flow *Bingham plastic* idealization is shown, but the flow behavior after yield may also be nonlinear. An example of a yielding fluid is toothpaste, which will not flow out of the tube until a finite stress is applied by squeezing.

A further complication of nonnewtonian behavior is the transient effect shown in Fig. 1.7b. Some fluids require a gradually increasing shear stress to maintain a constant strain rate and are called *rheopectic*. The opposite case of a fluid which thins out with

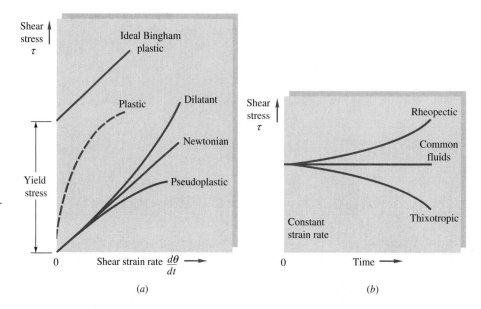

Fig. 1.7 Rheological behavior of various viscous materials: (*a*) stress versus strain rate; (*b*) effect of time on applied stress.

time and requires decreasing stress is termed *thixotropic*. We neglect nonnewtonian effects in this book; see Ref. 6 for further study.

Surface Tension

A liquid, being unable to expand freely, will form an *interface* with a second liquid or gas. The physical chemistry of such interfacial surfaces is quite complex, and whole textbooks are devoted to this specialty [15]. Molecules deep within the liquid repel each other because of their close packing. Molecules at the surface are less dense and attract each other. Since half of their neighbors are missing, the mechanical effect is that the surface is in tension. We can account adequately for surface effects in fluid mechanics with the concept of surface tension.

If a cut of length dL is made in an interfacial surface, equal and opposite forces of magnitude $Y\,dL$ are exposed normal to the cut and parallel to the surface, where Y is called the *coefficient of surface tension*. The dimensions of Y are $\{F/L\}$, with SI units of newtons per meter and BG units of pounds-force per foot. An alternate concept is to open up the cut to an area dA; this requires work to be done of amount $Y\,dA$. Thus the coefficient Y can also be regarded as the surface energy per unit area of the interface, in $N \cdot m/m^2$ or $ft \cdot lbf/ft^2$.

The two most common interfaces are water-air and mercury-air. For a clean surface at $20°C = 68°F$, the measured surface tension is

$$Y = \begin{cases} 0.0050 \text{ lbf/ft} = 0.073 \text{ N/m} & \text{air-water} \\ 0.033 \text{ lbf/ft} = 0.48 \text{ N/m} & \text{air-mercury} \end{cases} \tag{1.30}$$

These are design values and can change considerably if the surface contains contaminants like detergents or slicks. Generally Y decreases with liquid temperature and is zero at the critical point. Values of Y for water are given in Fig. 1.8.

If the interface is curved, a mechanical balance shows that there is a pressure difference across the interface, the pressure being higher on the concave side, as illustrated

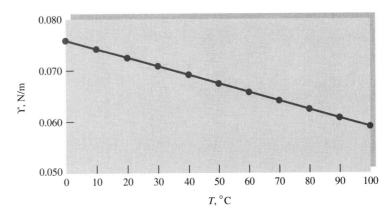

Fig. 1.8 Surface tension of a clean air-water interface. Data from Table A.5.

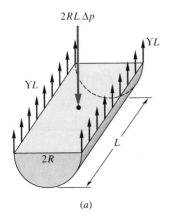
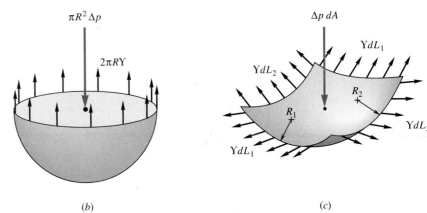

(a)   (b)   (c)

Fig. 1.9 Pressure change across a curved interface due to surface tension: (a) interior of a liquid cylinder; (b) interior of a spherical droplet; (c) general curved interface.

in Fig. 1.9. In Fig. 1.9a, the pressure increase in the interior of a liquid cylinder is balanced by two surface-tension forces

$$2RL\,\Delta p = 2YL$$

or

$$\Delta p = \frac{Y}{R} \tag{1.31}$$

We are not considering the weight of the liquid in this calculation. In Fig. 1.9b, the pressure increase in the interior of a spherical droplet balances a ring of surface-tension force

$$\pi R^2\,\Delta p = 2\pi R Y$$

or

$$\Delta p = \frac{2Y}{R} \tag{1.32}$$

We can use this result to predict the pressure increase inside a soap bubble, which has *two* interfaces with air, an inner and outer surface of nearly the same radius R:

$$\Delta p_{\text{bubble}} \approx 2\,\Delta p_{\text{droplet}} = \frac{4Y}{R} \tag{1.33}$$

Figure 1.9c shows the general case of an arbitrarily curved interface whose principal

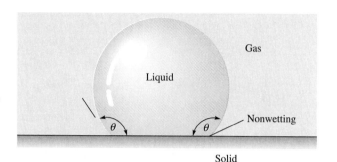

Fig. 1.10 Contact-angle effects at liquid-gas-solid interface. If $\theta < 90°$, the liquid "wets" the solid; if $\theta > 90°$, the liquid is nonwetting.

radii of curvature are R_1 and R_2. A force balance normal to the surface will show that the pressure increase on the concave side is

$$\Delta p = Y(R_1^{-1} + R_2^{-1}) \qquad (1.34)$$

Equations (1.31) to (1.33) can all be derived from this general relation; e.g., in Eq. (1.31), $R_1 = R$ and $R_2 = \infty$.

A second important surface effect is the *contact angle* θ which appears when a liquid interface intersects with a solid surface, as in Fig. 1.10. The force balance would then involve both Y and θ. If the contact angle is less than 90°, the liquid is said to *wet* the solid; if $\theta > 90°$, the liquid is termed *nonwetting*. For example, water wets soap but does not wet wax. Water is extremely wetting to a clean glass surface, with $\theta \approx 0°$. Like Y, the contact angle θ is sensitive to the actual physicochemical conditions of the solid-liquid interface. For a clean mercury-air-glass interface, $\theta = 130°$.

Example 1.9 illustrates how surface tension causes a fluid interface to rise or fall in a capillary tube.

EXAMPLE 1.9

Derive an expression for the change in height h in a circular tube of a liquid with surface tension Y and contact angle θ, as in Fig. E1.9.

Solution

The vertical component of the ring surface-tension force at the interface in the tube must balance the weight of the column of fluid of height h

$$2\pi R Y \cos \theta = \gamma \pi R^2 h$$

Solving for h, we have the desired result

$$h = \frac{2Y \cos \theta}{\gamma R} \qquad \textit{Ans.}$$

Thus the capillary height decreases inversely with tube radius R and is positive if $\theta < 90°$ (wetting liquid) and negative (capillary depression) if $\theta > 90°$.

Suppose that $R = 1$ mm. Then the capillary rise for a water-air-glass interface, $\theta \approx 0°$, $Y = 0.073$ N/m, and $\rho = 1000$ kg/m³ is

$$h = \frac{2(0.073 \text{ N/m})(\cos 0°)}{(1000 \text{ kg/m}^3)(9.81 \text{ m/s}^2)(0.001 \text{ m})} = 0.015 \text{ (N} \cdot \text{s}^2)/\text{kg} = 0.015 \text{ m} = 1.5 \text{ cm}$$

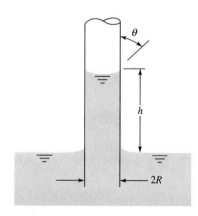

Fig. E1.9

For a mercury-air-glass interface, with $\theta = 130°$, $Y = 0.48$ N/m, and $\rho = 13,600$ kg/m³, the capillary rise is

$$h = \frac{2(0.48)(\cos\ 130°)}{13,600(9.81)(0.001)} = -0.46\ \text{cm}$$

When a small-diameter tube is used to make pressure measurements (Chap. 2), these capillary effects must be corrected for.

Vapor Pressure

Vapor pressure is the pressure at which a liquid boils and is in equilibrium with its own vapor. For example, the vapor pressure of water at 68°F is 49 lbf/ft², while that of mercury is only 0.0035 lbf/ft². If the liquid pressure is greater than the vapor pressure, the only exchange between liquid and vapor is evaporation at the interface. If, however, the liquid pressure falls below the vapor pressure, vapor bubbles begin to appear in the liquid. If water is heated to 212°F, its vapor pressure rises to 2116 lbf/ft², and thus water at normal atmospheric pressure will boil. When the liquid pressure is dropped below the vapor pressure due to a flow phenomenon, we call the process *cavitation*. As we shall see in Chap. 2, if water is accelerated from rest to about 50 ft/s, its pressure drops by about 15 lbf/in², or 1 atm. This can cause cavitation.

The dimensionless parameter describing flow-induced boiling is the *cavitation number*

$$\text{Ca} = \frac{p_a - p_v}{\frac{1}{2}\rho V^2} \tag{1.35}$$

where p_a = ambient pressure
p_v = vapor pressure
V = characteristic flow velocity

Depending upon the geometry, a given flow has a critical value of Ca below which the flow will begin to cavitate. Values of surface tension and vapor pressure of water are given in Table A.5. The vapor pressure of water is plotted in Fig. 1.11.

Fig. 1.11 Vapor pressure of water. Data from Table A.5.

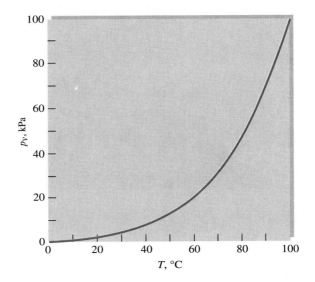

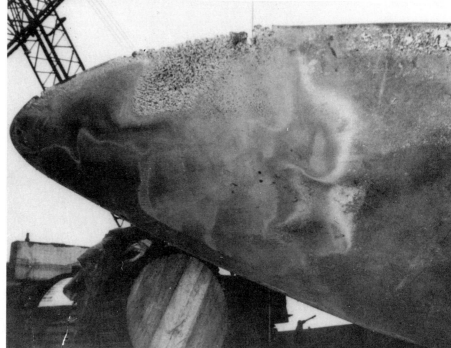

Fig. 1.12 Two aspects of cavitation bubble formation in liquid flows: (*a*) Beauty: spiral bubble sheets form from the surface of a marine propeller [*Courtesy of the Garfield Thomas Water Tunnel, Pennsylvania State University*]; (*b*) ugliness: collapsing bubbles erode a propeller surface [*Courtesy of Thomas T. Huang, David Taylor Research Center*].

Figure 1.12*a* shows cavitation bubbles being formed on the low-pressure surfaces of a marine propeller. When these bubbles move into a higher-pressure region, they collapse implosively. Cavitation collapse can rapidly spall and erode metallic surfaces and eventually destroy them, as shown in Fig. 1.12*b*.

No-Slip and No-Temperature-Jump Conditions

When a fluid flow is bounded by a solid surface, molecular interactions cause the fluid in contact with the surface to seek momentum and energy equilibrium with that surface. All liquids essentially are in equilibrium with the surface they contact. All gases are, too, except under the most rarefied conditions [8]. Excluding rarefied gases, then, all fluids at a point of contact with a solid take on the velocity and temperature of that surface

$$\mathbf{V}_{\text{fluid}} \equiv \mathbf{V}_{\text{wall}} \qquad T_{\text{fluid}} \equiv T_{\text{wall}} \tag{1.36}$$

These are called the *no-slip* and *no-temperature-jump conditions*, respectively. They serve as *boundary conditions* for analysis of fluid flow past a solid surface (Chap. 6). Figure 1.13 illustrates the no-slip condition for water flow past the top and bottom surfaces of a fixed thin plate. The flow past the upper surface is disorderly, or turbulent, while the lower surface flow is smooth, or laminar.[1] In both cases there is clearly no slip at the wall, where the water takes on the zero velocity of the fixed plate. The velocity profile is made visible by the discharge of a line of hydrogen bubbles from the wire shown stretched across the flow.

To decrease the mathematical difficulty, the no-slip condition is partially relaxed in the analysis of inviscid flow (Chap. 8). The flow is allowed to "slip" past the surface but not to permeate through the surface

$$V_{\text{normal}}(\text{fluid}) \equiv V_{\text{normal}}(\text{solid}) \tag{1.37}$$

---

[1] Laminar and turbulent flows are studied in Chaps. 6 and 7.

Fig. 1.13 The no-slip condition in water flow past a thin fixed plate. The upper flow is turbulent; the lower flow is laminar. The velocity profile is made visible by a line of hydrogen bubbles discharged from the wire across the flow. [*From* Illustrated Experiments in Fluid Mechanics (*The NCFMF Book of Film Notes*), *National Committee for Fluid Mechanics Films, Education Development Center, Inc., copyright 1972.*]

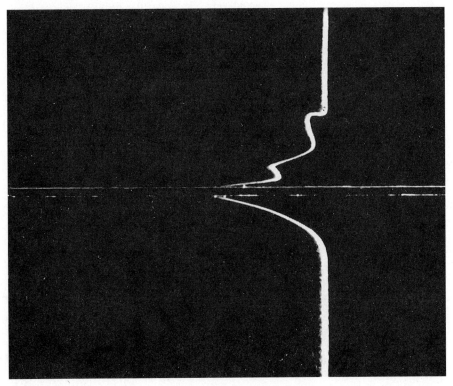

while the tangential velocity V_t is allowed to be independent of the wall. The analysis is much simpler, but the flow patterns are highly idealized.

Speed of Sound

In gas flow, one must be aware of *compressibility* effects (significant density changes caused by the flow). We shall see in Sec. 4.1 and in Chap. 9 that compressibility becomes important when the flow velocity reaches a significant fraction of the speed of sound of the fluid. The *speed of sound a* of a fluid is the rate of propagation of small-disturbance pressure pulses (''sound waves'') through the fluid. In Chap. 9 we shall show, from momentum and thermodynamic arguments, that the speed of sound is defined by

$$a^2 = \left(\frac{\partial p}{\partial p}\right)_s = k\left(\frac{\partial p}{\partial p}\right)_T \qquad k = \frac{c_p}{c_v} \tag{1.38}$$

This is true for either a liquid or a gas, but it is for *gases* that the problem of compressibility occurs. For an ideal gas, Eq. (1.10), we obtain the simple formula

$$a_{\text{ideal gas}} = (kRT)^{1/2} \tag{1.39}$$

where R is the gas constant, Eq. (1.11), and T the absolute temperature. For example, for air at 20°C, $a = \{(1.40)[287 \text{ m}^2/(\text{s}^2 \cdot \text{K})](293 \text{ K})\}^{1/2} \approx 343 \text{ m/s}$ (1126 ft/s = 768 mi/h). If, in this case, the air velocity reaches a significant fraction of a, say, 100 m/s, then we must account for compressibility effects (Chap. 9). Another way to state this is to account for compressibility when the *Mach number* Ma = V/a of the flow reaches about 0.3.

The speed of sound of water is tabulated in Table A.5. The speed of sound of air (or any approximately perfect gas) is simply calculated from Eq. (1.39).

1.8 Basic Flow-Analysis Techniques

There are three basic ways to attack a fluid-flow problem. They are equally important for a student learning the subject, and this book tries to give adequate coverage to each method:

1. Control-volume, or *integral* analysis (Chap. 3)
2. Infinitesimal system, or *differential* analysis (Chap. 4)
3. Experimental study, or *dimensional* analysis (Chap. 5)

In all cases, the flow must satisfy the three basic laws of mechanics[1] plus a thermodynamic state relation and associated boundary conditions:

1. Conservation of mass (continuity)
2. Linear momentum (Newton's second law)
3. First law of thermodynamics (conservation of energy)
4. A state relation like $\rho = \rho(p, T)$
5. Appropriate boundary conditions at solid surfaces, interfaces, inlets, and exits

In integral and differential analyses, these five relations are modeled mathematically

---

[1] In fluids which are variable mixtures of components, such as seawater, a fourth basic law is required, *conservation of species*. For an example of salt conservation analysis, see Ref. 16, Chap. 4.

and solved by computational methods. In an experimental study, the fluid itself performs this task without the use of any mathematics. In other words, these laws are believed to be fundamental to physics, and no fluid flow is known to violate them.

A control volume is a finite region, chosen carefully by the analyst, with open boundaries through which mass, momentum, and energy are allowed to cross. The analyst makes a budget, or balance, between the incoming and outgoing fluid and the resultant changes within the control volume. The result is a powerful tool but a crude one. Details of the flow are normally washed out or ignored in control-volume analyses. Nevertheless, the control-volume technique of Chap. 3 never fails to yield useful and quantitative information to the engineering analyst.

When the conservation laws are written for an infinitesimal system of fluid in motion, they become the basic differential equations of fluid flow. To apply them to a specific problem, one must integrate these equations mathematically subject to the boundary conditions of the particular problem. Exact analytic solutions are often possible only for very simple geometries and boundary conditions (Chap. 4). Otherwise, one attempts numerical integration on a digital computer, i.e., a summing procedure for finite-sized systems which one hopes will approximate the exact integral calculus [1]. Even computer analysis often fails to provide an accurate simulation, because of either inadequate storage or inability to model the finely detailed flow structure characteristic of irregular geometries or turbulent-flow patterns. Thus differential analysis sometimes promises more than it delivers, although we can successfully study a number of classic and useful solutions.

A properly planned experiment is very often the best way to study a practical engineering flow problem. Guidelines for planning flow experiments are given in Chap. 5. For example, no theory presently available, whether differential or integral, calculus or computer, is able to make an accurate computation of the aerodynamic drag and side force of an automobile moving down a highway with crosswinds. One must solve the problem by experiment. The experiment may be *full-scale*: One can test a real automobile on a real highway in real crosswinds. For that matter, there are wind tunnels in existence large enough to hold a full-scale car without significant blockage effects. Normally, however, in the design stage, one tests a small-model automobile in a small wind tunnel. Without proper interpretation, the model results may be poor and mislead the designer (Chap. 5). For example, the model may lack important details such as surface finish or underbody protuberances. The ''wind'' produced by the tunnel propellers may lack the turbulent gustiness of real winds. It is the job of the fluid-flow analyst, using such techniques as dimensional analysis, to plan an experiment which gives an accurate estimate of full-scale or *prototype* results expected in the final product.

It is possible to classify flows, but there is no general agreement on how to do it. Most classifications deal with the assumptions made in the proposed flow analysis. They come in pairs, and we normally assume that a given flow is either

$$\text{Steady} \quad \text{or} \quad \text{unsteady} \qquad (1.40a)$$

$$\text{Inviscid} \quad \text{or} \quad \text{viscous} \qquad (1.40b)$$

$$\text{Incompressible} \quad \text{or} \quad \text{compressible} \qquad (1.40c)$$

$$\text{Gas} \quad \text{or} \quad \text{liquid} \qquad (1.40d)$$

Fig. 1.14 Ready for a flow analysis? Then choose one assumption from each box.

As Fig. 1.14 indicates, we choose one assumption from each pair. We may have a steady viscous compressible gas flow or an unsteady inviscid ($\mu = 0$) incompressible liquid flow. Although there is no such thing as a truly inviscid fluid, the assumption $\mu = 0$ gives adequate results in many analyses (Chap. 8). Often the assumptions overlap: A flow may be viscous in the boundary layer near a solid surface (Fig. 1.13) and effectively inviscid away from the surface. The viscous part of the flow may be laminar or transitional or turbulent or combine patches of all three types of viscous flow. A flow may involve both a gas and a liquid and the free surface, or interface, between them (Chap. 10). A flow may be compressible in one region and have nearly constant density in another. Nevertheless, Eq. (1.40) and Fig. 1.14 give the basic binary assumptions of flow analysis, and Chaps. 6 to 10 try to separate them and isolate the basic effect of each assumption.

A Classic Example: Pressure Drop in Pipe Flow

In Chap. 6 we shall analyze the classic problem of viscous fluid flow through long, straight pipes. This flow is amenable to both analysis and experiment and is well documented in the literature. The pressure drop Δp from inlet to exit increases as the average fluid velocity through the pipe increases. The pipe diameter and the fluid physical properties are important, too.

Let the pipe be smooth, of 1-cm diameter. Figure 1.15 is a log-log plot of $\Delta p/L$ versus average velocity V for four different common fluids, as estimated from the data correlations to be developed in Chap. 6. This figure would have been state-of-the-art for engineers in 1880. It looks reasonable but has several intriguing features:

1. The pressure drops vary by seven orders of magnitude.
2. At low velocity $\Delta p/L$ rises linearly with V; then, after a small "jump" $\Delta p/L$ begins to rise quite a bit faster, nearly quadratically with V.
3. The jump, now called the *transition point*, occurs at four oddly erratic places.
4. The fluid behavior seems mischievous: Water and mercury are close together at low velocity but spread apart after the jump. Conversely, water and gasoline, somewhat apart at low velocity, come together after the jump.

All these features, and more, began to be explained clearly after a classic experiment in 1883 by Osborne Reynolds at the University of Manchester. Thus was dimensional analysis born, and Fig. 1.15 is clarified by what we now call the *Reynolds number*, $\rho VD/\mu$. A dimensionless pressure drop, or friction factor, collapses all the data of Fig. 1.15 into a single curve, as will be shown in Fig. 6.13.

1.9 Flow Patterns: Streamlines, Streaklines, and Pathlines

Fluid mechanics is a highly visual subject. The patterns of flow can be visualized in a dozen different ways, and you can view these sketches or photographs and learn a great deal qualitatively and often quantitatively about the flow. Appendix C lists a number

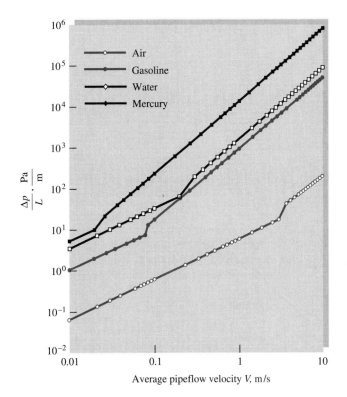

Fig. 1.15 Pressure drop per unit length for flow of four different fluids through a 1-cm-diameter smooth pipe. These curves are computed from the engineering data correlations in Chap. 6.

of fine films which have been made to illustrate various flow phenomena.

Four basic types of line patterns are used to visualize flows:

1. A *streamline* is a line everywhere tangent to the velocity vector at a given instant.
2. A *pathline* is the actual path traversed by a given fluid particle.
3. A *streakline* is the locus of particles which have earlier passed through a prescribed point.
4. A *timeline* is a set of fluid particles that form a line at a given instant.

The streamline is convenient to calculate mathematically, while the other three are easier to generate experimentally. Note that a streamline and a timeline are instantaneous lines, while the pathline and the streakline are generated by the passage of time. The velocity profile shown in Fig. 1.13 is really a timeline generated earlier by a single discharge of bubbles from the wire. A pathline can be found by a time exposure of a single marked particle moving through the flow. Streamlines are difficult to generate experimentally in unsteady flow unless one marks a great many particles and notes their direction of motion during a very short time interval [17, p. 35]. In steady flow the situation simplifies greatly:

Streamlines, pathlines, and streaklines are identical in steady flow.

In fluid mechanics the most common mathematical result for visualization purposes is the streamline pattern. Figure 1.16a shows a typical set of streamlines, and Fig. 1.16b

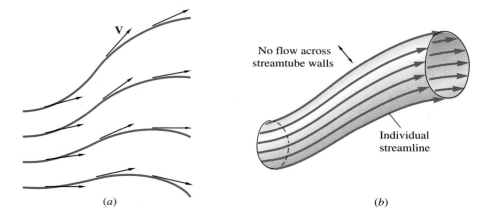

Fig. 1.16 The most common method of flow-pattern presentation: (*a*) Streamlines are everywhere tangent to the local velocity vector; (*b*) a streamtube is formed by a closed collection of streamlines.

No flow across streamtube walls

Individual streamline

(*a*)

(*b*)

shows a closed pattern called a *streamtube*. By definition the fluid within a streamtube is confined there because it cannot cross the streamlines; thus the streamtube walls need not be solid but may be fluid surfaces.

Figure 1.17 shows an arbitrary velocity vector. If the elemental arc length dr of a streamline is to be parallel to **V**, their respective components must be in proportion:

Streamline:
$$\frac{dx}{u} = \frac{dy}{v} = \frac{dz}{w} = \frac{dr}{V} \tag{1.41}$$

If the velocities (u, v, w) are known functions of position and time, Eq. (1.41) can be integrated to find the streamline passing through the initial point (x_0, y_0, z_0, t_0). The method is straightforward for steady flows (Example 1.10) but may be laborious for unsteady flow.

The pathline, or displacement of a particle, is defined by integration of the velocity components, as mentioned in Sec. 1.5:

Pathline:
$$x = \int u \, dt \qquad y = \int v \, dt \qquad z = \int w \, dt \tag{1.42}$$

Fig. 1.17 Geometric relations for defining a streamline.

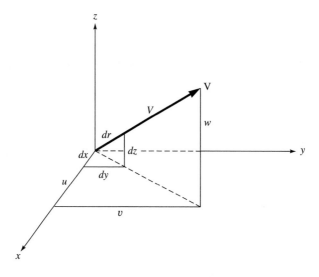

Given (u, v, w) as known functions of position and time, the integration is begun at a specified initial position (x_0, y_0, z_0, t_0). Again the integration may be laborious.

Streaklines, easily generated experimentally with smoke, dye, or bubble releases, are very difficult to compute analytically. See Ref. 18 for mathematical details.

EXAMPLE 1.10

Given the steady two-dimensional velocity distribution

$$u = Kx \qquad v = -Ky \qquad w = 0 \tag{1}$$

where K is a positive constant, compute and plot the streamlines of the flow, including directions, and give some possible interpretations of the pattern.

Solution

Since time does not appear explicitly in Eq. (1), the motion is steady, so that streamlines, pathlines, and streaklines will coincide. Since $w = 0$ everywhere, the motion is two dimensional, in the xy plane. The streamlines can be computed by substituting the expressions for u and v into Eq. (1.41):

$$\frac{dx}{Kx} = -\frac{dy}{Ky}$$

or

$$\int \frac{dx}{x} = -\int \frac{dy}{y}$$

Integrating, we obtain $\ln x = -\ln y + \ln C$, or

$$xy = C \qquad\qquad\qquad Ans. \ (2)$$

This is the general expression for the streamlines, which are hyperbolas. The complete pattern is plotted in Fig. E1.10 by assigning various values to the constant C. The arrowheads can be determined only by returning to Eqs. (1) to ascertain the velocity component direc-

Fig. E1.10 Streamlines for the velocity distribution given by Eq. (1), for $K > 0$.

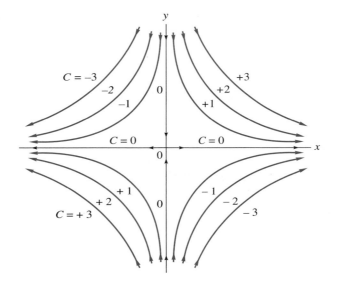

tions, assuming K is positive. For example, in the upper right quadrant ($x > 0$, $y > 0$), u is positive and v is negative; hence the flow moves down and to the right, establishing the arrowheads as shown.

Note that the streamline pattern is entirely independent of constant K. It could represent the impingement of two opposing streams, or the upper half could simulate the flow of a single downward stream against a flat wall. Taken in isolation, the upper right quadrant is similar to the flow in a 90° corner. This is definitely a realistic flow pattern and is discussed again in Chap. 8.

Finally note the peculiarity that the two streamlines ($C = 0$) have opposite directions and intersect. This is possible only at a point where $u = v = w = 0$, which occurs at the origin in this case. Such a point of zero velocity is called a *stagnation point*.

A streakline can be produced experimentally by the continuous release of marked particles (dye, smoke, or bubbles) from a given point. Figure 1.18 shows two examples. The flow in Fig. 1.18*b* is unsteady and periodic due to the flapping of the plate against the oncoming stream. We see that the dash-dot streakline does not coincide with either the streamline or the pathline passing through the same release point. This is characteristic of unsteady flow, but in Fig. 1.18*a* the smoke filaments form streaklines which are identical to the streamlines and pathlines. We noted earlier that this coincidence of lines is always true of steady flow: Since the velocity never changes magnitude or direction at any point, every particle which comes along repeats the behavior of its earlier neighbors.

Methods of experimental flow visualization include the following:

1. Dye, smoke, or bubble discharges
2. Surface powder or flakes on liquid flows
3. Floating or neutral-density particles
4. Optical techniques which detect density changes in gas flows: shadowgraph, schlieren, and interferometer
5. Tufts of yarn attached to boundary surfaces

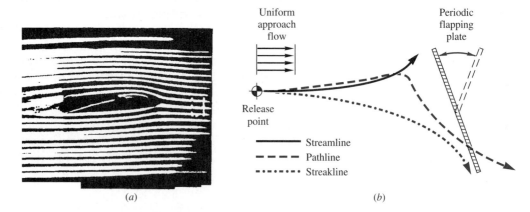

(a) (b)

Fig. 1.18 Experimental visualization of steady and unsteady flow: (a) steady flow past an airfoil visualized by smoke filaments (*C. A. A. SCIENTIFIC—Prime Movers Laboratory Systems*); (b) unsteady flow past an oscillating plate with a point bubble release (from an experiment in Ref. 17).

6. Evaporative coatings on boundary surfaces
7. Luminescent fluids or additives

These methods are illustrated in film 3 in App. C. The mathematical implications of flow-pattern analysis are discussed in detail in Ref. 18. References 19 and 20 are beautiful albums of photographs. References 21 and 22 are monographs on flow visualization.

1.10 History and Scope of Fluid Mechanics

Like most scientific disciplines, fluid mechanics has a history of erratically occurring early achievements, then an intermediate era of steady fundamental discoveries in the eighteenth and nineteenth centuries, leading to the twentieth-century era of ''modern practice,'' as we self-centeredly term our limited but up-to-date knowledge. Ancient civilizations had enough knowledge to solve certain flow problems. Sailing ships with oars and irrigation systems were both known in prehistoric times. The Greeks produced quantitative information. Archimedes and Hero of Alexandria both postulated the parallelogram law for addition of vectors in the third century B.C. Archimedes (285–212 B.C.) formulated the laws of buoyancy and applied them to floating and submerged bodies, actually deriving a form of the differential calculus as part of the analysis. The Romans built extensive aqueduct systems in the fourth century B.C. but left no records showing any quantitative knowledge of design principles.

From the birth of Christ to the Renaissance there was a steady improvement in the design of such flow systems as ships and canals and water conduits but no recorded evidence of fundamental improvements in flow analysis. Then Leonardo da Vinci (1452–1519) derived the equation of conservation of mass in one-dimensional steady flow. Leonardo was an excellent experimentalist, and his notes contain accurate descriptions of waves, jets, hydraulic jumps, eddy formation, and both low-drag (streamlined) and high-drag (parachute) designs. A Frenchman, Edme Mariotte (1620–1684), built the first wind tunnel and tested models in it.

Problems involving the momentum of fluids could finally be analyzed after Isaac Newton (1642–1727) postulated his laws of motion and the law of viscosity of the linear fluids now called newtonian. The theory first yielded to the assumption of a ''perfect'' or frictionless fluid, and eighteenth-century mathematicians (Daniel Bernoulli, Leonhard Euler, Jean d'Alembert, Joseph-Louis Lagrange, and Pierre-Simon Laplace) produced many beautiful solutions of frictionless-flow problems. Euler developed both the differential equations of motion and their integrated form, now called the Bernoulli equation. D'Alembert used them to show his famous paradox: that a body immersed in a frictionless fluid has zero drag. These beautiful results amounted to overkill, since perfect-fluid assumptions have very limited application in practice and most engineering flows are dominated by the effects of viscosity. Engineers began to reject what they regarded as a totally unrealistic theory and developed the science of *hydraulics*, relying almost entirely on experiment. Such experimentalists as Chézy, Pitot, Borda, Weber, Francis, Hagen, Pouiseuille, Darcy, Manning, Bazin, and Weisbach produced data on a variety of flows such as open channels, ship resistance, pipe flows, waves, and turbines. All too often the data were used in raw form without regard to the fundamental physics of flow.

At the end of the nineteenth century, unification between experimental *hydraulics* and theoretical *hydrodynamics* finally began. William Froude (1810–1879) and his son Robert (1846–1924) developed laws of model testing, Lord Rayleigh (1842–1919) proposed the technique of dimensional analysis, and Osborne Reynolds (1842–1912) published the classic pipe experiment in 1883 which showed the importance of the dimensionless Reynolds number named after him. Meanwhile, viscous-flow theory was available but unexploited, since Navier (1785–1836) and Stokes (1819–1903) had successfully added newtonian viscous terms to the equations of motion. The resulting Navier-Stokes equations were too difficult to analyze for arbitrary flows. Then, in 1904, a German engineer, Ludwig Prandtl (1875–1953), published perhaps the most important paper ever written on fluid mechanics. Prandtl pointed out that fluid flows with small viscosity, e.g., water flows and airflows, can be divided into a thin viscous layer, or *boundary layer*, near solid surfaces and interfaces, patched onto a nearly inviscid outer layer, where the Euler and Bernoulli equations apply. Boundary-layer theory has proved to be the single most important tool in modern flow analysis. The twentieth-century foundations for the present state of the art in fluid mechanics were laid in a series of broad-based experiments and theories by Prandtl and his two chief friendly competitors, Theodore von Kármán (1881–1963) and Sir Geoffrey I. Taylor (1886–1975). Many of the results sketched here from a historical point of view will, of course, be discussed in this textbook. More historical details can be found in Refs. 23 to 25.

Since the earth is 75 percent covered with water and 100 percent covered with air, the scope of fluid mechanics is vast and touches nearly every human endeavor. The sciences of meteorology, physical oceanography, and hydrology are concerned with naturally occurring fluid flows, as are medical studies of breathing and blood circulation. All transportation problems involve fluid motion, with well-developed specialties in aerodynamics of aircraft and rockets and in naval hydrodynamics of ships and submarines. Almost all our electric energy is developed either from water flow or from steam flow through turbine generators. All combustion problems involve fluid motion, as do the more classic problems of irrigation, flood control, water supply, sewage disposal, projectile motion, and oil and gas pipelines. The aim of this book is to present enough fundamental concepts and practical applications in fluid mechanics to prepare you to move smoothly into any of these specialized fields of the science of flow—and then be prepared to move out again as new technologies develop.

References

1. D. A. Anderson, J. C. Tannehill, and R. H. Pletcher, *Computational Fluid Mechanics and Heat Transfer*, McGraw-Hill, New York, 1984.
2. S. V. Patankar, *Numerical Heat Transfer and Fluid Flow*, Hemisphere, New York, 1980.
3. F. M. White, *Viscous Fluid Flow*, 2d ed., McGraw-Hill, New York, 1991.
4. R. J. Goldstein (ed.), *Fluid Mechanics Measurements*, Hemisphere, New York, 1983.
5. R. A. Granger, *Experiments in Fluid Mechanics*, Holt, New York, 1988.
6. R. B. Bird, R. C. Armstrong, and O. Hassager, *Dynamics of Polymeric Liquids*, vol. 1: *Fluid Mechanics* and vol. 2: *Kinetic Theory* (with C. F. Curtiss), Wiley, New York, 1987.
7. A. E. Bergeles and S. Ishigai, *Two-Phase Flow Dynamics and Reactor Safety*, McGraw-Hill, New York, 1981.
8. G. N. Patterson, *Introduction to the Kinetic Theory of Gas Flows*, University of Toronto Press, Toronto, 1971.
9. *ASME Orientation and Guide for Use of SI Units*, Guide no. SI-1, American Society of Mechanical Engineers, New York, 1982.

10. J. P. Holman, *Heat Transfer*, 7th ed., McGraw-Hill, New York, 1990.
11. R. C. Reid, J. M. Prausnitz, and T. K. Sherwood, *The Properties of Gases and Liquids*, 4th ed., McGraw-Hill, New York, 1987.
12. J. Hilsenrath et al., ''Tables of Thermodynamic and Transport Properties,'' *U.S. Nat. Bur. Stand. Circ. 564,* 1955; reprinted by Pergamon, New York, 1960.
13. C. A. Meyer et al., *ASME Steam Tables: With Mollier Chart*, 5th ed., American Society of Mechanical Engineers, New York, 1983.
14. O. A. Hougen and K. M. Watson, *Chemical Process Principles Charts*, Wiley, New York, 1960.
15. A. W. Adamson, *Physical Chemistry of Surfaces*, 5th ed., Interscience, New York, 1990.
16. J. A. Knauss, *Introduction to Physical Oceanography*, Prentice-Hall, Englewood Cliffs, N.J., 1978.
17. National Committee for Fluid Mechanics Films, *Illustrated Experiments in Fluid Mechanics*, M.I.T. Press, Cambridge, Mass., 1972.
18. I. G. Currie, *Fundamental Mechanics of Fluids*, 2d ed., McGraw-Hill, New York, 1993.
19. M. van Dyke, *An Album of Fluid Motion*, Parabolic Press, Stanford, Calif., 1982.
20. Y. Nakayama (ed.), *Visualized Flow*, Pergamon, Oxford, 1988.
21. W. J. Yang (ed.), *Handbook of Flow Visualization*, Hemisphere, New York, 1989.
22. W. Merzkirch, *Flow Visualization*, 2d ed., Academic, New York, 1987.
23. H. Rouse and S. Ince, *History of Hydraulics*, Iowa Institute of Hydraulic Research, University of Iowa, Iowa City, 1957; reprinted by Dover, New York, 1963.
24. H. Rouse, *Hydraulics in the United States 1776–1976*, Iowa Institute of Hydraulic Research, University of Iowa, Iowa City, 1976.
25. G. Garbrecht, *Hydraulics and Hydraulic Research: An Historical Review*, Gower Pub., Aldershot, United Kingdom, 1987.
26. *1986 SAE Handbook*, vols. 1 to 4, Society of Automotive Engineers, Warrendale, Penn., 1986.
27. J. R. van Wazer, *Viscosity and Flow Measurement*, Interscience, New York, 1963.

Recommended Films

Films numbered 3, 4, 6, 13, 16, and 17 in App. C.

PROBLEMS

Problem Distribution

Section	Topic	Problems
1.1, 1.2, 1.3	Fluid-continuum concept	1.1–1.3
1.4	Dimensions, units, dynamics	1.4–1.19
1.5	Velocity field	1.20–1.21
1.6	Thermodynamic properties	1.22–1.36
1.7	Viscosity; no-slip condition	1.37–1.61
1.7	Surface tension	1.62–1.71
1.7	Vapor pressure; cavitation	1.72–1.74
1.7	Speed of sound; Mach number	1.75–1.76
1.8	Basic flow analysis and classification	1.77–1.78
1.9	Streamlines and pathlines	1.79–1.84
1.10	History of fluid mechanics	1.85

1.1 A gas at 20°C may be considered *rarefied*, deviating from the continuum concept, when it contains fewer than 10^{12} molecules per cubic millimeter. If Avogadro's number is 6.023 E23 molecules per mole, what absolute pressure (in Pa) for air does this represent?

1.2 Table A.6 lists the density of the standard atmosphere as a function of altitude. Use these values to estimate crudely—say, within a factor of 2—the number of molecules of air in the entire atmosphere of the earth.

1.3 What is the number of molecules in 1 μm^3 of water at 20°C? According to the criterion of Sec. 1.3, at what pressure will (liquid) water become rarefied and deviate from the continuum concept?

1.4 A beaker approximates a right circular cone with diameter 6 in and height 8 in. When filled with liquid, it weighs 48 oz; when empty, it weighs 9 oz. Estimate the density of this liquid in both SI and BG units.

1.5 The *mean free path* of a gas ℓ is defined as the average distance traveled by molecules between collisions. A proposed formula for estimating ℓ of an ideal gas is

$$\ell = 1.26 \frac{\mu}{\rho\sqrt{RT}}$$

What are the dimensions of the constant 1.26? Use the formula to estimate the mean free path of air at 0°C and 5 kPa. Would you consider air *rarefied* at this condition?

1.6 A small village draws 1 acre · ft/day of water from its reservoir. Convert this water usage to (*a*) gallons per minute and (*b*) liters per second.

1.7 In the $\{MLT\Theta\}$ system, what is the dimensional representation of (*a*) entropy, (*b*) mass rate of flow, (*c*) drag force, (*d*) angular acceleration, and (*e*) modulus of elasticity?

1.8 Suppose we know little about the strength of materials but are told that the bending stress σ in a beam is *proportional* to the beam half-thickness y and also depends upon the bending moment M and the beam-area moment of inertia I. We also learn that, for the particular case $M = 2500$ in · lbf, $y = 1.5$ in, and $I = 0.4$ in^4, the predicted stress is 64.64 MPa. Use this information, without further study of structural analysis, to find the only possible dimensionally homogeneous formula for $\sigma = y\,f(M, I)$.

1.9 SAE 70 lubricating oil at 100°C weighs 55 lbf/ft^3 and has a viscosity of 0.0088 slug/(ft · s). In SI units, what are (*a*) its viscosity μ and (*b*) its kinematic viscosity $\nu = \mu/\rho$?

1.10 The Stokes-Oseen formula [18] for drag force F on a sphere of diameter D in a fluid stream of low velocity V, density ρ, and viscosity μ is

$$F = 3\pi\mu DV + \frac{9\pi}{16}\rho V^2 D^2$$

Is this formula dimensionally homogeneous?

1.11 Engineers sometimes use the following formula for the volume rate of flow Q of a liquid flowing through a hole of diameter D in the side of a tank

$$Q = 0.6\,\frac{\pi}{4}\,D^2(2gh)^{1/2}$$

where g is the acceleration of gravity and h is the height of the liquid surface above the hole. What are the dimensions of the constant 0.6?

1.12 For low-speed (laminar) steady flow through a circular pipe, as shown in Fig. P1.12, the velocity u varies with radius and takes the form

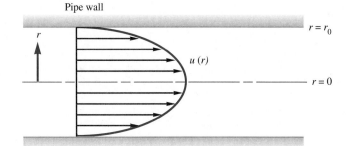

Fig. P1.12

$$u = B\,\frac{\Delta p}{\mu}\,(r_0^2 - r^2)$$

where μ is the fluid viscosity and Δp is the pressure drop from entrance to exit. What are the dimensions of the constant B?

1.13 The *efficiency* η of a pump is defined as the (dimensionless) ratio of the power developed by the flow to the power required to drive the pump

$$\eta = \frac{Q\,\Delta p}{\text{input power}}$$

where Q is the volume rate of flow and Δp is the pressure rise produced by the pump. Suppose that a certain pump develops a pressure rise of 25 lbf/in^2 when its flow rate is 60 L/s. If the input power is 18.5 hp, what is the efficiency?

1.14 Figure P1.14 shows the flow of water over a dam. The volume flow Q is known to depend only upon the crest width B, acceleration of gravity g, and upstream water height H above the dam crest. It is further known that Q is proportional to $H^{3/2}$. What is the form of the only possible dimensionally homogeneous relation for this flow rate?

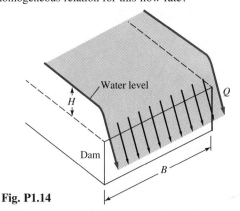

Fig. P1.14

1.15 The speed of propagation C of waves traveling at the interface between two fluids is given by

$$C = \left(\frac{\pi Y}{\rho_a \lambda}\right)^{1/2}$$

where λ is the wavelength and ρ_a the average density of the two fluids. If the formula is dimensionally consistent, what are the units of Y? What might it represent?

1.16 A popular formula in the hydraulics literature is the Hazen-Williams formula for volume flow rate Q in a pipe of diameter D and pressure gradient dp/dx:

$$Q = 61.9 D^{2.63} \left(\frac{dp}{dx}\right)^{0.54}$$

What are the dimensions of the constant 61.9? Can this formula be used with confidence for a variety of liquids and gases?

1.17 We have seen that algebraic physical equations such as that of Bernoulli, Eq. (1) of Example 1.3, are dimensionally consistent. Are differential equations in physics also consistent? For example, determine whether the heat-conduction equation

$$\rho c_p \frac{\partial T}{\partial t} = k \frac{\partial^2 T}{\partial x^2}$$

is dimensionally consistent. Can you draw a general conclusion from this result?

1.18 A ball of mass m is thrown directly upward from the initial position $z = 0$ and $V = V_0$. The air drag on the ball is KV^2, where K is a drag parameter to be correlated in Chap. 7. Set up a differential equation for the ball motion, and solve for the instantaneous velocity $V(t)$ and position $z(t)$. Find the maximum height z_{max} reached by the ball.

1.19 Apply the analysis of Prob. 1.18 to a baseball, with $m = 145$ g, $V_0 = 40$ m/s, and $K \approx 0.0013$ N $\cdot$ s^2/m^2. Compute the maximum height of the ball and the time at which it is reached, and compare your results with the classical case of zero air drag.

1.20 Extend the formula for fluid acceleration, from Example 1.5, to three dimensions. Write your final relation in compact vector form, using the velocity $\mathbf{V}$ and the operator ∇.

1.21 Apply the result from Example 1.5 to compute the acceleration vector for the velocity field $\mathbf{V} = Kx\mathbf{i} - Ky t\mathbf{j} + 0\mathbf{k}$, where K is a positive constant. Comment about the directions of the acceleration vectors for this particular (practical engineering) flow.

1.22 For a perfect gas, estimate the specific weight in N/m^3, on earth, of (a) carbon monoxide, (b) chlorine, and (c) uranium hexafluoride gas ^{238}UF$_6$ at 80°C and 125 kPa.

1.23 A tank contains 1.2 m^3 of helium at 150 kPa and 75°C. Estimate the total mass of this gas, in kg, (a) on earth and (b) on the moon. (c) How much heat transfer, in MJ, is required

to expand this gas at constant temperature to a new volume of 2.0 m^3?

1.24 When we in the United States say a tire is filled "to 30 lb," we mean that its internal pressure is 30 lbf/in^2 above the ambient atmosphere. If the tire is at sea level, has a volume of 3.0 ft^3, and is at 65°F, estimate the total weight of air, in lbf, inside the tire.

1.25 Wet atmospheric air at 100 percent relative humidity contains saturated water vapor, and by Dalton's law of partial pressures,

$$p_{atm} = p_{dry\ air} + p_{water\ vapor}$$

Suppose this wet atmosphere is at 30°C and 1 atm. Calculate the density of this 100 percent humid air, and compare with the density of dry air at the same conditions.

1.26 Air at 1 atm and 80°F has an internal energy of approximately 2.35 E6 ft^2/(s^2 $\cdot$ °R). If this air moves at 450 ft/s at an altitude $z = 25$ ft, what is its total energy, in ft $\cdot$ lbf/(slug $\cdot$ °R), relative to the datum $z = 0$? Are any energy contributions negligible?

1.27 For steam at 20 lbf/in^2, some values of temperature and specific volume are as follows, from Ref. 13:

T, °F	300	400	500	600	700
v ft^3/lbm	22.356	25.428	28.457	31.466	34.465

Is stream, for these conditions, nearly a perfect gas, or is it wildly nonideal? If reasonably perfect, find a least-squares value for the gas constant R, in m^2/(s^2 $\cdot$ K), estimate the percentage of error in this approximation, and compare with Table A.4.

1.28 A compressed-air tank holds 6 ft^3 of air at 20°C and 100 lbf/in^2 "gage," i.e., above atmospheric pressure. Estimate the energy, in ft $\cdot$ lbf, required to compress this air from the atmosphere, assuming an ideal isothermal process.

1.29 The density of (fresh) water at 1 atm, over the temperature range 0 to 100°C, is given in Table A.1. Fit these values to a least-squares equation of the form $\rho = a + bT + cT^2$, with T in °C, and estimate its accuracy. Use your formula to compute the density of water at 57°C, and compare with the accepted experimental value of 984.7 kg/m^3.

1.30 If 3 kg of CO_2 is confined in a rigid tank at 160°C and 135 kPa, estimate how much heat must be removed to lower the gas pressure to 85 kPa. Assume a perfect gas.

1.31 If water occupies 1 m^3 at 1-atm pressure, estimate the pressure required to reduce its volume by 2 percent.

1.32 Repeat Prob. 1.28 if the tank is filled with compressed *water* instead of air. Why is the result thousands of times less than the result of 204,000 ft $\cdot$ lbf in Prob. 1.28?

1.33 Some experimental values of the density of mercury versus pressure at 20°C are as follows:

p, atm	1	1,000	2,000
ρ, kg/m^3	13,545	13,599	13,652

Fit these data to the empirical state relation for liquids, Eq. (1.19), to find the best values of B and n for mercury. Then, assuming the data are nearly isentropic, use these values to estimate the speed of sound of mercury at 1 atm and compare with Table 9.1.

1.34 In Table A.4, most common gases (air, nitrogen, oxygen) have a specific-heat ratio $k \approx 1.40$. Why do argon and helium have such high values? Why does NH$_3$ have such a low value? What is the lowest k for any gas that you know of?

1.35 The *isentropic bulk modulus* B of a fluid is defined as the isentropic change in pressure per fractional change in density:

$$B = \rho \left(\frac{\partial p}{\partial \rho} \right)_s$$

What are the dimensions of B? Estimate the bulk modulus of (a) CO$_2$, assumed to be a perfect gas, and (b) water, at 20°C and 1 atm.

1.36 A near-ideal gas has a molecular weight of 59 and a specific heat $c_v = 2550$ ft · lbf/(slug · °R). What are (a) its specific-heat ratio k and (b) its speed of sound at 20°C?

1.37 In Fig. 1.6, if the fluid is glycerin at 20°C and the width between the plates is 4 mm, what shear stress (in Pa) is required to move the upper plate at 7.5 m/s? What is the Reynolds number if L is taken to be the distance between plates?

1.38 SAE 30 oil at 20°C is sheared between two plates 0.008 in apart. The lower plate is fixed, and the upper plate moves at 22 ft/s. What is the shear stress in the oil?

1.39 Knowing μ for air at 20°C from Table 1.4, estimate its viscosity at 650°C by (a) the power law and (b) the Sutherland law. (c) Also make an estimate from Fig. 1.5. Compare with the accepted value of $\mu \approx 3.98$ E-5 kg/(m · s).

1.40 In Fig. 1.5 in the range $3.0 < T/T_c < 10$, determine the best-fit value of the power-law viscosity exponent n in Eq. (1.27) for the low-density-limit curve.

1.41 For liquid viscosity as a function of temperature, a simplification of the log-quadratic law of Eq. (1.28) is *Andrade's equation* [11]

$$\mu \approx A \exp \left(\frac{B}{T} \right)$$

where (A, B) are curve-fit constants and T is absolute temperature. Fit this relation to the data for water in Table A.1, and estimate the percentage of error of the approximation.

1.42 Some experimental values of the viscosity of argon gas at 1 atm are as follows:

T, K	300	400	500	600	700	800
μ, kg/(m · s)	2.27 E-5	2.85 E-5	3.37 E-5	3.83 E-5	4.25 E-5	4.64 E-5

Fit these values to either (a) a power law or (b) the Sutherland law, Eq. (1.27).

1.43 Some measured values of the viscosity of ethyl alcohol at 1 atm are as follows:

T, °C	−40	0	40	80
μ, kg/(m · s)	0.00481	0.00177	0.000834	0.000430

Fit these values to Eq. (1.28) and assess the accuracy of the formula. Take $T_0 = 273.16$ K and compare also with Table A.3.

1.44 The values for SAE 30 oil in Table 1.4 are strictly "representative," not exact, because lubricating oils vary considerably according to the type of crude oil from which they are refined. The Society of Automotive Engineers [26] allows certain kinematic viscosity *ranges* for all lubricating oils: for SAE 30, $9.3 < \nu < 12.5$ cm^2/s at 100°C. SAE 30 oil density can also vary ± 2 percent from the tabulated value of 891 kg/m^3. Consider the following data for an acceptable grade of SAE 30 oil:

T, °C	0	20	40	60	80	100
μ, kg/(m · s)	2.00	0.40	0.11	0.042	0.017	0.0095

How does this oil compare with the plot in Fig. A.1? How well do the data fit Andrade's equation in Prob. 1.41?

1.45 A block of weight W slides down an inclined plane while lubricated by a thin film of oil, as in Fig. P1.45. The film contact area is A, and its thickness is h. Assuming a linear velocity distribution in the film, derive an expression for the "terminal" (zero-acceleration) velocity V of the block.

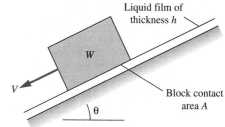

Fig. P1.45

1.46 Find the terminal velocity of the block in Fig. P1.45 if the block mass is 6 kg, $A = 35$ cm^2, $\theta = 15°$, and the film is 1-mm-thick SAE 30 oil at 20°C.

1.47 A shaft 6.00 cm in diameter is being pushed axially through a bearing sleeve 6.02 cm in diameter and 40 cm long. The clearance, assumed uniform, is filled with oil whose properties are $\nu = 0.003$ m^2/s and SG = 0.88. Estimate the force required to pull the shaft at a steady velocity of 0.4 m/s.

1.48 A thin plate is separated from two fixed plates by very viscous liquids μ_1 and μ_2, respectively, as in Fig. P1.48. The plate spacings h_1 and h_2 are unequal, as shown. The contact area is A between the center plate and each fluid. (*a*) Assuming a linear velocity distribution in each fluid, derive the force F required to pull the plate at velocity V. (*b*) Is there a necessary *relation* between the two viscosities μ_1 and μ_2?

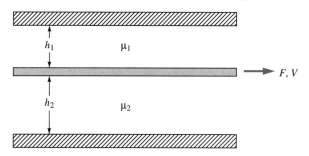

Fig. P1.48

1.49 The shaft in Prob. 1.47 is now fixed axially and rotated inside the sleeve at 1500 r/min. Estimate (*a*) the torque (in N · m) and (*b*) the power (in kW) required to rotate the shaft.

1.50 An amazing number of commercial and laboratory devices have been developed to measure the viscosity of fluids, as described in Ref. 27. The concentric rotating shaft of Prob. 1.49 is an example of a *rotational viscometer*. Let the inner and outer cylinders have radii r_i and r_o, respectively, with total sleeve length L. Let the rotational rate be Ω rad/s and the applied torque be M. Derive a theoretical relation for the viscosity of the clearance fluid μ in terms of these parameters.

1.51 Use the theory of Prob. 1.50 (or derive an ad hoc expression if you like) for a 8-cm-long shaft, rotating at 1200 r/min, with $r_i = 2.00$ cm and $r_o = 2.05$ cm. If the measured torque is 0.293 N · m, what is the fluid viscosity? Suppose that the uncertainties of the experiment are as follows: L, ± 0.5 mm; M, ± 0.003 N · m; Ω, ± 1 percent; and r_i or r_o, ± 0.02 mm. What is the uncertainty in the measured viscosity?

1.52 Air at 20°C forms a boundary layer near a solid wall of sine-wave-shaped velocity profile. The boundary-layer thickness is 6 mm, and the peak velocity is 10 m/s. Compute the shear stress in the boundary layer in Pa at y equal to (*a*), 0, (*b*) 3 mm, and (*c*) 6 mm (See Fig. P1.52).

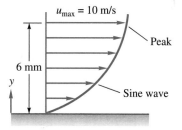

Fig. P1.52

1.53 A solid cone of angle 2θ, base radius r_0, and density ρ_c is rotating with initial angular velocity ω_0 inside a conical seat. The clearance h is filled with oil of viscosity μ. Neglecting air drag, derive an expression for the time required to reduce the cone's angular velocity from ω_0 to $0.2\omega_0$. (See Fig. P1.53).

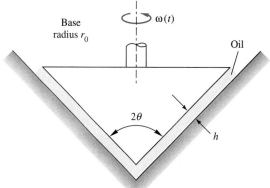

Fig. P1.53

1.54 A disk of radius R rotates at angular velocity Ω inside an oil bath of viscosity μ, as shown in Fig. P1.54. Assuming a linear velocity profile and neglecting shear on the outer disk edges, derive an expression for the viscous torque on the disk.

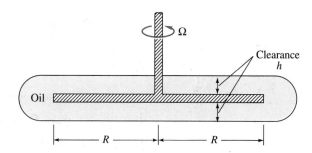

Fig. P1.54

1.55 The device in Fig. P1.54 is called a *rotating-disk viscometer* [27]. Suppose that $R = 5$ cm and $h = 1$ mm. If the torque required to rotate the disk at 900 r/min is 0.537 N · m, what is the viscosity of the fluid? If the uncertainty in each parameter (M, R, h, Ω) is ± 1 percent, what is the overall uncertainty in the viscosity?

1.56 The device in Fig. P1.56 is called a *cone-plate viscometer* [27]. The angle of the cone is very small, so that $\sin \theta \approx \theta$, and the gap is filled with the test liquid. The torque M to rotate the cone at a rate Ω is measured. Assuming a linear velocity profile in the fluid film, derive an expression for fluid viscosity μ as a function of (M, R, Ω, θ).

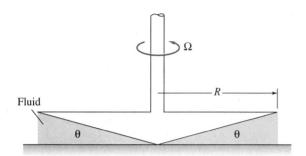

Fig. P1.56

1.57 For the cone-plate viscometer of Fig. P1.56, suppose that R = 6 cm and θ = 3°. If the torque required to rotate the cone at 600 r/min is 0.157 N · m, what is the viscosity of the fluid? If the uncertainty in each parameter (M, R, Ω, θ) is ±1 percent, what is the overall uncertainty in the viscosity?

1.58 The laminar-pipe flow example of Prob. 1.12 can be used to design a *capillary viscometer* [27]. If Q is the volume flow rate, L the pipe length, and Δp the pressure drop from entrance to exit, the theory of Chap. 6 yields a formula for viscosity:

$$\mu = \frac{\pi r_0^4 \, \Delta p}{8LQ}$$

Pipe end effects are neglected [27]. Suppose our capillary has r_0 = 2 mm and L = 25 cm. The following flow-rate and pressure-drop data are obtained for a certain fluid:

Q, m³/h	0.36	0.72	1.08	1.44	1.80
Δp, kPa	159	318	477	1274	1851

What is the viscosity of the fluid? *Note:* Only the first three points give the proper viscosity. What is wrong for the last two points, which were measured accurately?

1.59 A solid cylinder of diameter D, length L, and density ρ_s falls due to gravity inside a tube of diameter D_0. The clearance $D_0 - D \ll D$ is filled with fluid of density ρ and viscosity μ. Neglect the air above and below the cylinder. Derive a formula for the terminal fall velocity of the cylinder. Apply your formula to the case of a steel cylinder where D = 2 cm, D_0 = 2.04 cm, and L = 15 cm with a film of SAE 30 oil at 20°C.

1.60 Repeat the analysis of Eq. (1.26)—see Fig. 1.6—for fluid heated unevenly to cause the viscosity to vary linearly from $\mu/2$ at the lower surface to $3\mu/2$ at the upper surface. What is the ratio of the shear stress in this case to the shear stress for Fig. 1.6?

1.61 An air-hockey puck has a mass of 50 g and is 9 cm in diameter. When it is placed on the air table, a 20°C air film, of 0.12-mm thickness, forms under the puck. The puck is struck with an initial velocity of 10 m/s. Assuming a linear velocity distribution in the air film, how long will it take the puck to

(*a*) slow down to 1 m/s and (*b*) stop completely? (*c*) How far along this extremely long table will the puck have traveled for condition (*a*)?

1.62 The hydrogen bubbles which produced the velocity profiles in Fig. 1.13 are quite small; $D \approx 0.01$ mm. If the hydrogen-water interface is comparable to air-water and the water temperature is 30°C, estimate the excess pressure within the bubble.

1.63 Derive Eq. (1.34) by making a force balance on the fluid interface in Fig. 1.9c.

1.64 At 60°C the surface tension of mercury and of water is 0.47 and 0.0662 N/m, respectively. What capillary-height changes will occur in these two fluids when they are in contact with air in a clean glass tube of 0.4-mm diameter?

1.65 The system in Fig. P1.65 is used to calculate the pressure p_1 in the tank by measuring the 15-cm height of liquid in the 1-mm-diameter tube. The fluid is at 60°C (see Prob. 1.64). Calculate the true fluid height in the tube and the percentage of error due to capillarity if the fluid is (*a*) water and (*b*) mercury.

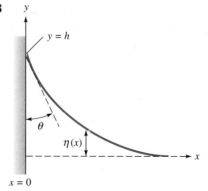

15 cm

P_1

Fig. P1.65

1.66 A thin wire ring, 3 cm in diameter, is lifted from a water surface at 20°C. Neglecting the wire weight, what is the force required to lift the ring? Is this a good way to measure surface tension? Should the wire be made of any particular material?

1.67 A 1-in-diameter soap bubble has an internal pressure 0.002 lbf/in² greater than the outside atmosphere. What is the surface tension of the soap-air interface, in lbf/ft?

1.68 Make an analysis of the shape of the water-air interface near

Fig. P1.68

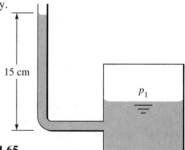

$y = h$

θ

$\eta(x)$

$x = 0$

a plane wall, assuming that the slope is small, $R^{-1} \approx d^2\eta/dx^2$, and that the pressure difference across the interface is balanced by the specific weight and the interface height, $\Delta p \approx \gamma\eta$. The boundary conditions are a wetting contact angle θ at $x = 0$ and a horizontal surface $\eta = 0$ as $x \to \infty$. What is the maximum height h at the wall? (See Fig. P1.68.)

1.69 Repeat Prob. 1.68 using the exact curvature expression $R^{-1} = \eta''/(1 + \eta'^2)^{3/2}$. Find the value of h.

1.70 Derive an expression for the capillary-height change h for a fluid of surface tension Y and contact angle θ between two vertical parallel plates a distance W apart. What will h be for water at 20°C if $W = 1$ mm? (See Fig. P1.70).

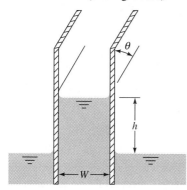

Fig. P1.70

1.71 A soap bubble of diameter D_1 coalesces with another bubble of diameter D_2 to form a single bubble of diameter D_3 with the same amount of air. Assuming an isothermal process, derive an expression for finding D_3 as a function of D_1, D_2, p_{atm}, and Y.

1.72 Early mountaineers boiled water to estimate their altitude. If they reach the top and find that water boils at 82°C, approximately how high is the mountain?

1.73 A small submersible moves at velocity V, in fresh water at 20°C, at a 2-m depth, where the ambient pressure is 121 kPa. Its critical cavitation number is known to be $Ca = 0.27$. At what velocity will cavitation bubbles begin to form on the body? Will the body cavitate if $V = 30$ m/s and the water is cold (5°C)?

1.74 A propeller is tested in a water tunnel at 20°C as in Fig. 1.12a. The lowest pressure on the blade can be estimated by a form of Bernoulli's equation (Example 1.3):

$$p_{min} \approx p_0 - \tfrac{1}{2}\rho V^2$$

where $p_0 = 1.5$ atm and $V =$ tunnel velocity. If we run the tunnel at $V = 18$ m/s, can we be sure that there will be no cavitation? If not, can we change the water temperature and avoid cavitation?

1.75 An airplane flies at 712 mi/h. At what altitude in the standard atmosphere will the airplane's Mach number be exactly unity?

1.76 The density of 20°C gasoline varies with pressure approximately as follows:

p, atm	1	500	1000	1500
ρ, lbm/ft³	42.45	44.85	46.60	47.98

Use these data to estimate (a) the speed of sound (m/s) and (b) the bulk modulus (MPa) of gasoline at 1 atm.

1.77 Examine the photographs in Figs. 1.12a, 1.13, 5.2a, 7.14a, and 9.10b and classify them according to the boxes in Fig. 1.14.

1.78 By using the physical property data in App. A, show that the "jumps" in the pressure drop curves in Fig. 1.15 all occur at about the same Reynolds number, $\rho VD/\mu$.

1.79 Repeat Example 1.10 by letting the velocity components increase linearly with time:

$$\mathbf{V} = Kxt\mathbf{i} - Kyt\mathbf{j} + 0\mathbf{k}$$

Find and sketch, for a few representative times, the instantaneous streamlines. How do they differ from the steady flow lines in Example 1.10?

1.80 A velocity field is given by $u = V \cos\theta$, $v = V \sin\theta$, and $w = 0$, where V and θ are constants. Find an expression for the streamlines of this flow.

1.81 A two-dimensional steady velocity field is given by $u = x^2 - y^2$, $v = -2xy$. Derive the streamline pattern and sketch a few streamlines in the upper half plane. *Hint:* The differential equation is exact.

1.82 Problems 1.80 and 1.81 illustrate the determination of the streamline pattern $f(x, y) = $ const from the known velocity components $u(x, y)$ and $v(x, y)$. Is the inverse of this problem possible? That is, can one compute u and v from a given streamline pattern $f(x, y) = $ constant?

1.83 A two-dimensional unsteady velocity field is given by $u = x(1 + 2t)$, $v = y$. Find the equation of the time-varying streamlines which all pass through the point (x_0, y_0) at some time t. Sketch some.

1.84 Repeat Prob. 1.83 to find the equation of the pathline which passes through (x_0, y_0) at time $t = 0$. Sketch it.

1.85 Do some reading and report to the class on the life and achievements, especially vis-à-vis fluid mechanics, of
 (a) Evangelista Torricelli (1608–1647)
 (b) Henri de Pitot (1695–1771)
 (c) Antoine Chézy (1718–1798)
 (d) Gotthilf Heinrich Ludwig Hagen (1797–1884)
 (e) Julius Weisbach (1806–1871)
 (f) George Gabriel Stokes (1819–1903)
 (g) Moritz Weber (1871–1951)
 (h) Theodor von Kármán (1881–1963)
 (i) Paul Richard Heinrich Blasius (1883–1970)

Chapter 2
Pressure Distribution in a Fluid

Motivation. Many fluid problems do not involve motion. They concern the pressure distribution in a static fluid and its effect on solid surfaces and on floating and submerged bodies.

When the fluid velocity is zero, denoted as the *hydrostatic condition*, the pressure variation is due only to the weight of the fluid. Assuming a known fluid in a given gravity field, the pressure may easily be calculated by integration. Important applications in this chapter are (1) pressure distribution in the atmosphere and the oceans, (2) the design of manometer pressure instruments, (3) forces on submerged flat and curved surfaces, (4) buoyancy on a submerged body, and (5) the behavior of floating bodies. The last two result in Archimedes' principles.

If the fluid is moving in *rigid-body motion*, such as a tank of liquid which has been spinning for a long time, the pressure also can be easily calculated, because the fluid is free of shear stress. We apply this idea here to simple rigid-body accelerations in Sec. 2.9. Pressure measurement instruments are discussed in Sec. 2.10. As a matter of fact, pressure also can be easily analyzed in arbitrary (nonrigid-body) motions $\mathbf{V}(x, y, z, t)$, but we defer that subject to Chap. 4.

2.1 Pressure and Pressure Gradient

In Fig. 1.1 we saw that a fluid at rest cannot support shear stress and thus Mohr's circle reduces to a point. In other words, the normal stress on any plane through a fluid element at rest is equal to a unique value called the *fluid pressure p*, taken positive for compression by common convention. This is such an important concept that we shall review it with another approach.

Figure 2.1 shows a small wedge of fluid at rest of size Δx by Δz by Δs and depth b into the paper. There is no shear by definition, but we postulate that the pressures p_x, p_z, and p_n may be different on each face. The weight of the element also may be important. Summation of forces must equal zero (no acceleration) in both the x and z directions.

$$\sum F_x = 0 = p_x b \, \Delta z - p_n b \, \Delta s \sin \theta$$

$$\sum F_z = 0 = p_z b \, \Delta x - p_n b \, \Delta s \cos \theta - \tfrac{1}{2} \gamma b \, \Delta x \, \Delta z \tag{2.1}$$

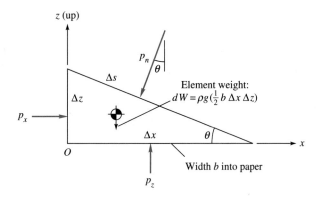

Fig. 2.1 Equilibrium of a small wedge of fluid at rest.

but the geometry of the wedge is such that

$$\Delta s \sin \theta = \Delta z \qquad \Delta s \cos \theta = \Delta x \tag{2.2}$$

Substitution into Eq. (2.1) and rearrangement give

$$p_x = p_n \qquad p_z = p_n + \tfrac{1}{2}\gamma\,\Delta z \tag{2.3}$$

These relations illustrate two important principles of the hydrostatic, or shear-free, condition: (1) There is no pressure change in the horizontal direction, and (2) there is a vertical change in pressure proportional to the density, gravity, and depth change. We shall exploit these results to the fullest, starting in Sec. 2.3.

In the limit as the fluid wedge shrinks to a "point," $\Delta z \rightarrow 0$ and Eqs. (2.3) become

$$p_x = p_z = p_n = p \tag{2.4}$$

Since θ is arbitrary, we conclude that the pressure p at a point in a static fluid is independent of orientation.

What about the pressure at a point in a moving fluid? If there are strain rates in a moving fluid, there will be viscous stresses, both shear and normal in general (Sec. 4.3). In that case (Chap. 4) the pressure is defined as the average of the three normal stresses σ_{ii} on the element

$$p = -\tfrac{1}{3}(\sigma_{xx} + \sigma_{yy} + \sigma_{zz}) \tag{2.5}$$

The minus sign occurs because a compression stress is considered to be negative whereas p is positive. Equation (2.5) is subtle and rarely needed since the great majority of viscous flows have negligible viscous normal stresses (Chap. 4).

Pressure Force on a Fluid Element

Pressure (or any other stress, for that matter) causes no net force on a fluid element unless it varies *spatially*.[1] To see this, consider the pressure acting on the two x faces in Fig. 2.2. Let the pressure vary arbitrarily

$$p = p(x, y, z, t) \tag{2.6}$$

The net force in the x direction on the element in Fig. 2.2 is given by

[1] An interesting application for a large element is in Fig. 3.7.

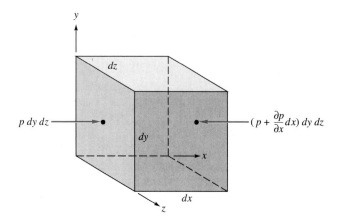

Fig. 2.2 Net x force on an element due to pressure variation.

$$dF_x = p \, dy \, dz - \left(p + \frac{\partial p}{\partial x} \, dx\right) dy \, dz = -\frac{\partial p}{\partial x} \, dx \, dy \, dz \qquad (2.7)$$

In like manner the net force dF_y involves $-\partial p/\partial y$, and the net force dF_z concerns $-\partial p/\partial z$. The total net-force vector on the element due to pressure is

$$d\mathbf{F}_{\text{press}} = \left(-\mathbf{i}\frac{\partial p}{\partial x} - \mathbf{j}\frac{\partial p}{\partial y} - \mathbf{k}\frac{\partial p}{\partial z}\right) dx \, dy \, dz \qquad (2.8)$$

We recognize the term in parentheses as the negative vector gradient of p. Denoting $\mathbf{f}$ as the net force per unit element volume, we rewrite Eq. (2.8) as

$$\mathbf{f}_{\text{press}} = -\nabla p \qquad (2.9)$$

Thus it is not the pressure but the pressure *gradient* causing a net force which must be balanced by gravity or acceleration or some other effect in the fluid.

2.2 Equilibrium of a Fluid Element

The pressure gradient is a *surface* force which acts on the sides of the element. There may also be a *body* force, due to electromagnetic or gravitational potentials, acting on the entire mass of the element. Here we consider only the gravity force, or weight of the element

$$d\mathbf{F}_{\text{grav}} = \rho\mathbf{g} \, dx \, dy \, dz$$

or

$$\mathbf{f}_{\text{grav}} = \rho\mathbf{g} \qquad (2.10)$$

In general, there may also be a surface force due to the gradient, if any, of the viscous stresses. For completeness, we write this term here without derivation and consider it more thoroughly in Chap. 4. For an incompressible fluid with constant viscosity, the net viscous force is

$$\mathbf{f}_{\text{VS}} = \mu\left(\frac{\partial^2 \mathbf{V}}{\partial x^2} + \frac{\partial^2 \mathbf{V}}{\partial y^2} + \frac{\partial^2 \mathbf{V}}{\partial z^2}\right) = \mu\nabla^2\mathbf{V} \qquad (2.11)$$

where VS stands for viscous stresses and μ is the coefficient of viscosity from Chap. 1. Note that the term $\mathbf{g}$ in Eq. (2.10) denotes the acceleration of gravity, a vector acting toward the center of the earth. On earth the average magnitude of **g** is 32.174 ft/s^2 = 9.807 m/s^2.

The total vector resultant of these three forces—pressure, gravity, and viscous stress—must either keep the element in equilibrium or cause it to move with acceleration **a**. From Newton's law, Eq. (1.2), we have

$$\rho\mathbf{a} = \sum \mathbf{f} = \mathbf{f}_{press} + \mathbf{f}_{grav} + \mathbf{f}_{visc} = -\nabla p + \rho\mathbf{g} + \mu\nabla^2\mathbf{V} \qquad (2.12)$$

This is one form of the differential momentum equation for a fluid element, and it is studied further in Chap. 4. Vector addition is implied by Eq. (2.12): The acceleration reflects the local balance of forces and is not necessarily parallel to the local-velocity vector, which reflects the direction of motion at that instant.

This chapter is concerned with cases where the velocity and acceleration are known, leaving one to solve for the pressure variation in the fluid. Later chapters will take up the more general problem where pressure, velocity, and acceleration are all unknown. Rewrite Eq. (2.12) as

$$\nabla p = \rho(\mathbf{g} - \mathbf{a}) + \mu\nabla^2\mathbf{V} = \mathbf{B}(x, y, z, t) \qquad (2.13)$$

where **B** is a short notation for the vector sum on the right-hand side. If **V** and **a** = $d\mathbf{V}/dt$ are known functions of space and time and the density and viscosity are known, we can solve Eq. (2.13) for $p(x, y, z, t)$ by direct integration. By components, Eq. (2.13) is equivalent to three simultaneous first-order differential equations

$$\frac{\partial p}{\partial x} = B_x(x, y, z, t) \qquad \frac{\partial p}{\partial y} = B_y(x, y, z, t) \qquad \frac{\partial p}{\partial z} = B_z(x, y, z, t) \qquad (2.14)$$

Since the right-hand sides are known functions, they can be integrated systematically to obtain the distribution $p(x, y, z, t)$ except for an unknown function of time, which remains because we have no relation for $\partial p/\partial t$. This extra function is found from a condition of known time variation $p_0(t)$ at some point (x_0, y_0, z_0). If the flow is steady (independent of time), the unknown function is a constant and is found from knowledge of a single known pressure p_0 at a point (x_0, y_0, z_0). If this sounds complicated, it is not; we shall illustrate with many examples. Finding the pressure distribution from a known velocity distribution is one of the easiest problems in fluid mechanics, which is why we put it in Chap. 2.

Examining Eq. (2.13), we can single out at least four special cases:

1. Flow at rest or at constant velocity: The acceleration and viscous terms vanish identically, and p depends only upon gravity and density. This is the *hydrostatic* condition. See Sec. 2.3.
2. Rigid-body translation and rotation: The viscous term vanishes identically, and p depends only upon the term $\rho(\mathbf{g} - \mathbf{a})$. See Sec. 2.9.
3. Irrotational motion ($\nabla \times \mathbf{V} \equiv 0$): The viscous term vanishes identically, and an exact integral called *Bernoulli's equation* can be found for the pressure distribution. See Sec. 4.9.
4. Arbitrary viscous motion: Nothing helpful happens, no general rules apply, but still the integration is quite straightforward. See Sec. 6.4.

Let us consider cases 1 and 2 here.

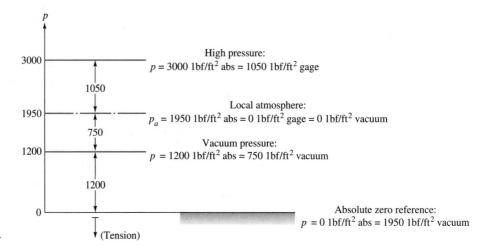

Fig. 2.3 Illustration of absolute, gage, and vacuum pressure readings.

Gage Pressure and Vacuum Pressure: Relative Terms

Before embarking on examples, we should note that engineers are apt to specify pressures as (1) the *absolute* or total magnitude or (2) the value *relative* to the local ambient atmosphere. The second case occurs because many pressure instruments are of *differential* type and record, not an absolute magnitude, but the difference between the fluid pressure and the atmosphere. The measured pressure may be either higher or lower than the local atmosphere, and each case is given a name:

1. $p > p_a$ *Gage* pressure: $p(\text{gage}) = p - p_a$
2. $p < p_a$ *Vacuum* pressure: $p(\text{vacuum}) = p_a - p$

This is a convenient shorthand, and one later adds (or subtracts) atmospheric pressure to determine the absolute fluid pressure.

A typical situation is shown in Fig. 2.3. The local atmosphere is at, say, 1950 lbf/ft^2, which might reflect a storm condition in a sea-level location or normal conditions at an altitude of 2300 ft. Thus, on this day, $p_a = 1950$ lbf/ft^2 absolute $= 0$ lbf/ft^2 gage $= 0$ lbf/ft^2 vacuum. Suppose gage 1 in a laboratory reads $p_1 = 3000$ lbf/ft^2 absolute. This value may be reported as a *gage* pressure $p_1 = 3000 - 1950 = 1050$ lbf/ft^2 gage. (One must also record the atmospheric pressure in the laboratory, since p_a changes gradually.) Suppose gage 2 reads $p_2 = 1200$ lbf/ft^2 absolute. Locally, this is a *vacuum* pressure and might be reported as $p_2 = 1950 - 1200 = 750$ lbf/ft^2 vacuum. From time to time, we may specify gage or vacuum pressure in problems to keep you on your toes.

2.3 Hydrostatic Pressure Distributions

If the fluid is at rest or at constant velocity, $\mathbf{a} = 0$ and $\nabla^2\mathbf{V} = 0$. Equation (2.13) for the pressure distribution reduces to

$$\nabla p = \rho\mathbf{g} \tag{2.15}$$

This is a *hydrostatic* distribution and is correct for all fluids at rest, regardless of their viscosity, because the viscous term vanishes identically.

Recall from vector analysis that the vector ∇p expresses the magnitude and direction of the maximum spatial rate of increase of the scalar property p. As a result, ∇p is perpendicular everywhere to surfaces of constant p. Thus Eq. (2.15) states that a fluid in hydrostatic equilibrium will align its constant-pressure surfaces everywhere normal to the local-gravity vector. The maximum pressure increase will be in the direction of gravity, i.e., "down." If the fluid is a liquid, its free surface, being at atmospheric pressure, will be normal to local gravity, or "horizontal." You probably knew all this before, but Eq. (2.15) is the proof of it.

In our customary coordinate system z is "up." Thus the local-gravity vector for small-scale problems is

$$\mathbf{g} = -g\mathbf{k} \tag{2.16}$$

where g is the magnitude of local gravity, for example, 9.807 m/s^2. For these coordinates Eq. (2.15) has the components

$$\frac{\partial p}{\partial x} = 0 \qquad \frac{\partial p}{\partial y} = 0 \qquad \frac{\partial p}{\partial z} = -\rho g = -\gamma \tag{2.17}$$

the first two of which tell us that p is independent of x and y. Hence $\partial p/\partial z$ can be replaced by the total derivative dp/dz, and the hydrostatic condition reduces to

$$\frac{dp}{dz} = -\gamma$$

or

$$p_2 - p_1 = -\int_1^2 \gamma \, dz \tag{2.18}$$

Equation (2.18) is the solution to the hydrostatic problem. The integration requires an assumption about the density and gravity distribution. Gases and liquids are usually treated differently.

We state the following conclusions about a hydrostatic condition:

Pressure in a continuously distributed uniform static fluid varies only with vertical distance and is independent of the shape of the container. The pressure is the same at all points on a given horizontal plane in the fluid. The pressure increases with depth in the fluid.

An illustration of this is shown in Fig. 2.4. The free surface of the container is atmos-

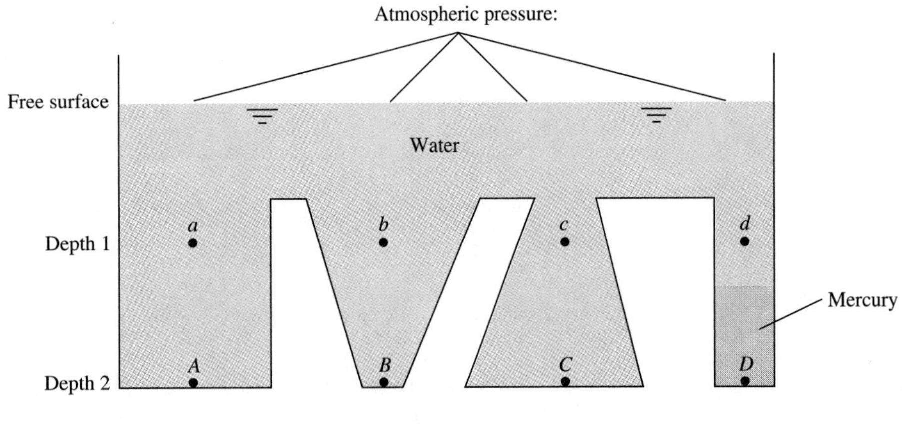

Fig. 2.4 Hydrostatic-pressure distribution. Points a, b, c, and d are at equal depths in water and therefore have identical pressures. Points A, B, and C are also at equal depths in water and have identical pressures higher than a, b, c, and d. Point D has a different pressure from A, B, and C because it is not connected to them by a water path.

pheric and forms a horizontal plane. Points a, b, c, and d are at equal depth in a horizontal plane and are interconnected by the same fluid, water; therefore all points have the same pressure. The same is true of points A, B, and C on the bottom, which all have the same higher pressure than at a, b, c, and d. However, point D, although at the same depth as A, B, and C, has a different pressure because it lies beneath a different fluid, mercury.

Effect of Variable Gravity

For a spherical planet of uniform density, the acceleration of gravity varies inversely as the square of the radius from its center

$$g = g_0 \left(\frac{r_0}{r} \right)^2 \tag{2.19}$$

where r_0 is the planet radius and g_0 is the surface value of g. For earth, $r_0 \approx 3960$ statute mi ≈ 6400 km. In typical engineering problems the deviation from r_0 extends from the deepest ocean, about 11 km, to the atmospheric height of supersonic transport operation, about 20 km. This gives a maximum variation in g of $(6400/6420)^2$, or 0.6 percent. We therefore neglect the variation of g in most problems.

Hydrostatic Pressure in Liquids

Liquids are so nearly incompressible that we can neglect their density variation in hydrostatics. In Example 1.7 we saw that water density increases only 4.6 percent at the deepest part of the ocean. Its effect on hydrostatics would be about half of this, or 2.3 percent. Thus we assume constant density in liquid hydrostatic calculations, for which Eq. (2.18) integrates to

Liquids:
$$p_2 - p_1 = -\gamma(z_2 - z_1) \tag{2.20}$$

or
$$z_1 - z_2 = \frac{p_2}{\gamma} - \frac{p_1}{\gamma}$$

We use the first form in most problems. The quantity γ is called the *specific weight* of the fluid, with dimensions of weight per unit volume; some values are tabulated in Table 2.1. The quantity p/γ is a length called the *pressure head* of the fluid.

For lakes and oceans, the coordinate system is usually chosen as in Fig. 2.5, with $z = 0$ at the free surface, where p equals the surface atmospheric pressure p_a. When

Table 2.1 Specific Weight of Some Common Fluids

Fluid	Specific weight γ at 68°F = 20°C	
	lbf/ft³	N/m³
Air (at 1 atm)	0.0752	11.8
Ethyl alcohol	49.2	7,733
SAE 30 oil	55.5	8,720
Water	62.4	9,790
Seawater	64.0	10,050
Glycerin	78.7	12,360
Carbon tetrachloride	99.1	15,570
Mercury	846	133,100

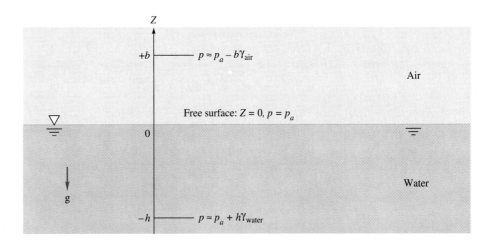

Fig. 2.5 Hydrostatic-pressure distribution in oceans and atmospheres.

we introduce the reference value $(p_1, z_1) = (p_a, 0)$, Eq. (2.20) becomes, for p at any (negative) depth z,

Lakes and oceans:
$$p = p_a - \gamma z \qquad (2.21)$$

where γ is the average specific weight of the lake or ocean. As we shall see, Eq. (2.21) holds in the atmosphere also with an accuracy of 2 percent for heights z up to 1000 m.

EXAMPLE 2.1

Newfound Lake, a freshwater lake near Bristol, New Hampshire, has a maximum depth of 60 m, and the mean atmospheric pressure is 91 kPa. Estimate the absolute pressure in kPa at this maximum depth.

Solution

From Table 2.1, take $\gamma \approx 9790$ N/m³. With $p_a = 91$ kPa and $z = -60$ m, Eq. (2.21) predicts that the pressure at this depth will be

$$p = 91 \text{ kN/m}^2 - (9790 \text{ N/m}^3)(-60 \text{ m}) \frac{1 \text{ kN}}{1000 \text{ N}}$$

$$= 91 \text{ kPa} + 587 \text{ kN/m}^2 = 678 \text{ kPa} \qquad \textit{Ans.}$$

By omitting p_a we could state the result as $p = 587$ kPa (gage).

The Mercury Barometer

The simplest practical application of the hydrostatic formula (2.20) is the barometer (Fig. 2.6), which measures atmospheric pressure. A tube is filled with mercury and inverted while submerged in a reservoir. This causes a near vacuum in the closed upper end because mercury has an extremely small vapor pressure at room temperatures (0.16 Pa at 20°C). Since atmospheric pressure forces a mercury column to rise a distance h into the tube, the upper mercury surface is at zero pressure.

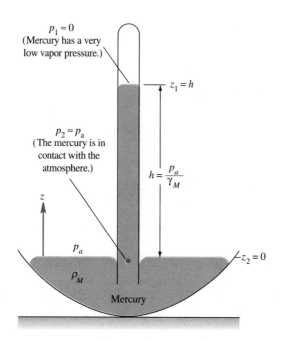

Fig. 2.6 The mercury barometer: The height of the mercury column is a measure of atmospheric pressure.

From Fig. 2.6, Eq. (2.20) applies with $p_1 = 0$ at $z_1 = h$ and $p_2 = p_z$ at $z_2 = 0$:

$$p_a - 0 = -\gamma_M(0 - h)$$

or
$$h = \frac{p_a}{\gamma_M} \tag{2.22}$$

At sea-level standard, with $p_a = 101{,}350$ Pa and $\gamma_M = 133{,}100 \text{ N/m}^3$ from Table 2.1, the barometric height is $h = 101{,}350/133{,}100 = 0.761$ m or 761 mm. In the United States the weather service reports this as an atmospheric "pressure" of 29.96 inHg (inches of mercury). Mercury is used because it is the heaviest common liquid. A water barometer would be 34 ft high.

Hydrostatic Pressure in Gases

Gases are compressible, with density nearly proportional to pressure. Thus density must be considered as a variable in Eq. (2.18) if the integration carries over large pressure changes. It is sufficiently accurate to introduce the perfect-gas law $p = \rho RT$ in Eq. (2.18)

$$\frac{dp}{dz} = -\rho g = -\frac{p}{RT} g$$

Separate the variables and integrate between points 1 and 2:

$$\int_1^2 \frac{dp}{p} = \ln \frac{p_2}{p_1} = -\frac{g}{R} \int_1^2 \frac{dz}{T} \tag{2.23}$$

The integral over z requires an assumption about the temperature variation $T(z)$. One common approximation is the *isothermal atmosphere*, where $T = T_0$:

$$p_2 = p_1 \exp\left[-\frac{g(z_2 - z_1)}{RT_0}\right] \tag{2.24}$$

The quantity in brackets is dimensionless. (Think that over; it must be dimensionless, right?) Equation (2.24) is a fair approximation for earth, but actually the earth's mean atmospheric temperature drops off nearly linearly with z up to an altitude of about 36,000 ft (11,000 m):

$$T \approx T_0 - Bz \tag{2.25}$$

Here T_0 is sea-level temperature (absolute) and B is the *lapse rate*, both of which vary somewhat from day to day. By international agreement [1] the following standard values are assumed to apply from 0 to 36,000 ft:

$$T_0 = 518.69°R = 288.16 \text{ K} = 15°C$$

$$B = 0.003566°R/ft = 0.00650 \text{ K/m} \tag{2.26}$$

This lower portion of the atmosphere is called the *troposphere*. Introducing Eq. (2.25) into (2.23) and integrating, we obtain the more accurate relation

$$p = p_a\left(1 - \frac{Bz}{T_0}\right)^{g/(RB)} \qquad \text{where } \frac{g}{RB} = 5.26 \text{ (air)} \tag{2.27}$$

in the troposphere, with $z = 0$ at sea level. The exponent $g/(RB)$ is dimensionless (again it must be) and has the standard value of 5.26 for air, with $R = 1717 \text{ft}^2/(s^2 \cdot °R)$.

The U.S. standard atmosphere [1] is sketched in Fig. 2.7. The pressure is seen to be nearly zero at $z = 30$ km. For tabulated properties see Table A.6.

Fig. 2.7 Temperature and pressure distribution in the U.S. standard atmosphere. (*From Ref. 1.*)

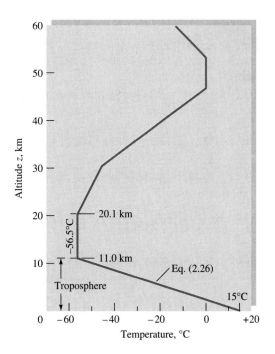

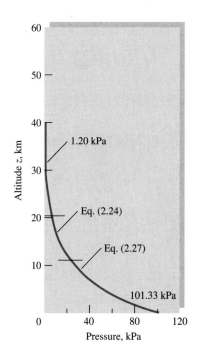

EXAMPLE 2.2

If sea-level pressure is 101,350 Pa, compute the standard pressure at an altitude of 5000 m, using (a) the exact formula and (b) an isothermal assumption at a standard sea-level temperature of 15°C. Is the isothermal approximation adequate?

Solution

Part (a)   Use absolute temperature in the exact formula, Eq. (2.27):

$$p = p_a \left[1 - \frac{(0.00650 \text{ K/m})(5000 \text{ m})}{288.16 \text{ K}} \right]^{5.26} = (101,350 \text{ Pa})(0.8872)^{5.26}$$

$$= 101,350(0.52388) = 54,000 \text{ Pa} \qquad\qquad \textit{Ans. (a)}$$

This is the standard-pressure result given at $z = 5000$ m in Table A.6.

Part (b)   If the atmosphere were isothermal at 288.16 K, Eq. (2.24) would apply:

$$p \approx p_a \exp\left(-\frac{gz}{RT} \right) = (101,350 \text{ Pa}) \exp\left\{ -\frac{(9.807 \text{ m/s}^2)(5000 \text{ m})}{[287 \text{ m}^2/(\text{s}^2 \cdot \text{K})](288.16 \text{ K})} \right\}$$

$$= (101,350 \text{ Pa}) \exp(-0.5929) \approx 60,100 \text{ Pa} \qquad\qquad \textit{Ans. (b)}$$

This is 11 percent higher than the exact result. The isothermal formula is inaccurate in the troposphere.

Is the Linear Formula Adequate for Gases?

The linear approximation from Eq. (2.20) or (2.21), $\Delta p \approx \gamma \Delta z$, is satisfactory for liquids, which are nearly incompressible. It may be used even over great depths in the ocean. For gases, which are highly compressible, it is valid only over moderate changes in altitude.

The error involved in using the linear approximation (2.21) can be evaluated by expanding the exact formula (2.27) into a series

$$\left(1 - \frac{Bz}{T_0} \right)^n = 1 - n\frac{Bz}{T_0} + \frac{n(n-1)}{2!} \left(\frac{Bz}{T_0} \right)^2 - \cdots \qquad\qquad (2.28)$$

where $n = g/(RB)$. Introducing these first three terms of the series into Eq. (2.27) and rearranging, we obtain

$$p = p_a - \gamma_a z \left(1 - \frac{n-1}{2}\frac{Bz}{T_0} + \cdots \right) \qquad\qquad (2.29)$$

Thus the error in using the linear formula (2.21) is small if the second term in parentheses in (2.29) is small compared with unity. This is true if

$$z \ll \frac{2T_0}{(n-1)B} = 20,800 \text{ m} \qquad\qquad (2.30)$$

We thus expect errors of less than 5 percent if z or δz is less than 1000 m.

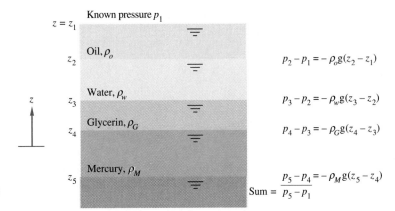

Known pressure p_1

$z = z_1$

Oil, ρ_o z_2 $p_2 - p_1 = -\rho_o g(z_2 - z_1)$

z z_3 Water, ρ_w $p_3 - p_2 = -\rho_w g(z_3 - z_2)$

z_4 Glycerin, ρ_G $p_4 - p_3 = -\rho_G g(z_4 - z_3)$

z_5 Mercury, ρ_M $\dfrac{p_5 - p_4 = -\rho_M g(z_5 - z_4)}{\text{Sum} = \ p_5 - p_1}$

Fig. 2.8 Evaluating pressure changes through a column of multiple fluids.

2.4 Application to Manometry

From the hydrostatic formula (2.20), a change in elevation $z_2 - z_1$ of a liquid is equivalent to a change in pressure $(p_2 - p_1)/\gamma$. Thus a static column of one or more liquids or gases can be used to measure pressure differences between two points. Such a device is called a *manometer*. If multiple fluids are used, we must change the density in the formula as we move from one fluid to another. Figure 2.8 illustrates the use of the formula with a column of multiple fluids. The pressure change through each fluid is calculated separately. If we wish to know the total change $p_5 - p_1$, we add the successive changes $p_2 - p_1, p_3 - p_2, p_4 - p_3$, and $p_5 - p_4$. The intermediate values of p cancel, and we have, for the example of Fig. 2.8,

$$p_5 - p_1 = -\gamma_0(z_2 - z_1) - \gamma_w(z_3 - z_2) - \gamma_G(z_4 - z_3) - \gamma_M(z_5 - z_4) \quad (2.31)$$

No additional simplification is possible on the right-hand side because of the different densities. Notice that we have placed the fluids in order from the lightest on top to the heaviest at bottom. This is the only stable configuration. If we attempt to layer them in any other manner, the fluids will overturn and seek the stable arrangement.

Figure 2.9 shows a simple open manometer for measuring p_A in a closed chamber relative to atmospheric pressure p_a, in other words, measuring the gage pressure. The chamber fluid ρ_1 is combined with a second fluid ρ_2, perhaps for two reasons: (1) to protect the environment from a corrosive chamber fluid or (2) because a heavier fluid

Fig. 2.9 Simple open manometer for measuring p_A relative to atmospheric pressure.

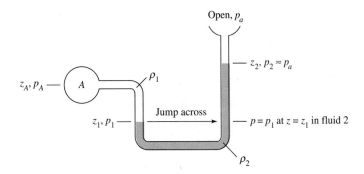

Open, p_a

$z_2, p_2 \approx p_a$

z_A, p_A — A ρ_1

z_1, p_1 — Jump across → $p = p_1$ at $z = z_1$ in fluid 2

ρ_2

p_2 will keep z_2 small and the open tube can be shorter. The basic hydrostatic relation (2.20) is applied in two steps, first from z_A to z_1 and then from z_1 to z_2:

$$p_A - p_1 = -\gamma_1(z_A - z_1) \qquad p_1 - p_2 = -\gamma_2(z_1 - z_2) \qquad (2.32)$$

The small amount of air between z_2 and the open end is neglected, and we assume that $p_2 \approx p_a$. When we add the two relations above, p_1 cancels and we obtain the desired result

$$p_A = p_a - \gamma_1(z_A - z_1) - \gamma_2(z_1 - z_2) \qquad (2.33)$$

Notice that the pressure at level z_1 is equal to p_1 on both sides of the U-tube in Fig. 2.9. This is because a continuous length of the same fluid connects the two equal levels. The hydrostatic relation (2.20) requires this as a form of Pascal's law:

> Any two points at the same elevation in a continuous mass of the same static fluid will be at the same pressure.

This rule can be used to facilitate calculations in multiple-U-tube problems. We can jump across the U-tube if we stay within the same fluid.

EXAMPLE 2.3

(a) Find the pressure p_A in Fig. 2.9 if $p_a = 2116$ lbf/ft^2, $z_A = 7$ in, $z_1 = 4$ in, $z_2 = 13$ in, fluid 1 is water, and fluid 2 is mercury. (b) What would the height z_2 be for the same pressure p_A if the mercury were replaced by glycerin?

Solution

Part (a) The pressure relation has already been derived in Eq. (2.33). From Table 2.1, $\gamma_1 = 62.4$ and $\gamma_2 = 846$ lbf/ft^3. We need z_A, z_1, and z_2 in ft to produce p in lbf/ft^2. Substitute into (2.33)

$$p_A = 2116 - 62.4(\tfrac{7}{12} - \tfrac{4}{12}) - 846(\tfrac{4}{12} - \tfrac{13}{12})$$

$$= 2116 - 16 + 635 = 2735 \text{ lbf/ft}^2 \qquad \textit{Ans. (a)}$$

Part (b) The specific weight of glycerin is 78.7 lbf/ft^3. The balance in Eq. (2.33) would now be

$$2735 = 2116 - 16 - 78.7\left(\frac{4}{12} - z_2\right)$$

or
$$z_2 = \frac{635}{78.7} + \frac{4}{12} = 8.4 \text{ ft} = 101 \text{ in} \qquad \textit{Ans. (b)}$$

This would require a much taller U-tube and is not a good idea in the long run because glycerin tends to mix with water over time.

Instead of attempting to remember manometer formulations, it is simpler to remember Eq. (2.20)[1] and derive the pressure-change relation for each new situation. Figure 2.10 illustrates a multiple-fluid manometer problem for finding the difference in pressure

---

[1] The author prefers as a memory device to keep the negative sign with γ so that the subscripts on p and z will be the same on both sides.

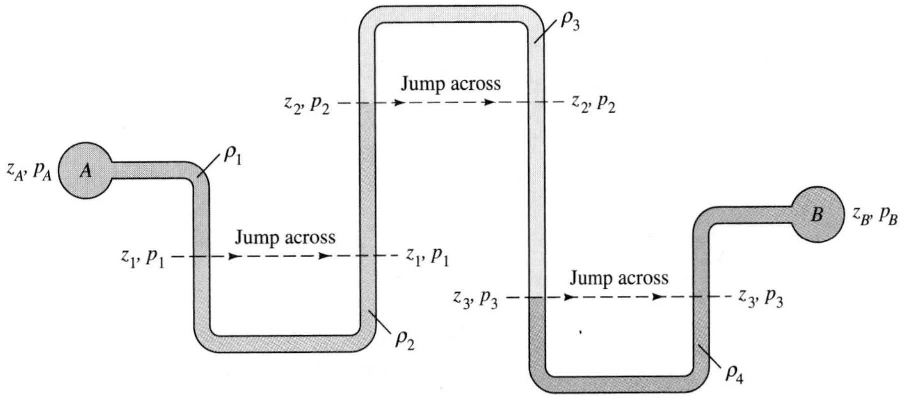

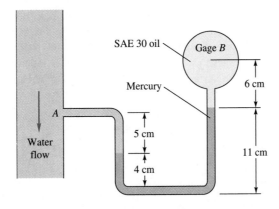

Fig. 2.10 A complicated multiple-fluid manometer to relate p_A to p_B. This system is not especially practical but makes a good homework or examination problem.

between two chambers A and B. We repeatedly apply Eq. (2.20), "jumping across" at equal pressures when we come to a continuous mass of the same fluid. Thus, in Fig. 2.10, we compute four pressure differences while making three jumps:

$$p_A - p_B = (p_A - p_1) + (p_1 - p_2) + (p_2 - p_3) + (p_3 - p_B)$$

$$= -\gamma_1(z_A - z_1) - \gamma_2(z_1 - z_2) - \gamma_3(z_2 - z_3) - \gamma_4(z_3 - z_B) \quad (2.34)$$

The intermediate pressures $p_{1,2,3}$ cancel. It looks complicated, but really it is merely *sequential*. One starts at A, goes down to 1, jumps across, goes up to 2, jumps across, goes down to 3, jumps across, and finally goes up to B. When evaluated, the pressure changes in Eq. (2.34) will be (positive, negative, positive, negative).

EXAMPLE 2.4

Pressure gage B is to measure the pressure at point A in a water flow. If the pressure at B is 87 kPa, estimate the pressure at A, in kPa. Assume all fluids are at 20°C. See Fig. E2.4.

Fig. E2.4

Solution

First list the specific weights from Table 2.1 or Table A.3:

$$\gamma_{\text{water}} = 9790 \text{ N/m}^3 \qquad \gamma_{\text{mercury}} = 133{,}100 \text{ N/m}^3 \qquad \gamma_{\text{oil}} = 8720 \text{ N/m}^3$$

Now proceed from A to B, calculating the pressure change in each fluid and adding:

$$p_A - \gamma_W(\Delta z)_W - \gamma_M(\Delta z)_M - \gamma_O(\Delta z)_O = p_B$$

or $p_A - (9790 \text{ N/m}^3)(-0.05 \text{ m}) - (133,100 \text{ N/m}^3)(0.07 \text{ m}) - (8720 \text{ N/m}^3)(0.06 \text{ m})$

$$= p_A + 489.5 \text{ Pa} - 9317 \text{ Pa} - 523.2 \text{ Pa} = p_B = 87,000 \text{ Pa}$$

where we replace N/m^2 by its short name, Pa. The value $\Delta z_M = 0.07$ m is the net elevation change in the mercury (11 cm $-$ 4 cm). Solving for the pressure at point A, we obtain

$$p_A = 96,351 \text{ Pa} = 96.4 \text{ kPa} \qquad\qquad Ans.$$

The intermediate six-figure result of 96,351 Pa is utterly fatuous, since the measurements cannot be made that accurately.

In making these manometer calculations we have neglected the capillary-height changes due to surface tension, which were discussed in Example 1.9. These effects cancel if there is a fluid interface, or *meniscus*, on both sides of the U-tube, as in Fig. 2.9. Otherwise, as in the right-hand U-tube of Fig. 2.10, a capillary correction can be made or the effect can be made negligible by using large-bore ($\geq$1 cm) tubes.

2.5 Hydrostatic Forces on Plane Surfaces

A common problem in the design of structures which interact with fluids is the computation of the hydrostatic force on a plane surface. If we neglect density changes in the fluid, Eq. (2.20) applies and the pressure on any submerged surface varies linearly with depth. For a plane surface, the linear stress distribution is exactly analogous to combined bending and compression of a beam in strength-of-materials theory. The hydrostatic problem thus reduces to simple formulas involving the centroid and moments of inertia of the plate cross-sectional area.

Figure 2.11 shows a plane panel of arbitrary shape completely submerged in a liquid. The panel plane makes an arbitrary angle θ with the horizontal free surface, so that the depth varies over the panel surface. If h is the depth to any element area dA of the plate, from Eq. (2.20) the pressure there is $p = p_a + \gamma h$.

To derive formulas involving the plate shape, establish an xy coordinate system in the plane of the plate with the origin at its centroid, plus a dummy coordinate ξ down from the surface in the plane of the plate. Then the total hydrostatic force on one side of the plate is given by

$$F = \int p\,dA = \int (p_a + \gamma h)\,dA = p_a A + \gamma \int h\,dA \qquad (2.35)$$

The remaining integral is evaluated by noticing from Fig. 2.11 that $h = \xi \sin \theta$ and, by definition, the centroidal slant distance from the surface to the plate is

$$\xi_{CG} = \frac{1}{A} \int \xi\,dA \qquad (2.36)$$

Therefore, since θ is constant along the plate, Eq. (2.35) becomes

$$F = p_a A + \gamma \sin \theta \int \xi\,dA = p_a A + \gamma \sin \theta\, \xi_{CG} A \qquad (2.37)$$

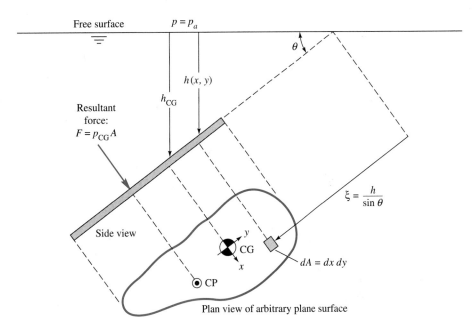

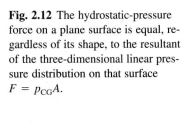

Fig. 2.11 Hydrostatic force and center of pressure on an arbitrary plane surface of area A inclined at an angle θ below the free surface.

Finally, unravel this by noticing that $\xi_{CG} \sin \theta = h_{CG}$, the depth straight down from the surface to the plate centroid. Thus

$$F = p_a A + \gamma h_{CG} A = (p_a + \gamma h_{CG})A = p_{CG}A \qquad (2.38)$$

The force on one side of any plane submerged surface in a uniform fluid equals the pressure at the plate centroid times the plate area, independent of the shape of the plate or the angle θ at which it is slanted.

Equation (2.38) can be visualized physically in Fig. 2.12 as the resultant of a linear stress distribution over the plate area. This simulates combined compression and bending of a beam of the same cross section. It follows that the "bending" portion of the

Fig. 2.12 The hydrostatic-pressure force on a plane surface is equal, regardless of its shape, to the resultant of the three-dimensional linear pressure distribution on that surface $F = p_{CG}A$.

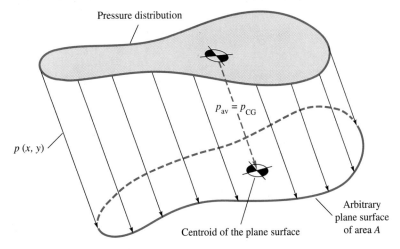

stress causes no force if its "neutral axis" passes through the plate centroid of area. Thus the remaining "compression" part must equal the centroid stress times the plate area. This is the result of Eq. (2.38).

However, to balance the bending-moment portion of the stress, the resultant force F does not act through the centroid but below it toward the high-pressure side. Its line of action passes through the *center of pressure* CP of the plate, as sketched in Fig. 2.11. To find the coordinates (x_{CP}, y_{CP}), we sum moments of the elemental force $p\,dA$ about the centroid and equate to the moment of the resultant F. To compute y_{CP}, we equate

$$F y_{CP} = \int yp\,dA = \int y(p_a + \gamma\xi \sin\theta)\,dA = \gamma \sin\theta \int y\xi\,dA \qquad (2.39)$$

The term $\int p_a y\,dA$ vanishes by definition of centroidal axes. Introducing $\xi = \xi_{CG} - y$, we obtain

$$F y_{CP} = \gamma \sin\theta \left(\xi_{CG} \int y\,dA - \int y^2\,dA \right) = -\gamma \sin\theta\, I_{xx} \qquad (2.40)$$

where again $\int y\,dA = 0$ and I_{xx} is the area moment of inertia of the plate area about its centroidal x axis, computed in the plane of the plate. Substituting for F gives the result

$$y_{CP} = -\gamma \sin\theta \frac{I_{xx}}{p_{CG}A} \qquad (2.41)$$

The negative sign in Eq. (2.41) shows that y_{CP} is below the centroid at a deeper level and, unlike F, depends upon angle θ. If we move the plate deeper, y_{CP} approaches the centroid because every term in Eq. (2.41) remains constant except p_{CG}, which increases. The determination of x_{CP} is exactly similar:

$$F x_{CP} = \int xp\,dA = \int x[p_a + \gamma(\xi_{CG} - y)\sin\theta]\,dA$$

$$= -\gamma \sin\theta \int xy\,dA = -\gamma \sin\theta\, I_{xy} \qquad (2.42)$$

where I_{xy} is the product of inertia of the plate, again computed in the plane of the plate. Substituting for F gives

$$x_{CP} = -\gamma \sin\theta \frac{I_{xy}}{p_{CG}A} \qquad (2.43)$$

For positive I_{xy}, x_{CP} is negative because the dominant pressure force acts in the third, or lower left, quadrant of the panel. If $I_{xy} = 0$, usually implying symmetry, $x_{CP} = 0$ and the center of pressure lies directly below the centroid on the y axis.

Gage-Pressure Formulas

In most cases the ambient pressure p_a is neglected because it acts on both sides of the plate; e.g., the other side of the plate is inside a ship or on the dry side of a gate or dam. In this case $p_{CG} = \gamma h_{CG}$, and the center of pressure becomes independent of specific weight

$$F = \gamma h_{CG}A \qquad y_{CP} = -\frac{I_{xx}\sin\theta}{h_{CG}A} \qquad x_{CP} = -\frac{I_{xy}\sin\theta}{h_{CG}A} \qquad (2.44)$$

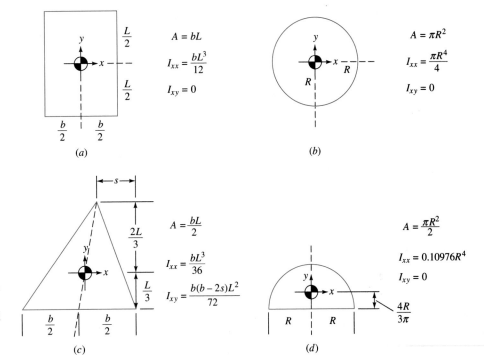

Fig. 2.13 Centroidal moments of inertia for various cross sections: (*a*) rectangle, (*b*) circle, (*c*) triangle, and (*d*) semicircle.

Figure 2.13 gives the area and moments of inertia of several common cross sections for use with these formulas.

EXAMPLE 2.5

The gate in Fig. E2.5a is 5 ft wide, is hinged at point *B*, and rests against a smooth wall at point *A*. Compute (*a*) the force on the gate due to seawater pressure, (*b*) the horizontal force *P* exerted by the wall at point *A*, and (*c*) the reactions at the hinge *B*.

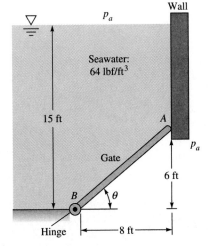

Fig. E2.5a

Solution

Part (a)   By geometry the gate is 10 ft long from A to B, and its centroid is halfway between, or at elevation 3 ft above point B. The depth h_{CG} is thus $15 - 3 = 12$ ft. The gate area is $5(10) = 50$ ft^2. Neglect p_a as acting on both sides of the gate. From Eq. (2.38) the hydrostatic force on the gate is

$$F = p_{CG}A = \gamma h_{CG}A = (64 \text{ lbf/ft}^3)(12 \text{ ft})(50 \text{ ft}^2) = 38{,}400 \text{ lbf} \qquad \textit{Ans. (a)}$$

Part (b)   First we must find the center of pressure of F. A free-body diagram of the gate is shown in Fig. E2.5b. The gate is a rectangle, hence

$$I_{xy} = 0 \qquad \text{and} \qquad I_{xx} = \frac{bL^3}{12} = \frac{(5 \text{ ft})(10 \text{ ft})^3}{12} = 417 \text{ ft}^4$$

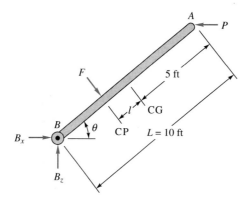

Fig. E2.5b

The distance l from the CG to the CP is given by Eq. (2.44) since p_a is neglected.

$$l = -y_{CP} = +\frac{I_{xx}\sin\theta}{h_{CG}A} = \frac{(417 \text{ ft}^4)(\frac{6}{10})}{(12 \text{ ft})(50 \text{ ft}^2)} = 0.417 \text{ ft}$$

The distance from point B to force F is thus $10 - l - 5 = 4.583$ ft. Summing moments counterclockwise about B gives

$$PL \sin\theta - F(5 - l) = P(6 \text{ ft}) - (38{,}400 \text{ lbf})(4.583 \text{ ft}) = 0$$

or

$$P = 29{,}300 \text{ lbf} \qquad \textit{Ans. (b)}$$

Part (c)   With F and P known, the reactions B_x and B_z are found by summing forces on the gate

$$\sum F_x = 0 = B_x + F \sin\theta - P = B_x + 38{,}400(0.6) - 29{,}300$$

or

$$B_x = 6300 \text{ lbf}$$

$$\sum F_z = 0 = B_z - F \cos\theta = B_z - 38{,}400(0.8)$$

or

$$B_z = 30{,}700 \text{ lbf} \qquad \textit{Ans. (c)}$$

This example should have reviewed your knowledge of statics.

EXAMPLE 2.6

A tank of oil has a right-triangular panel near the bottom, as in Fig. E2.6. Omitting p_a, find the (a) hydrostatic force and (b) CP on the panel.

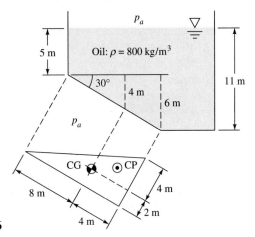

Fig. E2.6

Solution

Part (a)   The triangle has properties given in Fig. 2.13c. The centroid is one-third up (4 m) and one-third over (2 m) from the lower left corner, as shown. The area is

$$\tfrac{1}{2}(6 \text{ m})(12 \text{ m}) = 36 \text{ m}^2$$

The moments of inertia are

$$I_{xx} = \frac{bL^3}{36} = \frac{(6 \text{ m})(12 \text{ m})^3}{36} = 288 \text{ m}^4$$

and

$$I_{xy} = \frac{b(b - 2s)L^2}{72} = \frac{(6 \text{ m})[6 \text{ m} - 2(6 \text{ m})](12 \text{ m})^2}{72} = -72 \text{ m}^4$$

The depth to the centroid is $h_{CG} = 5 + 4 = 9$ m; thus the hydrostatic force from Eq. (2.44) is

$$F = \rho g h_{CG} A = (800 \text{ kg/m}^3)(9.807 \text{ m/s}^2)(9 \text{ m})(36 \text{ m}^2)$$

$$= 2.54 \times 10^6 \text{ (kg} \cdot \text{m)/s}^2 = 2.54 \times 10^6 \text{ N} = 2.54 \text{ MN} \qquad \textit{Ans. (a)}$$

Part (b)   The CP position is given by Eqs. (2.44):

$$y_{CP} = -\frac{I_{xx} \sin \theta}{h_{CG} A} = -\frac{(288 \text{ m}^4)(\sin 30°)}{(9 \text{ m})(36 \text{ m}^2)} = -0.444 \text{ m}$$

$$x_{CP} = -\frac{I_{xy} \sin \theta}{h_{CG} A} = -\frac{(-72 \text{ m}^4)(\sin 30°)}{(9 \text{ m})(36 \text{ m}^2)} = +0.111 \text{ m} \qquad \textit{Ans. (b)}$$

The resultant force $F = 2.54$ MN acts through this point, which is down and to the right of the centroid.

2.6 Hydrostatic Forces on Curved Surfaces

The resultant pressure force on a curved surface is most easily computed by separating it into horizontal and vertical components. Consider the arbitrary curved surface sketched in Fig. 2.14a. The incremental pressure forces, being normal to the local area element, vary in direction along the surface and thus cannot be added numerically. We could sum the separate three components of these elemental pressure forces, but it turns out that we need not perform a laborious three-way integration.

Figure 2.14b shows a free-body diagram of the column of fluid contained in the vertical projection above the curved surface. The desired forces F_H and F_V are exerted by the surface on the fluid column. Other forces are shown due to fluid weight and horizontal pressure on the vertical sides of this column. The column of fluid must be in static equilibrium. On the upper part of the column $bcde$, the horizontal components F_1 exactly balance and are not relevant to the discussion. On the lower, irregular portion of fluid abc adjoining the surface, summation of horizontal forces shows that the desired force F_H due to the curved surface is exactly equal to the force F_H on the vertical left side of the fluid column. This left-side force can be computed by the plane-surface formula, Eq. (2.38), based on a vertical projection of the area of the curved surface. This is a general rule and simplifies the analysis:

> The horizontal component of force on a curved surface equals the force on the plane area formed by the projection of the curved surface onto a vertical plane normal to the component.

If there are two horizontal components, both can be computed by this scheme.

Summation of vertical forces on the fluid free body then shows that

$$F_V = W_1 + W_2 + W_{air} \tag{2.45}$$

We can state this in words as our second general rule:

> The vertical component of pressure force on a curved surface equals in magnitude and direction the weight of the entire column of fluid, both liquid and atmosphere, above the curved surface.

Thus the calculation of F_V involves little more than finding centers of mass of a column of fluid—perhaps a little integration if the lower portion abc has a particularly vexing shape.

Fig. 2.14 Computation of hydrostatic force on a curved surface: (a) submerged curved surface; (b) free-body diagram of fluid above the curved surface.

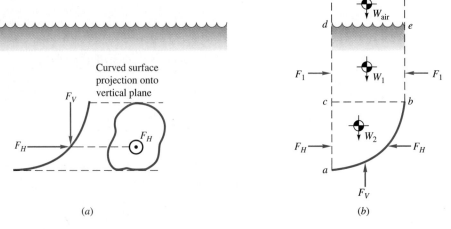

(a)   (b)

EXAMPLE 2.7

A dam has a parabolic shape $z/z_0 = (x/x_0)^2$ as shown in Fig. E2.7a, with $x_0 = 10$ ft and $z_0 = 24$ ft. The fluid is water, $\gamma = 62.4$ lbf/ft^3, and atmospheric pressure may be omitted. Compute the forces F_H and F_V on the dam and the position CP where they act. The width of the dam is 50 ft.

Solution

The vertical projection of this curved surface is a rectangle 24 ft high and 50 ft wide, with its centroid halfway down, or $h_{CG} = 12$ ft. The force F_H is thus

$$F_H = \gamma h_{CG} A_{proj} = (62.4 \text{ lbf/ft}^3)(12 \text{ ft})(24 \text{ ft})(50 \text{ ft})$$

$$= 899{,}000 \text{ lbf} = 899 \times 10^3 \text{ lbf} \qquad Ans.$$

The line of action of F_H is below the centroid by an amount

$$y_{CP} = -\frac{I_{xx} \sin \theta}{h_{CG} A_{proj}} = -\frac{\frac{1}{12}(50 \text{ ft})(24 \text{ ft})^3 (\sin 90°)}{(12 \text{ ft})(24 \text{ ft})(50 \text{ ft})} = -4 \text{ ft}$$

Thus F_H is $12 + 4 = 16$ ft, or two-thirds, down from the free surface or 8 ft from the bottom, as might have been evident by inspection of the triangular pressure distribution.

The vertical component F_V equals the weight of the parabolic portion of fluid above the curved surface. The geometric properties of a parabola are shown in Fig. E2.7b. The weight of this amount of water is

$$F_V = \gamma(\tfrac{2}{3}x_0 z_0 b) = (62.4 \text{ lbf/ft}^3)(\tfrac{2}{3})(10 \text{ ft})(24 \text{ ft})(50 \text{ ft})$$

$$= 499{,}000 \text{ lbf} = 499 \times 10^3 \text{ lbf} \qquad Ans.$$

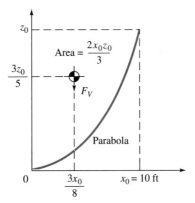

Fig. E2.7b

This acts downward on the surface at a distance $3x_0/8 = 3.75$ ft over from the origin of coordinates. Note that the vertical distance $3z_0/5$ in Fig. E2.7b is irrelevant.

The total resultant force acting on the dam is

$$F = (F_H^2 + F_V^2)^{1/2} = [(499)^2 + (899)^2]^{1/2} = 1028 \times 10^3 \text{ lbf}$$

As seen in Fig. E2.7c, this force acts down and to the right at an angle of $29° = \tan^{-1}\frac{499}{899}$.

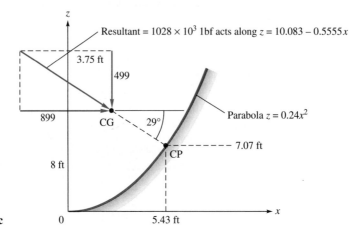

Fig. E2.7c

The force F passes through the point $(x, z) = (3.75 \text{ ft}, 8 \text{ ft})$. If we move down along the $29°$ line until we strike the dam, we find an equivalent center of pressure on the dam at

$$x_{CP} = 5.43 \text{ ft} \qquad z_{CP} = 7.07 \text{ ft} \qquad\qquad Ans.$$

This definition of CP is rather artificial, but this is an unavoidable complication of dealing with a curved surface.

2.7 Hydrostatic Forces in Layered Fluids

The formulas for plane and curved surfaces in Secs. 2.5 and 2.6 are valid only for a fluid of uniform density. If the fluid is layered with different densities, as in Fig. 2.15, a single formula cannot solve the problem because the slope of the linear pressure distribution changes between layers. However, the formulas apply separately to each layer, and thus the appropriate remedy is to compute and sum the separate layer forces and moments.

Consider the slanted plane surface immersed in a two-layer fluid in Fig. 2.15. The slope of the pressure distribution becomes steeper as we move down into the denser second layer. The total force on the plate does *not* equal the pressure at the centroid times the plate area, but the plate portion in each layer does satisfy the formula, so that we can sum forces to find the total:

$$F = \sum F_i = \sum p_{CG_i} A_i \tag{2.46}$$

Similarly, the centroid of the plate portion in each layer can be used to locate the center of pressure on that portion

$$y_{CP_i} = -\frac{\rho_i g \, \sin \theta_i \, I_{xx_i}}{p_{CG_i} A_i} \qquad x_{CP_i} = -\frac{\rho_i g \, \sin \theta_i \, I_{xy_i}}{p_{CG_i} A_i} \tag{2.47}$$

These formulas locate the center of pressure of that particular F_i with respect to the centroid of that particular portion of plate in the layer, not with respect to the centroid of the entire plate. The center of pressure of the total force $F = \sum F_i$ can then be found by summing moments about some convenient point such as the surface. The following example will illustrate.

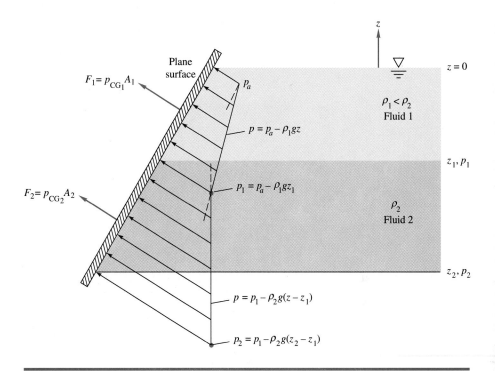

Fig. 2.15 Hydrostatic forces on a surface immersed in a layered fluid must be summed in separate pieces.

EXAMPLE 2.8

A tank 20 ft deep and 7 ft wide is layered with 8 ft of oil, 6 ft of water, and 4 ft of mercury. Compute (*a*) the total hydrostatic force and (*b*) the resultant center of pressure of the fluid on the right-hand side of the tank.

Solution

Part (a)   Divide the end panel into three parts as sketched in Fig. E2.8, and find the hydrostatic pressure at the centroid of each part, using the relation (2.38) in steps as in Fig. E2.8:

Fig. E2.8

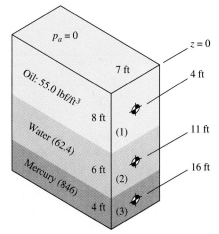

$$P_{CG_1} = (55.0 \text{ lbf/ft}^3)(4 \text{ ft}) = 220 \text{ lbf/ft}^2$$

$$P_{CG_2} = (55.0)(8) + 62.4(3) = 627 \text{ lbf/ft}^2$$

$$P_{CG_3} = (55.0)(8) + 62.4(6) + 846(2) = 2506 \text{ lbf/ft}^2$$

These pressures are then multiplied by the respective panel areas to find the force on each portion:

$$F_1 = P_{CG_1}A_1 = (220 \text{ lbf/ft}^2)(8 \text{ ft})(7 \text{ ft}) = 12{,}300 \text{ lbf}$$

$$F_2 = P_{CG_2}A_2 = 627(6)(7) = 26{,}300 \text{ lbf}$$

$$F_3 = P_{CG_3}A_3 = 2506(4)(7) = \underline{70{,}200 \text{ lbf}}$$

$$F = \sum F_i = 108{,}800 \text{ lbf} \qquad \textit{Ans. (a)}$$

Part (b)   Equations (2.47) can be used to locate the CP of each force F_i, noting that $\theta = 90°$ and $\sin \theta = 1$ for all part. The moments of inertia are $I_{xx_1} = (7 \text{ ft})(8 \text{ ft})^3/12 = 298.7 \text{ ft}^4$, $I_{xx_2} = 7(6)^3/12 = 126.0 \text{ ft}^4$, and $I_{xx_3} = 7(4)^3/12 = 37.3 \text{ ft}^4$. The centers of pressure are thus at

$$y_{CP_1} = -\frac{\rho_1 g I_{xx_1}}{F_1} = -\frac{(55.0 \text{ lbf/ft}^3)(298.7 \text{ ft}^4)}{12{,}300 \text{ lbf}} = -1.33 \text{ ft}$$

$$y_{CP_2} = -\frac{62.4(126.0)}{26{,}300} = -0.30 \text{ ft} \qquad y_{CP_3} = -\frac{846(37.3)}{70{,}200} = -0.45 \text{ ft}$$

This locates $z_{CP_1} = -4 - 1.33 = -5.33 \text{ ft}$, $z_{CP_2} = -11 - 0.30 = -11.30 \text{ ft}$, and $z_{CP_3} = -16 - 0.45 = -16.45 \text{ ft}$. Summing moments about the surface then gives

$$\sum F_i z_{CP_i} = F z_{CP}$$

or $$12{,}300(-5.33) + 26{,}300(-11.30) + 70{,}200(-16.45) = 108{,}800 z_{CP}$$

or $$z_{CP} = -\frac{1{,}518{,}000}{108{,}800} = -13.95 \text{ ft} \qquad \textit{Ans. (b)}$$

The center of pressure of the total resultant force on the right side of the tank lies 13.95 ft below the surface.

2.8 Buoyancy and Stability

The same principles used to compute hydrostatic forces on surfaces can be applied to the net pressure force on a completely submerged or floating body. The results are the two laws of buoyancy discovered by Archimedes in the third century B.C.:

1. A body immersed in a fluid experiences a vertical buoyant force equal to the weight of the fluid it displaces.
2. A floating body displaces its own weight in the fluid in which it floats.

These two laws are easily derived by referring to Fig. 2.16. In Fig. 2.16a, the body lies between an upper curved surface 1 and a lower curved surface 2. From Eq. (2.45) for vertical force, the body experiences a net upward force

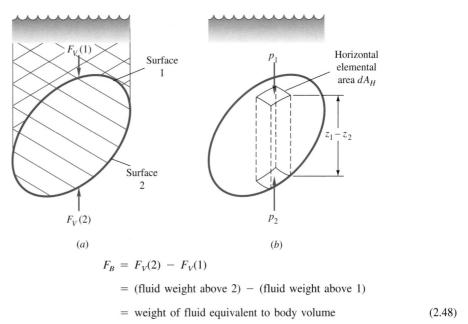

Fig. 2.16 Two different approaches to the buoyant force on an arbitrary immersed body: (a) forces on upper and lower curved surfaces; (b) summation of elemental vertical-pressure forces.

$$F_B = F_V(2) - F_V(1)$$

$$= \text{(fluid weight above 2)} - \text{(fluid weight above 1)}$$

$$= \text{weight of fluid equivalent to body volume} \qquad (2.48)$$

Alternatively, from Fig. 2.16b, we can sum the vertical forces on elemental vertical slices through the immersed body:

$$F_B = \int_{\text{body}} (p_2 - p_1)\, dA_H = -\gamma \int (z_2 - z_1)\, dA_H = (\gamma)(\text{body volume}) \qquad (2.49)$$

These are identical results and equivalent to law 1 above.

Equation (2.49) assumes that the fluid has uniform specific weight. The line of action of the buoyant force passes through the center of volume of the displaced body; i.e., its center of mass is computed as if it had uniform density. This point through which F_B acts is called the *center of buoyancy*, commonly labeled B or CB on a drawing. Of course, the point B may or may not correspond to the actual center of mass of the body's own material, which may have variable density.

Equation (2.49) can be generalized to a layered fluid (LF) by summing the weights of each layer of density ρ_i displaced by the immersed body:

$$(F_B)_{\text{LF}} = \sum \rho_i g(\text{displaced volume})_i \qquad (2.50)$$

Each displaced layer would have its own center of volume, and one would have to sum moments of the incremental buoyant forces to find the center of buoyancy of the immersed body.

Since liquids are relatively heavy, we are conscious of their buoyant forces, but gases also exert buoyancy on any body immersed in them. For example, human beings have an average specific weight of about 60 lbf/ft^3. We may record the weight of a person as 180 lbf and thus estimate the person's total volume as 3.0 ft^3. However, in so doing we are neglecting the buoyant force of the air surrounding the person. At standard conditions, the specific weight of air is 0.0763 lbf/ft^3; hence the buoyant force is approximately 0.23 lbf. If measured in vacuo, the person would weigh about 0.23 lbf more. For balloons and blimps the buoyant force of air, instead of being negligible, is

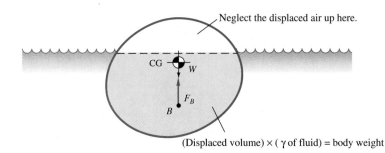

Fig. 2.17 Static equilibrium of a floating body.

Neglect the displaced air up here.

CG W

F_B

B

(Displaced volume) × (γ of fluid) = body weight

the controlling factor in the design. Also, many flow phenomena, e.g., natural convection of heat and vertical mixing in the ocean, are strongly dependent upon seemingly small buoyant forces.

Floating bodies are a special case; only a portion of the body is submerged, with the remainder poking up out of the free surface. This is illustrated in Fig. 2.17, where the shaded portion is the displaced volume. Equation (2.49) is modified to apply to this smaller volume

$$F_B = (\gamma)(\text{displaced volume}) = \text{floating-body weight} \tag{2.51}$$

Not only does the buoyant force equal the body weight, but also they are *collinear* since there can be no net moments for static equilibrium. Equation (2.51) is the mathematical equivalent of Archimedes' law 2, previously stated.

EXAMPLE 2.9

A block of concrete weighs 100 lbf in air and "weighs" only 60 lbf when immersed in fresh water (62.4 lbf/ft^3). What is the average specific weight of the block?

Solution

A free-body diagram of the submerged block (see Fig. E2.9) shows a balance between the apparent weight, the buoyant force, and the actual weight

$$\sum F_z = 0 = 60 + F_B - 100$$

or

$$F_B = 40 \text{ lbf} = (62.4 \text{ lbf/ft}^3)(\text{block volume, ft}^3)$$

Solving gives the volume of the block as $40/62.4 = 0.641$ ft^3. Therefore the specific weight of the block is

$$\gamma_{\text{block}} = \frac{100 \text{ lbf}}{0.641 \text{ ft}^3} = 156 \text{ lbf/ft}^3 \qquad\qquad Ans.$$

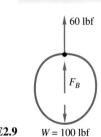

60 lbf

F_B

Fig. E2.9 $W = 100$ lbf

Occasionally, a body will have exactly the right weight and volume for its ratio to equal the specific weight of the fluid. If so, the body will be *neutrally buoyant* and will remain at rest at any point where it is immersed in the fluid. Small neutrally buoyant particles are sometimes used in flow visualization, and a neutrally buoyant body called a *Swallow float* [2] is used to track oceanographic currents. A submarine can achieve positive, neutral, or negative buoyancy by pumping water in or out of its ballast tanks.

Stability

A floating body as in Fig. 2.17 may not approve of the position in which it is floating. If so, it will overturn at the first opportunity and is said to be statically *unstable*, like a pencil balanced upon its point. The least disturbance will cause it to seek another equilibrium position which is stable. Engineers must design to avoid floating instability. The only way to tell for sure whether a floating position is stable is to "disturb" the body a slight amount mathematically and see whether it develops a restoring moment which will return it to its original position. If so, it is stable; if not, unstable. Such calculations for arbitrary floating bodies have been honed to a fine art by naval architects [3], but we can at least outline the basic principle of the static-stability calculation. Figure 2.18 illustrates the computation for the usual case of a symmetric floating body. The steps are as follows:

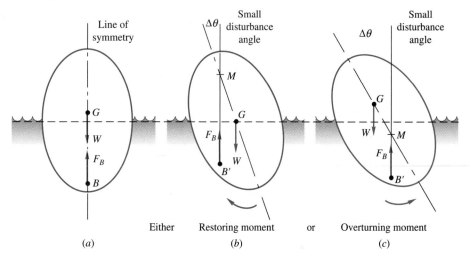

Fig. 2.18 Calculation of the metacenter *M* of a floating body to determine its static stability: (*a*) *B'* moves far out (point *M* above *G* denotes stability); (*c*) *B'* moves slightly (point *M* below *G* denotes instability).

1. The basic floating position is calculated from Eq. (2.51). The body's center of mass *G* and center of buoyancy *B* are computed.
2. The body is tilted a small angle $\Delta\theta$, and a new waterline is established for the body to float at this angle. The new position *B'* of the center of buoyancy is calculated. A vertical line drawn upward from *B'* intersects the line of symmetry at a point *M*, called the *metacenter*, which is independent of $\Delta\theta$ for small angles.
3. If point *M* is above *G*, that is, if the *metacentric height* $\overline{MG}$ is positive, a restoring moment is present and the original position is stable. If *M* is below *G* (negative $\overline{MG}$, the body is unstable and will overturn if disturbed. Stability increases with increasing $\overline{MG}$.

Thus the metacentric height is a property of the cross section for the given weight, and its value gives an indication of the stability of the body. For a body of varying cross section and draft, such as a ship, the computation of the metacenter can be very involved. We use a two-dimensional, or uniform, cross section as an example.

EXAMPLE 2.10

A barge has a uniform rectangular cross section of width 2*L* and vertical draft of height *H*. Determine (*a*) the metacentric height for a small tilt angle and (*b*) the range of ratio *L/H*

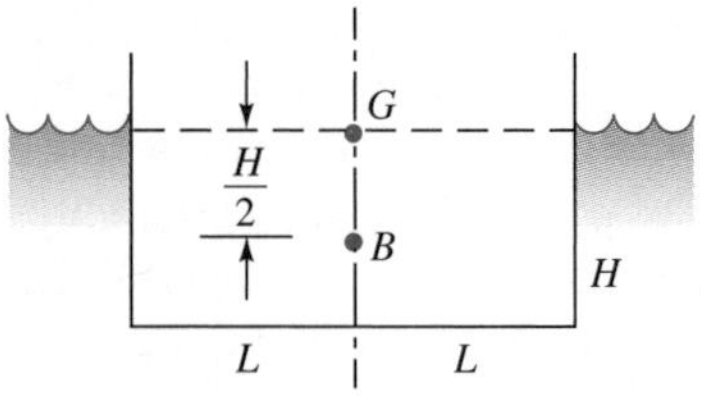

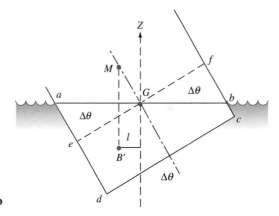

Fig. E2.10a

for which the barge is statically stable. Assume that the center of mass G of the barge is exactly at the waterline, as shown in Fig. E2.10a.

Solution

The barge in its tilted position $\Delta\theta$ is shown in Fig. E2.10b. Because of symmetry the tilted body floats, again with G at the waterline, and triangles aeG and fbG are identical in size.

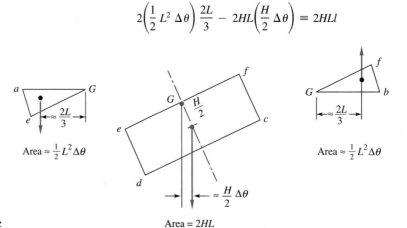

Fig. E2.10b

The new center of buoyancy B' can be found by summing moments of the submerged areas about, say, the point G and setting this equal to the total submerged area ($2LH$) times the distance l. The submerged area $aGbcde$ is the sum of rectangle $efdc$ plus triangle aeG minus triangle fbG, and the centroids of each of these pieces can easily be found for small angles of tilt (Fig. E2.10c). Summing moments of area counterclockwise about G, we have

$$2\left(\frac{1}{2}L^2\,\Delta\theta\right)\frac{2L}{3} - 2HL\left(\frac{H}{2}\,\Delta\theta\right) \equiv 2HLl$$

Fig. E2.10c

We can solve this for the distance $l = [L^2/(3H) - H/2]\,\Delta\theta$. From the tilted position showing M above, the distance $\overline{MG} \approx l/\Delta\theta$, for small angles. Thus we have the approximate result for metacentric height, independent of $\Delta\theta$,

$$\overline{MG} = \frac{L^2}{3H} - \frac{H}{2} \qquad\qquad Ans.\ (a)$$

This can be positive or stable only if $L^2 > 3H^2/2$ or

$$L > 1.225H \qquad \text{Ans. (b)}$$

The wider the barge relative to its draft, the more stable it is.

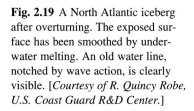

A Simple Estimate of Metacentric Height

The computations in Example 2.10 are equivalent to a sort of beam-bending problem, with the buoyancy force creating a moment about the waterline. The analysis may be generalized for any smoothly varying waterline to a formula [3] for distance between points M and B:

$$\overline{MB} = z_M - z_B = \frac{I_0}{\mathcal{V}_{\text{sub}}} \tag{2.52}$$

where I_0 is the area moment of inertia of the waterline cross section *about the over-turning centroidal axis* and $\mathcal{V}_{\text{sub}}$ is the submerged volume of the floating body. The formula requires that there be no discontinuities or notches at the waterline. Let us test it on Example 2.10: If b is the width into the paper, $I_0 = b(2L)^3/12$ and $\mathcal{V}_{\text{sub}} = bH(2L)$, whence $\overline{MB} = I_0/\mathcal{V}_{\text{sub}} = L^2/(3H)$. Subtract, from this, the distance $\overline{GB} = H/2$ (Fig. E2.10a), and we obtain the desired result for $\overline{MG}$:

$$\overline{MG} = \overline{MB} - \overline{GB} = \frac{L^2}{3H} - \frac{H}{2} \qquad \text{Ans. (a) of Example 2.10}$$

Floating bodies may be stable in more than one position. Reference 11 points out that even simple floating shapes, e.g., a cube of uniform density, may have infinitely many stable orientations, not necessarily symmetric. Circular cylinders may float with their axes tilted [11].

Floating instability occurs in nature. Giant icebergs may overturn after their shapes change due to underwater melting. Figure 2.19 shows a North Atlantic iceberg which

Fig. 2.19 A North Atlantic iceberg after overturning. The exposed surface has been smoothed by underwater melting. An old water line, notched by wave action, is clearly visible. [*Courtesy of R. Quincy Robe, U.S. Coast Guard R&D Center.*]

has overturned, perhaps more than once. The exposed surface is smooth and rounded, indicating that it was previously melting underwater. An old waterline, notched by surface wave action melting, is clearly visible. Iceberg overturning is a dramatic, rarely seen event.

2.9 Pressure Distribution in Rigid-Body Motion

In rigid-body motion, all particles are in combined translation and rotation, and there is no relative motion between particles. With no relative motion, there are no strains or strain rates, so that the viscous term $\mu\nabla^2\mathbf{V}$ in Eq. (2.13) vanishes, leaving a balance between pressure, gravity, and particle acceleration

$$\nabla p = \rho(\mathbf{g} - \mathbf{a}) \qquad (2.53)$$

The pressure gradient acts in the direction $\mathbf{g} - \mathbf{a}$, and lines of constant pressure (including the free surface, if any) are perpendicular to this direction. The general case of combined translation and rotation of a rigid body is discussed in Chap. 3, Fig. 3.12. If the center of rotation is at point O and the translational velocity is V_0 at this point, the velocity of an arbitrary point P on the body is given by[1]

$$\mathbf{V} = \mathbf{V}_0 + \mathbf{\Omega} \times \mathbf{r}_0$$

where $\mathbf{\Omega}$ is the angular-velocity vector and $\mathbf{r}_0$ is the position of point P. Differentiating, we obtain the most general form of the acceleration of a rigid body:

$$\mathbf{a} = \frac{d\mathbf{V}_0}{dt} + (\mathbf{\Omega} \times \mathbf{r}_0) + \frac{d\mathbf{\Omega}}{dt} \times \mathbf{r}_0 \qquad (2.54)$$

Looking at the right-hand side, we see that the first term is the translational acceleration; the second term is the *centripetal acceleration*, whose direction is from point P perpendicular toward the axis of rotation; and the third term is the linear acceleration due to changes in the angular velocity. It is rare for all three of these terms to apply to any one fluid flow. In fact, fluids can rarely move in rigid-body motion unless restrained by confining walls for a long time. For example, suppose a tank of water is in a car which starts a constant acceleration. The water in the tank would begin to slosh about, and that sloshing would damp out very slowly until finally the particles of water would be in approximately rigid-body acceleration. This would take so long that the car would have reached hypersonic speeds. Nevertheless, we can at least discuss the pressure distribution in a tank of rigidly accelerating water. The following is an example where the water in the tank will reach uniform acceleration rapidly.

EXAMPLE 2.11

A tank of water 1 m deep is in free fall under gravity with negligible drag. Compute the pressure at the bottom of the tank if $p_a = 101$ kPa.

Solution

Being unsupported in this condition, the water particles tend to fall downward as a rigid hunk of fluid. In free fall with no drag, the downward acceleration is $\mathbf{a} = \mathbf{g}$. Thus Eq. (2.53)

---

[1] For a more detailed derivation of rigid-body motion, see Ref. 4, Sec. 2.7.

for this situation gives $\nabla p = \rho(\mathbf{g} - \mathbf{g}) = 0$. The pressure in the water is thus *constant everywhere* and equal to the atmospheric pressure 101 kPa. In other words, the walls are doing no service in sustaining the pressure distribution which would normally exist.

Uniform Linear Acceleration

In this general case of uniform rigid-body acceleration, Eq. (2.53) applies, **a** having the same magnitude and direction for all particles. With reference to Fig. 2.20, the parallelogram sum of **g** and $-\mathbf{a}$ gives the direction of the pressure gradient or greatest rate of increase of p. The surfaces of constant pressure must be perpendicular to this and are thus tilted at an angle θ such that

$$\theta = \tan^{-1}\frac{a_x}{g + a_z} \tag{2.55}$$

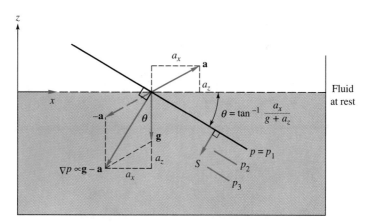

Fig. 2.20 Tilting of constant-pressure surfaces in a tank of liquid in rigid-body acceleration.

One of these tilted lines is the free surface, which is found by the requirement that the fluid retain its volume unless it spills out. The rate of increase of pressure in the direction $\mathbf{g} - \mathbf{a}$ is greater than in ordinary hydrostatics and is given by

$$\frac{dp}{ds} = \rho G \qquad \text{where } G = [a_x^2 + (g + a_z)^2]^{1/2} \tag{2.56}$$

These results are independent of the size or shape of the container as long as the fluid is continuously connected throughout the container.

EXAMPLE 2.12

A drag racer rests her coffee mug on a horizontal tray while she accelerates at 7 m/s². The mug is 10 cm deep and 6 cm in diameter and contains coffee 7 cm deep at rest. (*a*) Assuming rigid-body acceleration of the coffee, determine whether it will spill out of the mug. (*b*) Calculate the gage pressure in the corner at point A if the density of coffee is 1010 kg/m³.

Solution

Part (*a*)   The free surface tilts at the angle θ given by Eq. (2.55) regardless of the shape of the mug. With $a_z = 0$ and standard gravity,

$$\theta = \tan^{-1}\frac{a_x}{g} = \tan^{-1}\frac{7.0}{9.81} = 35.5°$$

If the mug is symmetric about its central axis, the volume of coffee is conserved if the tilted surface intersects the original rest surface exactly at the centerline, as shown in Fig. E2.12.

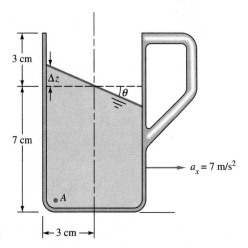

Fig. E2.12

Thus the deflection at the left side of the mug is

$$z = (3 \text{ cm})(\tan \theta) = 2.14 \text{ cm} \qquad \qquad Ans. (a)$$

This is less than the 3-cm clearance available, so the coffee will not spill unless it was sloshed during the start-up of acceleration.

Part (b)   When at rest, the gage pressure at point A is given by Eq. (2.20):

$$p_A = \rho g(z_{\text{surf}} - z_A) = (1010 \text{ kg/m}^3)(9.81 \text{ m/s}^2)(0.07 \text{ m}) = 694 \text{ N/m}^2 = 694 \text{ Pa}$$

During acceleration, Eq. (2.56) applies, with $G = [(7.0)^2 + (9.81)^2]^{1/2} = 12.05 \text{ m/s}^2$. The distance Δs down the normal from the tilted surface to point A is

$$\Delta s = (7.0 + 2.14)(\cos \theta) = 7.44 \text{ cm}$$

Thus the pressure at point A becomes

$$p_A = \rho G \, \Delta s = 1010(12.05)(0.0744) = 906 \text{ Pa} \qquad \qquad Ans. (b)$$

which is an increase of 31 percent over the pressure when at rest.

Rigid-Body Rotation

As a second special case, consider rotation of the fluid about the z axis without any translation, as sketched in Fig. 2.21. We assume that the container has been rotating long enough at constant Ω for the fluid to have attained rigid-body rotation. The fluid acceleration will then be the centripetal term in Eq. (2.54). In the coordinates of Fig. 2.21, the angular-velocity and position vectors are given by

$$\Omega = \mathbf{k}\Omega \qquad r_0 = \mathbf{i}_r r \qquad \qquad (2.57)$$

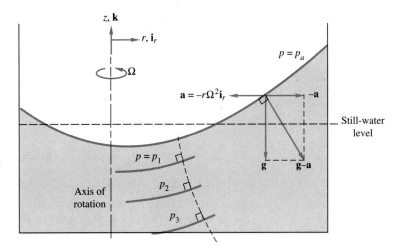

Fig. 2.21 Development of paraboloid constant-pressure surfaces in a fluid in rigid-body rotation. The dashed line along the direction of maximum pressure increase is an exponential curve.

Then the acceleration is given by

$$\boldsymbol{\Omega} \times (\boldsymbol{\Omega} \times \mathbf{r}_0) = -r\Omega^2 \mathbf{i}_r \tag{2.58}$$

as marked in the figure, and Eq. (2.53) for the force balance becomes

$$\nabla p = \mathbf{i}_r \frac{\partial p}{\partial r} + \mathbf{k} \frac{\partial p}{\partial z} = \rho(\mathbf{g} - \mathbf{a}) = \rho(r\Omega^2 \mathbf{i}_r - g\mathbf{k}) \tag{2.59}$$

Equating like components, we find the pressure field by solving two first-order partial differential equations

$$\frac{\partial p}{\partial r} = \rho r \Omega^2 \qquad \frac{\partial p}{\partial z} = -\gamma \tag{2.60}$$

This is our first specific example of the generalized three-dimensional problem described by Eqs. (2.14) for more than one independent variable. The right-hand sides of (2.60) are known functions of r and z. One can proceed as follows: Integrate the first equation "partially," i.e., holding z constant, with respect to r. The result is

$$p = \tfrac{1}{2}\rho r^2 \Omega^2 + f(z) \tag{2.61}$$

where the "constant" of integration is actually a function $f(z)$.[†] Now differentiate this with respect to z and compare with the second relation of (2.60):

$$\frac{\partial p}{\partial z} = 0 + f'(z) = -\gamma$$

or $$f(z) = -\gamma z + C \tag{2.62a}$$

where C is a constant. Thus Eq. (2.61) now becomes

$$p = \text{const} - \gamma z + \tfrac{1}{2}\rho r^2 \Omega^2 \tag{2.62b}$$

This is the pressure distribution in the fluid. The value of C is found by specifying the

[†] This is because $f(z)$ vanishes when differentiated with respect to r. If you don't see this, you should review your calculus.

pressure at one point. If $p = p_0$ at $(r, z) = (0, 0)$, then $C = p_0$. The final desired distribution is

$$p = p_0 - \gamma z + \tfrac{1}{2}\rho r^2 \Omega^2 \qquad (2.63)$$

The pressure is linear in z and parabolic in r. If we wish to plot a constant-pressure surface, say, $p = p_1$, Eq. (2.63) becomes

$$z = \frac{p_0 - p_1}{\gamma} + \frac{r^2 \Omega^2}{2g} = a + br^2 \qquad (2.64)$$

Thus the surfaces are paraboloids of revolution, concave upward, with their minimum point on the axis of rotation. Some examples are sketched in Fig. 2.21.

As in the previous example of linear acceleration, the position of the free surface is found by conserving the volume of fluid. For a noncircular container with the axis of rotation off-center, as in Fig. 2.21, a lot of laborious mensuration is required, and a single problem will take you all weekend. However, the calculation is easy for a cylinder rotating about its central axis, as in Fig. 2.22. Since the volume of a paraboloid is one-half the base area times its height, the still-water level is exactly halfway between the high and low points of the free surface. The center of the fluid drops an amount $h/2 = \Omega^2 R^2/(4g)$, and the edges rise an equal amount.

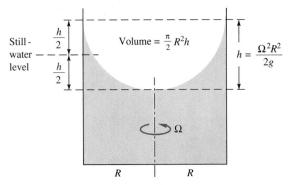

Fig. 2.22 Determining the free-surface position for rotation of a cylinder of fluid about its central axis.

EXAMPLE 2.13

The coffee cup in Example 2.12 is removed from the drag racer, placed on a turntable, and rotated about its central axis until a rigid-body mode occurs. Find (*a*) the angular velocity which will cause the coffee to just reach the lip of the cup and (*b*) the gage pressure at point *A* for this condition.

Solution

Part (a) The cup contains 7 cm of coffee. The remaining distance of 3 cm up to the lip must equal the distance $h/2$ in Fig. 2.22. Thus

$$\frac{h}{2} = 0.03 \text{ m} = \frac{\Omega^2 R^2}{4g} = \frac{\Omega^2 (0.03 \text{ m})^2}{4(9.81 \text{ m/s}^2)}$$

Solving, we obtain

$$\Omega^2 = 1308 \qquad \text{or} \qquad \Omega = 36.2 \text{ rad/s} = 345 \text{ r/min} \qquad \textit{Ans. (a)}$$

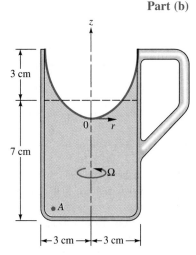

Fig. E2.13

Part (b) To compute the pressure, it is convenient to put the origin of coordinates r and z at the bottom of the free-surface depression, as shown in Fig. E2.13. The gage pressure here is $p_0 = 0$, and point A is at $(r, z) = (3 \text{ cm}, -4 \text{ cm})$. Equation (2.63) can then be evaluated

$$p_A = 0 - (1010 \text{ kg/m}^3)(9.81 \text{ m/s}^2)(-0.04 \text{ m})$$

$$+ \tfrac{1}{2}(1010 \text{ kg/m}^3)(0.03 \text{ m})^2(1308 \text{ rad}^2/\text{s}^2)$$

$$= 396 \text{ N/m}^2 + 594 \text{ N/m}^2 = 990 \text{ Pa} \qquad \text{Ans. (b)}$$

This is about 43 percent greater than the still-water pressure $p_A = 694 \text{ Pa}$.

Here, as in the linear-acceleration case, it should be emphasized that the paraboloid pressure distribution (2.63) sets up in *any* fluid under rigid-body rotation, regardless of the shape or size of the container. The container may even be closed and filled with fluid. It is only necessary that the fluid be continuously interconnected throughout the container. The following example will illustrate a peculiar case in which one can visualize an imaginary free surface extending outside the walls of the container.

EXAMPLE 2.14

A U-tube with a radius of 10 in and containing mercury to a height of 30 in is rotated about its center at 180 r/min until a rigid-body mode is achieved. The diameter of the tubing is negligible. Atmospheric pressure is 2116 lbf/ft². Find the pressure at point A in the rotating condition. See Fig. E2.14.

Solution

Convert the angular velocity to radians per second:

$$\Omega = (180 \text{ r/min})\frac{2\pi \text{ rad/r}}{60 \text{ s/min}} = 18.85 \text{ rad/s}$$

From Table 2.1 we find for mercury that $\gamma = 846 \text{ lbf/ft}^3$ and hence $\rho = 846/32.2 = 26.3$ slugs/ft³. At this high rotation rate, the free surface will slant upward at a fierce angle [about 84°; check this from Eq. (2.64)], but the tubing is so thin that the free surface will remain at approximately the same 30-in height, point B. Placing our origin of coordinates at this height, we can calculate the constant C in Eq. (2.62b) from the condition $p_B = 2116 \text{ lbf/ft}^2$ at $(r, z) = (10 \text{ in}, 0)$:

$$p_B = 2116 \text{ lbf/ft}^2 = C - 0 + \tfrac{1}{2}(26.3 \text{ slugs/ft}^3)(\tfrac{10}{12} \text{ ft})^2(18.85 \text{ rad/s})^2$$

or $\qquad\qquad\qquad\qquad C = 2116 - 3245 = -1129 \text{ lbf/ft}^2$

We then obtain p_A by evaluating Eq. (2.63) at $(r, z) = (0, -30 \text{ in})$:

$$p_A = -1129 - (846 \text{ lbf/ft}^3)(-\tfrac{30}{12} \text{ ft}) = -1129 + 2115 = 986 \text{ lbf/ft}^2 \qquad \text{Ans.}$$

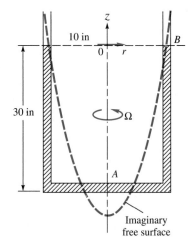

Fig. E2.14

This is less than atmospheric pressure, and we can see why if we follow the free-surface paraboloid down from point B along the dashed line in the figure. It will cross the horizontal portion of the U-tube (where p will be atmospheric) and fall *below* point A. From Fig. 2.22 the actual drop from point B will be

$$h = \frac{\Omega^2 R^2}{2g} = \frac{(18.85)^2(\frac{10}{12})^2}{2(32.2)} = 3.83 \text{ ft} = 46 \text{ in}$$

Thus p_A is about 16 inHg below atmospheric pressure, or about $\frac{16}{12}(846) = 1128 \text{ lbf/ft}^2$ below $p_a = 2116 \text{ lbf/ft}^2$, which checks with the answer above. When the tube is at rest,

$$p_A = 2116 - 846(-\tfrac{30}{12}) = 4231 \text{ lbf/ft}^2$$

Hence rotation has reduced the pressure at point A by 77 percent. Further rotation can reduce p_A to near-zero pressure, and cavitation can occur.

An interesting by-product of this analysis for rigid-body rotation is that the lines everywhere parallel to the pressure gradient form a family of curved surfaces, as sketched in Fig. 2.21. They are everywhere orthogonal to the constant-pressure surfaces, and hence their slope is the negative inverse of the slope computed from Eq. (2.64):

$$\left.\frac{dz}{dr}\right|_{GL} = -\frac{1}{(dz/dr)_{p=\text{const}}} = -\frac{1}{r\Omega^2/g}$$

where GL stands for gradient line

or
$$\frac{dz}{dr} = -\frac{g}{r\Omega^2} \tag{2.65}$$

Separating the variables and integrating, we find the equation of the pressure-gradient surfaces

$$r = C_1 \exp\left(-\frac{\Omega^2 z}{g}\right) \tag{2.66}$$

Notice that this result and Eq. (2.64) are independent of the density of the fluid. In the absence of friction and Coriolis effects, Eq. (2.66) defines the lines along which the apparent net gravitational field would act on a particle. Depending upon its density, a small particle or bubble would tend to rise or fall in the fluid along these exponential lines, as demonstrated experimentally in Ref. 5. Also, buoyant streamers would align themselves with these exponential lines, thus avoiding any stress other than pure tension. Figure 2.23 shows the configuration of such streamers before and during rotation.

2.10 Pressure Measurement

There are many devices available for measuring pressure, both in a static stream and in a moving stream. All take advantage of the fact that pressure applied to a finite area of material causes a force and stress and displacement in the material. These mechanical effects can then be quantified in various ways:

1. A force balance
2. The height of a liquid column (manometer)
3. Direct displacement measurement
4. Indirect (electrical) measurement of displacement

Force balances are commonly used to *calibrate* pressure instruments rather than as devices for routine measurement. The manometer, analyzed in Sec. 2.4, is a simple and inexpensive device with no moving parts except the liquid column itself. Manometers

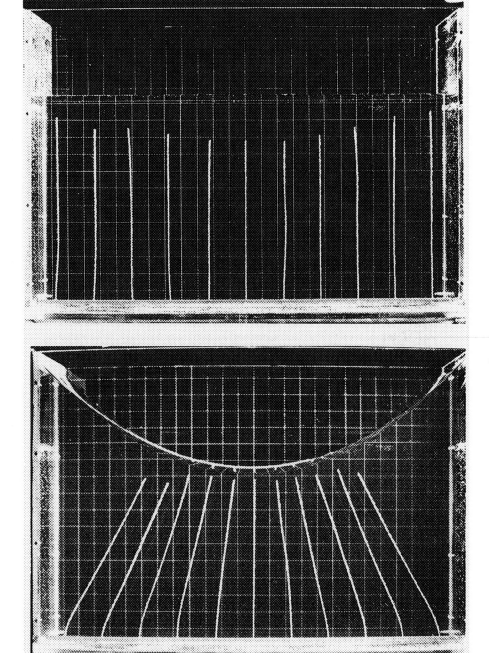

Fig. 2.23 Experimental demonstration with buoyant streamers of the fluid force field in rigid-body rotation: (*top*) fluid at rest (streamers hang vertically upward); (*bottom*) rigid-body rotation (streamers are aligned with the direction of maximum pressure gradient). (*From Ref. 5, courtesy of R. Ian Fletcher.*)

can be constructed with extreme accuracy by using fluids of small density differences, tilted liquid columns, and a micrometer-mounted pointer or eyepiece to locate the meniscus accurately. Examples are given in Fig. 2.24.

When pressure is measured in a moving fluid (the so-called *static pressure*), care

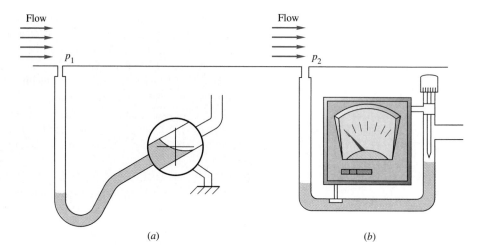

(a)

(b)

Fig. 2.24 Two types of accurate manometers for precise measurements: (*a*) tilted tube with eyepiece; (*b*) micrometer pointer with ammeter detector.

must be taken not to disturb the flow. The best way to do this is to take the measurement through a *static hole* in the wall of the flow, as illustrated for the two instruments in Fig. 2.24. The hole should be normal to the wall, and burrs should be avoided. If the hole is small enough (typically 1-mm diameter), there will be no flow into the measuring tube once the pressure has adjusted to a steady value. Thus the flow is almost undisturbed. An oscillating flow pressure, however, can cause a large error due to possible dynamic response of the tubing. Other devices of smaller dimensions are used for dynamic-pressure measurements (see Fig. 2.26*d*). Note that the manometers in Fig. 2.24 are arranged to measure the absolute pressures p_1 and p_2. If the pressure difference $p_1 - p_2$ is desired, a significant error is incurred by subtracting two independent measurements, and it would be far better to connect both ends of one instrument to the two static holes p_1 and p_2 so that one manometer reads the difference directly.

Fig. 2.25 Schematic of a bourdon-tube device for mechanical measurement of high pressures.

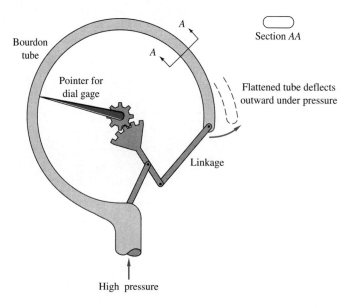

The third type of pressure gage is a direct displacement measurement. An inexpensive and reliable device is the *bourdon tube*, sketched in Fig. 2.25. A curved tube with a flattened cross section will deflect outward when pressurized internally. The deflection can be measured by a linkage attached to a calibrated dial-gage pointer. Extreme accuracy can be obtained through proper design, and commercial bourdon gages are available with an accuracy of ±0.1 percent of full scale.

The fourth type of pressure gage measures the displacement of the gage sensing element by electrical means. The common techniques are (1) resistive, (2) capacitive, (3) inductive, (4) reluctive, (5) piezoelectric, and (6) eddy currents. Some examples are sketched in Fig. 2.26.

The reluctive device in Fig. 2.26a is called a *linear variable differential transformer* (LVDT). Note that it uses a bourdon tube for convenience as a source of mechanical displacement from the applied pressure. The strain gages in Fig. 2.26b are attached to

Fig. 2.26 Four types of pressure transducers with electric output: (*a*) differential transformer (core motion causes a change in transformer reluctance); (*b*) strain-gage transducer (membrane deflection causes gage strain); (*c*) potentiometer transducer (capsule deflection causes variable-resistance change); (*d*) piezoelectric transducer (diaphragm deflection causes induced charge in crystals.)

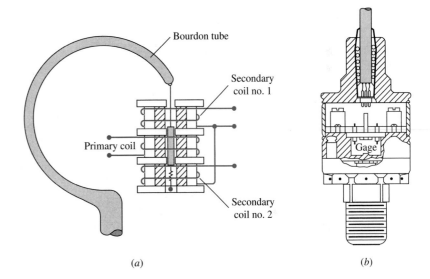

(*a*)

(*b*)

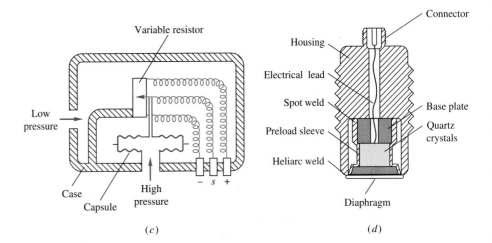

(*c*)

(*d*)

a membrane which deflects under pressure, while the potentiometer gage (Fig. 2.26c) has a small bellows which deflects the pickup on the variable resistor. The piezoelectric transducer (Fig. 2.26d) uses the discovery of Pierre and Jacques Curie in 1880 that certain quartz crystals generate an electric charge when stressed. The piezoelectric gage has no internal fluid volume; i.e., the diaphragm is installed flush with the wall and reacts almost intantaneously to a change in local pressure. Thus the dynamic response is excellent, and piezoelectric sensors are in wide use for rapid transient-pressure measurements such as blast waves or turbulent-pressure fluctuations.

All the pressure devices with electric sensors have the great advantage that their output can be recorded on a paper chart or magnetic tape or other such permanent storage. This advantage serves to offset the relatively high cost ($100 to $2000) of electromechanical transducers.

Further discussion of pressure-measuring devices can be found in Refs. 7 to 10.

Summary

This chapter has been devoted entirely to the computation of pressure distributions and the resulting forces and moments in a static fluid or a fluid with a known velocity field. All hydrostatic (Secs. 2.3 to 2.8) and rigid-body (Sec. 2.9) problems are solved in this manner and are classic cases which every student should understand. In arbitrary viscous flows, both pressure and velocity are unknowns and are solved together as a system of equations in the chapters which follow.

References

1. *U.S. Standard Atmosphere*, 1976, Government Printing Office, Washington, 1976.
2. G. Neumann and W. J. Pierson, Jr., *Principles of Physical Oceanography*, Prentice-Hall, Englewood Cliffs, N.J., 1966.
3. T. C. Gillmer, *Modern Ship Design*, chap. 5, United States Naval Institute, Annapolis, Md., 1970.
4. D. T. Greenwood, *Principles of Dynamics*, 2d ed., Prentice-Hall, Englewood Cliffs, N.J., 1988.
5. R. I. Fletcher, "The Apparent Field of Gravity in a Rotating Fluid System," *Am. J. Phys.* vol. 40, pp. 959–965, July 1972.
6. National Committee for Fluid Mechanics Films, *Illustrated Experiments in Fluid Mechanics*, M.I.T. Press, Cambridge, Mass., 1972.
7. J. P. Holman, *Experimental Methods for Engineers*, 5th ed., McGraw-Hill, New York, 1989.
8. R. P. Benedict, *Fundamentals of Temperature, Pressure, and Flow Measurement*, 3d ed., Wiley, New York, 1984.
9. T. G. Beckwith and R. G. Marangoni, *Mechanical Measurements*, 4th ed., Addison-Wesley, Reading, Mass., 1990.
10. J. W. Dally, W. F. Riley, and K. G. McConnell, *Instrumentation for Engineering Measurements*, Wiley, New York, 1984.
11. E. N. Gilbert, "How Things Float," *Am. Math. Monthly,* vol. 98, no. 3, pp. 201–216, 1991.

Recommended Films

Films numbered 5, 17, and 24 in App. C.

PROBLEMS

In addition to many traditional problems, categorized in the problem distribution list below, there are several **word problems**, *labeled W2.1 to W2.8, and a* **design project**, *denoted as D2.1.*

Problem Distribution

Section	Topic	Problems
2.1	Pressure and pressure gradient	2.1–2.3
2.2	Static equilibrium; gage pressure	2.4–2.5
2.3	Hydrostatic pressure; barometers	2.6–2.22
2.3	The atmosphere	2.23–2.29
2.4	Manometers; multiple fluids	2.30–2.47
2.5	Forces on plane surfaces	2.48–2.81
2.6	Forces on curved surfaces	2.82–2.100
2.7	Forces in layered fluids	2.101–2.103
2.8	Buoyancy; Archimedes' principles	2.104–2.126
2.8	Stability of floating bodies	2.127–2.136
2.9	Uniform acceleration	2.137–2.151
2.9	Rigid-body rotation	2.152–2.157
2.10	Pressure measurements	None

2.1 For the two-dimensional stress field shown in Fig. P2.1 it is found that

$$\sigma_{xx} = 2000 \text{ lbf/ft}^2 \qquad \sigma_{yy} = 1800 \text{ lbf/ft}^2$$

$$\sigma_{xy} = \sigma_{yx} = 100 \text{ lbf/ft}^2$$

Find the shear and normal stress in pounds per square foot on plane *AA* cutting through at a 30° angle as shown.

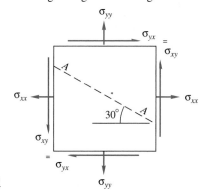

Fig. P2.1

2.2 For the stress field of Fig. P2.1 we are given

$$\sigma_{xx} = 2000 \text{ lbf/ft}^2 \qquad \sigma_{yy} = 1800 \text{ lbf/ft}^2$$

$$\sigma_n(AA) = 2100 \text{ lbf/ft}^2$$

Compute the shear stress on plane *AA* and the shear stress σ_{xy}.

2.3 Derive Eq. (2.18) by using the differential element in Fig. 2.2 with *z* "up," no fluid motion, and pressure varying only in the *z* direction.

2.4 Atlanta, Georgia, has an average altitude of 1100 ft. On a standard day, pressure gage *A* in a laboratory experiment reads 96 kPa, and gage *B* reads 100 kPa. Express these readings in gage pressure or vacuum pressure (Pa), whichever is appropriate.

2.5 Any pressure reading can be expressed as a length or *head* $h = p/\gamma$. What is standard sea-level pressure expressed in (*a*) ft of ethyl alcohol, (*b*) m of water, (*c*) inHg, and (*d*) mm of carbon tetrachloride?

2.6 Express the absolute pressure at point *B* in Pa in Fig. 2.4 if it lies 95 cm below the surface and the atmospheric pressure is 29.1 inHg.

2.7 The deepest known point in the ocean is 11,034 m in the Mariana Trench in the Pacific. At this depth the specific weight of seawater is approximately 10,520 N/m³. Estimate the absolute pressure at this depth, in atm.

2.8 Repeat Prob. 2.7 by integrating the more exact nonlinear pressure-density relation for water, Eq. (1.19), from the surface (*z* = 0) to the depth *z* = −11,034 m.

2.9 An approximate answer to Prob. 1.33 for mercury is $B \approx 41{,}300$ and $n \approx 6$. Consider this a reward if you read ahead this far. Now use this formula to compute the pressure in the Mariana Trench (Prob. 2.7) if the ocean were filled with mercury instead of seawater.

2.10 A closed tank contains 1.5 m of SAE 30 oil, 1 m of water, 20 cm of mercury, and an airspace on top, all at 20°C. The absolute pressure at the bottom of the tank is 60 kPa. What is the pressure in the airspace?

2.11 In Fig. P2.11, pressure gage *A* reads 1.5 kPa (gage). The fluids are at 20°C. Determine the elevations *z*, in m, of the

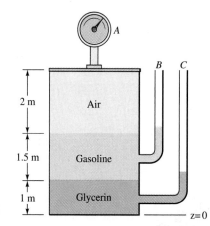

Fig. P2.11

liquid levels in the open piezometer tubes B and C.

2.12 When open tubes called *piezometers* are connected to a tank of liquid under pressure, the liquid rises to the *piezometer head*, or *pressure head*, of the liquid. If p_A is the pressure at point A, show that all three piezometers rise to the same level $h = p_A/\gamma$.

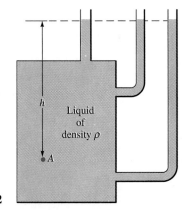

Fig. P2.12

2.13 In Fig. P2.13 the 20°C water and gasoline surfaces are open to the atmosphere and at the same elevation. What is the height h of the third liquid in the right leg?

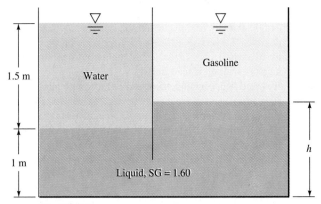

Fig. P2.13

2.14 The closed tank in Fig. P2.14 is at 20°C. If the pressure at

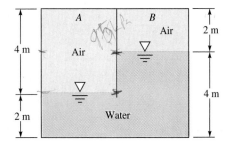

Fig. P2.14

point A is 95 kPa absolute, what is the absolute pressure at point B in kPa? What percent error do you make by neglecting the specific weight of the air?

2.15 The air-oil-water system in Fig. P2.15 is at 20°C. Knowing that gage A reads 15 lbf/in² absolute and gage B reads 1.25 lbf/in² less than gage C, compute (*a*) the specific weight of the oil in lbf/ft³ and (*b*) the actual reading of gage C in lbf/in² absolute.

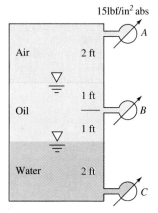

Fig. P2.15

2.16 A closed inverted cone, 100 cm high with diameter 60 cm at the top, is filled with air at 20°C and 1 atm. Water at 20°C is introduced at the bottom (the vertex) to compress the air isothermally until a gage at the top of the cone reads 30 kPa (gage). Estimate (*a*) the amount of water needed (cm³) and (*b*) the resulting absolute pressure at the bottom of the cone (kPa).

2.17 The system in Fig. P2.17 is at 20°C. If the pressure at point A is 1900 lbf/ft², determine the pressures at points B, C, and D in lbf/ft².

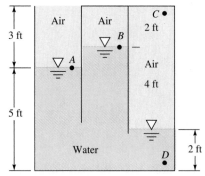

Fig. P2.17

2.18 The system in Fig. P2.18 is at 20°C. If atmospheric pressure is 101.33 kPa and the pressure at the bottom of the tank is 242 kPa, what is the specific gravity of fluid X?

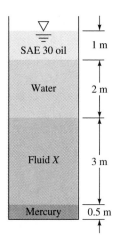

Fig. P2.18

2.19 The U-tube in Fig. P2.19 has a 1-cm ID and contains mercury as shown. If 20 cm³ of water is poured into the right-hand leg, what will the free-surface height in each leg be after the sloshing has died down?

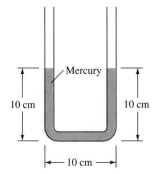

Fig. P2.19

2.20 The hydraulic jack in Fig. P2.20 is filled with oil at 56 lbf/ft³. Neglecting the weight of the two pistons, what force F on the handle is required to support the 2000-lbf weight for this design?

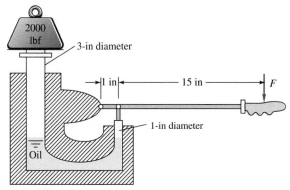

Fig. P2.20

2.21 At 20°C gage A reads 350 kPa absolute. What is the height h of the water in cm? What should gage B read in kPa absolute?

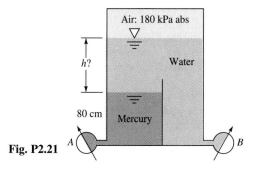

Fig. P2.21

2.22 The fuel gage for a gasoline tank in a car reads proportional to the bottom gage pressure as in Fig. P2.22. If the tank is 30 cm deep and accidentally contains 2 cm of water plus gasoline, how many centimeters of air remain at the top when the gage erroneously reads "full"?

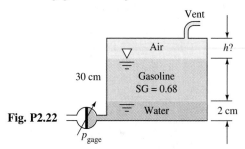

Fig. P2.22

2.23 In Prob. 1.2 we made a crude integration of the density distribution $\rho(z)$ in Table A.6 and estimated the mass of the earth's atmosphere to be $m \approx 6$ E18 kg. Can this result be used to estimate the sea-level pressure on earth? Conversely, can the actual sea-level pressure of 101.35 kPa be used to make a more accurate estimate of the atmospheric mass?

2.24 Venus has a mass of 4.90 E24 kg and a radius of 6050 km. Its atmosphere is 96 percent CO_2, but let us assume it to be 100 percent. Its surface temperature averages 730 K, decreasing to 250 K at an altitude of 70 km. The average surface pressure is 9.1 MPa. Estimate the atmospheric pressure of Venus at an altitude of 10 km.

2.25 Mars has a mass of 6.38 E23 kg and a radius of 3381 km. Its atmosphere is mostly CO_2—let us assume it to be 100 percent. Its surface temperature is highly variable but averages about 200 K. The average surface pressure is 800 Pa. Estimate the atmospheric pressure of Mars at an altitude of 10 km.

2.26 Investigate the effect of doubling the lapse rate on atmospheric pressure. Compare the standard atmosphere (Table A.6) with a lapse rate twice as high of $B_2 = 0.0130$ K/m.

Find the altitude at which the pressure deviation is (a) 1 percent and (b) 5 percent. What do you conclude?

2.27   Put Prob. 2.26 on an analytic basis by assuming arbitrary B in Eq. (2.27). Show that, approximately, the deviation in pressure $p(z)$ is less than 1 percent of p_a if $z < 0.14T_0/B$.

2.28   Earth's atmospheric conditions vary somewhat. On a certain day the sea-level temperature is 45°F, and the sea-level pressure is 29.5 inHg. An airplane overhead registers an air temperature of 18°F and a pressure of 12 lbf/in². Estimate the plane's altitude, in ft.

2.29   Under some conditions the atmosphere is *adiabatic*, $p \approx$ (const)(ρ^k), where k is the specific-heat ratio. Show that, for an adiabatic atmosphere, the pressure variation is given by

$$p = p_0\left[1 - \frac{(k-1)gz}{kRT_0}\right]^{k/(k-1)}$$

Compare this formula for air at $z = 10{,}000$ m with the standard atmosphere in Table A.6.

2.30   In Fig. P2.30 fluid 1 is SAE 30 oil, and fluid 2 is carbon tetrachloride. If $p_a = 99$ kPa, determine the absolute pressure at point A.

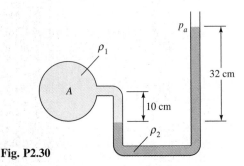

Fig. P2.30

2.31   In Fig. P2.31 all fluids are at 20°C. Determine the pressure difference (Pa) between points A and B.

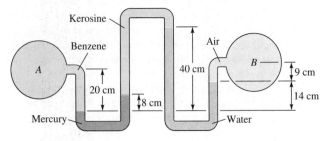

Fig. P2.31

2.32   For the inverted manometer of Fig. P2.32, all fluids are at 20°C. If $p_B - p_A = 97$ kPa, what must the height H be in cm?

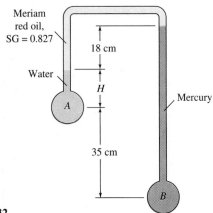

Fig. P2.32

2.33   In Fig. P2.33 the pressure at point A is 25 lbf/in². All fluids are at 20°C. What is the air pressure in the closed chamber B, in Pa?

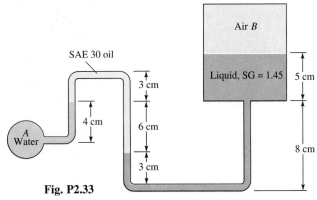

Fig. P2.33

2.34   Sometimes manometer dimensions have a significant effect. In Fig. P2.34 containers (a) and (b) are cylindrical and con-

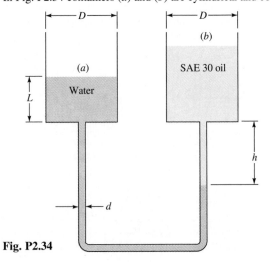

Fig. P2.34

ditions are such that $p_a = p_b$. Derive a formula for the pressure difference $p_a - p_b$ when the oil-water interface on the right rises a distance $\Delta h < h$, for (a) $d \ll D$ and (b) $d = 0.2D$. What is the percentage change in the value of Δp?

2.35 For a specific application of Prob. 2.34, take $D = 5$ cm, $L = 8$ cm, and $h = 10$ cm. Both fluids are at 20°C. Evaluate $p_a - p_b$ when $\Delta h = 1$ cm for (a) $d \approx 0$ and (b) $d = 1$ cm.

2.36 For Fig. 2.9 in the text, let fluid 1 be water and fluid 2 be mercury, at 20°C. The right leg is fitted with a scale to read p_A in kPa (gage). What should the length between scale graduations be, in mm?

2.37 The inclined manometer in Fig. 2.37 contains Meriam red manometer oil, SG = 0.827. Assume that the reservoir is very large. If the inclined arm is fitted with graduations 1 in apart, what should the angle θ be if each graduation corresponds to 1 lbf/ft^2 gage pressure for p_A?

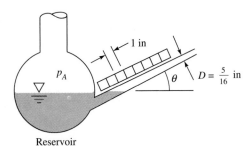

Fig. P2.37

2.38 Repeat Prob. 2.37 for a finite reservoir approximating a half-full hemisphere with a diameter of 6 in.

2.39 An 8-cm-diameter piston compresses manometer oil into an inclined 7-mm-diameter tube, as shown in Fig. P2.39. When a weight W is added to the top of the piston, the oil rises an additional distance of 10 cm up the tube, as shown. How large is the weight, in N?

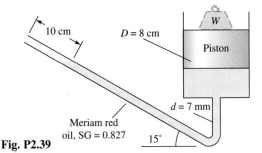

Fig. P2.39

2.40 A pump slowly introduces mercury into the bottom of the closed tank in Fig. P2.40. At the instant shown, the air pressure $p_B = 80$ kPa. The pump stops when the air pressure

rises to 110 kPa. All fluids remain at 20°C. What will be the manometer reading h at that time, in cm, if it is connected to standard sea-level ambient air p_{atm}?

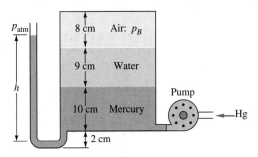

Fig. P2.40

2.41 The system in Fig. P2.41 is at 20°C. Compute the pressure at point A in lbf/ft^2 absolute.

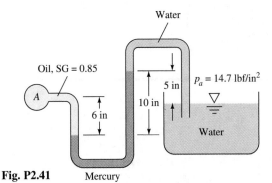

Fig. P2.41   Mercury

2.42 Very small pressure differences $p_A - p_B$ can be measured accurately by the two-fluid differential manometer in Fig. P2.42. Density ρ_2 is only slightly larger than that of the upper fluid ρ_1. Derive an expression for the proportionality between h and $p_A - p_B$ if the reservoirs are very large.

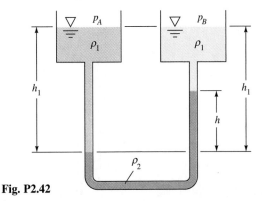

Fig. P2.42

2.43 To illustrate the effectiveness of the system in Fig. P2.42, consider that a height difference of 1 cm in a fluid with SG = 0.85 corresponds to a pressure difference of 83.2 Pa. In Fig. P2.42, what difference $p_A - p_B$ corresponds to $h = 1$ cm when $SG_1 = 0.84$ and $SG_2 = 0.86$? What is the increase in accuracy?

2.44 Water flows downward in a pipe at 45°, as shown in Fig. P2.44. The pressure drop $p_1 - p_2$ is partly due to gravity and partly due to friction. The mercury manometer reads a 6-in height difference. What is the total pressure drop $p_1 - p_2$ in lbf/in²? What is the pressure drop due to friction only between 1 and 2 in lbf/in²? Does the manometer reading correspond only to friction drop? Why?

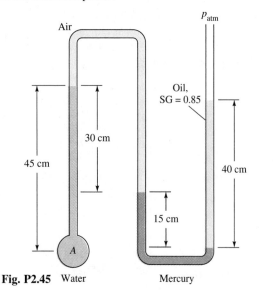

Fig. P2.44

2.45 Determine the gage pressure at point A in Pa. Is it higher or lower than atmospheric?

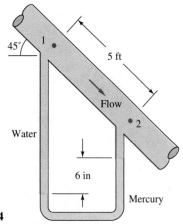

Fig. P2.45 Water

2.46 In Fig. P2.46 both ends of the manometer are open to the atmosphere. Estimate the specific gravity of fluid X.

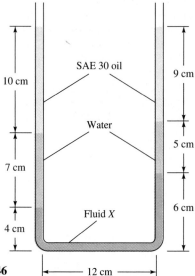

Fig. P2.46 |← 12 cm →|

2.47 The cylindrical tank in Fig. P2.47 is being filled with water at 20°C by a pump developing an exit pressure of 175 kPa. At the instant shown, the air pressure is 110 kPa and $H = 35$ cm. The pump stops when it can no longer raise the water pressure. For isothermal air compression, estimate H at that time.

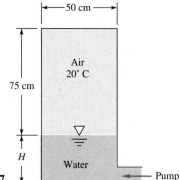

Fig. P2.47

2.48 Repeat Example 2.5, but instead let the hinge be at point A and let point B rest against a smooth bottom.

2.49 A vertical gate 6 ft wide and 8 ft high is hinged at the top and held closed by water, on one side, whose level is 7 ft above the gate top. What horizontal force applied at the bottom of the gate is required to open it? Neglect the atmospheric-pressure effect.

2.50 A vat filled with oil (SG = 0.87) is 6 m long and 4 m deep and has a trapezoidal cross section 3 m wide at the bottom and 5 m wide at the top. Compute (a) the weight of oil in the vat, (*b*) the force on the vat bottom, and (*c*) the force on the trapezoidal end panel.

2.51 Gate *AB* in Fig. P2.51 is 1.2 m long and 0.8 m into the paper. Neglecting atmospheric pressure, compute the force *F* on the gate and its center-of-pressure position *X*.

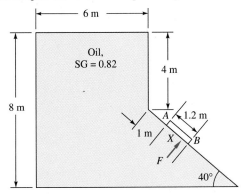

Fig. P2.51

2.52 Suppose that the tank in Fig. P2.51 is filled with liquid *X*, not oil. Gate *AB* is 0.8 m wide into the paper. Suppose that liquid *X* causes a force *F* on gate *AB* and that the moment of this force about point *B* is 26,500 N · m. What is the specific gravity of liquid *X*?

2.53 Figure P2.53 shows the elevation and right-side views of an open tank. If the tank is filled with water at 20°C, compute (*a*) the force of the water on panel *ABC* and (*b*) the moment of this force about line *AB*.

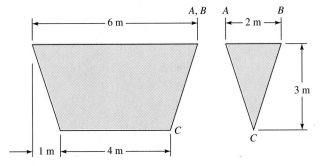

Fig. P2.53

2.54 Figure P2.53 shows the elevation and right-side views of an open tank. If the tank is filled with liquid *X*, the force of the liquid on panel *ABC* is found to be 26 kN. Compute (*a*) the moment of this force about line *AB* and (*b*) the specific gravity of liquid *X*.

2.55 Gate *AB* in Fig. P2.55 is 5 ft wide into the paper, hinged at *A*, and restrained by a stop at *B*. The water is at 20°C. Compute (*a*) the force on stop *B* and (*b*) the reactions at *A* if the water depth *h* = 9.5 ft.

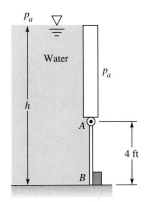

Fig. P2.55

2.56 In Fig. P2.55, gate *AB* is 5 ft wide into the paper, and stop *B* will break if the water force on it equals 9200 lbf. For what water depth *h* is this condition reached?

2.57 In Fig. P2.55, gate *AB* is 5 ft wide into the paper. Suppose that the fluid is liquid *X*, not water. Hinge *A* breaks when its reaction is 7800 lbf, and the liquid depth is *h* = 13 ft. What is the specific gravity of liquid *X*?

2.58 In Fig. P2.58 the cover gate *AB* closes a circular opening 80 cm in diameter. The gate is held closed by a 200-kg mass as shown. Assume standard gravity at 20°C. At what water level *h* will the gate be dislodged? Neglect the weight of the gate.

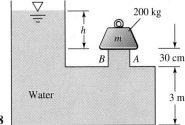

Fig. P2.58

2.59 When freshly poured between wooden forms, concrete approximates a fluid with SG = 2.40. Figure P2.59 shows an

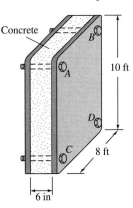

Fig. P2.59

8- by 10-ft by 6-in slab poured between wooden forms which are connected by four corner bolts A, B, C, D as shown. Neglecting end effects, compute the forces in all four bolts.

2.60   Find the net hydrostatic force per unit width on the rectangular gate AB in Fig. P2.60 and its line of action.

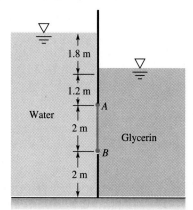

Fig. P2.60

2.61   Gate AB in Fig. P2.61 is a homogeneous mass of 180 kg, 1.2 m wide into the paper, hinged at A, and resting on a smooth bottom at B. All fluids are at 20°C. For what water depth h will the force at point B be zero?

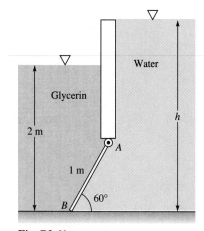

Fig. P2.61

2.62   Gate AB in Fig. P2.62 is 15 ft long and 8 ft wide into the paper and is hinged at B with a stop at A. The water is at 20°C. The gate is 1-in-thick steel, SG = 7.85. Compute the water level h for which the gate will start to fall.

2.63   The tank in Fig. P2.63 has a 4-cm-diameter plug at the bottom on the right. All fluids are at 20°C. The plug will pop out if the hydrostatic force on it is 25 N. For this condition,

what will be the reading h on the mercury manometer on the left side?

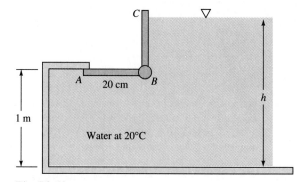

Fig. P2.62

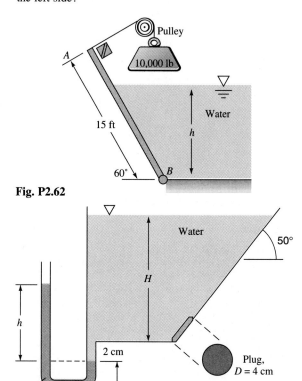

Fig. P2.63

2.64   Gate ABC in Fig. P2.64 has a fixed hinge line at B and is 2 m wide into the paper. The gate will open at A to release water if the water depth is high enough. Compute the depth h for which the gate will begin to open.

Fig. P2.64

2.65   Gate AB in Fig. P2.65 is semicircular, hinged at B, and held

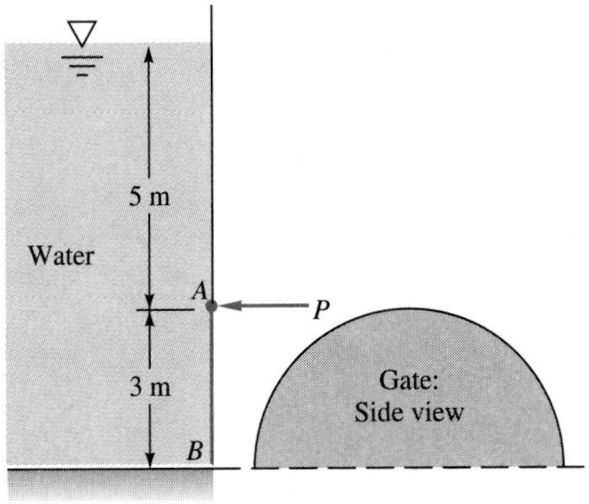

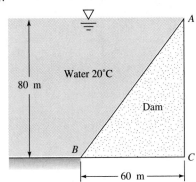

Fig. P2.65

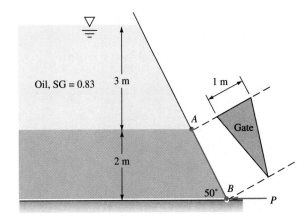

Fig. P2.68

by a horizontal force P at A. What force P is required for equilibrium?

2.66 Dam ABC in Fig. P2.66 is 30 m wide into the paper and made of concrete (SG = 2.4). Find the hydrostatic force on surface AB and its moment about C. Assuming no seepage of water under the dam, could this force tip the dam over? How does your argument change if there is seepage under the dam?

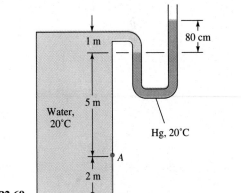

Fig. P2.66

2.67 Generalize Prob. 2.66 as follows. Denote length AB as H, length BC as L, and angle ABC as θ. Let the dam material have specific gravity SG. The width of the dam is b. Assume no seepage of water under the dam. Find an analytic relation between SG and the critical angle θ_c for which the dam will just tip over to the right. Use your relation to compute θ_c for the special case SG = 2.4 (concrete).

2.68 Isosceles triangle gate AB in Fig. P2.68 is hinged at A and weighs 1500 N. What horizontal force P is required at point B for equilibrium?

2.69 The water tank in Fig. P2.69 is pressurized, as shown by the mercury-manometer reading. Determine the hydrostatic force per unit depth on gate AB.

2.70 Calculate the force and center of pressure on one side of the

Fig. P2.69

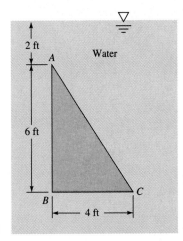

Fig. P2.70

vertical triangular panel ABC in Fig. P2.70. Neglect p_{atm}.

2.71 In Fig. P2.71 gate AB is 3 m wide into the paper and is connected by a rod and pulley to a concrete sphere (SG =

2.40). What diameter of the sphere is just sufficient to keep the gate closed?

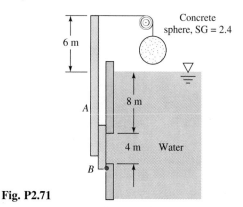

Fig. P2.71

2.72 The V-shaped container in Fig. P2.72 is hinged at A and held together by cable BC at the top. If cable spacing is 1 m into the paper, what is the cable tension?

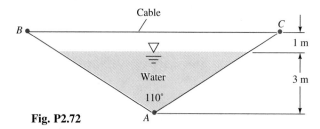

Fig. P2.72

2.73 Gate AB is 5 ft wide into the paper and opens to let fresh water out when the ocean tide is dropping. The hinge at A is 2 ft above the freshwater level. At what ocean level h will the gate first open? Neglect the gate weight.

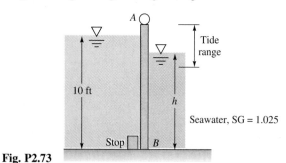

Fig. P2.73

2.74 In "soft" liquids (low bulk modulus β), it may be necessary to account for liquid compressibility in hydrostatic calculations. An approximate density relation would be

$$dp \approx \frac{\beta}{\rho}\, d\rho = a^2\, d\rho \quad \text{or} \quad p \approx p_0 + a^2(\rho - \rho_0)$$

where a is the speed of sound and (p_0, ρ_0) are the conditions at the liquid surface $z = 0$. Use this approximation to show that the density variation with depth in a soft liquid is

$$\rho = \rho_0 e^{-gz/a^2}$$

where g is the acceleration of gravity and z is positive upward. Then consider a vertical wall of width b, extending from the surface ($z = 0$) down to depth $z = -h$. Find an analytic expression for the hydrostatic force F on this wall, and compare it with the incompressible result $F = \rho_0 g h^2 b/2$. Would the center of pressure be below the incompressible position $z = -2h/3$?

2.75 Compute the force on one side of the parabolic panel ABC in Fig. P2.75, neglecting atmospheric pressure. Compute the vertical distance down to the center of pressure, given that $I_{xx} = 2bh^3/7$ for a parabola about a horizontal axis through A.

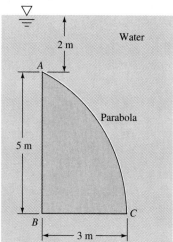

Fig. P2.75

2.76 Consider the angled gate ABC in Fig. P2.76, hinged at C and of width b into the paper. Derive an analytic formula

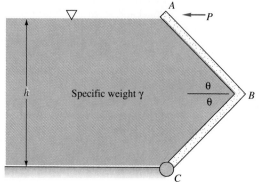

Fig. P2.76

for the horizontal force P required at the top for equilibrium, as a function of the angle θ.

2.77 The circular gate ABC in Fig. P2.77 has a 1-m radius and is hinged at B. Compute the force P just sufficient to keep the gate from opening when $h = 8$ m. Neglect atmospheric pressure.

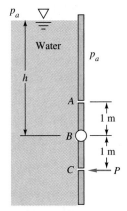

Fig. P2.77

2.78 Repeat Prob. 2.77 to derive an analytic expression for P as a function of h. Is there anything unusual about your solution?

2.79 Gate ABC in Fig. P2.79 is 1 m square and is hinged at B. It will open automatically when the water level h becomes high enough. Determine the lowest height for which the gate will open. Neglect atmospheric pressure. Is this result independent of the liquid density?

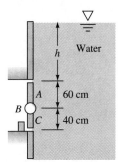

Fig. P2.79

2.80 For the closed tank in Fig. P2.80, all fluids are at 20°C, and the airspace is pressurized. It is found that the net outward hydrostatic force on the 30- by 40-cm panel at the bottom of the water layer is 8450 N. Estimate (*a*) the pressure in the airspace and (*b*) the reading h on the mercury manometer.

2.81 Gate AB is 7 ft into the paper and weighs 3000 lbf when submerged. It is hinged at B and rests against a smooth wall at A. Determine the water level h at the left which will just cause the gate to open.

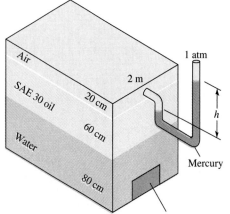

Fig. P2.80   Panel, 30 cm high, 40 cm wide

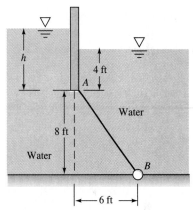

Fig. P2.81

2.82 The dam in Fig. P2.82 is a quarter circle 50 m wide into the paper. Determine the horizontal and vertical components of the hydrostatic force against the dam and the point CP where the resultant strikes the dam.

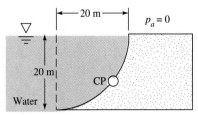

Fig. P2.82

2.83 Gate AB is a quarter circle 10 ft wide into the paper and hinged at B. Find the force F just sufficient to keep the gate from opening. The gate is uniform and weighs 3000 lbf.

2.84 Determine (*a*) the total hydrostatic force on the curved surface AB in Fig. P2.84 and (*b*) its line of action. Neglect

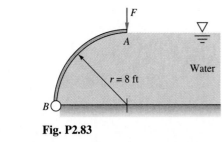

Fig. P2.83

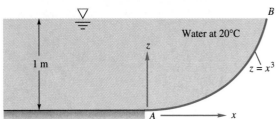

Fig. P2.84

atmospheric pressure, and let the surface have unit width.

2.85 Compute the horizontal and vertical components of the hydrostatic force on the quarter-circle panel at the bottom of the water tank in Fig. P2.85.

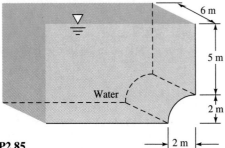

Fig. P2.85

2.86 Compute the horizontal and vertical components of the hydrostatic force on the hemispherical bulge at the bottom of the tank in Fig. P2.86.

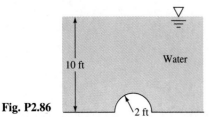

Fig. P2.86

2.87 The bottle of champagne (SG = 0.96) in Fig. P2.87 is under pressure, as shown by the mercury-manometer reading. Compute the net force on the 2-in-radius hemispherical end cap at the bottom of the bottle.

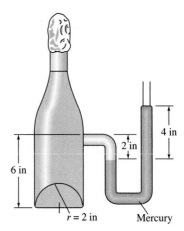

Fig. P2.87

2.88 Gate *ABC* is a circular arc, sometimes called a *Tainter gate*, which can be raised and lowered by pivoting about point *O*. See Fig. P2.88. For the position shown, determine (*a*) the hydrostatic force of the water on the gate and (*b*) its line of action. Does the force pass through point *O*?

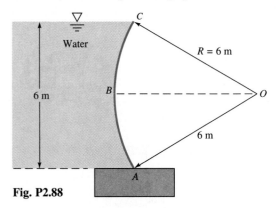

Fig. P2.88

2.89 Compute the hydrostatic force and its line of action on the semicylindrical bulge *ABC* in Fig. P2.89.

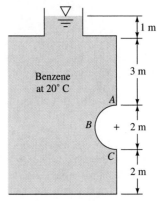

Fig. P2.89

2.90 A 1-ft-diameter hole in the bottom of the tank in Fig. P2.90 is closed by a conical 45° plug. Neglecting the weight of the plug, compute the force F required to keep the plug in the hole.

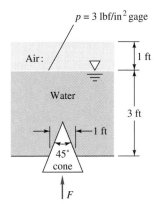

Fig. P2.90

2.91 The hemispherical dome in Fig. P2.91 weighs 30 kN and is filled with water and attached to the floor by six equally spaced bolts. What is the force in each bolt required to hold down the dome?

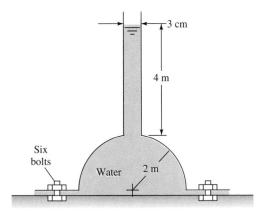

Fig. P2.91

2.92 A 4-m-diameter water tank consists of two half cylinders, each weighing 4.5 kN/m, bolted together as shown in Fig.

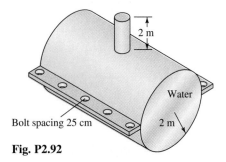

Fig. P2.92

P2.92. If the support of the end caps is neglected, determine the force induced in each bolt.

2.93 In Fig. P2.93 a one-quadrant spherical shell of radius R is submerged in liquid of specific gravity γ and depth $h > R$. Find an analytic expression for the resultant hydrostatic force, and its line of action, on the shell surface.

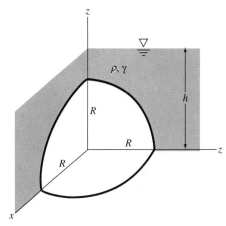

Fig. P2.93

2.94 The 4-ft-diameter log (SG = 0.80) in Fig. P2.94 is 8 ft long into the paper and dams water as shown. Compute the net vertical and horizontal reactions at point C.

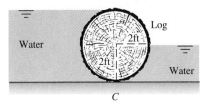

Fig. P2.94

2.95 The 2-m-diameter cylinder in Fig. P2.95 is 4 m long into the paper and rests in static equilibrium against the smooth wall at point B. Compute (*a*) the weight and (*b*) the specific gravity of the cylinder. Assume zero wall friction at point B.

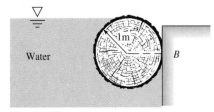

Fig. P2.95

2.96 The tank in Fig. P2.96 is 3 m wide into the paper. Neglecting atmospheric pressure, compute the hydrostatic (*a*) horizontal force, (*b*) vertical force, and (*c*) resultant force on quarter-circle panel *BC*.

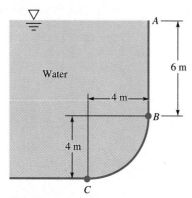

Fig. P2.96

2.97 Gate *AB* is a three-eighths circle, 3 m wide into the paper, hinged at *B*, and resting against a smooth wall at *A*. Compute the reaction forces at points *A* and *B*. See Fig. P2.97.

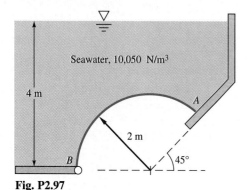

Fig. P2.97

2.98 Gate *ABC* in Fig. P2.98 is a quarter circle 8 ft wide into the paper. Compute the horizontal and vertical hydrostatic forces on the gate and the line of action of the resultant force.

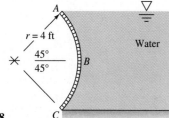

Fig. P2.98

2.99 A 2-ft-diameter sphere weighing 400 lbf closes a 1-ft-diameter hole in the bottom of the tank in Fig. P2.99. Compute

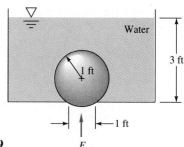

Fig. P2.99

the force *F* required to dislodge the sphere from the hole.

2.100 Pressurized water fills the tank in Fig. P2.100. Compute the net hydrostatic force on the conical surface *ABC*.

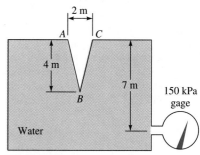

Fig. P2.100

2.101 A fuel truck has a tank cross section which is approximately elliptical, with a 3-m horizontal major axis and a 2-m vertical minor axis. The top is vented to the atmosphere. If the tank is filled half with water and half with gasoline, what is the hydrostatic force on the flat elliptical end panel?

2.102 In Fig. P2.80 suppose that the manometer reading is *h* = 25 cm. What will be the net hydrostatic force on the complete end wall, which is 160 cm high and 2 m wide?

2.103 The cylindrical tank in Fig. P2.103 has a hemispherical end cap *ABC* and contains oil and water as shown. Compute the resultant force and line of action of the fluids on the end cap *ABC*.

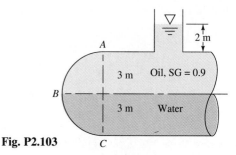

Fig. P2.103

2.104 The can in Fig. P2.104 floats in the position shown. What

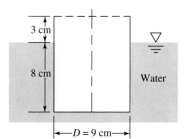

Fig. P2.104

is its weight in N?

2.105 It is said that Archimedes discovered the buoyancy laws when asked by King Hiero of Syracuse to determine whether his new crown was pure gold (SG = 19.3). Archimedes measured the weight of the crown in air to be 11.8 N and its weight in water to be 10.9 N. Was it pure gold?

2.106 It is found that a 10-cm cube of aluminum (SG = 2.71) will remain neutral under water (neither rise nor fall) if it is tied by a string to a submerged 18-cm-diameter sphere of buoyant foam. What is the specific weight of the foam, in N/m^3?

2.107 Repeat Prob. 2.62, assuming that the 10,000-lbf weight is aluminum (SG = 2.71) and is hanging submerged in the water.

2.108 A piece of yellow pine wood (SG = 0.65) is 5 cm square and 2.2 m long. How many newtons of lead (SG = 11.4) should be attached to one end of the wood so that it will float vertically with 30 cm out of the water?

2.109 A *hydrometer* floats at a level which is a measure of the specific gravity of the liquid. The stem is of constant diameter D, and a weight in the bottom stabilizes the body to float vertically, as shown in Fig. P2.109. If the position $h = 0$ is pure water (SG = 1.0), derive a formula for h as a function of total weight W, D, SG, and the specific weight γ_0 of water.

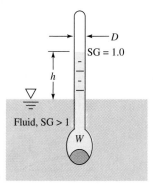

Fig. P2.109

2.110 A particular hydrometer in Fig. P2.109 has a mass of 20 g and has $D = 1$ cm. Compute the position h when the hydrometer floats in a liquid of density 1250 kg/m^3.

2.111 A hot-air balloon must be designed to support basket, cords, and one person for a total weight of 1300 N. The balloon material has a mass of 60 g/m^2. Ambient air is at 25°C and 1 atm. The hot air inside the balloon is at 70°C and 1 atm. What diameter spherical balloon will just support the total weight? Neglect the size of the hot-air inlet vent.

2.112 The uniform 5-m-long round wooden rod in Fig. P2.112 is tied to the bottom by a string. Determine (*a*) the tension in the string and (*b*) the specific gravity of the wood. Is it possible for the given information to determine the inclination angle θ? Explain.

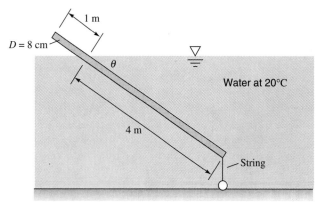

Fig. P2.112

2.113 A *spar buoy* is a buoyant rod weighted to float and protrude vertically, as in Fig. P2.113. It can be used for measurements or markers. Suppose that the buoy is maple wood (SG = 0.6), 2 in by 2 in by 10 ft, floating in seawater (SG = 1.025). How many pounds of steel (SG = 7.85) should be added to the bottom end so that $h = 18$ in?

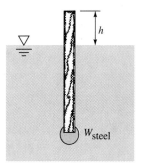

Fig. P2.113

2.114 A right circular cone is 10 cm in diameter and 18 cm high and weighs 2 N in air. How much force is required to push this cone with the vertex downward into SAE 30 oil at 20°C so that its base is exactly at the surface? How much additional force is required to push the base an additional 10 cm below the surface?

2.115 The 2-in by 2-in by 10-ft spar buoy from Fig. P2.113 has 5 lbm of steel attached and has gone aground on a rock, as in Fig. P2.115. Compute the angle θ at which the buoy will lean, assuming that the rock exerts no moments on the spar.

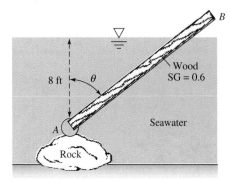

Fig. P2.115

2.116 The homogeneous 12-cm cube in Fig. 2.116 is balanced by a 2-kg mass on the beam scale when the cube is immersed in 20°C ethanol. What is the specific gravity of the cube?

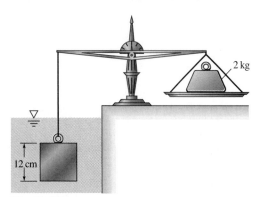

Fig. P2.116

2.117 The balloon in Fig. P2.117 is filled with helium and pressurized to 125 kPa. For the atmospheric conditions shown, compute the tension in the mooring line.

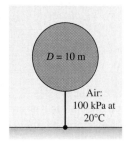

Fig. P2.117

2.118 A 14 in-diameter hollow sphere is made of steel (SG = 7.85) with 0.16-in wall thickness. How high will this sphere

float in 20°C water? How much weight must be added inside to make the sphere neutrally buoyant?

2.119 When a 5-lbf weight is placed on the end of the uniform floating wooden beam in Fig. P2.119, the beam tilts at an angle θ with its upper right corner at the surface, as shown. Determine (a) the angle θ and (b) the specific gravity of the wood. (*Hint:* Both the vertical forces and the moments about the beam centroid must be balanced.)

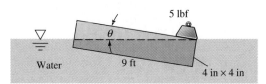

Fig. P2.119

2.120 A uniform wooden beam (SG = 0.65) is 10 cm by 10 cm by 3 m and is hinged at A, as in Fig. P2.120. At what angle θ will the beam float in the 20°C water?

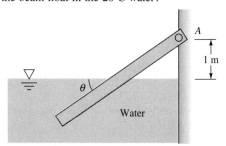

Fig. P2.120

2.121 The uniform beam in Fig. P2.121, of size L by h by b and with specific weight γ_b, floats exactly on its diagonal when a heavy uniform sphere is tied to the left corner, as shown. Show that this can only happen (a) when $\gamma_b = \gamma/3$ and (b) when the sphere has size

$$D = \left[\frac{Lhb}{\pi(SG - 1)} \right]^{1/3}$$

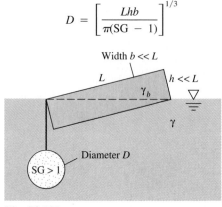

Fig. P2.121

2.122 A uniform block of steel (SG = 7.85) will "float" at a mercury-water interface as in Fig. P2.122. What is the ratio of the distances *a* and *b* for this condition?

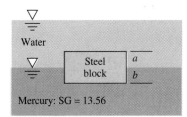

Fig. P2.122

2.123 In an estuary where fresh water meets and mixes with seawater, there often occurs a stratified salinity condition with fresh water on top and salt water on the bottom, as in Fig. P2.123. The interface is called a *halocline*. An idealization of this would be constant density on each side of the halocline as shown. A 35-cm-diameter sphere weighing 50 lbf would "float" near such a halocline. Compute the sphere position for the idealization in Fig. P2.123.

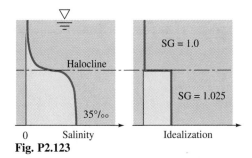

Fig. P2.123

2.124 A balloon weighing 3.5 lbf is 6 ft in diameter. It is filled with hydrogen at 18 lbf/in² absolute and 60°F and is released. At what altitude in the U.S. standard atmosphere will this balloon be neutrally buoyant?

2.125 Suppose that the balloon in Prob. 2.111 is constructed to have a diameter of 14 m, is filled at sea level with hot air at 70°C and 1 atm, and is released. If the air inside the balloon remains constant and the heater maintains it at 70°C, at what altitude in the U.S. standard atmosphere will this balloon be neutrally buoyant?

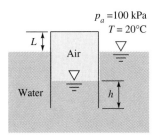

Fig. P2.126

2.126 An open can 15 cm in diameter and 30 cm long (Fig. P2.126) is eased downward so that the air within is trapped and compressed by the water. The can weighs 4 N and is made of sheet steel (SG = 7.85). Assuming isothermal compression of the air in the can, compute the height of water intrusion *h* and the height *L* of the can above the water when the can is floating. Assume that the position is stable.

2.127 Consider the 2-in by 2-in by 10-ft spar buoy of Prob. 2.113. How many pounds of steel (SG = 7.85) should be added at the bottom to ensure vertical floating with a metacentric height $\overline{MG}$ of (*a*) zero (neutral stability) or (*b*) 1 ft (reasonably stable)?

2.128 The iceberg of Fig. 2.19 can be idealized as a cube of side length *L*, as in Fig. P2.128. If seawater is denoted by S = 1.0, then glacier ice (which forms icebergs) has S = 0.88. Determine if this "cubic" iceberg is stable for the position shown in Fig. P2.128.

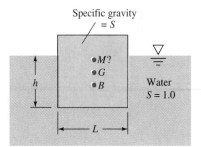

Fig. P2.128

2.129 The iceberg idealization in Prob. 2.128 may become unstable if its sides melt and its height exceeds its width. In Fig. P2.128 suppose that the height is *L* and the depth into the paper is *L*, but the width in the plane of the paper is $H < L$. Assuming S = 0.88 for the iceberg, find the ratio H/L for which it becomes neutrally stable, i.e., about to overturn.

2.130 Consider a wooden cylinder (SG = 0.6) 1 m in diameter and 2 m long. Would this cylinder be stable if placed to float with its axis vertical in oil (SG = 0.85)?

2.131 A barge is 15 ft wide and 40 ft long and floats with a draft of 4 ft. It is piled so high with gravel that its center of gravity is 3 ft above the waterline. Is it stable?

2.132 A solid right circular cone has SG = 0.99 and floats vertically as in Fig. P2.132. Is this a stable position for the cone?

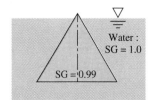

Fig. P2.132

2.133 Generalize Prob. 2.128 to determine the range of values of S between 0 and 1.0 for which the floating homogeneous cube is stable in Fig. P2.128.

2.134 When floating in water (SG = 1.0), an equilateral triangular body (SG = 0.9) might take one of the two positions shown in Fig. P2.134. Which is the more stable position? Assume large width into the paper.

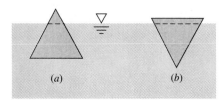

(a)   (b)

Fig. P2.134

2.135 Consider a homogeneous right circular cylinder of length L, radius R, and specific gravity SG, floating in water (SG = 1). Show that the body will be stable with its axis vertical if

$$\frac{R}{L} > [2SG(1 - SG)]^{1/2}$$

2.136 Consider a homogeneous right circular cylinder of length L, radius R, and specific gravity SG = 0.5, floating in water (SG = 1). Show that the body will be stable with its axis horizontal if $L/R > 2.0$.

2.137 A tank of water 4 m deep receives a constant upward acceleration a_z. Determine (a) the gage pressure at the tank bottom if $a_z = 5$ m²/s and (b) the value of a_z which causes the gage pressure at the tank bottom to be 1 atm.

2.138 A 12-fl-oz glass, of 3-in diameter, partly full of water, is attached to the edge of an 8-ft-diameter merry-go-round which is rotated at 12 r/min. How full can the glass be before water spills? (*Hint:* Assume that the glass is much smaller than the radius of the merry-go-round.)

2.139 The tank of water in Fig. P2.139 accelerates to the right with the fluid in rigid-body motion. Compute a_x in m/s². Does the solution change if the fluid is mercury?

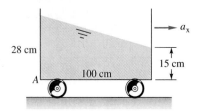

Fig. P2.139

2.140 Compute the gage pressure at point A in Fig. P2.139 if the fluid is glycerin at 20°C.

2.141 The same tank from Prob. 2.139 is now moving with con-

stant acceleration up a 30° inclined plane, as in Fig. P2.141. Assuming rigid-body motion, compute (a) the value of the acceleration a, (b) whether the acceleration is up or down, and (c) the gage pressure at point A if the fluid is mercury at 20°C.

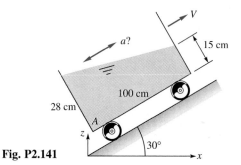

Fig. P2.141

2.142 The tank of water in Fig. P2.142 is 12 cm wide into the paper. If the tank is accelerated to the right in rigid-body motion at 6.0 m/s², compute (a) the water depth on side AB and (b) the water-pressure force on panel AB. Assume no spilling.

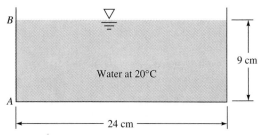

Fig. P2.142

2.143 The tank of water in Fig. P2.143 is full and open to the atmosphere at point A. For what acceleration a_x in ft/s² will the pressure at point B be atmospheric?

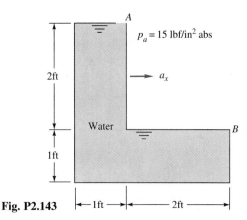

Fig. P2.143

2.144 For the water tank of Fig. P2.143, what acceleration a_x in ft/s^2 will cause the pressure at point B to be zero absolute? Neglect cavitation.

2.145 A fish tank 14 in deep by 16 by 27 in is to be carried in a car which may experience accelerations as high as 6 m/s^2. What is the maximum water depth which will avoid spilling in rigid-body motion? What is the proper alignment of the tank with respect to the car motion?

2.146 The tank in Fig. P2.146 is filled with water and has a vent hole at point A. The tank is 1 m wide into the paper. Inside the tank, a 10-cm balloon, filled with helium at 130 kPa, is tethered centrally by a string. If the tank accelerates to the right at 5 m/s^2 in rigid-body motion, at what angle will the balloon lean? Will it lean to the right or to the left?

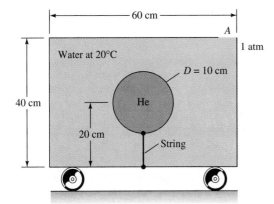

Fig. P2.146

2.147 The tank of water in Fig. P2.147 accelerates uniformly by freely rolling down a 30° incline. If the wheels are frictionless, what is the angle θ? Can you explain this interesting result?

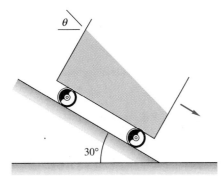

Fig. P2.147

2.148 Think about the following modification to Fig. P2.146. Let the 10-cm-diameter body instead be a concrete sphere (SG = 2.4) hanging by a string from the top of the tank. If the

tank accelerates to the right at 5 m/s^2 in rigid-body motion, at what angle will the sphere lean? Will it lean to the right or to the left?

2.149 The 6-ft-radius waterwheel in Fig. P2.149 is being used to lift water with its 1-ft-diameter half-cylinder blades. If the wheel rotates at 10 r/min and rigid-body motion is assumed, what is the water surface angle θ at position A?

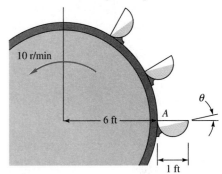

Fig. P2.149

2.150 A cheap accelerometer, probably worth the price, can be made from a U-tube as in Fig. P2.150. If $L = 18$ cm and $D = 5$ mm, what will h be if $a_x = 6$ m/s^2? Can the scale markings on the tube be linear multiples of a_x?

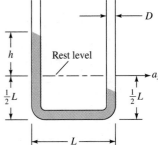

Fig. P2.150

2.151 The U-tube in Fig. P2.151 is open at A and closed at D. If accelerated to the right at uniform a_x, what acceleration will cause the pressure at point C to be atmospheric? The fluid is water (SG = 1.0).

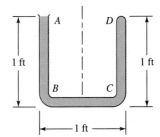

Fig. P2.151

2.152 A 16-cm-diameter open cylinder 27 cm high is full of water.

Compute the rigid-body rotation rate about its central axis, in r/min, (*a*) for which one-third of the water will spill out and (*b*) for which the bottom will be barely exposed.

2.153 Suppose the U-tube in Fig. P2.150 is not translated but rather rotated about its right leg at 95 r/min. What will be the level *h* in the left leg if $L = 18$ cm and $D = 5$ mm?

2.154 A very deep 18-cm-diameter can contains 12 cm of water overlaid with 10 cm of SAE 30 oil. If the can is rotated in rigid-body motion about its central axis at 150 r/min, what will be the shapes of the air-oil and oil-water interfaces? What will be the maximum fluid pressure in the can in Pa (gage)?

2.155 For what uniform rotation rate in r/min about axis *C* will the U-tube in Fig. P2.155 take the configuration shown? The fluid is mercury at 20°C.

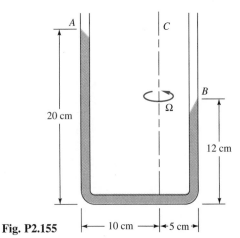

Fig. P2.155

2.156 Suppose that the U-tube of Fig. P2.151 is rotated about axis *DC*. If the fluid is water at 122°F and atmospheric pressure is 2116 lbf/ft² absolute, at what rotation rate will the fluid within the tube begin to vaporize? At what point will this occur?

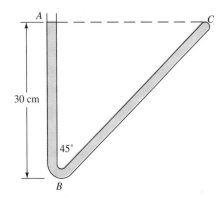

Fig. P2.157

2.157 The 45° V-tube in Fig. P2.157 contains water and is open at *A* and closed at *C*. What uniform rotation rate in r/min about axis *AB* will cause the pressure to be equal at points *B* and *C*? For this condition, at what point in leg *BC* will the pressure be a minimum?

Word Problems

W2.1 Consider a hollow cone with a vent hole in the vertex at the top, along with a hollow cylinder, open at the top, with the same base area as the cone. Fill both with water to the top. The *hydrostatic paradox* is that both containers have the same force on the bottom due to the water pressure, although the cone contains 67 percent less water. Can you explain the paradox?

W2.2 Can the temperature ever *rise* with altitude in the real atmosphere? Wouldn't this cause the air pressure to *increase* upward? Explain the physics of this situation.

W2.3 Consider a submerged curved surface which consists of a two-dimensional circular arc of arbitrary angle, arbitrary depth, and arbitrary orientation. Show that the resultant hydrostatic pressure force on this surface must pass through the center of curvature of the arc.

W2.4 Fill a glass approximately 80 percent with water, and add a large ice cube. Mark the water level. The ice cube, having SG ≈ 0.9, sticks up out of the water. Let the ice cube melt with negligible evaporation from the water surface. Will the water level be higher than, lower than, or the same as before?

W2.5 A ship, carrying a load of steel, is trapped while floating in a small closed lock. Members of the crew want to get out, but they can't quite reach the top wall of the lock. A crew member suggests throwing the steel overboard in the lock, claiming the ship will then rise and they can climb out. Will this plan work?

W2.6 Consider a balloon of mass *m* floating neutrally in the atmosphere, carrying a person/basket of mass $M > m$. Discuss the stability of this system to disturbances.

W2.7 Consider a helium balloon on a string tied to the seat of your stationary car. The windows are closed, so there is no air motion within the car. The car begins to accelerate forward. Which way will the balloon lean, forward or backward? (*Hint:* The acceleration sets up a horizontal pressure gradient in the air within the car.)

W2.8 Repeat your analysis of Prob. W2.7 to let the car move at constant velocity and go around a curve. Will the balloon lean in, toward the center of curvature, or out?

Design Project

D2.1 It is desired to have a bottom-moored, floating system which creates a nonlinear force in the mooring line as the water level rises. The design force F need only be accurate in the range of seawater depths h between 6 and 8 m, as shown in the accompanying table. Design a buoyant system which will provide this force distribution. The system should be practical, i.e., of inexpensive materials and simple construction.

h, m	F, N	h, m	F, N
6.00	400	7.25	554
6.25	437	7.50	573
6.50	471	7.75	589
6.75	502	8.00	600
7.00	530		

Chapter 3
Integral Relations
for a Control Volume

Motivation. In analyzing fluid motion, we might take one of two paths: (1) seeking to describe the detailed flow pattern at every point (x, y, z) in the field or (2) working with a finite region, making a balance of flow in versus flow out, and determining gross flow effects such as the force or torque on a body or the total energy exchange. The second is the ''control-volume'' method and is the subject of this chapter. The first is the ''differential'' approach and is developed in Chap. 4.

We first develop the concept of the control volume, in nearly the same manner as one does in a thermodynamics course, and we find the rate of change of an arbitrary gross fluid property, a result called the *Reynolds transport theorem*. We then apply this theorem, in sequence, to mass, linear momentum, angular momentum, and energy, thus deriving the four basic control-volume relations of fluid mechanics. There are many applications, of course. The chapter then ends with a special case of frictionless, shaft-work-free momentum and energy: the *Bernoulli equation*. The Bernoulli equation is a wonderful, historic relation, but it is extremely restrictive and should always be viewed with skepticism and care in applying it to a real (viscous) fluid motion.

3.1 Basic Physical Laws of Fluid Mechanics

It is time now to really get serious about flow problems. The fluid-statics applications of Chap. 2 were more like fun than work, at least in my opinion. Statics problems basically require only the density of the fluid and knowledge of the position of the free surface, but most flow problems require the analysis of an arbitrary state of variable fluid motion defined by the geometry, the boundary conditions, and the laws of mechanics. This chapter and the next two outline the three basic approaches to the analysis of arbitrary flow problems:

1. Control-volume, or large-scale, analysis (Chap. 3)
2. Differential, or small-scale, analysis (Chap. 4)
3. Experimental, or dimensional, analysis (Chap. 5)

The three approaches are roughly equal in importance, but control-volume analysis is ''more equal,'' being the single most valuable tool to the engineer for flow analysis. It gives ''engineering'' answers, sometimes gross and crude but always useful. In principle, the differential approach of Chap. 4 can be used for any problem, but in practice the lack of mathematical tools and the inability of the digital computer to model small-scale processes make the differential approach rather limited. Similarly, although the dimensional analysis of Chap. 5 can be applied to any problem, the lack of time and money and generality often makes experimentation a limited approach. But a control-volume analysis takes about half an hour and gives useful results. Thus, in a trio of approaches, the control volume is best. Oddly enough, it is the newest of the three. Differential analysis began with Euler and Lagrange in the eighteenth century, and dimensional analysis was pioneered by Lord Rayleigh in the late nineteenth century, but the control volume, although proposed by Euler, was not developed on a rigorous basis as an analytical tool until the 1940s.

Systems versus Control Volumes

All the laws of mechanics are written for a *system*, which is defined as an arbitrary quantity of mass of fixed identity. Everything external to this system is denoted by the term *surroundings*, and the system is separated from its surroundings by its *boundaries*. The laws of mechanics then state what happens when there is an interaction between the system and its surroundings.

First, the system is a fixed quantity of mass, denoted by m. Thus the mass of the system is conserved and does not change.[1] This is a law of mechanics and has a very simple mathematical form, called *conservation of mass*:

$$m_{\text{syst}} = \text{const}$$

or

$$\frac{dm}{dt} = 0 \tag{3.1}$$

This is so obvious in solid-mechanics problems that we often forget about it. In fluid mechanics, we must pay a lot of attention to mass conservation, and it takes a little analysis to make it hold.

Second, if the surroundings exert a net force $\mathbf{F}$ on the system, Newton's second law states that the mass will begin to accelerate[2]

$$\mathbf{F} = m\mathbf{a} = m\frac{d\mathbf{V}}{dt} = \frac{d}{dt}(m\mathbf{V}) \tag{3.2}$$

In Eq. (2.12) we saw this relation applied to a differential element of viscous incompressible fluid. In fluid mechanics Newton's law is called the linear-momentum relation. Note that it is a vector law which implies the three scalar equations $F_x = ma_x$, $F_y = ma_y$, and $F_z = ma_z$.

Third, if the surroundings exert a net moment $\mathbf{M}$ about the center of mass of the system, there will be a rotation effect

$$\mathbf{M} = \frac{d\mathbf{H}}{dt} \tag{3.3}$$

where $\mathbf{H} = \Sigma(\mathbf{r} \times \mathbf{V})\,\delta m$ is the angular momentum of the system about its center of

[1] We are neglecting nuclear reactions, where mass can be changed to energy.
[2] We are neglecting relativistic effects, where Newton's law must be modified.

mass. Here we call Eq. (3.3) the angular-momentum relation. Note that it is also a vector equation implying three scalar equations such as $M_x = dH_x/dt$.

For an arbitrary mass and arbitrary moment, **H** is quite complicated and contains nine terms (see, e.g., Ref. 1, p. 285). In elementary dynamics we commonly treat only a rigid body rotating about a fixed x axis, for which Eq. (3.3) reduces to

$$M_x = I_x \frac{d}{dt}(\omega_x) \tag{3.4}$$

where ω_x is the angular velocity of the body and I_x is its mass moment of inertia about the x axis. Unfortunately, fluid systems are not rigid and rarely reduce to such a simple relation, as we shall see in Sec. 3.5.

Fourth, if heat dQ is added to the system or work dW is done by the system, the system energy dE must change according to the energy relation, or first law of thermodynamics,

$$dQ - dW = dE$$

or $\qquad \dfrac{dQ}{dt} - \dfrac{dW}{dt} = \dfrac{dE}{dt}$ $\tag{3.5}$

Like mass conservation, Eq. (3.1), this is a scalar relation having only a single component.

Finally, the second law of thermodynamics relates entropy change dS to heat added dQ and absolute temperature T:

$$dS \geq \frac{dQ}{T} \tag{3.6}$$

This is valid for a system and can be written in control-volume form, but there are almost no practical applications in fluid mechanics except to analyze flow-loss details (see Sec. 9.5).

All these laws involve thermodynamic properties, and thus we must supplement them with state relations $p = p(\rho, T)$ and $e = e(\rho, T)$ for the particular fluid being studied, as in Sec. 1.6.

The purpose of this chapter is to put our four basic laws into the control-volume form suitable for arbitrary regions in a flow:

1. Conservation of mass (Sec. 3.3)
2. The linear-momentum relation (Sec. 3.4)
3. The angular-momentum relation (Sec. 3.5)
4. The energy equation (Sec. 3.6)

Wherever necessary to complete the analysis we also introduce a state relation such as the perfect-gas law.

Equations (3.1) to (3.6) apply to either fluid or solid systems. They are ideal for solid mechanics, where we follow the same system forever because it represents the product we are designing and building. For example, we follow a beam as it deflects under load. We follow a piston as it oscillates. We follow a rocket system all the way to Mars.

But fluid systems do not demand this concentrated attention. It is rare that we wish to follow the ultimate path of a specific particle of fluid. Instead it is likely that the fluid forms the environment whose effect on our product we wish to know. For the three examples cited above, we wish to know the wind loads on the beam, the fluid pressures on the piston, and the drag and lift loads on the rocket. This requires that the basic laws be rewritten to apply to a specific *region* in the neighborhood of our product. In other words, where the fluid particles in the wind go after they leave the beam is of little interest to a beam designer. The user's point of view underlies the need for the control-volume analysis of this chapter.

Although thermodynamics is not at all the main topic of this book, it would be a shame if the student did not review at least the first law and the state relations, as discussed, e.g., in Refs. 6 and 7.

In analyzing a control volume, we convert the system laws to apply to a specific region which the system may occupy for only an instant. The system passes on, and other systems come along, but no matter. The basic laws are reformulated to apply to this local region called a control volume. All we need to know is the flow field in this region, and often simple assumptions will be accurate enough (e.g., uniform inlet and/ or outlet flows). The flow conditions away from the control volume are then irrelevant. The technique for making such localized analyses is the subject of this chapter.

Volume and Mass Rate of Flow

All the analyses in this chapter involve evaluation of the volume flow Q or mass flow $\dot{m}$ passing through a surface (imaginary) defined in the flow.

Suppose that the surface S in Fig. 3.1a is a sort of (imaginary) wire mesh through which the fluid passes without resistance. How much volume of fluid passes through S in unit time? If, typically, $\mathbf{V}$ varies with position, we must integrate over the elemental surface dA in Fig. 3.1a. Also, typically $\mathbf{V}$ may pass through dA at an angle θ off the normal. Let $\mathbf{n}$ be defined as the unit vector normal to dA. Then the amount of fluid swept through dA in time dt is the volume of the slanted parallelopiped in Fig. 3.1b:

$$d\mathcal{V} = V\, dt\, dA \cos\theta = (\mathbf{V}\cdot\mathbf{n})\, dA\, dt$$

The integral of $d\mathcal{V}/dt$ is the total volume rate of flow Q through the surface S

$$Q = \int_s (\mathbf{V}\cdot\mathbf{n})\, dA = \int_s V_n\, dA \qquad (3.7)$$

Fig. 3.1 Volume rate of flow through an arbitrary surface: (*a*) an elemental area dA on the surface; (*b*) the incremental volume swept through dA equals $V\, dt\, dA \cos\theta$.

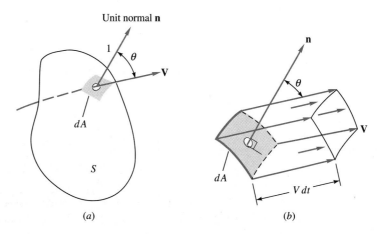

(*a*)   (*b*)

We could replace $\mathbf{V} \cdot \mathbf{n}$ by its equivalent, V_n, the component of $\mathbf{V}$ normal to dA, but the use of the dot product allows Q to have a sign to distinguish between inflow and outflow. By convention throughout this book we consider $\mathbf{n}$ to be the *outward* normal unit vector. Therefore $\mathbf{V} \cdot \mathbf{n}$ denotes outflow if it is positive and inflow if negative. This will be an extremely useful housekeeping device when we are computing volume and mass flow in the basic control-volume relations.

Volume flow can be multiplied by density to obtain the mass flow $\dot{m}$. If density varies over the surface, it must be part of the surface integral

$$\dot{m} = \int_s \rho(\mathbf{V} \cdot \mathbf{n}) \, dA = \int_s \rho V_n \, dA$$

If density is constant, it comes out of the integral and a direct proportionality results:

Constant density: $$\dot{m} = \rho Q$$

3.2 The Reynolds Transport Theorem

To convert a system analysis to a control-volume analysis, we must convert our mathematics to apply to a specific region rather than to individual masses. This conversion, called the *Reynolds transport theorem*, can be applied to all the basic laws. Examining the basic laws (3.1) to (3.3) and (3.5), we see that they are all concerned with the time derivative of fluid properties m, $\mathbf{V}$, $\mathbf{H}$, and E. Therefore what we need is to relate the time derivative of a system property to the rate of change of that property within a certain region.

The desired conversion formula differs slightly according to whether the control volume is fixed, moving, or deformable. Figure 3.2 illustrates these three cases. The fixed control volume in Fig. 3.2a encloses a stationary region of interest to a nozzle designer. The control surface is an abstract concept and does not hinder the flow in any way. It slices through the jet leaving the nozzle, circles around through the surrounding atmosphere, and slices through the flange bolts and the fluid within the nozzle. This particular control volume exposes the stresses in the flange bolts, which contribute to applied forces in the momentum analysis. In this sense the control volume resembles the *free-body* concept, which is applied to systems in solid-mechanics analyses.

Figure 3.2b illustrates a moving control volume. Here the ship is of interest, not the ocean, so that the control surface chases the ship at ship speed V. The control volume is of fixed volume, but the relative motion between water and ship must be considered.

Fig. 3.2 Fixed, moving, and deformable control volumes: (a) fixed control volume for nozzle-stress analysis; (b) control volume moving at ship speed for drag-force analysis; (c) control volume deforming within cylinder for transient pressure-variation analysis.

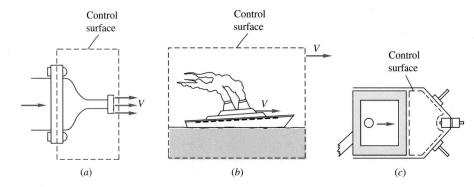

(a)   (b)   (c)

If V is constant, this relative motion is a steady-flow pattern, which simplifies the analysis.[1] If V is variable, the relative motion is unsteady, so that the computed results are time-variable and certain terms enter the momentum analysis to reflect the noninertial frame of reference.

Figure 3.2c shows a deforming control volume. Varying relative motion at the boundaries becomes a factor, and the rate of change of shape of the control volume enters the analysis. We begin by deriving the fixed-control-volume case, and we consider the other cases as advanced topics.

One-Dimensional Fixed Control Volume

As a simple first example, consider a duct or streamtube with a nearly one-dimensional flow $V = V(x)$, as shown in Fig. 3.3. The selected control volume is a portion of the duct which happens to be filled exactly by system 2 at a particular instant t. At time $t + dt$, system 2 has begun to move out, and a sliver of system 1 has entered from the left. The shaded areas show an outflow sliver of volume $A_b V_b \, dt$ and an inflow volume $A_a V_a \, dt$.

Now let B be any property of the fluid (energy, momentum, etc.), and let $\beta = dB/dm$ be the *intensive* value or the amount of B per unit mass in any small portion of the fluid. The total amount of B in the control volume is thus

$$B_{CV} = \int_{CV} \beta \rho \, d\mathcal{V} \qquad \beta = \frac{dB}{dm} \qquad (3.8)$$

[1] A *wind tunnel* uses a fixed model to simulate flow over a body moving through a fluid. A *tow tank* uses a moving model to simulate the same situation.

Fig. 3.3 Example of inflow and outflow as three systems pass through a control volume: (*a*) System 2 fills the control volume at time t; (*b*) at time $t + dt$ system 2 begins to leave and system 1 enters.

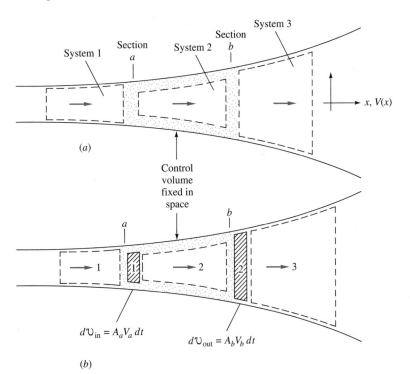

where $\rho\,d\mathcal{V}$ is a differential mass of the fluid. We want to relate the rate of change of B_{CV} to the rate of change of the amount of B in system 2 which happens to coincide with the control volume at time t. The time derivative of B_{CV} is defined by the calculus limit

$$\frac{d}{dt}(B_{CV}) = \frac{1}{dt}B_{CV}(t + dt) - \frac{1}{dt}B_{CV}(t)$$

$$= \frac{1}{dt}[B_2(t + dt) - (\beta\rho\,d\mathcal{V})_{out} + (\beta\rho\,d\mathcal{V})_{in}] - \frac{1}{dt}[B_2(t)]$$

$$= \frac{1}{dt}[B_2(t + dt) - B_2(t)] - (\beta\rho AV)_{out} + (\beta\rho AV)_{in}$$

The first term on the right is the rate of change of B within system 2 at the instant it occupies the control volume. By rearranging the last line of the above equation, we have the desired conversion formula relating changes in any property B of a local system to one-dimensional computations concerning a fixed control volume which instantaneously encloses the system.

$$\frac{d}{dt}(B_{syst}) = \frac{d}{dt}\left(\int_{CV}\beta\rho\,d\mathcal{V}\right) + (\beta\rho AV)_{out} - (\beta\rho AV)_{in} \tag{3.9}$$

This is the one-dimensional Reynolds transport theorem for a fixed volume. The three terms on the right-hand side are, respectively,

1. The rate of change of B within the control volume
2. The flux of B passing out of the control surface
3. The flux of B passing into the control surface

If the flow pattern is steady, the first term vanishes. Equation (3.9) can readily be generalized to an arbitrary flow pattern, as follows.

Arbitrary Fixed Control Volume

Figure 3.4 shows a generalized fixed control volume with an arbitrary flow pattern passing through. The only additional complication is that there are variable slivers of inflow and outflow of fluid all about the control surface. In general, each differential area dA of surface will have a different velocity $\mathbf{V}$ making a different angle θ with the local normal to dA. Some elemental areas will have inflow volume $(VA\cos\theta)_{in}\,dt$, and others will have outflow volume $(VA\cos\theta)_{out}\,dt$, as seen in Fig. 3.4. Some surfaces might correspond to streamlines ($\theta = 90°$) or solid walls ($\mathbf{V} = 0$) with neither inflow nor outflow. Equation (3.9) generalizes to

$$\frac{d}{dt}(B_{syst}) = \frac{d}{dt}\left(\int_{CV}\beta\rho\,d\mathcal{V}\right) + \int_{CS}\beta\rho V\cos\theta\,dA_{out} - \int_{CS}\beta\rho V\cos\theta\,dA_{in} \tag{3.10}$$

This is the Reynolds transport theorem for an arbitrary fixed control volume. By letting the property B be mass, momentum, angular momentum, or energy, we can rewrite all the basic laws in control-volume form. Note that all three of the control-volume integrals are concerned with the intensive property β. Since the control volume is fixed in space, the elemental volumes $d\mathcal{V}$ do not vary with time, so that the time derivative of the volume integral vanishes unless either β or ρ varies with time (unsteady flow).

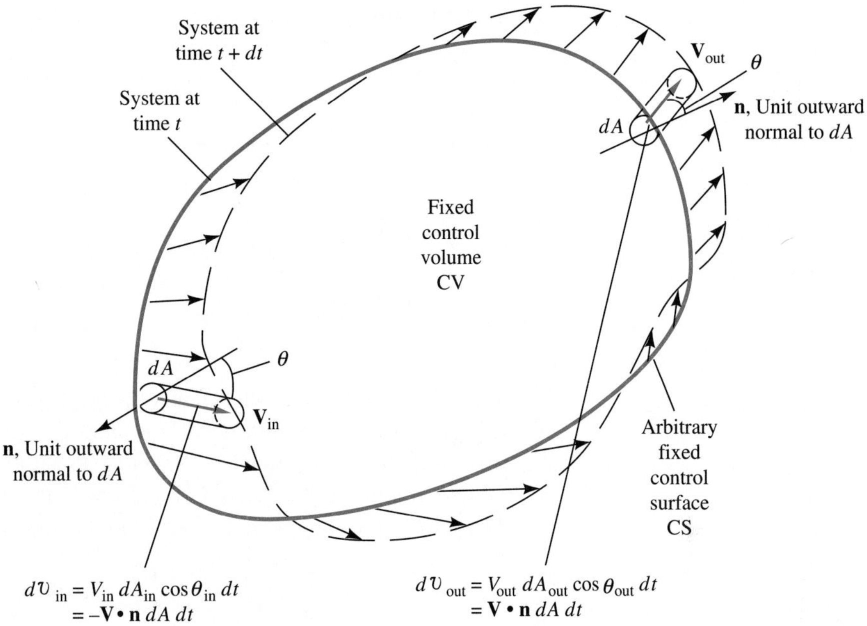

Fig. 3.4 Generalization of Fig. 3.3 to an arbitrary control volume with an arbitrary flow pattern.

$$d\mathcal{V}_{in} = V_{in}\, dA_{in} \cos\theta_{in}\, dt$$
$$= -\mathbf{V} \cdot \mathbf{n}\, dA\, dt$$

$$d\mathcal{V}_{out} = V_{out}\, dA_{out} \cos\theta_{out}\, dt$$
$$= \mathbf{V} \cdot \mathbf{n}\, dA\, dt$$

Equation (3.10) expresses the basic formula that a system derivative equals the rate of change of B within the control volume plus the flux of B out of the control surface minus the flux of B into the control surface. The quantity B (or β) may be any vector or scalar property of the fluid. Two alternate forms are possible for the flux terms. First we may notice that $V \cos\theta$ is the component of V normal to the area element of the control surface. Thus we can write

$$\text{Flux terms} = \int_{CS} \beta\rho V_n\, dA_{out} - \int_{CS} \beta\rho V_n\, dA_{in} = \int_{CS} \beta\, d\dot{m}_{out} - \int_{CS} \beta\, d\dot{m}_{in} \quad (3.11a)$$

where $d\dot{m} = \rho V_n\, dA$ is the differential mass flux through the surface. Form (3.11a) helps visualize what is being calculated.

A second alternate form offers elegance and compactness as advantages. If $\mathbf{n}$ is defined as the *outward* normal unit vector everywhere on the control surface, then $\mathbf{V} \cdot \mathbf{n} = V_n$ for outflow and $\mathbf{V} \cdot \mathbf{n} = -V_n$ for inflow. Therefore the flux terms can be represented by a single integral involving $\mathbf{V} \cdot \mathbf{n}$ which accounts for both positive outflow and negative inflow

$$\text{Flux terms} = \int_{CS} \beta\rho(\mathbf{V} \cdot \mathbf{n})\, dA \quad (3.11b)$$

The compact form of the Reynolds transport theorem is thus

$$\frac{d}{dt}(B_{syst}) = \frac{d}{dt}\left(\int_{CV} \beta\rho\, d\mathcal{V}\right) + \int_{CS} \beta\rho(\mathbf{V} \cdot \mathbf{n})\, dA \quad (3.12)$$

This is beautiful but only occasionally useful, when the coordinate system is ideally suited to the control volume selected. Otherwise the computations are easier when the flux of B out is added and the flux of B in is subtracted, according to (3.10) or (3.11a).

The time-derivative term can be written in the equivalent form

$$\frac{d}{dt} \left(\int_{CV} \beta \rho \, d\mathcal{V} \right) = \int_{CV} \frac{\partial}{\partial t} (\beta \rho) \, d\mathcal{V} \tag{3.13}$$

for the fixed control volume since the volume elements do not vary.

Control Volume Moving at Constant Velocity

If the control volume is moving uniformly at velocity $\mathbf{V}_s$, as in Fig. 3.2b, an observer fixed to the control volume will see a relative velocity $\mathbf{V}_r$ of fluid crossing the control surface, defined by

$$\mathbf{V}_r = \mathbf{V} - \mathbf{V}_s \tag{3.14}$$

where $\mathbf{V}$ is the fluid velocity relative to the same coordinate system in which the control volume motion $\mathbf{V}_s$ is observed. Note that Eq. (3.14) is a vector subtraction. The flux terms will be proportional to $\mathbf{V}_r$, but the volume integral is unchanged because the control volume moves as a fixed shape without deforming. The Reynolds transport theorem for this case of a uniformly moving control volume is

$$\frac{d}{dt} (B_{syst}) = \frac{d}{dt} \left(\int_{CV} \beta \rho \, d\mathcal{V} \right) + \int_{CS} \beta \rho (\mathbf{V}_r \cdot \mathbf{n}) \, dA \tag{3.15}$$

which reduces to Eq. (3.12) if $\mathbf{V}_s \equiv 0$.

Control Volume of Constant Shape but Variable Velocity[1]

If the control volume moves with a velocity $\mathbf{V}_s(t)$ which retains its shape, then the volume elements do not change with time but the boundary relative velocity $\mathbf{V}_r = \mathbf{V}(\mathbf{r}, t) - \mathbf{V}_s(t)$ becomes a somewhat more complicated function. Equation (3.15) is unchanged in form, but the area integral may be more laborious to evaluate.

Arbitrarily Moving and Deformable Control Volume[2]

The most general situation is when the control volume is both moving and deforming arbitrarily, as illustrated in Fig. 3.5. The flux of volume across the control surface is again proportional to the relative normal velocity component $\mathbf{V}_r \cdot \mathbf{n}$, as in Eq. (3.15). However, since the control surface has a deformation, its velocity $\mathbf{V}_s = \mathbf{V}_s(\mathbf{r}, t)$, so that the relative velocity $\mathbf{V}_r = \mathbf{V}(\mathbf{r}, t) - \mathbf{V}_s(\mathbf{r}, t)$ is or can be a complicated function, even though the flux integral is the same as in Eq. (3.15). Meanwhile, the volume integral in Eq. (3.15) must allow the volume elements to distort with time. Thus the time derivative must be applied *after* integration. For the deforming control volume, then, the transport theorem takes the form

$$\frac{d}{dt} (B_{syst}) = \frac{d}{dt} \left(\int_{CV} \beta \rho \, d\mathcal{V} \right) + \int_{CS} \beta \rho (\mathbf{V}_r \cdot \mathbf{n}) \, dA \tag{3.16}$$

This is the most general case, which we can compare with the equivalent form for a fixed control volume

---

[1] This section may be omitted without loss of continuity.
[2] This section may be omitted without loss of continuity.

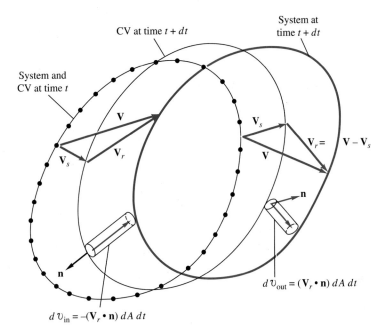

Fig. 3.5 Relative-velocity effects between a system and a control volume when both move and deform. The system boundaries move at velocity $\mathbf{V}$, and the control surface moves at velocity $\mathbf{V}_s$.

$$\frac{d}{dt}(B_{\text{syst}}) = \int_{\text{CV}} \frac{\partial}{\partial t}(\beta\rho)\, d\mathcal{V} + \int_{\text{CS}} \beta\rho(\mathbf{V}\cdot\mathbf{n})\, dA \tag{3.17}$$

The moving and deforming control volume, Eq. (3.16), contains only two complications: (1) The time derivative of the first integral on the right must be taken outside, and (2) the second integral involves the *relative* velocity $\mathbf{V}_r$ between the fluid system and the control surface. These differences and mathematical subtleties are best shown by examples.

One-Dimensional Flux-Term Approximations

In many applications, the flow crosses the boundaries of the control surface only at certain simplified inlets and exits which are approximately *one-dimensional*; i.e., the flow properties are nearly uniform over the cross section of the inlet or exit. Then the triple-integral flux terms required in Eq. (3.16) reduce to a simple sum of positive (exit) and negative (inlet) product terms involving the flow properties at each cross section

$$\int_{\text{CS}} \beta\rho(\mathbf{V}_r\cdot\mathbf{n})\, dA = \sum (\beta_i\rho_i V_{ri}A_i)_{\text{out}} - \sum (\beta_i\rho_i V_{ri}A_i)_{\text{in}} \tag{3.18}$$

An example of this situation is shown in Fig. 3.6. There are inlet flows at sections 1 and 4 and outflows at sections 2, 3, and 5. For this particular problem Eq. (3.18) would be

$$\int_{\text{CS}} \beta\rho(\mathbf{V}_r\cdot\mathbf{n})\, dA = \beta_2\rho_2 V_{r2}A_2 + \beta_3\rho_3 V_{r3}A_3$$

$$+ \beta_5\rho_5 V_{r5}A_5 - \beta_1\rho_1 V_{r1}A_1 - \beta_4\rho_4 V_{r4}A_4 \tag{3.19}$$

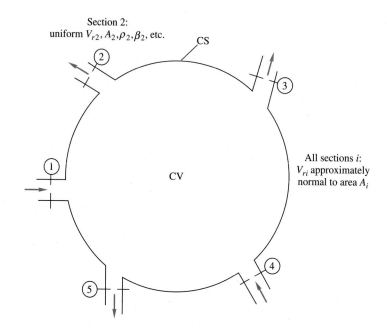

Section 2:
uniform $V_{r2}, A_2, \rho_2, \beta_2$, etc.   CS

All sections i:
V_{ri} approximately
normal to area A_i

Fig. 3.6 A control volume with simplified one-dimensional inlets and
exits.

with no contribution from any other portion of the control surface because there is no
flow across the boundary.

EXAMPLE 3.1

A fixed control volume has three one-dimensional boundary sections, as shown in Fig. E3.1.
The flow within the control volume is steady. The flow properties at each section are tabulated below. Find the rate of change of energy of the system which occupies the control
volume at this instant.

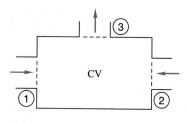

Fig. E3.1

Section	Type	ρ, kg/m^3	V, m/s	A, m^2	e, J/kg
1	Inlet	800	5.0	2.0	300
2	Inlet	800	8.0	3.0	100
3	Outlet	800	17.0	2.0	150

Solution

The property under study here is energy, and so $B = E$ and $\beta = dE/dm = e$, the energy
per unit mass. Since the control volume is fixed, Eq. (3.17) applies:

$$\left(\frac{dE}{dt}\right)_{syst} = \int_{CV} \frac{\partial}{\partial t}(e\rho)\, d\mathscr{V} + \int_{CS} e\rho(\mathbf{V} \cdot \mathbf{n})\, dA$$

The flow within is steady, so that $\partial(e\rho)/\partial t \equiv 0$ and the volume integral vanishes. The area
integral consists of two inlet sections and one outlet section, as given in the table

$$\left(\frac{dE}{dt}\right)_{syst} = -e_1\rho_1A_1V_1 - e_2\rho_2A_2V_2 + e_3\rho_3A_3V_3$$

Introducing the numerical values from the table, we have

$$\left(\frac{dE}{dt}\right)_{\text{syst}} = -(300 \text{ J/kg})(800 \text{ kg/m}^3)(2 \text{ m}^2)(5 \text{ m/s}) - 100(800)(3)(8) + 150(800)(2)(17)$$

$$= (-2{,}400{,}000 - 1{,}920{,}000 + 4{,}080{,}000) \text{ J/s}$$

$$= -240{,}000 \text{ J/s} = -0.24 \text{ MJ/s} \qquad\qquad\qquad Ans.$$

Thus the system is losing energy at the rate of 0.24 MJ/s = 0.24 MW. Since we have accounted for all fluid energy crossing the boundary, we conclude from the first law that there must be heat loss through the control surface or the system must be doing work on the environment through some device not shown. Notice that the use of SI units leads to a consistent result in joules per second without any conversion factors. We promised in Chap. 1 that this would be the case.

Note: This problem involves energy, but suppose we check the balance of mass also. Then $B = $ mass m, and $B = dm/dm = $ unity. Again the volume integral vanishes for steady flow, and Eq. (3.17) reduces to

$$\left(\frac{dm}{dt}\right)_{\text{syst}} = \int_{\text{CS}} \rho(\mathbf{V} \cdot \mathbf{n}) \, dA = -\rho_1 A_1 V_1 - \rho_2 A_2 V_2 + \rho_3 A_3 V_3$$

$$= -(800 \text{ kg/m}^3)(2 \text{ m}^2)(5 \text{ m/s}) - 800(3)(8) + 800(17)(2)$$

$$= (-8000 - 19{,}200 + 27{,}200) \text{ kg/s} = 0 \text{ kg/s}$$

Thus the system mass does not change, which correctly expresses the law of conservation of system mass, Eq. (3.1).

EXAMPLE 3.2

The balloon in Fig. E3.2 is being filled through section 1, where the area is A_1, velocity is V_1, and fluid density is ρ_1. The average density within the balloon is $\rho_b(t)$. Find an expression for the rate of change of system mass within the balloon at this instant.

Solution

It is convenient to define a deformable control surface just outside the balloon, expanding at the same rate $R(t)$. Equation (3.16) applies with $V_r = 0$ on the balloon surface and $V_r = V_1$ at the pipe entrance. For mass change, we take $B = m$ and $\beta = dm/dm = 1$. Equation (3.16) becomes

$$\left(\frac{dm}{dt}\right)_{\text{syst}} = \frac{d}{dt}\left(\int_{\text{CV}} \rho \, d\mathcal{V}\right) + \int_{\text{CS}} \rho(\mathbf{V}_r \cdot \mathbf{n}) \, dA$$

Mass flux occurs only at the inlet, so that the control-surface integral reduces to the single negative term $-\rho_1 A_1 V_1$. The fluid mass within the control volume is approximately the average density times the volume of a sphere. The equation thus becomes

$$\left(\frac{dm}{dt}\right)_{\text{syst}} = \frac{d}{dt}\left(\rho_b \frac{4}{3} \pi R^3\right) - \rho_1 A_1 V_1 \qquad\qquad\qquad Ans.$$

This is the desired result for the system mass rate of change. Actually, by the conservation

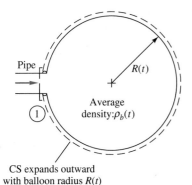

Pipe

$R(t)$

Average density: $\rho_b(t)$

①

CS expands outward with balloon radius $R(t)$

Fig. E3.2

law (3.1), this change must be zero. Thus the balloon density and radius are related to the inlet mass flux by

$$\frac{d}{dt}(\rho_b R^3) = \frac{3}{4\pi}\rho_1 A_1 V_1$$

This is a first-order differential equation which could form part of an engineering analysis of balloon inflation. It cannot be solved without further use of mechanics and thermodynamics to relate the four unknowns ρ_b, ρ_1, V_1, and R. The pressure and temperature and the elastic properties of the balloon would also have to be brought into the analysis.

For advanced study, many more details of the analysis of deformable control volumes can be found in Hansen [4] and Potter and Foss [5].

3.3 Conservation of Mass

The Reynolds transport theorem, Eq. (3.16) or (3.17), establishes a relation between system rates of change and control-volume surface and volume integrals. But system derivatives are related to the basic laws of mechanics, Eqs. (3.1) to (3.5). Eliminating system derivatives between the two gives the control-volume, or *integral*, forms of the laws of mechanics of fluids. The dummy variable B becomes, respectively, mass, linear momentum, angular momentum, and energy.

For conservation of mass, as discussed in Examples 3.1 and 3.2, $B = m$ and $\beta = dm/dm = 1$. Equation (3.1) becomes

$$\left(\frac{dm}{dt}\right)_{syst} = 0 = \frac{d}{dt}\left(\int_{CV} \rho \, d\mathcal{V}\right) + \int_{CS} \rho(\mathbf{V}_r \cdot \mathbf{n}) \, dA \tag{3.20}$$

This is the integral mass-conservation law for a deformable control volume. For a fixed control volume, we have

$$\int_{CV} \frac{\partial \rho}{\partial t} \, d\mathcal{V} + \int_{CS} \rho(\mathbf{V} \cdot \mathbf{n}) \, dA = 0 \tag{3.21}$$

If the control volume has only a number of one-dimensional inlets and outlets, we can write

$$\int_{CV} \frac{\partial \rho}{\partial t} \, d\mathcal{V} + \sum_i (\rho_i A_i V_i)_{out} - \sum_i (\rho_i A_i V_i)_{in} = 0 \tag{3.22}$$

Other special cases occur. Suppose that the flow within the control volume is steady; then $\partial \rho / \partial t \equiv 0$, and Eq. (3.21) reduces to

$$\int_{CS} \rho(\mathbf{V} \cdot \mathbf{n}) \, dA = 0 \tag{3.23}$$

This states that in steady flow the mass flows entering and leaving the control volume must balance exactly.[1] If, further, the inlets and outlets are one-dimensional, we have for steady flow

---

[1] Throughout this section we are neglecting *sources* or *sinks* of mass which might be embedded in the control volume. Equations (3.20) and (3.21) can readily be modified to add source and sink terms, but this is rarely necessary.

$$\sum_i (\rho_i A_i V_i)_{\text{in}} = \sum_i (\rho_i A_i V_i)_{\text{out}} \tag{3.24}$$

This simple approximation is widely used in engineering analyses. For example, referring to Fig. 3.6, we see that if the flow in that control volume is steady, the three outlet mass fluxes balance the two inlets:

$$\text{Outflow} = \text{inflow}$$

$$\rho_2 A_2 V_2 + \rho_3 A_3 V_3 + \rho_5 A_5 V_5 = \rho_1 A_1 V_1 + \rho_4 A_4 V_4 \tag{3.25}$$

The quantity $\rho A V$ is called the *mass flow* $\dot{m}$ passing through the one-dimensional cross section and has consistent units of kilograms per second (or slugs per second) for SI (or BG) units. Equation (3.25) can be rewritten in the short form

$$\dot{m}_2 + \dot{m}_3 + \dot{m}_5 = \dot{m}_1 + \dot{m}_4 \tag{3.26}$$

and, in general, the steady-flow–mass-conservation relation (3.23) can be written as

$$\sum_i (\dot{m}_i)_{\text{out}} = \sum_i (\dot{m}_i)_{\text{in}} \tag{3.27}$$

If the inlets and outlets are not one-dimensional, one has to compute $\dot{m}$ by integration over the section

$$\dot{m}_{\text{cs}} = \int_{\text{cs}} \rho(\mathbf{V} \cdot \mathbf{n}) \, dA \tag{3.28}$$

where "cs" stands for cross section. An illustration of this is given in Example 3.4.

Incompressible Flow

Still further simplification is possible if the fluid is incompressible, which we may define as having density variations which are negligible in the mass-conservation requirement.[1] As we saw in Chap. 1, all liquids are nearly incompressible, and gas flows can *behave* as if they were incompressible, particularly if the gas velocity is less than about 30 percent of the speed of sound of the gas.

Again consider the fixed control volume. If the fluid is nearly incompressible, $\partial \rho / \partial t$ is negligible and the volume integral in Eq. (3.21) may be neglected, after which the density can be slipped outside the surface integral and divided out since it is nonzero. The result is a conservation law for incompressible flows, whether steady or unsteady:

$$\int_{\text{CS}} (\mathbf{V} \cdot \mathbf{n}) \, dA = 0 \tag{3.29}$$

If the inlets and outlets are one-dimensional, we have

$$\sum_i (V_i A_i)_{\text{out}} = \sum_i (V_i A_i)_{\text{in}} \tag{3.30}$$

or

$$\sum Q_{\text{out}} = \sum Q_{\text{in}}$$

where $Q_i = V_i A_i$ is called the *volume flow* passing through the given cross section.

[1] Be warned that there is subjectivity in specifying incompressibility. Oceanographers consider a 0.1 percent density variation very significant, while aerodynamicists often neglect density variations in highly compressible, even hypersonic, gas flows. Your task is to justify the incompressible approximation when you make it.

Again, if consistent units are used, $Q = VA$ will have units of cubic meters per second (SI) or cubic feet per second (BG). If the cross section is not one-dimensional, we have to integrate

$$Q_{cs} = \int_{cs} (\mathbf{V} \cdot \mathbf{n}) \, dA \qquad (3.31)$$

Equation (3.31) allows us to define an *average velocity* V_{av} which, when multiplied by the section area, gives the correct volume flow

$$V_{av} = \frac{Q}{A} = \frac{1}{A} \int (\mathbf{V} \cdot \mathbf{n}) \, dA \qquad (3.32)$$

This could be called the *volume-average velocity*. If the density varies across the section, we can define an average density in the same manner:

$$\rho_{av} = \frac{1}{A} \int \rho \, dA \qquad (3.33)$$

But the mass flow would contain the product of density and velocity, and the average product $(\rho V)_{av}$ would in general have a different value from the product of the averages

$$(\rho V)_{av} = \frac{1}{A} \int \rho(\mathbf{V} \cdot \mathbf{n}) \, dA \approx \rho_{av} V_{av} \qquad (3.34)$$

We illustrate average velocity in Example 3.4. We can often neglect the difference or, if necessary, use a correction factor between mass average and volume average.

EXAMPLE 3.3

Write the conservation-of-mass relation for steady flow through a streamtube (flow everywhere parallel to the walls) with a single one-dimensional exit 1 and inlet 2 (Fig. E3.3).

Solution

For steady flow Eq. (3.24) applies with the single inlet and exit

$$\dot{m} = \rho_1 A_1 V_1 = \rho_2 A_2 V_2 = \text{const}$$

Thus, in a streamtube in steady flow, the mass flow is constant across every section of the tube. If the density is constant, then

$$Q = A_1 V_1 = A_2 V_2 = \text{const} \qquad \text{or} \qquad V_2 = \frac{A_1}{A_2} V_1$$

The volume flow is constant in the tube in steady incompressible flow, and the velocity increases as the section area decreases. This relation was derived by Leonardo da Vinci in 1500.

EXAMPLE 3.4

For steady viscous flow through a circular tube (Fig. E3.4), the axial velocity profile is given approximately by

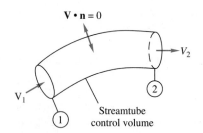

$\mathbf{V} \cdot \mathbf{n} = 0$

V_2

V_1

Streamtube
control volume

Fig. E3.3

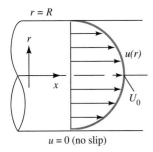

Fig. E3.4

$$u = U_0\left(1 - \frac{r}{R}\right)^m$$

so that u varies from zero at the wall ($r = R$), or no slip, up to a maximum $u = U_0$ at the centerline $r = 0$. For highly viscous (laminar) flow $m \approx \frac{1}{2}$, while for less viscous (turbulent) flow $m \approx \frac{1}{7}$. Compute the average velocity if the density is constant.

Solution

The average velocity is defined by Eq. (3.32). Here $\mathbf{V} = \mathbf{i}u$ and $\mathbf{n} = \mathbf{i}$, and thus $\mathbf{V} \cdot \mathbf{n} = u$. Since the flow is symmetric, the differential area can be taken as a circular strip $dA = 2\pi r\, dr$. Equation (3.32) becomes

$$V_{av} = \frac{1}{A} \int u\, dA = \frac{1}{\pi R^2} \int_0^R U_0\left(1 - \frac{r}{R}\right)^m 2\pi r\, dr$$

or
$$V_{av} = U_0 \frac{2}{(1 + m)(2 + m)} \qquad\qquad Ans.$$

For the laminar-flow approximation, $m \approx \frac{1}{2}$ and $V_{av} \approx 0.53U_0$. (The exact laminar theory in Chap. 6 gives $V_{av} = 0.50U_0$.) For turbulent flow, $m \approx \frac{1}{7}$ and $V_{av} \approx 0.82U_0$. (There is no exact turbulent theory, and so we accept this approximation.) The turbulent velocity profile is more uniform across the section, and thus the average velocity is only slightly less than maximum.

EXAMPLE 3.5

Consider the constant-density velocity field

$$u = \frac{V_0 x}{L} \qquad v = 0 \qquad w = -\frac{V_0 z}{L}$$

similar to Example 1.10. Use the triangular control volume in Fig. E3.5, bounded by $(0, 0)$, (L, L), and $(0, L)$, with depth b into the paper. Compute the volume flow through sections 1, 2, and 3, and compare to see whether mass is conserved.

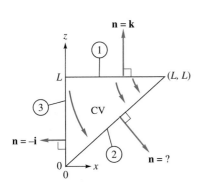

Fig. E3.5

Solution

The velocity field everywhere has the form $\mathbf{V} = \mathbf{i}u + \mathbf{k}w$. This must be evaluated along each section. We save section 2 until last because it looks tricky. Section 1 is the plane $z = L$ with depth b. The unit outward normal is $\mathbf{n} = \mathbf{k}$, as shown. The differential area is a strip of depth b varying with x: $dA = b\, dx$. The normal velocity is

$$(\mathbf{V} \cdot \mathbf{n})_1 = (\mathbf{i}u + \mathbf{k}w) \cdot \mathbf{k} = w|_1 = -\frac{V_0 z}{L}\bigg|_{z=L} = -V_0$$

The volume flow through section 1 is thus, from Eq. (3.31),

$$Q_1 = \int_1 (\mathbf{V} \cdot \mathbf{n})\, dA = \int_0^L (-V_0)b\, dx = -V_0 bL \qquad\qquad Ans.\ 1$$

Since this is negative, section 1 is a net inflow. Check the units: V_0bL is a velocity times an area; OK.

Section 3 is the plane $x = 0$ with depth b. The unit normal is $\mathbf{n} = -\mathbf{i}$, as shown, and $dA = b \, dz$. The normal velocity is

$$(\mathbf{V} \cdot \mathbf{n})_3 = (\mathbf{i}u + \mathbf{k}w) \cdot (-\mathbf{i}) = -u|_3 = -\left.\frac{V_0 x}{L}\right|_{x=0} = 0 \qquad \textit{Ans. 3}$$

Thus $V_n \equiv 0$ all along section 3; hence $Q_3 = 0$.

Finally, section 2 is the plane $x = z$ with depth b. The normal direction is to the right $\mathbf{i}$ and down $-\mathbf{k}$ but must have *unit* value; thus $\mathbf{n} = (1/\sqrt{2})(\mathbf{i} - \mathbf{k})$. The differential area is either $dA = \sqrt{2}b \, dx$ or $dA = \sqrt{2}b \, dz$. The normal velocity is

$$(\mathbf{V} \cdot \mathbf{n})_2 = (\mathbf{i}u + \mathbf{k}w) \cdot \frac{1}{\sqrt{2}}(\mathbf{i} - \mathbf{k}) = \frac{1}{\sqrt{2}}(u - w)_2$$

$$= \frac{1}{\sqrt{2}}\left[V_0 \frac{x}{L} - \left(-V_0 \frac{z}{L}\right)\right]_{x=z} = \frac{\sqrt{2}V_0 x}{L} \quad \text{or} \quad \frac{\sqrt{2}V_0 z}{L}$$

Then the volume flow through section 2 is

$$Q_2 = \int_2 (\mathbf{V} \cdot \mathbf{n}) \, dA = \int_0^L \frac{\sqrt{2}V_0 x}{L} (\sqrt{2}b \, dx) = V_0 bL \qquad \textit{Ans. 2}$$

This answer is positive, indicating an outflow. These are the desired results. We should note that the volume flow is zero through the front and back triangular faces of the prismatic control volume because $V_n = v = 0$ on those faces.

The sum of the three volume flows is

$$Q_1 + Q_2 + Q_3 = -V_0 bL + V_0 bL + 0 = 0$$

Mass is conserved in this constant-density flow, and there are no net sources or sinks within the control volume. This is a very realistic flow, as described in Example 1.10.

EXAMPLE 3.6

The tank in Fig. E3.6 is being filled with water by two one-dimensional inlets. Air is trapped at the top of the tank. The water height is h. (*a*) Find an expression for the change in water height dh/dt. (*b*) Compute dh/dt if $D_1 = 1$ in, $D_2 = 3$ in, $V_1 = 3$ ft/s, $V_2 = 2$ ft/s, and $A_t = 2$ ft², assuming water at 20°C.

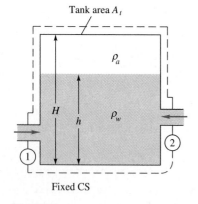

Tank area A_t

ρ_a

H

h ρ_w

(1)   (2)

Fixed CS

Fig. E3.6

Solution

Part (*a*)   A suggested control volume encircles the tank and cuts through the two inlets. The flow within is unsteady, and Eq. (3.22) applies with no outlets and two inlets:

$$\frac{d}{dt}\left(\int_{\mathrm{CV}} \rho \, d\mathcal{V}\right) - \rho_1 A_1 V_1 - \rho_2 A_2 V_2 = 0 \qquad (1)$$

Now if A_t is the tank cross-sectional area, the unsteady term can be evaluated as follows:

$$\frac{d}{dt}\left(\int_{\mathrm{CV}} \rho \, d\mathcal{V}\right) = \frac{d}{dt}(\rho_w A_t h) + \frac{d}{dt}[\rho_a A_t(H - h)] = \rho_w A_t \frac{dh}{dt} \qquad (2)$$

The ρ_a term vanishes because it is the rate of change of air mass and is zero because the air is trapped at the top. Substituting (2) into (1), we find the change of water height

$$\frac{dh}{dt} = \frac{\rho_1 A_1 V_1 + \rho_2 A_2 V_2}{\rho_w A_t} \qquad\qquad Ans.\ (a)$$

For water, $\rho_1 = \rho_2 = \rho_w$, and this result reduces to

$$\frac{dh}{dt} = \frac{A_1 V_1 + A_2 V_2}{A_t} = \frac{Q_1 + Q_2}{A_t} \qquad\qquad (3)$$

Part (b)   The two inlet volume flows are

$$Q_1 = A_1 V_1 = \tfrac{1}{4}\pi(\tfrac{1}{12}\text{ ft})^2(3\text{ ft/s}) = 0.016\text{ ft}^3/\text{s}$$

$$Q_2 = A_2 V_2 = \tfrac{1}{4}\pi(\tfrac{3}{12}\text{ ft})^2(2\text{ ft/s}) = 0.098\text{ ft}^3/\text{s}$$

Then, from Eq. (3),

$$\frac{dh}{dt} = \frac{(0.016 + 0.098)\text{ ft}^3/\text{s}}{2\text{ ft}^2} = 0.057\text{ ft/s} \qquad\qquad Ans.\ (b)$$

Suggestion: Repeat this problem with the top of the tank open.

An illustration of a mass balance with a deforming control volume has already been given in Example 3.2.

The control-volume mass relations, Eq. (3.20) or (3.21), are fundamental to all fluid-flow analyses. They involve only velocity and density. Vector directions are of no consequence except to determine the normal velocity at the surface and hence whether the flow is *in* or *out*. Although your specific analysis may concern forces or moments or energy, you must always make sure that mass is balanced as part of the analysis; otherwise the results will be unrealistic and probably rotten. We shall see in the examples which follow how mass conservation is constantly checked in performing an analysis of other fluid properties.

3.4 The Linear Momentum Equation

In Newton's law, Eq. (3.2), the property being differentiated is the linear momentum $m\mathbf{V}$. Therefore our dummy variable is $\mathbf{B} = m\mathbf{V}$ and $\beta = d\mathbf{B}/dm = \mathbf{V}$, and application of the Reynolds transport theorem gives the linear-momentum relation for a deformable control volume

$$\frac{d}{dt}(m\mathbf{V})_{\text{syst}} = \sum \mathbf{F} = \frac{d}{dt}\left(\int_{\text{CV}} \mathbf{V}\rho\, d\mathcal{V}\right) + \int_{\text{CS}} \mathbf{V}\rho(\mathbf{V}_r \cdot \mathbf{n})\, dA \qquad (3.35)$$

The following points concerning this relation should be strongly emphasized:

1. The term $\mathbf{V}$ is the fluid velocity relative to an *inertial* (nonaccelerating) coordinate system; otherwise Newton's law must be modified to include noninertial relative-acceleration terms (see the end of this section).
2. The term $\sum \mathbf{F}$ is the *vector* sum of all forces acting on the control-volume material considered as a free body; i.e., it includes surface forces on all fluids and solids

cut by the control surface plus all body forces (gravity and electromagnetic) acting on the masses within the control volume.

3. The entire equation is a vector relation; both the integrals are vectors due to the term $\mathbf{V}$ in the integrands. The equation thus has three components. If we want only, say, the x component, the equation reduces to

$$\sum F_x = \frac{d}{dt}\left(\int_{\mathrm{CV}} u\rho \, d\mathcal{V}\right) + \int_{\mathrm{CS}} u\rho(\mathbf{V}_r \cdot \mathbf{n}) \, dA \qquad (3.36)$$

and similarly, $\sum F_y$ and $\sum F_z$ would involve v and w, respectively. Failure to account for the vector nature of the linear-momentum relation (3.35) is probably the greatest source of student error in control-volume analyses.

For a fixed control volume, the relative velocity $\mathbf{V}_r \equiv \mathbf{V}$, and

$$\sum \mathbf{F} = \frac{d}{dt}\left(\int_{\mathrm{CV}} \mathbf{V}\rho \, d\mathcal{V}\right) + \int_{\mathrm{CS}} \mathbf{V}\rho(\mathbf{V} \cdot \mathbf{n}) \, dA \qquad (3.37)$$

Again we stress that this is a vector relation and that $\mathbf{V}$ must be an inertial-frame velocity. Most of the momentum analyses in this text are concerned with Eq. (3.37).

One-Dimensional Momentum Flux

By analogy with the term *mass flow* used in Eq. (3.28), the surface integral in Eq. (3.37) is called the *momentum-flux term*. If we denote momentum by $\mathbf{M}$, then

$$\dot{\mathbf{M}}_{\mathrm{cs}} = \int_{\mathrm{sec}} \mathbf{V}\rho(\mathbf{V} \cdot \mathbf{n}) \, dA \qquad (3.38)$$

Because of the dot product, the result will be negative for inlet momentum flux and positive for outlet flux. If the cross section is one-dimensional, $\mathbf{V}$ and ρ are uniform over the area and the integrated result is

$$\dot{\mathbf{M}}_{\mathrm{sec}\,i} = \mathbf{V}_i(\rho_i V_{ni} A_i) = \dot{m}_i \mathbf{V}_i \qquad (3.39)$$

for outlet flux and $-\dot{m}_i \mathbf{V}_i$ for inlet flux. Thus if the control volume has only one-dimensional inlets and outlets, Eq. (3.37) reduces to

$$\sum \mathbf{F} = \frac{d}{dt}\left(\int_{\mathrm{CV}} \mathbf{V}\rho \, d\mathcal{V}\right) + \sum (\dot{m}_i \mathbf{V}_i)_{\mathrm{out}} - \sum (\dot{m}_i \mathbf{V}_i)_{\mathrm{in}} \qquad (3.40)$$

This is a commonly used approximation in engineering analyses. It is crucial to realize that we are dealing with vector sums. Equation (3.40) states that the net vector force on a fixed control volume equals the rate of change of vector momentum within the control volume plus the vector sum of outlet momentum fluxes minus the vector sum of inlet fluxes.

Net Pressure Force on a Closed Control Surface

Generally speaking, the surface forces on a control volume are due to (1) forces exposed by cutting through solid bodies which protrude through the surface and (2) forces due to pressure and viscous stresses of the surrounding fluid. The computation of pressure force is relatively simple, as shown in Fig. 3.7. Recall from Chap. 2 that the external pressure force on a surface is normal to the surface and *inward*. Since the unit vector $\mathbf{n}$ is defined as *outward*, one way to write the pressure force is

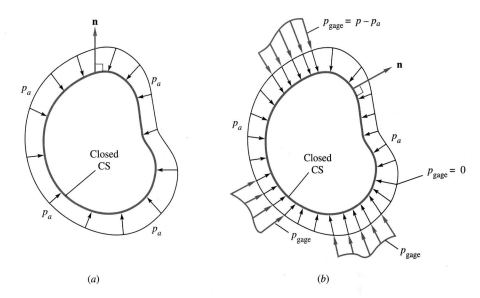

Fig. 3.7 Pressure-force computation by subtracting a uniform distribution: (*a*) uniform pressure, $\mathbf{F} = -p_a \int \mathbf{n} \, dA \equiv 0$; (*b*) nonuniform pressure, $\mathbf{F} = -\int (p - p_a)\mathbf{n} \, dA$.

$$\mathbf{F}_{\text{press}} = \int_{\text{CS}} p(-\mathbf{n}) \, dA \tag{3.41}$$

Now if the pressure has a uniform value p_a all around the surface, as in Fig. 3.7*a*, the net pressure force is zero

$$\mathbf{F}_{\text{UP}} = \int p_a(-\mathbf{n}) \, dA = -p_a \int \mathbf{n} \, dA \equiv 0 \tag{3.42}$$

where the subscript UP stands for uniform pressure. This result is *independent of the shape of the surface*[1] as long as the surface is closed, and all our control volumes are closed. Thus a seemingly complicated pressure-force problem can be simplified by subtracting any convenient uniform pressure p_a and working only with the pieces of gage pressure which remain, as illustrated in Fig. 3.7*b*. Thus Eq. (3.41) is entirely equivalent to

$$\mathbf{F}_{\text{press}} = \int_{\text{CS}} (p - p_a)(-\mathbf{n}) \, dA = \int_{\text{CS}} p_{\text{gage}}(-\mathbf{n}) \, dA$$

This trick can mean quite a saving in computation.

EXAMPLE 3.7

A control volume of a nozzle section has surface pressures of 40 lbf/in^2 absolute at section 1 and atmospheric pressure of 15 lbf/in^2 absolute at section 2 and on the external rounded part of the nozzle, as in Fig. E3.7*a*. Compute the net pressure force if $D_1 = 3$ in and $D_2 = 1$ in.

Solution

We do not have to bother with the outer surface if we subtract 15 lbf/in^2 from all surfaces. This leaves 25 lbf/in^2 gage at section 1 and 0 lbf/in^2 gage everywhere else, as in Fig. E3.7*b*.

---

[1] Can you prove this? It is a consequence of Gauss' theorem from vector analysis.

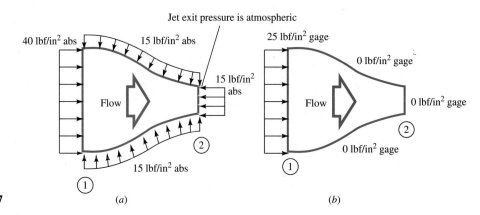

Fig. E3.7

(a)   (b)

Then the net pressure force is computed from section 1 only

$$\mathbf{F} = p_{g1}(-\mathbf{n})_1 A_1 = (25 \text{ lbf/in}^2) \frac{\pi}{4} (3 \text{ in})^2 \mathbf{i} = 177\mathbf{i} \text{ lbf} \qquad\qquad Ans.$$

Notice that we did not change inches to feet in this case because, with pressure in pounds-force per square inch and area in square inches, the product gives force directly in pounds. More often, though, the change back to standard units is necessary and desirable. *Note:* This problem computes pressure force only. There are probably other forces involved in Fig. E3.7, e.g., nozzle-wall stresses in the cuts through sections 1 and 2 and the weight of the fluid within the control volume.

Pressure Condition at a Jet Exit

Figure E3.7 illustrates a pressure boundary condition commonly used for jet exit-flow problems. When a fluid flow leaves a confined internal duct and exits into an ambient "atmosphere," its free surface is exposed to that atmosphere. Therefore the jet itself will essentially be at atmospheric pressure also. This condition was used at section 2 in Fig. E3.7.

Only two effects could maintain a pressure difference between the atmosphere and a free exit jet. The first is surface tension, Eq. (1.31), which is usually negligible. The second effect is a *supersonic* jet, which can separate itself from an atmosphere with expansion or compression waves (Chap. 9). For the majority of applications, therefore, we shall set the pressure in an exit jet as atmospheric.

EXAMPLE 3.8

A fixed control volume of a streamtube in steady flow has a uniform inlet flow (ρ_1, A_1, V_1) and a uniform exit flow (ρ_2, A_2, V_2), as shown in Fig. 3.8. Find an expression for the net force on the control volume.

Solution

Equation (3.40) applies with one inlet and exit

$$\sum \mathbf{F} = \dot{m}_2 \mathbf{V}_2 - \dot{m}_1 \mathbf{V}_1 = (\rho_2 A_2 V_2)\mathbf{V}_2 - (\rho_1 A_1 V_1)\mathbf{V}_1$$

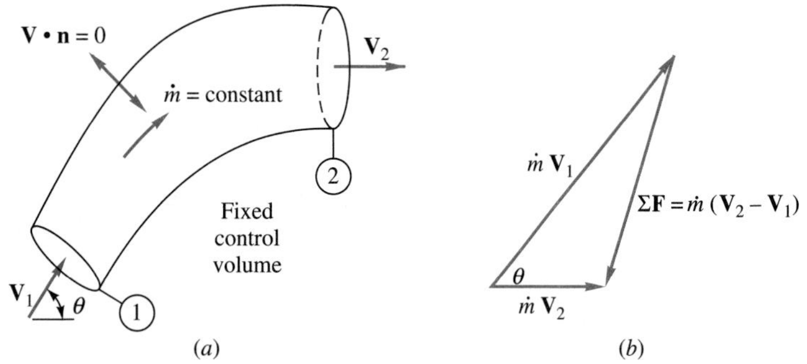

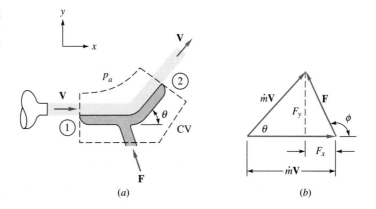

Fig. 3.8 Net force on a one-dimensional streamtube in steady flow: (*a*) streamtube in steady flow; (*b*) vector diagram for computing net force.

The volume-integral term vanishes for steady flow, but from conservation of mass in Example 3.3 we saw that

$$\dot{m}_1 = \dot{m}_2 = \dot{m} = \text{const}$$

Therefore a simple form for the desired result is

$$\sum \mathbf{F} = \dot{m}(\mathbf{V}_2 - \mathbf{V}_1) \qquad\qquad Ans.$$

This is a *vector* relation and is sketched in Fig. 3.8*b*. The term $\sum \mathbf{F}$ represents the net force acting on the control volume due to all causes; it is needed to balance the change in momentum of the fluid as it turns and decelerates while passing through the control volume.

EXAMPLE 3.9

As shown in Fig. 3.9*a*, a fixed vane turns a water jet of area A through an angle θ without changing its velocity magnitude. The flow is steady, pressure is p_a everywhere, and friction on the vane is negligible. (*a*) Find the components F_x and F_y of the applied vane force. (*b*) Find expressions for the force magnitude F and the angle ϕ between F and the horizontal; plot them versus θ.

Solution

Part (a)   The control volume selected in Fig. 3.9*a* cuts through the inlet and exit of the jet and through the vane support, exposing the vane force **F**. Since there is no cut along the vane-jet interface,

Fig. 3.9 Net applied force on a fixed jet-turning vane: (*a*) geometry of the vane turning the water jet; (*b*) vector diagram for the net force.

vane friction is internally self-canceling. The pressure force is zero in the uniform atmosphere. We neglect the weight of fluid and the vane weight within the control volume. Then Eq. (3.40) reduces to

$$\mathbf{F}_{\text{vane}} = \dot{m}_2 \mathbf{V}_2 - \dot{m}_1 \mathbf{V}_1$$

But the magnitude $V_1 = V_2 = V$ as given, and conservation of mass for the streamtube requires $\dot{m}_1 = \dot{m}_2 = \dot{m} = \rho AV$. The vector diagram for force and momentum change becomes an isosceles triangle with legs $\dot{m}\mathbf{V}$ and base $\mathbf{F}$, as in Fig. 3.9b. We can readily find the force components from this diagram

$$F_x = \dot{m}V(\cos \theta - 1) \qquad F_y = \dot{m}V \sin \theta \qquad \qquad Ans. \ (a)$$

where $\dot{m}V = \rho AV^2$ for this case. This is the desired result.

Part (b)   The force magnitude is obtained from part (a):

$$F = (F_x^2 + F_y^2)^{1/2} = \dot{m}V[\sin^2 \theta + (\cos \theta - 1)^2]^{1/2} = 2\dot{m}V \sin \frac{\theta}{2} \qquad Ans. \ (b)$$

From the geometry of Fig. 3.9b we obtain

$$\phi = 180° - \tan^{-1} \frac{F_y}{F_x} = 90° + \frac{\theta}{2} \qquad \qquad Ans. \ (b)$$

Fig. E3.9

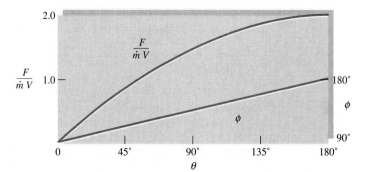

These can be plotted versus θ as shown in Fig. E3.9. Two special cases are of interest. First, the maximum force occurs at $\theta = 180°$, that is, when the jet is turned around and thrown back in the opposite direction with its momentum completely reversed. This force is $2\dot{m}V$ and acts to the *left*; that is, $\phi = 180°$. Second, at very small turning angles ($\theta < 10°$) we obtain approximately

$$F \approx \dot{m}V\theta \qquad \phi \approx 90°$$

The force is linearly proportional to the turning angle and acts nearly normal to the jet. This is the principle of a lifting vane, or airfoil, which causes a slight change in the oncoming flow direction and thereby creates a lift force normal to the basic flow.

EXAMPLE 3.10

A water jet of velocity V_j impinges normal to a flat plate which moves to the right at velocity V_c, as shown in Fig. 3.10a. Find the force required to keep the plate moving at constant velocity if the jet density is 1000 kg/m³, the jet area is 3 cm², and V_j and V_c are 20 and 15

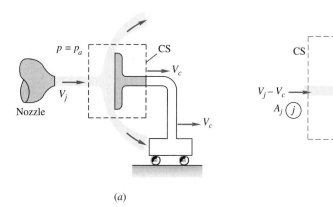

Fig. 3.10 Force on a plate moving at constant velocity: (*a*) jet striking a moving plate normally; (*b*) control volume fixed relative to the plate.

(*a*) (*b*)

m/s, respectively. Neglect the weight of the jet and plate, and assume steady flow with respect to the moving plate with the jet splitting into an equal upward and downward half-jet.

Solution

The suggested control volume in Fig. 3.10*a* cuts through the plate support to expose the desired forces R_x and R_y. This control volume moves at speed V_c and thus is fixed relative to the plate, as in Fig. 3.10*b*. We must satisfy both mass and momentum conservation for the assumed steady-flow pattern in Fig. 3.10*b*. There are two outlets and one inlet, and Eq. (3.30) applies for mass conservation

$$\dot{m}_{\text{out}} = \dot{m}_{\text{in}}$$

or

$$\rho_1 A_1 V_1 + \rho_2 A_2 V_2 = \rho_j A_j (V_j - V_c) \tag{1}$$

We assume that the water is incompressible $\rho_1 = \rho_2 = \rho_j$, and we are given that $A_1 = A_2 = \frac{1}{2} A_j$. Therefore Eq. (1) reduces to

$$V_1 + V_2 = 2(V_j - V_c) \tag{2}$$

Strictly speaking, this is all that mass conservation tells us. However, from the symmetry of the jet deflection and the neglect of fluid weight, we conclude that the two velocities V_1 and V_2 must be equal, and hence (2) becomes

$$V_1 = V_2 = V_j - V_c \tag{3}$$

For the given numerical values, we have

$$V_1 = V_2 = 20 - 15 = 5 \text{ m/s}$$

Now we can compute R_x and R_y from the two components of momentum conservation. Equation (3.40) applies with the unsteady term zero

$$\sum F_x = R_x = \dot{m}_1 u_1 + \dot{m}_2 u_2 - \dot{m}_j u_j \tag{4}$$

where from the mass analysis, $\dot{m}_1 = \dot{m}_2 = \frac{1}{2} \dot{m}_j = \frac{1}{2} \rho_j A_j (V_j - V_c)$. Now check the flow directions at each section: $u_1 = u_2 = 0$, and $u_j = V_j - V_c = 5$ m/s. Thus Eq. (4) becomes

$$R_x = -\dot{m}_j u_j = -[\rho_j A_j (V_j - V_c)](V_j - V_c) \tag{5}$$

For the given numerical values we have

$$R_x = -(1000 \text{ kg/m}^3)(0.0003 \text{ m}^2)(5 \text{ m/s})^2 = -7.5 \text{ (kg} \cdot \text{m)/s}^2 = -7.5 \text{ N} \qquad Ans.$$

This acts to the *left*; i.e., it requires a restraining force to keep the plate from accelerating to the right due to the continuous impact of the jet. The vertical force is

$$F_y = R_y = \dot{m}_1 v_1 + \dot{m}_2 v_2 - \dot{m}_j v_j$$

Check directions again: $v_1 = V_1, v_2 = -V_2, v_j = 0$. Thus

$$R_y = \dot{m}_1(V_1) + \dot{m}_2(-V_2) = \tfrac{1}{2}\dot{m}_j(V_1 - V_2) \qquad (6)$$

But since we found earlier that $V_1 = V_2$, this means that $R_y = 0$, as we could expect from the symmetry of the jet deflection.[1] Two other results are of interest. First, the relative velocity at section 1 was found to be 5 m/s up, from Eq. (3). If we convert this to absolute motion by adding on the control-volume speed $V_c = 15$ m/s to the right, we find that the absolute velocity $\mathbf{V}_1 = 15\mathbf{i} + 5\mathbf{j}$ m/s, or 15.8 m/s at an angle of 18.4° upward, as indicated in Fig. 3.10a. Thus the absolute jet speed changes after hitting the plate. Second, the computed force R_x does not change if we assume the jet deflects in all radial directions along the plate surface rather than just up and down. Since the plate is normal to the x axis, there would still be zero outlet x-momentum flux when Eq. (4) was rewritten for a radial-deflection condition.

EXAMPLE 3.11

The previous example treated a plate at normal incidence to an oncoming flow. In Fig. 3.11 the plate is parallel to the flow. The stream is not a jet but a broad river, or *free stream*, of uniform velocity $\mathbf{V} = U_0\mathbf{i}$. The pressure is assumed uniform, and so it has no net force on the plate. The plate does not block the flow as in Fig. 3.10, so that the only effect is due to boundary shear, which was neglected in the previous example. The no-slip condition at the wall brings the fluid there to a halt, and these slowly moving particles retard their neighbors above, so that at the end of the plate there is a significant retarded shear layer, or *boundary layer*, of thickness $y = \delta$. The viscous stresses along the wall can sum to a finite drag force on the plate. These effects are illustrated in Fig. 3.11. The problem is to make an integral

[1] Symmetry can be a powerful tool if used properly. Try to learn more about the uses and misuses of symmetry conditions. Here we doggedly computed the results without invoking symmetry.

Fig. 3.11 Control-volume analysis of drag force on a flat plate due to boundary shear.

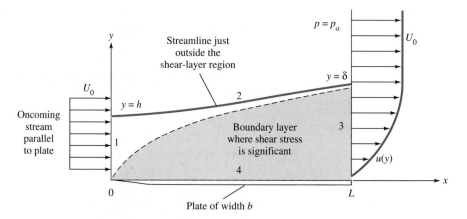

analysis and find the drag force D in terms of the flow properties ρ, U_0, and δ and the plate dimensions L and b.[†]

Solution

Like most practical cases, this problem requires a combined mass and momentum balance. A proper selection of control volume is essential, and we select the four-sided region from 0 to h to δ to L and back to the origin 0, as shown in Fig. 3.11. Had we chosen to cut across horizontally from left to right along the height $y = h$, we would have cut through the shear layer and exposed unknown shear stresses. Instead we follow the streamline passing through $(x, y) = (0, h)$, which is outside the shear layer and also has no mass flow across it. The four control-volume sides are thus

1. From $(0, 0)$ to $(0, h)$: a one-dimensional inlet, $\mathbf{V} \cdot \mathbf{n} = -U_0$
2. From $(0, h)$ to (L, δ): a streamline, no shear, $\mathbf{V} \cdot \mathbf{n} \equiv 0$
3. From (L, δ) to $(L, 0)$: a two-dimensional outlet, $\mathbf{V} \cdot \mathbf{n} = + u(y)$
4. From $(L, 0)$ to $(0, 0)$: a streamline just above the plate surface, $\mathbf{V} \cdot \mathbf{n} = 0$, shear forces summing to the drag force $-D\mathbf{i}$ acting from the plate onto the retarded fluid

The pressure is uniform, and so there is no net pressure force. Since the flow is assumed incompressible and steady, Eq. (3.37) applies with no unsteady term and fluxes only across sections 1 and 3:

$$\sum F_x = -D = \rho \int_1 u(\mathbf{V} \cdot \mathbf{n})\, dA + \rho \int_3 u(\mathbf{V} \cdot \mathbf{n})\, dA$$

$$= \rho \int_0^h U_0(-U_0) b\, dy + \rho \int_0^\delta u(+u) b\, dy$$

Evaluating the first integral and rearranging give

$$D = \rho U_0^2 b h - \rho b \int_0^\delta u^2\, dy \tag{1}$$

This could be considered the answer to the problem, but it not useful because the height h is not known with respect to the shear-layer thickness δ. This is found by applying mass conservation, since the control volume forms a streamtube

$$\rho \int_{CS} (\mathbf{V} \cdot \mathbf{n})\, dA = 0 = \rho \int_0^h (-U_0) b\, dy + \rho \int_0^\delta u b\, dy$$

or

$$U_0 h = \int_0^\delta u\, dy \tag{2}$$

after canceling b and ρ and evaluating the first integral. Introduce this value of h into Eq. (1) for a much cleaner result

$$D = \rho b \int_0^\delta u(U_0 - u)\, dy \,\bigg|_{x=L} \qquad\qquad\qquad \textit{Ans.} \text{ (3)}$$

This result was first derived by Theodore von Kármán in 1921.[1] It relates the friction drag

---

[†] The general analysis of such wall-shear problems, called *boundary-layer theory*, is treated in Sec. 7.3.

[1] The autobiography of this great twentieth-century engineer and teacher [2] is recommended for its historical and scientific insight.

on one side of a flat plate to the integral of the *momentum defect* $u(U_0 - u)$ across the trailing cross section of the flow past the plate. Since $U_0 - u$ vanishes as y increases, the integral has a finite value. Equation (3) is an example of *momentum-integral theory* for boundary layers, which is treated in Chap. 7. To illustrate the magnitude of this drag force, we can use a simple parabolic approximation for the outlet-velocity profile $u(y)$ which simulates low-speed, or *laminar*, shear flow

$$u \approx U_0\left(\frac{2y}{\delta} - \frac{y^2}{\delta^2}\right) \qquad \text{for } 0 \le y \le \delta \tag{4}$$

Substituting into Eq. (3) and letting $\eta = y/\delta$ for convenience, we obtain

$$D = \rho b U_0^2 \delta \int_0^1 (2\eta - \eta^2)(1 - 2\eta + \eta^2)\, d\eta = \tfrac{2}{15}\rho U_0^2 b\delta \tag{5}$$

This is within 1 percent of the accepted result from laminar boundary-layer theory (Chap. 7) in spite of the crudeness of the Eq. (4) approximation. This is a happy situation and has led to the wide use of Kármán's integral theory in the analysis of viscous flows. Note that D increases with the shear-layer thickness δ, which itself increases with plate length and the viscosity of the fluid (see Sec. 7.4).

Momentum-Flux Correction Factor

For flow in a duct, the axial velocity is usually nonuniform, as in Example 3.4. For this case the simple momentum-flux calculation $\int u\rho(\mathbf{V} \cdot \mathbf{n})\, dA = \dot{m}V = \rho AV^2$ is somewhat in error and should be corrected to $\beta\rho AV^2$, where β is the dimensionless momentum-flux correction factor, $\beta \ge 1$.

The factor β accounts for the variation of u^2 across the duct section. That is, we compute the exact flux and set it equal to a flux based on average velocity in the duct

$$\rho \int u^2\, dA = \beta \dot{m} V_{\text{av}} = \beta\rho AV_{\text{av}}^2$$

$$\beta = \frac{1}{A}\int \left(\frac{u}{V_{\text{av}}}\right)^2 dA$$

or

$$\tag{3.43a}$$

Values of β can be computed based on typical duct velocity profiles similar to those in Example 3.4. The results are as follows:

Laminar flow:
$$u = U_0\left(1 - \frac{r^2}{R^2}\right) \qquad \beta = \frac{4}{3} \tag{3.43b}$$

Turbulent flow:
$$u \approx U_0\left(1 - \frac{r}{R}\right)^m \qquad \frac{1}{9} \le m \le \frac{1}{5}$$

$$\beta = \frac{(1+m)^2(2+m)^2}{2(1+2m)(2+2m)} \tag{3.43c}$$

The turbulent correction factors have the following range of values:

Turbulent flow:	m	$\frac{1}{5}$	$\frac{1}{6}$	$\frac{1}{7}$	$\frac{1}{8}$	$\frac{1}{9}$
	β	1.037	1.027	1.020	1.016	1.013

These are so close to unity that they are normally neglected. The laminar correction may sometimes be important.

To illustrate a typical use of these correction factors, the solution to Example 3.8 for nonuniform velocities at sections 1 and 2 would be given as

$$\sum \mathbf{F} = \dot{m}(\beta_2 \mathbf{V}_2 - \beta_1 \mathbf{V}_1) \tag{3.43d}$$

Note that the basic parameters and vector character of the result are not changed at all by this correction.

Noninertial Reference Frame[1]

All previous derivations and examples in this section have assumed that the coordinate system is inertial, i.e., at rest or moving at constant velocity. In this case the rate of change of velocity equals the absolute acceleration of the system, and Newton's law applies directly in the form of Eqs. (3.2) and (3.35).

In many cases it is convenient to use a *noninertial*, or accelerating, coordinate system. An example would be coordinates fixed to a rocket during takeoff. A second example is any flow on the earth's surface, which is accelerating relative to the fixed stars because of the rotation of the earth. Atmospheric and oceanographic flows experience the so-called *Coriolis acceleration*, outlined below. It is typically less than $10^{-5}g$, where g is the acceleration of gravity, but its accumulated effect over distances of many kilometers can be dominant in geophysical flows. By contrast, the Coriolis acceleration is negligible in small-scale problems like pipe or airfoil flows.

Suppose that the fluid flow has velocity $\mathbf{V}$ relative to a noninertial xyz coordinate system, as shown in Fig. 3.12. Then $d\mathbf{V}/dt$ will represent a noninertial acceleration which must be added vectorially to a relative acceleration $\mathbf{a}_{rel}$ to give the absolute acceleration $\mathbf{a}_i$ relative to some inertial coordinate system XYZ, as in Fig. 3.12. Thus

$$\mathbf{a}_i = \frac{d\mathbf{V}}{dt} + \mathbf{a}_{rel} \tag{3.44}$$

[1] This section may be omitted without loss of continuity.

Fig. 3.12 Geometry of fixed versus accelerating coordinates.

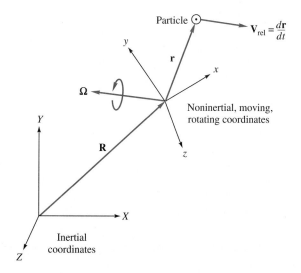

Since Newton's law applies to the absolute acceleration,

$$\sum \mathbf{F} = m\mathbf{a}_i = m\left(\frac{d\mathbf{V}}{dt} + \mathbf{a}_{rel}\right)$$

or

$$\sum \mathbf{F} - m\mathbf{a}_{rel} = m\frac{d\mathbf{V}}{dt} \tag{3.45}$$

Thus Newton's law in noninertial coordinates xyz is equivalent to adding more "force" terms $-m\mathbf{a}_{rel}$ to account for noninertial effects. In the most general case, sketched in Fig. 3.12, the term $\mathbf{a}_{rel}$ contains four parts, three of which account for the angular velocity $\mathbf{\Omega}(t)$ of the inertial coordinates. By inspection of Fig. 3.12, the absolute displacement of a particle is

$$\mathbf{S}_i = \mathbf{r} + \mathbf{R} \tag{3.46}$$

Differentiation gives the absolute velocity

$$\mathbf{V}_i = \mathbf{V} + \frac{d\mathbf{R}}{dt} + \mathbf{\Omega} \times \mathbf{r} \tag{3.47}$$

A second differentiation gives the absolute acceleration:

$$\mathbf{a}_i = \frac{d\mathbf{V}}{dt} + \frac{d^2\mathbf{R}}{dt^2} + \frac{d\mathbf{\Omega}}{dt} \times \mathbf{r} + 2\mathbf{\Omega} \times \mathbf{V} + \mathbf{\Omega} \times (\mathbf{\Omega} \times \mathbf{r}) \tag{3.48}$$

By comparison with Eq. (3.44), we see that the last four terms on the right represent the additional relative acceleration:

1. $d^2\mathbf{R}/dt^2$ is the acceleration of the noninertial origin of coordinates xyz.
2. $(d\mathbf{\Omega}/dt) \times \mathbf{r}$ is the angular-acceleration effect.
3. $2\mathbf{\Omega} \times \mathbf{V}$ is the Coriolis acceleration.
4. $\mathbf{\Omega} \times (\mathbf{\Omega} \times \mathbf{r})$ is the centripetal acceleration, directed from the particle normal to the axis of rotation with magnitude $\Omega^2 L$, where L is the normal distance to the axis.[1]

Equation (3.45) differs from Eq. (3.2) only in the added inertial forces on the left-hand side. Thus the control-volume formulation of linear momentum in noninertial coordinates merely adds inertia terms by integrating the added relative acceleration over each differential mass in the control volume

$$\sum \mathbf{F} - \int_{CV} \mathbf{a}_{rel}\,dm = \frac{d}{dt}\left(\int_{CV} \mathbf{V}\rho\,d\mathcal{V}\right) + \int_{CS} \mathbf{V}\rho(\mathbf{V}_r \cdot \mathbf{n})\,dA \tag{3.49}$$

where

$$\mathbf{a}_{rel} = \frac{d^2\mathbf{R}}{dt^2} + \frac{d\mathbf{\Omega}}{dt} \times \mathbf{r} + 2\mathbf{\Omega} \times \mathbf{V} + \mathbf{\Omega} \times (\mathbf{\Omega} \times \mathbf{r})$$

This is the noninertial equivalent to the inertial form given in Eq. (3.35). To analyze such problems, one must have knowledge of the displacement $\mathbf{R}$ and angular velocity $\mathbf{\Omega}$ of the noninertial coordinates.

If the control volume is nondeformable, Eq. (3.49) reduces to

[1] A complete discussion of these noninertial coordinate terms is given, e.g., in Ref. 4, pp. 49–51.

$$\sum \mathbf{F} - \int_{CV} \mathbf{a}_{rel} \; dm = \frac{d}{dt} \left(\int_{CV} \mathbf{V} \rho \; d\mathcal{V} \right) + \int_{CS} \mathbf{V} \rho (\mathbf{V} \cdot \mathbf{n}) \; dA \qquad (3.50)$$

In other words, the right-hand side reduces to that of Eq. (3.37).

EXAMPLE 3.12

Repeat Example 3.10 with the plate and its cart unrestrained horizontally and thus allowed to accelerate to the right. Derive (*a*) the equation of motion for cart velocity $V_c(t)$ and (*b*) the time required for the cart to accelerate from rest to 95 percent of the jet velocity. (*c*) Compute actual numerical values from (*b*) for the conditions of Example 3.10 and a cart mass of 3 kg. Neglect cart wheel friction.

Solution

Part (a)
The control volume is shown in Fig. E3.12 to include the cart and its wheel. The control volume moves at speed $V_c(t)$. The flow within the control volume is unsteady because the inlet velocity $V_j - V_c$ varies with time. The mass-conservation relation is Eq. (3.22)

$$\frac{d}{dt} \left(\int_{CV} \rho \; d\mathcal{V} \right) + \rho_1 A_1 V_1 + \rho_2 A_2 V_2 - \rho_j A_j (V_j - V_c) = 0 \qquad (1)$$

Again assume incompressible flow so that the density cancels. The integral is the mass within the control volume, which remains constant if the jet cross section is constant. Therefore we conclude that the time derivative of the integral is zero, and the previous result holds:

$$V_1 = V_2 = V_j - V_c \qquad (2)$$

These speeds V_1 and V_2 are relative to the moving cart. The momentum relation (3.50) is now applied to the *x* direction with the coordinates *xyz* fixed to the accelerating cart

$$\sum F_x - \int_{CV} a_{x,rel} \; dm = \frac{d}{dt} \left(\int_{CV} u \rho \; d\mathcal{V} \right) + \int_{CS} u \rho (\mathbf{V} \cdot \mathbf{n}) \; dA$$

Fig. E3.12

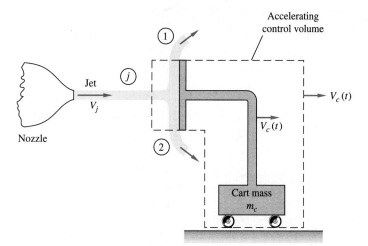

Now the cart is unrestrained, and the pressure is constant; hence $\Sigma F_x = 0$. The relative acceleration of the control volume is none other than the rate of change of cart speed since the cart is not rotating relative to inertial coordinates

$$a_{x,\text{rel}} = \frac{d}{dt}(V_c) \tag{3}$$

The area integrals on the right-hand side are the same as found in Example 3.10

$$\int_{\text{CS}} u\rho(\mathbf{V} \cdot \mathbf{n}) \, dA = -\dot{m}_j u_j = -\rho_j A_j (V_j - V_c)^2 \tag{4}$$

with only the jet inlet flux having nonzero u velocity. Finally, evaluation of the two remaining integrals requires an assumption about the mass and x momentum of the fluid within the control volume. Since these are probably small with respect to the *cart* mass and momentum, we apply a little art: We neglect the contribution of fluid mass to the volume integrals,[1] so that the integrals are, approximately,

$$\int_{\text{CV}} a_{x,\text{rel}} \, dm \approx m_c \frac{dV_c}{dt} \qquad \frac{d}{dt}\left(\int_{\text{CV}} u\rho \, d\mathcal{V}\right) \approx 0$$

where m_c is the mass of the cart and plate. Substituting back gives

$$0 - m_c \frac{dV_c}{dt} = 0 - \rho A_j (V_j - V_c)^2$$

or $\qquad\qquad \dfrac{dV_c}{dt} = K(V_j - V_c)^2 \qquad K = \dfrac{\rho A_j}{m_c} \qquad\qquad$ *Ans. (a)* (5)

This is the desired differential equation for the cart speed.

Part (b) We can find the time to reach 95 percent of the jet speed by integrating Eq. (5), assuming that K and V_j are constant. Separate the variables and use a lower limit starting from rest, that is, $V_c = 0$ at $t = 0$

$$\int_0^{V_c} (V_j - V_c)^{-2} \, dV_c = \int_0^t K \, dt$$

Evaluate the integrals to get

$$\frac{1}{V_j - V_c} - \frac{1}{V_j} = Kt$$

or $\qquad\qquad \dfrac{V_c}{V_j} = \dfrac{V_j Kt}{1 + V_j Kt} \qquad\qquad\qquad$ (6)

This is the general solution for the cart speed $V_c(t)$ when starting from rest. The time t^* when $V_c/V_j = 0.95$ is thus given by

$$0.95 = \frac{V_j K t^*}{1 + V_j K t^*}$$

or $\qquad\qquad t^* = \dfrac{19}{KV_j} = \dfrac{19 m_c}{\rho A_j V_j} \qquad\qquad$ *Ans. (b)*

[1] Have your instructor assign you to analyze the conditions under which these assumptions are valid.

Part (c) The constant $1/(KV_j)$ is an indication of the response time of the cart when struck by the jet. For the given conditions,

$$t^* = \frac{19(3 \text{ kg})}{(1000 \text{ kg/m}^3)(0.0003 \text{ m}^2)(20 \text{ m/s})} = 9.5 \text{ s} \qquad \textit{Ans. (c)}$$

3.5 The Angular-Momentum Theorem[1]

A control-volume analysis can be applied to the angular-momentum relation, Eq. (3.3), by letting our dummy variable **B** be the angular-momentum vector **H**. However, since the system considered here is typically a group of nonrigid fluid particles of variable velocity, the concept of mass moment of inertia is of no help and we have to calculate the instantaneous angular momentum by integration over the elemental masses dm. If O is the point about which moments are desired, the angular momentum about O is given by

$$\mathbf{H}_O = \int_{\text{syst}} (\mathbf{r} \times \mathbf{V}) \, dm \qquad (3.51)$$

where **r** is the position vector from O to the elemental mass dm and **V** is the velocity of that element. The amount of angular momentum per unit mass is thus seen to be

$$\boldsymbol{\beta} = \frac{d\mathbf{H}_O}{dm} = \mathbf{r} \times \mathbf{V}$$

The Reynolds transport theorem (3.16) then tells us that

$$\left. \frac{d\mathbf{H}_O}{dt} \right|_{\text{syst}} = \frac{d}{dt} \left[\int_{\text{CV}} (\mathbf{r} \times \mathbf{V}) \rho \, d\mathscr{V} \right] + \int_{\text{CS}} (\mathbf{r} \times \mathbf{V}) \rho (\mathbf{V}_r \cdot \mathbf{n}) \, dA \qquad (3.52)$$

for the most general case of a deformable control volume. But from the angular-momentum theorem (3.3), this must equal the sum of all the moments about point O applied to the control volume

$$\frac{d\mathbf{H}_O}{dt} = \sum \mathbf{M}_O = \sum (\mathbf{r} \times \mathbf{F})_O$$

Note that the total moment equals the summation of moments of all applied forces about point O. Recall, however, that this law, like Newton's law (3.2), assumes that the particle velocity **V** is relative to an *inertial* coordinate system. If not, the moments about point O of the relative acceleration terms $\mathbf{a}_{\text{rel}}$ in Eq. (3.49) must also be included

$$\sum \mathbf{M}_O = \sum (\mathbf{r} \times \mathbf{F})_O - \int_{\text{CV}} (\mathbf{r} \times \mathbf{a}_{\text{rel}}) \, dm \qquad (3.53)$$

where the four terms constituting $\mathbf{a}_{\text{rel}}$ are given in Eq. (3.49). Thus the most general case of the angular-momentum theorem is for a deformable control volume associated with a noninertial coordinate system. We combine Eqs. (3.52) and (3.53) to obtain

$$\sum (\mathbf{r} \times \mathbf{F})_O - \int_{\text{CV}} (\mathbf{r} \times \mathbf{a}_{\text{rel}}) \, dm = \frac{d}{dt} \left[\int_{\text{CV}} (\mathbf{r} \times \mathbf{V}) \rho \, d\mathscr{V} \right] + \int_{\text{CS}} (\mathbf{r} \times \mathbf{V}) \rho (\mathbf{V}_r \cdot \mathbf{n}) \, dA$$

$$(3.54)$$

[1] This section may be omitted without loss of continuity.

For a nondeformable inertial control volume, this reduces to

$$\sum \mathbf{M}_O = \frac{\partial}{\partial t}\left[\int_{CV} (\mathbf{r} \times \mathbf{V})\rho \, d\mathcal{V}\right] + \int_{CS} (\mathbf{r} \times \mathbf{V})\rho(\mathbf{V} \cdot \mathbf{n}) \, dA \qquad (3.55)$$

Further, if there are only one-dimensional inlets and exits, the angular-momentum flux terms evaluated on the control surface become

$$\int_{CS} (\mathbf{r} \times \mathbf{V})\rho(\mathbf{V} \cdot \mathbf{n}) \, dA = \sum (\mathbf{r} \times \mathbf{V})_{out}\dot{m}_{out} - \sum (\mathbf{r} \times \mathbf{V})_{in}\dot{m}_{in} \qquad (3.56)$$

Although at this stage the angular-momentum theorem can be considered to be a supplementary topic, it has direct application to many important fluid-flow problems involving torques or moments. A particularly important case is the analysis of rotating fluid-flow devices, usually called *turbomachines* (Chap. 11).

EXAMPLE 3.13

As shown in Fig. E3.13a, a pipe bend is supported at point A and connected to a flow system by flexible couplings at sections 1 and 2. The fluid is incompressible, and ambient pressure p_a is zero. (a) Find an expression for the torque T which must be resisted by the support at A, in terms of the flow properties at sections 1 and 2 and the distances h_1 and h_2. (b) Compute this torque if $D_1 = D_2 = 3$ in, $p_1 = 100$ lbf/in² gage, $p_2 = 80$ lbf/in² gage, $V_1 = 40$ ft/s, $h_1 = 2$ in, $h_2 = 10$ in, and $\rho = 1.94$ slugs/ft³.

Fig. E3.13a

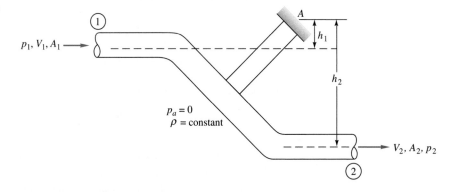

Solution

Part (a)   The control volume chosen in Fig. E3.13b cuts through sections 1 and 2 and through the support at A, where the torque T_A is desired. The flexible-couplings description specifies that there is no torque at either section 1 or 2, and so the cuts there expose no moments. For the angular-momentum terms $\mathbf{r} \times \mathbf{V}$, $\mathbf{r}$ should be taken from point A to sections 1 and 2. Note that the gage pressure forces p_1A_1 and p_2A_2 both have moments about A. Equation (3.55) with one-dimensional flux terms becomes

$$\sum \mathbf{M}_A = \mathbf{T}_A + \mathbf{r}_1 \times (-p_1A_1\mathbf{n}_1) + \mathbf{r}_2 \times (-p_2A_2\mathbf{n}_2)$$

$$= (\mathbf{r}_2 \times \mathbf{V}_2)(+\dot{m}_{out}) + (\mathbf{r}_1 \times \mathbf{V}_1)(-\dot{m}_{in}) \qquad (1)$$

Figure E3.13c shows that all the cross products are associated either with $r_1 \sin \theta_1 = h_1$ or

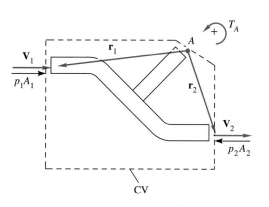

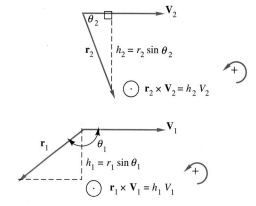

Fig. E3.13b   **Fig. E3.13c**

$r_2 \sin \theta_2 = h_2$, the perpendicular distances from point A to the pipe axes at 1 and 2. Remember that $\dot{m}_{\text{in}} = \dot{m}_{\text{out}}$ from the steady-flow continuity relation. In terms of counterclockwise moments, Eq. (1) then becomes

$$T_A + p_1 A_1 h_1 - p_2 A_2 h_2 = \dot{m}(h_2 V_2 - h_1 V_1) \qquad (2)$$

Rewriting this, we find the desired torque to be

$$T_A = h_2(p_2 A_2 + \dot{m} V_2) - h_1(p_1 A_1 + \dot{m} V_1) \qquad \text{Ans. (a)} \quad (3)$$

counterclockwise. The quantities p_1 and p_2 are gage pressures. Note that this result is independent of the shape of the pipe bend and varies only with the properties at sections 1 and 2 and the distances h_1 and h_2.[†]

Part (b) The inlet and exit areas are the same:

$$A_1 = A_2 = \frac{\pi}{4} (3)^2 = 7.07 \text{ in}^2 = 0.0491 \text{ ft}^2$$

Since the density is constant, we conclude from continuity that $V_2 = V_1 = 40$ ft/s. The mass flow is

$$\dot{m} = \rho A_1 V_1 = 1.94(0.0491)(40) = 3.81 \text{ slug/s}$$

Equation (3) can be evaluated as

$$T_A = (\tfrac{10}{12} \text{ ft})[80(7.07) \text{ lbf} + 3.81(40) \text{ lbf}] - (\tfrac{2}{12} \text{ ft})[100(7.07) \text{ lbf} + 3.81(40) \text{ lbf}]$$

$$= 598 - 143 = 455 \text{ ft} \cdot \text{lbf counterclockwise} \qquad \text{Ans. (b)}$$

We got a little daring there and multiplied p in lbf/in^2 gage times A in in^2 to get lbf without changing units to lbf/ft^2 and ft^2.

EXAMPLE 3.14

Figure 3.13 shows a schematic of a centrifugal pump. The fluid enters axially and passes

---

[†] Indirectly, the pipe-bend shape probably affects the pressure change from p_1 to p_2.

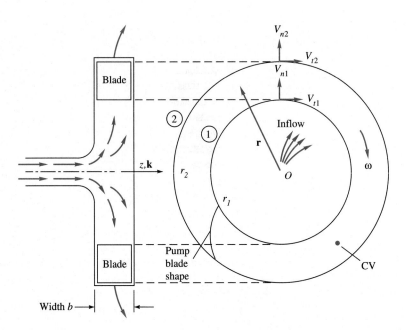

Fig. 3.13 Schematic of a simplified centrifugal pump.

through the pump blades, which rotate at angular velocity ω; the velocity of the fluid is changed from V_1 to V_2 and its pressure from p_1 to p_2. (*a*) Find an expression for the torque T_O which must be applied to these blades to maintain this flow. (*b*) The power supplied to the pump would be $P = \omega T_O$. To illustrate numerically, suppose $r_1 = 0.2$ m, $r_2 = 0.5$ m, and $b = 0.15$ m. Let the pump rotate at 600 r/min and deliver water at 2.5 m³/s with a density of 1000 kg/m³. Compute the idealized torque and power supplied.

Solution

Part (*a*)
The control volume is chosen to be the angular region between sections 1 and 2 where the flow passes through the pump blades (see Fig. 3.13). The flow is steady and assumed incompressible. The contribution of pressure to the torque about axis O is zero since the pressure forces at 1 and 2 act radially through O. Equation (3.55) becomes

$$\sum \mathbf{M}_O = \mathbf{T}_O = (\mathbf{r}_2 \times \mathbf{V}_2)\dot{m}_{\text{out}} - (\mathbf{r}_1 \times \mathbf{V}_1)\dot{m}_{\text{in}} \tag{1}$$

where steady-flow continuity tells us that

$$\dot{m}_{\text{in}} = \rho V_{n1} 2\pi r_1 b = \dot{m}_{\text{out}} = \rho V_{n2} 2\pi r_2 b = \rho Q$$

The cross product $\mathbf{r} \times \mathbf{V}$ is found to be clockwise about O at both sections:

$$\mathbf{r}_2 \times \mathbf{V}_2 = r_2 V_{t2} \sin 90° \; \mathbf{k} = r_2 V_{t2}\mathbf{k} \qquad \text{clockwise}$$

$$\mathbf{r}_1 \times \mathbf{V}_1 = r_1 V_{t1}\mathbf{k} \qquad \text{clockwise}$$

Equation (1) thus becomes the desired formula for torque

$$\mathbf{T}_O = \rho Q(r_2 V_{t2} - r_1 V_{t1})\mathbf{k} \qquad \text{clockwise} \qquad\qquad \textit{Ans. (a)} \quad (2a)$$

This relation is called *Euler's turbine formula*. In an idealized pump, the inlet and outlet tangential velocities would match the blade rotational speeds $V_{t1} = \omega r_1$ and $V_{t2} = \omega r_2$. Then the formula for torque supplied becomes

$$T_O = \rho Q \omega (r_2^2 - r_1^2) \qquad \text{clockwise} \qquad (2b)$$

Part (b) Convert ω to $600(2\pi/60) = 62.8$ rad/s. The normal velocities are not needed here but follow from the flow rate

$$V_{n1} = \frac{Q}{2\pi r_1 b} = \frac{2.5 \ m^3/s}{2\pi(0.2 \ m)(0.15 \ m)} = 13.3 \ m/s$$

$$V_{n2} = \frac{Q}{2\pi r_2 b} = \frac{2.5}{2\pi(0.5)(0.15)} = 5.3 \ m/s$$

For the idealized inlet and outlet, tangential velocity equals tip speed

$$V_{t1} = \omega r_1 = (62.8 \ \text{rad/s})(0.2 \ m) = 12.6 \ m/s$$

$$V_{t2} = \omega r_2 = 62.8(0.5) = 31.4 \ m/s$$

Equation (2a) predicts the required torque to be

$$T_O = (1000 \ kg/m^3)(2.5 \ m^3/s)[(0.5 \ m)(31.4 \ m/s) - (0.2 \ m)(12.6 \ m/s)]$$

$$= 33,000 \ (kg \cdot m^2)/s^2 = 33,000 \ N \cdot m \qquad Ans.$$

The power required is

$$P = \omega T_O = (62.8 \ \text{rad/s})(33,000 \ N \cdot m) = 2,070,000 \ (N \cdot m)/s$$

$$= 2.07 \ MW \ (2780 \ hp) \qquad Ans.$$

In actual practice the tangential velocities are considerably less than the impeller-tip speeds, and the design power requirements for this pump may be only 1 MW or less.

EXAMPLE 3.15

Figure 3.14 shows a lawn-sprinkler arm viewed from above. The arm rotates about O at constant angular velocity ω. The volume flux entering the arm at O is Q, and the fluid is incompressible. There is a retarding torque at O, due to bearing friction, of amount $-T_O \mathbf{k}$. Find an expression for the rotation ω in terms of the arm and flow properties.

Solution

The entering velocity is $V_0 \mathbf{k}$, where $V_0 = Q/A_{\text{pipe}}$. Equation (3.55) applies to the control volume sketched in Fig. 3.14 only if $\mathbf{V}$ is the absolute velocity relative to an inertial frame. Thus the exit velocity at section 2 is

$$\mathbf{V}_2 = V_0 \mathbf{i} - R\omega \mathbf{i}$$

Equation (3.55) then predicts that, for steady flow,

$$\sum \mathbf{M}_O = -T_O \mathbf{k} = (\mathbf{r}_2 \times \mathbf{V}_2)\dot{m}_{\text{out}} - (\mathbf{r}_1 \times \mathbf{V}_1)\dot{m}_{\text{in}} \qquad (1)$$

where, from continuity, $\dot{m}_{\text{out}} = \dot{m}_{\text{in}} = \rho Q$. The cross products with reference to point O are

$$\mathbf{r}_2 \times \mathbf{V}_2 = R\mathbf{j} \times (V_0 - R\omega)\mathbf{i} = (R^2\omega - RV_0)\mathbf{k}$$

$$\mathbf{r}_1 \times \mathbf{V}_1 = 0\mathbf{j} \times V_0\mathbf{k} = 0$$

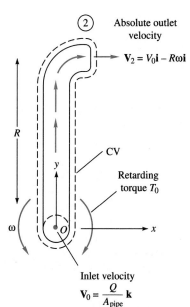

② Absolute outlet velocity

$\mathbf{V}_2 = V_0\mathbf{i} - R\omega\mathbf{i}$

R

CV

Retarding torque T_0

ω

y

x

O

Inlet velocity

$V_0 = \dfrac{Q}{A_{\text{pipe}}} \mathbf{k}$

Fig. 3.14 View from above of a single arm of a rotating lawn sprinkler.

Equation (1) thus becomes

$$-T_O\mathbf{k} = \rho Q(R^2\omega - RV_0)\mathbf{k}$$

or
$$\omega = \frac{V_0}{R} - \frac{T_O}{\rho QR^2} \qquad\qquad Ans.$$

The result may surprise you: Even if the retarding torque T_O is negligible, the arm rotational speed is limited to the value V_0/R imposed by the inlet speed and the arm length.

3.6 The Energy Equation[1]

As our fourth and final basic law, we apply the Reynolds transport theorem (3.12) to the first law of thermodynamics, Eq. (3.5). The dummy variable B becomes energy E, and the energy per unit mass is $\beta = dE/dm = e$. Equation (3.5) can then be written for a fixed control volume as follows:[2]

$$\frac{dQ}{dt} - \frac{dW}{dt} = \frac{dE}{dt} = \frac{d}{dt}\left(\int_{CV} e\rho \, d\mathcal{V}\right) + \int_{CS} e\rho(\mathbf{V} \cdot \mathbf{n}) \, dA \qquad (3.57)$$

Recall that positive Q denotes heat added to the system and positive W denotes work done by the system.

The system energy per unit mass e may be of several types:

$$e = e_{\text{internal}} + e_{\text{kinetic}} + e_{\text{potential}} + e_{\text{other}}$$

where e_{other} could encompass chemical reactions, nuclear reactions, and electrostatic or magnetic field effects. We neglect e_{other} here and consider only the first three terms as discussed in Eq. (1.9), with z defined as "up":

$$e = \hat{u} + \tfrac{1}{2}V^2 + gz \qquad (3.58)$$

The heat and work terms could be examined in detail. If this were a heat-transfer book, dQ/dT would be broken down into conduction, convection, and radiation effects and whole chapters written on each (see, e.g., Ref. 3). Here we leave the term untouched and consider it only occasionally.

Using for convenience the overdot to denote the time derivative, we divide the work term into three parts:

$$\dot{W} = \dot{W}_{\text{shaft}} + \dot{W}_{\text{press}} + \dot{W}_{\text{viscous stresses}} = \dot{W}_s + \dot{W}_p + \dot{W}_v$$

The work of gravitational forces has already been included as potential energy in Eq. (3.58). Other types of work, e.g., those due to electromagnetic forces, are excluded here.

The shaft work isolates that portion of the work which is deliberately done by a machine (pump impeller, fan blade, piston, etc.) protruding through the control surface into the control volume. No further specification other than $\dot{W}_s$ is desired at this point, but calculations of the work done by turbomachines will be performed in Chap. 11.

---

[1] This section should be read for information and enrichment even if you lack formal background in thermodynamics.

[2] The energy equation for a deformable control volume is rather complicated and is not discussed here. See Refs. 4 and 5 for further details.

The rate of work $\dot{W}_p$ done on pressure forces occurs at the surface only; all work on internal portions of the material in the control volume is by equal and opposite forces and is self-canceling. The pressure work equals the pressure force on a small surface element dA times the normal velocity component into the control volume

$$d\dot{W}_p = -(p\ dA)V_{n,\text{in}} = -p(-\mathbf{V}\cdot\mathbf{n})\ dA$$

The total pressure work is the integral over the control surface

$$\dot{W}_p = \int_{\text{CS}} p(\mathbf{V}\cdot\mathbf{n})\ dA \tag{3.59}$$

A cautionary remark: If part of the control surface is the surface of a machine part, we prefer to delegate that portion of the pressure to the *shaft work* term $\dot{W}_s$, not to $\dot{W}_p$, which is primarily meant to isolate the fluid-flow pressure-work terms.

Finally, the shear work due to viscous stresses occurs at the control surface, the internal work terms again being self-canceling, and consists of the product of each viscous stress (one normal and two tangential) and the respective velocity component

$$d\dot{W}_v = -\tau\cdot\mathbf{V}\ dA$$

or

$$\dot{W}_v = -\int_{\text{CS}} \tau\cdot\mathbf{V}\ dA \tag{3.60}$$

where τ is the stress vector on the elemental surface dA. This term may vanish or be negligible according to the particular type of surface at that part of the control volume:

Solid surface. For all parts of the control surface which are solid confining walls, $\mathbf{V} = 0$ from the viscous no-slip condition; hence $\dot{W}_v = $ zero identically.

Surface of a machine. Here the viscous work is contributed by the machine, and so we absorb this work in the term $\dot{W}_s$.

An inlet or outlet. At an inlet or outlet, the flow is approximately normal to the element dA; hence the only viscous-work term comes from the normal stress $\tau_{nn}V_n\ dA$. Since viscous normal stresses are extremely small in all but rare cases, e.g., the interior of a shock wave, it is customary to neglect viscous work at inlets and outlets of the control volume.

Streamline surface. If the control surface is a streamline such as the upper curve in the boundary-layer analysis of Fig. 3.11, the viscous-work term must be evaluated and retained if shear stresses are significant along this line. In the particular case of Fig. 3.11, the streamline is outside the boundary layer, and viscous work is negligible.

The net result of the above discussion is that the rate-of-work term in Eq. (3.57) consists essentially of

$$\dot{W} = \dot{W}_s + \int_{\text{CS}} p(\mathbf{V}\cdot\mathbf{n})\ dA - \int_{\text{CS}} (\tau\cdot\mathbf{V})_{SS}\ dA \tag{3.61}$$

where the subscript SS stands for stream surface. When we introduce (3.61) and (3.58) into (3.57), we find that the pressure-work term can be combined with the energy-flux term since both involve surface integrals of $\mathbf{V}\cdot\mathbf{n}$. The control-volume energy equation thus becomes

$$\dot{Q} - \dot{W}_s - (\dot{W}_v)_{ss} = \frac{\partial}{\partial t}\left(\int_{CV} e\rho \, d\mathcal{V}\right) + \int_{CS}\left(e + \frac{p}{\rho}\right)\rho(\mathbf{V} \cdot \mathbf{n}) \, dA \qquad (3.62)$$

Using e from (3.58), we see that the enthalpy $\hat{h} = \hat{u} + p/\rho$ occurs in the control-surface integral. The final general form for the energy equation for a fixed control volume becomes

$$\dot{Q} - \dot{W}_s - \dot{W}_v = \frac{\partial}{\partial t}\left[\int_{CV}\left(\hat{u} + \frac{1}{2}V^2 + gz\right)\rho \, d\mathcal{V}\right] + \int_{CS}\left(\hat{h} + \frac{1}{2}V^2 + gz\right)\rho(\mathbf{V} \cdot \mathbf{n}) \, dA$$

$$(3.63)$$

As mentioned above, the shear-work term $\dot{W}_v$ is rarely important.

One-Dimensional Energy-Flux Terms

If the control volume has a series of one-dimensional inlets and outlets, as in Fig. 3.6, the surface integral in (3.63) reduces to a summation of outlet fluxes minus inlet fluxes

$$\int_{CS}(\hat{h} + \tfrac{1}{2}V^2 + gz)\rho(\mathbf{V} \cdot \mathbf{n}) \, dA$$

$$= \sum (\hat{h} + \tfrac{1}{2}V^2 + gz)_{out}\dot{m}_{out} - \sum (\hat{h} + \tfrac{1}{2}V^2 + gz)_{in}\dot{m}_{in} \qquad (3.64)$$

where the values of $\hat{h}$, $\tfrac{1}{2}V^2$, and gz are taken to be averages over each cross section.

EXAMPLE 3.16

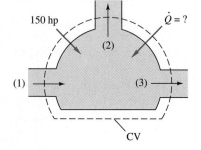

Fig. E3.16

A steady-flow machine (Fig. E3.16) takes in air at section 1 and discharges it at sections 2 and 3. The properties at each section are as follows:

Section	A, ft^2	Q, ft^3/s	T, °F	p, lbf/in^2 abs	z, ft
1	0.4	100	70	20	1.0
2	1.0	40	100	30	4.0
3	0.25	50	200	?	1.5

Work is provided to the machine at the rate of 150 hp. Find the pressure p_3 in lbf/in^2 absolute and the heat transfer $\dot{Q}$ in Btu/s. Assume that air is a perfect gas with $R = 1715$ and $c_p = 6003$ ft · lbf/(slug · °R).

Solution

The control volume chosen cuts across the three desired sections and otherwise follows the solid walls of the machine. Therefore the shear-work term $\dot{W}_v$ is negligible. We have enough information to compute $V_i = Q_i/A_i$ immediately

$$V_1 = \frac{100}{0.4} = 250 \text{ ft/s} \qquad V_2 = \frac{40}{1.0} = 40 \text{ ft/s} \qquad V_3 = \frac{50}{0.25} = 200 \text{ ft/s}$$

and the densities $\rho_i = p_i/(RT_i)$

$$\rho_1 = \frac{20(144)}{1715(70 + 460)} = 0.00317 \text{ slug/ft}^3$$

$$\rho_2 = \frac{30(144)}{1715(560)} = 0.00450 \text{ slug/ft}^3$$

but ρ_3 is determined from the steady-flow continuity relation:

$$\dot{m}_1 = \dot{m}_2 + \dot{m}_3$$

$$\rho_1 Q_1 = \rho_2 Q_2 + \rho_3 Q_3 \tag{1}$$

$$0.00317(100) = 0.00450(40) + \rho_3(50)$$

or

$$50\rho_3 = 0.317 - 0.180 = 0.137 \text{ slug/s}$$

$$\rho_3 = \frac{0.137}{50} = 0.00274 \text{ slug/ft}^3 = \frac{144 p_3}{1715(660)}$$

$$p_3 = 21.5 \text{ lbf/in}^2 \text{ absolute} \qquad\qquad\qquad Ans.$$

Note that the volume flux $Q_1 \neq Q_2 + Q_3$ because of the density changes.

For steady flow, the volume integral in (3.63) vanishes, and we have agreed to neglect viscous work. With one inlet and two outlets, we obtain

$$\dot{Q} - \dot{W}_s = -\dot{m}_1(\hat{h}_1 + \tfrac{1}{2}V_1^2 + gz_1) + \dot{m}_2(\hat{h}_2 + \tfrac{1}{2}V_2^2 + gz_2) + \dot{m}_3(\hat{h}_3 + \tfrac{1}{2}V_3^2 + gz_3) \tag{2}$$

where $\dot{W}_s$ is given in hp and can be quickly converted to consistent BG units:

$$\dot{W}_s = -150 \text{ hp } [550 \text{ ft} \cdot \text{lbf/(s} \cdot \text{hp)}]$$

$$= -82,500 \text{ ft} \cdot \text{lbf/s} \qquad \text{negative work on system}$$

For a perfect gas with constant c_p, $\hat{h} = c_p T$ plus an arbitrary constant. It is instructive to separate the flux terms in Eq. (2) above to examine their magnitudes:

Enthalpy flux:

$$c_p(-\dot{m}_1 T_1 + \dot{m}_2 T_2 + \dot{m}_3 T_3) = [6003 \text{ ft} \cdot \text{lbf/(slug} \cdot {}^\circ\text{R)}][(-0.317 \text{ slug/s})(530 \ {}^\circ\text{R})$$

$$+ 0.180(560) + 0.137(660)]$$

$$= -1,009,000 + 605,000 + 543,000$$

$$= +139,000 \text{ ft} \cdot \text{lbf/s}$$

Kinetic-energy flux:

$$-\dot{m}_1(\tfrac{1}{2}V_1^2) + \dot{m}_2(\tfrac{1}{2}V_2^2) + \dot{m}_3(\tfrac{1}{2}V_3^2) = \tfrac{1}{2}[-0.317(250)^2 + 0.180(40)^2 + 0.137(200)^2]$$

$$= -9900 + 150 + 2750 = -7000 \text{ ft} \cdot \text{lbf/s}$$

Potential-energy flux:

$$g(-\dot{m}_1 z_1 + \dot{m}_2 z_2 + \dot{m}_3 z_3) = 32.2[-0.317(1.0) + 0.180(4.0) + 0.137(1.5)]$$

$$= -10 + 23 + 7 = +20 \text{ ft} \cdot \text{lbf/s}$$

These are typical effects: The potential-energy flux is negligible in gas flows, the kinetic-energy flux is small in low-speed flows, and the enthalpy flux is dominant. It is only when we neglect heat-transfer effects that the kinetic and potential energies become important. Anyway, we can now solve for the heat flux

$$\dot{Q} = -82{,}500 + 139{,}000 - 7000 + 20 = 49{,}520 \text{ ft} \cdot \text{lbf/s} \tag{3}$$

Converting, we get

$$\dot{Q} = \frac{49{,}520}{778.2 \text{ ft} \cdot \text{lbf/Btu}} = +63.6 \text{ Btu/s} \qquad\qquad \textit{Ans.}$$

The Steady-Flow Energy Equation   For steady flow with one inlet and one outlet, both assumed one-dimensional, Eq. (3.63) reduces to a celebrated relation used in many engineering analyses. Let section 1 be the inlet and section 2 the outlet. Then

$$\dot{Q} - \dot{W}_s - \dot{W}_v = -\dot{m}_1(\hat{h}_1 + \tfrac{1}{2}V_1^2 + gz_1) + \dot{m}_2(\hat{h}_2 + \tfrac{1}{2}V_2^2 + gz_2) \tag{3.65}$$

But, from continuity, $\dot{m}_1 = \dot{m}_2 = \dot{m}$, and we can rearrange (3.65) as follows:

$$\hat{h}_1 + \tfrac{1}{2}V_1^2 + gz_1 = (\hat{h}_2 + \tfrac{1}{2}V_2^2 + gz_2) - q + w_s + w_v \tag{3.66}$$

where $q = \dot{Q}/\dot{m} = dQ/dm$, the heat transferred to the fluid per unit mass. Similarly, $w_s = \dot{W}_s/\dot{m} = dW_s/dm$ and $w_v = \dot{W}_v/\dot{m} = dW_v/dm$. Equation (3.66) is a general form of the *steady-flow energy equation*, which states that the upstream *stagnation enthalpy* $H_1 = (\hat{h} + \tfrac{1}{2}V^2 + gz)_1$ differs from the downstream value H_2 only if there is heat transfer, shaft work, or viscous work as the fluid passes between sections 1 and 2. Recall that q is positive if heat is added to the control volume and that w_s and w_v are positive if work is done by the fluid on the surroundings.

Each term in Eq. (3.66) has the dimensions of energy per unit mass, or velocity squared, which is a form commonly used by mechanical engineers. If we divide through by g, each term becomes a length, or head, which is a form preferred by civil engineers. The traditional symbol for head is h, which we do not wish to confuse with enthalpy. Therefore we use internal energy in rewriting the head form of the energy relation:

$$\frac{p_1}{\gamma} + \frac{\hat{u}_1}{g} + \frac{V_1^2}{2g} + z_1 = \frac{p_2}{\gamma} + \frac{\hat{u}_2}{g} + \frac{V_2^2}{2g} + z_2 - h_q + h_s + h_v \tag{3.67}$$

where $h_q = q/g$, $h_s = w_s/g$, and $h_v = w_v/g$ are the head forms of the heat added, shaft work done, and viscous work done, respectively. The term p/γ is called *pressure head* and the term $V^2/2g$ is denoted as *velocity head*.

Friction Losses in Low-Speed Flow   A very common application of the steady-flow energy equation is for low-speed flow with no shaft work and negligible viscous work, such as liquid flow in pipes. For this case Eq. (3.67) may be written in the form

$$\frac{p_1}{\gamma} + \frac{V_1^2}{2g} + z_1 = \left(\frac{p_2}{\gamma} + \frac{V_2^2}{2g} + z_2\right) + \frac{\hat{u}_2 - \hat{u}_1 - q}{g} \tag{3.68}$$

The term in parentheses is called the useful head or *available head* or *total head* of the flow, denoted as h_0. The last term on the right is the difference between the available head upstream and downstream and is normally *positive*, representing the loss in head due to friction, denoted as h_f. Thus, in low-speed (nearly incompressible) flow with no shaft work, one inlet, and one exit, we may write

$$h_{0,\text{in}} = h_{0,\text{out}} + h_f$$

or   (Available head)$_{\text{in}}$ = (available head)$_{\text{out}}$ + (frictional head loss)   (3.69)

The frictional loss occurs in all real flows and is the result of viscous dissipation converting mechanical energy to nonrecoverable internal energy plus heat transfer. In Chap. 6 we shall develop methods of correlating h_f with flow conditions for such frictional effects as pipes, valves, fittings, and diffusers.

EXAMPLE 3.17

Gasoline at 20°C is pumped through a smooth 12-cm-diameter pipe 10 km long, at a flow rate of 75 m³/h (330 gal/min). The inlet is fed by a pump at an absolute pressure of 24 atm. The exit is at standard atmospheric pressure and is 150 m higher. Estimate the frictional head loss h_f, and compare it to the velocity head of the flow $V^2/(2g)$. (These numbers are quite realistic for liquid flow through long pipelines.)

Solution

For gasoline at 20°C, from Table A.3, $\rho = 680$ kg/m³, or $\gamma = (680)(9.81) = 6670$ N/m³. There is no shaft work, hence Eq. (3.68) applies and can be evaluated:

$$\frac{p_{\text{in}}}{\gamma} + \frac{V_{\text{in}}^2}{2g} + z_{\text{in}} = \frac{p_{\text{out}}}{\gamma} + \frac{V_{\text{out}}^2}{2g} + z_{\text{out}} + h_f \tag{1}$$

The pipe is of uniform cross section, and thus the average velocity everywhere is

$$V_{\text{in}} = V_{\text{out}} = \frac{Q}{A} = \frac{75/3600 \text{ m}^3/\text{s}}{(\pi/4)(0.12 \text{ m})^2} \approx 1.84 \text{ m/s}$$

Being equal at inlet and exit, this term will cancel out of Eq. (1) above, but we are asked to compute the velocity head of the flow for comparison purposes:

$$\frac{V^2}{2g} = \frac{(1.84 \text{ m/s})^2}{2(9.81 \text{ m/s}^2)} \approx 0.173 \text{ m}$$

Now we are in a position to evaluate all terms in Eq. (1) except the friction head loss:

$$\frac{(24)(101{,}350 \text{ N/m}^2)}{6670 \text{ N/m}^3} + 0.173 \text{ m} + 0 \text{ m} = \frac{101{,}350 \text{ N/m}^2}{6670 \text{ N/m}^3} + 0.173 \text{ m} + 150 \text{ m} + h_f$$

or $h_f = 364.7 - 15.2 - 150 \approx 199$ m   *Ans.*

The friction head is larger than the elevation change Δz, and the pump must drive the flow against both changes, hence the high inlet pressure. The ratio of friction to velocity head is

$$\frac{h_f}{V^2/(2g)} \approx \frac{199 \text{ m}}{0.173 \text{ m}} \approx 1150 \qquad \textit{Ans.}$$

This high ratio is typical of long pipelines. (Note that we did not make direct use of the 10,000-m pipe length, whose effect is hidden within h_f.) In Chap. 6 we can state this problem in a more direct fashion: Given the flow rate, fluid, and pipe size, what inlet pressure is needed? Our correlations for h_f will lead to the estimate $p_{\text{inlet}} \approx 24$ atm, as stated above.

EXAMPLE 3.18

Air [$R = 1715$, $c_p = 6003$ ft · lbf/(slug · °R)] flows steadily, as shown in Fig. E3.18, through a turbine which produces 700 hp. For the inlet and exit conditions shown, estimate (a) the exit velocity V_2 and (b) the heat transferred $\dot{Q}$ in Btu/h.

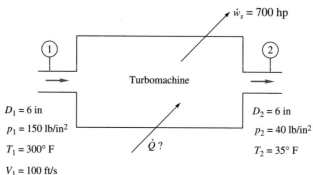

$\dot{w}_s = 700$ hp

Turbomachine

$D_1 = 6$ in
$p_1 = 150$ lb/in^2
$T_1 = 300°$ F

$\dot{Q}$?

$D_2 = 6$ in
$p_2 = 40$ lb/in^2
$T_2 = 35°$ F

Fig. E3.18 $V_1 = 100$ ft/s

Solution

Part (a)   The inlet and exit densities can be computed from the perfect-gas law:

$$\rho_1 = \frac{p_1}{RT_1} = \frac{150(144)}{1715(460 + 300)} = 0.0166 \text{ slug/ft}^3$$

$$\rho_2 = \frac{p_2}{RT_2} = \frac{40(144)}{1715(460 + 35)} = 0.00679 \text{ slug/ft}^3$$

The mass flow is determined by the inlet conditions

$$\dot{m} = \rho_1 A_1 V_1 = (0.0166)\frac{\pi}{4}\left(\frac{6}{12}\right)^2 (100) = 0.325 \text{ slug/s}$$

Knowing mass flow, we compute the exit velocity

$$\dot{m} = 0.325 = \rho_2 A_2 V_2 = (0.00679)\frac{\pi}{4}\left(\frac{6}{12}\right)^2 V_2$$

or $V_2 = 244$ ft/s   *Ans. (a)*

Part (b)   The steady-flow energy equation (3.65) applies with $\dot{W}_v = 0$, $z_1 = z_2$, and $\hat{h} = c_p T$:

$$\dot{Q} - \dot{W}_s = \dot{m}(c_p T_2 + \tfrac{1}{2}V_2^2 - c_p T_1 - \tfrac{1}{2}V_1^2)$$

Convert the turbine work to foot-pounds-force per second with the conversion factor 1 hp = 550 ft · lbf/s. The turbine work is positive

$$\dot{Q} - 700(550) = 0.325[6003(495) + \tfrac{1}{2}(244)^2 - 6003(760) - \tfrac{1}{2}(100)^2]$$

$$= -510,000 \text{ ft} \cdot \text{lbf/s}$$

or $\dot{Q} = -125,000$ ft · lbf/s

Convert this to British thermal units as follows:

$$\dot{Q} = (-125,000 \text{ ft} \cdot \text{lbf/s}) \frac{3600 \text{ s/h}}{778.2 \text{ ft} \cdot \text{lbf/Btu}}$$

$$= -576,000 \text{ Btu/h} \qquad\qquad\qquad\qquad\qquad Ans. (b)$$

The negative sign indicates that this heat transfer is a *loss* from the control volume.

Kinetic-Energy Correction Factor

Often the flow entering or leaving a port is not strictly one-dimensional. In particular, the velocity may vary over the cross section, as in Fig. E3.4. In this case the kinetic-energy term in Eq. (3.64) for a given port should be modified by a dimensionless correction factor α so that the integral can be proportional to the square of the average velocity through the port

$$\int_{\text{port}} (\tfrac{1}{2}V^2)\rho(\mathbf{V} \cdot \mathbf{n}) \, dA \equiv \alpha(\tfrac{1}{2}V_{\text{av}}^2)\dot{m}$$

where $$V_{\text{av}} = \frac{1}{A}\int u \, dA \qquad \text{for incompressible flow}$$

If the density is also variable, the integration is very cumbersome; we shall not treat this complication. By letting u be the velocity normal to the port, the first equation above becomes, for incompressible flow,

$$\tfrac{1}{2}\rho \int u^3 \, dA = \tfrac{1}{2}\rho\alpha V_{\text{av}}^3 A$$

or $$\alpha = \frac{1}{A}\int \left(\frac{u}{V_{\text{av}}}\right)^3 dA \qquad\qquad\qquad (3.70)$$

This is the kinetic-energy correction factor, having a value of about 2.0 for fully developed laminar pipe flow and from 1.04 to 1.11 for turbulent pipe flow. The incompressible steady-flow energy equation would become

$$\frac{p_1}{\rho} + \frac{1}{2}\alpha_1 V_1^2 + gz_1 = \left(\frac{p_2}{\rho} + \frac{1}{2}\alpha_2 V_2^2 + gz_2\right) + w_s + \Delta H_{\text{losses}} \qquad (3.71)$$

To compute numerical values, we can use these approximations to be discussed in Chap. 6:

Laminar flow: $$u = U_0\left[1 - \left(\frac{r}{R}\right)^2\right]$$

from which $$V_{\text{av}} = 0.5U_0$$

and $$\alpha = 2.0 \qquad\qquad\qquad (3.72)$$

Turbulent flow: $$u \approx U_0\left(1 - \frac{r}{R}\right)^m \qquad m \approx \frac{1}{7}$$

from which, in Example 3.4,

$$V_{\text{av}} = \frac{2U_0}{(1 + m)(2 + m)}$$

Substituting into Eq. (3.70) gives

$$\alpha = \frac{(1 + m)^3 (2 + m)^3}{4(1 + 3m)(2 + 3m)} \tag{3.73}$$

and numerical values are as follows:

Turbulent flow:

m	$\frac{1}{5}$	$\frac{1}{6}$	$\frac{1}{7}$	$\frac{1}{8}$	$\frac{1}{9}$
α	1.106	1.077	1.058	1.046	1.037

These values are only slightly different from unity and are often neglected in elementary turbulent-flow analyses. However, α should never be neglected in laminar flow.

EXAMPLE 3.19

A hydroelectric power plant (Fig. E3.19) takes in 30 m³/s of water through its turbine and discharges it to the atmosphere at $V_2 = 2$ m/s. The head loss in the turbine and penstock system is $h_f = 20$ m. Assuming turbulent flow, $\alpha \approx 1.06$, estimate the power in MW extracted by the turbine.

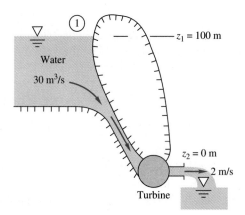

Fig. E3.19

Solution

We neglect viscous work and heat transfer and take section 1 at the reservoir surface (Fig. E3.19), where $V_1 \approx 0$, $p_1 = p_{atm}$, and $z_1 = 100$ m. Section 2 is at the turbine outlet. The steady-flow energy equation (3.71) becomes, in head form,

$$\frac{p_1}{\gamma} + \frac{\alpha_1 V_1^2}{2g} + z_1 = \frac{p_2}{\gamma} + \frac{\alpha_2 V_2^2}{2g} + z_2 + h_s + h_f$$

$$\frac{p_a}{\gamma} + \frac{1.06(0)^2}{2(9.81)} + 100 \text{ m} = \frac{p_a}{\gamma} + \frac{1.06(2.0 \text{ m/s})^2}{2(9.81 \text{ m/s}^2)} + 0 \text{ m} + h_s + 20 \text{ m}$$

The pressure terms cancel, and we may solve for the turbine head (which is positive):

$$h_s = 100 - 20 - 0.2 \approx 79.8 \text{ m}$$

The turbine extracts about 79.8 percent of the 100-m head available from the dam. The total power extracted may be evaluated from the water mass flow:

$$P = \dot{m} w_s = (\rho Q)(g h_s) = (998 \text{ kg/m}^3)(30 \text{ m}^3/\text{s})(9.81 \text{ m/s}^2)(79.8 \text{ m})$$

$$= 23.4 \text{ E6 kg} \cdot \text{m}^2/\text{s}^3 = 23.4 \text{ E6 N} \cdot \text{m/s} = 23.4 \text{ MW} \qquad \qquad Ans.$$

The turbine drives an electric generator which probably has losses of about 15 percent, so the net power generated by this hydroelectric plant is about 20 MW.

EXAMPLE 3.20

The pump in Fig. E3.20 delivers water (62.4 lbf/ft^3) at $3 \text{ ft}^3/\text{s}$ to a machine at section 2, which is 20 ft higher than the reservoir surface. The losses between 1 and 2 are given by $h_f = KV_2^2/(2g)$, where $K \approx 7.5$ is a dimensionless loss coefficient (see Sec. 6.7). Take $\alpha \approx 1.07$. Find the horsepower required for the pump if it is 80 percent efficient.

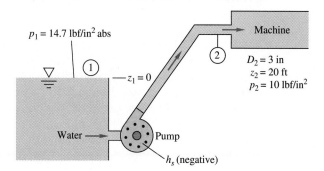

$p_1 = 14.7 \text{ lbf/in}^2 \text{ abs}$

Machine

(1)

(2)

$z_1 = 0$

$D_2 = 3 \text{ in}$
$z_2 = 20 \text{ ft}$
$p_2 = 10 \text{ lbf/in}^2$

Water

Pump

h_s (negative)

Fig. E3.20

Solution

If the reservoir is large, the flow is steady, with $V_1 \approx 0$. We can compute V_2 from the given flow rate and the pipe diameter:

$$V_2 = \frac{Q}{A_2} = \frac{3 \text{ ft}^2/\text{s}}{(\pi/4)(\frac{3}{12} \text{ ft})^2} = 61.1 \text{ ft/s}$$

The viscous work is zero because of the solid walls and near-one-dimensional inlet and exit. The steady-flow energy equation (3.71) becomes

$$\frac{p_1}{\gamma} + \frac{\alpha_1 V_1^2}{2g} + z_1 = \frac{p_2}{\gamma} + \frac{\alpha_2 V_2^2}{2g} + z_2 + h_s + h_f$$

Introducing $V_1 \approx 0$, $z_1 = 0$, and $h_f = KV_2^2/(2g)$, we may solve for the pump head:

$$h_s = \frac{p_1 - p_2}{\gamma} - z_2 - (\alpha_2 + K)\left(\frac{V_2^2}{2g}\right)$$

The pressures should be in lbf/ft^2 for consistent units. For the given data, we obtain

$$h_s = \frac{(14.7 - 10.0)(144) \text{ lbf/ft}^2}{62.4 \text{ lbf/ft}^3} - 20 \text{ ft} - (1.07 + 7.5)\frac{(61.1 \text{ ft/s})^2}{2(32.2 \text{ ft/s}^2)}$$

$$= 11 - 20 - 497 = -506 \text{ ft}$$

The pump head is negative, indicating work done *on* the fluid. As in Example 3.19, the power delivered is computed from

$$P = \dot{m} w_s = \rho Q g h_s = (1.94 \text{ slug/ft}^3)(3.0 \text{ ft}^3/\text{s})(32.2 \text{ ft/s}^2)(-507 \text{ ft}) = -94,900 \text{ ft} \cdot \text{lbf/s}$$

or $\quad \text{hp} = \dfrac{94,900 \text{ ft} \cdot \text{lbf/s}}{550 \text{ ft} \cdot \text{lbf/(s} \cdot \text{hp)}} \approx 173 \text{ hp}$

We drop the negative sign when merely referring to the "power" required. If the pump is 80 percent efficient, the input power required to drive it is

$$P_{\text{input}} = \frac{P}{\text{efficiency}} = \frac{173 \text{ hp}}{0.8} \approx 216 \text{ hp} \qquad\qquad Ans.$$

The inclusion of the kinetic-energy correction factor α in this case made a difference of about 1 percent in the result.

3.7 Frictionless Flow: The Bernoulli Equation

Closely related to the steady-flow energy equation is a relation between pressure, velocity, and elevation in a frictionless flow, now called the *Bernoulli equation*. It was stated (vaguely) in words in 1738 in a textbook by Daniel Bernoulli. A complete derivation of the equation was given in 1755 by Leonhard Euler. The Bernoulli equation is very famous and very widely used, but one should be wary of its restrictions—all fluids are viscous and thus all flows have friction to some extent. To use the Bernoulli equation correctly, one must confine it to regions of the flow which are nearly frictionless. This section (and, in more detail, Chap. 8) will address the proper use of the Bernoulli relation.

Consider Fig. 3.15, which is an elemental fixed streamtube control volume of variable area $A(s)$ and length ds, where s is the streamline direction. The properties (ρ, V, p) may vary with s and time but are assumed to be uniform over the cross section A. The streamtube orientation θ is arbitrary, with an elevation change $dz = ds \sin \theta$. Friction on the streamtube walls is shown and then neglected—a very restrictive assumption.

Conservation of mass (3.20) for this elemental control volume yields

$$\frac{d}{dt}\left(\int_{\text{CV}} \rho \, d\mathcal{V} \right) + \dot{m}_{\text{out}} - \dot{m}_{\text{in}} = 0 \approx \frac{\partial \rho}{\partial t} d\mathcal{V} + d\dot{m}$$

where $\dot{m} = \rho A V$ and $d\mathcal{V} \approx A \, ds$. Then our desired form of mass conservation is

Fig. 3.15 The Bernoulli equation for frictionless flow along a streamline: (*a*) forces and fluxes; (*b*) net pressure force after uniform subtraction of *p*.

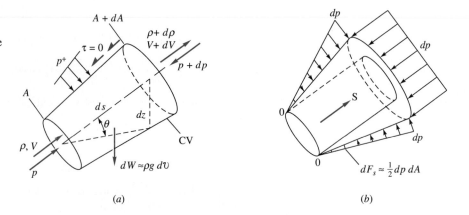

(a)   (b)

$$dm = d(\rho A V) = -\frac{\partial \rho}{\partial t} A \, ds \qquad (3.74)$$

This relation does not require an assumption of frictionless flow.

Now write the linear-momentum relation (3.37) in the streamwise direction:

$$\sum dF_s = \frac{d}{dt}\left(\int_{CV} V\rho \, d\mathcal{V}\right) + (\dot{m}V)_{\text{out}} - (\dot{m}V)_{\text{in}} \approx \frac{\partial}{\partial t}(\rho V) A \, ds + d(\dot{m}V)$$

where $V_s = V$ itself because s is the streamline direction. If we neglect the shear force on the walls (frictionless flow), the forces are due to pressure and gravity. The streamwise gravity force is due to the weight component of the fluid within the control volume:

$$dF_{s,\text{grav}} = -dW \sin \theta = -\gamma A \, ds \sin \theta = -\gamma A \, dz$$

The pressure force is more easily visualized, in Fig. 3.15b, by first subtracting a uniform value p from all surfaces, remembering from Fig. 3.7 that the net force is not changed. The pressure along the slanted side of the streamtube has a streamwise component which acts not on A itself but on the outer ring of area increase dA. The net pressure force is thus

$$dF_{s,\text{press}} = \tfrac{1}{2} dp \, dA - dp(A + dA) \approx -A \, dp$$

to first order. Substitute these two force terms into the linear-momentum relation:

$$\sum dF_s = -\gamma A \, dz - A \, dp = \frac{\partial}{\partial t}(\rho V) A \, ds + d(\dot{m}V)$$

$$= \frac{\partial \rho}{\partial t} VA \, ds + \frac{\partial V}{\partial t} \rho A \, ds + \dot{m} \, dV + V \, d\dot{m}$$

The first and last terms on the right cancel by virtue of the continuity relation (3.74). Divide what remains by ρA and rearrange into the final desired relation:

$$\frac{\partial V}{\partial t} ds + \frac{dp}{\rho} + V \, dV + g \, dz = 0 \qquad (3.75)$$

This is Bernoulli's equation for *unsteady frictionless flow along a streamline*. It is in differential form and can be integrated between any two points 1 and 2 on the streamline:

$$\int_1^2 \frac{\partial V}{\partial t} ds + \int_1^2 \frac{dp}{\rho} + \frac{1}{2}(V_2^2 - V_1^2) + g(z_2 - z_1) = 0 \qquad (3.76)$$

To evaluate the two remaining integrals, one must estimate the unsteady effect $\partial V/\partial t$ and the variation of density with pressure. At this time we consider only steady ($\partial V/\partial t = 0$) incompressible (constant-density) flow, for which Eq. (3.76) becomes

$$\frac{p_2 - p_1}{\rho} + \frac{1}{2}(V_2^2 - V_1^2) + g(z_2 - z_1) = 0$$

or

$$\frac{p_1}{\rho} + \frac{1}{2}V_1^2 + gz_1 = \frac{p_2}{\rho} + \frac{1}{2}V_2^2 + gz_2 = \text{const} \qquad (3.77)$$

This is the Bernoulli equation for steady frictionless incompressible flow along a streamline.

Relation between the Bernoulli and Steady-Flow Energy Equations

Equation (3.77) is a widely used form of the Bernoulli equation for incompressible steady frictionless streamline flow. It is clearly related to the steady-flow energy equation for a streamtube (flow with one inlet and one outlet), from Eq. (3.66), which we state as follows:

$$\frac{p_1}{\rho} + \frac{\alpha_1 V_1^2}{2} + gz_1 = \frac{p_2}{\rho} + \frac{\alpha_2 V_2^2}{2} + gz_2 + (\hat{u}_2 - \hat{u}_1 - q) + w_s + w_v \qquad (3.78)$$

This relation is much more general than the Bernoulli equation, because it allows for (1) friction, (2) heat transfer, (3) shaft work, and (4) viscous work (another frictional effect).

If we compare the Bernoulli equation (3.77) with the energy equation (3.78), we see that the Bernoulli equation contains even more restrictions than might first be realized. The complete list of assumptions for Eq. (3.77) is as follows:

1. *Steady flow*—a common assumption applicable to many flows.
2. *Incompressible flow*—acceptable if the flow Mach number is less than 0.3.
3. *Frictionless flow*—very restrictive, solid walls introduce friction effects.
4. *Flow along a single streamline*—different streamlines may have different "Bernoulli constants" $w_0 = p/\rho + V^2/2 + gz$, depending upon flow conditions.
5. *No shaft work between 1 and 2*—no pumps or turbines on the streamline.
6. *No heat transfer between 1 and 2*—either added or removed.

Thus our warning: Be wary of misuse of the Bernoulli equation. Only a certain limited set of flows satisfies all six assumptions above. The usual momentum or "mechanical force" derivation of the Bernoulli equation does not even reveal items 5 and 6, which are thermodynamic limitations. The basic reason for restrictions 5 and 6 is that heat transfer and work transfer, in real fluids, are married to frictional effects, which therefore invalidate our assumption of frictionless flow.

Figure 3.16 illustrates some practical limitations on the use of Bernoulli's equation (3.77). For the wind-tunnel model test of Fig. 3.16*a*, the Bernoulli equation is valid in the core flow of the tunnel but not in the tunnel-wall boundary layers, the model surface boundary layers, or the wake of the model, all of which are regions with high friction.

In the propeller flow of Fig. 3.16*b*, Bernoulli's equation is valid both upstream and downstream, but with a different constant $w_0 = p/\rho + V^2/2 + gz$, caused by the work addition of the propeller. The Bernoulli relation (3.77) is not valid near the propeller blades or in the helical vortices (not shown, see Fig. 1.12*a*) shed downstream of the blade edges. Also, the Bernoulli constants are higher in the flowing "slipstream" than in the ambient atmosphere because of the slipstream kinetic energy.

For the chimney flow of Fig. 3.16*c*, Eq. (3.77) is valid before and after the fire, but with a change in Bernoulli constant that is caused by heat addition. The Bernoulli equation is not valid within the fire itself or in the chimney-wall boundary layers.

The moral is to apply Eq. (3.77) only when all six restrictions can be satisfied: steady incompressible flow along a streamline with no friction losses, no heat transfer, and no shaft work between sections 1 and 2.

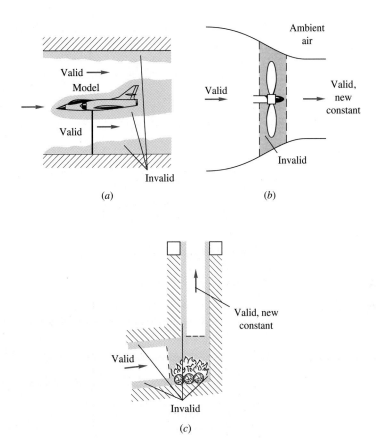

Fig. 3.16 Illustration of regions of validity and invalidity of the Bernoulli equation: (*a*) tunnel model, (*b*) propeller, (*c*) chimney.

Hydraulic and Energy Grade Lines

A useful visual interpretation of Bernoulli's equation is to sketch two grade lines of a flow. The *energy grade line* (EGL) shows the height of the total Bernoulli constant $h_0 = z + p/(\gamma) + V^2/(2g)$. In frictionless flow with no work or heat transfer, Eq. (3.77), the EGL has constant height. The *hydraulic grade line* (HGL) shows the height corresponding to elevation and pressure head $z + p/(\gamma)$, that is, the EGL minus the velocity head $V^2/(2g)$. The HGL is the height to which liquid would rise in a piezometer tube (see Prob. 2.12) attached to the flow. In an open-channel flow the HGL is identical to the free surface of the water.

Figure 3.17 illustrates the EGL and HGL for frictionless flow at sections 1 and 2 of a duct. The piezometer tubes measure the static-pressure head $z + p/\gamma$ and thus outline the HGL. The pitot stagnation-velocity tubes measure the total head $z + p/\gamma + V^2/(2g)$, which corresponds to the EGL. In this particular case the EGL is constant, and the HGL rises due to a drop in velocity.

In more general flow conditions, the EGL will drop slowly due to friction losses and will drop sharply due to a substantial loss (a valve or obstruction) or due to work extraction (to a turbine). The EGL can rise only if there is work addition (as from a pump or propeller). The HGL generally follows the behavior of the EGL with respect to losses or work transfer, and it rises and/or falls if the velocity decreases and/or increases.

As mentioned before, no conservation factors are needed in computations with the

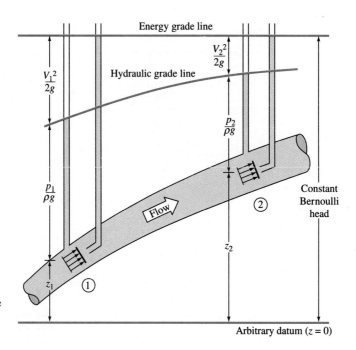

Fig. 3.17 Hydraulic and energy grade lines for frictionless flow in a duct.

Bernoulli equation if consistent SI or BG units are used, as the following examples will show.

In all Bernoulli-type problems in this text, we consistently take point 1 upstream and point 2 downstream.

EXAMPLE 3.21

Find a relation between nozzle discharge velocity V^2 and tank free-surface height h as in Fig. E3.21. Assume steady frictionless flow.

Fig. E3.21

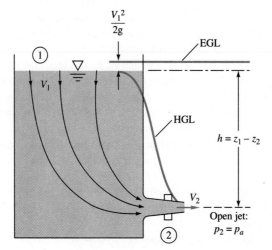

Solution

As mentioned, we always choose point 1 upstream and point 2 downstream. Try to choose points 1 and 2 where maximum information is known or desired. Here we select point 1 as the tank free surface, where elevation and pressure are known, and point 2 as the nozzle exit, where again pressure and elevation are known. The two unknowns are V_1 and V_2.

Mass conservation is usually a vital part of Bernoulli analyses. If A_1 is the tank cross section and A_2 the nozzle area, this is approximately a one-dimensional flow with constant density, Eq. (3.30),

$$A_1 V_1 = A_2 V_2 \qquad (1)$$

Bernoulli's equation (3.77) gives

$$\frac{p_1}{\rho} + \tfrac{1}{2} V_1^2 + g z_1 = \frac{p_2}{\rho} + \tfrac{1}{2} V_2^2 + g z_2$$

But since sections 1 and 2 are both exposed to atmospheric pressure $p_1 = p_2 = p_a$, the pressure terms cancel, leaving

$$V_2^2 - V_1^2 = 2g(z_1 - z_2) = 2gh \qquad (2)$$

Eliminating V_1 between Eqs. (1) and (2), we obtain the desired result:

$$V_2^2 = \frac{2gh}{1 - A_2^2/A_1^2} \qquad \text{Ans.} \quad (3)$$

Generally the nozzle area A_2 is very much smaller than the tank area A_1, so that the ratio A_2^2/A_1^2 is doubly negligible, and an accurate approximation for the outlet velocity is

$$V_2 \approx (2gh)^{1/2} \qquad \text{Ans.} \quad (4)$$

This formula, discovered by Evangelista Torricelli in 1644, states that the discharge velocity equals the speed which a frictionless particle would attain if it fell freely from point 1 to point 2. In other words, the potential energy of the surface fluid is entirely converted to kinetic energy of efflux, which is consistent with the neglect of friction and the fact that no net pressure work is done. Note that Eq. (4) is independent of the fluid density, a characteristic of gravity-driven flows.

Except for the wall boundary layers, the streamlines from 1 to 2 all behave in the same way, and we can assume that the Bernoulli constant h_0 is the same for all the core flow. However, the outlet flow is likely to be nonuniform, not one-dimensional, so that the average velocity is only approximately equal to Torricelli's result. The engineer will then adjust the formula to include a dimensionless *discharge coefficient* c_d

$$(V_2)_{\text{av}} = \frac{Q}{A_2} = c_d (2gh)^{1/2} \qquad (5)$$

As discussed in Sec. 6.10, the discharge coefficient of a nozzle varies from about 0.6 to 1.0 as a function of (dimensionless) flow conditions and nozzle shape.

Before proceeding with more examples, we should note carefully that a solution by Bernoulli's equation (3.77) does *not* require a control-volume analysis, only a selection of two points 1 and 2 along a given streamline. The control volume was used to derive the differential relation (3.75), but the integrated form (3.77) is valid all along the streamline for frictionless flow with no heat transfer or shaft work, and a control volume is not necessary.

EXAMPLE 3.22

Rework Example 3.21 to account, at least approximately, for the unsteady-flow condition caused by the draining of the tank.

Solution

Essentially we are asked to include the unsteady integral term involving $\partial V/\partial t$ from Eq. (3.76). This will result in a new term added to Eq. (2) from Example 3.21:

$$2 \int_1^2 \frac{\partial V}{\partial t} \, ds + V_2^2 - V_1^2 = 2gh \tag{1}$$

Since the flow is incompressible, the continuity equation still retains the simple form $A_1 V_1 = A_2 V_2$ from Example 3.21. To integrate the unsteady term, we must estimate the acceleration all along the streamline. Most of the streamline is in the tank region where $\partial V/\partial t \approx dV_1/dt$. The length of the average streamline is slightly longer than the nozzle depth h. A crude estimate for the integral is thus

$$\int_1^2 \frac{\partial V}{\partial t} \, ds \approx \int_1^2 \frac{dV_1}{dt} \, ds \approx \frac{dV_1}{dt} h \tag{2}$$

But since A_1 and A_2 are constant, $dV_1/dt \approx (A_2/A_1)(dV_2/dt)$. Substitution into Eq. (1) gives

$$2h \frac{A_2}{A_1} \frac{dV_2}{dt} + V_2^2 \left(1 - \frac{A_2^2}{A_1^2}\right) \approx 2gh \tag{3}$$

This is a first-order differential equation for $V_2(t)$. It is complicated by the fact that the depth h is variable $h = h(t)$, as determined by the variation in $V_1(t)$

$$h(t) = h_0 - \int_0^t V_1 \, dt \tag{4}$$

Equations (3) and (4) must be solved simultaneously, but the problem is well posed and can be handled analytically or numerically. We can also estimate the size of the first term in Eq. (3) by using the approximation $V_2 \approx (2gh)_{1/2}$ from the previous example. After differentiation, we obtain

$$2h \frac{A_2}{A_1} \frac{dV_2}{dt} \approx -\left(\frac{A_2}{A_1}\right)^2 V_2^2 \tag{5}$$

which is negligible if $A_2 \ll A_1$, as originally postulated.

EXAMPLE 3.23

A constriction in a pipe will cause the velocity to rise and the pressure to fall at section 2 in the throat. The pressure difference is a measure of the flow rate through the pipe. The smoothly necked-down system shown in Fig. E3.23 is called a *venturi tube*. Find an expression for the mass flux in the tube as a function of the pressure change.

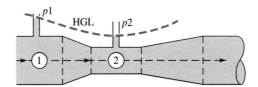

Fig. E3.23

Solution

Bernoulli's equation is assumed to hold along the center streamline

$$\frac{p_1}{\rho} + \tfrac{1}{2}V_1^2 + gz_1 = \frac{p_2}{\rho} + \tfrac{1}{2}V_2^2 + gz_2$$

If the tube is horizontal, $z_1 = z_2$ and we can solve for V_2:

$$V_2^2 - V_1^2 = \frac{2\,\Delta p}{\rho} \qquad \Delta p = p_1 - p_2 \tag{1}$$

We relate the velocities from the incompressible continuity relation

$$A_1V_2 = A_2V_2$$

or

$$V_1 = \beta^2 V^2 \qquad \beta = \frac{D_2}{D_1} \tag{2}$$

Combining (1) and (2), we obtain a formula for the velocity in the throat

$$V_2 = \left[\frac{2\,\Delta p}{\rho(1 - \beta^4)}\right]^{1/2} \tag{3}$$

The mass flux is given by

$$\dot{m} = \rho A_2 V_2 = A_2\left(\frac{2\rho\,\Delta p}{1 - \beta^4}\right)^{1/2} \tag{4}$$

This is the ideal frictionless mass flux. In practice, we measure $\dot{m}_{\text{actual}} = c_d\dot{m}_{\text{ideal}}$ and correlate the discharge coefficient c_d.

EXAMPLE 3.24

A 10-cm fire hose with a 3-cm nozzle discharges 1.5 m³/min to the atmosphere. Assuming frictionless flow, find the force F_B exerted by the flange bolts to hold the nozzle on the hose.

Solution

We use Bernoulli's equation and continuity to find the pressure p_1 upstream of the nozzle and then we use a control-volume momentum analysis to compute the bolt force, as in Fig. E3.24.

The flow from 1 to 2 is a constriction exactly similar in effect to the venturi in Example 3.23 for which Eq. (1) gave

$$p_1 = p_2 + \tfrac{1}{2}\rho(V_2^2 - V_1^2) \tag{1}$$

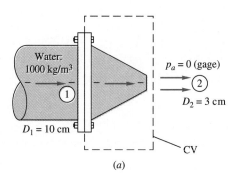

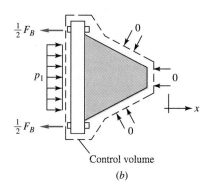

Fig. E3.24   (a)   (b)

The velocities are found from the known flow rate $Q = 1.5$ m^3/min or 0.025 m^3/s:

$$V_2 = \frac{Q}{A_2} = \frac{0.025 \text{ m}^3/\text{s}}{(\pi/4)(0.03 \text{ m})^2} = 35.4 \text{ m/s}$$

$$V_1 = \frac{Q}{A_1} = \frac{0.025 \text{ m}^3/\text{s}}{(\pi/4)(0.1 \text{ m})^2} = 3.2 \text{ m/s}$$

We are given $p_2 = p_a = 0$ gage pressure. Then Eq. (1) becomes

$$p_1 = \tfrac{1}{2}(1000 \text{ kg/m}^3)[(35.4^2 - 3.2^2) \text{ m}^2/\text{s}^2]$$

$$= 620,000 \text{ kg/(m} \cdot \text{s}^2) = 620,000 \text{ Pa gage}$$

The control-volume force balance is shown in Fig. E3.24b:

$$\sum F_x = -F_B + p_1 A_1$$

and the zero gage pressure on all other surfaces contributes no force. The x-momentum flux is $+\dot{m}V_2$ at the outlet and $-\dot{m}V_1$ at the inlet. The steady-flow momentum relation (3.40) thus gives

$$-F_B + p_1 A_1 = \dot{m}(V_2 - V_1)$$

or $$F_B = p_1 A_1 - \dot{m}(V_2 - V_1) \qquad (2)$$

Substituting the given numerical values, we find

$$\dot{m} = \rho Q = (1000 \text{ kg/m}^3)(0.025 \text{ m}^3/\text{s}) = 25 \text{ kg/s}$$

$$A_1 = \frac{\pi}{4} D_1^2 = \frac{\pi}{4}(0.1 \text{ m})^2 = 0.00785 \text{ m}^2$$

$$F_B = (620,000 \text{ N/m}^2)(0.00785 \text{ m}^2) - (25 \text{ kg/s})[(35.4 - 3.2) \text{ m/s}]$$

$$= 4872 \text{ N} - 805 \text{ (kg} \cdot \text{m)/s}^2 = 4067 \text{ N } (915 \text{ lbf}) \qquad \textit{Ans.}$$

This gives an idea of why it takes more than one firefighter to hold a fire hose at full discharge.

___

Notice from these examples that the solution of a typical problem involving Bernoulli's equation almost always leads to a consideration of the continuity equation as an equal partner in the analysis. The only exception is when the complete velocity distribution is already known from a previous or given analysis, but that means that the continuity relation has already been used to obtain the given information. The point is that the continuity relation is always an important element in a flow analysis.

Summary

This chapter has analyzed the four basic equations of fluid mechanics: conservation of (1) mass, (2) linear momentum, (3) angular momentum, and (4) energy. The equations were attacked ''in the large,'' i.e., applied to whole regions of a flow. As such, the typical analysis will involve an approximation of the flow field within the region, giving somewhat crude but always instructive quantitative results. However, the basic control-volume relations are rigorous and correct and will give exact results if applied to the exact flow field.

There are two main points to a control-volume analysis. The first is the selection of a proper, clever, workable control volume. There is no substitute for experience, but the following guidelines apply. The control volume should cut through the place where the information or solution is desired. It should cut through places where maximum information is already known. If the momentum equation is to be used, it should *not* cut through solid walls unless absolutely necessary, since this will expose possible unknown stresses and forces and moments which make the solution for the desired force difficult or impossible. Finally, every attempt should be made to place the control volume in a frame of reference where the flow is steady or quasi-steady, since the steady formulation is much simpler to evaluate.

The second main point to a control-volume analysis is the reduction of the analysis to a case which applies to the problem at hand. The 24 examples in this chapter give only an introduction to the search for appropriate simplifying assumptions. You will need to solve 24 or 124 more examples to become truly experienced in simplifying the problem just enough and no more. In the meantime, it would be wise for the beginner to adopt a very general form of the control-volume conservation laws and then make a series of simplifications to achieve the final analysis. Starting with the general form, one can ask a series of questions:

1. Is the control volume nondeforming or nonaccelerating?
2. Is the flow field steady? Can we change to a steady-flow frame?
3. Can friction be neglected?
4. Is the fluid incompressible? If not, is the perfect-gas law applicable?
5. Are gravity or other body forces negligible?
6. Is there heat transfer, shaft work, or viscous work?
7. Are the inlet and outlet flows approximately one-dimensional?
8. Is atmospheric pressure important to the analysis? Is the pressure hydrostatic on any portions of the control surface?
9. Are there reservoir conditions which change so slowly that the velocity and time rates of change can be neglected?

In this way, by approving or rejecting a list of basic simplifications like those above, one can avoid pulling Bernoulli's equation off the shelf when it does not apply.

References

1. D. T. Greenwood, *Principles of Dynamics*, Prentice-Hall, Englewood Cliffs, N.J., 1965.
2. T. von Kármán, *The Wind and Beyond*, Little, Brown, Boston, 1967.
3. J. P. Holman, *Heat Transfer*, 7th ed., McGraw-Hill, New York, 1990.
4. A. G. Hansen, *Fluid Mechanics*, Wiley, New York, 1967.
5. M. C. Potter and J. F. Foss, *Fluid Mechanics*, Ronald, New York, 1975.
6. G. J. Van Wylen and R. E. Sonntag, *Fundamentals of Classical Thermodynamics,* 3d ed., Wiley, New York, 1985.
7. W. C. Reynolds and H. C. Perkins, *Engineering Thermodynamics*, 2d ed., McGraw-Hill, New York, 1977.

PROBLEMS

In addition to many traditional problems, categorized in the problem distribution list below, there are several word problems, labeled W3.1 to W3.7, and a design project, denoted as D3.1.

Problem Distribution

Section	Topic	Problems
3.1	Basic physical laws; volume flow	3.1–3.8
3.2	Reynolds transport theorem	3.9–3.11
3.3	Conservation of mass	3.12–3.38
3.4	Linear-momentum equation	3.39–3.109
3.5	Angular-momentum theorem	3.110–3.125
3.6	Energy equation	3.126–3.146
3.7	Bernoulli's equation	3.147–3.182

3.1 Discuss Newton's second law (the linear-momentum relation) in these three forms:

$$\sum \mathbf{F} = m\mathbf{a} \qquad \sum \mathbf{F} = \frac{d}{dt}(m\mathbf{V})$$

$$\sum \mathbf{F} = \frac{d}{dt}\left(\int_{\text{system}} \mathbf{V}\rho \, d\mathcal{V} \right)$$

Are they all equally valid? Are they equivalent? Are some forms better for fluid mechanics as opposed to solid mechanics?

3.2 Consider the angular-momentum relation in the form

$$\sum \mathbf{M}_O = \frac{d}{dt}\left[\int_{\text{system}} (\mathbf{r} \times \mathbf{V})\rho \, d\mathcal{V} \right]$$

What does $\mathbf{r}$ mean in this relation? Is this relation valid in both solid and fluid mechanics? Is it related to the *linear-momentum* equation (Prob. 3.1)? In what manner?

3.3 For steady low-Reynolds-number (laminar) flow through a long tube (see Prob. 1.12), the axial velocity distribution is given by $u = C(R^2 - r^2)$, where R is the tube radius and $r \leq R$. Integrate $u(r)$ to find the total volume flow Q through the tube.

3.4 Discuss whether the following flows are steady or unsteady: (a) flow near an airplane moving at 900 km/h, (b) flow in a pipe as the downstream valve is opened at a uniform rate, (c) flow of a river past a bridge pier, (d) water motion near a beach as a uniform train of waves passes by, (e) flow over the spillway of a dam. Elaborate if these questions seem ambiguous.

3.5 A theory proposed by S. I. Pai in 1953 gives the following velocity values $u(r)$ for turbulent (high-Reynolds-number) airflow in a 4-cm-diameter tube:

r, cm	0	0.25	0.5	0.75	1.0	1.25	1.5	1.75	2.0
u, m/s	6.00	5.97	5.88	5.72	5.51	5.23	4.89	4.43	0.00

Comment on these data vis-à-vis laminar flow, Prob. 3.3. Estimate, as best you can, the total volume flow Q through the tube, in m³/s.

3.6 When a gravity-driven liquid jet issues from a slot in a tank, as in Fig. P3.6, an approximation for the exit velocity distribution is $u \approx \sqrt{2g(h - z)}$, where h is the depth of the jet centerline. Near the slot, the jet is horizontal, two-dimensional, and of thickness $2L$, as shown. Find an general expression for the total volume flow Q issuing from the slot; then take the limit of your result if $L \ll h$.

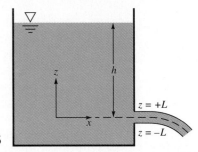

Fig. P3.6

3.7 Consider flow of a uniform stream U toward a circular cylinder of radius R, as in Fig. P3.7. An approximate theory for the velocity distribution near the cylinder is developed

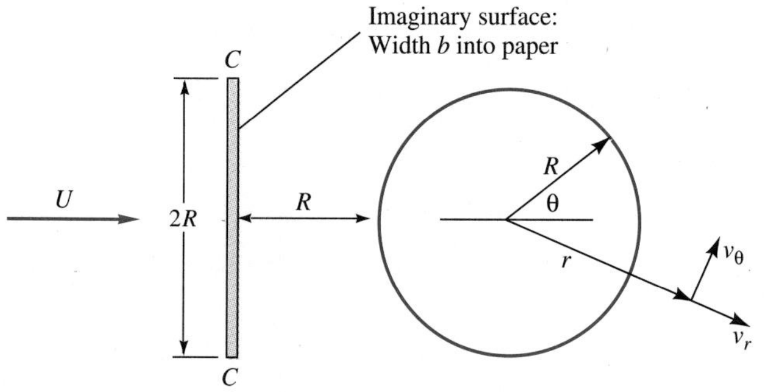

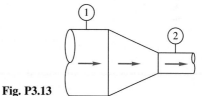

Fig. P3.7

in Chap. 8, in polar coordinates, for $r \geq R$:

$$v_r = U \cos \theta \left(1 - \frac{R^2}{r^2}\right) \qquad v_\theta = -U \sin \theta \left(1 + \frac{R^2}{r^2}\right)$$

where the positive directions for radial (v_r) and circumferential (v_θ) velocities are shown in Fig. P3.7. Compute the volume flow Q passing through the (imaginary) surface CC in the figure. Comment. (If CC were far upstream of the cylinder, the flow would be $Q = 2URb$.)

3.8 Oil (SG = 0.89) flows through a 24-in-diameter pipeline at 6500 gal/min. Compute (*a*) the volume flow in ft³/s, (*b*) the average velocity in ft/s, and (*c*) the mass flow in lbm/s.

3.9 A laboratory test tank contains seawater of salinity S and density ρ. Water enters the tank at conditions (S_1, ρ_1, A_1, V_1) and is assumed to mix immediately in the tank. Tank water leaves through an outlet A_2 at velocity V_2. If salt is a "conservative" property (neither created nor destroyed), use the Reynolds transport theorem to find an expression for the rate of change of salt mass M_{salt} within the tank.

3.10 Laminar steady flow, through a tube of radius R and length L, is being heated at the wall. The fluid entered the tube at uniform temperature $T_0 = T_w/3$. As the fluid exits the tube, its axial velocity and enthalpy profiles are approximated by

$$u = U_0 \left(1 - \frac{r^2}{R^2}\right) \qquad h = \frac{c_p T_w}{2} \left(1 + \frac{r^2}{R^2}\right)$$

$$c_p = \text{const}$$

(*a*) Sketch these profiles and comment on their physical realism. (*b*) Compute the total flux of enthalpy through the exit section.

3.11 A room contains dust of uniform concentration $C = \rho_{dust}/\rho$. It is to be cleaned up by introducing fresh air at velocity V_i through a duct of area A_i on one wall and exhausting the room air at velocity V_0 through a duct A_0 on the opposite wall. Find an expression for the instantaneous rate of change of dust mass within the room.

3.12 Water at 20°C flows steadily through a closed tank, as in

Fig. P3.12. At section 1, $D_1 = 6$ cm and the volume flow is 100 m³/h. At section 2, $D_2 = 5$ cm and the average velocity is 8 m/s. If $D_3 = 4$ cm, what is (*a*) Q_3 in m³/h and (*b*) average V_3 in m/s?

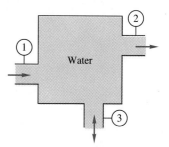

Fig. P3.12

3.13 Water at 20°C flows steadily at 40 kg/s through the nozzle in Fig. P3.13. If $D_1 = 18$ cm and $D_2 = 5$ cm, compute the average velocity, in m/s, at (*a*) section 1 and (*b*) section 2.

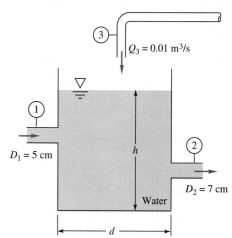

Fig. P3.13

3.14 The open tank in Fig. P3.14 contains water at 20°C and is being filled through section 1 at $V_1 = 3$ m/s and through section 3 at $Q_3 = 0.01$ m³/s. If the water level h is constant, determine the exit velocity V_2.

Fig. P3.14

3.15 Generalize Prob. 3.14 as follows. Let the volume flows (Q_1, Q_2, Q_3) be arbitrary, but assume the liquid is incompressible. Derive an expression for the water-level change dh/dt for the given tank size.

3.16 An incompressible fluid flows past an impermeable flat plate, as in Fig. P3.16, with a uniform inlet profile $u = U_0$ and a cubic polynomial exit profile

$$u \approx U_0 \left(\frac{3\eta - \eta^3}{2} \right) \qquad \text{where } \eta = \frac{y}{\delta}$$

Compute the volume flow Q across the top surface of the control volume.

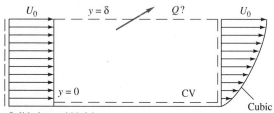

Solid plate, width b into paper

Fig. P3.16

3.17 Incompressible steady flow in the inlet between parallel plates in Fig. P3.17 is uniform, $u = U_0 = 8$ cm/s, while downstream the flow develops into the parabolic laminar profile $u = az(z_0 - z)$, where a is a constant. If $z_0 = 4$ cm and the fluid is SAE 30 oil at 20°C, what is the value of u_{max} in cm/s?

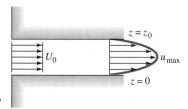

Fig. P3.17

3.18 Modify Prob. 3.17 as follows. Let the fluid be water at 20°C, so that the flow downstream is at higher Reynolds number and develops into a *turbulent* profile

$$u \approx u_{max}(2z/z_0)^{1/7} \qquad \text{for } 0 < z < \frac{z_0}{2}$$

and the flow is symmetric about the channel centerline. Estimate u_{max} in cm/s.

3.19 The tank in Fig. P3.19 admits water at 20°C and 75 N/s weight flow while ejecting gasoline at 60 N/s. If all fluids are approximately incompressible, how much air in N/h is passing through the vent? In which direction?

3.20 Oil (SG = 0.91) enters at section 1 in Fig. P3.20 at a weight flow of 250 N/h to lubricate a thrust bearing. The steady oil flow exits radially through the narrow clearance between thrust plates. Compute (*a*) the outlet volume flux in mL/s

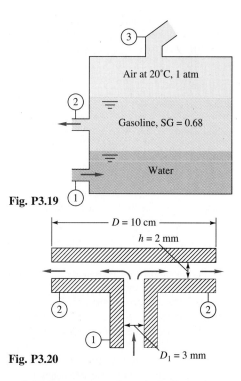

Fig. P3.19

Fig. P3.20

and (*b*) the average outlet velocity in cm/s.

3.21 A dehumidifier brings in saturated wet air (100 percent relative humidity) at 30°C and 1 atm, through an inlet of 8-cm diameter and average velocity 3 m/s. After some of the water vapor condenses and is drained off at the bottom, the somewhat drier air leaves at approximately 30°C, 1 atm, and 50 percent relative humidity. For steady operation, estimate the amount of water drained off in kg/h. (This problem is idealized from a real dehumidifier.)

3.22 The converging-diverging nozzle shown in Fig. P3.22 expands and accelerates dry air to supersonic speeds at the exit, where $p_2 = 8$ kPa and $T_2 = 240$ K. At the throat, $p_1 = 284$ kPa, $T_1 = 665$ K, and $V_1 = 517$ m/s. For steady compressible flow of an ideal gas, estimate (*a*) the mass flow in kg/h, (*b*) the velocity V_2, and (*c*) the Mach number Ma_2.

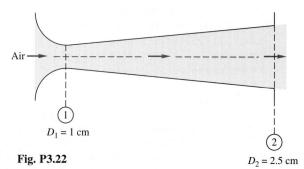

Fig. P3.22

3.23 The hypodermic needle in Fig. P3.23 contains some sort of serum (SG = 1.02). If the serum is to be injected steadily at 6 cm^3/s, how fast, in in/s, should the plunger be advanced? Neglect leakage in the plunger clearance.

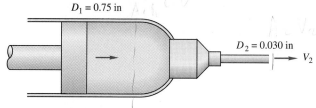

$D_1 = 0.75$ in

$D_2 = 0.030$ in

V_2

Fig. P3.23

3.24 Modify Prob. 3.23 as follows. Suppose that the leakage back past the plunger equals 10 percent of the needle flow. If the plunger is advanced at 0.5 in/s, how much serum will be delivered through the needle, in cm^3/s?

3.25 As will be discussed in Chaps. 7 and 8, the flow of a stream U_0 past a blunt flat plate creates a broad low-velocity wake behind the plate. A simple model is given in Fig. P3.25, with only half of the flow shown due to symmetry. The velocity profile behind the plate is idealized as "dead air" (near-zero velocity) behind the plate, plus a higher velocity, decaying vertically above the wake according to the variation $u \approx U_0 + \Delta U\, e^{-z/L}$, where L is the plate height and $z = 0$ is the top of the wake. Find Δu as a function of stream speed U_0.

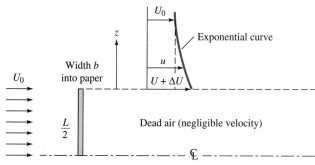

U_0

z

Exponential curve

u

Width b into paper

$U + \Delta U$

U_0

$\dfrac{L}{2}$

Dead air (negligible velocity)

$\mathcal{L}$

Fig. P3.25

3.26 A thin layer of liquid, draining from an inclined plane, as in Fig. P3.26, will have a laminar velocity profile $u \approx U_0(2y/h - y^2/h^2)$, where U_0 is the surface velocity. If the plane has width b into the paper, determine the volume rate of flow in the film.

3.27 Suppose that Fig. P3.26 represents a water-channel flow $h = 5$ ft with a turbulent velocity profile $u \approx U_0(y/h)^{1/7}$. If 6000 gal/min per foot of channel width is flowing down the slope, what is the value of the surface velocity U_0 in ft/s?

3.28 Consider a cylindrical water tank of diameter D and water depth h. According to elementary theory, the flow rate from

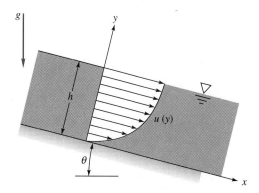

g

y

h

$u\,(y)$

θ

x

Fig. P3.26

a small hole of area A in the bottom of the tank would be $Q \approx CA\sqrt{2gh}$, where $C \approx 0.6$. If the initial water level is h_0 and the hole is opened, derive an expression for the time required for the water level to drop to $\frac{1}{2}h_0$.

3.29 In elementary compressible-flow theory (Chap. 9), compressed air will exhaust from a small hole in a tank at the mass flow rate $\dot{m} \approx C\rho$, where ρ is the air density in the tank and C is a constant. If ρ_0 is the initial density in a tank of volume $\mathcal{V}$, derive a formula for the density change $\rho(t)$ after the hole is opened. Apply your formula to the following case: a spherical tank of diameter 50 cm, with initial pressure 300 kPa and temperature 100°C, and a hole whose initial exhaust rate is 0.01 kg/s. Find the time required for the tank density to drop by 50 percent.

3.30 The V-shaped tank in Fig. P3.30 has width b into the paper and is filled from the inlet pipe at volume flow Q. Derive expressions for (a) the rate of change dh/dt and (b) the time required for the surface to rise from h_1 to h_2.

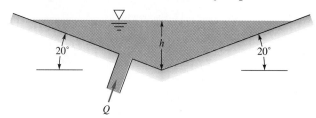

$20°$

h

$20°$

Q

Fig. P3.30

3.31 A bellows may be modeled as a deforming wedge-shaped volume as in Fig. P3.31. The check valve on the left (pleated) end is closed during the stroke. If b is the bellows width into the paper, derive an expression for outlet mass flow $\dot{m}_0$ as a function of stroke $\theta(t)$.

3.32 Traffic engineers have long noted that on any crowded highway the "number flux" of cars passing any given section increases with car speed up to about 50 mi/h and then decreases. The reason apparently is that drivers keep greater separation distance between cars at high speeds. Analyze

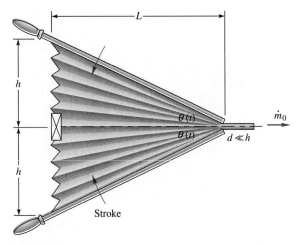

Fig. P3.31

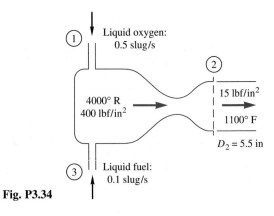

Fig. P3.34

this problem to determine whether there is indeed a maximum car flux when the separation distance is proportional to (a) car speed and (b) car speed squared. If a maximum is found at 50 mi/h, estimate the separation distance at this speed.

3.33 In some wind tunnels the test section is perforated to suck out fluid and provide a thin viscous boundary layer. The test section wall in Fig. P3.33 contains 1200 holes of 5-mm diameter each per square meter of wall area. The suction velocity through each hole is $V_s = 8$ m/s, and the test-section entrance velocity is $V_1 = 35$ m/s. Assuming incompressible steady flow of air at 20°C, compute (a) V_0, (b) V_2, and (c) V_f, in m/s.

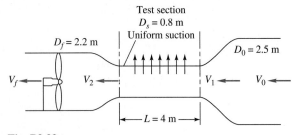

Fig. P3.33

3.34 A rocket motor is operating steadily, as shown in Fig. P3.34. The products of combustion flowing out the exhaust nozzle approximate a perfect gas with a molecular weight of 28. For the given conditions calculate V_2 in ft/s.

3.35 In contrast to the liquid rocket in Fig. P3.34, the solid-propellant rocket in Fig. P3.35 is self-contained and has no entrance ducts. Using a control-volume analysis for the conditions shown in Fig. P3.35, compute the rate of mass loss of the propellant, assuming that the exit gas has a molecular weight of 28.

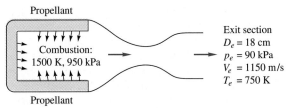

Fig. P3.35

3.36 The jet pump in Fig. P3.36 injects water at $U_1 = 40$ m/s through a 3-pipe and entrains a secondary flow of water $U_2 = 3$ m/s in the annular region around the small pipe. The two flows become fully mixed downstream, where U_3 is approximately constant. For steady incompressible flow, compute U_3 in m/s.

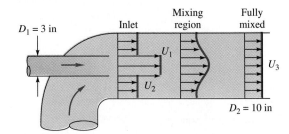

Fig. P3.36

3.37 When it's raining and you have on your new clothes and no umbrella, some say it's better to run and others say you should walk to keep drier. Suppose that it is raining straight down at a volume of q m³/s per meter of ground area. You have to go a distance L in the rain. Assume that a human approximates a box h high, b wide, and w deep. Analyze this situation to see if you keep drier walking at speed V_0 or running at speed $4V_0$.

3.38 An incompressible fluid in Fig. P3.38 is being squeezed outward between two large circular disks by the uniform down-

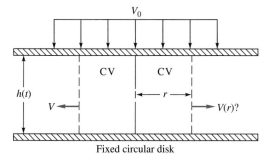

Fig. P3.38

ward motion V_0 of the upper disk. Assuming one-dimensional radial outflow, use the control volume shown to derive an expression for $V(r)$.

3.39 For the elbow duct in Fig. P3.39, SAE 30 oil at 20°C enters section 1 at 350 N/s, where the flow is laminar, and exits at section 2, where the flow is turbulent:

$$u_1 \approx V_{av,1}\left(1 - \frac{r^2}{R_1^2}\right) \qquad u_2 \approx V_{av,2}\left(1 - \frac{r}{R_2}\right)^{1/7}$$

Assuming steady incompressible flow, compute the force, and its direction, of the oil on the elbow due to momentum change only (no pressure change or friction effects) for (*a*) unit momentum-flux correction factors and (*b*) actual correction factors β_1 and β_2.

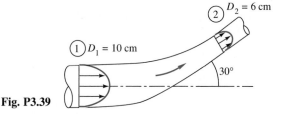

Fig. P3.39

3.40 The water jet in Fig. P3.40 strikes normal to a fixed plate. Neglect gravity and friction, and compute the force F in newtons required to hold the plate fixed.

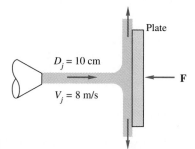

Fig. P3.40

3.41 In Fig. P3.41 the vane turns the water jet completely around.

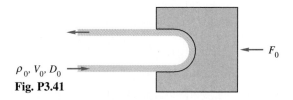

Fig. P3.41

Find an expression for the maximum jet velocity V_0 if the maximum possible support force is F_0.

3.42 A liquid of density ρ flows through the sudden contraction in Fig. P3.42 and exits to the atmosphere. Assume uniform conditions (p_1, V_1, D_1) at section 1 and (p_2, V_2, D_2) at section 2. Find an expression for the force F exerted by the fluid on the contraction.

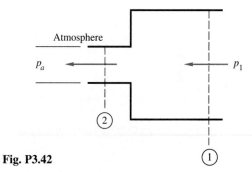

Fig. P3.42

3.43 Water at 20°C flows through a 5-cm-diameter pipe which has a 180° vertical bend, as in Fig. P3.43. The total length of pipe between flanges 1 and 2 is 75 cm. When the weight flow rate is 230 N/s, $p_1 = 165$ kPa and $p_2 = 134$ kPa. Neglecting pipe weight, determine the total force which the flanges must withstand for this flow.

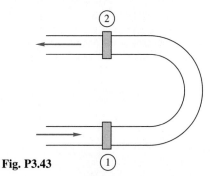

Fig. P3.43

3.44 When a uniform stream flows past an immersed thick cylinder, a broad low-velocity *wake* is created downstream, idealized as a V shape in Fig. P3.44. Pressures p_1 and p_2 are approximately equal. If the flow is two-dimensional and incompressible, with width b into the paper, derive a formula for the drag force F on the cylinder. Rewrite your result in the form of a dimensionless *drag coefficient* based on body length $C_D = F/(\rho U^2 bL)$.

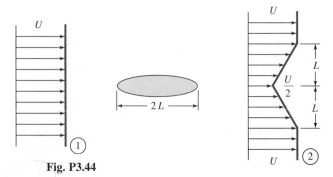

Fig. P3.44

3.45 In Fig. P3.45 a perfectly balanced weight and platform are supported by a steady water jet. If the total weight supported is 700 N, what is the proper jet velocity?

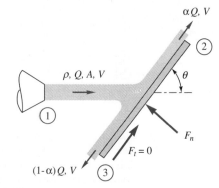

Fig. P3.45

3.46 When a jet strikes an inclined fixed plate, as in Fig. P3.46, it breaks into two jets at 2 and 3 of equal velocity $V = V_{\text{jet}}$ but unequal fluxes αQ at 2 and $(1 - \alpha)Q$ at section 3, α being a fraction. The reason is that for frictionless flow the fluid can exert no tangential force F_t on the plate. The condition $F_t = 0$ enables us to solve for α. Perform this analysis, and find α as a function of the plate angle θ. Why doesn't the answer depend upon the properties of the jet?

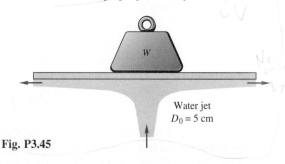

Fig. P3.46

3.47 A liquid jet of velocity V_j and diameter D_j strikes a fixed hollow cone, as in Fig. P3.47, and deflects back as a conical sheet at the same velocity. Find the cone angle θ for which the restraining force $F = \frac{3}{2}\rho A_j V_j^2$.

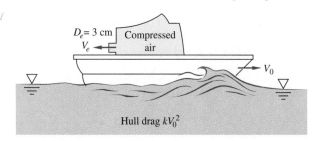

Fig. P3.47

3.48 The small boat in Fig. P3.48 is driven at a steady speed V_0 by a jet of compressed air issuing from a 3-cm-diameter hole at $V_e = 343$ m/s. Jet exit conditions are $p_e = 1$ atm and $T_e = 30°C$. Air drag is negligible, and the hull drag is kV_0^2, where $k \approx 19$ N $\cdot$ s^2/m^2. Estimate the boat speed V_0, in m/s.

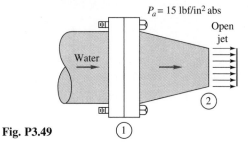

Fig. P3.48

3.49 The horizontal nozzle in Fig. P3.49 has $D_1 = 12$ in and $D_2 = 6$ in, with inlet pressure $p_1 = 38$ lbf/in^2 absolute and $V_2 = 56$ ft/s. For water at 20°C, compute the horizontal force provided by the flange bolts to hold the nozzle fixed.

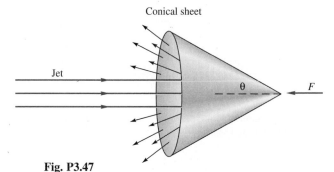

Fig. P3.49

3.50 The jet engine on a test stand in Fig. P3.50 admits air at 20°C and 1 atm at section 1, where $A_1 = 0.5$ m^2 and $V_1 = 250$ m/s. The fuel-to-air ratio is 1 : 30. The air leaves section

2 at atmospheric pressure and higher temperature, where $V_2 = 900$ m/s and $A_2 = 0.4$ m². Compute the horizontal test stand reaction R_x needed to hold this engine fixed.

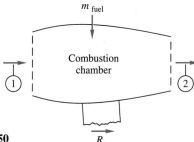

Fig. P3.50

3.51 A liquid jet of velocity V_j and area A_j strikes a single 180° bucket on a turbine wheel rotating at angular velocity Ω, as in Fig. P3.51. Derive an expression for the power P delivered to this wheel at this instant as a function of the system parameters. At what angular velocity is the maximum power delivered? How would your analysis differ if there were many, many buckets on the wheel, so that the jet was continually striking at least one bucket?

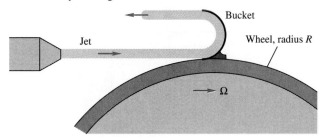

Fig. P3.51

3.52 The vertical gate in a water channel is partially open, as in Fig. P3.52. Assuming no change in water level and a hydrostatic pressure distribution, derive an expression for the streamwise force F_x on one-half of the gate as a function of $(\rho, h, w, \theta, V_1)$. Apply your result to the case of water at 20°C, $V_1 = 0.8$ m/s, $h = 2$ m, $w = 1.5$ m, and $\theta = 50°$.

3.53 Consider incompressible flow in the entrance of a circular tube, as in Fig. P3.53. The inlet flow is uniform, $u_1 = U_0$. The flow at section 2 is developed pipe flow. Find the wall drag force F as a function of (p_1, p_2, ρ, U_0, R) if the flow at section 2 is

(a) Laminar: $u_2 = u_{max}\left(1 - \dfrac{r^2}{R^2}\right)$

(b) Turbulent: $u_2 \approx u_{max}\left(1 - \dfrac{r}{R}\right)^{1/7}$

3.54 For the pipe-flow-reducing section of Fig. P3.54, $D_1 = 8$

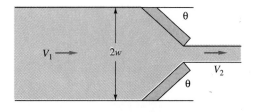

Top view

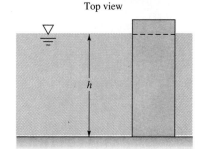

Fig. P3.52   Side view

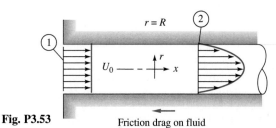

Fig. P3.53   Friction drag on fluid

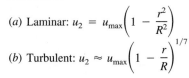

Fig. P3.54

cm, $D_2 = 5$ cm, and $p_2 = 1$ atm. All fluids are at 20°C. If $V_1 = 5$ m/s and the manometer reading is $h = 58$ cm, estimate the total force resisted by the flange bolts.

3.55 In Fig. P3.55 the jet strikes a vane which moves to the right at contant velocity V_c on a frictionless cart. Compute (a) the force F_x required to restrain the cart and (b) the power P delivered to the cart. Also find the cart velocity for which (c) the force F_x is a maximum and (d) the power P is a maximum.

3.56 For the flat-plate boundary-layer flow of Fig. 3.11, assume

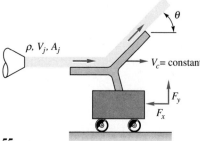

that the exit profile is given by $u \approx U_0 \sin[\pi y/(2\delta)]$ for water flow at 20°C: $U_0 = 3$ m/s, $\delta = 2$ mm, and $L = 45$ cm. Estimate the total drag force on the plate, in N, per unit depth into the paper.

3.57 Laminar-flow theory [Ref. 3 of Chap. 1, p. 260] gives the following expression for the wake behind a flat plate of length L (see Fig. P3.44 for a crude sketch of wake):

$$u = U\left[1 - \frac{0.664}{\pi}\left(\frac{L}{x}\right)^{1/2}\exp\left(-\frac{y^2\rho U}{4x\mu}\right)\right]$$

where U is the stream velocity, x is distance downstream of the plate, and $y = 0$ is the plane of the plate. Sketch two wake profiles, for $u_{min} = 0.9U$ and $u_{min} = 0.8U$. For these two profiles, evaluate the momentum-flux *defect*, i.e., the difference between the momentum of a uniform stream U and the actual wake profile. Comment on your results.

3.58 The water tank in Fig. P3.58 stands on a frictionless cart and feeds a jet of diameter 4 cm and velocity 8 m/s, which is deflected 60° by a vane. Compute the tension in the supporting cable.

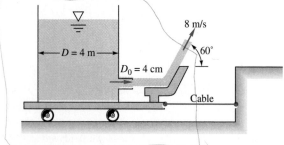

Fig. P3.58

3.59 When a pipe flow suddenly expands from A_1 to A_2, as in Fig. P3.59, low-speed, low-friction eddies appear in the corners and the flow gradually expands to A_2 downstream. Using the suggested control volume for incompressible steady flow and assuming that $p \approx p_1$ on the corner annular ring as shown, show that the downstream pressure is given by

$$p_2 = p_1 + \rho V_1^2 \frac{A_1}{A_2}\left(1 - \frac{A_1}{A_2}\right)$$

Neglect wall friction.

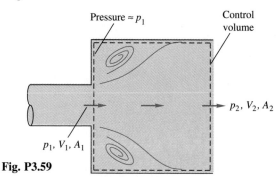

Fig. P3.59

3.60 Water at 20°C flows through the elbow in Fig. P3.60 and exits to the atmosphere. The pipe diameter is $D_1 = 10$ cm, while $D_2 = 3$ cm. At a weight flow rate of 150 N/s, the pressure $p_1 = 2.3$ atm (gage). Neglecting the weight of water and elbow, estimate the force on the flange bolts at section 1.

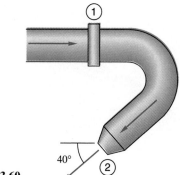

Fig. P3.60

3.61 A 20°C water jet strikes a vane mounted on a tank with frictionless wheels, as in Fig. P3.61. The jet turns and falls

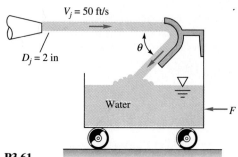

Fig. P3.61

into the tank without spilling out. If $\theta = 30°$, evaluate the horizontal force F required to hold the tank stationary.

3.62 Water at 20°C exits to the standard sea-level atmosphere through the split nozzle in Fig. P3.62. Duct areas are $A_1 = 0.02$ m² and $A_2 = A_3 = 0.008$ m². If $p_1 = 135$ kPa (absolute) and the flow rate is $Q_2 = Q_3 = 275$ m³/h, compute the force on the flange bolts at section 1.

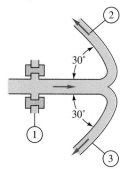

Fig. P3.62

3.63 The sluice gate in Fig. P3.63 can control and measure flow in open channels. At sections 1 and 2, the flow is uniform and the pressure is hydrostatic. The channel width is b into the paper. Neglecting bottom friction, derive an expression for the force F required to hold the gate. For what condition h_2/h_1 is the force largest? For very low velocity $V_1^2 \ll gh_1$, for what value of h_2/h_1 will the force be one-half of the maximum?

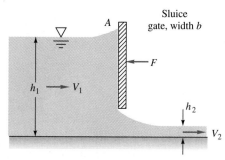

Fig. P3.63

3.64 The 6-cm-diameter 20°C water jet in Fig. P3.64 strikes a plate containing a hole of 4-cm diameter. Part of the jet passes through the hole, and part is deflected. Determine the horizontal force required to hold the plate.

3.65 The box in Fig. P3.65 has three 0.5-in holes on the right side. The volume flows of 20°C water shown are steady, but the details of the interior are not known. Compute the force, if any, which this water flow causes on the box.

3.66 The tank in Fig. P3.66 weighs 500 N empty and contains 600 L of water at 20°C. Pipes 1 and 2 have equal diameters

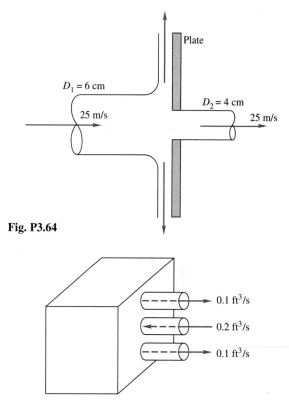

Fig. P3.64

Fig. P3.65

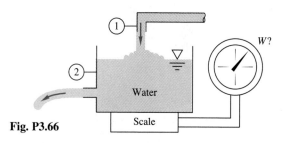

Fig. P3.66

of 6 cm and equal steady volume flows of 300 m³/h. What should the scale reading W be in N?

3.67 Gravel is dumped from a hopper, at a rate of 650 N/s, onto a moving belt, as in Fig. P3.67. The gravel then passes off the end of the belt. The drive wheels are 80 cm in diameter and rotate clockwise at 150 r/min. Neglecting system friction and air drag, estimate the power required to drive this belt.

3.68 The rocket in Fig. P3.68 has a supersonic exhaust, and the exit pressure p_e is not necessarily equal to p_a. Show that the force F required to hold this rocket on the test stand is

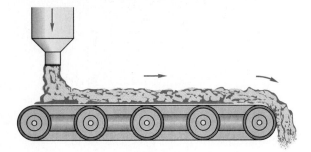

Fig. P3.67

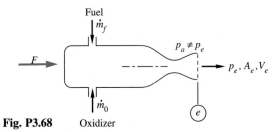

Fig. P3.68   Oxidizer

$F = \rho_e A_e V_e^2 + A_e(p_e - p_a)$. Is this force F what we term the *thrust* of the rocket?

3.69 The solution to Prob. 3.22 is a mass flow of 218 kg/h with $V_2 = 1060$ m/s and $Ma_2 = 3.41$. If the conical section 1–2 in Fig. P3.22 is 12 cm long, estimate the force on these conical walls caused by this high-speed gas flow.

3.70 The dredger in Fig. P3.70 is loading sand (SG = 2.6) onto a barge. The sand leaves the dredger pipe at 4 ft/s with a weight flux of 850 lbf/s. Estimate the tension on the mooring line caused by this loading process.

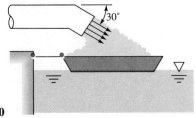

Fig. P3.70

3.71 Suppose that a deflector is deployed at the exit of the jet engine of Prob. 3.50, as shown in Fig. P3.71. What will the reaction R_x on the test stand be now? Is this reaction sufficient to serve as a braking force during airplane landing?

3.72 When immersed in a uniform stream, a thick elliptical cylinder creates a broad downstream wake, as idealized in Fig. P3.72. The pressure at the upstream and downstream sections are approximately equal, and the fluid is water at 20°C. If $U_0 = 4$ m/s and $L = 80$ cm, estimate the drag force on the cylinder per unit width into the paper. Also compute the

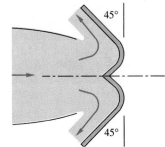

Fig. P3.71

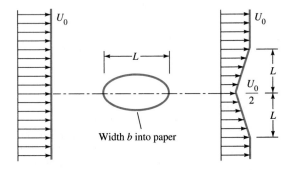

Width b into paper

Fig. P3.72

dimensionless drag coefficient $C_D = 2F/(\rho U_0^2 bL)$.

3.73 A pump in a tank of water at 20°C directs a jet at 45 ft/s and 200 gal/min against a vane, as shown in Fig. P3.73. Compute the force F to hold the cart stationary if the jet follows path A. The tank holds 250 gal of water.

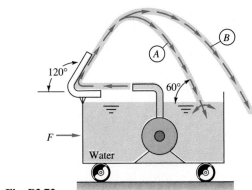

Fig. P3.73

3.74 Modify Prob. 3.73 to compute the force required if the jet follows path B. The tank holds 250 gal of water at this instant.

3.75 For the rocket engine of Prob. 3.34 compute the thrust in lbf if atmospheric pressure is 6 lbf/in^2.

3.76 The rocket engine of Prob. 3.35 has an initial mass of 250 kg and is mounted on the rear of a 1300-kg racing car. The rocket is fired up, and the car accelerates on level ground. If the car has an air drag of kV^2, where $k \approx 0.65$ N $\cdot$ s^2/m^2, and rolling resistance cV, where $c \approx 16$ N $\cdot$ s/m, estimate the velocity of the car after it travels 0.25 mi (1320 ft).

3.77 Water at 20°C flows steadily through a reducing pipe bend, as in Fig. P3.77. Known conditions are $p_1 = 350$ kPa, $D_1 = 25$ cm, $V_1 = 2.2$ m/s, $p_2 = 120$ kPa, and $D_2 = 8$ cm. Neglecting bend and water weight, estimate the total force which must be resisted by the flange bolts.

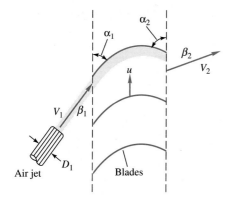

Fig. P3.77

3.78 A fluid jet of diameter D_1 enters a cascade of moving blades at absolute velocity V_1 and angle β_1, and it leaves at absolute velocity V_1 and angle β_2, as in Fig. P3.78. The blades move at velocity u. Derive a formula for the power P delivered to the blades as a function of these parameters.

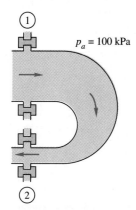

Fig. P3.78

3.79 Apply the analysis of Prob. 3.78 to the following specific case: air, $\rho = 1.2$ kg/m^3, $V_1 = 85$ m/s, $\beta_1 = 25°$, $\beta_2 = 55°$, and $u = 50$ m/s. Estimate (a) the outlet velocity V_2 and (b) the power P delivered to the blades, if $D_1 = 6$ cm.

3.80 A river of width b and depth h_1 passes over a submerged obstacle, or "drowned weir," in Fig. P3.80, emerging at a new flow condition (V_2, h_2). Neglect atmospheric pressure, and assume that the water pressure is hydrostatic at both sections 1 and 2. Derive an expression for the force exerted by the river on the obstacle in terms of V_1, h_1, h_2, b, ρ, and g. Neglect water friction on the river bottom.

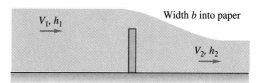

Fig. P3.80

3.81 Torricelli's idealization of efflux from a hole in the side of a tank is $V \approx \sqrt{2gh}$, as shown in Fig. P3.81. The tank weighs 250 N when empty and contains water at 20°C. The tank bottom is on very smooth ice (static friction coefficient $\zeta \approx 0.01$). For what water depth h will the tank just begin to move to the right?

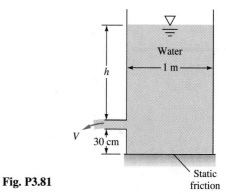

Fig. P3.81

3.82 The model car in Fig. P3.82 weighs 17 N and is to be accelerated from rest by a 1-cm-diameter water jet moving at 75 m/s. Neglecting air drag and wheel friction, estimate the velocity of the car after it has moved forward 1 m.

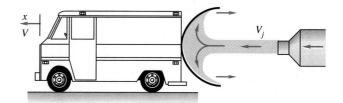

Fig. P3.82

3.83 Gasoline at 20°C is flowing at $V_1 = 12$ m/s in a 5-cm-diameter pipe when it encounters a 1-m length of uniform radial wall suction. At the end of this suction region, the average fluid velocity has dropped to $V_2 = 10$ m/s. If $p_1 = 120$ kPa, estimate p_2 if the wall friction losses are neglected.

3.84 Air at 20°C and 1 atm flows in a 25-cm-diameter duct at 15 m/s, as in Fig. P3.84. The exit is choked by a 90° cone, as shown. Estimate the force of the airflow on the cone.

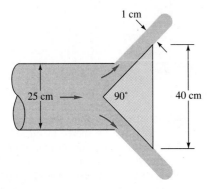

Fig. P3.84

3.85 The thin-plate orifice in Fig. P3.85 causes a large pressure drop. For 20°C water flow at 500 gal/min, with pipe $D = 10$ cm and orifice $d = 6$ cm, $p_1 - p_2 \approx 145$ kPa. If the wall friction is negligible, estimate the force of the water on the orifice plate.

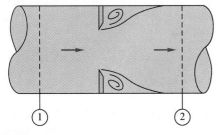

Fig. P3.85

3.86 For the water-jet pump of Prob. 3.36, add the following data: $p_1 = p_2 = 25$ lbf/in², and the distance between sections 1 and 3 is 80 in. If the average wall shear stress between sections 1 and 3 is 7 lbf/ft², estimate the pressure p_3. Why is it higher than p_1?

3.87 Figure P3.87 simulates a *manifold* flow, with fluid removed from a porous wall or perforated section of pipe. Assume incompressible flow with negligible wall friction and small suction $V_w \ll V_1$. If (p_1, V_1, V_w, ρ, D) are known, derive expressions for (a) V_2 and (b) p_2.

3.88 The boat in Fig. P3.88 is jet-propelled by a pump which develops a volume flow rate Q and ejects water out the stern at velocity V_j. If the boat drag force is $F = kV^2$, where k is

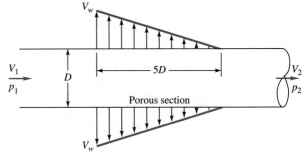

Fig. P3.87

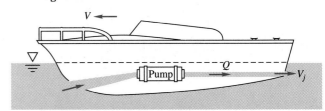

Fig. P3.88

a constant, develop a formula for the steady forward speed V of the boat.

3.89 Consider Fig. P3.36 as a general problem for analysis of a mixing ejector pump. If all conditions (p, ρ, V) are known at sections 1 and 2 and if the wall friction is negligible, derive formulas for estimating (a) V_3 and (b) p_3.

3.90 As shown in Fig. P3.90, a liquid column of height h is confined in a vertical tube of cross-sectional area A by a stopper. At $t = 0$ the stopper is suddenly removed, exposing the bottom of the liquid to atmospheric pressure. Using a control-volume analysis of mass and vertical momentum, derive the differential equation for the downward motion $V(t)$ of the liquid. Assume one-dimensional, incompressible, frictionless flow.

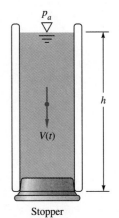

Fig. P3.90   Stopper

3.91 Extend Prob. 3.90 to include a linear (laminar) average wall shear stress resistance of the form $\tau \approx cV$, where c is a constant. Find the differential equation for dV/dt and then solve for $V(t)$, assuming for simplicity that the wall area remains constant.

3.92 A more involved version of Prob. 3.90 is the elbow-shaped tube in Fig. P3.92, with constant cross-sectional area A and diameter $D \ll h, L$. Assume incompressible flow, neglect friction, and derive a differential equation for dV/dt when the stopper is opened. *Hint:* Combine two control volumes, one for each leg of the tube.

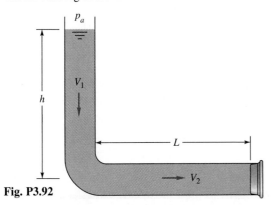

Fig. P3.92

3.93 Extend Prob. 3.92 to include a linear (laminar) average wall shear stress resistance of the form $\tau \approx cV$, where c is a constant. Find the differential equation for dV/dt and then solve for $V(t)$, assuming for simplicity that the wall area remains constant.

3.94 Attempt a numerical solution of Prob. 3.93 for SAE 30 oil at 20°C. Let $h = 20$ cm, $L = 15$ cm, and $D = 4$ mm. Use the laminar shear approximation from Sec. 6.4: $\tau \approx 8\mu V/D$, where μ is the fluid viscosity. Account for the decrease in wall area wetted by the fluid. Solve for the time required to empty (a) the vertical leg and (b) the horizontal leg.

3.95 Attempt a numerical solution of Prob. 3.93 for mercury at 20°C. Let $h = 20$ cm, $L = 15$ cm, and $D = 4$ mm. For mercury the flow will be *turbulent*, with the wall shear stress estimated from Sec. 6.4: $\tau \approx 0.005\rho V^2$, where ρ is the fluid density. Account for the decrease in wall area wetted by the fluid. Solve for the time required to empty (a) the vertical leg and (b) the horizontal leg. Compare with a frictionless flow solution.

3.96 Extend Prob. 3.90 to the case of the liquid motion in a frictionless U-tube whose liquid column is displaced a distance Z upward and then released, as in Fig. P3.96. Neglect the short horizontal leg and combine control-volume analyses for the left and right legs to derive a single differential equation for $V(t)$ of the liquid column.

3.97 Extend Prob. 3.96 to include a linear (laminar) average wall shear stress resistance of the form $\tau \approx 8\mu V/D$, where μ is

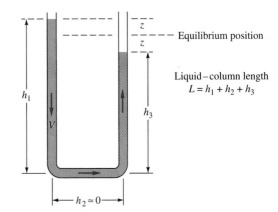

Fig. P3.96

the fluid viscosity. Find the differential equation for dV/dt and then solve for $V(t)$, assuming an initial desplacement $z = z_0$, $V = 0$ at $t = 0$. The result should be a damped oscillation tending toward $z = 0$.

3.98 Consider a rocket of initial mass M_0, steady exhaust mass flux $\dot{m}$, and exit velocity V_e relative to the rocket. The rocket moves straight up, as in Fig. P3.98. Set up the differential equation for rocket motion $V(t)$, and show that the solution is

$$V = -V_e \ln\left(1 - \frac{\dot{m}t}{M_0}\right) - gt$$

if air resistance is neglected and the flow pattern within the rocket is steady.

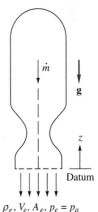

Fig. P3.98 $\rho_e, V_e, A_e, p_e = p_a$

3.99 Suppose that the rocket motor of Prob. 3.34 is attached to a missile which starts from rest at sea level and moves straight up, as in Fig. P3.98. If the system weighs 950 lbf, which includes 300 lbf of fuel and oxidizer, estimate the velocity and height of the missile (a) after 10 s and (b) after 20 s. Neglect air drag.

3.100 Suppose that the solid-propellant rocket of Prob. 3.35 is built into a missile of diameter 70 cm and length 4 m. The system weighs 1800 N, which includes 700 N of propellant. Neglect air drag. If the missile is fired vertically from rest at sea level, estimate (a) its velocity and height at fuel burnout and (b) the maximum height it will attain.

3.101 Modify Prob. 3.100 by accounting for air drag on the missile $F \approx C\rho D^2 V^2$, where $C \approx 0.02$, ρ is the air density, D is the missile diameter, and V is the missile velocity. Solve numerically for (a) the velocity and altitude at burnout and (b) the maximum altitude attained.

3.102 As can often be seen in a kitchen sink when the faucet is running, a high-speed channel flow (V_1, h_1) may "jump" to a low-speed, low-energy condition (V_2, h_2) as in Fig. P3.102. The pressure at sections 1 and 2 is approximately hydrostatic, and wall friction is negligible. Use the continuity and momentum relations to find h_2 and V_2 in terms of (h_1, V_1).

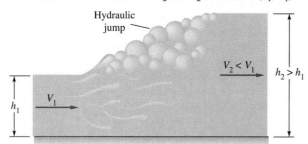

Fig. P3.102

3.103 Suppose that the solid-propellant rocket of Prob. 3.35 is mounted on a 1000-kg car to propel it up a long slope of 15°. The rocket motor weighs 900 N, which includes 500 N of propellant. If the car starts from rest when the rocket is fired, and if air drag and wheel friction are neglected, estimate the maximum distance that the car will travel up the hill.

3.104 A rocket is attached to a rigid horizontal rod hinged at the origin as in Fig. P3.104. Its initial mass is M_0, and its exit properties are $\dot{m}$ and V_e relative to the rocket. Set up the differential equation for rocket motion, and solve for the angular velocity $\omega(t)$ of the rod. Neglect gravity, air drag, and the rod mass.

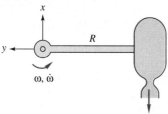

Fig. P3.104

3.105 Extend Prob. 3.104 to the case where the rocket has a linear air drag force $F = cV$, where c is a constant. Assuming no burnout, solve for $\omega(t)$ and find the *terminal* angular velocity, i.e., the final motion when the angular acceleration is zero. Apply to the case $M_0 = 6$ kg, $R = 3$ m, $m = 0.05$ kg/s, $V_e = 1100$ m/s, and $c = 0.075$ N·s/m to find the angular velocity after 12 s of burning.

3.106 Extend Prob. 3.104 to the case where the rocket has a quadratic air drag force $F = kV^2$, where k is a constant. Assuming no burnout, solve for $\omega(t)$ and find the *terminal* angular velocity, i.e., the final motion when the angular acceleration is zero. Apply to the case $M_0 = 6$ kg, $R = 3$ m, $m = 0.05$ kg/s, $V_e = 1100$ m/s, and $k = 0.0011$ N·s^2/m^2 to find the angular velocity after 12 s of burning.

3.107 The cart in Fig. P3.107 moves at constant velocity $V_0 = 12$ m/s and takes on water with a scoop 80 cm wide which dips $h = 2.5$ cm into a pond. Neglect air drag and wheel friction. Estimate the force required to keep the cart moving.

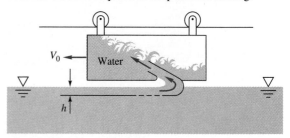

Fig. P3.107

3.108 A rocket sled of mass M is to be decelerated by a scoop, as in Fig. P3.108, which has width b into the paper and dips into the water a depth h, creating an upward jet at 60°. The rocket thrust is T to the left. Let the initial velocity be V_0, and neglect air drag and wheel friction. Find an expression for $V(t)$ of the sled for (a) $T = 0$ and (b) finite $T \neq 0$.

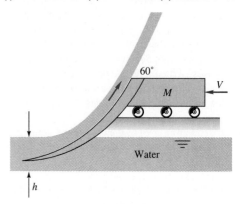

Fig. P3.108

3.109 Apply Prob. 3.108 to the following case: $M_{\text{total}} = 900$ kg,

$b = 60$ cm, $h = 2$ cm, $V_0 = 120$ m/s, with the rocket of Prob. 3.35 attached and burning. Estimate V after 3 s.

3.110 The horizontal lawn sprinkler in Fig. P3.110 has a water flow rate of 4.0 gal/min introduced vertically through the center. Estimate (*a*) the retarding torque required to keep the arms from rotating and (*b*) the rotation rate (r/min) if there is no retarding torque.

3.111 In Prob. 3.60 find the torque caused around flange 1 if the center point of exit 2 is 1.2 m directly below the flange center.

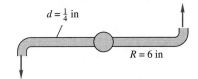

$d = \frac{1}{4}$ in

$R = 6$ in

Fig. P3.110

3.112 The wye joint in Fig. P3.112 splits the pipe flow into equal amounts $Q/2$, which exit, as shown, a distance R_0 from the axis. Neglect gravity and friction. Find an expression for the torque T about the x axis required to keep the system rotating at angular velocity Ω.

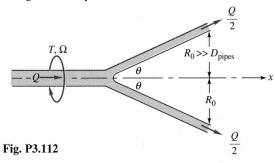

T, Ω

Q

$\dfrac{Q}{2}$

$R_0 \gg D_{pipes}$

θ

θ

R_0

x

$\dfrac{Q}{2}$

Fig. P3.112

3.113 Modify Example 3.14 so that the arm starts from rest and spins up to its final rotation speed. The moment of inertia of the arm about O is I_0. Neglecting air drag, find $d\omega/dt$ and integrate to determine the angular velocity $\omega(t)$, assuming $\omega = 0$ at $t = 0$.

3.114 The three-arm lawn sprinkler of Fig. P3.114 receives 20°C

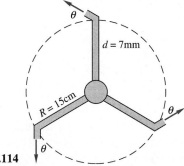

θ

$d = 7$mm

$R = 15$cm

θ

θ

Fig. P3.114

water through the center at 2.7 m³/h. If collar friction is negligible, what is the steady rotation rate in r/min for (*a*) $\theta = 0°$ and (*b*) $\theta = 40°$?

3.115 Water at 20°C flows at 30 gal/min through the 0.75-in-diameter double pipe bend of Fig. P3.115. The pressures are $p_1 = 30$ lbf/in² and $p_2 = 24$ lbf/in². Compute the torque T at point B necessary to keep the pipe from rotating.

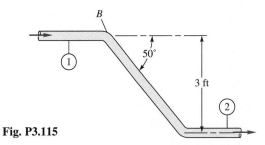

B

(1)

50°

3 ft

(2)

Fig. P3.115

3.116 The centrifugal pump of Fig. P3.116 has a flow rate Q and exits the impeller at an angle θ_2 relative to the blades, as shown. The fluid enters axially at section 1. Assuming incompressible flow at shaft angular velocity ω, derive a formula for the power P required to drive the impeller.

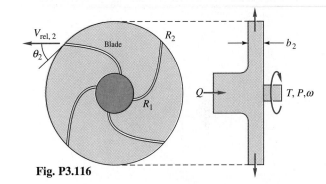

$V_{rel, 2}$

θ_2

Blade

R_2

R_1

b_2

Q

T, P, ω

Fig. P3.116

3.117 Apply Prob. 3.116 to the following case: water at 20°C, $Q = 1400$ gal/min, $R_1 = 9$ cm, $R_2 = 18$ cm, $b_2 = 3$ cm, $\theta_2 = 40°$, rotation rate of 1200 r/min. Estimate the power P, in W, required to drive the impeller.

3.118 Reverse the flow in Fig. P3.116, so that the system operates as a radial-inflow *turbine*. Assuming that the outflow into section 1 has no tangential velocity, derive an expression for the power P extracted by the turbine.

3.119 Revisit the turbine cascade system of Prob. 3.78, and derive a formula for the power P delivered, using the *angular-momentum* theorem of Eq. (3.55).

3.120 A centrifugal pump impeller delivers 4000 gal/min of water at 20°C with a shaft rotation rate of 1750 r/min. Neglect losses. If $r_1 = 6$ in, $r_2 = 14$ in, $b_1 = b_2 = 1.75$ in, $V_{t1} = 10$ ft/s, and $V_{t2} = 110$ ft/s, compute the absolute velocities

(a) V_1 and (b) V_2 and (c) the horsepower required. (d) Compare with the ideal horsepower required.

3.121 The pipe bend of Fig. P3.121 has $D_1 = 27$ cm and $D_2 = 13$ cm. When water at 20°C flows through the pipe at 4000 gal/min, $p_1 = 194$ kPa (gage). Compute the torque required at point B to hold the bend stationary.

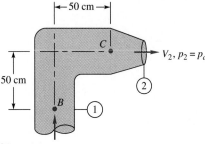

Fig. P3.121

3.122 Extend Prob. 3.46 to the problem of computing the center of pressure L of the normal face F_n, as in Fig. P3.122. (At the center of pressure, no moments are required to hold the plate at rest.) Neglect friction. Express your result in terms of the sheet thickness h_1 and the angle θ between the plate and the oncoming jet 1.

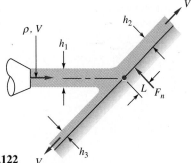

Fig. P3.122

3.123 The waterwheel in Fig. P3.123 is being driven at 200 r/min by a 150-ft/s jet of water at 20°C. The jet diameter is 2.5 in. Assuming no losses, what is the horsepower developed by the wheel? For what speed Ω r/min will the horsepower developed be a maximum? Assume that there are many buckets on the waterwheel.

3.124 A rotating dishwasher arm delivers at 60°C to six nozzles, as in Fig. P3.124. The total flow rate is 3.0 gal/min. Each nozzle has a diameter of $\frac{3}{16}$ in. If the nozzle flows are equal and friction is neglected, estimate the steady rotation rate of the arm, in r/min.

3.125 A liquid of density ρ flows through a 90° bend as shown in Fig. P3.125 and issues vertically from a uniformly porous section of length L. Neglecting pipe and liquid weight, de-

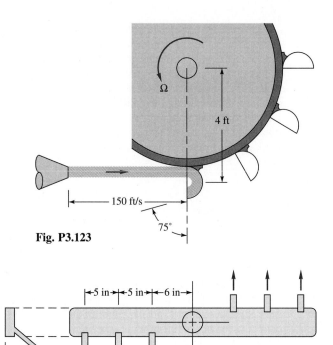

Fig. P3.123

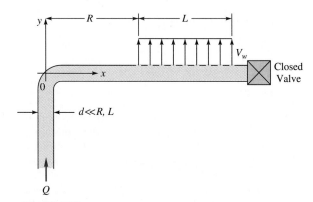

Fig. P3.124

Fig. P3.125

rive an expression for the torque M at point 0 required to hold the pipe stationary.

3.126 Given is steady isothermal flow of water at 20°C through the device in Fig. P3.126. Heat-transfer, gravity, and temperature effects are negligible. Known data are $D_1 = 9$ cm, $Q_1 = 220$ m³/h, $p_1 = 150$ kPa, $D_2 = 7$ cm, $Q_2 = 100$ m³/h, $p_2 = 225$ kPa, $D_3 = 4$ cm, and $p_3 = 265$ kPa. Compute the rate of shaft work done for this device and its direction.

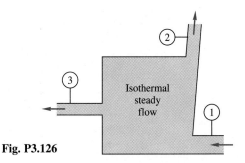

Fig. P3.126

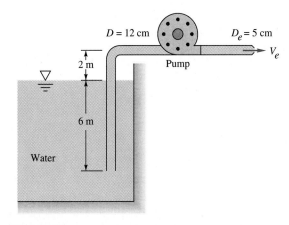

Fig. P3.130

3.127 A power plant on a river, as in Fig. P3.127, must eliminate 55 MW of waste heat to the river. The river conditions upstream are $Q_i = 2.5$ m³/s and $T_i = 18°C$. The river is 45 m wide and 2.7 m deep. If heat losses to the atmosphere and ground are negligible, estimate the downstream river conditions (Q_0, T_0).

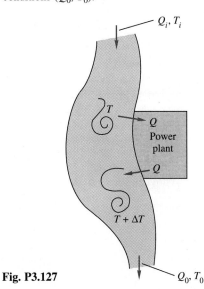

Fig. P3.127

3.128 For the conditions of Prob. 3.127, if the power plant is to heat the nearby river water by no more than 12°C, what should be the minimum flow rate Q, in m³/s, through the plant heat exchanger? How will the value of Q affect the downstream conditions (Q_0, T_0)?

3.129 Multnomah Falls in the Columbia River Gorge has a sheer drop of 543 ft. Using the steady-flow energy equation, estimate the water temperature change in °F caused by this drop.

3.130 When the pump in Fig. P3.130 draws 220 m³/h of water at 20°C from the reservoir, the total friction head loss is 5 m. The flow discharges through a nozzle to the atmosphere. Estimate the pump power in kW delivered to the water.

3.131 When the pump in Fig. P3.130 delivers 25 kW of power to

the water, the friction head loss is 4 m. Estimate (a) the exit velocity V_e and (b) the flow rate Q.

3.132 If shaft work and kinetic-energy changes are negligible in the horizontal laminar pipe flow of Prob. 3.10, find an expression for the total heat transfer dQ/dt from the tube walls to the fluid.

3.133 The long pipe in Fig. P3.133 is filled with water at 20°C. When valve A is closed, $p_1 - p_2 = 75$ kPa. When the valve is open and water flows at 500 m³/h, $p_1 - p_2 = 160$ kPa. What is the friction head loss between 1 and 2, in m, for the flowing condition?

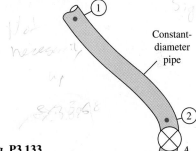

Fig. P3.133

3.134 A 36-in-diameter pipeline carries oil (SG = 0.89) at 1 million barrels per day (bbl/day) (1 bbl = 42 U.S. gal). The friction head loss is 13 ft/1000 ft of pipe. It is planned to place pumping stations every 10 mi along the pipe. Estimate the horsepower which must be delivered to the oil by each pump.

3.135 The *pump-turbine* system in Fig. P3.135 draws water from the upper reservoir in the daytime to produce power for a city. At night, it pumps water from lower to upper reservoirs to restore the situation. For a design flow rate of 15,000 gal/min in either direction, the friction head loss is 17 ft. Estimate the power in kW (a) extracted by the turbine and (b) delivered by the pump.

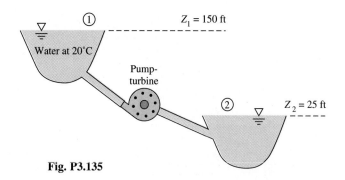

Fig. P3.135

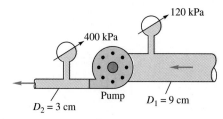

Fig. P3.139

3.136 A pump is to deliver water at 20°C from a pond to an elevated tank. The pump is 1 m above the pond, and the tank free surface is 20 m above the pump. The head loss in the system is $h_f \approx cQ^2$, where $c = 0.08$ h²/m⁵. If the pump is 72 percent efficient and is driven by a 500-W motor, what flow rate Q m³/h will result?

3.137 A fireboat draws seawater (SG = 1.025) from a submerged pipe and discharges it through a nozzle, as in Fig. P3.137. The total head loss is 6.5 ft. If the pump efficiency is 75 percent, what horsepower motor is required to drive it?

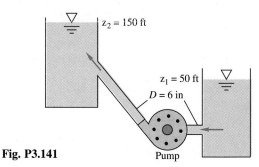

Fig. P3.141

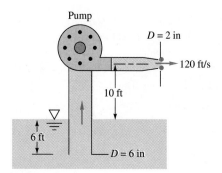

Fig. P3.137

3.138 Air enters a steady-flow compressor at 20°C, 100 kPa, and 15 m/s and is discharged at 45°C, 225 kPa, and 65 m/s. The weight flow is 400 N/min, and heat losses are 1200 W. Compute the rate of shaft work, in kW, of this compressor.

3.139 The horizontal pump in Fig. P3.139 discharges 20°C water at 57 m³/h. Neglecting losses, what power in kW is delivered to the water by the pump?

3.140 Steam enters a horizontal turbine at 350 lbf/in² absolute, 580°C, and 12 ft/s and is discharged at 110 ft/s and 25°C saturated conditions. The mass flow is 2.5 lbm/s, and the heat losses are 7 Btu/lb of steam. If head losses are negligible, how much horsepower does the turbine develop?

3.141 Water at 20°C is pumped at 1500 gal/min from the lower to the upper reservoir, as in Fig. P3.141. Pipe friction losses

are approximated by $h_f \approx 27V^2/(2g)$, where V is the average velocity in the pipe. If the pump is 75 percent efficient, what horsepower is needed to drive it?

3.142 A typical pump has a head which, for a given shaft rotation rate, varies with the flow rate, resulting in a *pump performance curve* as in Fig. P3.142. Suppose that this pump is 75 percent efficient and is used for the system in Prob. 3.141. Estimate (*a*) the flow rate, in gal/min, and (*b*) the horsepower needed to drive the pump.

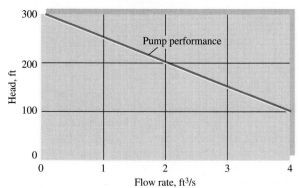

Fig. P3.142

3.143 The insulated tank in Fig. P3.143 is to be filled from a high-pressure air supply. Initial conditions in the tank are $T = 20$°C and $p = 200$ kPa. When the valve is opened, the initial mass flow rate into the tank is 0.013 kg/s. Assuming an ideal gas, estimate the initial rate of temperature rise of the air in the tank.

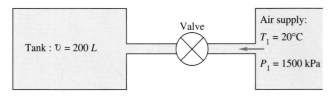

Fig. P3.143

3.144 The pump in Fig. P3.144 creates a 20°C water jet oriented to travel a maximum horizontal distance. System friction head losses are 6.5 m. The jet may be approximated by the trajectory of frictionless particles. What power must be delivered by the pump?

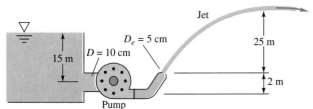

Fig. P3.144

3.145 The large turbine in Fig. P3.145 diverts the river flow under a dam as shown. System friction losses are $h_f = 3.5V^2/(2g)$, where V is the average velocity in the supply pipe. For what river flow rate in m³/s will the power extracted be 25 MW? Which of the *two* possible solutions has a better "conversion efficiency"?

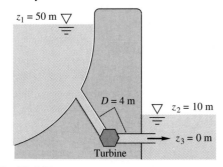

Fig. P3.145

3.146 Kerosine at 20°C flows through the pump in Fig. P3.146 at 2.3 ft³/s. Head losses between 1 and 2 are 8 ft, and the pump delivers 8 hp to the flow. What should the mercury-manometer reading h ft be?

3.147 Repeat Prob. 3.49 by assuming that p_1 is unknown and using Bernoulli's equation with no losses. Compute the new bolt force for this assumption. What is the head loss between 1 and 2 for the data of Prob. 3.49?

3.148 Reanalyze Prob. 3.54 to estimate the manometer reading h

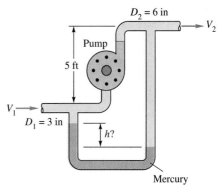

Fig. P3.146

if Bernoulli's equation is valid with zero losses. For the reading $h \approx 58$ cm in Prob. 3.54, what is the head loss between sections 1 and 2?

3.149 A jet of alcohol strikes the vertical plate in Fig. P3.149. A force $F \approx 425$ N is required to hold the plate stationary. Assuming there are no losses in the nozzle, estimate (a) the mass flow rate of alcohol and (b) the absolute pressure at section 1.

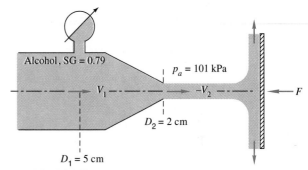

Fig. P3.149

3.150 Verify that Bernoulli's equation is not valid for the sudden expansion of Prob. 3.59 and that the actual head loss is given by

$$h_f \approx \frac{V^2}{2g}\left(1 - \frac{A_1}{A_2}\right)^2$$

See Sec. 6.7 for further details.

3.151 In Prob. 3.63 the velocity approaching the sluice gate was assumed to be known. If Bernoulli's equation is valid with no losses, derive an expression for V_1 as a function of only h_1, h_2, and g.

3.152 A free liquid jet, as in Fig. P3.152, has constant ambient pressure and small losses; hence from Bernoulli's equation $z + V^2/(2g)$ is constant along the jet. For the fire nozzle in the figure, what are (a) the minimum and (b) the maximum values of θ for which the water jet will clear the corner of

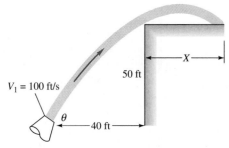

Fig. P3.152

the building? For which case will the jet velocity be higher when it strikes the roof of the building?

3.153 For the container of Fig. P3.153 use Bernoulli's equation to derive a formula for the distance X where the free jet leaving horizontally will strike the floor, as a function of h and H. For what ratio h/H will X be maximum? Sketch the three trajectories for $h/H = 0.4, 0.5$, and 0.6.

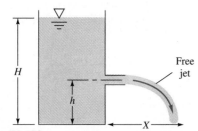

Fig. P3.153

3.154 In Fig. P3.154 the exit nozzle is horizontal. If losses are negligible, what should the water level h cm be for the free jet to just clear the wall?

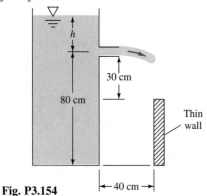

Fig. P3.154

3.155 Bernoulli's 1738 treatise *Hydrodynamica* contains many excellent sketches of flow patterns related to his frictionless relation. One, however, redrawn here as Fig. P3.155, seems physically misleading. Can you explain what might be

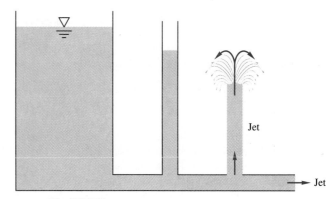

Fig. P3.155

wrong with the figure?

3.156 A blimp cruises at 65 mi/h through sea-level standard air. A differential pressure transducer connected between the nose and the side of the blimp registers 800 Pa. Estimate (*a*) the absolute pressure at the nose and (*b*) the absolute velocity of the air near the blimp side.

3.157 The manometer fluid in Fig. P3.157 is mercury. Estimate the volume flow in the tube if the flowing fluid is (*a*) gasoline and (*b*) nitrogen, at 20°C and 1 atm.

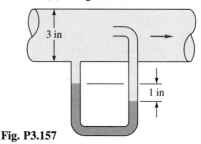

Fig. P3.157

3.158 In Fig. P3.158 the flowing fluid is CO_2 at 20°C. Neglect losses. If $p_1 = 170$ kPa and the manometer fluid is Meriam red oil (SG = 0.827), estimate (*a*) p_2 and (*b*) the gas flow rate in m^3/h.

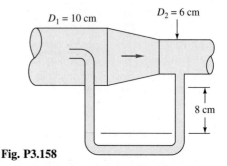

Fig. P3.158

3.159 The garden is 125 ft away from the faucet, but the hose is only 50 ft long. The hose diameter is $\frac{5}{8}$ in, and its nozzle can be adjusted to any small exit area. Assuming no losses, if the hose jet is to reach the garden, what minimum gage pressure is required at the faucet?

3.160 The air-cushion vehicle in Fig. P3.160 brings in sea-level standard air through a fan and discharges it at high velocity through an annular skirt of 3-cm clearance. If the vehicle weighs 50 kN, estimate (a) the required airflow rate and (b) the fan power in kW.

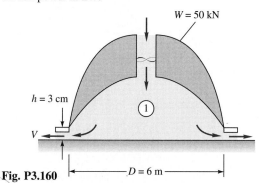

Fig. P3.160

3.161 A necked-down section in a pipe flow, called a *venturi*, develops a low throat pressure which can aspirate fluid upward from a reservoir, as in Fig. P3.161. Using Bernoulli's equation with no losses, derive an expression for the velocity V_1 which is just sufficient to bring reservoir fluid into the throat.

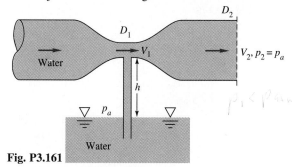

Fig. P3.161

3.162 The solution to Prob. 3.102 is

$$h_2 = \frac{1}{2} h_1 \left[\left(1 + \frac{8V_1^2}{gh_1} \right)^{1/2} - 1 \right]$$

Show that Bernoulli's equation, when applied between sections 1 and 2, does *not* give this result. Then derive an expression for the head loss h_f for a hydraulic jump.

3.163 The liquid in Fig. P3.163 is kerosine at 20°C. Estimate the flow flow rate from the tank for (a) no losses and (b) pipe losses $h_f \approx 4.5V^2/(2g)$.

3.164 In Fig. P3.164 all fluids are at 20°C. Compute the exit mass flow of water in lbm/s for (a) no losses and (b) pipe losses $h_f \approx 2.5V^2/(2g)$.

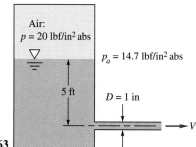

Fig. P3.163

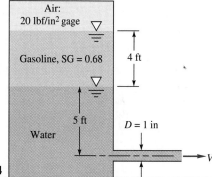

Fig. P3.164

3.165 A *venturi meter*, shown in Fig. P3.165, is a carefully designed constriction whose pressure difference is a measure of the flow rate in a pipe. Using Bernoulli's equation for steady incompressible flow with no losses, show that the flow rate Q is related to the manometer reading h by

$$Q = \frac{A_2}{\sqrt{1 - (D_2/D_1)^4}} \sqrt{\frac{2gh(\rho_M - \rho)}{\rho}}$$

where ρ_M is the density of the manometer fluid.

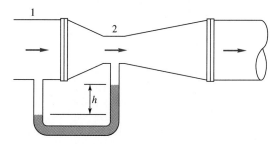

Fig. P3.165

3.166 An open-circuit wind tunnel draws in sea-level standard air and accelerates it through a contraction into a 1-m by 1-m test section. A differential transducer mounted in the test section wall measures a pressure difference of 45 mm of water between the inside and outside. Estimate (a) the test section velocity in mi/h and (b) the absolute pressure on the front nose of a small model mounted in the test section.

3.167 In Fig. P3.167 the fluid is gasoline at 20°C at a weight flux of 120 N/s. Assuming no losses, estimate the gage pressure at section 1.

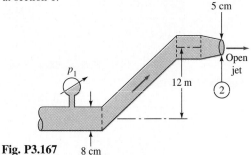

Fig. P3.167

3.168 In Fig. P3.168 both fluids are at 20°C. If $V_1 = 1.7$ ft/s and losses are neglected, what should the manometer reading h ft be?

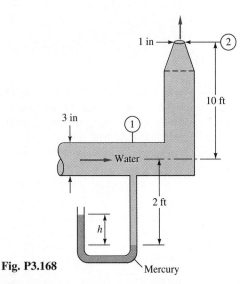

Fig. P3.168

3.169 Once it has been started by sufficient suction, the *siphon* in Fig. P3.169 will run continuously as long as reservoir fluid is available. Using Bernoulli's equation with no losses, show (a) that the exit velocity V_2 depends only upon gravity and the distance H and (b) that the lowest (vacuum) pressure occurs at point 3 and depends on the distance $L + H$.

3.170 If losses are neglected in Fig. P3.170, for what water level h will the flow begin to form vapor cavities at the throat of the nozzle?

3.171 For the 40°C water flow in Fig. P3.171, estimate the volume flow through the pipe, assuming no losses; then explain what is wrong with this seemingly innocent question. If the actual flow rate is $Q = 40$ m³/h, compute (a) the head loss in ft

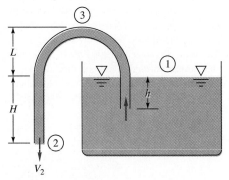

Fig. P3.169

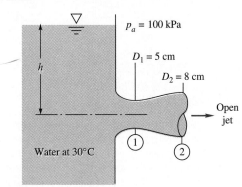

Fig. P3.170

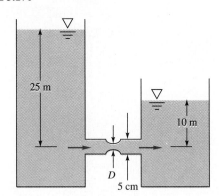

Fig. P3.171

and (b) the constriction diameter D which causes cavitation, assuming that the throat divides the head loss equally and that changing the constriction causes no additional losses.

3.172 The 35°C water flow of Fig. P3.172 discharges to sea-level standard atmosphere. Neglecting losses, for what nozzle diameter D will cavitation begin to occur? To avoid cavitation, should you increase or decrease D from this critical value?

3.173 The horizontal wye fitting in Fig. P3.173 splits the 20°C water flow rate equally. If $Q_1 = 5$ ft³/s and $p_1 = 25$ lbf/in²

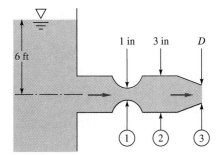

Fig. P3.172

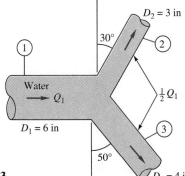

Fig. P3.173

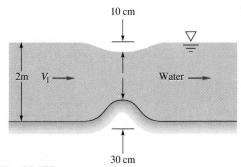

Fig. P3.175

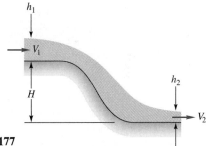

Fig. P3.176

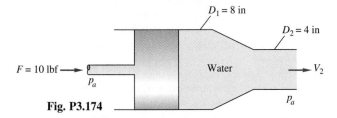

Fig. P3.174

(gage) and losses are neglected, estimate (a) p_2, (b) p_3, and (c) the vector force required to keep the wye in place.

3.174 In Fig. P3.174 the piston drives water at 20°C. Neglecting losses, estimate the exit velocity V_2 ft/s. If D_2 is further constricted, what is the maximum possible value of V_2?

3.175 If the approach velocity is not too high, a hump in the bottom of a water channel causes a dip Δh in the water level, which can serve as a flow measurement. If, as shown in Fig. P3.175, $\Delta h = 10$ cm when the bump is 30 cm high, what is the volume flow Q_1 per unit width, assuming no losses? In general, is Δh proportional to Q_1?

3.176 In the spillway flow of Fig. P3.176, the flow is assumed uniform and hydrostatic at sections 1 and 2. If losses are neglected, compute (a) V_2 and (b) the force per unit width of the water on the spillway.

3.177 For the water-channel flow of Fig. P3.177, $h_1 = 1.5$ m, $H = 4$ m, and $V_1 = 3$ m/s. Neglecting losses and assuming

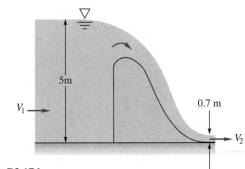

Fig. P3.177

uniform flow at sections 1 and 2, find the downstream depth h_2, and show that *two* realistic solutions are possible.

3.178 For the water-channel flow of Fig. P3.178, $h_1 = 0.45$ ft,

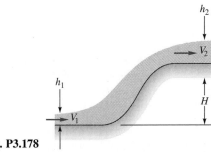

Fig. P3.178

$H = 2.2$ ft, and $V_1 = 16$ ft/s. Neglecting losses and assuming uniform flow at sections 1 and 2, find the downstream depth h_2; show that *two* realistic solutions are possible.

3.179 A cylindrical tank of diameter D contains liquid to an initial height h_0. At time $t = 0$ a small stopper of diameter d is removed from the bottom. Using Bernoulli's equation with no losses, derive (*a*) a differential equation for the free-surface height $h(t)$ during draining and (*b*) an expression for the time t_0 to drain the entire tank.

3.180 The large tank of incompressible liquid in Fig. P3.180 is at rest when, at $t = 0$, the valve is opened to the atmosphere. Assuming $h \approx$ constant (negligible velocities and accelerations in the tank), use the unsteady frictionless Bernoulli equation to derive and solve a differential equation for $V(t)$ in the pipe.

3.181 Modify Prob. 3.180 as follows. Let the top of the tank be enclosed and under constant gage pressure p_0. Repeat the analysis to find $V(t)$ in the pipe.

3.182 The incompressible-flow form of Bernoulli's relation, Eq.

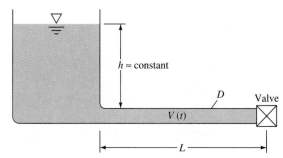

Fig. P3.180

(3.77), is accurate only for Mach numbers less than about 0.3. At higher speeds, variable density must be accounted for. The most common assumption for compressible fluids is *isentropic flow of an ideal gas*, or $p = C\rho^k$, where $k = c_p/c_v$. Substitute this relation into Eq. (3.75), integrate, and eliminate the constant C. Compare your compressible result with Eq. (3.77) and comment.

Word Problems

W3.1 Derive a control-volume form of the *second* law of thermodynamics. Suggest some practical uses for your relation in analyzing real fluid flows.

W3.2 Suppose that it is desired to estimate volume flow Q in a pipe by measuring the axial velocity $u(r)$ at specific points. For cost reasons only *three* measuring points are to be used. What are the best radii selections for these three points?

W3.3 Consider water flowing by gravity through a short pipe connecting two reservoirs whose surface levels differ by an amount Δz. Why does the incompressible frictionless Bernoulli equation lead to an absurdity when the flow rate through the pipe is computed? Does the paradox have something to do with the length of the short pipe? Does the paradox disappear if we round the entrance and exit edges of the pipe?

W3.4 Use the steady-flow energy equation to analyze flow through a water faucet whose supply pressure is p_0. What physical mechanism causes the flow to vary continuously from zero to maximum as we open the faucet valve?

W3.5 Consider a long sewer pipe, half full of water, sloping downward at angle θ. Antoine Chézy in 1768 determined that the average velocity of such an open-channel flow should be $V \approx C\sqrt{R \tan \theta}$, where R is the pipe radius and C is a constant. How does this famous formula relate to the steady-flow energy equation applied to a length L of the channel?

W3.6 Put a table tennis ball in a funnel, and attach the small end of the funnel to an air supply. You probably won't be able to blow the ball either up or down out of the funnel. Explain why.

W3.7 How does a *siphon* work? Are there any limitations (e.g., how high or how low can you siphon water away from a tank)? Also, how far—could you use a flexible tube to siphon water from a tank to a point 100 ft away?

Design Project

D3.1 Let us generalize Probs. 3.141 and 3.142, in which a pump performance curve was used to determine the flow rate between reservoirs. The particular pump in Fig. P3.142 is one of a family of pumps of similar shape, whose dimensionless performance is as follows:

Head:

$$\phi \approx 6.04 - 161\zeta \qquad \phi = \frac{gh}{n^2 D_p^2} \quad \text{and} \quad \zeta = \frac{Q}{nD_p^3}$$

Efficiency:

$$\eta \approx 70\zeta - 91500\zeta^3 \qquad \eta = \frac{\text{power to water}}{\text{power input}}$$

where h_p is the pump head (ft), n is the shaft rotation rate (r/s), and D_p is the impeller diameter (ft). The range of validity is $0 < \zeta < 0.027$. The pump of Fig. P3.142 had $D_p = 2$ ft in diameter and rotated at $n = 20$ r/s (1200 r/min). The solution to Prob. 3.142, namely, $Q \approx 2.57$ ft³/s and $h_p \approx 172$ ft, corresponds to $\phi \approx 3.46$, $\zeta \approx 0.016$, $\eta \approx 0.75$ (or 75 percent), and power to the water = $\rho g Q h_p \approx 27{,}500$ ft · lbf/s (50 hp). Please check these numerical values before beginning this project.

Now restudy Prob. 3.142 to select a *low-cost* pump which rotates at a rate now slower than 600 r/min and delivers no less than 1.0 ft³/s of water. Assume that the cost of the pump is linearly proportional to the power input required. Comment on any limitations to your results.

Chapter 4
Differential Relations for a Fluid Particle

Motivation. In analyzing fluid motion, we might take one of two paths: (1) seeking an estimate of gross effects (mass flow, induced force, energy change) over a *finite* region or control volume or (2) seeking the point-by-point details of a flow pattern by analyzing an *infinitesimal* region of the flow. The former or gross-average viewpoint was the subject of Chap. 3.

This chapter treats the second in our trio of techniques for analyzing fluid motion, small-scale, or *differential*, analysis. That is, we apply our four basic conservation laws to an infinitesimally small control volume or, alternately, to an infinitesimal fluid system. In either case the results yield the basic *differential equations* of fluid motion. Appropriate *boundary conditions* are also developed.

In their most basic form, these differential equations of motion are quite difficult to solve, and very little is known about their general mathematical properties. However, certain things can be done which have great educational value. First, e.g., as shown in Chap. 5, the equations (even if unsolved) reveal the basic dimensionless parameters which govern fluid motion. Second, as shown in Chap. 6, a great number of useful solutions can be found if one makes two simplifying assumptions: (1) steady flow and (2) incompressible flow. A third and rather drastic simplification, frictionless flow, makes our old friend the Bernoulli equation valid and yields a wide variety of idealized, or *perfect-fluid*, possible solutions. These idealized flows are treated in Chap. 8, and we must be careful to ascertain whether such solutions are in fact realistic when compared with actual fluid motion. Finally, even the difficult general differential equations now yield to the approximating technique known as *numerical analysis*, whereby the derivatives are simulated by algebraic relations between a finite number of grid points in the flow field which are then solved on a digital computer. Reference 1 is an example of a textbook devoted entirely to numerical analysis of fluid motion.

4.1 The Acceleration Field of a Fluid

In Sec. 1.5 we established the cartesian vector form of a velocity field which varies in space and time:

$$\mathbf{V}(\mathbf{r}, \mathbf{t}) = \mathbf{i}u(x, y, z, t) + \mathbf{j}v(x, y, z, t) + \mathbf{k}w(x, y, z, t) \qquad (1.7)$$

This is the most important variable in fluid mechanics: Knowledge of the velocity vector field is nearly equivalent to *solving* a fluid-flow problem. Our coordinates are fixed in space, and we observe the fluid as it passes by—as if we had scribed a set of coordinate lines on a glass window in a wind tunnel. This is the *eulerian* frame of reference, as opposed to the lagrangian frame, which follows the moving position of individual particles.

To write Newton's second law for an infinitesimal fluid system, we need to calculate the acceleration vector field **a** of the flow. Thus we compute the total time derivative of the velocity vector, similar to Example 1.5:

$$\mathbf{a} = \frac{d\mathbf{V}}{dt} = \mathbf{i}\frac{du}{dt} + \mathbf{j}\frac{dv}{dt} + \mathbf{k}\frac{dw}{dt}$$

Since each scalar component (u, v, w) is a function of the four variables (x, y, z, t), we use the chain rule to obtain each scalar time derivative. For example,

$$\frac{du(x, y, z, t)}{dt} = \frac{\partial u}{\partial t} + \frac{\partial u}{\partial x}\frac{dx}{dt} + \frac{\partial u}{\partial y}\frac{dy}{dt} + \frac{\partial u}{\partial z}\frac{dz}{dt}$$

But, by definition, dx/dt is the local velocity component u, and $dy/dt = v$, and $dz/dt = w$. The total derivative of u may thus be written in the compact form

$$\frac{du}{dt} = \frac{\partial u}{\partial t} + u\frac{\partial u}{\partial x} + v\frac{\partial u}{\partial y} + w\frac{\partial u}{\partial z} = \frac{\partial u}{\partial t} + (\mathbf{V} \cdot \nabla)u \tag{4.1}$$

Exactly similar expressions, with u replaced by v or w, hold for dv/dt or dw/dt. Summing these into a vector, we obtain the total acceleration:

$$\mathbf{a} = \frac{d\mathbf{V}}{dt} = \underbrace{\frac{\partial \mathbf{V}}{\partial t}}_{\text{Local}} + \underbrace{\left(u\frac{\partial \mathbf{V}}{\partial x} + v\frac{\partial \mathbf{V}}{\partial y} + w\frac{\partial \mathbf{V}}{\partial z}\right)}_{\text{Convective}} = \frac{\partial \mathbf{V}}{\partial t} + (\mathbf{V} \cdot \nabla)\mathbf{V} \tag{4.2}$$

The term $\partial\mathbf{V}/\partial t$ is called the *local acceleration*, which vanishes if the flow is steady, i.e., independent of time. The three terms in parentheses are called the *convective acceleration*, which arises when the particle moves through regions of spatially varying velocity, as in a nozzle or diffuser. Flows which are nominally "steady" may have large accelerations due to the convective terms.

Note our use of the compact dot product involving **V** and the gradient operator ∇:

$$u\frac{\partial}{\partial x} + v\frac{\partial}{\partial y} + w\frac{\partial}{\partial z} = \mathbf{V} \cdot \nabla \qquad \text{where} \qquad \nabla = \mathbf{i}\frac{\partial}{\partial x} + \mathbf{j}\frac{\partial}{\partial y} + \mathbf{k}\frac{\partial}{\partial z}$$

The total time derivative—sometimes called the *substantial* or *material* derivative—concept may be applied to any variable, e.g., the pressure:

$$\frac{dp}{dt} = \frac{\partial p}{\partial t} + u\frac{\partial p}{\partial x} + v\frac{\partial p}{\partial y} + w\frac{\partial p}{\partial z} = \frac{\partial p}{\partial t} + (\mathbf{V} \cdot \nabla)p \tag{4.3}$$

Wherever convective effects occur in the basic laws involving mass, momentum, or energy, the basic differential equations become nonlinear and are usually more complicated than flows which do not involve convective changes.

We emphasize that this total time derivative follows a particle of fixed identity, making it convenient for expressing laws of particle mechanics in the eulerian fluid-field description. The operator d/dt is sometimes assigned a special symbol such as D/Dt as a further reminder that it contains four terms and follows a fixed particle.

EXAMPLE 4.1

Given the eulerian velocity-vector field

$$\mathbf{V} = 3t\mathbf{i} + xz\mathbf{j} + ty^2\mathbf{k}$$

find the acceleration of a particle.

Solution

First note the specific given components

$$u = 3t \qquad v = xz \qquad w = ty^2$$

Then evaluate the vector derivatives required for Eq. (4.2)

$$\frac{\partial \mathbf{V}}{\partial t} = \mathbf{i}\frac{\partial u}{\partial t} + \mathbf{j}\frac{\partial v}{\partial t} + \mathbf{k}\frac{\partial w}{\partial t} = 3\mathbf{i} + y^2\mathbf{k}$$

$$\frac{\partial \mathbf{V}}{\partial x} = z\mathbf{j} \qquad \frac{\partial \mathbf{V}}{\partial y} = 2ty\mathbf{k} \qquad \frac{\partial \mathbf{V}}{\partial z} = x\mathbf{j}$$

This could have been worse: There are only five terms in all, whereas there could have been as many as twelve. Substitute directly into Eq. (4.2):

$$\frac{d\mathbf{V}}{dt} = (3\mathbf{i} + y^2\mathbf{k}) + (3t)(z\mathbf{j}) + (xz)(2ty\mathbf{k}) + (ty^2)(x\mathbf{j})$$

Collect terms for the final result

$$\frac{d\mathbf{V}}{dt} = 3\mathbf{i} + (3tz + txy^2)\mathbf{j} + (2xyzt + y^2)\mathbf{k} \qquad\qquad Ans.$$

Assuming that $\mathbf{V}$ is valid everywhere as given, this acceleration applies to all positions and times within the flow field.

4.2 The Differential Equation of Mass Conservation

All the basic differential equations can be derived by considering either an elemental control volume or an elemental system. Here we choose an infinitesimal fixed control volume (dx, dy, dz), as in Fig. 4.1, and use our basic control-volume relations from Chap. 3. The flow through each side of the element is approximately one-dimensional, and so the appropriate mass-conservation relation to use here is

$$\int_{CV} \frac{\partial \rho}{\partial t}\, d\mathcal{V} + \sum_i (\rho_i A_i V_i)_{\text{out}} - \sum_i (\rho_i A_i V_i)_{\text{in}} = 0 \qquad (3.22)$$

The element is so small that the volume integral simply reduces to a differential term

$$\int_{CV} \frac{\partial \rho}{\partial t}\, d\mathcal{V} \approx \frac{\partial \rho}{\partial t}\, dx\, dy\, dz$$

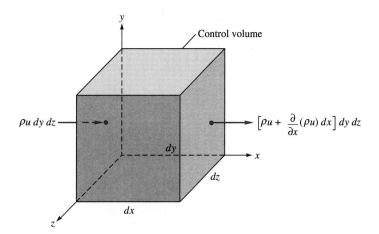

Fig. 4.1 Elemental cartesian fixed control volume showing the inlet and outlet mass flows on the x faces.

The mass-flow terms occur on all six faces, three inlets and three outlets. We make use of the field or continuum concept from Chap. 1, where all fluid properties are considered to be uniformly varying functions of time and position, such as $\rho = \rho(x, y, z, t)$. Thus, if T is the temperature on the left face of the element in Fig. 4.1, the right face will have a slightly different temperature $T + (\partial T/\partial x)\, dx$. For mass conservation, if ρu is known on the left face, the value of this product on the right face is $\rho u + (\partial \rho u/\partial x)\, dx$.

Figure 4.1 shows only the mass flows on the x or left and right faces. The flows on the y (bottom and top) and the z (back and front) faces have been omitted to avoid cluttering up the drawing. We can list all these six flows as follows:

Face	Inlet mass flow	Outlet mass flow
x	$\rho u\, dy\, dz$	$\left[\rho u + \dfrac{\partial}{\partial x}(\rho u)\, dx\right] dy\, dz$
y	$\rho v\, dx\, dz$	$\left[\rho v + \dfrac{\partial}{\partial y}(\rho v)\, dy\right] dx\, dz$
z	$\rho w\, dx\, dy$	$\left[\rho w + \dfrac{\partial}{\partial z}(\rho w)\, dz\right] dx\, dy$

Introduce these terms into Eq. (3.22) above and we have

$$\frac{\partial \rho}{\partial t}\, dx\, dy\, dz + \frac{\partial}{\partial x}(\rho u)\, dx\, dy\, dz + \frac{\partial}{\partial y}(\rho v)\, dx\, dy\, dz + \frac{\partial}{\partial z}(\rho w)\, dx\, dy\, dz = 0$$

The element volume cancels out of all terms, leaving a partial differential equation involving the derivatives of density and velocity

$$\frac{\partial \rho}{\partial t} + \frac{\partial}{\partial x}(\rho u) + \frac{\partial}{\partial y}(\rho v) + \frac{\partial}{\partial z}(\rho w) = 0 \tag{4.4}$$

This is the desired result: conservation of mass for an infinitesimal control volume. It is often called the *equation of continuity* because it requires no assumptions except that the density and velocity are continuum functions. That is, the flow may be either steady or unsteady, viscous or frictionless, compressible or incompressible.[1] However, the equation does not allow for any source or sink singularities within the element.

The vector-gradient operator

$$\mathbf{\nabla} = \mathbf{i}\,\frac{\partial}{\partial x} + \mathbf{j}\,\frac{\partial}{\partial y} + \mathbf{k}\,\frac{\partial}{\partial z}$$

enables us to rewrite the equation of continuity in a compact form, not that it helps much in finding a solution. The last three terms of Eq. (4.4) are equivalent to the divergence of the vector $\rho\mathbf{V}$

$$\frac{\partial}{\partial x}\,(\rho u) + \frac{\partial}{\partial y}\,(\rho v) + \frac{\partial}{\partial z}\,(\rho w) \equiv \mathbf{\nabla}\cdot(\rho\mathbf{V}) \tag{4.5}$$

so that the compact form of the continuity relation is

$$\frac{\partial\rho}{\partial t} + \mathbf{\nabla}\cdot(\rho\mathbf{V}) = 0 \tag{4.6}$$

In this vector form the equation is still quite general and can readily be converted to other than cartesian coordinate systems.

Cylindrical Polar Coordinates

The most common alternative to the cartesian system is the *cylindrical polar* coordinate system, sketched in Fig. 4.2. An arbitrary point P is defined by a distance z along the axis, a radial distance r from the axis, and a rotation angle θ about the axis. The three independent velocity components are an axial velocity v_z, a radial velocity v_r, and a circumferential velocity v_θ, which is positive counterclockwise, i.e., in the direction of

Fig. 4.2 Definition sketch for the cylindrical coordinate system.

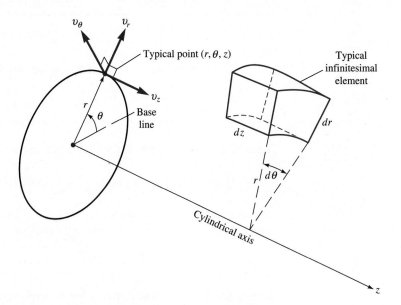

---

[1] One case where Eq. (4.4) might need special care is *two-phase flow*, where the density is discontinuous between the phases. For further details on this case, see, e.g., Ref. 2.

increasing θ. In general, all components, as well as pressure and density and other fluid properties, are continuous functions of r, θ, z, and t.

The divergence of any vector function $\mathbf{A}(r, \theta, z, t)$ is found by making the transformation of coordinates

$$r = (x^2 + y^2)^{1/2} \qquad \theta = \tan^{-1} \frac{y}{x} \qquad z = z \tag{4.7}$$

and the result is given here without proof[1]

$$\nabla \cdot \mathbf{A} = \frac{1}{r} \frac{\partial}{\partial r} (rA_r) + \frac{1}{r} \frac{\partial}{\partial \theta} (A_\theta) + \frac{\partial}{\partial z} (A_z) \tag{4.8}$$

The general continuity equation (4.6) in cylindrical polar coordinates is thus

$$\frac{\partial \rho}{\partial t} + \frac{1}{r} \frac{\partial}{\partial r} (r\rho v_r) + \frac{1}{r} \frac{\partial}{\partial \theta} (\rho v_\theta) + \frac{\partial}{\partial z} (\rho v_z) = 0 \tag{4.9}$$

There are other orthogonal curvilinear coordinate systems, notably *spherical polar* coordinates, which occasionally merit use in a fluid-mechanics problem. We shall not treat these systems here except in Prob. 4.12.

There are also other ways to derive the basic continuity equation (4.6) which are interesting and instructive. Ask your instructor about these alternate approaches.

Steady Compressible Flow

If the flow is steady, $\partial/\partial t \equiv 0$ and all properties are functions of position only. Equation (4.6) reduces to

Cartesian:
$$\frac{\partial}{\partial x} (\rho u) + \frac{\partial}{\partial y} (\rho v) + \frac{\partial}{\partial z} (\rho w) = 0$$

Cylindrical:
$$\frac{1}{r} \frac{\partial}{\partial r} (r\rho v_r) + \frac{1}{r} \frac{\partial}{\partial \theta} (\rho v_\theta) + \frac{\partial}{\partial z} (\rho v_z) = 0 \tag{4.10}$$

Since density and velocity are both variables, these are still nonlinear and rather formidable, but a number of special-case solutions have been found.

Incompressible Flow

A special case which affords great simplification is incompressible flow, where the density changes are negligible. Then $\partial \rho/\partial t \approx 0$ regardless of whether the flow is steady or unsteady, and the density can be slipped out of the divergence in Eq. (4.6) and divided out. The result is

$$\nabla \cdot \mathbf{V} = 0 \tag{4.11}$$

valid for steady or unsteady incompressible flow. The two coordinate forms are

Cartesian:
$$\frac{\partial u}{\partial x} + \frac{\partial v}{\partial y} + \frac{\partial w}{\partial z} = 0 \tag{4.12a}$$

Cylindrical:
$$\frac{1}{r} \frac{\partial}{\partial r} (rv_r) + \frac{1}{r} \frac{\partial}{\partial \theta} (v_\theta) + \frac{\partial}{\partial z} (v_z) = 0 \tag{4.12b}$$

[1] See, e.g., Ref. 3, p. 783.

These are *linear* differential equations, and a wide variety of solutions are known, as discussed in Chaps. 6 to 8. Since no author or instructor can resist a wide variety of solutions, it follows that a great deal of time is spent studying incompressible flows. Fortunately, this is exactly what should be done, because most practical engineering flows are approximately incompressible, the chief exception being the high-speed gas flows treated in Chap. 9.

When is a given flow approximately incompressible? We can derive a nice criterion by playing a little fast and loose with density approximations. In essence, we wish to slip the density out of the divergence in Eq. (4.6) and approximate a typical term as, e.g.,

$$\frac{\partial}{\partial x}(\rho u) \approx \rho \frac{\partial u}{\partial x} \tag{4.13}$$

This is equivalent to the strong inequality

$$\left| u \frac{\partial \rho}{\partial x} \right| \ll \left| \rho \frac{\partial u}{\partial x} \right|$$

or

$$\left| \frac{\delta \rho}{\rho} \right| \ll \left| \frac{\delta V}{V} \right| \tag{4.14}$$

As we shall see in Chap. 9, the pressure change is approximately proportional to the density change and the square of the speed of sound a of the fluid

$$\delta p \approx a^2 \, \delta \rho \tag{4.15}$$

Meanwhile, if elevation changes are negligible, the pressure is related to the velocity change by Bernoulli's equation (3.77)

$$\delta p \approx -\rho V \, \delta V \tag{4.16}$$

Combining Eqs. (4.14) to (4.16), we obtain an explicit criterion for incompressible flow:

$$\frac{V^2}{a^2} = \text{Ma}^2 \ll 1 \tag{4.17}$$

where $\text{Ma} = V/a$ is the dimensionless *Mach number* of the flow. How small is small? The commonly accepted limit is

$$\text{Ma} \leq 0.3 \tag{4.18}$$

For air at standard conditions, a flow can thus be considered incompressible if the velocity is less than about 100 m/s (330 ft/s). This encompasses a wide variety of airflows: automobile and train motions, light aircraft, landing and takeoff of high-speed aircraft, most pipe flows, and turbomachinery at moderate rotational speeds. Further, it is clear that almost all liquid flows are incompressible, since flow velocities are small and the speed of sound is very large.[1]

---

[1] An exception occurs in geophysical flows, where a density change is imposed thermally or mechanically rather than by the flow conditions themselves. An example is fresh water layered upon saltwater or warm air layered upon cold air in the atmosphere. We say that the fluid is *stratified*, and we must account for vertical density changes in Eq. (4.6) even if the velocities are small.

Before attempting to analyze the continuity equation, we shall proceed with the derivation of the momentum and energy equations, so that we can analyze them as a group. A very clever device called the *stream function* can often make short work of the continuity equation, but we shall save it until Sec. 4.7.

One further remark is appropriate: The continuity equation is always important and must always be satisfied for a rational analysis of a flow pattern. Any newly discovered momentum or energy ''solution'' will ultimately crash in flames when subjected to critical analysis if it does not also satisfy the continuity equation.

EXAMPLE 4.2

Under what conditions does the velocity field

$$\mathbf{V} = (a_1x + b_1y + c_1z)\mathbf{i} + (a_2x + b_2y + c_2z)\mathbf{j} + (a_3x + b_3y + c_3z)\mathbf{k}$$

where a_1, b_1, etc. = const, represent an incompressible flow which conserves mass?

Solution

Recalling that $\mathbf{V} = u\mathbf{i} + v\mathbf{j} + w\mathbf{k}$, we see that $u = (a_1x + b_1y + c_1z)$, etc. Substituting into Eq. (4.12a) for incompressible continuity, we obtain

$$\frac{\partial}{\partial x}(a_1x + b_1y + c_1z) + \frac{\partial}{\partial y}(a_2x + b_2y + c_2z) + \frac{\partial}{\partial z}(a_3x + b_3y + c_3z) = 0$$

or
$$a_1 + b_2 + c_3 = 0 \qquad\qquad Ans.$$

At least two of constants a_1, b_2, and c_3 must have opposite signs. Continuity imposes no restrictions whatever on constants b_1, c_1, a_2, c_2, a_3, and b_3, which do not contribute to a mass increase or decrease of a differential element.

EXAMPLE 4.3

An incompressible velocity field is given by

$$u = a(x^2 - y^2) \qquad v \text{ unknown} \qquad w = b$$

where a and b are constants. What must the form of the velocity component v be?

Solution

Again Eq. (4.12a) applies

$$\frac{\partial}{\partial x}(ax^2 - ay^2) + \frac{\partial v}{\partial y} + \frac{\partial b}{\partial z} = 0$$

or
$$\frac{\partial v}{\partial y} = -2ax \qquad\qquad (1)$$

This is easily integrated partially with respect to y

$$v(x, y, z, t) = -2axy + f(x, z, t) \qquad\qquad Ans.$$

This is the only possible form for v which satisfies the incompressible continuity equation. The function of integration f is entirely arbitrary since it vanishes when v is differentiated with respect to y.[†]

EXAMPLE 4.4

A centrifugal impeller of 40-cm diameter is used to pump hydrogen at 15°C and 1-atm pressure. What is the maximum allowable impeller rotational speed to avoid compressibility effects at the blade tips?

Solution

The speed of sound of hydrogen for these conditions is $a = 1300$ m/s. Assume that the gas velocity leaving the impeller is approximately equal to the impeller-tip speed

$$V = \Omega r = \tfrac{1}{2}\Omega D$$

Our rule of thumb, Eq. (4.18), neglects compressibility if

$$V = \tfrac{1}{2}\Omega D \le 0.3a = 390 \text{ m/s}$$

or
$$\tfrac{1}{2}\Omega(0.4 \text{ m}) \le 390 \text{ m/s} \qquad \Omega \le 1950 \text{ rad/s}$$

Thus we estimate the allowable speed to be quite large

$$\Omega \le 310 \text{ r/s (18,600 r/min)} \qquad\qquad Ans.$$

An impeller moving at this speed in air would create shock waves at the tips but not in a light gas like hydrogen.

4.3 The Differential Equation of Linear Momentum

Having done it once in Sec. 4.2 for mass conservation, we can move along a little faster this time. We use the same elemental control volume as in Fig. 4.1, for which the appropriate form of the linear-momentum relation is

$$\sum \mathbf{F} = \frac{\partial}{\partial t}\left(\int_{CV} \mathbf{V}\rho \, d\mathcal{V}\right) + \sum (\dot{m}_i \mathbf{V}_i)_{\text{out}} - \sum (\dot{m}_i \mathbf{V}_i)_{\text{in}} \qquad (3.40)$$

Again the element is so small that the volume integral simply reduces to a derivative term

$$\frac{\partial}{\partial t}\left(\int_{CV} \mathbf{V}\rho \, d\mathcal{V}\right) \approx \frac{\partial}{\partial t}(\rho\mathbf{V}) \, dx \, dy \, dz \qquad (4.19)$$

The momentum fluxes occur on all six faces, three inlets and three outlets. Referring again to Fig. 4.1, we can form a table of momentum fluxes by exact analogy with the discussion which led up to the equation for net mass flux:

[†] This is a very realistic flow which simulates the turning of an inviscid fluid through a 60° angle; see Examples 4.7 and 4.9.

Faces	Inlet momentum flux	Outlet momentum flux
x	$\rho u \mathbf{V} \, dy \, dz$	$\left[\rho u \mathbf{V} + \dfrac{\partial}{\partial x} (\rho u \mathbf{V}) \, dx \right] dy \, dz$
y	$\rho v \mathbf{V} \, dx \, dz$	$\left[\rho v \mathbf{V} + \dfrac{\partial}{\partial y} (\rho v \mathbf{V}) \, dy \right] dx \, dz$
z	$\rho w \mathbf{V} \, dx \, dy$	$\left[\rho w \mathbf{V} + \dfrac{\partial}{\partial z} (\rho w \mathbf{V}) \, dz \right] dx \, dy$

Introduce these terms and Eq. (4.19) into Eq. (3.40), and get the intermediate result

$$\sum \mathbf{F} = dx \, dy \, dz \left[\frac{\partial}{\partial t} (\rho \mathbf{V}) + \frac{\partial}{\partial x} (\rho u \mathbf{V}) + \frac{\partial}{\partial y} (\rho v \mathbf{V}) + \frac{\partial}{\partial z} (\rho w \mathbf{V}) \right] \qquad (4.20)$$

Note that this is a vector relation. A simplification occurs if we split up the term in brackets as follows:

$$\frac{\partial}{\partial t} (\rho \mathbf{V}) + \frac{\partial}{\partial x} (\rho u \mathbf{V}) + \frac{\partial}{\partial y} (\rho v \mathbf{V}) + \frac{\partial}{\partial z} (\rho w \mathbf{V})$$

$$= \mathbf{V} \left[\frac{\partial \rho}{\partial t} + \nabla \cdot (\rho \mathbf{V}) \right] + \rho \left(\frac{\partial \mathbf{V}}{\partial t} + u \frac{\partial \mathbf{V}}{\partial x} + v \frac{\partial \mathbf{V}}{\partial y} + w \frac{\partial \mathbf{V}}{\partial z} \right) \qquad (4.21)$$

The term in brackets on the right-hand side is seen to be the equation of continuity, Eq. (4.6), which vanishes identically. The long term in parentheses on the right-hand side is seen from Eq. (4.2) to be the total acceleration of a particle which instantaneously occupies the control volume

$$\frac{\partial \mathbf{V}}{\partial t} + u \frac{\partial \mathbf{V}}{\partial x} + v \frac{\partial \mathbf{V}}{\partial y} + w \frac{\partial \mathbf{V}}{\partial z} = \frac{d\mathbf{V}}{dt} \qquad (4.2)$$

Thus we have now reduced Eq. (4.20) to

$$\sum \mathbf{F} = \rho \frac{d\mathbf{V}}{dt} \, dx \, dy \, dz \qquad (4.22)$$

It might be good for you to stop and rest now and think about what we have just done. What is the relation between Eqs. (4.22) and (3.40) for an infinitesimal control volume? Could we have *begun* the analysis at Eq. (4.22)?

Equation (4.22) points out that the net force on the control volume must be of differential size and proportional to the element volume. These forces are of two types, *body* forces and *surface* forces. Body forces are due to external fields (gravity, magnetism, electric potential) which act upon the entire mass within the element. The only body force we shall consider in this book is gravity. The gravity force on the differential mass $\rho \, dx \, dy \, dz$ within the control volume is

$$d\mathbf{F}_{\text{grav}} = \rho \mathbf{g} \, dx \, dy \, dz \qquad (4.23)$$

where $\mathbf{g}$ may in general have an arbitrary orientation with respect to the coordinate system. In many applications, such as Bernoulli's equation, we take z "up," and $\mathbf{g} = -g\mathbf{k}$.

The surface forces are due to the stresses on the sides of the control surface. These stresses, as discussed in Chap. 2, are the sum of hydrostatic pressure plus viscous stresses τ_{ij} which arise from motion with velocity gradients

$$\sigma_{ij} = \begin{vmatrix} -p + \tau_{xx} & \tau_{yx} & \tau_{zx} \\ \tau_{xy} & -p + \tau_{yy} & \tau_{zy} \\ \tau_{xz} & \tau_{yz} & -p + \tau_{zz} \end{vmatrix} \qquad (4.24)$$

The subscript notation for stresses is given in Fig. 4.3.

It is not these stresses but their *gradients*, or differences, which cause a net force on the differential control surface. This is seen by referring to Fig. 4.4, which shows only

Fig. 4.3 Notation for stresses.

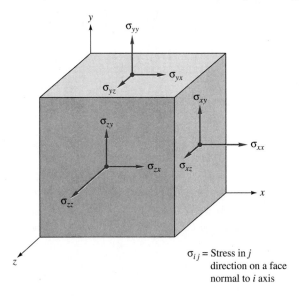

σ_{ij} = Stress in j direction on a face normal to i axis

Fig. 4.4 Elemental cartesian fixed control volume showing the surface forces in the x direction only.

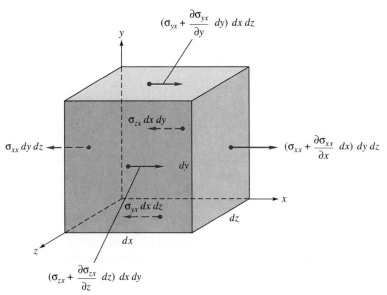

the *x*-directed stresses to avoid cluttering up the drawing. For example, the leftward force $\sigma_{xx}\,dy\,dz$ on the left face is balanced by the rightward force $\sigma_{xx}\,dy\,dz$ on the right face, leaving only the net rightward force $(\partial\sigma_{xx}/\partial x)\,dx\,dy\,dz$ on the right face. The same thing happens on the other four faces, so that the net surface force in the *x* direction is given by

$$dF_{x,\text{ surf}} = \left[\frac{\partial}{\partial x}(\sigma_{xx}) + \frac{\partial}{\partial y}(\sigma_{yx}) + \frac{\partial}{\partial z}(\sigma_{zx})\right] dx\,dy\,dz \qquad (4.25)$$

We see that this force is proportional to the element volume. Notice that the stress terms are taken from the *top row* of the array in Eq. (4.24). Splitting this row into pressure plus viscous stresses, we can rewrite Eq. (4.25) as

$$\frac{dF_x}{d\mathcal{V}} = -\frac{\partial p}{\partial x} + \frac{\partial}{\partial x}(\tau_{xx}) + \frac{\partial}{\partial y}(\tau_{yx}) + \frac{\partial}{\partial z}(\tau_{zx}) \qquad (4.26)$$

In exactly similar manner, we can derive the *y* and *z* forces per unit volume on the control surface

$$\frac{dF_y}{d\mathcal{V}} = -\frac{\partial p}{\partial y} + \frac{\partial}{\partial x}(\tau_{xy}) + \frac{\partial}{\partial y}(\tau_{yy}) + \frac{\partial}{\partial z}(\tau_{zy})$$

$$\frac{dF_z}{d\mathcal{V}} = -\frac{\partial p}{\partial z} + \frac{\partial}{\partial x}(\tau_{xz}) + \frac{\partial}{\partial y}(\tau_{yz}) + \frac{\partial}{\partial z}(\tau_{zz}) \qquad (4.27)$$

Now we multiply Eqs. (4.26) and (4.27) by **i**, **j**, and **k**, respectively, and add to obtain an expression for the net vector surface force

$$\left(\frac{d\mathbf{F}}{d\mathcal{V}}\right)_{\text{surf}} = -\nabla p + \left(\frac{d\mathbf{F}}{d\mathcal{V}}\right)_{\text{viscous}} \qquad (4.28)$$

where the viscous force has a total of nine terms:

$$\left(\frac{d\mathbf{F}}{d\mathcal{V}}\right)_{\text{viscous}} = \mathbf{i}\left(\frac{\partial\tau_{xx}}{\partial x} + \frac{\partial\tau_{yx}}{\partial y} + \frac{\partial\tau_{zx}}{\partial z}\right)$$

$$+ \mathbf{j}\left(\frac{\partial\tau_{xy}}{\partial x} + \frac{\partial\tau_{yy}}{\partial y} + \frac{\partial\tau_{zy}}{\partial z}\right)$$

$$+ \mathbf{k}\left(\frac{\partial\tau_{xz}}{\partial x} + \frac{\partial\tau_{yz}}{\partial y} + \frac{\partial\tau_{zz}}{\partial z}\right) \qquad (4.29)$$

Since each term in parentheses in (4.29) represents the divergence of a stress-component vector acting on the *x*, *y*, and *z* faces, respectively, Eq. (4.29) is sometimes expressed in divergence form

$$\left(\frac{d\mathbf{F}}{d\mathcal{V}}\right)_{\text{viscous}} = \nabla \cdot \tau_{ij} \qquad (4.30)$$

where

$$\tau_{ij} = \begin{bmatrix} \tau_{xx} & \tau_{yx} & \tau_{zx} \\ \tau_{xy} & \tau_{yy} & \tau_{zy} \\ \tau_{xz} & \tau_{yz} & \tau_{zz} \end{bmatrix} \qquad (4.31)$$

is the viscous-stress tensor acting on the element. The surface force is thus the sum of the *pressure-gradient* vector and the divergence of the viscous-stress tensor. Substituting into Eq. (4.22) and utilizing Eq. (4.23), we have the basic differential momentum equation for an infinitesimal element

$$\rho \mathbf{g} - \nabla p + \nabla \cdot \tau_{ij} = \rho \frac{d\mathbf{V}}{dt} \tag{4.32}$$

where

$$\frac{d\mathbf{V}}{dt} = \frac{\partial \mathbf{V}}{\partial t} + u \frac{\partial \mathbf{V}}{\partial x} + v \frac{\partial \mathbf{V}}{\partial y} + w \frac{\partial \mathbf{V}}{\partial z} \tag{4.33}$$

We can also express Eq. (4.32) in words:

Gravity force per unit volume + pressure force per unit volume

$$+ \text{ viscous force per unit volume } = \text{ density } \times \text{ acceleration} \tag{4.34}$$

Equation (4.32) is so brief and compact that its inherent complexity is almost invisible. It is a *vector* equation, each of whose component equations contains nine terms. Let us therefore write out the component equations in full to illustrate the mathematical difficulties inherent in the momentum equation:

$$\rho g_x - \frac{\partial p}{\partial x} + \frac{\partial \tau_{xx}}{\partial x} + \frac{\partial \tau_{yx}}{\partial y} + \frac{\partial \tau_{zx}}{\partial z} = \rho \left(\frac{\partial u}{\partial t} + u \frac{\partial u}{\partial x} + v \frac{\partial u}{\partial y} + w \frac{\partial u}{\partial z} \right)$$

$$\rho g_y - \frac{\partial p}{\partial y} + \frac{\partial \tau_{xy}}{\partial x} + \frac{\partial \tau_{yy}}{\partial y} + \frac{\partial \tau_{zy}}{\partial z} = \rho \left(\frac{\partial v}{\partial t} + u \frac{\partial v}{\partial x} + v \frac{\partial v}{\partial y} + w \frac{\partial v}{\partial z} \right) \tag{4.35}$$

$$\rho g_z - \frac{\partial p}{\partial z} + \frac{\partial \tau_{xz}}{\partial x} + \frac{\partial \tau_{yz}}{\partial y} + \frac{\partial \tau_{zz}}{\partial z} = \rho \left(\frac{\partial w}{\partial t} + u \frac{\partial w}{\partial x} + v \frac{\partial w}{\partial y} + w \frac{\partial w}{\partial z} \right)$$

This is the differential momentum equation in its full glory, and it is valid for any fluid in any general motion, particular fluids being characterized by particular viscous-stress terms. Note that the last three "convective" terms on the right-hand side of each component equation in (4.35) are nonlinear, which complicates the general mathematical analysis.

Inviscid Flow: Euler's Equation

Equation (4.35) is not ready to use until we write the viscous stresses in terms of velocity components. The simplest assumption is frictionless flow $\tau_{ij} = 0$, for which Eq. (4.35) reduces to

$$\rho \mathbf{g} - \nabla p = \rho \frac{d\mathbf{V}}{dt} \tag{4.36}$$

This is Euler's equation for inviscid flow. We show in Sec. 4.9 that Euler's equation can be integrated along a streamline to yield the frictionless Bernoulli equation, (3.75) or (3.77). The complete analysis of inviscid flow fields, using continuity and the Bernoulli relation, is given in Chap. 8.

Newtonian Fluid: Navier-Stokes Equations

For a newtonian fluid, as discussed in Sec. 1.7, the viscous stresses are proportional to the element strain rates and the coefficient of viscosity. For incompressible flow, the generalization of Eq. (1.23) to three-dimensional viscous flow is[1]

$$\tau_{xx} = 2\mu\,\frac{\partial u}{\partial x} \qquad \tau_{yy} = 2\mu\,\frac{\partial v}{\partial y} \qquad \tau_{zz} = 2\mu\,\frac{\partial w}{\partial z}$$

$$\tau_{xy} = \tau_{yx} = \mu\!\left(\frac{\partial u}{\partial y} + \frac{\partial v}{\partial x}\right) \qquad \tau_{xz} = \tau_{zx} = \mu\!\left(\frac{\partial w}{\partial x} + \frac{\partial u}{\partial z}\right) \tag{4.37}$$

$$\tau_{yz} = \tau_{zy} = \mu\!\left(\frac{\partial v}{\partial z} + \frac{\partial w}{\partial y}\right)$$

where μ is the viscosity coefficient. Substitution into Eq. (4.35) gives the differential momentum equation for a newtonian fluid with constant density and viscosity

$$\rho g_x - \frac{\partial p}{\partial x} + \mu\!\left(\frac{\partial^2 u}{\partial x^2} + \frac{\partial^2 u}{\partial y^2} + \frac{\partial^2 u}{\partial z^2}\right) = \rho\,\frac{du}{dt}$$

$$\rho g_y - \frac{\partial p}{\partial y} + \mu\!\left(\frac{\partial^2 v}{\partial x^2} + \frac{\partial^2 v}{\partial y^2} + \frac{\partial^2 v}{\partial z^2}\right) = \rho\,\frac{dv}{dt} \tag{4.38}$$

$$\rho g_z - \frac{\partial p}{\partial z} + \mu\!\left(\frac{\partial^2 w}{\partial x^2} + \frac{\partial^2 w}{\partial y^2} + \frac{\partial^2 w}{\partial z^2}\right) = \rho\,\frac{dw}{dt}$$

These are the *Navier-Stokes equations*, named after C. L. M. H. Navier (1785–1836) and Sir George G. Stokes (1819–1903), who are credited with their derivation. They are second-order nonlinear partial differential equations and are quite formidable, but surprisingly many solutions have been found to a variety of interesting viscous-flow problems, some of which are discussed in Sect. 4.11 and in Chap. 6 (see also Refs. 4 and 5). For compressible flow, see eq. (2.29) of Ref. 5.

Equation (4.38) has four unknowns: p, u, v, and w. It should be combined with the incompressible continuity relation (4.12) to form four equations in these four unknowns. We shall discuss this again in Sec. 4.6, which presents the appropriate boundary conditions for these equations.

EXAMPLE 4.5

Take the velocity field of Example 4.3, with $b = 0$ for algebraic convenience

$$u = a(x^2 - y^2) \qquad v = -2axy \qquad w = 0$$

and determine under what conditions it is a solution to the Navier-Stokes momentum equation (4.38). Assuming that these conditions are met, determine the resulting pressure distribution when z is "up" $(g_x = 0,\ g_y = 0,\ g_z = -g)$.

Solution

Make a direct substitution of u, v, w into Eq. (4.38):

$$\rho(0) - \frac{\partial p}{\partial x} + \mu(2a - 2a) = 2a^2\rho(x^3 + xy^2) \tag{1}$$

---

[1] When compressibility is significant, additional small terms arise containing the element volume expansion rate and a *second* coefficient of viscosity; see Refs. 4 and 5 for details.

$$\rho(0) - \frac{\partial p}{\partial y} + \mu(0) = 2a^2\rho(x^2y + y^3) \tag{2}$$

$$\rho(-g) - \frac{\partial p}{\partial z} + \mu(0) = 0 \tag{3}$$

The viscous terms vanish identically (although μ is *not* zero). Equation (3) can be integrated partially to obtain

$$p = -\rho g z + f_1(x, y) \tag{4}$$

i.e., the pressure is hydrostatic in the z direction, which follows anyway from the fact that the flow is two-dimensional ($w = 0$). Now the question is: Do Eqs. (1) and (2) show that the given velocity field *is* a solution? One way to find out is to form the mixed derivative $\partial^2 p/(\partial x\,\partial y)$ from (1) and (2) separately and then compare them.

Differentiate Eq. (1) with respect to y

$$\frac{\partial^2 p}{\partial x\,\partial y} = -4a^2\rho xy \tag{5}$$

Now differentiate Eq. (2) with respect to x

$$\frac{\partial^2 p}{\partial x\,\partial y} = -\frac{\partial}{\partial x}[2a^2\rho(x^2y + y^3)] = -4a^2\rho xy \tag{6}$$

Since these are identical, the given velocity field is an *exact* solution to the Navier-Stokes equation.   *Ans.*

To find the pressure distribution, substitute Eq. (4) into Eqs. (1) and (2), which will enable us to find $f_1(x, y)$

$$\frac{\partial f_1}{\partial x} = -2a^2\rho(x^3 + xy^2) \tag{7}$$

$$\frac{\partial f_1}{\partial y} = -2a^2\rho(x^2y + y^2) \tag{8}$$

Integrate Eq. (7) partially with respect to x

$$f_1 = -\tfrac{1}{2}a^2\rho(x^4 + 2x^2y^2) + f_2(y) \tag{9}$$

Differentiate this with respect to y and compare with Eq. (8)

$$\frac{\partial f_1}{\partial y} = -2a^2\rho x^2y + f_2'(y) \tag{10}$$

Comparing (8) and (10), we see they are equivalent if

$$f_2'(y) = -2a^2\rho y^3$$

or

$$f_2(y) = -\tfrac{1}{2}a^2\rho y^4 + C \tag{11}$$

where C is a constant. Combine Eqs. (4), (9), and (11) to give the complete expression for pressure distribution

$$p(x, y, z) = -\rho g z - \tfrac{1}{2}a^2\rho(x^4 + y^4 + 2x^2y^2) + C \qquad \textit{Ans.} \tag{12}$$

This is the desired solution. Do you recognize it? Not unless you go back to the beginning and square the velocity components:

$$u^2 + v^2 + w^2 = V^2 = a^2(x^4 + y^4 + 2x^2y^2) \tag{13}$$

Comparing with Eq. (12), we can rewrite the pressure distribution as

$$p + \tfrac{1}{2}\rho V^2 + \rho gz = C \tag{14}$$

This is Bernoulli's equation (3.77). That is no accident, because the velocity distribution given in this problem is one of a family of flows which are solutions to the Navier-Stokes equation and which satisfy Bernoulli's incompressible equation everywhere in the flow field. They are called *irrotational flows*, for which curl $\mathbf{V} = \nabla \times \mathbf{V} \equiv 0$. This subject is discussed again in Sec. 4.9.

4.4 The Differential Equation of Angular Momentum

Having now been through the same approach for both mass and linear momentum, we can go rapidly through a derivation of the differential angular-momentum relation. The appropriate form of the integral angular-momentum equation for a fixed control volume is

$$\sum \mathbf{M}_O = \frac{\partial}{\partial t}\left[\int_{CV} (\mathbf{r} \times \mathbf{V})\rho \, d\mathcal{V}\right] + \int_{CS} (\mathbf{r} \times \mathbf{V})\rho(\mathbf{V} \cdot \mathbf{n}) \, dA \tag{3.55}$$

We shall confine ourselves to an axis O which is parallel to the z axis and passes through the centroid of the elemental control volume. This is shown in Fig. 4.5. Let θ be the angle of rotation about O of the fluid within the control volume. The only stresses which have moments about O are the shear stresses τ_{xy} and τ_{yx}. We can evaluate the moments about O and the angular-momentum terms about O. A lot of algebra is involved, and we give here only the result

$$\left[\tau_{xy} - \tau_{yx} + \frac{1}{2}\frac{\partial}{\partial x}(\tau_{xy}) \, dx - \frac{1}{2}\frac{\partial}{\partial y}(\tau_{yx}) \, dy\right] dx \, dy \, dz$$

$$= \frac{1}{12}\rho(dx \, dy \, dz)(dx^2 + dy^2)\frac{d^2\theta}{dt^2} \tag{4.39}$$

Assuming that the angular acceleration $d^2\theta/dt^2$ is not infinite, we can neglect all higher-

Fig. 4.5 Elemental cartesian fixed control volume showing shear stresses which may cause a net angular acceleration about O axis.

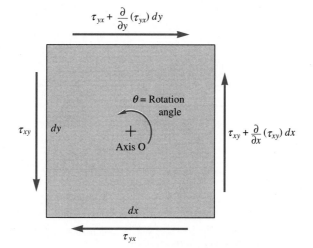

order differential terms, which leaves a finite and interesting result

$$\tau_{xy} \approx \tau_{yx} \tag{4.40}$$

Had we summed moments about axes parallel to y or x, we would have obtained exactly analogous results

$$\tau_{xz} \approx \tau_{zx} \qquad \tau_{yz} \approx \tau_{zy} \tag{4.41}$$

There is *no* differential angular-momentum equation. Application of the integral theorem to a differential element gives the result, well known to students of stress analysis, that the shear stresses are symmetric: $\tau_{ij} = \tau_{ji}$. This is the only result of this section.[1] There is no differential equation to remember, which leaves room in your brain for the next topic, the differential energy equation.

4.5 The Differential Equation of Energy[2]

We are now so used to this type of derivation that we can race through the energy equation at a bewildering pace. The appropriate integral relation for the fixed control volume of Fig. 4.1 is

$$\dot{Q} - \dot{W}_s - \dot{W}_v = \frac{\partial}{\partial t}\left(\int_{\text{CV}} e\rho \, d\mathcal{V}\right) + \int_{\text{CS}}\left(e + \frac{p}{\rho}\right)\rho(\mathbf{V} \cdot \mathbf{n}) \, dA \tag{3.62}$$

where $\dot{W}_s = 0$ because there can be no infinitesimal shaft protruding into the control volume. By analogy with Eq. (4.20), the right-hand side becomes, for this tiny element,

$$\dot{Q} - \dot{W}_v = \left[\frac{\partial}{\partial t}(\rho e) + \frac{\partial}{\partial x}(\rho u \zeta) + \frac{\partial}{\partial y}(\rho v \zeta) + \frac{\partial}{\partial z}(\rho w \zeta)\right] dx \, dy \, dz \tag{4.42}$$

where $\zeta = e + p/\rho$. When we use the continuity equation by analogy with Eq. (4.21), this becomes

$$\dot{Q} - \dot{W}_v = \left(\rho\frac{de}{dt} + \mathbf{V} \cdot \nabla p\right) dx \, dy \, dz \tag{4.43}$$

To evaluate $\dot{Q}$, we neglect radiation and consider only heat conduction through the sides of the element. The heat flow by conduction follows Fourier's law from Chap. 1

$$\mathbf{q} = -k\,\nabla T \tag{1.29}$$

where k is the coefficient of thermal conductivity of the fluid. Figure 4.6 shows the heat flow passing through the x faces, the y and z heat flows being omitted for clarity. We can list these six heat-flux terms:

Faces	Inlet heat flux	Outlet heat flux
x	$q_x \, dy \, dz$	$\left[q_x + \dfrac{\partial}{\partial x}(q_x)\,dx\right] dy \, dz$
y	$q_y \, dx \, dz$	$\left[q_y + \dfrac{\partial}{\partial y}(q_y)\,dy\right] dx \, dz$
z	$q_z \, dx \, dy$	$\left[q_z + \dfrac{\partial}{\partial z}(q_z)\,dz\right] dx \, dy$

[1] We are neglecting the possibility of a finite *couple* being applied to the element by some powerful external force field. See, e.g., Ref. 6, p. 217.

[2] This section may be omitted without loss of continuity.

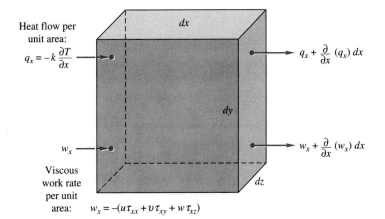

Fig. 4.6 Elemental cartesian control volume showing heat-flow and viscous-work-rate terms in the x direction.

Heat flow per unit area:
$$q_x = -k \frac{\partial T}{\partial x}$$

$$q_x + \frac{\partial}{\partial x}(q_x)\,dx$$

$$w_x$$

$$w_x + \frac{\partial}{\partial x}(w_x)\,dx$$

Viscous work rate per unit area: $w_x = -(u\tau_{xx} + v\tau_{xy} + w\tau_{xz})$

By adding the inlet terms and subtracting the outlet terms, we obtain the net heat added to the element

$$\dot{Q} = -\left[\frac{\partial}{\partial x}(q_x) + \frac{\partial}{\partial y}(q_y) + \frac{\partial}{\partial z}(q_z) \right] dx\,dy\,dz = -\nabla \cdot \mathbf{q}\,dx\,dy\,dz \qquad (4.44)$$

As expected, the heat flux is proportional to the element volume. Introducing Fourier's law from Eq. (1.29), we have

$$\dot{Q} = \nabla \cdot (k\,\nabla T)\,dx\,dy\,dz \qquad (4.45)$$

The rate of work done by viscous stresses equals the product of the stress component, its corresponding velocity component, and the area of the element face. Figure 4.6 shows the work rate on the left x face is

$$\dot{W}_{v,\text{LF}} = w_x\,dy\,dz \qquad \text{where } w_x = -(u\tau_{xx} + v\tau_{xy} + w\tau_{xz}) \qquad (4.46)$$

(where the subscript LF stands for left face) and a slightly different work on the right face due to the gradient in w_x. These work fluxes could be tabulated in exactly the same manner as the heat fluxes in the previous table, with w_x replacing q_x, etc. After outlet terms are subtracted from inlet terms, the net viscous-work rate becomes

$$\dot{W}_v = \left[\frac{\partial}{\partial x}(u\tau_{xx} + v\tau_{xy} + w\tau_{xz}) + \frac{\partial}{\partial y}(u\tau_{yx} + v\tau_{yy} + w\tau_{yz}) \right.$$

$$\left. + \frac{\partial}{\partial z}(u\tau_{zx} + v\tau_{zy} + w\tau_{zz}) \right] dx\,dy\,dz$$

$$= -\nabla \cdot (\mathbf{V} \cdot \tau_{ij})\,dx\,dy\,dz \qquad (4.47)$$

We now substitute Eqs. (4.45) and (4.47) into Eq. (4.43) to obtain one form of the differential energy equation

$$\rho \frac{de}{dt} + \mathbf{V} \cdot \nabla p = \nabla \cdot (k\,\nabla T) + \nabla \cdot (\mathbf{V} \cdot \tau_{ij}) \qquad \text{where } e = \hat{u} + \tfrac{1}{2}V^2 + gz \qquad (4.48)$$

A more useful form is obtained if we split up the viscous-work term

$$\nabla \cdot (\mathbf{V} \cdot \tau_{ij}) \equiv \mathbf{V} \cdot (\nabla \cdot \tau_{ij}) + \Phi \qquad (4.49)$$

where Φ is short for the *viscous-dissipation function*.[1] For a newtonian incompressible viscous fluid, this function has the form

$$\Phi = \mu\left[2\left(\frac{\partial u}{\partial x}\right)^2 + 2\left(\frac{\partial v}{\partial y}\right)^2 + 2\left(\frac{\partial w}{\partial z}\right)^2 + \left(\frac{\partial v}{\partial x} + \frac{\partial u}{\partial y}\right)^2 \right.$$
$$\left. + \left(\frac{\partial w}{\partial y} + \frac{\partial v}{\partial z}\right)^2 + \left(\frac{\partial u}{\partial z} + \frac{\partial w}{\partial x}\right)^2\right] \tag{4.50}$$

Since all terms are quadratic, viscous dissipation is always positive, so that a viscous flow always tends to lose its available energy due to dissipation, in accordance with the second law of thermodynamics.

Now substitute Eq. (4.49) into Eq. (4.48), using the linear-momentum equation (4.33) to eliminate $\nabla \cdot \tau_{ij}$. This will cause the kinetic and potential energies to cancel, leaving a more customary form of the general differential energy equation

$$\rho\frac{d\hat{u}}{dt} + p(\nabla \cdot \mathbf{V}) = \nabla \cdot (k\,\nabla T) + \Phi \tag{4.51}$$

This equation is valid for a newtonian fluid under very general conditions of unsteady, compressible, viscous, heat-conducting flow, except that it neglects radiation heat transfer and internal *sources* of heat that might occur during a chemical or nuclear reaction.

Equation (4.51) is too difficult to analyze except on a digital computer [1]. It is customary to make the following approximations:

$$d\hat{u} \approx c_v\,dT \qquad c_v, \mu, k, \rho \approx \text{const} \tag{4.52}$$

Equation (4.51) then takes the simpler form

$$\rho c_v\frac{dT}{dt} = k\nabla^2 T + \Phi \tag{4.53}$$

which involves temperature T as the sole primary variable plus velocity as a secondary variable through the total time-derivative operator

$$\frac{dT}{dt} = \frac{\partial T}{\partial t} + u\frac{\partial T}{\partial x} + v\frac{\partial T}{\partial y} + w\frac{\partial T}{\partial z} \tag{4.54}$$

A great many interesting solutions to Eq. (4.53) are known for various flow conditions, and extended treatments are given in advanced books on viscous flow [4, 5] and books on heat transfer [7, 8].

One well-known special case of Eq. (4.53) occurs when the fluid is at rest or has negligible velocity, where the dissipation Φ and convective terms become negligible

$$\rho c_v\frac{\partial T}{\partial t} = k\,\nabla^2 T \tag{4.55}$$

This is called the *heat-conduction equation* in applied mathematics and is valid for solids and fluids at rest. The solution to Eq. (4.55) for various conditions is a large part of courses and books on heat transfer.

This completes the derivation of the basic differential equations of fluid motion.

---

[1] For further details, see, e.g., Ref. 5, p. 72.

4.6 Boundary Conditions for the Basic Equations

There are three basic differential equations of fluid motion, just derived. Let us summarize them here:

Continuity:
$$\frac{\partial \rho}{\partial t} + \nabla \cdot (\rho \mathbf{V}) = 0 \tag{4.56}$$

Momentum:
$$\rho \frac{d\mathbf{V}}{dt} = \rho \mathbf{g} - \nabla p + \nabla \cdot \tau_{ij} \tag{4.57}$$

Energy
$$\rho \frac{d\hat{u}}{dt} + p(\nabla \cdot \mathbf{V}) = \nabla \cdot (k \nabla T) + \Phi \tag{4.58}$$

where Φ is given by Eq. (4.50). In general, the density is variable, so that these three equations contain five unknowns, ρ, V, p, $\hat{u}$, and T. Therefore we need two additional relations to complete the system of equations. These are provided by data or algebraic expressions for the state relations of the thermodynamic properties

$$\rho = \rho(p, T) \qquad \hat{u} = \hat{u}(p, T) \tag{4.59}$$

For example, for a perfect gas with constant specific heats, we complete the system with

$$\rho = \frac{p}{RT} \qquad \hat{u} = \int c_v \, dT \approx c_v \, T + \text{const} \tag{4.60}$$

It is shown in advanced books [4, 5] that this system of equations (4.56) to (4.59), is well posed and can be solved analytically or numerically, subject to the proper boundary conditions.

What are the proper boundary conditions? First, if the flow is unsteady, there must be an *initial condition* or initial spatial distribution known for each variable:

At $t = 0$:
$$\rho, V, p, \hat{u}, T = \text{known } f(x, y, z) \tag{4.61}$$

Thereafter, for all times t to be analyzed, we must know something about the variables at each *boundary* enclosing the flow.

Figure 4.7 illustrates the three most common types of boundaries encountered in fluid-flow analysis: a solid wall, an inlet or outlet, a liquid-gas interface.

First, for a solid, impermeable wall, there is no slip and no temperature jump in a viscous heat-conducting fluid

$$\mathbf{V}_{\text{fluid}} = \mathbf{V}_{\text{wall}} \qquad T_{\text{fluid}} = T_{\text{wall}} \qquad \text{solid wall} \tag{4.62}$$

The only exception to Eq. (4.62) occurs in an extremely rarefied gas flow, where slippage can be present [5].

Second, at any inlet or outlet section of the flow, the complete distribution of velocity, pressure, and temperature must be known for all times:

Inlet or outlet:
$$\text{Known } \mathbf{V}, p, T \tag{4.63}$$

These inlet and outlet sections can be and often are at $\pm\infty$, simulating a body immersed in an infinite expanse of fluid.

Finally, the most complex conditions occur at a liquid-gas interface, or free surface, as sketched in Fig. 4.7. Let us denote the interface by

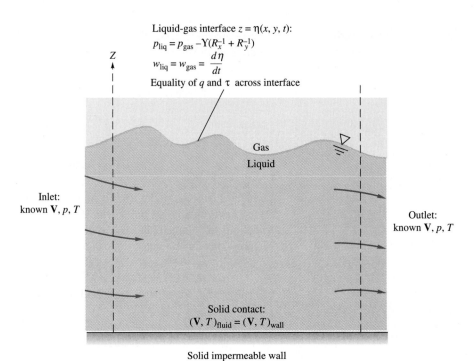

Fig. 4.7 Typical boundary conditions in a viscous heat-conducting fluid-flow analysis.

Interface: $\qquad\qquad\qquad\qquad z = \eta(x, y, t)$ $\qquad\qquad$ (4.64)

Then there must be equality of vertical velocity across the interface, so that no holes appear between liquid and gas:

$$w_{\text{liq}} = w_{\text{gas}} = \frac{d\eta}{dt} = \frac{\partial\eta}{\partial t} + u\frac{\partial\eta}{\partial x} + v\frac{\partial\eta}{\partial y} \qquad\qquad (4.65)$$

This is called the *kinematic boundary condition.*

There must be mechanical equilibrium across the interface. The viscous-shear stresses must balance

$$(\tau_{zy})_{\text{liq}} = (\tau_{zy})_{\text{gas}} \qquad (\tau_{zx})_{\text{liq}} = (\tau_{zx})_{\text{gas}} \qquad\qquad (4.66)$$

Neglecting the viscous normal stresses, the pressures must balance at the interface except for surface-tension effects

$$p_{\text{liq}} = p_{\text{gas}} - Y(R_x^{-1} + R_y^{-1}) \qquad\qquad (4.67)$$

which is equivalent to Eq. (1.34). The radii of curvature can be written in terms of the free-surface position η

$$R_x^{-1} + R_y^{-1} = \frac{\partial}{\partial x}\left[\frac{\partial\eta/\partial x}{\sqrt{1 + (\partial\eta/\partial x)^2 + (\partial\eta/\partial y)^2}}\right]$$
$$+ \frac{\partial}{\partial y}\left[\frac{\partial\eta/\partial y}{\sqrt{1 + (\partial\eta/\partial x)^2 + (\partial\eta/\partial y)^2}}\right] \qquad (4.68)$$

Finally, the heat transfer must be the same on both sides of the interface, since no heat can be stored in the infinitesimally thin interface

$$(q_z)_{\text{liq}} = (q_z)_{\text{gas}} \tag{4.69}$$

Neglecting radiation, this is equivalent to

$$\left(k\frac{\partial T}{\partial z}\right)_{\text{liq}} = \left(k\frac{\partial T}{\partial z}\right)_{\text{gas}} \tag{4.70}$$

This is as much detail as we wish to give at this level of exposition. Further and even more complicated details on fluid-flow boundary conditions are given in Refs. 5 and 9.

Simplified Free-Surface Conditions

In the introductory analyses given in this book, such as open-channel flows in Chap. 10, we shall back away from the exact conditions (4.65) to (4.69) and assume that the upper fluids is an ''atmosphere'' which merely exerts pressure upon the lower fluid, with shear and heat conduction negligible. We also neglect nonlinear terms involving the slopes of the free surface. We then have a much simpler and linear set of conditions at the surface

$$p_{\text{liq}} \approx p_{\text{gas}} - \Upsilon\left(\frac{\partial^2 \eta}{\partial x^2} + \frac{\partial^2 \eta}{\partial y^2}\right) \qquad w_{\text{liq}} \approx \frac{\partial \eta}{\partial t}$$

$$\left(\frac{\partial V}{\partial z}\right)_{\text{liq}} \approx 0 \qquad \left(\frac{\partial T}{\partial z}\right)_{\text{liq}} \approx 0 \tag{4.71}$$

In many cases, such as open-channel flow, we can also neglect surface tension, so that

$$p_{\text{liq}} \approx p_{\text{atm}} \tag{4.72}$$

These are the types of approximations which will be used in Chap. 10. The nondimensional forms of these conditions will also be useful in Chap. 5.

Incompressible Flow with Constant Properties

Flow with constant ρ, μ, and k is a basic simplification which will be used, e.g., throughout Chap. 6. The basic equations of motion (4.56) to (4.58) reduce to:

Continuity:
$$\nabla \cdot V = 0 \tag{4.73}$$

Momentum:
$$\rho\frac{dV}{dt} = \rho g - \nabla p + \mu \nabla^2 V \tag{4.74}$$

Energy:
$$\rho c_v \frac{dT}{dt} = k \nabla^2 T + \Phi \tag{4.75}$$

Since ρ is constant, there are only three unknowns: p, V, and T. The system is closed.[1] Not only that, the system splits apart: Continuity and momentum are independent of T. Thus we can solve Eqs. (4.73) and (4.74) entirely separately for the pressure and velocity, using such boundary conditions as

Solid surface:
$$V = V_{\text{wall}} \tag{4.76}$$

[1] For this system, what are the thermodynamic equivalents to Eq. (4.59)?

Inlet or outlet: $\qquad\qquad\qquad$ Known $\mathbf{V}$, p $\qquad\qquad\qquad\qquad$ (4.77)

Free surface: $\qquad\qquad\qquad p \approx p_a \qquad w \approx \dfrac{\partial\eta}{\partial t}$ $\qquad\qquad\qquad$ (4.78)

Later, entirely at our leisure,[1] we can solve for the temperature distribution from Eq. (4.75), which depends upon velocity $\mathbf{V}$ through the dissipation Φ and the total time-derivative operator d/dt.

Inviscid-Flow Approximations   Chapter 8 assumes inviscid flow throughout, for which the viscosity $\mu = 0$. The momentum equation (4.74) reduces to

$$\rho\frac{d\mathbf{V}}{dt} = \rho\mathbf{g} - \nabla p \qquad\qquad (4.79)$$

This is *Euler's equation*; it can be integrated along a streamline to obtain Bernoulli's equation (see Sec. 4.9). By neglecting viscosity we have lost the second-order derivative of $\mathbf{V}$ in Eq. (4.74); therefore we must relax one boundary condition on velocity. The only mathematically sensible condition to drop is the no-slip condition at the wall. We let the flow slip parallel to the wall but do not allow it to flow into the wall. The proper inviscid condition is that the normal velocities must match at any solid surface:

Inviscid flow: $\qquad\qquad\qquad (V_n)_{\text{fluid}} = (V_n)_{\text{wall}}$ $\qquad\qquad\qquad$ (4.80)

In most cases the wall is fixed; therefore the proper inviscid-flow condition is

$$V_n = 0 \qquad\qquad (4.81)$$

There is *no* condition whatever on the tangential velocity component at the wall in inviscid flow. The tangential velocity will be part of the solution, and the correct value will appear after the analysis is completed (see Chap. 8).

EXAMPLE 4.6

For steady incompressible laminar flow through a long tube, the velocity distribution is given by

$$v_z = U\left(1 - \frac{r^2}{R^2}\right) \qquad v_r = v_\theta = 0$$

where U is the maximum, or centerline, velocity and R is the tube radius. If the wall temperature is constant at T_w and the temperature $T = T(r)$ only, find $T(r)$ for this flow.

Solution

With $T = T(r)$, Eq. (4.75) reduces for steady flow to

$$\rho c_v v_r \frac{dT}{dr} = \frac{k}{r}\frac{d}{dr}\left(r\frac{dT}{dr}\right) + \mu\left(\frac{dv_z}{dr}\right)^2 \qquad\qquad (1)$$

---

[1] Since temperature is entirely *uncoupled* by this assumption, we may never get around to solving for it here and may ask you to wait until a course on heat transfer.

But since $v_r = 0$ for this flow, the convective term on the left vanishes. Introduce v_z into Eq. (1) to obtain

$$\frac{k}{r} \frac{d}{dr} \left(r \frac{dT}{dr} \right)^2 = -\mu \left(\frac{dv_z}{dr} \right)^2 = -\frac{4U^2 \mu r^2}{R^4} \tag{2}$$

Multiply through by r/k and integrate once:

$$r \frac{dT}{dr} = -\frac{\mu U^2 r^4}{kR^4} + C_1 \tag{3}$$

Divide through by r and integrate once again:

$$T = -\frac{\mu U^2 r^4}{4kR^4} + C_1 \ln r + C_2 \tag{4}$$

Now we are in position to apply our boundary conditions to evaluate C_1 and C_2.

First, since the logarithm of zero is $-\infty$, the temperature at $r = 0$ will be infinite unless

$$C_1 = 0 \tag{5}$$

Thus we eliminate the possibility of a logarithmic singularity. The same thing will happen if we apply the *symmetry* condition $dT/dr = 0$ at $r = 0$ to Eq. (3). The constant C_2 is then found by the wall-temperature condition at $r = R$

$$T = T_w = -\frac{\mu U^2}{4k} + C_2$$

or

$$C_2 = T_w + \frac{\mu U^2}{4k} \tag{6}$$

The correct solution is thus

$$T(r) = T_w + \frac{\mu U^2}{4k} \left(1 - \frac{r^2}{R^4} \right) \qquad Ans. \tag{7}$$

which is a fourth-order parabolic distribution with a maximum value $T_0 = T_w + \mu U^2/(4k)$ at the centerline.

4.7 The Stream Function

We have seen in Sec. 4.6 that even if the temperature is uncoupled from our system of equations of motion, we must solve the continuity and momentum equations simultaneously for pressure and velocity. The *stream function* ψ is a clever device which allows us to wipe out the continuity equation and solve the momentum equation directly for the single variable ψ.

The stream-function idea works only if the continuity equation (4.56) can be reduced to *two* terms. In general, we have *four* terms:

Cartesian:
$$\frac{\partial \rho}{\partial t} + \frac{\partial}{\partial x} (\rho u) + \frac{\partial}{\partial y} (\rho v) + \frac{\partial}{\partial z} (\rho w) = 0$$

$$\tag{4.82}$$

Cylindrical:
$$\frac{\partial \rho}{\partial t} + \frac{1}{r} \frac{\partial}{\partial r} (r \rho v_r) + \frac{1}{r} \frac{\partial}{\partial \theta} (\rho v_\theta) + \frac{\partial}{\partial z} (\rho v_z) = 0$$

First, let us eliminate unsteady flow, which is a peculiar and unrealistic application of the stream-function idea. Reduce either of Eqs. (4.82) to any *two* terms. The most common application is incompressible flow in the *xy* plane

$$\frac{\partial u}{\partial x} + \frac{\partial v}{\partial y} = 0 \tag{4.83}$$

This equation is satisfied *identically* if a function $\psi(x, y)$ is defined such that Eq. (4.83) becomes

$$\frac{\partial}{\partial x}\left(\frac{\partial \psi}{\partial y}\right) + \frac{\partial}{\partial y}\left(-\frac{\partial \psi}{\partial x}\right) \equiv 0 \tag{4.84}$$

Comparison of (4.83) and (4.84) shows that this new function ψ must be defined such that

$$u = \frac{\partial \psi}{\partial y} \qquad v = -\frac{\partial \psi}{\partial x} \tag{4.85}$$

or

$$\mathbf{V} = \mathbf{i}\,\frac{\partial \psi}{\partial y} - \mathbf{j}\,\frac{\partial \psi}{\partial x}$$

Is this legitimate? Yes, it is just a mathematical trick of replacing two variables (u and v) by a single higher-order function ψ. The vorticity, or curl $\mathbf{V}$, is an interesting function

$$\text{curl } \mathbf{V} = 2\mathbf{k}\omega_z = -\mathbf{k}\,\nabla^2\psi \qquad \text{where} \qquad \nabla^2\psi = \frac{\partial^2 \psi}{\partial x^2} + \frac{\partial^2 \psi}{\partial y^2} \tag{4.86}$$

Thus, if we take the curl of the momentum equation (4.74) and utilize Eq. (4.86), we obtain a single equation for ψ

$$\frac{\partial \psi}{\partial y}\frac{\partial}{\partial x}\,(\nabla^2\psi) - \frac{\partial \psi}{\partial x}\frac{\partial}{\partial y}\,(\nabla^2\psi) = \nu\,\nabla^2(\nabla^2\psi) \tag{4.87}$$

where $\nu = \mu/\rho$ is the kinematic viscosity. This is partly a victory and partly a defeat: Eq. (4.87) is scalar and has only one variable, ψ, but it now contains *fourth*-order derivatives and probably will require computer analysis. There will be four boundary conditions required on ψ. For example, for the flow of a uniform stream in the x direction past a solid body, the four conditions would be

At infinity:

$$\frac{\partial \psi}{\partial y} = U_\infty \qquad \frac{\partial \psi}{\partial x} = 0$$

$$\tag{4.88}$$

At the body:

$$\frac{\partial \psi}{\partial y} = \frac{\partial \psi}{\partial x} = 0$$

Many examples of numerical solution of Eqs. (4.87) and (4.88) are given in Ref. 1.

One important application is inviscid *irrotational* flow in the xy plane, where $\omega_z \equiv 0$. Equations (4.86) and (4.87) reduce to

$$\nabla^2\psi = \frac{\partial^2 \psi}{\partial x^2} + \frac{\partial^2 \psi}{\partial y^2} = 0 \tag{4.89}$$

This is the second-order *Laplace equation* (Chap. 8), for which many solutions and analytical techniques are known. Also, boundary conditions like Eq. (4.88) reduce to

At infinity: $\qquad\qquad\qquad\qquad\qquad \psi = U_\infty y + \text{const}$ $\qquad\qquad\qquad$ (4.90)

At the body: $\qquad\qquad\qquad\qquad\qquad \psi = \text{const}$

It is well within our capability to find some useful solutions to Eqs. (4.89) and (4.90), which we shall do in Chap. 8.

Geometric Interpretation of ψ

The fancy mathematics above would serve by itself to make the stream function immortal and always useful to engineers. Even better, though, ψ has a beautiful geometric interpretation: Lines of constant ψ are *streamlines* of the flow. This can be shown as follows. From Eq. (1.44) the definition of a streamline in two-dimensional flow is

$$\frac{dx}{u} = \frac{dy}{v}$$

or $\qquad\qquad\qquad\qquad u\,dy - v\,dx = 0 \qquad \text{streamline} \qquad$ (4.91)

Introducing the stream function from Eq. (4.85), we have

$$\frac{\partial \psi}{\partial x}\,dx + \frac{\partial \psi}{\partial y}\,dy = 0 = d\psi \qquad\qquad\qquad (4.92)$$

Thus the change in ψ is zero along a streamline, or

$$\psi = \text{const along a streamline} \qquad\qquad\qquad (4.93)$$

Having found a given solution $\psi(x, y)$, we can plot lines of constant ψ to give the streamlines of the flow.

There is also a physical interpretation which relates ψ to volume flow. From Fig. 4.8, we can compute the volume flow dQ through an element ds of control surface of unit depth

$$dQ = (\mathbf{V}\cdot\mathbf{n})\,dA = \left(\mathbf{i}\frac{\partial \psi}{\partial y} - \mathbf{j}\frac{\partial \psi}{\partial x}\right)\cdot\left(\mathbf{i}\frac{dy}{ds} - \mathbf{j}\frac{dx}{ds}\right)ds(1)$$

$$= \frac{\partial \psi}{\partial x}\,dx + \frac{\partial \psi}{\partial y}\,dy = d\psi \qquad\qquad\qquad (4.94)$$

Fig. 4.8 Geometric interpretation of stream function: volume flow through a differential portion of a control surface.

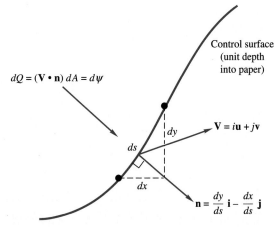

$dQ = (\mathbf{V}\bullet\mathbf{n})\,dA = d\psi$

Control surface
(unit depth
into paper)

dy

$\mathbf{V} = i\mathbf{u} + j\mathbf{v}$

ds

dx

$\mathbf{n} = \dfrac{dy}{ds}\,\mathbf{i} - \dfrac{dx}{ds}\,\mathbf{j}$

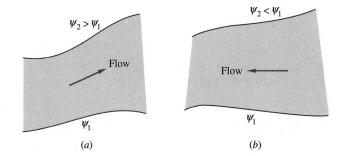

Fig. 4.9 Sign convention for flow in terms of change in stream function: (a) flow to the right if ψ_U is greater; (b) flow to the left if ψ_L is greater.

Thus the change in ψ across the element is numerically equal to the volume flow through the element. The volume flow between any two points in the flow field is equal to the change in stream function between those points:

$$Q_{1\to 2} = \int_1^2 (\mathbf{V} \cdot \mathbf{n})\, dA = \int_1^2 d\psi = \psi_2 - \psi_1 \tag{4.95}$$

Further, the direction of the flow can be ascertained by noting whether ψ increases or decreases. As sketched in Fig. 4.9, the flow is to the right if ψ_U is greater than ψ_L, where the subscripts stand for upper and lower, as before; otherwise the flow is to the left.

Both the stream function and the velocity potential were invented by the French mathematician Joseph Louis Lagrange and published in his treatise on fluid mechanics in 1781.

EXAMPLE 4.7

If a stream function exists for the velocity field of Example 4.5

$$u = a(x^2 - y^2) \qquad v = -2axy \qquad w = 0$$

find it, plot it, and interpret it.

Solution

Since this flow field was shown expressly in Example 4.3 to satisfy the equation of continuity, we are pretty sure that a stream function does exist. We can check again to see if

$$\frac{\partial u}{\partial x} + \frac{\partial v}{\partial y} = 0$$

Substitute: $\qquad\qquad 2ax + (-2ax) = 0 \qquad$ checks

Therefore we are certain that a stream function exists. To find ψ, we simply set

$$u = \frac{\partial \psi}{\partial y} = ax^2 - ay^2 \tag{1}$$

$$v = -\frac{\partial \psi}{\partial x} = -2axy \tag{2}$$

and work from either one toward the other. Integrate (1) partially

$$\psi = ax^2y - \frac{ay^3}{3} + f(x) \qquad (3)$$

Differentiate (3) with respect to x and compare with (2)

$$\frac{\partial\psi}{\partial x} = 2axy + f'(x) = 2axy \qquad (4)$$

Therefore $f'(x) = 0$, or $f = $ constant. The complete stream function is thus found

$$\psi = a\left(x^2y - \frac{y^3}{3}\right) + C \qquad Ans. \quad (5)$$

To plot this, set $C = 0$ for convenience and plot the function

$$3x^2y - y^3 = \frac{3\psi}{a} \qquad (6)$$

for constant values of ψ. The result is shown in Fig. E4.7a to be six 60° wedges of circulating motion, each with identical flow patterns except for the arrows. Once the streamlines are labeled, the flow directions follow from the sign convention of Fig. 4.9. How can the flow be interpreted? Since there is slip along all streamlines, no streamline can truly represent a solid surface in a viscous flow. However, the flow could represent the impingement of three incoming streams at 60, 180, and 300°. This would be a rather unrealistic yet exact solution to the Navier-Stokes equation, as we showed in Example 4.5.

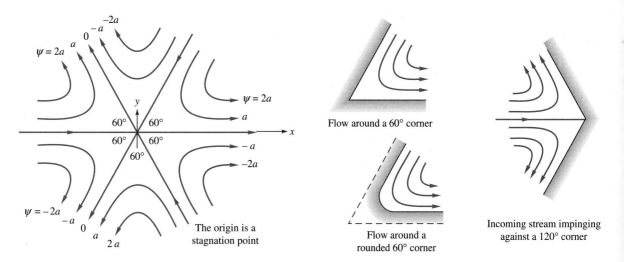

Fig. E4.7a

Flow around a 60° corner

The origin is a
stagnation point

Flow around a
rounded 60° corner

Incoming stream impinging
against a 120° corner

Fig. E4.7b

By allowing the flow to slip as a frictionless approximation, we could let any given streamline be a body shape. Some examples are shown in Fig. E4.7b.

A stream function also exists in a variety of other physical situations where only two coordinates are needed to define the flow. Three examples are illustrated here.

Steady Plane Compressible Flow

Suppose now that the density is variable but that $w = 0$, so that the flow is in the xy plane. Then the equation of continuity becomes

$$\frac{\partial}{\partial x}(\rho u) + \frac{\partial}{\partial y}(\rho v) = 0 \qquad (4.96)$$

We see that this is in exactly the same form as Eq. (4.84). Therefore a compressible-flow stream function can be defined such that

$$\rho u = \frac{\partial \psi}{\partial y} \qquad \rho v = -\frac{\partial \psi}{\partial x} \qquad (4.97)$$

Again lines of constant ψ are streamlines of the flow, but the change in ψ is now equal to the *mass* flow, not the volume flow

$$d\dot{m} = \rho(\mathbf{V} \cdot \mathbf{n})\, dA = d\psi$$

or $\qquad\qquad \dot{m}_{1\to2} = \int_1^2 \rho(\mathbf{V} \cdot \mathbf{n})\, dA = \psi_2 - \psi_1 \qquad (4.98)$

The sign convention on flow direction is the same as in Fig. 4.9. This particular stream function combines density with velocity and must be substituted into not only momentum but also the energy and state relations (4.58) and (4.59) with pressure and temperature as companion variables. Thus the compressible stream function is not a great victory, and further assumptions must be made to effect an analytical solution to a typical problem (see, e.g., Ref. 5, chap. 7).

Incompressible Plane Flow in Polar Coordinates

Suppose that the important coordinates are r and θ, with $v_z = 0$, and that the density is constant. Then Eq. (4.82b) reduces to

$$\frac{1}{r}\frac{\partial}{\partial r}(r v_r) + \frac{1}{r}\frac{\partial}{\partial \theta}(v_\theta) = 0 \qquad (4.99)$$

After multiplying through by r, we see that this is the same as the analogous form of Eq. (4.84)

$$\frac{\partial}{\partial r}\left(\frac{\partial \psi}{\partial \theta}\right) + \frac{\partial}{\partial \theta}\left(-\frac{\partial \psi}{\partial r}\right) = 0 \qquad (4.100)$$

By comparison of (4.99) and (4.100) we deduce the form of the incompressible polar-coordinate stream function

$$v_r = \frac{1}{r}\frac{\partial \psi}{\partial \theta} \qquad v_\theta = -\frac{\partial \psi}{\partial r} \qquad (4.101)$$

Once again lines of constant ψ are streamlines, and the change in ψ is the *volume flow* $Q_{1\to2} = \psi_2 - \psi_1$. The sign convention is the same as in Fig. 4.9. This type of stream function is very useful in analyzing flows with cylinders, vortices, sources, and sinks (Chap. 8).

Incompressible Axisymmetric Flow

As a final example, suppose that the flow is three-dimensional (v_r, v_z) but with no circumferential variations, $v_\theta = \partial/\partial\theta = 0$ (see Fig. 4.2 for definition of coordinates).

Such a flow is termed *axisymmetric*, and the flow pattern is the same when viewed on any meridional plane through the axis of revolution z. For incompressible flow, Eq. (4.82) becomes

$$\frac{1}{r}\frac{\partial}{\partial r}(rv_r) + \frac{\partial}{\partial z}(v_z) = 0 \tag{4.102}$$

This doesn't seem to work: Can't we get rid of the one r outside? But when we realize that r and z are independent coordinates, Eq. (4.102) can be rewritten as

$$\frac{\partial}{\partial r}(rv_r) + \frac{\partial}{\partial z}(rv_z) = 0 \tag{4.103}$$

By analogy with Eq. (4.84), this has the form

$$\frac{\partial}{\partial r}\left(-\frac{\partial \psi}{\partial z}\right) + \frac{\partial}{\partial z}\left(\frac{\partial \psi}{\partial r}\right) = 0 \tag{4.104}$$

By comparing (4.103) and (4.104), we deduce the form of an incompressible axisymmetric stream function $\psi(r, z)$

$$v_r = -\frac{1}{r}\frac{\partial \psi}{\partial z} \qquad v_z = \frac{1}{r}\frac{\partial \psi}{\partial r} \tag{4.105}$$

Here again lines of constant ψ are streamlines, but there is a factor (2π) in the volume flow: $Q_{1\to2} = 2\pi(\psi_2 - \psi_1)$. The sign convention on flow is the same as in Fig. 4.9.

EXAMPLE 4.8

Investigate the stream function in polar coordinates

$$\psi = U \sin \theta \left(r - \frac{R^2}{r}\right) \tag{1}$$

where U and R are constants, a velocity and a length, respectively. Plot the streamlines. What does the flow represent? Is it a realistic solution to the basic equations?

Solution

The streamlines are lines of constant ψ, which has units of square meters per second. Note that $\psi/(UR)$ is dimensionless. Rewrite Eq. (1) in dimensionless form

$$\frac{\psi}{UR} = \sin \theta \left(\eta - \frac{1}{\eta}\right) \qquad \eta = \frac{r}{R} \tag{2}$$

Of particular interest is the special line $\psi = 0$. From Eq. (1) or (2) this occurs when (*a*) $\theta = 0$ or $180°$ and (*b*) $r = R$. Case (*a*) is the x axis, and case (*b*) is a circle of radius R, both of which are plotted in Fig. E4.8.

For any other nonzero value of ψ it is easiest to pick a value of r and solve for θ:

$$\sin \theta = \frac{\psi/(UR)}{r/R - R/r} \tag{3}$$

In general, there will be two solutions for θ because of the symmetry about the y axis. For example take $\psi/(UR) = +1.0$:

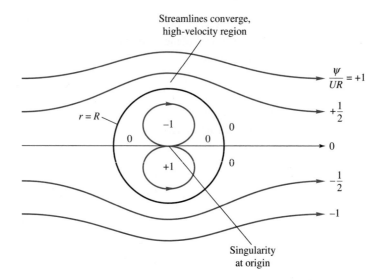

Fig. E4.8

Guess r/R	3.0	2.5	2.0	1.8	1.7	1.618
Compute θ	22°	28°	42°	54°	64°	90°
	158°	152°	138°	156°	116°	

This line is plotted in Fig. E4.8 and passes over the circle $r = R$. You have to watch it, though, because there is a second curve for $\psi/(UR) = +1.0$ for small $r < R$ below the x axis:

Guess r/R	0.618	0.6	0.5	0.4	0.3	0.2	0.1
Compute θ	−90°	−70°	−42°	−28°	−19°	−12°	−6°
		−110°	−138°	−152°	−161°	−168°	−174°

This second curve plots as a closed curve inside the circle $r = R$. There is a singularity of infinite velocity and indeterminate flow direction at the origin. Figure E4.8 shows the full pattern.

The given stream function, Eq. (1), is an exact and classic solution to the momentum equation (4.38) for frictionless flow. Outside the circle $r = R$ it represents two-dimensional inviscid flow of a uniform stream past a circular cylinder (Sec. 8.3). Inside the circle it represents a rather unrealistic trapped circulating motion of what is called a *line doublet*.

4.8 Vorticity and Irrotationality

The assumption of zero fluid angular velocity, or irrotationality, is a very useful simplification. Here we show that angular velocity is associated with the curl of the local-velocity vector.

The differential relations for deformation of a fluid element can be derived by examining Fig. 4.10. Two fluid lines AB and BC, initially perpendicular at time t, move and deform so that at $t + dt$ they have slightly different lengths $A'B'$ and $B'C'$ and are slightly off the perpendicular by angles $d\alpha$ and $d\beta$. Such deformation occurs kinematically because A, B, and C have slightly different velocities when the velocity field $\mathbf{V}$

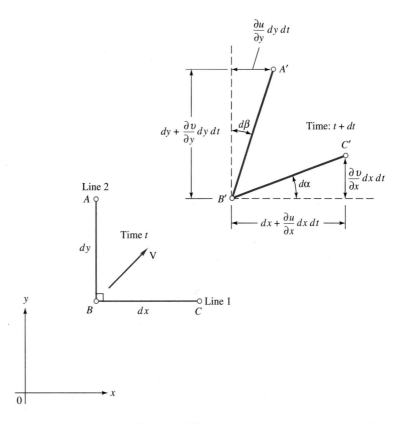

Fig. 4.10 Angular velocity and strain rate of two fluid lines deforming in the *xy* plane.

has spatial gradients. All these differential changes in the motion of A, B, and C are noted in Fig. 4.10.

We define the angular velocity ω_z about the z axis as the average rate of counterclockwise turning of the two lines

$$\omega_z = \frac{1}{2}\left(\frac{d\alpha}{dt} - \frac{d\beta}{dt}\right) \tag{4.106}$$

But from Fig. 4.10, $d\alpha$ and $d\beta$ are each directly related to velocity derivatives in the limit of small dt

$$d\alpha = \lim_{dt \to 0}\left[\tan^{-1}\frac{(\partial v/\partial x)\,dx\,dt}{dx + (\partial u/\partial x)\,dx\,dt}\right] = \frac{\partial v}{\partial x}\,dt$$

$$d\beta = \lim_{dt \to 0}\left[\tan^{-1}\frac{(\partial u/\partial y)\,dy\,dt}{dy + (\partial v/\partial y)\,dy\,dt}\right] = \frac{\partial u}{\partial y}\,dt \tag{4.107}$$

Combining Eqs. (4.106) and (4.107) gives the desired result:

$$\omega_z = \frac{1}{2}\left(\frac{\partial v}{\partial x} - \frac{\partial u}{\partial y}\right) \tag{4.108}$$

In exactly similar manner we determine the other two rates:

$$\omega_x = \frac{1}{2}\left(\frac{\partial w}{\partial y} - \frac{\partial v}{\partial z}\right) \qquad \omega_y = \frac{1}{2}\left(\frac{\partial u}{\partial z} - \frac{\partial w}{\partial x}\right) \tag{4.109}$$

The vector $\boldsymbol{\omega} = \mathbf{i}\omega_x + \mathbf{j}\omega_y + \mathbf{k}\omega_z$ is thus one-half the curl of the velocity vector

$$\boldsymbol{\omega} = \frac{1}{2}(\text{curl } \mathbf{V}) = \frac{1}{2}\begin{vmatrix} \mathbf{i} & \mathbf{j} & \mathbf{k} \\ \dfrac{\partial}{\partial x} & \dfrac{\partial}{\partial y} & \dfrac{\partial}{\partial z} \\ u & v & w \end{vmatrix} \tag{4.110}$$

Since the factor of $\frac{1}{2}$ is annoying, many workers prefer to use a vector twice as large, called the *vorticity*:

$$\zeta = 2\boldsymbol{\omega} = \text{curl } \mathbf{V} \tag{4.111}$$

Many flows have negligible or zero vorticity and are called *irrotational*

$$\text{curl } \mathbf{V} \equiv 0 \tag{4.112}$$

The next section expands on this idea. Such flows can be incompressible or compressible, steady or unsteady.

We may also note that Fig. 4.10 demonstrates the *shear-strain rate* of the element, which is defined as the rate of closure of the initially perpendicular lines

$$\dot{\epsilon}_{xy} = \frac{d\alpha}{dt} + \frac{d\beta}{dt} = \frac{\partial v}{\partial x} + \frac{\partial u}{\partial y} \tag{4.113}$$

When multiplied by viscosity μ, this equals the shear stress τ_{xy} in a newtonian fluid, as discussed earlier in Eqs. (4.37). Appendix E lists strain-rate and vorticity components in cylindrical coordinates.

4.9 Frictionless Irrotational Flows

When a flow is both frictionless and irrotational, pleasant things happen. First, the momentum equation (4.38) reduces to Euler's equation

$$\rho \frac{d\mathbf{V}}{dt} = \rho\mathbf{g} - \nabla p \tag{4.114}$$

Second, there is a great simplification in the acceleration term. Recall from Sec. 4.1 that acceleration has two terms

$$\frac{d\mathbf{V}}{dt} = \frac{\partial \mathbf{V}}{\partial t} + (\mathbf{V} \cdot \nabla)\mathbf{V} \tag{4.2}$$

A beautiful vector identity exists for the second term [11]:

$$(\mathbf{V} \cdot \nabla)\mathbf{V} \equiv \nabla(\tfrac{1}{2}V^2) + \zeta \times \mathbf{V} \tag{4.115}$$

where $\zeta = \text{curl } \mathbf{V}$ from Eq. (4.111) is the fluid vorticity.

Now combine (4.114) and (4.115), divide by ρ, and rearrange on the left-hand side. Dot the entire equation into an arbitrary vector displacement $d\mathbf{r}$:

$$\left[\frac{\partial \mathbf{V}}{\partial t} + \nabla\left(\frac{1}{2}V^2\right) + \zeta \times \mathbf{V} + \frac{1}{\rho}\nabla p - \mathbf{g}\right] \cdot d\mathbf{r} = 0 \tag{4.116}$$

Nothing works right unless we can get rid of the third term. We want

$$(\zeta \times \mathbf{V}) \cdot (d\mathbf{r}) \equiv 0 \tag{4.117}$$

This will be true under various conditions:

1. $\mathbf{V}$ is zero; trivial, no flow (hydrostatics).
2. ζ is zero; irrotational flow.
3. $d\mathbf{r}$ is perpendicular to $\zeta \times \mathbf{V}$; this is rather specialized and rare.
4. $d\mathbf{r}$ is parallel to $\mathbf{V}$; we integrate *along a streamline* (see Sec. 3.7).

Condition 4 is the common assumption. If we integrate along a streamline in frictionless compressible flow and take, for convenience, $\mathbf{g} = -g\mathbf{k}$, Eq. (4.116) reduces to

$$\frac{\partial \mathbf{V}}{\partial t} \cdot d\mathbf{r} + d\left(\frac{1}{2} V^2\right) + \frac{dp}{\rho} + g \, dz = 0 \tag{4.118}$$

Except for the first term, these are exact differentials. Integrate between any two points 1 and 2 along the streamline:

$$\int_1^2 \frac{\partial V}{\partial t} \, ds + \int_1^2 \frac{dp}{\rho} + \frac{1}{2} (V_2^2 - V_1^2) + g(z_2 - z_1) = 0 \tag{4.119}$$

where ds is the arc length along the streamline. Equation (4.119) is Bernoulli's equation for frictionless unsteady flow along a streamline and is identical to Eq. (3.76). For incompressible steady flow, it reduces to

$$\frac{p}{\rho} + \frac{1}{2} V^2 + gz = \text{constant along streamline} \tag{4.120}$$

The constant may vary from streamline to streamline unless the flow is also irrotational (assumption 2). For irrotational flow $\zeta = 0$, the offending term Eq. (4.117) vanishes regardless of the direction of $d\mathbf{r}$, and Eq. (4.120) then holds all over the flow field with the same constant.

Velocity Potential

Irrotationality gives rise to a scalar function ϕ similar and complementary to the stream function ψ. From a theorem in vector analysis [11], a vector with zero curl must be the gradient of a scalar function

$$\text{If} \qquad \nabla \times \mathbf{V} \equiv 0 \qquad \text{then} \qquad \mathbf{V} = \nabla\phi \tag{4.121}$$

where $\phi = \phi(x, y, z, t)$ is called the *velocity potential function*. Knowledge of ϕ thus immediately gives the velocity components

$$u = \frac{\partial\phi}{\partial x} \qquad v = \frac{\partial\phi}{\partial y} \qquad w = \frac{\partial\phi}{\partial z} \tag{4.122}$$

Lines of constant ϕ are called the *potential lines* of the flow.

Note that ϕ, unlike the stream function, is fully three-dimensional and not limited to two coordinates. It reduces a velocity problem with three unknowns u, v, and w to a single unknown potential ϕ; many examples are given in Chap. 8. The velocity potential also simplifies the unsteady Bernoulli equation (4.118) because if ϕ exists, we obtain

$$\frac{\partial \mathbf{V}}{\partial t} \cdot d\mathbf{r} = \frac{\partial}{\partial t} (\nabla\phi) \cdot d\mathbf{r} = d\left(\frac{\partial\phi}{\partial t}\right) \tag{4.123}$$

Equation (4.118) then becomes a relation between ϕ and p

$$\frac{\partial \phi}{\partial t} + \int \frac{dp}{\rho} + \frac{1}{2} |\nabla \phi|^2 + gz = \text{const} \tag{4.124}$$

This is the unsteady irrotational Bernoulli equation. It is very important in the analysis of accelerating flow fields (see, e.g., Refs. 10 and 15), but the only application in this text will be in Sec. 9.3 for steady flow.

Orthogonality of Streamlines and Potential Lines

If a flow is both irrotational and described by only two coordinates, ψ and ϕ both exist and the streamlines and potential lines are everywhere mutually perpendicular except at a stagnation point. For example, for incompressible flow in the xy plane, we would have

$$u = \frac{\partial \psi}{\partial y} = \frac{\partial \phi}{\partial x} \tag{4.125}$$

$$v = -\frac{\partial \psi}{\partial x} = \frac{\partial \phi}{\partial y} \tag{4.126}$$

Can you tell by inspection not only that these relations imply orthogonality but also that ϕ and ψ satisfy Laplace's equation?[1] A line of constant ϕ would be such that the change in ϕ is zero

$$d\phi = \frac{\partial \phi}{\partial x} dx + \frac{\partial \phi}{\partial y} dy = 0 = u\, dx + v\, dy \tag{4.127}$$

Solving, we have

$$\left(\frac{dy}{dx}\right)_{\phi=\text{const}} = -\frac{u}{v} = -\frac{1}{(dy/dx)_{\psi=\text{const}}} \tag{4.128}$$

Equation (4.128) is the mathematical condition that lines of constant ϕ and ψ be mutually orthogonal. It may not be true at a stagnation point, where both u and v are zero, so that their ratio in Eq. (4.128) is indeterminate.

Generation of Rotationality

This is the second time we have discussed Bernoulli's equation under different circumstances (the first was in Sec. 3.7). Such reinforcement is useful, since this is probably the most widely used equation in fluid mechanics. It requires frictionless flow with no shaft work or heat transfer between sections 1 and 2. The flow may or may not be irrotational, the latter being an easier condition, allowing a universal Bernoulli constant.

The only remaining question is: *When* is a flow irrotational? In other words, when does a flow have negligible angular velocity? The exact analysis of fluid rotationality under arbitrary conditions is a topic for advanced study, e.g., Ref. 10, sec. 8.5; Ref. 9, sec. 5.2; and Ref. 5, sec. 2.10. We shall simply state those results here without proof.

A fluid flow which is initially irrotational may become rotational if

1. There are significant viscous forces induced by jets, wakes, or solid boundaries. In this case Bernoulli's equation will not be valid in such viscous regions.

---

[1] Equations (4.125) and (4.126) are called the *Cauchy-Riemann equations* and are studied in complex-variable theory.

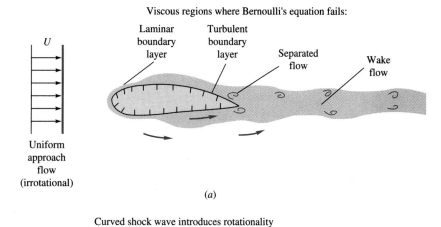

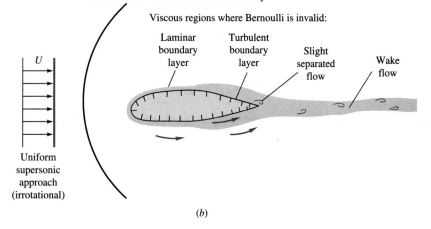

Fig. 4.11 Typical flow patterns illustrating viscous regions patched onto nearly frictionless regions: (a) low subsonic flow past a body ($U \ll a$); frictionless, irrotational potential flow outside the boundary layer (Bernoulli and Laplace equations valid); (b) supersonic flow past a body ($U > a$); frictionless, rotational flow outside the boundary layer (Bernoulli equation valid, potential flow invalid).

2. There are entropy gradients caused by curved shock waves (see Fig. 4.11b).
3. There are density gradients caused by *stratification* (uneven heating) rather than by pressure gradients.
4. There are significant *noninertial* effects such as the earth's rotation (the Coriolis acceleration).

In cases 2 to 4, Bernoulli's equation still holds along a streamline if friction is negligible. We shall not study cases 3 and 4 in this book. Case 2 will be treated briefly in Chap. 9 on gas dynamics. Primarily we are concerned with case 1, where rotation is induced by viscous stresses. This occurs near solid surfaces, where the no-slip condition creates a boundary layer through which the stream velocity drops to zero, and in jets and wakes, where streams of different velocities meet in a region of high shear.

Internal flows, such as pipes and ducts, are mostly viscous, and the wall layers grow to meet in the core of the duct. Bernoulli's equation does not hold in such flows unless it is modified for viscous losses.

External flows, such as a body immersed in a stream, are partly viscous and partly inviscid, the two regions being patched together at the edge of the shear layer or boundary layer. Two examples are shown in Fig. 4.11. Figure 4.11a shows a low-speed subsonic flow past a body. The approach stream is irrotational; i.e., the curl of a constant is zero, but viscous stresses create a rotational shear layer beside and downstream of the body. Generally speaking (see Chap. 6), the shear layer is laminar, or smooth, near the front of the body and turbulent, or disorderly, toward the rear. A separated, or deadwater, region usually occurs near the trailing edge, followed by an unsteady turbulent wake extending far downstream. Some sort of laminar or turbulent viscous theory must be applied to these viscous regions; they are then patched onto the outer flow, which is frictionless and irrotational. If the stream Mach number is less than about 0.3, we can combine Eq. (4.122) with the incompressible continuity equation (4.73).

$$\nabla \cdot \mathbf{V} = \nabla \cdot (\nabla \phi) = 0$$

or
$$\nabla^2 \phi = 0 = \frac{\partial^2 \phi}{\partial x^2} + \frac{\partial^2 \phi}{\partial y^2} + \frac{\partial^2 \phi}{\partial z^2} \tag{4.129}$$

This is Laplace's equation in three dimensions, there being no restraint on the number of coordinates in potential flow. A great deal of Chap. 8 will be concerned with solving Eq. (4.129) for practical engineering problems; it holds in the entire region of Fig. 4.11a outside the shear layer.

Figure 4.11b shows a supersonic flow past a body. A curved shock wave generally forms in front, and the flow downstream is *rotational* due to entropy gradients (case 2). We can use Euler's equation (4.114) in this frictionless region but not potential theory. The shear layers have the same general character as in Fig. 4.11a except that the separation zone is slight or often absent and the wake is usually thinner. Theory of separated flow is presently qualitative, but we can make quantitative estimates of laminar and turbulent boundary layers and wakes.

EXAMPLE 4.9

If a velocity potential exists for the velocity field of Example 4.5

$$u = a(x^2 - y^2) \qquad v = -2axy \qquad w = 0$$

find it, plot it, and compare with Example 4.7.

Solution

Since $w = 0$, the curl of $\mathbf{V}$ has only one z component, and we must show that it is zero:

$$(\nabla \times \mathbf{V})_z = 2\omega_z = \frac{\partial v}{\partial x} - \frac{\partial u}{\partial y} = \frac{\partial}{\partial x}(-2axy) - \frac{\partial}{\partial y}(ax^2 - ay^2)$$

$$= -2ay + 2ay = 0 \qquad \text{checks} \qquad \textit{Ans.}$$

The flow is indeed irrotational. A potential exists.
   To find $\phi(x, y)$, set

$$u = \frac{\partial \phi}{\partial x} = ax^2 - ay^2 \tag{1}$$

$$v = \frac{\partial \phi}{\partial y} = -2axy \tag{2}$$

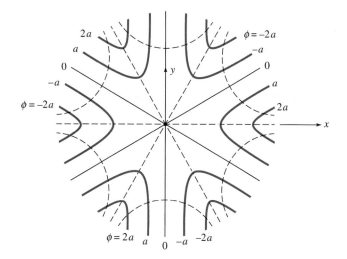

Fig. E4.9

Integrate (1)

$$\phi = \frac{ax^3}{3} - axy^2 + f(y) \tag{3}$$

Differentiate (3) and compare with (2)

$$\frac{\partial \phi}{\partial y} = -2axy + f'(y) = -2axy \tag{4}$$

Therefore $f' = 0$, or $f = $ constant. The velocity potential is

$$\phi = \frac{ax^3}{3} - axy^2 + C \qquad\qquad Ans.$$

Letting $C = 0$, we can plot the ϕ lines in the same fashion as in Example 4.7. The result is shown in Fig. E4.9 (no arrows on ϕ). For this particular problem, the ϕ lines form the same pattern as the ψ lines of Example 4.7 (which are shown here as dashed lines) but are displaced 30°. The ϕ and ψ lines are everywhere perpendicular except at the origin, a stagnation point, where they are 30° apart. We expected trouble at the stagnation point, and there is no general rule for determining the behavior of the lines at that point.

4.10 Some Illustrative Plane Potential Flows

Chapter 8 is devoted entirely to a detailed study of inviscid incompressible flows, especially those which possess both a stream function and a velocity potential. As sketched in Fig. 4.11a, inviscid flow is valid away from solid surfaces, and this inviscid pattern is ''patched'' onto the near-wall viscous layers—an idea developed in Chap. 7. Various body shapes can be simulated by the inviscid-flow pattern. Here we discuss plane flows, three of which are illustrated in Fig. 4.12.

Uniform Stream in the x Direction

A uniform stream $\mathbf{V} = \mathbf{i}U$, as in Fig. 4.12a, possesses both a stream function and a velocity potential, which may be found as follows:

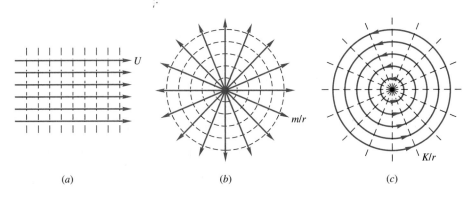

Fig. 4.12 Three elementary plane potential flows. Solid lines are streamlines; dashed lines are potential lines.

(a)   (b)   (c)

$$u = U = \frac{\partial \phi}{\partial x} = \frac{\partial \psi}{\partial y} \qquad v = 0 = \frac{\partial \phi}{\partial y} = -\frac{\partial \psi}{\partial x}$$

We may integrate each expression and discard the constants of integration, which do not affect the velocities in the flow. The results are

Uniform stream iU: $\psi = Uy \qquad \phi = Ux$ (4.130)

The streamlines are horizontal straight lines ($y = $ const), and the potential lines are vertical ($x = $ const), i.e., orthogonal to the streamlines, as expected.

Line Source or Sink at the Origin

Suppose that the z axis were a sort of thin-pipe manifold through which fluid issued at total rate Q uniformly along its length b. Looking at the xy plane, we would see a cylindrical radial outflow or *line source*, as sketched in Fig. 4.12b. Plane polar coordinates are appropriate (see Fig. 4.2), and there is no circumferential velocity. At any radius r, the velocity is

$$v_r = \frac{Q}{2\pi rb} = \frac{m}{r} = \frac{1}{r}\frac{\partial \psi}{\partial \theta} = \frac{\partial \phi}{\partial r} \qquad v_\theta = 0 = -\frac{\partial \psi}{\partial r} = \frac{1}{r}\frac{\partial \phi}{\partial \theta}$$

where we have used the polar-coordinate forms of the stream function and the velocity potential. Integrating and again discarding the constants of integration, we obtain the proper functions for this simple radial flow:

Line source or sink: $\psi = m\theta \qquad \phi = m \ln r$ (4.131)

where $m = Q/(2\pi b)$ is a constant, positive for a source, negative for a sink. As shown in Fig. 4.12b, the streamlines are radial spokes (constant θ), and the potential lines are circles (constant r).

Line Irrotational Vortex

A (two-dimensional) line vortex is a purely circulating steady motion, $v_\theta = f(r)$ only, $v_r = 0$. This satisfies the continuity equation identically, as may be checked from Eq. (4.12b). We may also note that a variety of velocity distributions $v_\theta(r)$ satisfy the θ-momentum equation of a viscous fluid, Eq. (E.6). We may show, as a problem exercise, that only one function $v_\theta(r)$ is *irrotational*, i.e., curl $\mathbf{V} = 0$, and that is $v_\theta = K/r$, where K is a constant. This is sometimes called a *free vortex*, for which the stream function and velocity may be found:

$$v_r = 0 = \frac{1}{r}\frac{\partial\psi}{\partial\theta} = \frac{\partial\phi}{\partial r} \qquad v_\theta = \frac{K}{r} = -\frac{\partial\psi}{\partial r} = \frac{1}{r}\frac{\partial\phi}{\partial\theta}$$

We may again integrate to determine the appropriate functions:

$$\psi = -K \ln r \qquad \phi = K\theta \qquad\qquad (4.132)$$

where K is a constant called the *strength* of the vortex. As shown in Fig. 4.12c, the streamlines are circles (constant r), and the potential lines are radial spokes (constant θ). Note the similarity between Eqs. (4.131) and (4.132). A free vortex is a sort of reversed image of a source. The ''bathtub vortex,'' formed when water drains through a bottom hole in a tank, is a good approximation to the free-vortex pattern.

Superposition: Source Plus an Equal Sink

Each of the three elementary flow patterns in Fig. 4.12 is an incompressible irrotational flow and therefore satisfies both plane ''potential flow'' equations $\nabla^2\psi = 0$ and $\nabla^2\phi = 0$. Since these are linear partial differential equations, any *sum* of such basic solutions is also a solution. Some of these composite solutions are quite interesting and useful.

For example, consider a source $+m$ at $(x, y) = (-a, 0)$, combined with a sink of equal strength $-m$, placed at $(+a, 0)$, as in Fig. 4.13. The resulting stream function is simply the sum of the two. In cartesian coordinates,

$$\psi = \psi_{\text{source}} + \psi_{\text{sink}} = m\tan^{-1}\frac{y}{x+a} - m\tan^{-1}\frac{y}{x-a}$$

Fig. 4.13 Potential flow due to a line source plus an equal line sink, from Eq. (4.133). Solid lines are streamlines, dashed lines are potential lines.

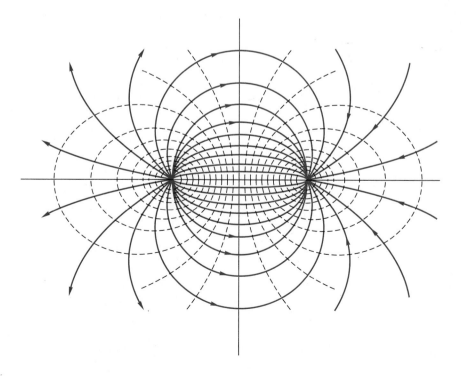

Similarly, the composite velocity potential is

$$\phi = \phi_{\text{source}} + \phi_{\text{sink}} = \frac{1}{2} m \ln [(x + a)^2 + y^2] - \frac{1}{2} m \ln [(x - a)^2 + y^2]$$

By using trigonometric and logarithmic identities, these may be simplified to

$$\text{Source plus sink:} \qquad \psi = -m \tan^{-1} \frac{2ay}{x^2 + y^2 - a^2}$$

$$\phi = \frac{1}{2} m \ln \frac{(x + a)^2 + y^2}{(x - a)^2 + y^2} \tag{4.133}$$

These lines are plotted in Fig. 4.13 and are seen to be two families of orthogonal circles, with the streamlines passing through the source and sink and the potential lines encircling them. They are harmonic (laplacian) functions which are exactly analogous in electromagnetic theory to the electric-current and electric-potential patterns of a magnet with poles at $(\pm a, 0)$.

Sink Plus a Vortex at the Origin

An interesting flow pattern, approximated in nature, occurs by superposition of a sink and a vortex, both centered at the origin. The composite stream function and velocity potential are

$$\text{Sink plus vortex:} \qquad \psi = m\theta - K \ln r \qquad \phi = m \ln r + K\theta \tag{4.134}$$

When plotted, these form two orthogonal families of logarithmic spirals, as shown in Fig. 4.14. This is a fairly realistic simulation of a tornado (where the sink flow moves up the z axis into the atmosphere) or a rapidly draining bathtub vortex. At the center

Fig. 4.14 Superposition of a sink plus a vortex, Eq. (4.134), simulates a tornado.

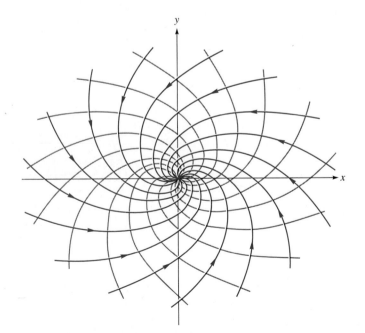

of a real (viscous) vortex, where Eq. (4.134) predicts infinite velocity, the actual circulating flow is highly *rotational* and approximates solid-body rotation $v_\theta \approx Cr$.

Uniform Stream Plus a Sink at the Origin: The Rankine Half-Body

If we superimpose a uniform x-directed stream against an isolated source, a half-body shape appears. If the source is at the origin, the combined stream function is, in polar coordinates,

Uniform stream plus source: $\qquad \psi = Ur \sin \theta + m\theta \qquad$ (4.135)

We can set this equal to various constants and plot the streamlines, as shown in Fig. 4.15. A curved, roughly elliptical, *half-body* shape appears, which separates the source flow from the stream flow. The body shape, which is named after the Scottish engineer W. J. M. Rankine (1820–1872), is formed by the particular streamlines $\psi = \pm \pi m$. The half-width of the body far downstream is $\pi m / U$. The upper surface may be plotted from the relation

$$r = \frac{m(\pi - \theta)}{U \sin \theta} \qquad (4.136)$$

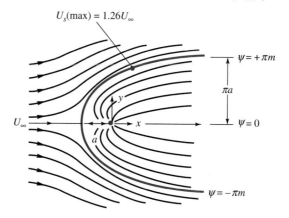

Fig. 4.15 Superposition of a source plus a uniform stream forms a Rankine half-body.

It is not a true ellipse. The nose of the body, which is a "stagnation" point where $V = 0$, stands at $(x, y) = (-a, 0)$, where $a = m/U$. The streamline $\psi = 0$ also crosses this point—recall that streamlines can cross only at a stagnation point.

The cartesian velocity components are found by differentiation:

$$u = \frac{\partial \psi}{\partial y} = U + \frac{m}{r} \cos \theta \qquad v = -\frac{\partial \psi}{\partial x} = \frac{m}{r} \sin \theta \qquad (4.137)$$

Setting $u = v = 0$, we find a single stagnation point at $\theta = 180°$ and $r = m/U$, or $(x, y) = (-m/U, 0)$, as stated. The resultant velocity at any point is

$$V^2 = u^2 + v^2 = U^2 \left(1 + \frac{a^2}{r^2} + \frac{2a}{r} \cos \theta \right) \qquad (4.138)$$

where we have substituted $m = Ua$. If we evaluate the velocities along the upper surface $\psi = \pi m$, we find a maximum value $U_{s,\max} \approx 1.26U$ at $\theta = 63°$. This point is labeled in Fig. 4.15 and, by Bernoulli's equation, is the point of minimum pressure on the body surface. After this point, the surface flow decelerates, the pressure rises, and the viscous layer grows thicker and more susceptible to "flow separation," as we shall see in Chap. 7.

EXAMPLE 4.10

The bottom of a river has a 4-m-high bump which approximates a Rankine half-body, as in Fig. E4.10. The pressure at point B on the bottom is 130 kPa, and the river velocity is 2.5 m/s. Use inviscid theory to estimate the water pressure at point A on the bump, which is 2 m above point B.

Fig. E4.10

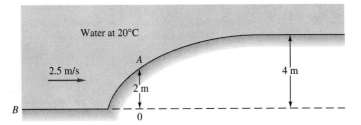

Water at 20°C

2.5 m/s

A

2 m

4 m

B

0

Solution

As in all inviscid theories, we ignore the low-velocity boundary layers which form on solid surfaces due to the no-slip condition. From Eq. (4.136) and Fig. 4.15, the downstream bump half-height equals πa. Therefore, for our case, $a = (4 \text{ m})/\pi = 1.27$ m. We have to find the spot where the bump height is half that much, $h = 2 \text{ m} = \pi a/2$. From Eq. (4.136) we may compute

$$r = h_A = \frac{a(\pi - \theta)}{\sin \theta} = \frac{\pi}{2} a \quad \text{or} \quad \theta = \frac{\pi}{2} = 90°$$

Thus point A in Fig. E4.10 is directly above the (initially unknown) origin of coordinates (labeled O in Fig. E4.10) and is 1.27 m to the right of the nose of the bump. With $r = \pi a/2$ and $\theta = \pi/2$ known, we compute the velocity at point A from Eq. (4.138):

$$V_A^2 = U^2 \left[1 + \frac{a^2}{(\pi a/2)^2} + \frac{2a}{\pi a/2} \cos \frac{\pi}{2} \right] = 1.405 U^2$$

or

$$V_A \approx 1.185U = 1.185(2.5 \text{ m/s}) = 2.96 \text{ m/s}$$

For water at 20°C, take $\rho = 998 \text{ kg/m}^2$ and $\gamma = 9790 \text{ N/m}^3$. Now, since the velocity and elevation are known at point A, we are in a position to use Bernoulli's inviscid, incompressible-flow equation (4.120) to estimate p_A from the known properties at point B (on the same streamline):

$$\frac{p_A}{\gamma} + \frac{V_A^2}{2g} + z_A \approx \frac{p_B}{\gamma} + \frac{V_B^2}{2g} + z_B$$

or

$$\frac{p_A}{9790 \text{ N/m}^3} + \frac{(2.96 \text{ m/s})^2}{2(9.81 \text{ m/s}^2)} + 2 \text{ m} \approx \frac{130,000}{9790} + \frac{(2.5)^2}{2(9.81)} + 0$$

Solving, we find

$$p_A = (13.60 - 2.45)(9790) \approx 109,200 \text{ Pa} \qquad \textit{Ans.}$$

If the approach velocity is uniform, this should be a pretty good approximation, since water is relatively inviscid and its boundary layers are thin.

4.11 Some Illustrative Incompressible Viscous Flows

The inviscid flows of Sec. 4.10 do *not* satisfy the no-slip condition. They "slip" at the wall but do not flow through the wall. To look at fully viscous no-slip conditions, we must attack the complete Navier-Stokes equations (4.74), and the result is usually not at all irrotational, nor does a velocity potential exist. We look here at three cases: (1) flow between parallel plates due to a moving upper wall, (2) flow between parallel plates due to pressure gradient, and (3) flow between concentric cylinders when the inner one rotates. Other cases will be given as problem assignments or considered in Chap. 6. Extensive solutions for viscous flows are discussed in Refs. 4 and 5.

Couette Flow between a Fixed and a Moving Plate

Consider two-dimensional incompressible plane ($\partial/\partial z = 0$) viscous flow between parallel plates a distance $2h$ apart, as shown in Fig. 4.16. We assume that the plates are very wide and very long, so that the flow is essentially axial, $u \neq 0$ but $v = w = 0$. The present case is Fig. 4.16a, where the upper plate moves at velocity V but there is no pressure gradient. Neglect gravity effects. We learn from the continuity equation (4.73) that

$$\frac{\partial u}{\partial x} + \frac{\partial y}{\partial y} + \frac{\partial w}{\partial z} = 0 = \frac{\partial u}{\partial x} + 0 + 0 \qquad \text{or} \qquad u = u(y) \text{ only}$$

Thus there is a single nonzero axial-velocity component which varies only across the channel. The flow is said to be *fully developed* (far downstream of the entrance). Substitute $u = u(y)$ into the x component of the Navier-Stokes momentum equation (4.74) for two-dimensional (x, y) flow:

$$\rho\left(u\frac{\partial u}{\partial x} + v\frac{\partial u}{\partial y}\right) = -\frac{\partial p}{\partial x} + \rho g_x + \mu\left(\frac{\partial^2 u}{\partial x^2} + \frac{\partial^2 u}{\partial y^2}\right)$$

or

$$\rho(0 + 0) = 0 + 0 + \mu\left(0 + \frac{d^2 u}{dy^2}\right) \tag{4.139}$$

Fig. 4.16 Incompressible viscous flow between parallel plates: (*a*) no pressure gradient, upper plate moving; (*b*) pressure gradient $\partial p/\partial x$ with both plates fixed.

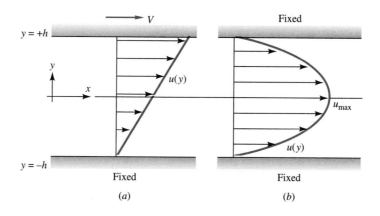

(a)   (b)

Most of the terms drop out, and the momentum equation simply reduces to

$$\frac{d^2u}{dy^2} = 0 \quad \text{or} \quad u = C_1 y + C_2$$

The two constants are found by applying the no-slip condition at the upper and lower plates:

At $y = +h$: $\qquad\qquad\qquad u = V = C_1 h + C_2$

At $y = -h$: $\qquad\qquad\qquad u = 0 = C_1(-h) + C_2$

or $\qquad\qquad\qquad\qquad C_1 = \frac{V}{2h} \quad \text{and} \quad C_2 = \frac{V}{2}$

Therefore the solution for this case (a), flow between plates with a moving upper wall, is

$$u = \frac{V}{2h} y + \frac{V}{2} \qquad -h \le y \le +h \tag{4.140}$$

This is *Couette flow* due to a moving wall: a linear velocity profile with no-slip at each wall, as anticipated and sketched in Fig. 4.16a. Note that the origin has been placed in the center of the channel, for convenience in case (b) below.

What we have just presented is a rigorous derivation of the more informally discussed flow of Fig. 1.6 (where y and h were defined differently).

Flow due to Pressure Gradient between Two Fixed Plates

Case (b) is sketched in Fig. 4.16b. Both plates are fixed $(V = 0)$, but the pressure varies in the x direction. If $v = w = 0$, the continuity equation leads to the same conclusion as case (a), namely, that $u = u(y)$ only. The x-momentum equation (4.138) changes only because the pressure is variable:

$$\mu \frac{d^2u}{dy^2} = \frac{\partial p}{\partial x} \tag{4.141}$$

Also, since $v = w = 0$ and gravity is neglected, the y- and z-momentum equations lead to

$$\frac{\partial p}{\partial y} = 0 \quad \text{and} \quad \frac{\partial p}{\partial z} = 0 \quad \text{or} \quad p = p(x) \text{ only}$$

Thus the pressure gradient in Eq. (4.141) is the total and only gradient:

$$\mu \frac{d^2u}{dy^2} = \frac{dp}{dx} = \text{const} < 0 \tag{4.142}$$

Why did we add the fact that dp/dx is *constant*? Recall a useful conclusion from the theory of separation of variables: If two quantities are equal and one varies only with y and the other varies only with x, then they must both equal the same constant. Otherwise they would not be independent of each other.

Why did we state that the constant is *negative*? Physically, the pressure must decrease in the flow direction in order to drive the flow against resisting wall shear stress. Thus the velocity profile $u(y)$ must have negative curvature everywhere, as anticipated and sketched in Fig. 4.16b.

The solution to Eq. (4.142) is accomplished by double integration:

$$u = \frac{1}{\mu}\frac{dp}{dx}\frac{y^2}{2} + C_1 y + C_2$$

The constants are found from the no-slip condition at each wall:

At $y = \pm h$: $u = 0$ or $C_1 = 0$ and $C_2 = -\frac{dp}{dx}\frac{h^2}{2\mu}$

Thus the solution to case (b), flow in a channel due to pressure gradient, is

$$u = -\frac{dp}{dx}\frac{h^2}{2\mu}\left(1 - \frac{y^2}{h^2}\right) \tag{4.143}$$

The flow forms a *Poiseuille* parabola of constant negative curvature. The maximum velocity occurs at the centerline $y = 0$:

$$u_{max} = -\frac{dp}{dx}\frac{h^2}{2\mu} \tag{4.144}$$

Other (laminar) flow parameters are computed in the following example.

EXAMPLE 4.11

For case (b) above, flow between parallel plates due to the pressure gradient, compute (a) the wall shear stress, (b) the stream function, (c) the vorticity, (d) the velocity potential, and (e) the average velocity.

Solution

All parameters can be computed from the basic solution, Eq. (4.143), by mathematical manipulation.

(a) The wall shear follows from the definition of a newtonian fluid, Eq. (4.37):

$$\tau_w = \tau_{xy\,\text{wall}} = \mu\left(\frac{\partial u}{\partial y} + \frac{\partial v}{\partial x}\right)\Bigg|_{y=\pm h} = \mu\frac{\partial}{\partial y}\left[\left(-\frac{dp}{dx}\right)\left(\frac{h^2}{2\mu}\right)\left(1 - \frac{y^2}{h^2}\right)\right]\Bigg|_{y=\pm h}$$

$$= \pm\frac{dp}{dx}h = \mp\frac{2\mu u_{max}}{h} \qquad\qquad Ans.\ (a)$$

The wall shear has the same magnitude at each wall, but by our sign convention of Fig. 4.3, the upper wall has negative shear stress.

(b) Since the flow is plane, steady, and incompressible, a stream function exists:

$$u = \frac{\partial\psi}{\partial y} = u_{max}\left(1 - \frac{y^2}{h^2}\right) \qquad v = -\frac{\partial\psi}{\partial x} = 0$$

Integrating and setting $\psi = 0$ at the centerline for convenience, we obtain

$$\psi = u_{max}\left(y - \frac{y^3}{3h^2}\right) \qquad\qquad Ans.\ (b)$$

At the walls, $y = \pm h$ and $\psi = \pm 2u_{max}h/3$, respectively.

(c) In plane flow, there is only a single nonzero vorticity component:

$$\zeta_z = (\text{curl } \mathbf{V})_z = \frac{\partial v}{\partial x} - \frac{\partial u}{\partial y} = \frac{2u_{max}}{h^2} y \qquad \textit{Ans. (c)}$$

The vorticity is highest at the wall and is positive (counterclockwise) in the upper half and negative (clockwise) in the lower half of the fluid. Viscous flows are typically full of vorticity and are not at all irrotational.

(d) From part (c), the vorticity is finite. Therefore the flow is not irrotational, and the velocity potential *does not exist*.   *Ans. (d)*

(e) The average velocity is defined as $V_{av} = Q/A$, where $Q = \int u\, dA$ over the cross section. For our particular distribution $u(y)$ from Eq. (4.143), we obtain

$$V_{av} = \frac{1}{A} \int u\, dA = \frac{1}{b(2h)} \int_{-h}^{+h} u_{max}\left(1 - \frac{y^2}{h^2}\right) b\, dy = \frac{2}{3} u_{max} \qquad \textit{Ans. (e)}$$

In plane Poiseuille flow between parallel plates, the average velocity is two-thirds of the maximum (or centerline) value. This result could also have been obtained from the stream function derived in part (b). From Eq. (4.95),

$$Q_{channel} = \psi_{upper} - \psi_{lower} = \frac{2u_{max}h}{3} - \left(-\frac{2u_{max}h}{3}\right) = \frac{4}{3} u_{max}h \text{ per unit width}$$

whence $V_{av} = Q/A_{b=1} = (4u_{max}h/3)/(2h) = 2u_{max}/3$, the same result.

This example illustrates a statement made earlier: Knowledge of the velocity vector **V** [as in Eq. (4.143)] is essentially the *solution* to a fluid-mechanics problem, since all other flow properties can then be calculated.

Flow between Long Concentric Cylinders

Consider a fluid of constant (ρ, μ) between two concentric cylinders, as in Fig. 4.17. There is no axial motion or end effect $v_z = \partial/\partial z = 0$. Let the inner cylinder rotate at angular velocity Ω_i. Let the outer cylinder be fixed. There is circular symmetry, so the velocity does not vary with θ and varies only with r.

Fig. 4.17 Coordinate system for incompressible viscous flow between a fixed outer cylinder and a steadily rotating inner cylinder.

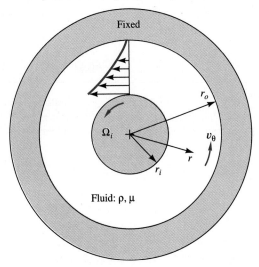

The continuity equation for this problem is Eq. (E.2):

$$\frac{1}{r}\frac{\partial}{\partial r}(rv_r) + \frac{1}{r}\frac{\partial v_\theta}{\partial \theta} = 0 = \frac{1}{r}\frac{d}{dr}(rv_r) \qquad \text{or} \qquad rv_r = \text{const}$$

Note that v_θ does not vary with θ. Since $v_r = 0$ at both the inner and outer cylinders, it follows that $v_r = 0$ everywhere and the motion can only be purely circumferential, $v_\theta = v_\theta(r)$. The θ-momentum equation (E.6) becomes

$$\rho(\mathbf{V}\cdot\nabla)v_\theta + \frac{\rho v_r v_\theta}{r} = -\frac{1}{r}\frac{\partial p}{\partial \theta} + \rho g_\theta + \mu\left(\nabla^2 v_\theta - \frac{v_\theta}{r^2}\right)$$

For the conditions of the present problem, all terms are zero except the last. Therefore the basic differential equation for flow between rotating cylinders is

$$\nabla^2 v_\theta = \frac{1}{r}\frac{d}{dr}\left(r\frac{dv_\theta}{dr}\right) = \frac{v_\theta}{r^2} \tag{4.145}$$

This is a linear second-order ordinary differential equation with the solution

$$v_\theta = C_1 r + \frac{C_2}{r}$$

The constants are found by the no-slip condition at the inner and outer cylinders:

Outer, at $r = r_o$: $\qquad\qquad v_\theta = 0 = C_1 r_o + \dfrac{C_2}{r_o}$

Inner, at $r = r_i$: $\qquad\qquad v_\theta = \Omega_i r_i = C_1 r_i + \dfrac{C_2}{r_i}$

The final solution for the velocity distribution is

Rotating inner cylinder: $\qquad\qquad v_\theta = \Omega_i r_i \dfrac{r_o/r - r/r_o}{r_o/r_i - r_i/r_o} \tag{4.146}$

The velocity profile closely resembles the sketch in Fig. 4.17. Variations of this case, such as a rotating outer cylinder, are given in the problem assignments.

Instability of Rotating Inner Cylinder Flow

The classic *Couette-flow* solution[1] of Eq. (4.146) describes a physically satisfying concave, two-dimensional, laminar-flow velocity profile as in Fig. 4.17. The solution is mathematically exact for an incompressible fluid. However, it becomes unstable at a relatively low rate of rotation of the inner cylinder, as shown in 1923 in a classic paper by G. I. Taylor [17]. At a critical value of what is now called the *Taylor number*, denoted Ta,

$$\text{Ta}_{\text{crit}} = \frac{r_i(r_o - r_i)^3 \Omega_i^2}{\nu^2} \approx 1700 \tag{4.147}$$

the plane flow of Fig. 4.17 vanishes and is replaced by a laminar *three-dimensional* flow pattern consisting of rows of nearly square alternating toroidal vortices. An ex-

[1] Named after M. Couette, whose pioneering paper in 1890 established rotating cylinders as a method, still used today, for measuring the viscosity of fluids.

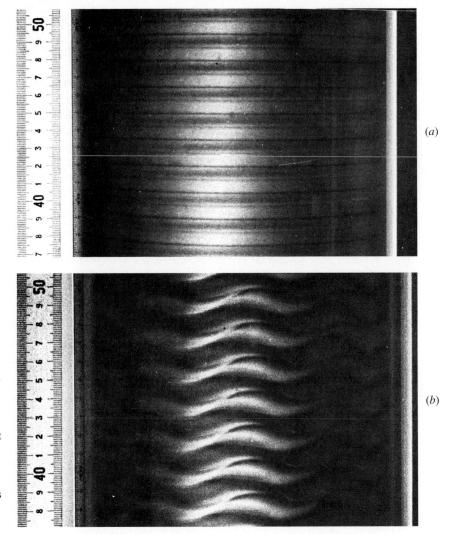

Fig. 4.18 Experimental verification of the instability of flow between a fixed outer and a rotating inner cylinder. (*a*) Toroidal Taylor vortices exist at 1.16 times the critical speed; (*b*) at 8.5 times the critical speed, the vortices are doubly periodic (*after Koschmieder, Ref. 18*). This instability does not occur if only the outer cylinder rotates.

perimental demonstration of toroidal ''Taylor vortices'' is shown in Fig. 4.18*a*, measured at Ta $\approx$ 1.16 Ta$_{crit}$ by Koschmieder [18]. At higher Taylor numbers, the vortices also develop a circumferential periodicity but are still laminar, as illustrated in Fig. 4.18*b*. At still higher Ta, turbulence ensues. This interesting instability reminds us that the Navier-Stokes equations, being nonlinear, do admit to multiple (nonunique) laminar solutions in addition to the usual instabilities associated with turbulence and chaotic dynamic systems.

Summary

This chapter complements Chap. 3 by using an infinitesimal control volume to derive the basic partial differential equations of mass, momentum, and energy for a fluid. These equations, together with thermodynamic state relations for the fluid and appropriate boundary conditions, in principle can be solved for the complete flow field in any given fluid-mechanics problem. Except for Chap. 9, in most of the problems to be studied here an incompressible fluid with constant viscosity is assumed.

In addition to deriving the basic equations of mass, momentum, and energy, this chapter introduced some supplementary ideas—the stream function, vorticity, irrotationality, and the velocity potential—which will be useful in coming chapters, especially Chap. 8. Temperature and density variations will be neglected except in Chap. 9, where compressibility is studied.

This chapter ended by discussing a few classical solutions for inviscid flows (uniform stream, source, sink, vortex, half-body) and for viscous flows (Couette flow due to moving walls and Poiseuille flow due to pressure gradient). Whole books [11, 13] are written on the basic equations of fluid mechanics. Whole books [4, 5, 15] are written on classical solutions to fluid-flow problems. Reference 12 contains 360 solved problems which relate fluid mechanics to the whole of continuum mechanics. This does not mean that all problems can be readily solved mathematically, even with the modern digital-computer codes now avaiable. Often the geometry and boundary conditions are so complex that experimentation (Chap. 5) is a necessity.

References

1. D. A. Anderson, J. C. Tannehill, and R. H. Pletcher, *Computational Fluid Mechanics and Heat Transfer*, McGraw-Hill, New York, 1984.
2. G. B. Wallis, *One-Dimensional Two-Phase Flow*, McGraw-Hill, New York, 1969.
3. S. M. Selby, *CRC Handbook of Tables for Mathematics*, 4th ed., CRC Press Inc., Cleveland, Ohio, 1976.
4. H. Schlichting, *Boundary Layer Theory*, 7th ed., McGraw-Hill, New York, 1979.
5. F. M. White, *Viscous Fluid Flow*, 2d ed., McGraw-Hill, New York, 1991.
6. L. E. Malvern, *Introduction to Mechanics of a Continuous Medium*, Prentice-Hall, Englewood Cliffs, N.J., 1969.
7. J. P. Holman, *Heat Transfer*, 7th ed., McGraw-Hill, New York, 1990.
8. W. M. Kays and M. E. Crawford, *Convective Heat and Mass Transfer*, 3d ed., McGraw-Hill, New York, 1993.
9. G. K. Batchelor, *An Introduction to Fluid Dynamics*, Cambridge University Press, Cambridge, England, 1967.
10. L. Prandtl and O. G. Tietjens, *Fundamentals of Hydro- and Aeromechanics*, Dover, New York, 1957.
11. R. Aris, *Vectors, Tensors, and the Basic Equations of Fluid Mechanics*, Prentice-Hall, Englewood Cliffs, N.J., 1962.
12. G. E. Mase, *Continuum Mechanics*, Schaum's Outline Series, McGraw-Hill, New York, 1970.
13. W. F. Hughes and E. W. Gaylord, *Basic Equations of Engineering Science*, Schaum's Outline Series, McGraw-Hill, New York, 1964.
14. G. Astarita and G. Marrucci, *Principles of Non-Newtonian Fluid Mechanics*, McGraw-Hill, New York, 1974.
15. H. Lamb, *Hydrodynamics*, 6th ed., Dover, New York, 1945.
16. A. Szeri, *Tribology: Friction, Lubrication, and Wear*, McGraw-Hill, New York, 1980.
17. G. I. Taylor, "Stability of a Viscous Liquid Contained between Two Rotating Cylinders," *Philos. Trans. Roy. Soc. London Ser. A*, vol. 223, 1923, pp. 289–343.
18. E. L. Koschmieder, "Turbulent Taylor Vortex Flow," *J. Fluid Mech.*, vol. 93, pt. 3, 1979, pp. 515–527.

Recommended Films

Films numbered 2 to 5 and 16 in App. C.

PROBLEMS

In addition to many traditional problems, categorized in the problem distribution list below, there are several word problems, labeled W4.1 to W4.10.

Problem Distribution

Section	Topic	Problems
4.1	The acceleration of a fluid	4.1–4.8
4.2	The continuity equation	4.9–4.25
4.3	Linear momentum: Navier-Stokes	4.26–4.36
4.4	Angular momentum: couple stresses	4.37
4.5	The differential energy equation	4.38–4.42
4.6	Boundary conditions	4.43–4.46
4.7	Stream function	4.47–4.55
4.8	Vorticity, irrotationality	4.56–4.60
4.9	Velocity potential	4.61–4.67
4.10	Plane potential flows	4.68–4.78
4.11	Incompressible viscous flows	4.79–4.90

4.1 An idealized velocity field is given by the formula

$$\mathbf{V} = 4tx\mathbf{i} - 2t^2y\mathbf{j} + 4xz\mathbf{k}$$

Is this flow field steady or unsteady? Is it two- or three-dimensional? At the point $(x, y, z) = (-1, 1, 0)$, compute (a) the acceleration vector and (b) any unit vector normal to the acceleration.

4.2 Flow through the converging nozzle in Fig. P4.2 can be approximated by the one-dimensional velocity distribution

$$u \approx V_0\left(1 + \frac{2x}{L}\right) \qquad v \approx 0 \qquad w \approx 0$$

(a) Find a general expression for the fluid acceleration in the nozzle. (b) For the specific case $V_0 = 12$ ft/s and $L = 8$ in, compute the acceleration, in g's, at the entrance and at the exit.

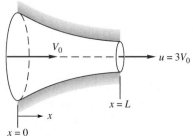

Fig. P4.2 $x = 0$

4.3 A two-dimensional velocity field is given by

$$\mathbf{V} = (x^2 - y^2 + x)\mathbf{i} - (2xy + y)\mathbf{j}$$

in arbitrary units. At $(x, y) = (1, 2)$, compute (a) the accelerations a_x and a_y, (b) the velocity component in the direction $\theta = 40°$, (c) the direction of maximum velocity, and (d) the direction of maximum acceleration.

4.4 Suppose that the pressure field $p = 3x^3 - 4y^2$, in arbitrary units, is associated with the velocity field of Prob. 4.3. Compute the rate of change dp/dt at $(x, y) = (1, 2)$.

4.5 The velocity field near a stagnation point (see Example 1.10) may be written in the form

$$u = \frac{U_0x}{L} \qquad v = \frac{-U_0y}{L} \qquad U_0 \text{ and } L \text{ are constants}$$

(a) Show that the acceleration vector is purely radial. (b) For the particular case $L = 1.5$ m, if the acceleration at $(x, y) = (1 \text{ m}, 1 \text{ m})$ is 25 m/s², what is the value of U_0?

4.6 Assume that flow in the converging nozzle of Fig. P4.2 has the form

$$\mathbf{V} \approx V_0\left(1 + \frac{x}{L}\right)\mathbf{i}$$

Compute (a) the fluid acceleration at $x = L$ and (b) the time required for a fluid particle to travel from $x = 0$ to $x = L$.

4.7 Consider a sphere of radius R immersed in a uniform stream U_0, as shown in Fig. P4.7. According to the theory of Chap. 8, the fluid velocity along streamline AB is given by

$$\mathbf{V} = u\mathbf{i} = U_0\left(1 + \frac{R^3}{x^3}\right)\mathbf{i}$$

Find (a) the position of maximum fluid acceleration along AB and (b) the time required for a fluid particle to travel from A to B.

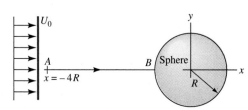

Fig. P4.7

4.8 When a valve is opened, fluid flows in the expansion duct of Fig. P4.8 according to the approximation

$$V = iU\left(1 - \frac{x}{2L}\right) \tanh \frac{Ut}{L}$$

Find (a) the fluid acceleration at $(x, t) = (L, L/U)$ and (b) the time for which the fluid acceleration at $x = L$ is zero. Why does the fluid acceleration become negative after condition (b)?

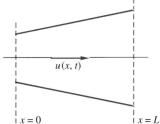

Fig. P4.8 $x = 0$ $x = L$

4.9 Show that the general continuity equation (4.4) can be written in the equivalent form $d\rho/dt + \rho(\nabla \cdot \mathbf{V}) = 0$.

4.10 Write the special cases of the equation of continuity for (a) steady compressible flow in the yz plane, (b) unsteady incompressible flow in the xz plane, (c) unsteady compressible flow in the y direction only, (d) steady compressible flow in plane polar coordinates.

4.11 Derive Eq. (4.12b) for cylindrical coordinates by considering the flux of an incompressible fluid in and out of the elemental control volume in Fig. 4.2.

4.12 Spherical polar coordinates (r, θ, ϕ) are defined in Fig. P4.12. The cartesian transformations are

$$x = r \sin \theta \cos \phi$$
$$y = r \sin \theta \sin \phi$$
$$z = r \cos \theta$$

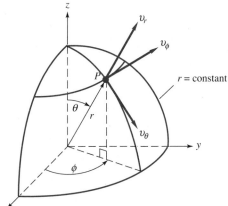

Fig. P4.12 x

Show that the cartesian incompressible continuity relation (4.12a) can be transformed to the spherical polar form

$$\frac{1}{r^2} \frac{\partial}{\partial r} (r^2 v_r) + \frac{1}{r \sin \theta} \frac{\partial}{\partial \theta} (v_\theta \sin \theta) + \frac{1}{r \sin \theta} \frac{\partial}{\partial \phi} (v_\phi) = 0$$

What is the most general form of v_r when the flow is purely radial, that is, v_θ and v_ϕ are zero?

4.13 A two-dimensional velocity field is given by

$$u = -\frac{Ky}{x^2 + y^2} \qquad v = \frac{Kx}{x^2 + y^2}$$

where K is constant. Does this field satisfy incompressible continuity? Transform these velocities to polar components v_r and v_θ. What might the flow represent?

4.14 For incompressible polar-coordinate flow, what is the most general form of a purely circulatory motion, $v_\theta = v_\theta(r, \theta, t)$ and $v_r = 0$, which satisfies continuity?

4.15 What is the most general form of a purely radial polar-coordinate incompressible-flow pattern, $v_r = v_r(r, \theta, t)$ and $v_\theta = 0$, which satisfies continuity?

4.16 An incompressible steady-flow pattern is given by $u = x^3 + 2z^2$ and $w = y^3 - 2yz$. What is the most general form of the third component, $v(x, y, z)$, which satisfies continuity?

4.17 A reasonable approximation for the two-dimensional incompressible laminar boundary layer on the flat surface in Fig. P4.17 is

$$u \approx U \sin \frac{\pi y}{2\delta} \quad \text{for } y \leq \delta \quad \text{where} \quad \delta \approx Cx^{1/2}, C = \text{const}$$

(a) Assuming a no-slip condition at the wall, find an expression for the velocity component $v(x, y)$ for $y \leq \delta$. (b) Then find the maximum value of v at the station $x = 1$ m, for the particular case of airflow, when $U = 3$ m/s and $\delta = 1.1$ cm.

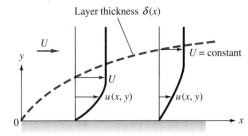

Fig. P4.17

4.18 A piston compresses gas in a cylinder by moving at constant speed V, as in Fig. P4.18. Let the gas density and length at $t = 0$ be ρ_0 and L_0, respectively. Let the gas velocity vary linearly from $u = V$ at the piston face to $u = 0$ at $x = L$. If the gas density varies only with time, find an expression for $\rho(t)$.

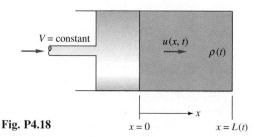

Fig. P4.18

$x = 0$ $x = L(t)$

4.19 An incompressible flow field has the cylinder components $v_\theta = Cr$, $v_z = K(R^2 - r^2)$, $v_r = 0$, where C and K are constants and $r \leq R$, $z \leq L$. Does this flow satisfy continuity? What might it represent physically?

4.20 A two-dimensional incompressible velocity field has $u = K(1 - e^{-ay})$, for $x \leq L$ and $0 \leq y \leq \infty$. What is the most general form of $v(x, y)$ for which continuity is satisfied and $v = v_0$ at $y = 0$? What are the proper dimensions for constants K and a?

4.21 Air flows under steady, approximately one-dimensional conditions through the conical nozzle in Fig. P4.21. If the speed of sound is approximately 340 m/s, what is the minimum nozzle-diameter ratio D_e/D_0 for which we can safely neglect compressibility effects if $V_0 = $ (a) 10 m/s and (b) 30 m/s?

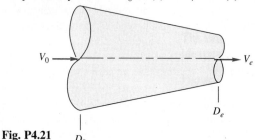

Fig. P4.21 D_0

4.22 Air at a certain temperature and pressure flows through a contracting nozzle of length L whose area decreases linearly, $A \approx A_0[1 - x/(2L)]$. The air average velocity increases nearly linearly from 76 m/s at $x = 0$ to 167 m/s at $x = L$. If the density at $x = 0$ is 2.0 kg/m³, estimate the density at $x = L$.

4.23 A tank volume $\mathcal{V}$ contains gas at conditions (ρ_0, p_0, T_0). At time $t = 0$ it is punctured by a small hole of area A. According to the theory of Chap. 9, the mass flow out of such a hole is approximately proportional to A and to the tank pressure. If the tank temperature is assumed constant and the gas is ideal, find an expression for the variation of density within the tank.

4.24 Reconsider Fig. P4.17 in the following general way. It is known that the boundary layer thickness $\delta(x)$ increases monotonically and that there is no slip at the wall ($y = 0$). Further, $u(x, y)$ merges smoothly with the outer stream flow, where $u \approx U = $ constant outside the layer. Use these facts to prove

that (a) the component $v(x, y)$ is positive everywhere within the layer, (b) v increases parabolically with y very near the wall, and (c) v is a maximum at $y = \delta$.

4.25 An incompressible flow in polar coordinates is given by

$$v_r = K \cos \theta \left(1 - \frac{b}{r^2} \right)$$

$$v_\theta = -K \sin \theta \left(1 + \frac{b}{r^2} \right)$$

Does this field satisfy continuity? For consistency, what should the dimensions of constants K and b be? Sketch the surface where $v_r = 0$ and interpret.

4.26 Curvilinear, or streamline, coordinates are defined in Fig. P4.26, where n is normal to the streamline in the plane of the radius of curvature R. Show that Euler's frictionless momentum equation (4.36) in streamline coordinates becomes

$$\frac{\partial V}{\partial t} + V \frac{\partial V}{\partial s} = -\frac{1}{\rho} \frac{\partial p}{\partial s} + g_s \tag{1}$$

$$-V \frac{\partial \theta}{\partial t} - \frac{V^2}{R} = -\frac{1}{\rho} \frac{\partial p}{\partial n} + g_n \tag{2}$$

Further show that the integral of Eq. (1) with respect to s is none other than our old friend Bernoulli's equation (3.76).

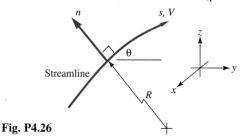

Fig. P4.26

4.27 A frictionless, incompressible steady-flow field is given by

$$V = 2xy\mathbf{i} - y^2\mathbf{j}$$

in arbitrary units. Let the density be $\rho_0 = $ constant and neglect gravity. Find an expression for the pressure gradient in the x direction.

4.28 If z is "up," what are the conditions on constants a and b for which the velocity field $u = ay$, $v = bx$, $w = 0$ is an exact solution to the continuity and Navier-Stokes equations for incompressible flow?

4.29 Consider the incompressible-flow field $u = Ax + By$, $v = Cx + Dy$, $w = 0$. For what conditions on constants A, B, C, D is this flow an exact solution to the continuity and Navier-Stokes equations with negligible gravity?

4.30 Show that the two-dimensional flow field of Example 4.30 is an exact solution to the incompressible Navier-Stokes equations (4.38). Neglecting gravity, compute the pressure field $p(x, y)$ and relate it to the absolute velocity $V^2 = u^2 + v^2$. Interpret the result.

4.31 According to potential theory (Chap. 8) for the flow approaching a rounded two-dimensional body, as in Fig. P4.31, the velocity approaching the stagnation point is given by $u = U(1 - a^2/x^2)$, where a is the nose radius and U is the velocity far upstream. Compute the value and position of the maximum viscous normal stress along this streamline. Is this also the position of maximum fluid deceleration? Evaluate the maximum viscous normal stress if the fluid is SAE 30 oil at 20°C, with $U = 2$ m/s and $a = 6$ cm.

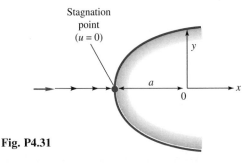

Fig. P4.31

4.32 The answer to Prob. 4.14 is $v_\theta = f(r)$ only. Do not reveal this to your friends if they are still working on Prob. 4.14. Show that this flow field is an exact solution to the Navier-Stokes equations (4.38) for only two special cases of the function $f(r)$. Neglect gravity. Interpret these two cases physically.

4.33 From Prob. 4.15 the purely radial polar-coordinate flow which satisfies continuity is $v_r = f(\theta)/r$, where f is an arbitrary function. Determine what particular forms of $f(\theta)$ satisfy the full Navier-Stokes equations in polar-coordinate form from Eqs. (E.5) and (E.6).

4.34 The fully developed laminar-pipe-flow solution of Prob. 3.53, $v_z = u_{\max}(1 - r^2/R^2)$, $v_\theta = 0$, $v_r = 0$, is an exact solution to the cylindrical Navier-Stokes equations (App. E). Neglecting gravity, compute the pressure distribution in the pipe $p(r, z)$ and the shear-stress distribution $\tau(r, z)$, using R, $u_{\max}$, and μ as parameters. Why does the maximum shear occur at the wall? Why does the density not appear as a parameter?

4.35 From the Navier-Stokes equations for incompressible flow in polar coordinates (App. E for cylindrical coordinates), find the most general case of purely circulating motion $v_\theta(r)$, $v_r = v_z = 0$, for flow with no slip between two fixed concentric cylinders, as in Fig. P4.35.

4.36 A constant-thickness film of viscous liquid flows in laminar motion down a plate inclined at angle θ, as in Fig. P4.36. The velocity profile is

$$u = Cy(2h - y) \qquad v = w = 0$$

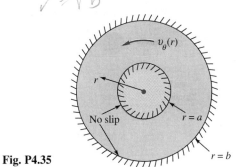

Fig. P4.35

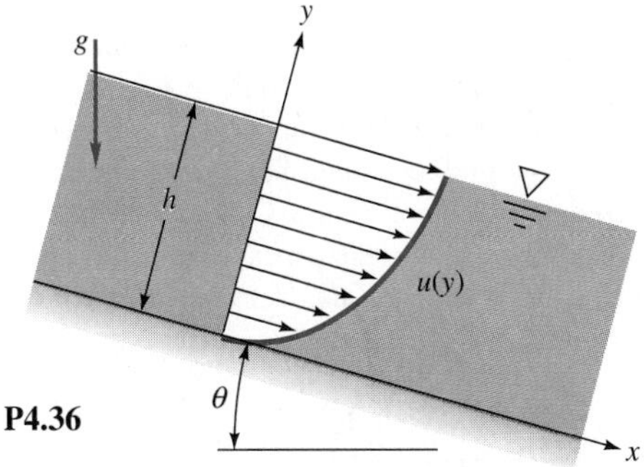

Fig. P4.36

Find the constant C in terms of the specific weight and viscosity and the angle θ. Find the volume flux Q per unit width in terms of these parameters.

4.37 Reconsider the angular-momentum balance of Fig. 4.5 by adding a concentrated *body couple* C_z about the z axis [6]. Determine a relation between the body couple and shear stress for equilibrium. What are the proper dimensions for C_z? (Body couples are important in continuous media with microstructure, such as granular materials.)

4.38 Manipulate the general differential energy equation (4.51) to show that the rate of change of entropy s in a newtonian fluid with constant k is given by

$$\rho T \frac{ds}{dt} = k\,\nabla^2 T + \Phi$$

Hint: Recall from thermodynamics that $T\,ds = d\hat{h} - dp/\rho$.

4.39 Problems involving viscous dissipation of energy are dependent on viscosity μ, thermal conductivity k, stream velocity U_0, and stream temperature T_0. Group these parameters into the dimensionless *Brinkman number*, which is proportional to μ.

4.40 As mentioned in Sec. 4.11, the velocity profile for laminar flow between two plates, as in Fig. P4.40, is

$$u = \frac{4u_{\max}y(h - y)}{h^2} \qquad v = w = 0$$

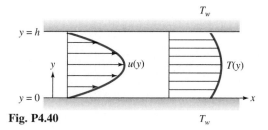

Fig. P4.40

If the wall temperature is T_w at both walls, use the incompressible-flow energy equation (4.75) to solve for the temperature distribution $T(y)$ between the walls for steady flow.

4.41 Repeat the analysis of Prob. 4.40 if the temperature of the lower wall is T_0 and of the upper wall is T_1, both constant.

4.42 In duct-flow problems with heat transfer, one often defines an average fluid temperature. Consider the duct flow of Fig. P4.40 of width b into the paper. Using a control-volume integral analysis with constant density and specific heat, derive an expression for the temperature arising if the entire duct flow poured into a bucket and was stirred uniformly. Assume arbitrary $u(y)$ and $T(y)$. This average is called the *cup-mixing temperature* of the flow.

4.43 For the draining liquid film of Fig. P4.36, what are the appropriate boundary conditions (a) at the bottom $y = 0$ and (b) at the surface $y = h$?

4.44 Suppose that we wish to analyze the sudden pipe-expansion flow of Fig. P3.59, using the full continuity and Navier-Stokes equations. What are the proper boundary conditions to handle this problem?

4.45 Suppose that we wish to analyze the U-tube oscillation flow of Fig. P3.96, using the full continuity and Navier-Stokes equations. What are the proper boundary conditions to handle this problem?

4.46 Fluid from a large reservoir at temperature T_0 flows into a circular pipe of radius R. The pipe walls are wound with an electric-resistance coil which delivers heat to the fluid at a rate q_w (energy per unit wall area). If we wish to analyze this problem by using the full continuity, Navier-Stokes, and energy equations, what are the proper boundary conditions for the analysis?

4.47 A two-dimensional incompressible flow is given by the velocity field $\mathbf{V} = 2y\mathbf{i} + 3x\mathbf{j}$, in arbitrary units. Does this flow satisfy continuity? If so, find the stream function $\psi(x, y)$ and plot a few streamlines, with arrows.

4.48 Determine the incompressible two-dimensional stream function $\psi(x, y)$ which represents the flow field given in Example 1.10.

4.49 Investigate the stream function $\psi = K(x^2 - y^2)$, $K = $ constant. Plot the streamlines in the full xy plane, find any stagnation points, and interpret what the flow could represent.

4.50 Investigate the polar-coordinate stream function $\psi = Kr^{1/2} \sin \frac{1}{2}\theta$, $K = $ constant. Plot the streamlines in the full xy plane, find any stagnation points, and interpret.

4.51 Investigate the polar-coordinate stream function $\psi = Kr^{2/3} \sin (2\theta/3)$, $K = $ constant. Plot the streamlines in all except the bottom right quadrant, and interpret.

4.52 A two-dimensional, incompressible, frictionless fluid is guided by wedge-shaped walls into a small slot at the origin, as in Fig. P4.52. The width into the paper is b, and the volume flow rate is Q. At any given distance r from the slot, the flow is radial inward, with constant velocity. Find an expression for the polar-coordinate stream function of this flow.

Fig. P4.52

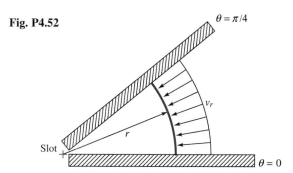

4.53 For the fully developed laminar-pipe-flow solution of Prob. 4.34, find the axisymmetric stream function $\psi(r, z)$. Use this result to determine the average velocity $V = Q/A$ in the pipe as a ratio of $u_{\max}$.

4.54 An incompressible stream function is defined by

$$\psi(x, y) = \frac{U}{L^2} (3x^2y - y^3)$$

where U and L are (positive) constants. Where in this chapter are the streamlines of this flow plotted? Use this stream function to find the volume flow Q passing through the rectangular surface whose corners are defined by $(x, y, z) = (2L, 0, 0)$, $(2L, 0, b)$, $(0, L, b)$, and $(0, L, 0)$. Show the direction of Q.

4.55 In spherical polar coordinates, as in Fig. P4.12, the flow is called *axisymmetric* if $v_\phi \equiv 0$ and $\partial/\partial\phi \equiv 0$, so that $v_r = v_r(r, \theta)$ and $v_\theta = v(r, \theta)$. Show that a stream function $\psi(r, \theta)$ exists for this case and is given by

$$v_r = \frac{1}{r^2 \sin \theta} \frac{\partial \psi}{\partial \theta} \qquad v_\theta = -\frac{1}{r \sin \theta} \frac{\partial \psi}{\partial r}$$

This is called the *Stokes stream function* [5, p. 204].

4.56 Investigate the velocity potential $\phi = Kxy$, $K = $ constant. Sketch the potential lines in the full xy plane, find any stagnation points, and sketch in by eye the orthogonal streamlines. What could the flow represent?

4.57 Determine the incompressible two-dimensional velocity potential $\phi(x, y)$ which represents the flow field given in Example 1.10. Sketch a few potential lines and streamlines.

4.58 Show that the incompressible velocity potential in plane polar coordinates $\phi(r, \theta)$ is such that

$$v_r = \frac{\partial \phi}{\partial r} \qquad v_\theta = \frac{1}{r} \frac{\partial \phi}{\partial \theta}$$

Further show that the angular velocity about the z axis in such a flow would be given by

$$2\omega_z = \frac{1}{r} \frac{\partial}{\partial r} (rv_\theta) - \frac{1}{r} \frac{\partial}{\partial \theta} (v_r)$$

Finally show that ϕ as defined above satisfies Laplace's equation in polar coordinates for incompressible flow.

4.59 Consider the simple flow defined by $\mathbf{V} = x\mathbf{i} - y\mathbf{j}$, in arbitrary units. At $t = 0$, consider the rectangular fluid element defined by the lines $x = 2$, $x = 3$ and $y = 2$, $y = 3$. Determine, and draw to scale, the location of this fluid element at $t = 0.5$ unit. Relate this new element shape to whether the flow is irrotational or incompressible.

4.60 Liquid drains from a small hole in a tank, as shown in Fig. P4.60, such that the velocity field set up is given by $v_r \approx 0$, $v_z \approx 0$, $v_\theta = \omega R^2 / r$, where $z = H$ is the depth of the water far from the hole. Is this flow pattern rotational or irrotational? Find the depth z_0 of the water at the radius $r = R$.

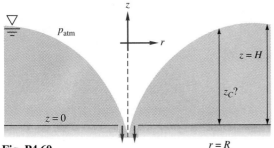

Fig. P4.60

4.61 Investigate the polar-coordinate velocity potential $\phi = Kr^{1/2} \cos \frac{1}{2}\theta$, $K = $ constant. Plot the potential lines in the full xy plane, sketch in by eye the orthogonal streamlines, and interpret.

4.62 Show that the linear Couette flow between plates in Fig. 1.6 has a stream function but no velocity potential. Why is this so?

4.63 Find the two-dimensional velocity potential $\phi(r, \theta)$ for the polar-coordinate flow pattern $v_r = Q/r$, $v_\theta = K/r$, where Q and K are constants.

4.64 Show that the velocity potential $\phi(r, z)$ in axisymmetric cylindrical coordinates (see Fig. 4.2) is defined such that

$$v_r = \frac{\partial \phi}{\partial r} \qquad v_z = \frac{\partial \phi}{\partial z}$$

Further show that for incompressible flow this potential satisfies Laplace's equation in (r, z) coordinates.

4.65 A two-dimensional incompressible flow is defined by

$$u = -\frac{Ky}{x^2 + y^2} \qquad v = \frac{Kx}{x^2 + y^2}$$

where $K = $ constant. Is this flow irrotational? if so, find its velocity potential, sketch a few potential lines, and interpret the flow pattern.

4.66 A plane polar-coordinate velocity potential is defined by

$$\phi = \frac{K \cos \theta}{r} \qquad K = \text{const}$$

Find the stream function for this flow, sketch some streamlines and potential lines, and interpret the flow pattern.

4.67 A stream function for a plane, irrotational, polar-coordinate flow is

$$\psi = C\theta - K \ln r \qquad C \text{ and } K = \text{const}$$

Find the velocity potential for this flow. Sketch some streamlines and potential lines, and interpret the flow pattern.

4.68 Find the stream function and plot some streamlines for the combination of a line source m at $(x, y) = (0, +a)$ and an equal line source placed at $(0, -a)$.

4.69 Find the stream function and plot some streamlines for the combination of a counterclockwise line vortex K at $(x, y) = (+a, 0)$ and an equal line vortex placed at $(-a, 0)$.

4.70 Find the stream function for a vertical uniform stream $\mathbf{V} = U\mathbf{j}$ plus a line source m at the origin. Plot the streamlines and interpret the pattern.

4.71 Find the stream function and plot some streamlines for the combination of a counterclockwise line vortex K at $(x, y) = (+a, 0)$ and an opposite (clockwise) line vortex placed at $(-a, 0)$.

4.72 A coastal power plant takes in cooling water through a vertical perforated manifold, as in Fig. P4.72. The total volume flow intake is 110 m³/s. Currents of 25 cm/s flow past the manifold, as shown. Estimate (a) how far downstream and

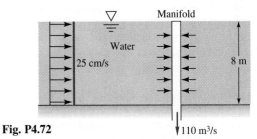

Fig. P4.72

(b) how far normal to the paper the effects of the intake are felt in the ambient 8-m-deep waters.

4.73 A two-dimensional Rankine half-body, 8 cm thick, is placed in a water tunnel at 20°C. The water pressure far upstream along the body centerline is 120 kPa. What is the nose radius of the half-body? At what tunnel flow velocity will cavitation bubbles begin to form on the surface of the body?

4.74 Find the stream function and plot some streamlines for the combination of a uniform stream $\mathbf{i}U$ and a clockwise line vortex $-K$ at the origin. Are there any stagnation points in the flow field?

4.75 Find the stream function and plot some streamlines for the combination of a line source $2m$ at $(x, y) = (+a, 0)$ and a line source m at $(-a, 0)$. Are there any stagnation points in the flow field?

4.76 Consider the half-body shape in Fig. 4.15. At what point on the body is the surface slope exactly 45°? What is the flow velocity at this point?

4.77 A tornado is simulated by a line sink $m = -1000$ m²/s plus a line vortex $K = +1600$ m²/s. Find the angle between any streamline and a radial line, and show that it is independent of both r and θ. If this tornado forms in sea-level standard air, at what radius will the local pressure be equivalent to 29 inHg?

4.78 We wish to study the flow due to a line source of strength m placed at position $(x, y) = (+L, 0)$ above the plane horizontal wall $y = 0$. Using Bernoulli's equation, find (a) the point(s) of minimum pressure on the plane wall and (b) the magnitude of the maximum flow velocity along the wall.

4.79 Study the combined effect of the two viscous flows in Fig. 4.16. That is, find $u(y)$ when the upper plate moves at speed V and there is also a constant pressure gradient (dp/dx). Is superposition possible? If so, explain why. Plot representative velocity profiles for (a) zero, (b) positive, and (c) negative pressure gradients for the same upper-wall speed V.

4.80 Apply the analysis of Prob. 4.79 to the following case: $V = 3$ m/s, $h = 1$ cm, in SAE 30 oil at 20°C. Find the pressure gradient, in Pa/m, for which the shear stress at the lower wall is zero. Also find the shear stress at the upper wall for this same condition.

4.81 Modify the analysis of Fig. 4.17 to find the velocity u_θ when the inner cylinder is fixed and the outer cylinder rotates at angular velocity Ω_0. May this solution be *added* to Eq. (4.146) to represent the flow caused when both inner and outer cylinders rotate? Explain your conclusion.

4.82 A solid circular cylinder of radius R rotates at angular velocity Ω in a viscous incompressible fluid which is at rest far from the cylinder, as in Fig. P4.82. Make simplifying assumptions and derive the governing differential equation and boundary conditions for the velocity field v_θ in the fluid. Do not solve unless you are obsessed with this problem. What is the steady-state flow field for this problem?

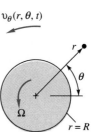

$v_\theta(r, \theta, t)$

Fig. P4.82

$r = R$

4.83 The flow pattern in bearing lubrication can be illustrated by Fig. P4.83, where a viscous oil (ρ, μ) is forced into the gap $h(x)$ between a fixed slipper block and a wall moving at velocity U. If the gap is thin, $h \ll L$, it can be shown that the pressure and velocity distributions are of the form $p = p(x)$, $u = u(y)$, $v = w = 0$. Neglecting gravity, reduce the Navier-Stokes equations (4.38) to a single differential equation for $u(y)$. What are the proper boundary conditions? Integrate and show that

$$u = \frac{1}{2\mu} \frac{dp}{dx} (y^2 - yh) + U\left(1 - \frac{y}{h}\right)$$

where $h = h(x)$ may be an arbitrary slowly varying gap width. (For further information on lubrication theory, see Ref. 16.)

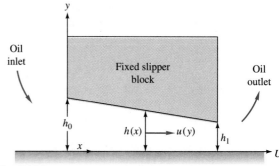

Oil inlet

Fixed slipper block

Oil outlet

h_0

$h(x)$ — $u(y)$

h_1

U

Fig. P4.83

Moving wall

4.84 Consider a viscous film of liquid draining uniformly down the side of a vertical rod of radius a, as in Fig. P4.84. At some distance down the rod the film will approach a terminal or *fully developed* draining flow of constant outer radius b, with $v_z = v_z(r)$, $v_\theta = v_r = 0$. Assume that the atmosphere offers no shear resistance to the film motion. Derive a differential equation for v_z, state the proper boundary conditions, and solve for the film velocity distribution. How does the film radius b relate to the total film volume flow rate Q?

4.85 A flat plate of essentially infinite width and breadth oscillates sinusoidally in its own plane beneath a viscous fluid, as in Fig. P4.85. The fluid is at rest far above the plate. Making as many simplifying assumptions as you can, set up the governing differential equation and boundary conditions for finding

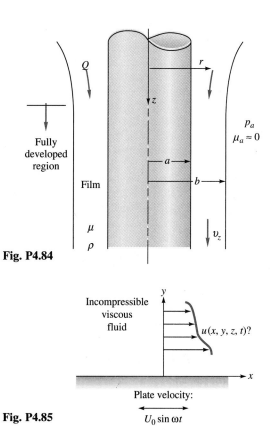

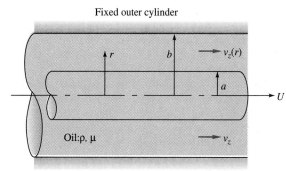

Fig. P4.84

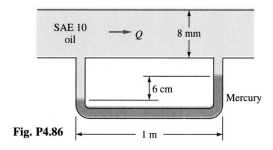

Fig. P4.85

tively. Simplify the differential energy equation appropriately for this problem, state the boundary conditions, and find the temperature distribution in the fluid. Neglect gravity.

4.88 The viscous oil in Fig. P4.88 is set into steady motion by a concentric inner cylinder moving axially at velocity U inside a fixed outer cylinder. Assuming constant pressure and density and a purely axial fluid motion, solve Eqs. (4.38) for the fluid velocity distribution $v_z(r)$. What are the proper boundary conditions?

Fig. P4.88

4.89 Modify Prob. 4.88 so that the outer cylinder also moves to the *left* at constant speed V. Find the velocity distribution $v_z(r)$. For what ratio V/U will the wall shear stress be the same at both cylinder surfaces?

4.90 A 5-cm-diameter rod is pulled steadily at ⌐ m/s through a fixed cylinder whose clearance is filled with SAE 10 oil at 20°C, as in Fig. P4.90. Estimate the (steady) force required to pull the inner rod.

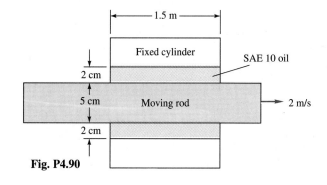

Fig. P4.90

the velocity field u in the fluid. Do not solve (if you *can* solve it immediately, you might be able to get exempted from the balance of this course with credit).

4.86 SAE 10 oil at 20°C flows between parallel plates 8 cm apart, as in Fig. P4.86. A mercury manometer, with wall pressure taps 1 m apart, registers a 6-cm height, as shown. Estimate the flow rate of oil for this condition.

Fig. P4.86

4.87 Suppose in Fig. 4.17 that neither cylinder is rotating. The fluid has constant (ρ, μ, k, c_p). What, then, is the steady-flow solution for $v_\theta(r)$? For this condition, suppose that the inner and outer cylinder surface temperatures are T_i and T_o, respec-

Word Problems

W4.1 The total acceleration of a fluid particle is given by Eq. (4.2) in the eulerian system, where **V** is a known function of space and time. Explain how we might evaluate particle acceleration in the lagrangian frame, where particle position $\mathbf{r}$ is a known function of time and initial position, $\mathbf{r} = \text{fcn}(\mathbf{r}_0, t)$. Can you give an illustrative example?

W4.2 Is is true that the continuity relation, Eq. (4.6), is valid for both viscous and inviscid, newtonian and nonnewtonian, compressible and incompressible flow? If so, are there *any* limitations on this equation?

W4.3 Consider a CD compact disk rotating at angular velocity Ω. Does it have *vorticity* in the sense of this chapter? If so, how much vorticity?

W4.4 How much acceleration can fluids endure? Are fluids like astronauts, who feel that $5g$ is severe? Perhaps use the flow pattern of Example 4.8, at $r = R$, to make some estimates of fluid-acceleration magnitudes.

W4.5 State the conditions (there are more than one) under which the analysis of temperature distribution in a flow field can be completely uncoupled, so that a separate analysis for velocity and pressure is possible. Can we do this for both laminar and turbulent flow?

W4.6 Consider liquid flow over a dam or weir. How might the boundary conditions and the flow pattern change when we compare water flow over a large prototype to SAE 30 oil flow over a tiny scale model?

W4.7 What is the difference between the stream function ψ and our method of finding the streamlines from Sec. 1.9? Or are they essentially the same?

W4.8 Under what conditions do both the stream function ψ and the velocity potential ϕ exist for a flow field? When does one exist but not the other?

W4.9 How might the remarkable three-dimensional Taylor instability of Fig. 4.18 be predicted? Discuss a general procedure for examining the stability of a given flow pattern.

W4.10 Consider an irrotational, incompressible, axisymmetric ($\partial/\partial\theta = 0$) flow in (r, z) coordinates. Does a stream function exist? If so, does it satisfy Laplace's equation? Are lines of constant ψ equal to the flow streamlines? Does a velocity potential exist? If so, does it satisfy Laplace's equation? Are lines of constant ϕ everywhere perpendicular to the ψ lines?

Chapter 5
Dimensional Analysis
and Similarity

Motivation. In this chapter we discuss the planning, presentation, and interpretation of experimental data. We shall try to convince you that such data are best presented in *dimensionless* form. Experiments which might result in tables of output, or even multiple volumes of tables, might be reduced to a single set of curves—or even a single curve—when suitably nondimensionalized. The technique for doing this is *dimensional analysis*.

Chapter 3 presented gross control-volume balances of mass, momentum, and energy which led to estimates of global parameters: mass flow, force, torque, total heat transfer. Chapter 4 presented infinitesimal balances which led to the basic partial differential equations of fluid flow and some particular solutions. These two chapters covered *analytical* techniques, which are limited to fairly simple geometries and well-defined boundary conditions. Probably one-third of fluid-flow problems can be attacked in this analytical or theoretical manner.

The other two-thirds of all fluid problems are too complex, both geometrically and physically, to be solved analytically. They must be tested by experiment. Their behavior is reported as experimental data. Such data are much more useful if they are expressed in compact, economic form. Graphs are especially useful, since tabulated data cannot be absorbed, nor can the trends and rates of change be observed, by most engineering eyes. These are the motivations for dimensional analysis. The technique is traditional in fluid mechanics and is useful in all engineering and physical sciences, with notable uses also seen in the biological and social sciences.

Dimensional analysis can also be useful in theories, as a compact way to present an analytical solution or output from a computer model. Here we concentrate on the presentation of experimental fluid-mechanics data.

5.1 Introduction

Basically, dimensional analysis is a method for reducing the number and complexity of experimental variables which affect a given physical phenomenon, by using a sort of compacting technique. If a phenomenon depends upon n dimensional variables, dimensional analysis will reduce the problem to only k *dimensionless* variables, where the reduction $n - k = 1, 2, 3,$ or 4, depending upon the problem complexity. Generally $n - k$ equals the number of different dimensions (sometimes called basic or primary or fundamental dimensions) which govern the problem. In fluid mechanics, the four basic dimensions are usually taken to be mass M, length L, time T, and temperature Θ, or an $MLT\Theta$ system for short. Sometimes one uses an $FLT\Theta$ system, with force F replacing mass.

Although its purpose is to reduce variables and group them in dimensionless form, dimensional analysis has several side benefits. The first is enormous savings in time and money. Suppose one knew that the force F on a particular body immersed in a stream of fluid depended only on the body length L, stream velocity V, fluid density ρ, and fluid viscosity μ, that is,

$$F = f(L, V, \rho, \mu) \tag{5.1}$$

Suppose further that the geometry and flow conditions are so complicated that our integral theories (Chap. 3) and differential equations (Chap. 4) fail to yield the solution for the force. Then we must find the function $f(L, V, \rho, \mu)$ experimentally.

Generally speaking, it takes about 10 experimental points to define a curve. To find the effect of body length in Eq. (5.1), we have to run the experiment for 10 lengths L. For each L we need 10 values of V, 10 values of ρ, and 10 values of μ, making a grand total of 10^4, or 10,000, experiments. At \$50 per experiment—well, you see what we are getting into. However, with dimensional analysis, we can immediately reduce Eq. (5.1) to the equivalent form

$$\frac{F}{\rho V^2 L^2} = g\left(\frac{\rho V L}{\mu}\right)$$

or
$$C_F = g(\text{Re}) \tag{5.2}$$

i.e., the dimensionless *force coefficient* $F/(\rho V^2 L^2)$ is a function only of the dimensionless *Reynolds number* $\rho V L/\mu$. We shall learn exactly how to make this reduction in Secs. 5.2 and 5.3.

The function g is different mathematically from the original function f, but it contains all the same information. Nothing is lost in a dimensional analysis. And think of the savings: We can establish g by running the experiment for only 10 values of the single variable called the Reynolds number. We do not have to vary L, V, ρ, or μ separately but only the *grouping* $\rho V L/\mu$. This we do merely by varying velocity V in, say, a wind tunnel or drop test or water channel, and there is no need to build 10 different bodies or find 100 different fluids with 10 densities and 10 viscosities. The cost is now about \$500, maybe less.

A second side benefit of dimensional analysis is that it helps our thinking and planning for an experiment or theory. It suggests dimensionless ways of writing equations before we waste money on computer time to find solutions. It suggests variables which can be discarded; sometimes dimensional analysis will immediately reject variables, and at other times it groups them off to the side, where a few simple tests will show them to be unimportant. Finally, dimensional analysis will often give a great deal of insight into the form of the physical relationship we are trying to study.

A third benefit is that dimensional analysis provides *scaling laws* which can convert data from a cheap, small *model* to design information for an expensive, large *prototype*. We do not build a million-dollar airplane and see whether it has enough lift force. We measure the lift on a small model and use a scaling law to predict the lift on the full-scale prototype airplane. There are rules we shall explain for finding scaling laws. When the scaling law is valid, we say that a condition of *similarity* exists between the model and the prototype. In the simple case of Eq. (5.1), similarity is achieved if the Reynolds number is the same for the model and prototype because the function g then requires the force coefficient to be the same also:

$$\text{If} \quad \text{Re}_m = \text{Re}_p \quad \text{then} \quad C_{Fm} = C_{Fp} \tag{5.3}$$

where subscripts m and p mean model and prototype, respectively. From the definition of force coefficient, this means that

$$\frac{F_p}{F_m} = \frac{\rho_p}{\rho_m} \left(\frac{V_p}{V_m}\right)^2 \left(\frac{L_p}{L_m}\right)^2 \tag{5.4}$$

for data taken where $\rho_p V_p L_p / \mu_p = \rho_m V_m L_m / \mu_m$. Equation (5.4) is a scaling law: If you measure the model force at the model Reynolds number, the prototype force at the same Reynolds number equals the model force times the density ratio times the velocity ratio squared times the length ratio squared. We shall give more examples later.

Do you understand these introductory explanations? Be careful; learning dimensional analysis is like learning to play tennis: There are levels of the game. We can establish some ground rules and do some fairly good work in this brief chapter, but dimensional analysis in the broad view has many subtleties and nuances which only time and practice and maturity enable you to master. Although dimensional analysis has a firm physical and mathematical foundation, considerable art and skill are needed to use it effectively.

EXAMPLE 5.1

A copepod is a water crustacean approximately 1 mm in diameter. We want to know the drag force on the copepod when it moves slowly in fresh water. A scale model 100 times larger is made and tested in glycerin at $V = 30$ cm/s. The measured drag on the model is 1.3 N. For similar conditions, what are the velocity and drag of the actual copepod in water? Assume that Eq. (5.1) applies and the temperature is 20°C.

Solution

From Table A.3 the fluid properties are:

Water (prototype): $\mu_p = 0.001$ kg/(m · s) $\rho_p = 998$ kg/m^3

Glycerin (model): $\mu_m = 1.5$ kg/(m · s) $\rho_m = 1263$ kg/m^3

The length scales are $L_m = 100$ mm and $L_p = 1$ mm. We are given enough model data to compute the Reynolds number and force coefficient

$$\text{Re}_m = \frac{\rho_m V_m L_m}{\mu_m} = \frac{(1263 \text{ kg/m}^3)(0.3 \text{ m/s})(0.1 \text{ m})}{1.5 \text{ kg/(m · s)}} = 25.3$$

$$C_{Fm} = \frac{F_m}{\rho_m V_m^2 L_m^2} = \frac{1.3 \text{ N}}{(1263 \text{ kg/m}^3)(0.3 \text{ m/s})^2(0.1 \text{ m})^2} = 1.14$$

Both these numbers are dimensionless, as you can check. For conditions of similarity, the prototype Reynolds number must be the same, and Eq. (5.2) then requires the prototype force coefficient to be the same

$$\text{Re}_p = \text{Re}_m = 25.3 = \frac{998V_p(0.001)}{0.001}$$

or
$$V_p = 0.0253 \text{ m/s} = 2.53 \text{ cm/s} \qquad \textit{Ans.}$$

$$C_{Fp} = C_{Fm} = 1.14 = \frac{F_p}{998(0.0253)^2(0.001)^2}$$

or
$$F_p = 7.31 \times 10^{-7} \text{ N} \qquad \textit{Ans.}$$

It would obviously be difficult to measure such a tiny drag force.

Historically, the first person to write extensively about units and dimensional reasoning in physical relations was Euler in 1765. Euler's ideas were far ahead of his time, as were those of Joseph Fourier, whose 1822 book *Analytical Theory of Heat* outlined what is now called the *principle of dimensional homogeneity* and even developed some similarity rules for heat flow. There were no further significant advances until Lord Rayleigh's book in 1877, *Theory of Sound*, which proposed a "method of dimensions" and gave several examples of dimensional analysis. The final breakthrough which established the method as we know it today is generally credited to E. Buckingham in 1914 [29], whose paper outlined what is now called the *Buckingham pi theorem* for describing dimensionless parameters (see Sec. 5.3). However, it is now known that a Frenchman, A. Vaschy, in 1892 and a Russian, D. Riabouchinsky, in 1911 had independently published papers reporting results equivalent to the pi theorem. Following Buckingham's paper, P. W. Bridgman published a classic book in 1922 [1], outlining the general theory of dimensional analysis. The subject continues to be controversial because there is so much art and subtlety in using dimensional analysis. Thus, since Bridgman there have been at least 25 books published on the subject [1 to 25]. There will probably be more, but seeing the whole list might make some fledgling authors think twice. Nor is dimensional analysis limited to fluid mechanics or even engineering. Specialized books have been written on the application of dimensional analysis to metrology [26], astrophysics [27], and even economics [28].

5.2 The Principle of Dimensional Homogeneity

In making the remarkable jump from the five-variable Eq. (5.1) to the two-variable Eq. (5.2), we were exploiting a rule which is almost a self-evident axiom in physics. This rule, the *principle of dimensional homogeneity*, can be stated as follows:

> If an equation truly expresses a proper relationship between variables in a physical process, it will be *dimensionally homogeneous*; i.e., each of its additive terms will have the same dimensions.

All the equations which are derived from the theory of mechanics are of this form. For example, consider the relation which expresses the displacement of a falling body

$$S = S_0 + V_0 t + \tfrac{1}{2}gt^2 \qquad (5.5)$$

Each term in this equation is a displacement, or length, and has dimensions $\{L\}$. The equation is dimensionally homogeneous. Note also that any consistent set of units can be used to calculate a result.

Consider Bernoulli's equation for incompressible flow

$$\frac{p}{\rho} + \frac{1}{2}V^2 + gz = \text{const} \tag{5.6}$$

Each term, including the constant, has dimensions of velocity squared, or $\{L^2T^{-2}\}$. The equation is dimensionally homogeneous and gives proper results for any consistent set of units.

Students count on dimensional homogeneity and use it to check themselves when they cannot quite remember an equation during an exam. For example, which is it:

$$S = \tfrac{1}{2}gt^2? \quad \text{or} \quad S = \tfrac{1}{2}g^2t? \tag{5.7}$$

By checking the dimensions, we reject the second form and back up our faulty memory. We are exploiting the principle of dimensional homogeneity (PDH), and this chapter simply exploits it further.

Equations (5.5) and (5.6) also illustrate some other factors that often enter into a dimensional analysis:

Dimensional variables are the quantities which actually vary during a given case and would be plotted against each other to show the data. In Eq. (5.5), they are S and t; in Eq. (5.6) they are p, V, and z. All have dimensions, and all can be nondimensionalized as a dimensional-analysis technique.

Dimensional constants may vary from case to case but are held constant during a given run. In Eq. (5.5) they are S_0, V_0, and g, and in Eq. (5.6) they are ρ, g, and C. They all have dimensions and conceivably could be nondimensionalized, but they are normally used to help nondimensionalize the variables in the problem.

Pure constants have no dimensions and never did. They arise from mathematical manipulations. In both Eqs. (5.5) and (5.6) they are $\frac{1}{2}$ and the exponent 2, both of which came from an integration: $\int t\, dt = \frac{1}{2}t^2$, $\int V\, dV = \frac{1}{2}V^2$. Other common dimensionless constants are π and e.

Note that integration and differentiation of an equation may change the dimensions but not the homogeneity of the equation. For example, integrate or differentiate Eq. (5.5):

$$\int S\, dt = S_0 t + \tfrac{1}{2}V_0 t^2 + \tfrac{1}{6}gt^3 \tag{5.8a}$$

$$\frac{dS}{dt} = V_0 + gt \tag{5.8b}$$

In the integrated form (5.8a) every term has dimensions of $\{LT\}$, while in the derivative form (5.8b) every term is a velocity $\{LT^{-1}\}$.

Finally, there are some physical variables that are naturally dimensionless by virtue of their definition as ratios of dimensional quantities. Some examples are strain (change in length per unit length), Poisson's ratio (ratio of transverse strain to longitudinal strain), and specific gravity (ratio of density to standard water density). All angles are dimensionless (ratio of arc length to radius) and should be taken in radians for this reason.

The motive behind dimensional analysis is that any dimensionally homogeneous equation can be written in an entirely equivalent nondimensional form which is more compact. Usually there is more than one method of presenting one's dimensionless data or theory. Let us illustrate these concepts more thoroughly by using the falling-body relation (5.5) as an example.

Ambiguity: The Choice of Variables and Scaling Parameters[1]

Equation (5.5) is familiar and simple, yet illustrates most of the concepts of dimensional analysis. It contains five terms (S, S_0, V_0, t, g) which we may divide, in our thinking, into variables and parameters. The *variables* are the things which we wish to plot, the basic output of the experiment or theory: in this case, S versus t. The *parameters* are those quantities whose effect upon the variables we wish to know: in this case S_0, V_0, and g. Almost any engineering study can be subdivided in this manner.

To nondimensionalize our results, we need to know how many dimensions are contained among our variables and parameters: in this case, only two, length $\{L\}$ and time $\{T\}$. Check each term to verify this:

$$\{S\} = \{S_0\} = \{L\} \qquad \{t\} = \{T\} \qquad \{V_0\} = \{LT^{-1}\} \qquad \{g\} = \{LT^{-2}\}$$

Among our parameters, we therefore select two to be *scaling parameters*, used to define dimensionless variables. What remains will be the ''basic'' parameter(s) whose effect we wish to show in our plot. These choices will not affect the content of our data, only the form of their presentation. Clearly there is ambiguity in these choices, something that often vexes the beginning experimenter. But the ambiguity is deliberate. Its purpose is to show a particular effect, and the choice is yours to make.

For the falling-body problem, we select any two of the three parameters to be scaling parameters. Thus we have three options. Let us discuss and display them in turn.

Option 1: Scaling parameters S_0 and V_0: the effect of gravity g.

First use the scaling parameters (S_0, V_0) to define dimensionless (*) displacement and time. There is only one suitable definition for each[2]:

$$S^* = \frac{S}{S_0} \qquad t^* = \frac{V_0 t}{S_0} \tag{5.9}$$

Substitute these variables into Eq. (5.5) and clean everything up until each term is dimensionless. The result is our first option:

$$S^* = 1 + t^* + \frac{1}{2}\alpha t^{*2} \qquad \alpha = \frac{gS_0}{V_0^2} \tag{5.10}$$

This result is shown plotted in Fig. 5.1a. There is a single dimensionless parameter α, which shows here the effect of gravity. It cannot show the direct effects of S_0 and V_0, since these two are hidden in the ordinate and abscissa. We see that gravity increases the parabolic rate of fall for $t^* > 0$, but not the initial slope at $t^* = 0$. We would learn the same from falling-body data, and the plot, within experimental accuracy, would look like Fig. 5.1a.

---

[1] I am indebted to Prof. Jacques Lewalle of Syracuse University for suggesting, outlining, and clarifying this entire discussion.

[2] Make them *proportional* to S and t. Do not define dimensionless terms upside down: S_0/S or $S_0/(V_0 t)$. The plots will look funny, users of your data will be confused, and your supervisor will be angry. It is not a good idea.

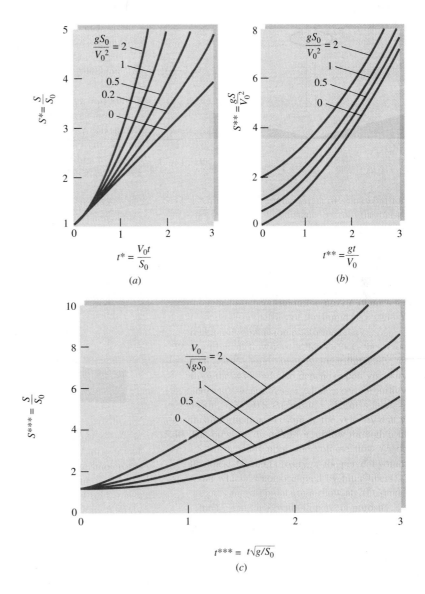

Fig. 5.1 Three entirely equivalent dimensionless presentations of the falling-body problem, Eq. (5.5): the effect of (*a*) gravity, (*b*) initial displacement, and (*c*) initial velocity. All plots contain the same information.

Option 2: Scaling parameters V_0 and g: the effect of initial displacement S_0.

Now use the new scaling parameters (V_0, g) to define dimensionless (**) displacement and time. Again there is only one suitable definition:

$$S^{**} = S\frac{g}{V_0^2} \qquad t^{**} = t\frac{g}{V_0} \tag{5.11}$$

Substitute these variables into Eq. (5.5) and clean everything up again. The result is our second option:

$$S^{**} = \alpha + t^{**} + \frac{1}{2}t^{**2} \qquad \alpha = \frac{gS_0}{V_0^2} \tag{5.12}$$

This result is plotted in Fig. 5.1b. The same single parameter α again appears and here shows the effect of initial *displacement*, which merely moves the curves upward without changing their shape.

Option 3: Scaling parameters S_0 and g: the effect of initial speed V_0.

Finally use the scaling parameters (S_0, g) to define dimensionless (***) displacement and time. Again there is only one suitable definition:

$$S^{***} = \frac{S}{S_0} \qquad t^{***} = t\left(\frac{g}{S_0}\right)^{1/2} \tag{5.13}$$

Substitute these variables into Eq. (5.5) and clean everything up as usual. The result is our third and final option:

$$S^{***} = 1 + \beta t^{***} + \frac{1}{2}t^{***2} \qquad \beta = \frac{1}{\sqrt{\alpha}} = \frac{V_0}{\sqrt{gS_0}} \tag{5.14}$$

This final presentation is shown in Fig. 5.1c. Once again the parameter α appears, but we have redefined it upside down, $\beta = 1/\sqrt{\alpha}$, so that our display parameter V_0 is in the numerator and is linear. This is our free choice and simply improves the display. Figure 5.1c shows that initial *velocity* increases the falling displacement and that the increase is proportional to time.

Note that, in all three options, the same parameter α appears but has a different meaning: dimensionless gravity, initial displacement, and initial velocity. The graphs, which contain exactly the same information, change their appearance to reflect these differences.

Whereas the original problem, Eq. (5.5), involved five quantities, the dimensionless presentations involve only three, having the form

$$S' = \text{fcn}(t', \alpha) \qquad \alpha = \frac{gS_0}{V_0^2} \tag{5.15}$$

The reduction $5 - 3 = 2$ should equal the number of fundamental dimensions involved in the problem $\{L, T\}$. This idea led to the pi theorem (Sec. 5.3).

The choice of scaling variables is left to the user, and the resulting dimensionless parameters have differing interpretations. For example, in the dimensionless drag-force formulation, Eq. (5.2), it is now clear that the scaling parameters were ρ, V, and L, since they appear in both the drag coefficient and the Reynolds number. Equation (5.2) can thus be interpreted as the variation of dimensionless *force* with dimensionless *viscosity*, with the scaling-parameter effects mixed between C_F and Re and therefore not immediately evident.

Suppose that we wish to study drag force versus *velocity*. Then we would not use V as a scaling parameter. We would use (ρ, μ, L) instead, and the final dimensionless function would become

$$C_F' = \frac{\rho F}{\mu^2} = \text{fcn}(\text{Re}) \qquad \text{Re} = \frac{\rho VL}{\mu} \tag{5.16}$$

In plotting these data, we would not be able to discern the effect of ρ or μ, since they appear in both dimensionless groups. The grouping C_F' again would mean dimensionless force, and Re is now interpreted as either dimensionless velocity or size.[1] The plot would be quite different compared to Eq. (5.2), although it contains exactly the same information. The development of parameters such as C_F' and Re from the initial variables is the subject of the pi theorem (Sec. 5.3).

Some Peculiar Engineering Equations

The foundation of the dimensional-analysis method rests on two assumptions: (1) The proposed physical relation is dimensionally homogeneous, and (2) all the relevant variables have been included in the proposed relation.

If a relevant variable is missing, dimensional analysis will fail, giving either algebraic difficulties or, worse, yielding a dimensionless formulation which does not resolve the process. A typical case is Manning's open-channel formula, discussed in Example 1.4:

$$V = \frac{1.49}{n} R^{2/3} S^{1/2} \qquad (1)$$

Since V is velocity, R is a radius, and n and S are dimensionless, the formula is not dimensionally homogeneous. This should be a warning that (1) the formula changes if the *units* of V and R change and (2) if valid, it represents a very special case. Equation (1) in Example 1.4 (see above) predates the dimensional-analysis technique and is valid only for water in rough channels at moderate velocities and large radii in BG units.

Such dimensionally inhomogeneous formulas abound in the hydraulics literature. Another example is the Hazen-Williams formula [30] for volume flow of water through a straight smooth pipe

$$Q = 61.9 D^{2.63} \left(\frac{dp}{dx} \right)^{0.54} \qquad (5.17)$$

where D is diameter and dp/dx is the pressure gradient. Some of these formulas arise because numbers have been inserted for fluid properties and other physical data into perfectly legitimate homogeneous formulas. We shall not give the units of Eq. (5.17) to avoid encouraging its use.

On the other hand, some formulas are "constructs" which cannot be made dimensionally homogeneous. The "variables" they relate cannot be analyzed by the dimensional-analysis technique. Most of these formulas are raw empiricisms convenient to a small group of specialists. Here are three examples:

$$B = \frac{25,000}{100 - R} \qquad (5.18)$$

$$S = \frac{140}{130 + \text{API}} \qquad (5.19)$$

$$0.0147 D_E - \frac{3.74}{D_E} = 0.26 t_R - \frac{172}{t_R} \qquad (5.20)$$

Equation (5.18) relates the Brinell hardness B of a metal to its Rockwell hardness R. Equation (5.19) relates the specific gravity S of an oil to its density in degrees API.

---

[1] We were lucky to achieve a size effect because in this case L, a scaling parameter, did not in fact appear in the drag coefficient.

Equation (5.20) relates the viscosity of a liquid in D_E, or degrees Engler, to its viscosity t_R in Saybolt seconds. Such formulas have a certain usefulness when communicated between fellow specialists, but we cannot handle them here. Variables like Brinell hardness and Saybolt viscosity are not suited to an $MLT\Theta$ dimensional system.

5.3 The Pi Theorem

There are several methods of reducing a number of dimensional variables into a smaller number of dimensionless groups. The scheme given here was proposed in 1914 by Buckingham [29] and is now called the *Buckingham pi theorem*. The name *pi* comes from the mathematical notation Π, meaning a product of variables. The dimensionless groups found from the theorem are power products denoted by Π_1, Π_2, Π_3, etc. The method allows the pis to be found in sequential order without resorting to free exponents.

The first part of the pi theorem explains what reduction in variables to expect:

If a physical process satisfies the PDH and involves n dimensional variables, it can be reduced to a relation between only k dimensionless variables or Π's. The reduction $j = n - k$ equals the maximum number of variables which do not form a pi among themselves and is always less than or equal to the number of dimensions describing the variables.

Take the specific case of force on an immersed body: Eq. (5.1) contains five variables F, L, U, ρ, and μ described by three dimensions $\{MLT\}$. Thus $n = 5$ and $j \leq 3$. Therefore it is a good guess that we can reduce the problem to k pis, with $k = n - j \geq 5 - 3 = 2$. And this is exactly what we obtained: two dimensionless variables $\Pi_1 = C_F$ and $\Pi_2 = \text{Re}$. On rare occasions it may take more pis than this minimum (see Example 5.5).

The second part of the theorem shows how to find the pis one at a time:

Find the reduction j, then select j scaling variables which do not form a pi among themselves.[1] Each desired pi group will be a power product of these j variables plus one additional variable which is assigned any convenient nonzero exponent. Each pi group thus found is independent.

To be specific, suppose that the process involves five variables

$$v_1 = f(v_2, v_3, v_4, v_5)$$

Suppose that there are three dimensions $\{MLT\}$ and we search around and find that indeed $j = 3$. Then $k = 5 - 3 = 2$ and we expect, from the theorem, two and only two pi groups. Pick out three convenient variables which do *not* form a pi, and suppose these turn out to be v_2, v_3, and v_4. Then the two pi groups are formed by power products of these three plus one additional variable:

$$\Pi_1 = (v_2)^a(v_3)^b(v_4)^c v_1 = M^0 L^0 T^0 \qquad \Pi_2 = (v_2)^a(v_3)^b(v_4)^c v_5 = M^0 L^0 T^0$$

Here we have arbitrarily chosen v_1 and v_5, the added variables, to have unit exponents. Equating exponents of the various dimensions is guaranteed by the theorem to give unique values of a, b, and c for each pi. And they are independent because only Π_1

---

[1] Make a clever choice here because all pi's will contain these j variables in various groupings.

Table 5.1 Dimensions of Fluid-Mechanics Properties

Quantity	Symbol	Dimensions	
		MLTΘ	*FLTΘ*
Length	L	L	L
Area	A	L^2	L^2
Volume	$\mathcal{V}$	L^3	L^3
Velocity	V	LT^{-1}	LT^{-1}
Speed of sound	a	LT^{-1}	LT^{-1}
Volume flow	Q	L^3T^{-1}	L^3T^{-1}
Mass flow	$\dot{m}$	MT^{-1}	FTL^{-1}
Pressure, stress	p, σ	$ML^{-1}T^{-2}$	FL^{-2}
Strain rate	$\dot{\epsilon}$	T^{-1}	T^{-1}
Angle	θ	None	None
Angular velocity	ω	T^{-1}	T^{-1}
Viscosity	μ	$ML^{-1}T^{-1}$	FTL^{-2}
Kinematic viscosity	ν	L^2T^{-1}	L^2T^{-1}
Surface tension	Y	MT^{-2}	FL^{-1}
Force	F	MLT^{-2}	F
Moment, torque	M	ML^2T^{-2}	FL
Power	P	ML^2T^{-3}	FLT^{-1}
Work, energy	W, E	ML^2T^{-2}	FL
Density	ρ	ML^{-3}	FT^2L^{-4}
Temperature	T	Θ	Θ
Specific heat	c_p, c_v	$L^2T^{-2}\Theta^{-1}$	$L^2T^{-2}\Theta^{-1}$
Thermal conductivity	k	$MLT^{-3}\Theta^{-1}$	$FT^{-1}\Theta^{-1}$
Expansion coefficient	β	Θ^{-1}	Θ^{-1}

contains v_1 and only Π_2 contains v_5. It is a very neat system once you get used to the procedure. We shall illustrate it with several examples.

Typically, six steps are involved:

1. List and count the n variables involved in the problem. If any important variables are missing, dimensional analysis will fail.
2. List the dimensions of each variable according to {$MLT\Theta$} or {$FLT\Theta$}. A list is given in Table 5.1.
3. Find j. Initially guess j equal to the number of different dimensions present, and look for j variables which do not form a pi product. If no luck, reduce j by 1 and look again. With practice, you will find j rapidly.
4. Select j scaling parameters which do not form a pi product. Make sure they please you and have some generality if possible, because they will then appear in every one of your pi groups. Pick density or velocity or length. Do not pick surface tension, e.g., or you will form six different independent Weber-number parameters and thoroughly annoy your colleagues.
5. Add one additional variable to your j repeating variables, and form a power product. Algebraically find the exponents which make the product dimensionless. Try to arrange for your output or *dependent* variables (force, pressure drop, torque, power) to appear in the numerator, and your plots will look better. Do this sequentially, adding one new variable each time, and you will find all $n - j = k$ desired pi products.
6. Write the final dimensionless function, and check your work to make sure all pi groups are dimensionless.

EXAMPLE 5.2

Repeat the development of Eq. (5.2) from Eq. (5.1), using the pi theorem.

Solution

Step 1 Write the function and count variables:

$$F = f(L, U, \rho, \mu) \qquad \text{there are five variables } (n = 5)$$

Step 2 List dimensions of each variable. From Table 5.1

F	L	U	ρ	μ
$\{MLT^{-2}\}$	$\{L\}$	$\{LT^{-1}\}$	$\{ML^{-3}\}$	$\{ML^{-1}T^{-1}\}$

Step 3 Find j. No variable contains the dimension Θ, and so j is less than or equal to 3 (MLT). We inspect the list and see that L, U, and ρ cannot form a pi group because only ρ contains mass and only U contains time. Therefore j does equal 3, and $n - j = 5 - 3 = 2 = k$. The pi theorem guarantees for this problem that there will be exactly two independent dimensionless groups.

Step 4 Select repeating j variables. The group L, U, ρ we found in step 3 will do fine.

Step 5 Combine L, U, ρ with one additional variable, in sequence, to find the two pi products.
First add force to find Π_1. You may select *any* exponent on this additional term as you please, to place it in the numerator or denominator to any power. Since F is the output, or dependent, variable, we select it to appear to the first power in the numerator:

$$\Pi_1 = L^a U^b \rho^c F = (L)^a (LT^{-1})^b (ML^{-3})^c (MLT^{-2}) = M^0 L^0 T^0$$

Equate exponents:

Length: $\qquad\qquad\qquad\qquad a + b - 3c + 1 = 0$

Mass: $\qquad\qquad\qquad\qquad\qquad\qquad c + 1 = 0$

Time: $\qquad\qquad\qquad\qquad -b \qquad\quad -2 = 0$

We can solve explicitly for

$$a = -2 \qquad b = -2 \qquad c = -1$$

Therefore

$$\Pi_1 = L^{-2} U^{-2} \rho^{-1} F = \frac{F}{\rho U^2 L^2} = C_F \qquad\qquad Ans.$$

This is exactly the right pi group as in Eq. (5.2). By varying the exponent on F, we could have found other equivalent groups such as $UL\rho^{1/2}/F^{1/2}$.
Finally, add viscosity to L, U, and ρ to find Π_2. Select any power you like for viscosity. By hindsight and custom, we select the power -1 to place it in the denominator:

$$\Pi_2 = L^a U^b \rho^c \mu^{-1} = L^a (LT^{-1})^b (ML^{-3})^c (ML^{-1}T^{-1})^{-1} = M^0 L^0 T^0$$

Equate exponents:

Length: $\qquad\qquad\qquad\qquad a + b - 3c + 1 = 0$

Mass: $$c - 1 = 0$$

Time: $$-b + 1 = 0$$

from which we find

$$a = b = c = 1$$

Therefore $$\Pi_2 = L^1 U^1 \rho^1 \mu^{-1} = \frac{\rho UL}{\mu} = \text{Re} \qquad \textit{Ans.}$$

We know we are finished; this is the second and last pi group. The theorem guarantees that the functional relationship must be of the equivalent form

$$\frac{F}{\rho U^2 L^2} = g\left(\frac{\rho UL}{\mu}\right) \qquad \textit{Ans.}$$

which is exactly Eq. (5.2).

EXAMPLE 5.3

Reduce the falling-body relationship, Eq. (5.5), to a function of dimensionless variables. Why are there three different formulations?

Solution

Write the function and count variables

$$S = f(t, S_0, V_0, g) \qquad \text{five variables } (n = 5)$$

List the dimensions of each variable, from Table 5.1:

S	t	S_0	V_0	g
$\{L\}$	$\{T\}$	$\{L\}$	$\{LT^{-1}\}$	$\{LT^{-2}\}$

There are only two primary dimensions (L, T), so that $j \leq 2$. By inspection we can easily find two variables which cannot be combined to form a pi, for example, V_0 and g. Then $j = 2$, and we expect $5 - 2 = 3$ pi products. Select j variables among the parameters S_0, V_0, and g. Avoid S and t since they are the dependent variables, which should not be repeated in pi groups.

There are three different options for repeating variables among the group (S_0, V_0, g). Therefore we can obtain three different dimensionless formulations, just as we did informally with the falling-body equation in Sec. 5.2. Take each option in turn:

1. Choose S_0 and V_0 as repeating variables. Combine them in turn with (S, t, g):

$$\Pi_1 = S^1 S_0^a V_0^b \qquad \Pi_2 = t^1 S_0^c V_0^d \qquad \Pi_3 = g^1 S_0^e V_0^f$$

Set each power product equal to $L^0 T^0$, and solve for the exponents (a, b, c, d, e, f). Please allow us to give the results here, and you may check the algebra as an exercise:

$$a = -1 \quad b = 0 \quad c = -1 \quad d = 1 \quad e = 1 \quad f = -2$$

$$\qquad \textit{Ans.}$$

$$\Pi_1 = S^* = \frac{S}{S_0} \qquad \Pi_2 = t^* = \frac{V_0 t}{S_0} \qquad \Pi_3 = \alpha = \frac{g S_0}{V_0^2}$$

Thus, for option 1, we know that $S^* = \text{fcn}(t^*, \alpha)$. We have found, by dimensional analysis, the same variables as in Eq. (5.10). But here there is no *formula* for the functional relation—we might have to experiment with falling bodies to establish Fig. 5.1a.

2. Choose V_0 and g as repeating variables. Combine them in turn with (S, t, S_0):

$$\Pi_1 = S^1 V_0^a g^b \qquad \Pi_2 = t^1 V_0^c g^d \qquad \Pi_3 = S_0^1 V_0^e g^f$$

Set each power product equal to $L^0 T^0$, and solve for the exponents (a, b, c, d, e, f). Once more allow us to give the results here, and you may check the algebra as an exercise.

$$a = -2 \qquad b = 1 \qquad c = -1 \qquad d = 1 \qquad e = 1 \qquad f = -2$$

Ans.

$$\Pi_1 = S^{**} = \frac{Sg}{V_0^2} \qquad \Pi_2 = t^{**} = \frac{tg}{V_0} \qquad \Pi_3 = \alpha = \frac{gS_0}{V_0^2}$$

Thus, for option 2, we now know that $S^{**} = \text{fcn}(t^{**}, \alpha)$. We have found, by dimensional analysis, the same groups as in Eq. (5.12). The data would plot as in Fig. 5.1b.

3. Finally choose S_0 and g as repeating variables. Combine them in turn with (S, t, V_0):

$$\Pi_1 = S^1 S_0^a g^b \qquad \Pi_2 = t^1 S_0^c g^d \qquad \Pi_3 = V_0^1 S_0^e g^f$$

Set each power product equal to $L^0 T^0$, and solve for the exponents (a, b, c, d, e, f). One more time allow us to give the results here, and you may check the algebra as an exercise:

$$a = -1 \qquad b = 0 \qquad c = -\tfrac{1}{2} \qquad d = \tfrac{1}{2} \qquad e = -\tfrac{1}{2} \qquad f = -\tfrac{1}{2}$$

Ans.

$$\Pi_1 = S^{***} = \frac{S}{S_0} \qquad \Pi_2 = t^{***} = t\sqrt{\frac{g}{S_0}} \qquad \Pi_3 = \beta = \frac{V_0}{\sqrt{gS_0}}$$

Thus, for option 3, we now know that $S^{***} = \text{fcn}(t^{***}, \beta = 1/\sqrt{\alpha})$. We have found, by dimensional analysis, the same groups as in Eq. (5.14). The data would plot as in Fig. 5.1c.

Dimensional analysis here has yielded the same pi groups as the use of scaling parameters with Eq. (5.5). Three different formulations appeared, because we could choose three different pairs of repeating variables to complete the pi theorem.

EXAMPLE 5.4

At low velocities (laminar flow), the volume flow Q through a small-bore tube is a function only of the tube radius R, the fluid viscosity μ, and the pressure drop per unit tube length dp/dx. Using the pi theorem, find an appropriate dimensionless relationship.

Solution

Write the given relation and count variables:

$$Q = f\left(R, \mu, \frac{dp}{dx}\right) \qquad \text{four variables } (n = 4)$$

Make a list of the dimensions of these variables from Table 5.1:

Q	R	μ	dp/dx
$\{L^3T^{-1}\}$	$\{L\}$	$\{ML^{-1}T^{-1}\}$	$\{ML^{-2}T^{-2}\}$

There are three primary dimensions (M, L, T), hence $j \leq 3$. By trial and error we determine that R, μ, and dp/dx cannot be combined into a pi group. Then $j = 3$, and $n - j = 4 - 3 = 1$. There is only *one* pi group, which we find by combining Q in a power product with the other three:

$$\Pi_1 = R^a \mu^b \left(\frac{dp}{dx}\right)^c Q^1 = (L)^a (ML^{-1}T^{-1})^b (ML^{-2}T^{-2})^c (L^3 T^{-1})$$

$$= M^0 L^0 T^0$$

Equate exponents:

Mass: $b + c = 0$

Length: $a - b - 2c + 3 = 0$

Time: $-b - 2c - 1 = 0$

Solving simultaneously, we obtain $a = -4, b = 1, c = -1$. Then

$$\Pi_1 = R^{-4} \mu^1 \left(\frac{dp}{dx}\right)^{-1} Q$$

or

$$\Pi_1 = \frac{Q\mu}{R^4(dp/dx)} = \text{const} \qquad\qquad\qquad Ans.$$

Since there is only one pi group, it must equal a dimensionless constant. This is as far as dimensional analysis can take us. The laminar-flow theory of Sec. 6.4 shows that the value of the constant is $\pi/8$.

EXAMPLE 5.5

Assume that the tip deflection δ of a cantilever beam is a function of the tip load P, beam length L, area moment of inertia I, and material modulus of elasticity E; that is, $\delta = f(P, L, I, E)$. Rewrite this function in dimensionless form, and comment on its complexity and the peculiar value of j.

Solution

List the variables and their dimensions:

δ	P	L	I	E
$\{L\}$	$\{MLT^{-2}\}$	$\{L\}$	$\{L^4\}$	$\{ML^{-1}T^{-2}\}$

There are five variables ($n = 5$) and three primary dimensions (M, L, T), hence $j \leq 3$. But try as we may, we *cannot* find any combination of three variables which does not form a pi group. This is because $\{M\}$ and $\{T\}$ occur only in P and E and only in the same form, $\{MT^{-2}\}$. Thus we have encountered a special case of $j = 2$, which is less than the number of dimensions (M, L, T). To gain more insight into this peculiarity, you should rework the problem, using the (F, L, T) system of dimensions.

With $j = 2$, we select L and E as two variables which cannot form a pi group and then add other variables to form the three desired pi's:

$$\Pi_1 = L^a E^b I^1 = (L)^a (ML^{-1}T^{-2})^b (L^4) = M^0 L^0 T^0$$

from which, after equating exponents, we find that $a = -4$, $b = 0$, or $\Pi_1 = I/L^4$. Then

$$\Pi_2 = L^a E^b P^1 = (L)^a (ML^{-1}T^{-2})^b (MLT^{-2}) = M^0 L^0 T^0$$

from which we find $a = -2$, $b = -1$, or $\Pi_2 = P/(EL^2)$, and

$$\Pi_3 = L^a E^b \delta^1 = (L)^a (ML^{-1}T^{-2})^b (L) = M^0 L^0 T^0$$

from which $a = -1$, $b = 0$, or $\Pi_3 = \delta/L$. The proper dimensionless function is $\Pi_3 = f(\Pi_2, \Pi_1)$, or

$$\frac{\delta}{L} = f\left(\frac{P}{EL^2}, \frac{I}{L^4}\right) \qquad\qquad Ans. \quad (1)$$

This is a complex three-variable function, but dimensional analysis alone can take us no further.

We can "improve" Eq. (1) by taking advantage of some physical reasoning, as Langhaar points out [8, p. 91]. For small elastic deflections, δ is proportional to load P and inversely proportional to moment of inertia I. Since P and I occur separately in Eq. (1), this means that Π_3 must be proportional to Π_2 and inversely proportional to Π_1. Thus, for these conditions,

$$\frac{\delta}{L} = (\text{const}) \frac{P}{EL^2} \frac{L^4}{I}$$

or

$$\delta = (\text{const}) \frac{PL^3}{EI} \qquad\qquad (2)$$

This could not be predicted by a pure dimensional analysis. Strength-of-materials theory predicts that the value of the constant is $\frac{1}{3}$.

5.4 Nondimensionalization of the Basic Equations

We could use the pi-theorem method of the previous section to analyze problem after problem after problem, finding the dimensionless parameters which govern in each case. Textbooks on dimensional analysis [for example, 7] do this. An alternate and very powerful technique is to attack the basic equations of flow from Chap. 4. Even though these equations cannot be solved in general, they will reveal basic dimensionless parameters, e.g., Reynolds number, in their proper form and proper position, giving clues to when they are negligible. The boundary conditions must also be nondimensionalized.

Let us briefly apply this technique to the incompressible-flow continuity and momentum equations with constant viscosity:

Continuity: $$\nabla \cdot \mathbf{V} = 0 \qquad\qquad (5.21a)$$

Momentum: $$\rho \frac{d\mathbf{V}}{dt} = \rho \mathbf{g} - \nabla p + \mu \nabla^2 \mathbf{V} \qquad\qquad (5.21b)$$

Typical boundary conditions for these two equations are

Fixed solid surface: $$\mathbf{V} = 0$$

Inlet or outlet: Known **V**, p (5.22)

Free surface, $z = \eta$: $w = \dfrac{d\eta}{dt}$ $p = p_a - Y(R_x^{-1} + R_y^{-1})$

We omit the energy equation (4.75) and assign its dimensionless form in the problems (Probs. 5.42 and 5.45).

Equations (5.21), and (5.22) contain the three basic dimensions M, L, and T. All variables p, **V**, x, y, z, and t can be nondimensionalized by using density and two reference constants which might be characteristic of the particular fluid flow:

$$\text{Reference velocity} = U \qquad \text{Reference length} = L$$

For example, U may be the inlet or upstream velocity and L the diameter of a body immersed in the stream.

Now define all relevant dimensionless variables, denoting them by an asterisk:

$$\mathbf{V^*} = \frac{\mathbf{V}}{U}$$

$$x^* = \frac{x}{L} \qquad y^* = \frac{y}{L} \qquad z^* = \frac{z}{L} \qquad (5.23)$$

$$t^* = \frac{tU}{L} \qquad p^* = \frac{p + \rho gz}{\rho U^2}$$

All these are fairly obvious except for p^*, where we have slyly introduced the gravity effect, assuming that z is up. This is a hindsight idea suggested by Bernoulli's equation (3.77).

Since ρ, U, and L are all constants, the derivatives in Eqs. (5.21) can all be handled in dimensionless form with dimensional coefficients. For example,

$$\frac{\partial u}{\partial x} = \frac{\partial (Uu^*)}{\partial (Lx^*)} = \frac{U}{L}\frac{\partial u^*}{\partial x^*}$$

Substitute the variables from Eqs. (5.23) into Eqs. (5.21) and (5.2) and divide through by the leading dimensional coefficient, in the same way as we handled Eq. (5.12). The resulting dimensionless equations of motion are:

Continuity: $\mathbf{\nabla^* \cdot V^*} = 0$ (5.24a)

Momentum: $\dfrac{d\mathbf{V^*}}{dt^*} = -\mathbf{\nabla^*}p^* + \dfrac{\mu}{\rho UL}\mathbf{\nabla^{*2}(V^*)}$ (5.24b)

The dimensionless boundary conditions are:

Fixed solid surface: $\mathbf{V^*} = 0$

Inlet or outlet: Known $\mathbf{V^*}$, p^*

Free surface, $z^* = \eta^*$: $w^* = \dfrac{d\eta^*}{dt^*}$ (5.25)

$$p^* = \frac{p_a}{\rho U^2} + \frac{gL}{U^2}z^* + \frac{Y}{\rho U^2 L}(R_x^{*-1} + R_y^{*-1})$$

These equations reveal a total of four dimensionless parameters, one in the momentum equation and three in the free-surface-pressure boundary condition.

Dimensionless Parameters

In the continuity equation there are no parameters. The momentum equation contains one, generally accepted as the most important parameter in fluid mechanics:

$$\text{Reynolds number Re} = \frac{\rho UL}{\mu}$$

It is named after Osborne Reynolds (1842–1912), a British engineer who first proposed it in 1883 (Ref. 4 of Chap. 6). The Reynolds number is always important, with or without a free surface, and can be neglected only in flow regions away from high-velocity gradients, e.g., away from solid surfaces, jets, or wakes.

The no-slip and inlet-exit boundary conditions contain no parameters. The free-surface-pressure condition contains three:

$$\text{Euler number (pressure coefficient) Eu} = \frac{p_a}{\rho U^2}$$

This is named after Leonhard Euler (1707–1783) and is rarely important unless the pressure drops low enough to cause vapor formation (cavitation) in a liquid. The Euler number is often written in terms of pressure differences: $\text{Eu} = \Delta p/(\rho U^2)$. If Δp involves vapor pressure p_v, it is called the *cavitation number* $\text{Ca} = (p_a - p_v)/(\rho U^2)$.

The second pressure parameter is much more important:

$$\text{Froude number Fr} = \frac{U^2}{gL}$$

It is named after William Froude (1810–1879), a British naval architect who, with his son Robert, developed the ship-model towing-tank concept and proposed similarity rules for free-surface flows (ship resistance, surface waves, open channels). The Froude number is the dominant effect in free-surface flows and is totally unimportant if there is no free surface. Chapter 10 investigates Froude number effects in detail.

The final free-surface parameter is

$$\text{Weber number We} = \frac{\rho U^2 L}{Y}$$

It is named after Moritz Weber (1871–1951) of the Polytechnic Institute of Berlin, who developed the laws of similitude in their modern form. It was Weber who named Re and Fr after Reynolds and Froude. The Weber number is important only if it is of order unity or less, which typically occurs when the surface curvature is comparable in size to the liquid depth, e.g., in droplets, capillary flows, ripple waves, and very small hydraulic models. If We is large, its effect may be neglected.

If there is no free surface, Fr, Eu, and We drop out entirely, except for the possibility of cavitation of a liquid at very small Eu. Thus, in low-speed viscous flows with no free surface, the Reynolds number is the only important dimensionless parameter.

Compressibility Parameters

In high-speed flow of a gas there are significant changes in pressure, density, and temperature which must be related by an equation of state such as the perfect-gas law,

Eq. (1.10). These thermodynamic changes introduce two additional dimensionless parameters mentioned briefly in earlier chapters:

$$\text{Mach number Ma} = \frac{U}{a} \qquad \text{Specific-heat ratio } k = \frac{c_p}{c_v}$$

The Mach number is named after Ernst Mach (1838–1916), an Austrian physicist. The effect of k is only slight to moderate, but Ma exerts a strong effect on compressible-flow properties if it is greater than about 0.3. These effects are studied in Chap. 9.

Oscillating Flows

If the flow pattern is oscillating, a seventh parameter enters through the inlet boundary condition. For example, suppose that the inlet stream is of the form

$$u = U \cos \omega t$$

Nondimensionalization of this relation results in

$$\frac{u}{U} = u* = \cos\left(\frac{\omega L}{U} t*\right)$$

The argument of the cosine contains the new parameter

$$\text{Strouhal number St} = \frac{\omega L}{U}$$

The dimensionless forces and moments, friction, and heat transfer, etc., of such an oscillating flow would be a function of both Reynolds and Strouhal numbers. This parameter is named after V. Strouhal, a German physicist who experimented in 1878 with wires singing in the wind.

Some flows which you might guess to be perfectly steady actually have an oscillatory pattern which is dependent on the Reynolds number. An example is the periodic vortex shedding behind a blunt body immersed in a steady stream of velocity U. Figure 5.2a shows an array of alternating vortices shed from a circular cylinder immersed in a steady crossflow. This regular, periodic shedding is called a *Kármán vortex street*, after T. von Kármán, who explained it theoretically in 1912. The shedding occurs in the range $10^2 < \text{Re} < 10^7$, with an average Strouhal number $\omega d/(2\pi U) \approx 0.21$. Figure 5.2$b$ shows measured shedding frequencies.

Resonance can occur if a vortex shedding frequency is near a body's structural-vibration frequency. Electric transmission wires sing in the wind, undersea mooring lines gallop at certain current speeds, and slender structures flutter at critical wind or vehicle speeds. A striking example is the disastrous failure of the Tacoma Narrows suspension bridge in 1940, when wind-excited vortex shedding caused resonance with the natural torsional oscillations of the bridge.

Other Dimensionless Parameters

We have discussed seven important parameters in fluid mechanics, and there are others. Four additional parameters arise from nondimensionalization of the energy equation (4.75) and its boundary conditions. These four (Prandtl number, Eckert number, Grashof number, and wall-temperature ratio) are listed in Table 5.2 just in case you fail to solve Prob. 5.42. Another important and rather sneaky parameter is the wall-roughness ratio ϵ/L (in Table 5.2).[1] Slight changes in surface roughness have a striking effect in the

---

[1] Roughness is easy to overlook because it is a slight geometric effect which does not appear in the equations of motion.

(a)

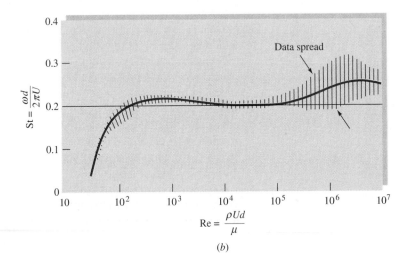

Fig. 5.2 Vortex shedding from a circular cylinder: (*a*) vortex street behind a circular cylinder (*from Ref. 33, courtesy of U.S. Naval Research Laboratory*); (*b*) experimental shedding frequencies (*data from Refs. 31 and 32*).

(b)

Table 5.2 Dimensionless Groups in Fluid Mechanics

Parameter	Definition	Qualitative ratio of effects	Importance
Reynolds number	$\text{Re} = \dfrac{\rho U L}{\mu}$	$\dfrac{\text{Inertia}}{\text{Viscosity}}$	Always
Mach number	$\text{Ma} = \dfrac{U}{a}$	$\dfrac{\text{Flow speed}}{\text{Sound speed}}$	Compressible flow
Froude number	$\text{Fr} = \dfrac{U^2}{gL}$	$\dfrac{\text{Inertia}}{\text{Gravity}}$	Free-surface flow
Weber number	$\text{We} = \dfrac{\rho U^2 L}{Y}$	$\dfrac{\text{Inertia}}{\text{Surface tension}}$	Free-surface flow
Cavitation number (Euler number)	$\text{Ca} = \dfrac{p - p_v}{\rho U^2}$	$\dfrac{\text{Pressure}}{\text{Inertia}}$	Cavitation
Prandtl number	$\text{Pr} = \dfrac{\mu c_p}{k}$	$\dfrac{\text{Dissipation}}{\text{Conduction}}$	Heat convection
Eckert number	$\text{Ec} = \dfrac{U^2}{c_p T_0}$	$\dfrac{\text{Kinetic energy}}{\text{Enthalpy}}$	Dissipation
Specific-heat ratio	$\dfrac{c_p}{c_v}$	$\dfrac{\text{Enthalpy}}{\text{Internal energy}}$	Compressible flow
Strouhal number	$\text{St} = \dfrac{\omega L}{U}$	$\dfrac{\text{Oscillation}}{\text{Mean speed}}$	Oscillating flow
Roughness ratio	$\dfrac{\epsilon}{L}$	$\dfrac{\text{Wall roughness}}{\text{Body length}}$	Turbulent, rough walls
Grashof number	$\text{Gr} = \dfrac{\beta \Delta T g L^3 \rho^2}{\mu^2}$	$\dfrac{\text{Buoyancy}}{\text{Viscosity}}$	Natural convection
Temperature ratio	$\dfrac{T_w}{T_0}$	$\dfrac{\text{Wall temperature}}{\text{Stream temperature}}$	Heat transfer
Pressure coefficient	$C_p = \dfrac{p - p_\infty}{\frac{1}{2}\rho U^2}$	$\dfrac{\text{Static pressure}}{\text{Dynamic pressure}}$	Aerodynamics, hydrodynamics
Lift coefficient	$C_L = \dfrac{L}{\frac{1}{2}\rho U^2 A}$	$\dfrac{\text{Lift force}}{\text{Dynamic force}}$	Aerodynamics, hydrodynamics
Drag coefficient	$C_D = \dfrac{D}{\frac{1}{2}\rho U^2 A}$	$\dfrac{\text{Drag force}}{\text{Dynamic force}}$	Aerodynamics, hydrodynamics

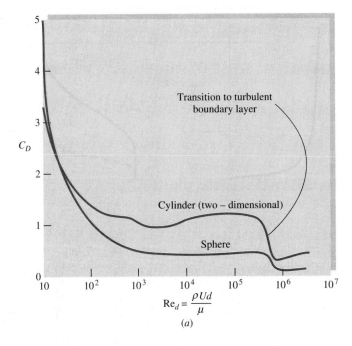

Cylinder length effect $(10^4 < Re < 10^5)$	
L/d	C_D
∞	1.20
40	0.98
20	0.91
10	0.82
5	0.74
3	0.72
2	0.68
1	0.64

$$Re_d = \frac{\rho U d}{\mu}$$

(a)

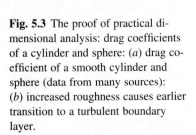

Fig. 5.3 The proof of practical dimensional analysis: drag coefficients of a cylinder and sphere: (a) drag coefficient of a smooth cylinder and sphere (data from many sources): (b) increased roughness causes earlier transition to a turbulent boundary layer.

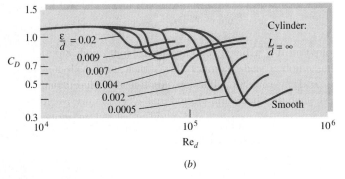

(b)

turbulent-flow or high-Reynolds-number range, as we shall see in Chap. 6 and in Fig. 5.3.

This book is primarily concerned with Reynolds-, Mach-, and Froude-number effects, which dominate most flows. Note that we discovered all these parameters (except ϵ/L) simply by nondimensionalizing the basic equations without actually solving them.

If the reader is not satiated with the 15 parameters given in Table 5.2, Ref. 34 contains a list of over 300 dimensionless parameters in use in engineering.

A Successful Application

Dimensional analysis is fun, but does it work? Yes; if all important variables are included in the proposed function, the dimensionless function found by dimensional analysis will collapse all the data onto a single curve or set of curves.

An example of the success of dimensional analysis is given in Fig. 5.3 for the measured drag on smooth cylinders and spheres. The flow is normal to the axis of the cylinder, which is extremely long, $L/d \rightarrow \infty$. The data are from many sources, for both liquids and gases, and include bodies from several meters in diameter down to fine wires and balls less than 1 mm in size. Both curves in Fig. 5.3a are entirely experimental; the analysis of immersed body drag is one of the weakest areas of modern fluid-mechanics theory. Except for some isolated digital-computer calculations, there is no theory for cylinder and sphere drag except *creeping flow*, Re < 1.

The Reynolds number of both bodies is based upon diameter, hence the notation Re_d. But the drag coefficients are defined differently:

$$C_D = \begin{cases} \dfrac{\text{drag}}{\frac{1}{2}\rho U^2 L d} & \text{cylinder} \\[2ex] \dfrac{\text{drag}}{\frac{1}{2}\rho U^2 \frac{1}{4}\pi d^2} & \text{sphere} \end{cases} \qquad (5.26)$$

They both have a factor $\frac{1}{2}$ as a traditional tribute to Bernoulli and Euler, and both are based on the projected area, i.e., the area one sees when looking toward the body from upstream. The usual definition of C_D is thus

$$C_D = \frac{\text{drag}}{\frac{1}{2}\rho U^2 (\text{projected area})} \qquad (5.27)$$

However, one should carefully check the definitions of C_D, Re, etc., before using data in the literature. Airfoils, e.g., use the planform area.

Figure 5.3a is for long, smooth cylinders. If wall roughness and cylinder length are included as variables, we obtain from dimensional analysis a complex three-parameter function

$$C_D = f\left(\text{Re}_d, \frac{\epsilon}{d}, \frac{L}{d}\right) \qquad (5.28)$$

To describe this function completely would require 1000 or more experiments. Therefore it is customary to explore the length and roughness effects separately to establish trends.

The table with Fig. 5.3a shows the length effect with zero wall roughness. As length decreases, the drag decreases by up to 50 percent. Physically, the pressure is "relieved" at the ends as the flow is allowed to skirt around the tips instead of deflecting over and under the body.

Figure 5.3b shows the effect of wall roughness for an infinitely long cylinder. The sharp drop in drag occurs at lower Re_d as roughness causes an earlier transition to a turbulent boundary layer on the surface of the body. Roughness has the same effect on sphere drag, a fact which is exploited in sports by deliberate dimpling of golf balls to give them less drag at their flight $\text{Re}_d \approx 10^5$.

Figure 5.3 is a typical experimental study of a fluid-mechanics problem, aided by dimensional analysis. As time and money and demand allow, the complete three-parameter relation (5.28) could be filled out by further experiments.

EXAMPLE 5.6

The capillary rise h of a liquid in a tube varies with tube diameter d, gravity g, fluid density ρ, surface tension Y, and the contact angle θ. (a) Find a dimensionless statement of this relation. (*b*) If $h = 3$ cm in a given experiment, what will h be in a similar case if the diameter and surface tension are half as much, the density is twice as much, and the contact angle is the same?

Solution

Part (a) **Step 1**   Write down the function and count variables:

$$h = f(d, g, \rho, Y, \theta) \qquad n = 6 \text{ variables}$$

Step 2   List the dimensions $\{FLT\}$ from Table 5.2:

h	d	g	ρ	Y	θ
$\{L\}$	$\{L\}$	$\{LT^{-2}\}$	$\{FT^2L^{-4}\}$	$\{FL^{-1}\}$	none

Step 3   Find j. Several groups of three form no pi: Y, ρ, and g or ρ, g, and d. Therefore $j = 3$, and we expect $n - j = 6 - 3 = 3$ dimensionless groups. One of these is obviously θ, which is already dimensionless:

$$\Pi_3 = \theta \qquad\qquad\qquad Ans. (a)$$

If we had carelessly chosen to search for it by using steps 4 and 5, we would still find $\Pi_3 = \theta$.

Step 4   Select j repeating variables which do not form a pi group: ρ, g, d.

Step 5   Add one additional variable in sequence to form the pis:

Add h:
$$\Pi_1 = \rho^a g^b d^c h = (FT^2L^{-4})^a (LT^{-2})^b (L)^c (L) = F^0 L^0 T^0$$

Solve for

$$a = b = 0 \qquad c = -1$$

$$\Pi_1 = \rho^0 g^0 d^{-1} h = \frac{h}{d} \qquad\qquad Ans. (a)$$

Therefore

Finally add Y, again selecting its exponent to be 1:

$$\Pi_2 = \rho^a g^b d^c Y = (FT^2L^{-4})^a (LT^{-2})^b (L)^c (FL^{-1}) = F^0 L^0 T^0$$

Solve for

$$a = b = -1 \qquad c = -2$$

Therefore
$$\Pi_2 = \rho^{-1} g^{-1} d^{-2} Y = \frac{Y}{\rho g d^2} \qquad\qquad Ans. (a)$$

Step 6   The complete dimensionless relation for this problem is thus

$$\frac{h}{d} = F\left(\frac{Y}{\rho g d^2}, \theta\right) \qquad\qquad Ans. (a) \quad (1)$$

This is as far as dimensional analysis goes. Theory, however, establishes that h is proportional to Y. Since Y occurs only in the second parameter, we can slip it outside

$$\left(\frac{h}{d}\right)_{\text{actual}} = \frac{Y}{\rho g d^2} F_1(\theta) \qquad \text{or} \qquad \frac{h \rho g d}{Y} = F_1(\theta)$$

Example 1.9 showed theoretically that $F_1(\theta) = 4 \cos \theta$.

Part (b)   We are given h_1 for certain conditions d_1, Y_1, ρ_1, and θ_1, and θ_1. If $h_1 = 3$ cm, what is h_2 for $d_2 = \frac{1}{2}d$, $Y_2 = \frac{1}{2}Y_1$, $\rho_2 = 2\rho_1$, and $\theta_2 = \theta_1$? We know the functional relation, Eq. (1), must still hold at condition 2

$$\frac{h_2}{d_2} = F\left(\frac{Y_2}{\rho_2 g d_2^2}, \theta_2\right)$$

But

$$\frac{Y_2}{\rho_2 g d_2^2} = \frac{\frac{1}{2}Y_1}{2\rho_1 g(\frac{1}{2}d_1)^2} = \frac{Y_1}{\rho_1 g d_1^2}$$

Therefore, functionally,

$$\frac{h_2}{d_2} = F\left(\frac{Y_1}{\rho_1 g d_1^2}, \theta_1\right) = \frac{h_1}{d_1}$$

We are given a condition 2 which is exactly similar to condition 1, and therefore a scaling law holds

$$h_2 = h_1 \frac{d_2}{d_1} = (3 \text{ cm}) \frac{\frac{1}{2}d_1}{d_1} = 1.5 \text{ cm} \qquad\qquad Ans. (b)$$

If the pi groups had not been exactly the same for both conditions, we would have had to know more about the functional relation F to calculate h_2.

5.5 Modeling and Its Pitfalls

So far we have learned about dimensional homogeneity and the pi-theorem method, using power products, for converting a homogeneous physical relation to dimensionless form. This is straightforward mathematically, but there are certain engineering difficulties which need to be discussed.

First, we have more or less taken for granted that the variables which affect the process can be listed and analyzed. Actually, selection of the important variables requires considerable judgment and experience. The engineer must decide, e.g., whether viscosity can be neglected. Are there significant temperature effects? Is surface tension important? What about wall roughness? Each pi group which is retained increases the expense and effort required. Judgment in selecting variables will come through practice and maturity; this book should provide some of the necessary experience.

Once the variables are selected and the dimensional analysis is performed, the experimenter seeks to achieve *similarity* between the model tested and the prototype to be designed. With sufficient testing, the model data will reveal the desired dimensionless function between variables

$$\Pi_1 = f(\Pi_2, \Pi_3, \ldots, \Pi_k) \qquad\qquad (5.29)$$

With Eq. (5.29) available in chart, graphical, or analytical form, we are in a position to ensure complete similarity between model and prototype. A formal statement would be as follows:

> Flow conditions for a model test are completely similar if all relevant dimensionless parameters have the same corresponding values for the model and the prototype.

This follows mathematically from Eq. (5.29). If $\Pi_{2m} = \Pi_{2p}$, $\Pi_{3m} = \Pi_{3p}$, etc., Eq. (5.29) guarantees that the desired output Π_{1m} will equal Π_{1p}. But this is easier said than done, as we now discuss.

Instead of complete similarity, the engineering literature speaks of particular types of similarity, the most common being geometric, kinematic, dynamic, and thermal. Let us consider each separately.

Geometric Similarity

Geometric similarity concerns the length dimension $\{L\}$ and must be ensured before any sensible model testing can proceed. A formal definition is as follows:

> A model and prototype are *geometrically similar* if and only if all body dimensions in all three coordinates have the same linear-scale ratio.

Note that *all* length scales must be the same. It is as if you took a photograph of the prototype and reduced it or enlarged it until it fitted the size of the model. If the model is to be made one-tenth the prototype size, its length, width, and height must each be one-tenth as large. Not only that, but also its entire shape must be one-tenth as large, and technically we speak of *homologous* points, which are points that have the same relative location. For example, the nose of the prototype is homologous to the nose of the model. The left wingtip of the prototype is homologous to the left wingtip of the model. Then geometric similarity requires that all homologous points be related by the same linear-scale ratio. This applies to the fluid geometry as well as the model geometry.

> All angles are preserved in geometric similarity. All flow dirctions are preserved. The orientations of model and prototype with respect to the surroundings must be identical.

Figure 5.4 illustrates a prototype wing and a one-tenth-scale model. The model lengths are all one-tenth as large, but its angle of attack with respect to the free stream is the same: $10°$ not $1°$. All physical details on the model must be scaled, and some are rather subtle and sometimes overlooked:

1. The model nose radius must be one-tenth as large.
2. The model surface roughness must be one-tenth as large.

Fig. 5.4 Geometric similarity in model testing: (*a*) prototype; (*b*) one-tenth-scale model.

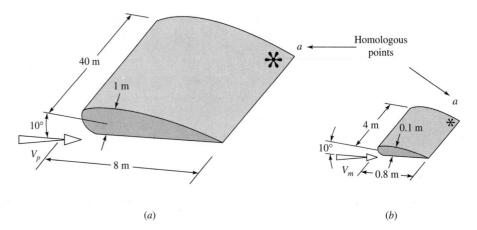

(*a*)

(*b*)

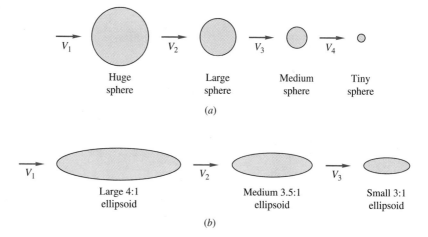

Fig. 5.5 Geometric similarity and dissimilarity of flows: (*a*) similar; (*b*) dissimilar.

3. If the prototype has a 5-mm boundary-layer trip wire 1.5 m from the leading edge, the model should have a 0.5-mm trip wire 0.15 m from its leading edge.
4. If the prototype is constructed with protruding fasteners, the model should have homologous protruding fasteners one-tenth as large.

And so on. Any departure from these details is a violation of geometric similarity and must be justified by experimental comparison to show that the prototype behavior was not significantly affected by the discrepancy.

Models which appear similar in shape but which clearly violate geometric similarity should not be compared except at your own risk. Figure 5.5 illustrates this point. The spheres in Fig. 5.5*a* are all geometrically similar and can be tested with a high expectation of success if the Reynolds number or Froude number, etc., is matched. But the ellipsoids in Fig. 5.5*b* merely *look* similar. They actually have different linear-scale ratios and therefore cannot be compared in a rational manner, even though they may have identical Reynolds and Froude numbers, etc. The data will not be the same for these ellipsoids, and any attempt to "compare" them is a matter of rough engineering judgment.

Kinematic Similarity

Kinematic similarity requires that the model and prototype have the same length-scale ratio and the same time-scale ratio. The result is that the velocity-scale ratio will be the same for both. As Langhaar [8] states it:

> The motions of two systems are kinematically similar if homologous particles lie at homologous points at homologous times.

Length-scale equivalence simply implies geometric similarity, but time-scale equivalence may require additional dynamic considerations such as equivalence of the Reynolds and Mach numbers.

One special case is incompressible frictionless flow with no free surface, as sketched in Fig. 5.6*a*. These perfect-fluid flows are kinematically similar with independent length and time scales, and no additional parameters are necessary (see Chap. 8 for further details).

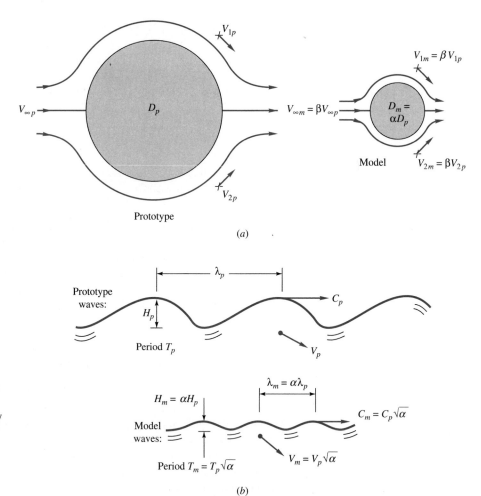

Fig. 5.6 Frictionless low-speed flows are kinematically similar: (a) Flows with no free surface are kinematically similar with independent length- and time-scale ratios; (b) free-surface flows are kinematically similar with length and time scales related by the Froude number.

Frictionless flows with a free surface, as in Fig. 5.6b, are kinematically similar if their Froude numbers are equal

$$\text{Fr}_m = \frac{V_m^2}{gL_m} = \frac{V_p^2}{gL_p} = \text{Fr}_p \tag{5.30}$$

Note that Froude number contains only length and time dimensions and hence is a purely kinematic parameter which fixes the relation between length and time. From Eq. (5.30), if the length scale is

$$L_m = \alpha L_p \tag{5.31}$$

where α is a dimensionless ratio, the velocity scale is

$$\frac{V_m}{V_p} = \left(\frac{L_m}{L_p}\right)^{1/2} = \sqrt{\alpha} \tag{5.32}$$

and the time scale is

$$\frac{T_m}{T_p} = \frac{L_m/V_m}{L_p/V_p} = \sqrt{\alpha} \tag{5.33}$$

These Froude-scaling kinematic relations are illustrated in Fig. 5.6b for wave-motion modeling. If the waves are related by the length scale α, then the wave period, propagation speed, and particle velocities are related by $\sqrt{\alpha}$.

If viscosity, surface tension, or compressibility is important, kinematic similarity is dependent upon the achievement of dynamic similarity.

Dynamic Similarity

Dynamic similarity exists when the model and the prototype have the same length-scale ratio, time-scale ratio, and force-scale (or mass-scale) ratio. Again geometric similarity is a first requirement; without it, proceed no further. Then dynamic similarity exists, simultaneous with kinematic similarity, if the model and prototype force and pressure coefficients are identical. This is ensured if:

1. For compressible flow, the model and prototype Reynolds number and Mach number and specific-heat ratio are correspondingly equal.
2. For incompressible flow
   a. With no free surface: model and prototype Reynolds numbers are equal.
   b. With a free surface: model and prototype Reynolds number, Froude number, and (if necessary) Weber number and cavitation number are correspondingly equal.

Mathematically, Newton's law for any fluid particle requires that the sum of the pressure force, gravity force, and friction force equal the acceleration term, or inertia force,

$$\mathbf{F}_p + \mathbf{F}_g + \mathbf{F}_f = \mathbf{F}_i$$

The dynamic-similarity laws listed above ensure that each of these forces will be in the same ratio and have equivalent directions between model and prototype. Figure 5.7 shows an example for flow through a sluice gate. The force polygons at homologous points have exactly the same shape if the Reynolds and Froude numbers are equal (neglecting surface tension and cavitation, of course). Kinematic similarity is also ensured by these model laws.

Fig. 5.7 Dynamic similarity in sluice-gate flow. Model and prototype yield identical homologous force polygons if the Reynolds and Froude numbers are the same corresponding values: (a) prototype; (b) model.

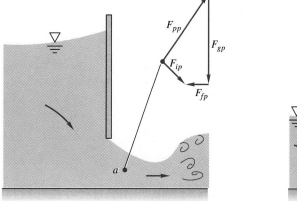

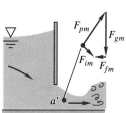

(a)

(b)

Discrepancies in Water and Air Testing

The perfect dynamic similarity shown in Fig. 5.7 is more of a dream than a reality because true equivalence of Reynolds and Froude numbers can be achieved only by dramatic changes in fluid properties, whereas in fact most model testing is simply done with water or air, the cheapest fluids avaialble.

First consider hydraulic model testing with a free surface. Dynamic similarity requires equivalent Froude numbers, Eq. (5.30), *and* equivalent Reynolds numbers

$$\frac{V_m L_m}{\nu_m} = \frac{V_p L_p}{\nu_p} \tag{5.34}$$

But both velocity and length are constrained by the Froude number, Eqs. (5.31) and (5.32). Therefore, for a given length-scale ratio α, Eq. (5.34) is true only if

$$\frac{\nu_m}{\nu_p} = \frac{L_m}{L_p}\frac{V_m}{V_p} = \alpha\sqrt{\alpha} = \alpha^{3/2} \tag{5.35}$$

For example, for a one-tenth-scale model, $\alpha = 0.1$ and $\alpha^{3/2} = 0.032$. Since ν_p is undoubtedly water, we need a fluid with only 0.032 times the kinematic viscosity of water to achieve dynamic similarity. Referring to Table 1.4, we see that this is impossible: Even mercury has only one-ninth the kinematic viscosity of water, and a mercury hydraulic model would be expensive and bad for your health. In practice, water is used for both the model and the prototype, and the Reynolds-number similarity (5.34) is unavoidably violated. The Froude number is held constant since it is the dominant parameter in free-surface flows. Typically the Reynolds number of the model flow is too small by a factor of 10 to 1000. As shown in Fig. 5.8, the low-Reynolds-number model data are used to estimate by extrapolation the desired high-Reynolds-number prototype data. As the figure indicates, there is obviously considerable uncertainty in using such an extrapolation, but there is no other practical alternative in hydraulic model testing.

Second, consider aerodynamic model testing in air with no free surface. The important parameters are the Reynolds number and the Mach number. Equation (5.34) should be satisfied, plus the compressibility criterion

$$\frac{V_m}{a_m} = \frac{V_p}{a_p} \tag{5.36}$$

Fig. 5.8 Reynolds-number extrapolation, or scaling, of hydraulic data with equal Froude numbers.

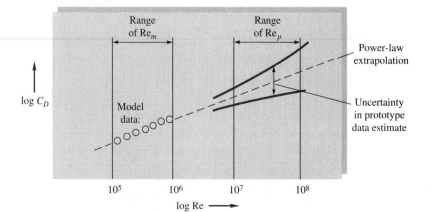

$\log C_D$

Range of Re_m

Range of Re_p

Power-law extrapolation

Model data:

Uncertainty in prototype data estimate

10^5 $\qquad$ 10^6 $\qquad$ 10^7 $\qquad$ 10^8

$\log \text{Re} \longrightarrow$

Elimination of V_m/V_p between (5.34) and (5.36) gives

$$\frac{\nu_m}{\nu_p} = \frac{L_m}{L_p}\frac{a_m}{a_p} \tag{5.37}$$

Since the prototype is no doubt an air operation, we need a wind-tunnel fluid of low viscosity and high speed of sound. Hydrogen is the only practical example, but clearly it is too expensive and dangerous. Therefore wind tunnels normally operate with air as the working fluid. Cooling and pressurizing the air will bring Eq. (5.37) into better agreement but not enough to satisfy a length-scale reduction of, say, one-tenth. Therefore Reynolds-number scaling is also commonly violated in aerodynamic testing, and an extrapolation like that in Fig. 5.8 is required here also.

Finally, a serious discrepancy of another type occurs in hydraulic models of natural flow systems such as rivers, harbors, estuaries, and embayments. Such flows have large horizontal dimensions and small relative vertical dimensions. If we were to scale an estuary model by a uniform linear length ratio of, say, 1:1000, the resulting model would be only a few millimeters deep and dominated by entirely spurious surface-tension or Weber-number effects. Therefore such hydraulic models commonly violate *geometric* similarity by "distorting" the vertical scale by a factor of 10 or more. Figure 5.9 shows a hydraulic model of a barrier-beach inlet in South Carolina. The horizontal scale reduction is 1:300, but the vertical scale is only 1:60. Since a deeper channel flows more efficiently, the model channel bottom is deliberately roughened more than the natural channel to correct for the geometric discrepancy. Thus the friction effect of the discrepancy can be corrected, but its effect on, say, dispersion of heat and mass is less well known.

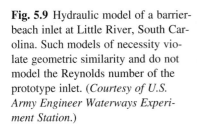

Fig. 5.9 Hydraulic model of a barrier-beach inlet at Little River, South Carolina. Such models of necessity violate geometric similarity and do not model the Reynolds number of the prototype inlet. (*Courtesy of U.S. Army Engineer Waterways Experiment Station.*)

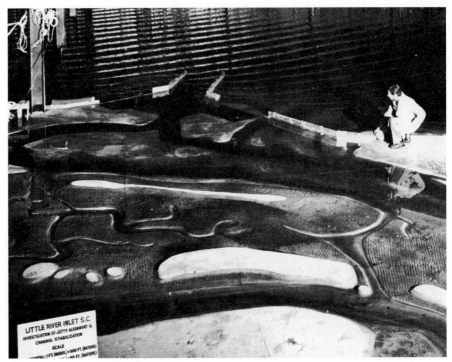

EXAMPLE 5.7

The pressure drop due to friction for flow in a long smooth pipe is a function of average flow velocity, density, viscosity, and pipe length and diameter: $\Delta p = \text{fcn}(V, \rho, \mu, L, D)$. We wish to know how Δp varies with V. (a) Use the pi theorem to rewrite this function in dimensionless form. (b) Then plot this function, using the following data for three pipes and three fluids:

D, cm	L, m	Q, m³/h	Δp, Pa	ρ, kg/m³	μ, kg/(m · s)	V, m/s*
1.0	5.0	0.3	4,680	680[†]	2.92 E-4[†]	1.06
1.0	7.0	0.6	22,300	680[†]	2.92 E-4[†]	2.12
1.0	9.0	1.0	70,800	680[†]	2.92 E-4[†]	3.54
2.0	4.0	1.0	2,080	998[‡]	0.0010[‡]	0.88
2.0	6.0	2.0	10,500	998[‡]	0.0010[‡]	1.77
2.0	8.0	3.1	30,400	998[‡]	0.0010[‡]	2.74
3.0	3.0	0.5	540	13,550[§]	1.56 E-3[§]	0.20
3.0	4.0	1.0	2,480	13,550[§]	1.56 E-3[§]	0.39
3.0	5.0	1.7	9,600	13,550[§]	1.56 E-3[§]	0.67

* $V = Q/A$, $A = \pi D^2/4$.
[†] Gasoline.
[‡] Water.
[§] Mercury.

(c) Suppose it is further known that Δp is proportional to L (which is quite true for long pipes with well-rounded entrances). Use this information to simplify and improve the pi-theorem formulation. Plot the dimensionless data in this improved manner and comment upon the results.

Solution

There are six variables with three primary dimensions involved $\{MLT\}$. Therefore we expect that $j = 6 - 3 = 3$ pi groups. We are correct, for we can find three variables which do not form a pi product, for example, (ρ, V, L). Carefully select three (j) repeating variables, but not including Δp or V, which we plan to plot versus each other. We select (ρ, μ, D), and the pi theorem guarantees that three independent power-product groups will occur:

$$\Pi_1 = \rho^a \mu^b D^c \, \Delta p \qquad \Pi_2 = \rho^d \mu^e D^f V \qquad \Pi_3 = \rho^g \mu^h D^i L$$

or

$$\Pi_1 = \frac{\rho D^2 \, \Delta p}{\mu^2} \qquad \Pi_2 = \frac{\rho V D}{\mu} \qquad \Pi_3 = \frac{L}{D}$$

We have omitted the algebra of finding $(a, b, c, d, e, f, g, h, i)$ by setting all exponents to zero M^0, L^0, T^0. Therefore we wish to plot the dimensionless relation

$$\frac{\rho D^2 \, \Delta p}{\mu^2} = \text{fcn}\!\left(\frac{\rho V D}{\mu}, \frac{L}{D}\right) \qquad\qquad Ans.\ (a)$$

We plot Π_1 versus Π_2 with Π_3 as a parameter. There will be nine data points. For example, the first row in the data above yields

$$\frac{\rho D^2 \, \Delta p}{\mu^2} = \frac{(680)(0.01)^2(4680)}{(2.92 \ \text{E-4})^2} = 3.73 \ \text{E9}$$

$$\frac{\rho V D}{\mu} = \frac{(680)(1.06)(0.01)}{2.92 \ \text{E-4}} = 24{,}700 \qquad \frac{L}{D} = 500$$

The nine data points are plotted as the open circles in Fig. 5.10. The values of L/D are listed for each point, and we see a significant length effect. In fact, if we connect the only two points which have the same L/D ($= 200$), we could see (and cross-plot to verify) that Δp increases linearly with L, as stated in the last part of the problem. Since L occurs only in $\Pi_3 = L/D$, the function $\Pi_1 = \text{fcn}(\Pi_2, \Pi_3)$ must reduce to $\Pi_1 = (L/D) \, \text{fcn}(\Pi_2)$, or simply a function involving only *two* parameters:

$$\frac{\rho D^3 \, \Delta p}{L \mu^2} = \text{fcn}\left(\frac{\rho V D}{\mu}\right) \qquad \text{flow in a long pipe} \qquad \text{Ans. (c)}$$

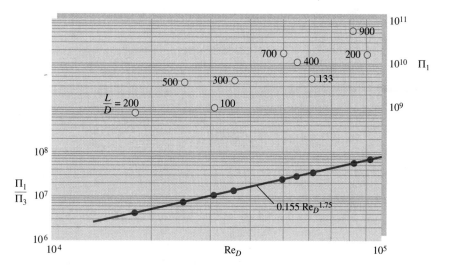

Fig. 5.10 Two different correlations of the data in Example 5.7: Open circles when plotting $\rho D^2 \, \Delta p / \mu^2$ versus Re_D, L/D is a parameter; once it is known that Δp is proportional to L, a replot (solid circles) of $\rho D^3 \, \Delta p / (L \mu^2)$ versus Re_D collapses into a single power-law curve.

We now modify each data point in Fig. 5.10 by dividing it by its L/D value. For example, for the first row of data, $\rho D^3 \, \Delta p / (L \mu^2) = (3.73 \ \text{E9})/500 = 7.46 \ \text{E6}$. We replot these new data points as solid circles in Fig. 5.10. They correlate almost perfectly into a straight-line power-law function:

$$\frac{\rho D^3 \, \Delta p}{L \mu^2} \approx 0.155 \left(\frac{\rho V D}{\mu}\right)^{1.75} \qquad \text{Ans. (c)}$$

All newtonian pipe flows should correlate in this manner. This example is a variation of the first completely successful dimensional analysis, pipe-flow friction, performed by Prandtl's student Paul Blasius, who published a related plot in 1911. For this range of (turbulent-flow) Reynolds numbers, the pressure drop increases approximately as $V^{1.75}$.

EXAMPLE 5.8

The smooth-sphere data plotted in Fig. 5.3a represent dimensionless drag versus dimensionless *viscosity*, since (ρ, V, d) were selected as scaling or repeating variables. (a) Replot these data to display the effect of dimensionless *velocity* on the drag. (b) Use your new figure to predict the terminal (zero-acceleration) velocity of a 1-cm-diameter steel ball (SG = 7.86) falling through water at 20°C.

Solution

To display the effect of velocity, we must not use V as a repeating variable. Instead we choose (ρ, μ, d) as our j variables to nondimensionalize Eq. (5.1), $F = $ fcn(d, V, ρ, μ). (See Example 5.2 for an alternate approach to this problem.) The pi groups form as follows:

$$\Pi_1 = \rho^a \mu^b d^c F = \frac{\rho F}{\mu^2} \qquad \Pi_2 = \rho^e \mu^f d^g V = \frac{\rho V d}{\mu} \qquad \text{Ans. (a)}$$

That is, $a = 1$, $b = -2$, $c = 0$, $e = 1$, $f = -1$, and $g = 1$, by using our power-product techniques of Examples 5.2 to 5.6. Therefore a plot of $\rho F/\mu^2$ versus Re will display the direct effect of velocity on sphere drag. This replot is shown as Fig. 5.11. The drag increases rapidly with velocity up to transition, where there is a slight drop, after which it increases

Fig. 5.11 Cross-plot of sphere-drag data from Fig. 5.3a to isolate diameter and velocity.

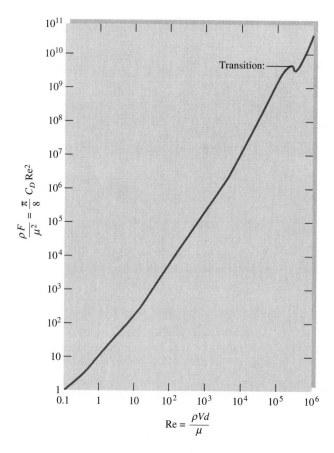

more quickly than ever. If the force is known, we may predict the velocity from the figure.

For water at 20°C, take $\rho = 998$ kg/m^3 and $\mu = 0.001$ kg/(m · s). For steel, $\rho_s = 7.86\rho_{water} \approx 7840$ kg/m^3. For terminal velocity, the drag equals the net weight of the sphere in water. Thus

$$F = W_{net} = (\rho_s - \rho_w)g\frac{\pi}{6}d^3 = (7840 - 998)(9.81)\left(\frac{\pi}{6}\right)(0.01)^3 = 0.0351 \text{ N}$$

Therefore the ordinate of Fig. 5.11 is known:

Falling steel sphere: $\quad \dfrac{\rho F}{\mu^2} = \dfrac{(998 \text{ kg/m}^3)(0.0351 \text{ N})}{[0.001 \text{ kg/(m · s)}]^2} \approx 3.5 \text{ E7}$

From Fig. 5.11, at $\rho F/\mu^2 \approx 3.5$ E7, a magnifying glass reveals that Re$_d \approx 2$ E4. Then a crude estimate of the terminal fall velocity is

$$\frac{\rho V d}{\mu} \approx 20,000 \quad \text{or} \quad V \approx \frac{20,000[0.001\text{kg/(m · s)}]}{(998 \text{ kg/m}^3)(0.01 \text{ m})} \approx 2.0\,\frac{\text{m}}{\text{s}} \qquad Ans.\ (b)$$

Better accuracy could be obtained by expanding the scale of Fig. 5.11 in the region of the given force coefficient. However, there is considerable uncertainty in published drag data for spheres, so the predicted fall velocity is probably uncertain by at least ± 5 percent.

Note that we found the answer directly from Fig. 5.11. We could use Fig. 5.3a also but would have to iterate between the ordinate and abscissa to obtain the final result, since V is contained in both plotted variables.

Summary

Chapters 3 and 4 presented integral and differential methods of mathematical analysis of fluid flow. This chapter introduces the third and final method: experimentation, as supplemented by the technique of dimensional analysis. Tests and experiments are used both to strengthen existing theories and to provide useful engineering results when theory is inadequate.

The chapter begins with a discussion of some familiar physical relations and how they can be recast in dimensionless form because they satisfy the principle of dimensional homogeneity. A general technique, the pi theorem, is then presented for systematically finding a set of dimensionless parameters by grouping a list of variables which govern any particular physical process. Alternately, direct application of dimensional analysis to the basic equations of fluid mechanics yields the fundamental parameters governing flow patterns: Reynolds number, Froude number, Prandtl number, Mach number, and others.

It is shown that model testing in air and water often leads to scaling difficulties for which compromises must be made. Many model tests do not achieve true dynamic similarity. The chapter ends by pointing out that classic dimensionless charts and data can be manipulated and recast to provide direct solutions to problems that would otherwise be quite cumbersome and laboriously iterative.

References

1. P. W. Bridgman, *Dimensional Analysis*, Yale University Press, New Haven, Conn., 1922, rev. ed., 1931.
2. A. W. Porter, *The Method of Dimensions*, Methuen, London, 1933.

3. F. M. Lanchester, *The Theory of Dimensions and Its Applications for Engineers*, Crosby-Lockwood, London, 1940.

4. R. Esnault-Pelterie, *L'Analyse dimensionelle*, F. Rouge, Lausanne, Switzerland, 1946.

5. G. W. Stubbings, *Dimensions in Engineering Theory*, Crosby-Lockwood, London, 1948.

6. G. Murphy, *Similitude in Engineering*, Ronald, New York, 1950.

7. H. E. Huntley, *Dimensional Analysis*, Rinehart, New York, 1951.

8. H. L. Langhaar, *Dimensional Analysis and the Theory of Models*, Wiley, New York, 1951.

9. W. J. Duncan, *Physical Similarity and Dimensional Analysis*, Arnold, London, 1953.

10. C. M. Focken, *Dimensional Methods and Their Applications*, Arnold, London, 1953.

11. L. I. Sedov, *Similarity and Dimensional Methods in Mechanics*, Academic, New York, 1959.

12. E. C. Ipsen, *Units, Dimensions, and Dimensionless Numbers*, McGraw-Hill, New York, 1960.

13. E. E. Jupp, *An Introduction to Dimensional Methods*, Cleaver-Hume, London, 1962.

14. R. Pankhurst, *Dimensional Analysis and Scale Factors*, Reinhold, New York, 1964.

15. S. J. Kline, *Similitude and Approximation Theory*, McGraw-Hill, New York, 1965.

16. B. S. Massey, *Units, Dimensional Analysis, and Physical Similarity*, Van Nostrand Reinhold, New York, 1971.

17. J. Zierep, *Similarity Laws and Modeling*, Dekker, New York, 1971.

18. W. E. Baker et al., *Similarity Methods in Engineering Dynamics*, Spartan, Rochelle Park, N. J., 1973.

19. E. S. Taylor, *Dimensional Analysis for Engineers*, Clarendon Press, Oxford, England, 1974.

20. E. de St. Q. Isaacson and M. de St. Q. Isaacson, *Dimensional Methods in Engineering and Physics*, Arnold, London, 1975.

21. P. LeCorbeiller, *Dimensional Analysis*, Irvington, New York, 1966.

22. V. J. Skoglund, *Similitude—Theory and Applications*, International, Scranton, Pa., 1967.

23. M. S. Yalin, *Theory of Hydraulic Models*, Macmillan, London, 1971.

24. J. J. Sharp, *Hydraulic Modeling*, Butterworth, London, 1981.

25. G. I. Barenblatt, *Dimensional Analysis*, Gordon and Breach, New York, 1987.

26. R. Esnault-Pelterie, *Dimensional Analysis and Metrology*, F. Rouge, Lausanne, Switzerland, 1950.

27. R. Kurth, *Dimensional Analysis and Group Theory in Astrophysics*, Pergamon, New York, 1972.

28. F. J. Long, *Dimensional Analysis for Economists*, North Holland, Amsterdam, 1967.

29. E. Buckingham, "On Physically Similar Systems: Illustrations of the Use of Dimensional Equations," *Phys. Rev.*, vol. 4, no. 4, 1914, pp. 345–376.

30. "Flow of Fluids through Valves, Fittings, and Pipe," *Crane Co. Tech. Pap.* 410, Chicago, 1957.

31. A. Roshko, "On the Development of Turbulent Wakes from Vortex Streets," *NACA Rep.* 1191, 1954.

32. G. W. Jones, Jr., "Unsteady Lift Forces Generated by Vortex Shedding about a Large, Stationary, Oscillating Cylinder at High Reynolds Numbers," *ASME Symp. Unsteady Flow*, 1968.

33. O. M. Griffin and S. E. Ramberg, "The Vortex Street Wakes of Vibrating Cylinders," *J. Fluid Mech.*, vol. 66, pt. 3, 1974, pp. 553–576.

34. *Encyclopedia of Science and Technology*, 7th ed., McGraw-Hill, New York, 1993.

35. H. A. Becker, *Dimensionless Parameters*, Halstead Press (Wiley), New York, 1976.

Recommended Films   Films numbered 1, 12, 30, and 35 in App. C.

PROBLEMS

In addition to many traditional problems, categorized in the problem distribution list below, there are word problems, labeled W5.1 to W5.10.

Problem Distribution

Section	Topic	Problems
5.1	Introduction	5.1–5.6
5.2	Choosing proper scaling parameters	5.7–5.9
5.2	The principle of dimensional homogeneity	5.10–5.17
5.3	The pi theorem	5.18–5.41
5.4	Nondimensionalizing the basic equations	5.42–5.47
5.4	Data for spheres and cylinders	5.48–5.57
5.5	Scaling of model data	5.58–5.74
5.5	Froude- and Mach-number scaling	5.75–5.84
5.5	Inventive rescaling of the data	5.85–5.91

5.1   For axial flow through a circular tube, the Reynolds number for transition to turbulence is approximately 2300 [see Eq. (6.2)], based upon the diameter and average velocity. If $d = 5$ cm and the fluid is kerosine at 20°C, find the volume flow rate in m^3/h which causes transition.

5.2   In flow past a thin flat body such as an airfoil, transition to turbulence occurs at about Re $= 1$ E6, based on the distance x from the leading edge of the wing. If an airplane flies at 450 mi/h at 8-km standard altitude and undergoes transition at the 12 percent chord position, how long is its chord (wing length from leading to trailing edge)?

5.3   An airplane has a chord length $L = 1.2$ m and flies at a Mach number of 0.7 in the standard atmosphere. If its Reynolds number, based on chord length, is 7 E6, how high is it flying?

5.4   When tested in water at 20°C flowing at 2 m/s, an 8-cm-diameter sphere has a measured drag of 5 N. What will be the velocity and drag force on a 1.5-m-diameter weather balloon moored in sea-level standard air under dynamically similar conditions?

5.5   An automobile has a characteristic length and area of 8 ft and 60 ft^2, respectively. When tested in sea-level standard air, it has the following measured drag force versus speed:

V, mi/h	20	40	60
Drag, lbf	31	115	249

The same car travels in Colorado at 55 mi/h at an altitude of 3500 m. Using dimensional analysis, estimate (a) its drag force and (b) the horsepower required to overcome air drag.

5.6   SAE 10 oil at 20°C flows past an 8-cm-diameter sphere. At flow velocities of 1, 2, and 3 m/s, the measured sphere drag forces are 1.5, 5.3, and 11.2 N, respectively. Estimate the drag force if the same sphere is tested at a velocity of 11 m/s in glycerin at 20°C.

5.7   A body is dropped on the moon ($g = 1.62$ m/s²) with an initial velocity of 12 m/s. By using option 2 variables, Eq. (5.11), the ground impact occurs at $t^{**} = 0.34$ and $S^{**} = 0.84$. Estimate (a) the initial displacement, (b) the final displacement, and (c) the time of impact.

5.8   The Bernoulli equation (5.6) can be written in the form

$$p = p_0 - \tfrac{1}{2}\rho V^2 - \rho g z \qquad (1)$$

where p_0 is the "stagnation" pressure at zero velocity and elevation. (a) State how many scaling variables are needed to nondimensionalize this equation. (b) Suppose that we wish to nondimensionalize Eq. (1) in order to plot dimensionless pressure versus velocity, with elevation as a parameter. Select the proper scaling variables and carry out and plot the resulting dimensionless relation.

5.9   Modify Prob. 5.8 as follows. Suppose that we wish to nondimensionalize Eq. (1) in order to plot dimensionless pressure versus gravity, with velocity as a parameter. Select the proper scaling variables and carry out and plot the resulting dimensionless relation.

5.10   Determine the dimension $\{MLT\Theta\}$ of the following quantities:

(a) $\rho u \dfrac{\partial u}{\partial x}$ (b) $\displaystyle\int_1^2 (p - p_0)\, dA$ (c) $\rho c_p \dfrac{\partial^2 T}{\partial x\, \partial y}$

(d) $\displaystyle\iiint \rho \dfrac{\partial u}{\partial t}\, dx\, dy\, dz$

All quantities have their standard meanings; for example, ρ is density, etc.

5.11   For a particle moving in a circle, its centripetal acceleration takes the form $a = \text{fcn}(V, R)$, where V is its velocity and R the radius of its path. By pure dimensional reasoning, rewrite this function in algebraic form.

5.12   The velocity of sound a of a gas varies with pressure p and density ρ. Show by dimensional reasoning that the proper form must be $a = (\text{const})(p/\rho)^{1/2}$.

5.13   The speed of propagation C of a capillary wave in deep water is known to be a function only of density ρ, wavelength λ, and surface tension Y. Find the proper functional relationship, completing it with a dimensionless constant. For a given density and wavelength, how does the propagation speed change if the surface tension is doubled?

5.14   An airplane has a characteristic length of 125 ft and is designed to fly at 300 mi/h at 10,000-ft standard altitude. The drag coefficient as defined by Eq. (5.2) is measured with a small model and found to be 0.01. What is the horsepower required to drive the prototype airplane?

5.15 It is desired to measure the drag on an airplane whose velocity is 300 mi/h. Is it feasible to test a one-twentieth-scale model of the plane in a wind tunnel at the same pressure and temperature to determine the prototype drag coefficient?

5.16 Convection heat-transfer data are often reported as a *heat-transfer coefficient h*, defined by

$$\dot{Q} = hA\,\Delta T$$

where $\dot{Q}$ = heat flow, J/s
A = surface area, m^2
ΔT = temperature difference, K

The dimensionless form of h, called the *Stanton number*, is a combination of h, fluid density ρ, specific heat c_p, and flow velocity V. Derive the Stanton number if it is proportional to h.

5.17 In some heat-transfer textbooks, e.g., J. P. Holman, *Heat Transfer*, 5th ed., McGraw-Hill, 1981, p. 285, simplified formulas are given for the heat-transfer coefficient from Prob. 5.16 for buoyant or *natural* convection over hot surfaces. An example formula is

$$h = 1.42\left(\frac{\Delta T}{L}\right)^{1/4}$$

where L is the length of the hot surface. Comment on the dimensional homogeneity of this formula. What might be the SI units of constants 1.42 and $\frac{1}{4}$? What parameters might be missing or hidden?

5.18 Under laminar conditions, the volume flow Q through a small triangular-section pore of side length b and length L is a function of viscosity μ, pressure drop per unit length $\Delta p/L$, and b. Using the pi theorem, rewrite this relation in dimensionless form. How does the volume flow change if the pore size b is doubled?

5.19 The period of oscillation T of a water surface wave is assumed to be a function of density ρ, wavelength λ, depth h, gravity g, and surface tension Y. Rewrite this relationship in dimensionless form. What results if Y is negligible?

5.20 The power input P to a centrifugal pump is assumed to be a function of the volume flow Q, impeller diameter D, rotational rate Ω, and the density ρ and viscosity μ of the fluid. Rewrite this as a dimensionless relationship.

5.21 In Example 5.1 we used the pi theorem to develop Eq. (5.2) from Eq. (5.1). Instead of merely listing the primary dimensions of each variable, some workers list the *powers* of each primary dimension for each variable in an array:

$$\begin{array}{c} \\ M \\ L \\ T \end{array} \begin{array}{cccccc} F & L & U & \rho & \mu \\ \left[\begin{array}{ccccc} 1 & 0 & 0 & 1 & 1 \\ 1 & 1 & 1 & -3 & -1 \\ -2 & 0 & -1 & 0 & -1 \end{array}\right] \end{array}$$

This array of exponents is called the *dimensional matrix* for the given function. Show that the *rank* of this matrix (the size of the largest nonzero determinant) is equal to $j = n - k$, the desired reduction between original variables and the pi groups. This is a general property of dimensional matrices, as noted by Buckingham [29].

5.22 The resistance force F of a surface ship is a function of its length L, velocity V, gravity g, and the density ρ and viscosity μ of the water. Rewrite in dimensionless form.

5.23 The period T of vibration of a beam is a function of its length L, area moment of inertia I, modulus of elasticity E, density ρ, and Poisson's ratio σ. Rewrite this relation in dimensionless form. What further reduction can we make if E and I can occur only in the product form EI?

5.24 The lift force F on a missile is a function of its length L, velocity V, diameter D, angle of attack α, density ρ, viscosity μ, and speed of sound a of the air. Write out the dimensional matrix of this function and determine its rank. (See Prob. 5.21 for an explanation of this concept.) Rewrite the function in terms of pi groups.

5.25 When a viscous fluid is confined between two long concentric cylinders as in Fig. 4.17, the torque per unit length T' required to turn the inner cylinder at angular velocity Ω is a function of Ω, cylinder radii a and b, and viscosity μ. Find the equivalent dimensionless function. What happens to the torque if both a and b are doubled?

5.26 A pendulum has an oscillation period T which is assumed to depend upon its length L, bob mass m, angle of swing θ, and the acceleration of gravity. A pendulum 1 m long, with a bob mass of 200 g, is tested on earth and found to have a period of 2.04 s when swinging at 20°. (*a*) What is its period when it swings at 45°? A similarly constructed pendulum, with $L = 30$ cm and $m = 100$ g, is to swing on the moon ($g = 1.62$ m/s^2) at $\theta = 20°$. (*b*) What will be its period?

5.27 The pressure rise Δp across a pump depends upon fluid density ρ, volume flow rate Q, impeller diameter D, and rotation rate Ω. Express this in the form of a dimensionless pressure versus a dimensionless flow rate.

5.28 A simply supported beam of diameter D, length L, and modulus of elasticity E is subjected to a fluid crossflow of velocity V, density ρ, and viscosity μ. Its center deflection δ is assumed to be a function of all these variables. (*a*) Rewrite this proposed function in dimensionless form. (*b*) Suppose it is known that δ is independent of μ, inversely proportional to E, and dependent only upon ρV^2, not ρ and V separately. Simplify the dimensionless function accordingly.

5.29 When fluid in a pipe is accelerated linearly from rest, it begins as laminar flow and then undergoes transition to turbulence at a time t_{tr} which depends upon the pipe diameter D, fluid acceleration a, density ρ, and viscosity μ. Arrange this into a dimensionless relation between t_{tr} and D.

5.30 In forced convection, the heat-transfer coefficient h, as defined in Prob. 5.16, is known to be a function of stream felocity U, body size L, and fluid properties ρ, μ, c_p, and k. Rewrite this function in dimensionless form, and note by name any parameters you recognize.

5.31 The heat-transfer rate per unit area q to a body from a fluid in natural or gravitational convection is a function of the temperature difference ΔT, gravity g, body length L, and three fluid properties: kinematic viscosity ν, conductivity k, and thermal expansion coefficient β. Rewrite in dimensionless form if it is known that g and β appear only as the product $g\beta$.

5.32 A *weir* is an obstruction in a channel flow which can be calibrated to measure the flow rate, as in Fig. P5.32. The volume flow Q varies with gravity g, weir width b into the paper, and upstream water height H above the weir crest. If it is known that Q is proportional to b, use the pi theorem to find a unique functional relationship $Q(g, b, H)$.

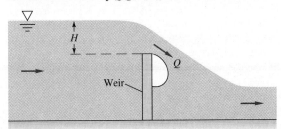

Fig. P5.32

5.33 A spar buoy (see Prob. 2.113) has a period T of vertical (heave) oscillation which depends upon the waterline cross-sectional area A, buoy mass m, and fluid specific weight γ. How does the period change due to doubling of (*a*) the mass and (*b*) the area? Instrument buoys should have long periods to avoid wave resonance. Sketch a possible long-period buoy design.

5.34 To good approximation, the thermal conductivity k of a gas (see Ref. 8 of Chap. 1) depends only upon the density ρ, mean free path ℓ, gas constant R, and absolute temperature T. For air at 20°C and 1 atm, $k \approx 0.026$ W/(m · K) and $\ell \approx 6.5$ E-8 m. Use this information to determine k for hydrogen at 20°C and 1 atm if $\ell \approx 1.2$ E-7 m.

5.35 The torque M required to turn the cone-plate viscometer in Fig. P5.35 depends upon the radius R, rotation rate Ω, fluid viscosity μ, and cone angle θ. Rewrite this relation in dimensionless form. How does the relation simplify it if it is known that M is proportional to θ?

5.36 The flow velocity u very near a rotating disk varies only with disk angular velocity ω, local radius R, distance z from the disk, and kinematic viscosity ν. Rewrite this relation in dimensionless form.

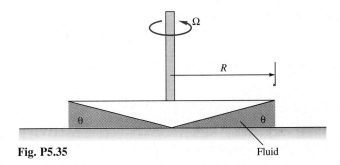

Fig. P5.35   Fluid

5.37 The pressure difference Δp across an explosion or blast wave is a function of the distance r from the blast center, time t, speed of sound a of the medium, and total energy E in the blast. Rewrite this relation in dimensionless form (see Ref. 18, chap. 4, for further details of blast-wave scaling). How does Δp change if E is doubled?

5.38 The size d of droplets produced by a liquid spray nozzle is thought to depend upon the nozzle diameter D, jet velocity U, and the properties of the liquid ρ, μ, and Y. Rewrite this relation in dimensionless form.

5.39 In turbulent flow past a flat surface, the velocity u near the wall varies approximately logarithmically with distance y from the wall and also depends upon viscosity μ, density ρ, and wall shear stress τ_w. For a certain airflow at 20°C and 1 atm, $\tau_w = 0.8$ Pa and $u = 15$ m/s at $y = 3.6$ mm. Use this information to estimate the velocity u at $y = 6$ mm.

5.40 The pressure drop Δp for airflow through a filter, as in Fig. P5.40, depends upon the volume flow Q, density ρ, filter thickness H, and porosity σ (the percent volume of filter material which is not occupied by filter fibers). The following are pressure-drop data in airflow at 20°C and 1 atm through a filter 3 cm thick with 45 percent porosity:

Δp, in water	0.31	1.24	2.79	4.96	7.75	11.2
Q, ft³/min	200	400	600	800	1000	1200

Use these data to determine the pressure drop, in P, of the same filter material if the thickness is increased to 6 cm and the flow rate is 750 ft³/min.

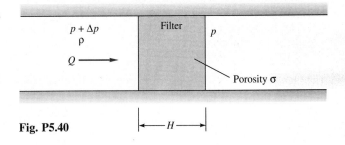

Fig. P5.40

5.41 A certain axial-flow turbine has an output torque M which is proportional to the volume flow rate Q and also depends upon the density ρ, rotor diameter D, and rotation rate Ω. How does the torque change due to a doubling of (a) D and (b) Ω?

5.42 Nondimensionalize the energy equation (4.75) and its boundary conditions (4.62), (4.63), and (4.70) by defining $T^* = T/T_0$, where T_0 is the inlet temperature, assumed constant. Use other dimensionless variables as needed from Eqs. (5.23). Isolate all dimensionless parameters you find, and relate them to the list given in Table 5.2.

5.43 The differential equation of salt conservation for flowing seawater is

$$\frac{\partial S}{\partial t} + u\frac{\partial S}{\partial x} + v\frac{\partial S}{\partial y} + w\frac{\partial S}{\partial z} = \kappa\left(\frac{\partial^2 S}{\partial x^2} + \frac{\partial^2 S}{\partial y^2} + \frac{\partial^2 S}{\partial z^2}\right)$$

where κ is a (constant) coefficient of diffusion, with typical units of square meters per second, and S is the salinity in parts per thousand. Nondimensionalize this equation and discuss any parameters which appear.

5.44 The differential energy equation for incompressible two-dimensional flow through a "Darcy-type" porous medium is approximately

$$\rho c_p \frac{\sigma}{\mu}\frac{\partial p}{\partial x}\frac{\partial T}{\partial x} + \rho c_p \frac{\sigma}{\mu}\frac{\partial p}{\partial y}\frac{\partial T}{\partial y} + k\frac{\partial^2 T}{\partial y^2} = 0$$

where σ is the *permeability* of the porous medium. All other symbols have their usual meanings. (a) What are the appropriate dimensions for σ? (b) Nondimensionalize this equation, using (L, U, ρ, T_0) as scaling constants, and discuss any dimensionless parameters which arise.

5.45 In natural-convection problems, the variation of density due to the temperature difference ΔT creates an important buoyancy term in the momentum equation (5.30). To first-order accuracy, the density variation would be $\rho \approx \rho_0(1 - \beta\,\Delta T)$, where β is the thermal-expansion coefficient. The momentum equation thus becomes

$$\rho_0 \frac{d\mathbf{V}}{dt} = -\boldsymbol{\nabla}(p + \rho_0 gz) + \rho_0\beta\,\Delta T\,g\mathbf{k} + \mu\,\nabla^2\mathbf{V}$$

where we have assumed that z is up. Nondimensionalize this equation, using Eqs. (5.23), and relate the parameters you find to the list in Table 5.2.

5.46 The differential equation for compressible inviscid flow of a gas in the xy plane is

$$\frac{\partial^2\phi}{\partial t^2} + \frac{\partial}{\partial t}(u^2 + v^2) + (u^2 - a^2)\frac{\partial^2\phi}{\partial x^2}$$
$$+ (v^2 - a^2)\frac{\partial^2\phi}{\partial y^2} + 2uv\frac{\partial^2\phi}{\partial x\,\partial y} = 0$$

where ϕ is the velocity potential and a is the (variable) speed of sound of the gas. Nondimensionalize this relation, using a reference length L and the inlet speed of sound a_0 as parameters for defining dimensionless variables.

5.47 The differential equation for small-amplitude vibrations $y(x, t)$ of a simple beam is given by

$$\rho A\frac{\partial^2 y}{\partial t^2} + EI\frac{\partial^4 y}{\partial x^4} = 0$$

where ρ = beam material density
    A = cross-sectional area
    I = area moment of inertia
    E = Young's modulus

Use only the quantities ρ, E, and A to nondimensionalize y, x, and t, and rewrite the differential equation in dimensionless form. Do any parameters remain? Could they be removed by further manipulation of the variables?

5.48 A smooth steel (SG = 7.86) sphere is immersed in a stream of ethanol at 20°C moving at 1.5 m/s. Estimate its drag in N from Fig. 5.3a. What stream velocity would quadruple its drag? Take $D = 2.5$ cm.

5.49 The sphere in Prob. 5.48 is dropped in gasoline at 20°C. Ignoring its acceleration phase, what will its terminal (constant) fall velocity be, from Fig. 5.3a?

5.50 Repeat Prob. 5.49 if the sphere is dropped in glycerin at 20°C.

5.51 A ship is towing a sonar array which approximates a submerged cylinder 1 ft in diameter and 30 ft long with its axis normal to the direction of tow. If the tow speed is 12 kn (1 kn = 1.69 ft/s), estimate the horsepower required to tow this cylinder. What will be the frequency of vortices shed from the cylinder? Use Figs. 5.2 and 5.3.

5.52 A 1-in-diameter telephone wire is mounted in air at 20°C and has a natural vibration frequency of 12 Hz. What wind velocity in ft/s will cause the wire to sing? At this condition what will the average drag force per unit wire length be?

5.53 Vortex shedding can be used to design a *vortex flowmeter* (Fig. 6.32). A blunt rod stretched across the pipe sheds vortices whose frequency is read by the sensor downstream. Suppose the pipe diameter is 5 cm and the rod is a cylinder of diameter 8 mm. If the sensor reads 5400 counts per minute, estimate the volume flow rate of water in m^3/h. How might the meter react to other liquids?

5.54 A fishnet is made of 1-mm-diameter strings knotted into 2×2 cm squares. Estimate the horsepower required to tow 300 ft^2 of this netting at 3 kn in seawater at 20°C. The net plane is normal to the flow direction.

5.55 The radio antenna on a car begins to vibrate wildly at 500 Hz when the car is driven at 55 mi/h. Estimate the diameter of the antenna.

5.56 A wooden flagpole, of diameter 5 in and height 30 ft, fractures at its base in hurricane winds at sea level. If the fracture stress is 3500 lbf/in², estimate the wind velocity in mi/h.

5.57 The simply supported 1040 carbon-steel rod of Fig. P5.57 is subjected to a crossflow stream of air at 20°C and 1 atm. For what stream velocity U will the rod center deflection be approximately 1 cm?

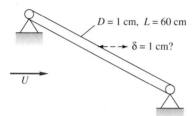

$D = 1$ cm, $L = 60$ cm

$\delta = 1$ cm?

U

Fig. P5.57

5.58 For the steel rod of Prob. 5.57, at what airstream velocity U will the rod begin to vibrate laterally in resonance in its first mode (a half sine wave)? (*Hint:* Consult a vibration text under "lateral beam vibration.")

5.59 We wish to know the drag of a blimp which will move in 20°C air at 6 m/s. If a one-thirtieth-scale model is tested in water at 20°C, what should the water velocity be? At this velocity, if the measured water drag on the model is 2700 N, what is the drag on the prototype blimp and the power required to propel it?

5.60 A prototype water pump has an impeller diameter of 2 ft and is designed to pump 12 ft³/s at 750 r/min. A 1-ft-diameter model pump is tested in 20°C air at 1800 r/min, and Reynolds-number effects are found to be negligible. For similar conditions, what will the volume flow of the model be in ft³/s? If the model pump requires 0.082 hp to drive it, what horsepower is required for the prototype?

5.61 If viscosity is neglected, typical pump-flow results from Prob. 5.20 are shown in Fig. P5.61 for a model pump tested in water. The pressure rise decreases and the power required increases with the dimensionless flow coefficient. Curve-fit

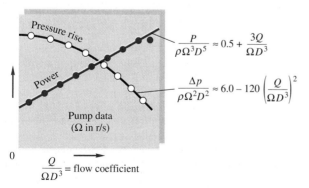

$$\frac{P}{\rho \Omega^3 D^5} \approx 0.5 + \frac{3Q}{\Omega D^3}$$

$$\frac{\Delta p}{\rho \Omega^2 D^2} \approx 6.0 - 120 \left(\frac{Q}{\Omega D^3}\right)^2$$

Pump data
(Ω in r/s)

$\frac{Q}{\Omega D^3}$ = flow coefficient

Fig. P5.61

expressions are given for the data. Suppose a similar pump of 12-cm diameter is built to move gasoline at 20°C and a flow rate of 25 m³/h. If the pump rotation speed is 30 r/s, find (*a*) the pressure rise and (*b*) the power required.

5.62 Modify Prob. 5.61 so that the rotation speed is unknown but $D = 12$ cm and $Q = 25$ m³/h. What is the maximum rotation speed for which the power will not exceed 300 W? What will the pressure rise be for this condition?

5.63 The pressure drop per unit length $\Delta p/L$ in smooth pipe flow is known to be a function only of the average velocity V, diameter D, and fluid properties ρ and μ. The following data were obtained for flow of water at 20°C in an 8-cm-diameter pipe 50 m long:

Q, m³/s	0.005	0.01	0.015	0.020
Δp, Pa	5800	20,300	42,100	70,800

Verify that these data are slightly outside the range of Fig. 5.10. What is a suitable power-law curve fit for the present data? Use these data to estimate the pressure drop for flow of kerosine at 20°C in a smooth pipe of diameter 5 cm and length 200 m if the flow rate is 50 m³/h.

5.64 The natural frequency ω of vibration of a mass M attached to a rod, as in Fig. P5.64, depends only upon M and the stiffness EI and length L of the rod. Tests with a 2-kg mass attached to a 1040 carbon-steel rod of diameter 12 mm and length 40 cm reveal a natural frequency of 0.9 Hz. Use these data to predict the natural frequency of a 1-kg mass attached to a 2024 aluminum-alloy rod of the same size.

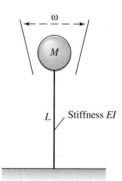

ω

M

L Stiffness EI

Fig. P5.64

5.65 In turbulent flow near a flat wall, the local velocity u varies only with distance y from the wall, wall shear stress τ_w, and fluid properties ρ and μ. The following data were taken in the University of Rhode Island wind tunnel for airflow, $\rho = 0.0023$ slug/ft³, $\mu = 3.81$ E-7 slug/(ft · s), and $\tau_w = 0.029$ lbf/ft²:

y, in	0.021	0.035	0.055	0.080	0.12	0.16
u, ft/s	50.6	54.2	57.6	59.7	63.5	65.9

(*a*) Plot these data in the form of dimensionless u versus dimensionless y, and suggest a suitable power-law curve fit. (*b*) Suppose that the tunnel speed is increased until $u = 90$ ft/s at $y = 0.11$ in. Estimate the new wall shear stress, in lbf/ft^2.

5.66 A torpedo 8 m below the surface in 20°C seawater cavitates at a speed of 21 m/s when atmospheric pressure is 101 kPa. If Reynolds-number and Froude-number effects are negligible, at what speed will it cavitate when running at a depth of 20 m? At what depth should it be to avoid cavitation at 30 m/s?

5.67 A one-fifth-scale model automobile is tested in a wind tunnel in the same air properties as the prototype. The prototype velocity is 50 km/h. For dynamically similar conditions the model drag is 350 N. What are the drag of the prototype automobile and the power in kW required to overcome this drag?

5.68 A rotary mixer is to be designed for stirring ethyl alcohol. Tests with a one-fourth-scale model in SAE 30 oil indicate most efficient mixing at 1770 r/min. What should the speed of the prototype mixer be in r/min?

5.69 A one-sixteenth-scale model of a weir (see Fig. P5.32) has a measured flow rate $Q = 2.1$ ft^3/s when the upstream water height is $H = 6.3$ in. If Q is proportional to weir width b, predict the prototype flow rate when $H_{\text{proto}} = 3.2$ ft.

5.70 A diamond-shaped body, of characteristic length 9 in, has the following measured drag forces when placed in a wind tunnel at sea-level standard conditions:

V, ft/s	30	38	48	56	61
F, lbf	1.25	1.95	3.02	4.05	4.81

Use these data to predict the drag force of a similar 15-in diamond placed at similar orientation in 20°C water flowing at 2.2 m/s.

5.71 The pressure drop in a venturi meter (Fig. P3.165) varies only with the fluid density, pipe approach velocity, and diameter ratio of the meter. A model venturi meter tested in water at 20°C shows a 5-kPa drop when the approach velocity is 4 m/s. A geometrically similar prototype meter is used to measure gasoline at 20°C and a flow rate of 9 m^3/min. If the prototype pressure gage is most accurate at 15 kPa, what should the upstream pipe diameter be?

5.72 A one-fifteenth-scale model of a parachute has a drag of 450 lbf when tested at 20 ft/s in a water tunnel. If Reynolds-number effects are negligible, estimate the terminal fall velocity at 5000-ft standard altitude of a parachutist using the prototype if chute and chutist together weigh 160 lbf. Neglect the drag coefficient of the woman.

5.73 The yawing moment on a torpedo control surface is tested on a one-eighth-scale model in a water tunnel at 20 m/s, using

Reynolds scaling. If the model measured moment is 14 N · m, what will the prototype moment be under similar conditions?

5.74 A one-tenth-scale model of a supersonic wing tested at 700 m/s in air at 20°C and 1 atm shows a pitching moment of 0.25 kN · m. If Reynolds-number effects are negligible, what will the pitching moment of the prototype wing be flying at the same Mach number at 8-km standard altitude?

5.75 A one-twelfth-scale model of an airplane is to be tested at 20°C in a pressurized wind tunnel. The prototype is to fly at 240 m/s at 10-km standard altitude. What should the tunnel pressure be in atm to scale both the Mach number and the Reynolds number accurately?

5.76 A 2-ft-long model of a ship is tested in a freshwater tow tank. The measured drag may be split into "friction" drag (Reynolds scaling) and "wave" drag (Froude scaling). The model data are as follows:

Tow speed, ft/s	0.8	1.6	2.4	3.2	4.0	4.8
Friction drag, lbf	0.016	0.057	0.122	0.208	0.315	0.441
Wave drag, lbf	0.002	0.021	0.083	0.253	0.509	0.697

The prototype ship is 150 ft long. Estimate its total drag when cruising at 15 kn in seawater at 20°C.

5.77 A dam spillway is to be tested by using Froude scaling with a one-thirtieth-scale model. The model flow has an average velocity of 0.6 m/s and a volume flow of 0.05 m^3/s. What will the velocity and flow of the prototype be? If the measured force on a certain part of the model is 1.5 N, what will the corresponding force on the prototype be?

5.78 A prototype spillway has a characteristic velocity of 3 m/s and a characteristic length of 10 m. A small model is constructed by using Froude scaling. What is the minimum scale ratio of the model which will ensure that its minimum Weber number is 100? Both flows use water at 20°C.

5.79 An East Coast estuary has a tidal period of 12.42 h (the semidiurnal lunar tide) and tidal currents of approximately 80 cm/s. If a one-five-hundredth-scale model is constructed with tides driven by a pump and storage apparatus, what should the period of the model tides be and what model current speeds are expected?

5.80 A prototype ship is 35 m long and designed to cruise at 11 m/s (about 21 kn). Its drag is to be simulated by a 1-m-long model pulled in a tow tank. For Froude scaling find (*a*) the tow speed, (*b*) the ratio of prototype to model drag, and (*c*) the ratio of prototype to model power.

5.81 An airplane, of overall length 55 ft, is designed to fly at 680 m/s at 8000-m standard altitude. A one-thirtieth-scale model is to be tested in a pressurized helium wind tunnel at 20°C. What is the appropriate tunnel pressure in atm? Even at this (high) pressure, exact dynamic similarity is not achieved. Why?

5.82 A prototype ship is 400 ft long and has a wetted area of 30,000 ft². A one-eightieth-scale model is tested in a tow tank according to Froude scaling at speeds of 1.3, 2.0, and 2.7 kn (1 kn = 1.689 ft/s). The measured friction drag of the model at these speeds is 0.11, 0.24, and 0.41 lbf, respectively. What are the three prototype speeds? What is the estimated prototype friction drag at these speeds if we correct for Reynolds-number discrepancy by extrapolation?

5.83 A one-fortieth-scale model of a ship's propeller is tested in a tow tank at 1200 r/min and exhibits a power output of 1.4 ft · lbf/s. According to Froude scaling laws, what should the revolutions per minute and horsepower output of the prototype propeller be under dynamically similar conditions?

5.84 A prototype ocean-platform piling is expected to encounter currents of 150 cm/s and waves of 12-s period and 3-m height. If a one-fifteenth-scale model is tested in a wave channel, what current speed, wave period, and wave height should be encountered by the model?

5.85 Solve Prob. 5.49, using the modified sphere-drag plot of Fig. 5.11.

5.86 Solve Prob. 5.50, using the modified sphere-drag plot of Fig. 5.11.

5.87 In Prob. 5.62 it was difficult to solve for Ω because it appeared in both power and flow coefficients. Rescale the problem, using the data of Fig. P5.61, to make a plot of dimensionless power versus dimensionless rotation speed. Enter this plot directly to solve Prob. 5.62 for Ω.

5.88 Modify Prob. 5.62 as follows: Let Ω = 32 r/s and Q = 24 m³/h for a geometrically similar pump. What is the maximum diameter if the power is not to exceed 340 W? Solve this problem by rescaling the data of Fig. P5.61 to make a plot of dimensionless power versus dimensionless diameter. Enter this plot directly to find the desired diameter.

5.89 Knowing that Δp is proportional to L, rescale the data of Example 5.7 to plot dimensionless Δp versus dimensionless *diameter*. Use this plot to find the diameter required in the first row of data in Example 5.7 if the pressure drop is increased to 10 kPa for the same flow rate, length, and fluid.

5.90 Knowing that Δp is proportional to L, rescale the data of Example 5.7 to plot dimensionless Δp versus dimensionless *viscosity*. Use this plot to find the viscosity required in the first row of data in Example 5.7 if the pressure drop is increased to 10 kPa for the same flow rate, length, and density.

5.91 Develop a plot of dimensionless Δp versus dimensionless viscosity, as described in Prob. 5.90. Suppose that L = 200 m, Q = 60 m³/h, and the fluid is kerosine at 20°C. Use your plot to determine the minimum pipe diameter for which the pressure drop is no more than 220 kPa.

Word Problems

W5.1 In 98 percent of data analysis cases, the "reducing factor" j, which lowers the number n of dimensional variables to $n - j$ dimensionless groups, exactly equals the number of relevant dimensions (M, L, T, Θ). In one case (Example 5.5) this was not so. Explain in words why this situation happens.

W5.2 Consider the following equation: **1 dollar bill $\approx$ 6 in.** Is this relation dimensionally inconsistent? Does it satisfy the PDH? Why?

W5.3 In making a dimensional analysis, what rules do you follow for choosing your scaling variables?

W5.4 In an earlier edition, the writer asked the following question about Fig. 5.1: "Which of the three graphs is a more effective presentation?" Why was this a dumb question?

W5.5 This chapter discusses the difficulty of scaling Mach and Reynolds numbers together (an airplane) and Froude and Reynolds numbers together (a ship). Give an example of a flow which would combine Mach and Froude numbers. Would there be scaling problems for common fluids?

W5.6 What is different about a very *small* model of a weir or dam (Fig. P5.32) which would make the test results difficult to relate to the prototype?

W5.7 What else are you studying this term? Give an example of a popular equation or formula from another course (thermodynamics, strength of materials, etc.) which does not satisfy the principle of dimensional homogeneity. Explain what is wrong and whether it can be modified to be homogeneous.

W5.8 Some colleges (e.g., Colorado State University) have environmental wind tunnels which can be used to study, e.g., wind flow over city buildings. What details of scaling might be important in such studies?

W5.9 If the model scale ratio is $\alpha = L_m/L_p$, as in Eq. (5.31), and the Weber number is important, how must the model and prototype surface tension be related to α for dynamic similarity?

W5.10 For a typical incompressible velocity potential analysis in Chap. 4 we solve $\nabla^2\phi = 0$, subject to known values of $\partial\phi/\partial n$ on the boundaries. What dimensionless parameters govern this type of motion?

Chapter 6
Viscous Flow in Ducts

Motivation. This chapter is completely devoted to an important practical fluids engineering problem: flow in ducts with various velocities, various fluids, and various duct shapes. Piping systems are encountered in almost every engineering design and thus have been studied extensively. There is a small amount of theory plus a large amount of experimentation.

The basic piping problem is this: Given the pipe geometry and its added components (such as fittings, valves, bends, and diffusers) plus the desired flow rate and fluid properties, what pressure drop is needed to drive the flow? Of course, it may be stated in alternate form: Given the pressure drop available from a pump, what flow rate will ensue? The correlations discussed in this chapter are adequate to solve most such piping problems.

6.1 Reynolds-Number Regimes

Now that we have derived and studied the basic flow equations in Chap. 4, you would think that we could just whip off myriad beautiful solutions illustrating the full range of fluid behavior, of course expressing all these educational results in dimensionless form, using our new tool from Chap. 5, dimensional analysis.

The fact of the matter is that no general analysis of fluid motion yet exists. There are several dozen known particular solutions, there are some rather specific digital-computer solutions, and there are a great many experimental data. There is a lot of theory available if we neglect such important effects as viscosity and compressibility (Chap. 8), but there is no general theory and there may never be. The reason is that a profound and vexing change in fluid behavior occurs at moderate Reynolds numbers. The flow ceases being smooth and steady (*laminar*) and becomes fluctuating and agitated (*turbulent*). The changeover is called *transition* to turbulence. In Fig. 5.3a we saw that transition on the cylinder and sphere occurred at about $Re = 3 \times 10^5$, where the sharp drop in the drag coefficient appeared. Transition depends upon many effects, e.g., wall roughness (Fig. 5.3b) or fluctuations in the inlet stream, but the primary parameter is the Reynolds number. There are a great many data on transition but only a small amount of theory [1 to 3].

Turbulence can be detected from a measurement by a small, sensitive instrument such as a hot-wire anemometer (Fig. 6.29e) or a piezoelectric pressure transducer (Fig. 2.26d). The flow will appear steady on average but will reveal rapid, random fluctuations if turbulence is present, as sketched in Fig. 6.1. If the flow is laminar, there may

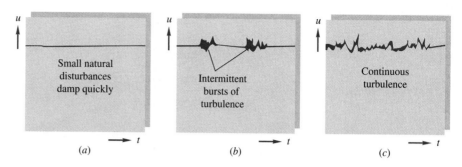

Fig. 6.1 The three regimes of viscous flow: (*a*) laminar flow at low Re; (*b*) transition at intermediate Re; (*c*) turbulent flow at high Re.

be occasional natural disturbances which damp out quickly (Fig. 6.1*a*). If transition is occurring, there will be sharp bursts of turbulent fluctuation (Fig. 6.1*b*) as the increasing Reynolds number causes a breakdown or instability of laminar motion. At sufficiently large Re, the flow will fluctuate continually (Fig. 6.1*c*) and is termed *fully turbulent*. The fluctuations, typically ranging from 1 to 20 percent of the average velocity, are not strictly periodic but are random and encompass a continuous range, or spectrum, of frequencies. In a typical wind-tunnel flow at high Re, the turbulent frequency ranges from 1 to 10,000 Hz, and the wavelength ranges from about 0.01 to 400 cm.

EXAMPLE 6.1

The accepted transition Reynolds number for flow in a circular pipe is $\mathrm{Re}_{d,\mathrm{crit}} \approx 2300$. For flow through a 5-cm-diameter pipe, at what velocity will this occur at 20°C for (*a*) airflow and (*b*) water flow?

Solution

Almost all pipe-flow formulas are based on the *average* velocity $V = Q/A$, not centerline or any other point velocity. Thus transition is specified at $\rho V d/\mu \approx 2300$. With d known, we introduce the appropriate fluid properties at 20°C from Tables A.3 and A.4:

(*a*) Air: $\quad \dfrac{\rho V d}{\mu} = \dfrac{(1.205 \text{ kg/m}^3)V(0.05 \text{ m})}{1.80 \text{ E-5 kg/(m} \cdot \text{s)}} = 2300 \quad$ or $\quad V \approx 0.7 \, \dfrac{\text{m}}{\text{s}}$

(*b*) Water: $\quad \dfrac{\rho V d}{\mu} = \dfrac{(998 \text{ kg/m}^3)V(0.05 \text{ m})}{0.001 \text{ kg/(m} \cdot \text{s)}} = 2300 \quad$ or $\quad V = 0.046 \, \dfrac{\text{m}}{\text{s}}$

These are very low velocities, so most engineering air and water pipe flows are turbulent, not laminar. We might expect laminar duct flow with more viscous fluids such as lubricating oils or glycerin.

In free-surface flows, turbulence can be observed directly. Figure 6.2 shows liquid flow issuing from the open end of a tube. The low-Reynolds-number jet (Fig. 6.2*a*) is smooth and laminar, with the fast center motion and slower wall flow forming different trajectories joined by a liquid sheet. The higher-Reynolds-number turbulent flow (Fig. 6.2*b*) is unsteady and irregular but, when averaged over time, is steady and predictable.

How did turbulence form inside the pipe? The laminar parabolic flow profile, which is similar to Eq. (4.143), became unstable and, at $\mathrm{Re}_d \approx 2300$, began to form "slugs"

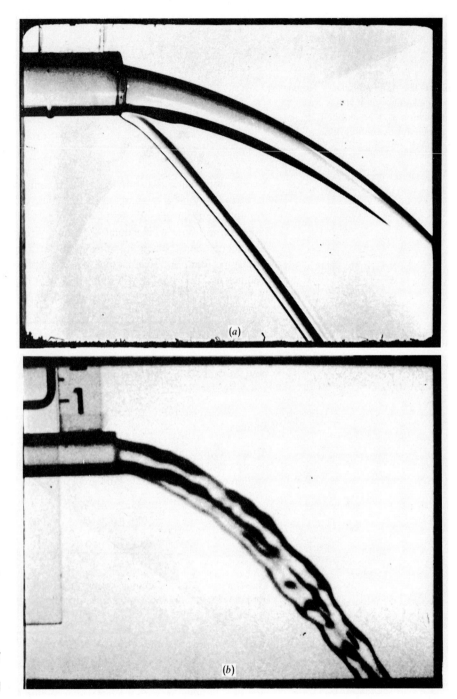

Fig. 6.2 Flow issuing at constant speed from a pipe: (*a*) high-viscosity, low-Reynolds-number, laminar flow; (*b*) low-viscosity, high-Reynolds-number, turbulent flow. [*From* Illustrated Experiments in Fluid Mechanics (*The NCFMF Book of Film Notes*), *National Committee for Fluid Mechanics Films, Education Development Center, Inc., copyright 1972.*]

or ''puffs'' of intense turbulence. A puff has a fast-moving front and a slow-moving rear and may be visualized by experimenting with glass tube flow. Figure 6.3 shows a puff as photographed by Bandyopadhyay [45]. Near the entrance (Fig. 6.3*a* and *b*) there

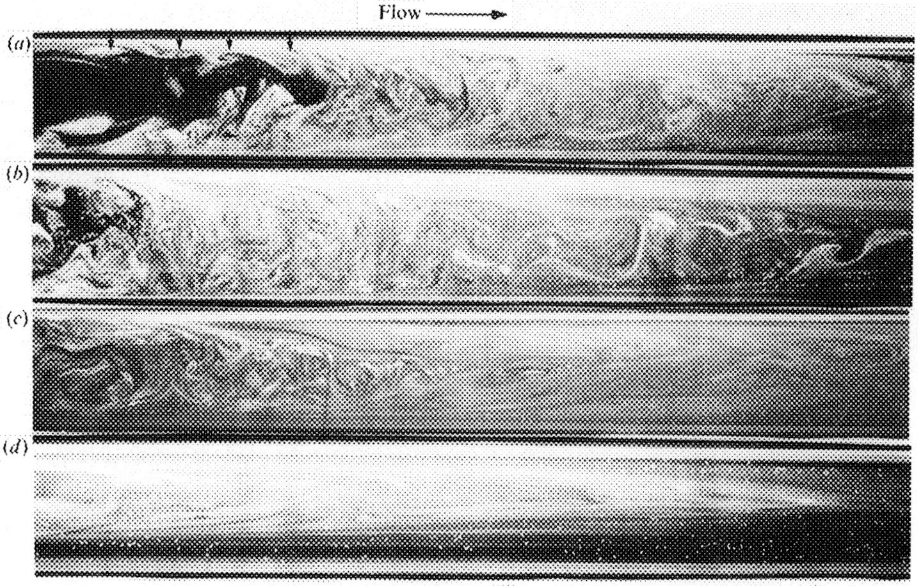

Flow ────────▶

Fig. 6.3 Formation of a turbulent puff in pipe flow: (*a*) and (*b*) near the entrance; (*c*) somewhat downstream; (*d*) far downstream. (*From Ref. 45, courtesy of P. R. Bandyopadhyay.*)

is an irregular laminar-turbulent interface, and vortex roll-up is visible. Further downstream (Fig. 6.3*c*) the puff becomes fully turbulent and very active, with helical motions visible. Far downstream (Fig. 6.3*d*), the puff is cone-shaped and less active, with a fuzzy ill-defined interface, sometimes called the "relaminarization" region.

A complete description of the statistical aspects of turbulence is given in Ref. 1, while theory and data on transition effects are given in Refs. 2 and 3. At this introductory level we merely point out that the primary parameter affecting transition is the Reynolds number. If $Re = UL/\nu$, where U is the average stream velocity and L is the "width," or transverse thickness, of the shear layer, the following approximate ranges occur:

$$
\begin{array}{ll}
0 < Re < \quad 1: & \text{highly viscous laminar "creeping" motion} \\
1 < Re < 100: & \text{laminar, strong Reynolds-number dependence} \\
100 < Re < 10^3: & \text{laminar, boundary-layer theory useful} \\
10^3 < Re < 10^4: & \text{transition to turbulence} \\
10^4 < Re < 10^6: & \text{turbulent, moderate Reynolds-number dependence} \\
10^6 < Re < \quad \infty: & \text{turbulent, slight Reynolds-number dependence}
\end{array}
$$

These are representative ranges which vary somewhat with flow geometry, surface roughness, and the level of fluctuations in the inlet stream. The great majority of our analyses are concerned with laminar flow or with turbulent flow, and one should not normally design a flow operation in the transition region.

Historical Outline

Since turbulent flow is more prevalent than laminar flow, experimenters have observed turbulence for centuries without being aware of the details. Before 1930 flow instruments were too insensitive to record rapid fluctuations, and workers simply reported mean values of velocity, pressure, force, etc. But turbulence can change the mean values dramatically, e.g., the sharp drop in drag coefficient in Fig. 5.3. A German engineer named G. H. L. Hagen first reported in 1839 that there might be *two* regimes of viscous flow. He measured water flow in long brass pipes and deduced a pressure-drop law

$$\Delta p = (\text{const}) \frac{LQ}{R^4} + \text{entrance effect} \tag{6.1}$$

This is exactly our laminar-flow scaling law from Example 5.4, but Hagen did not realize that the constant was proportional to the fluid viscosity.

The formula broke down as Hagen increased Q beyond a certain limit, i.e., past the critical Reynolds number, and he stated in his paper that there must be a second mode of flow characterized by "strong movements of water for which Δp varies as the second power of the discharge. . . ." He admitted that he could not clarify the reasons for the change.

A typical example of Hagen's data is shown in Fig. 6.4. The pressure drop varies linearly with $V = Q/A$ up to about 1.1 ft/s, where there is a sharp change. Above about $V = 2.2$ ft/s the pressure drop is nearly quadratic with V. The actual power $\Delta p \propto V^{1.75}$ seems impossible on dimensional grounds but is easily explained when the dimensionless pipe-flow data (Fig. 5.10) are displayed.

In 1883 Osborne Reynolds, a British engineering professor, showed that the change depended upon the parameter $\rho V d / \mu$, now named in his honor. By introducing a dye

Fig. 6.4 Experimental evidence of transition for water flow in a $\frac{1}{4}$-in smooth pipe 10 ft long.

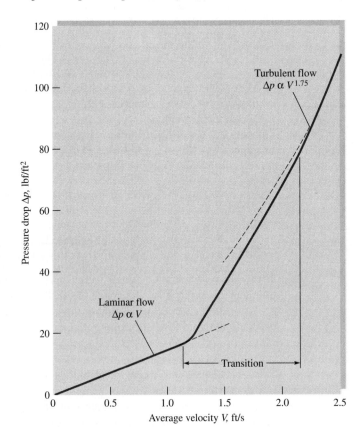

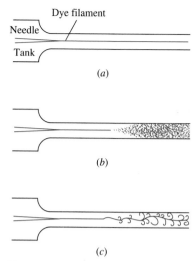

Dye filament

Needle

Tank

(a)

(b)

(c)

Fig. 6.5 Reynolds' sketches of pipe-flow transition: (a) low-speed, laminar flow; (b) high-speed, turbulent flow; (c) spark photograph of condition (b). (*From Ref. 4.*)

streak into a pipe flow, Reynolds could observe transition and turbulence. His sketches of the flow behavior are shown in Fig. 6.5.

If we examine Hagen's data and compute the Reynolds number at $V = 1.1$ ft/s, we obtain $\text{Re}_d = 2100$. The slow became fully turbulent, $V = 2.2$ ft/s, at $\text{Re}_d = 4200$. The accepted design value for pipe-flow transition is now taken to be

$$\text{Re}_{d,\text{crit}} \approx 2300 \qquad (6.2)$$

This is accurate for commercial pipes (Fig. 6.13), although with special care in providing a rounded entrance, smooth walls, and a steady inlet stream, $\text{Re}_{d,\text{crit}}$ can be delayed until much higher values.

Transition also occurs in external flows around bodies such as the sphere and cylinder in Fig. 5.3. Ludwig Prandtl, a German engineering professor, showed in 1914 that the thin boundary layer surrounding the body was undergoing transition from laminar to turbulent flow. Thereafter the force coefficient of a body was acknowledged to be a function of the Reynolds number [Eq. (5.2)].

There are now extensive theories and experiments of laminar-flow instability which explain why a flow changes to turbulence. Reference 5 is an advanced textbook on this subject.

Laminar-flow theory is now well developed, and many solutions are known [2, 3], but there are no analyses, even digital-computer solutions, which can stimulate the fine-scale random fluctuations of turbulent flow.[1] Therefore existing turbulent-flow theory is semiempirical, based upon dimensional analysis and physical reasoning; it is concerned with the mean flow properties only and the mean of the fluctuations, not their rapid variations. The turbulent-flow ''theory'' presented here in Chaps. 6 and 7 is unbelievably crude yet surprisingly effective. We shall attempt a rational approach which places turbulent-flow analysis on a firm physical basis.

6.2 Internal versus External Viscous Flows

Both laminar and turbulent flow may be either internal, i.e., ''bounded'' by walls, or external and unbounded. This chapter treats internal flows, and Chap. 7 studies external flows.

An internal flow is constrained by the bounding walls, and the viscous effects will grow and meet and permeate the entire flow. Figure 6.6 shows an internal flow in a long duct. There is an *entrance region* where a nearly inviscid upstream flow converges and enters the tube. Viscous boundary layers grow downstream, retarding the axial flow $u(r, x)$ at the wall and thereby accelerating the center-core flow to maintain the incompressible continuity requirement

$$Q = \int u \, dA = \text{const} \qquad (6.3)$$

At a finite distance from the entrance, the boundary layers merge and the inviscid core disappears. The tube flow is then entirely viscous, and the axial velocity adjusts slightly further until at $x = L_e$ it no longer changes with x and is said to be *fully developed*, $u \approx u(r)$ only. Downstream of $x = L_e$ the velocity profile is constant, the

[1] Reference 32 is a computer model of large-scale turbulent fluctuations.

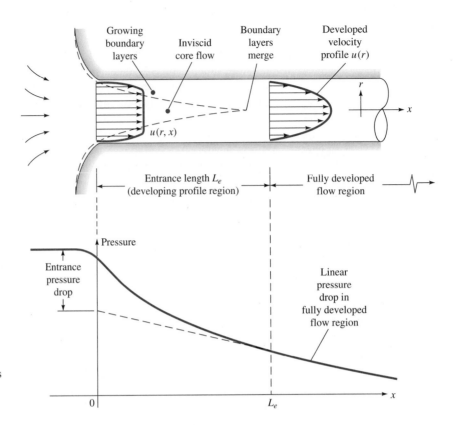

Fig. 6.6 Developing velocity profiles and pressure changes in the entrance of a duct flow.

wall shear is constant, and the pressure drops linearly with x, for either laminar or turbulent flow. All these details are shown in Fig. 6.6.

Dimensional analysis shows that the Reynolds number is the only parameter affecting entrance length. If

$$L_e = f(d, V, \rho, \mu) \qquad V = \frac{Q}{A}$$

then

$$\frac{L_e}{d} = g\left(\frac{\rho V d}{\mu}\right) = g(\text{Re}) \tag{6.4}$$

For laminar flow [2, 3], the accepted correlation is

$$\frac{L_e}{d} \approx 0.06 \, \text{Re} \qquad \text{laminar} \tag{6.5}$$

The maximum laminar entrance length, at $\text{Re}_{d,\text{crit}} = 2300$, is $L_e = 138d$, which is the longest development length possible.

In turbulent flow the boundary layers grow faster, and L_e is relatively shorter, according to the approximation

$$\frac{L_e}{d} \approx 4.4 \, \text{Re}_d^{1/6} \qquad \text{turbulent} \tag{6.6}$$

Some computed turbulent entrance lengths are thus

Re_d	4000	10^4	10^5	10^6	10^7	10^8
L_e/d	18	20	30	44	65	95

Now 44 diameters may seem "long," but typical pipe-flow applications involve an L/d value of 1000 or more, in which case the entrance effect may be neglected and a simple analysis made for fully developed flow (Sec. 6.4). This is possible for both laminar and turbulent flows, including rough walls and noncircular cross sections.

EXAMPLE 6.2

A $\frac{1}{2}$-in-diameter water pipe is 60 ft long and delivers water at 5 gal/min at 20°C. What fraction of this pipe is taken up by the entrance region?

Solution

Convert

$$Q = (5 \text{ gal/min}) \frac{0.00223 \text{ ft}^3/\text{s}}{1 \text{ gal/min}} = 0.0111 \text{ ft}^3/\text{s}$$

The average velocity is

$$V = \frac{Q}{A} = \frac{0.0111 \text{ ft}^3/\text{s}}{(\pi/4)(\frac{1}{2}/12 \text{ ft})^2} = 8.17 \text{ ft/s}$$

From Table 1.4 read for water $\nu = 1.01 \times 10^{-6} \text{ m}^2/\text{s} = 1.09 \times 10^{-5} \text{ ft}^2/\text{s}$. Then the pipe Reynolds number is

$$\mathrm{Re}_d = \frac{Vd}{\nu} = \frac{(8.17 \text{ ft/s})(\frac{1}{2}/12 \text{ ft})}{1.09 \times 10^{-5} \text{ ft}^2/\text{s}} = 31{,}300$$

This is greater than 4000; hence the flow is fully turbulent, and Eq. (6.6) applies for entrance length

$$\frac{L_e}{d} \approx 4.4 \, \mathrm{Re}_d^{1/6} = (4.4)(31{,}300)^{1/6} = 25$$

The actual pipe has $L/d = (60 \text{ ft})/[(\frac{1}{2}/12) \text{ ft}] = 1440$. Hence the entrance region takes up the fraction

$$\frac{L_e}{L} = \frac{25}{1440} = 0.017 = 1.7\% \qquad\qquad Ans.$$

This is a very small percentage, so that we can reasonably treat this pipe flow as essentially fully developed.

Shortness can be a virtue in duct flow if one wishes to maintain the inviscid core. For example, a "long" wind tunnel would be ridiculous, since the viscous core would invalidate the purpose of simulating free-flight conditions. A typical laboratory low-speed wind-tunnel test section is 1 m in diameter and 5 m long, with $V = 30$ m/s. If we take $\nu_{\mathrm{air}} = 1.51 \times 10^{-5} \text{ m}^2/\text{s}$ from Table 1.4, then $\mathrm{Re}_d = 1.99 \times 10^6$ and, from Eq. (6.6), $L_e/d \approx 49$. The test section has $L/d = 5$, which is much shorter than the development length. At the end of the section the wall boundary layers are only 10 cm thick, leaving 80 cm of inviscid core suitable for model testing.

An external flow has no restraining walls and is free to expand no matter how thick the viscous layers on the immersed body may become. Thus, far from the body the flow is nearly inviscid, and our analytical technique, treated in Chap. 7, is to patch an inviscid-flow solution onto a viscous boundary-layer solution computed for the wall region. There is no external equivalent of fully developed internal flow.

6.3 Semiempirical Turbulent Shear Correlations

Throughout this chapter we assume constant density and viscosity and no thermal interaction, so that only the continuity and momentum equations are to be solved for velocity and pressure

Continuity:
$$\frac{\partial u}{\partial x} + \frac{\partial v}{\partial y} + \frac{\partial w}{\partial z} = 0$$

$$\tag{6.7}$$

Momentum:
$$\rho \frac{d\mathbf{V}}{dt} = -\nabla p + \rho g + \mu \nabla^2 \mathbf{V}$$

subject to no slip at the walls and known inlet and exit conditions. (We shall save our free-surface solutions for Chap. 10.)

Both laminar and turbulent flows satisfy Eqs. (6.7). For laminar flow, where there are no random fluctuations, we go right to the attack and solve them for a variety of geometries [2, 3], leaving many more, of course, for the problems.

Reynolds' Time-Averaging Concept

For turbulent flow, because of the fluctuations, every velocity and pressure term in Eqs. (6.7) is a rapidly varying random function of time and space. At present our mathematics cannot handle such instantaneous fluctuating variables. No single pair of random functions $\mathbf{V}(x, y, z, t)$ and $p(x, y, z, t)$ is known to be a solution to Eqs. (6.7). Moreover, our attention as engineers is toward the average or *mean* values of velocity, pressure, shear stress, etc., in a high-Reynolds-number (turbulent) flow. This approach led Osborne Reynolds in 1895 to rewrite Eqs. (6.7) in terms of mean or time-averaged turbulent variables.

The time mean $\bar{u}$ of a turbulent function $u(x, y, z, t)$ is defined by

$$\bar{u} = \frac{1}{T} \int_0^T u \, dt \tag{6.8}$$

where T is an averaging period taken to be longer than any significant period of the fluctuations themselves. The mean values of turbulent velocity and pressure are illustrated in Fig. 6.7. For turbulent gas and water flows, an averaging period $T \approx 5$ s is usually quite adequate.

The *fluctuation* u' is defined as the deviation of u from its average value

$$u' = u - \bar{u} \tag{6.9}$$

also shown in Fig. 6.7. It follows by definition that a fluctuation has zero mean value

$$\bar{u'} = \frac{1}{T} \int_0^T (u - \bar{u}) \, dt = \bar{u} - \bar{u} = 0 \tag{6.10}$$

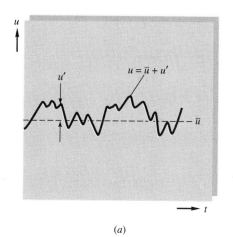

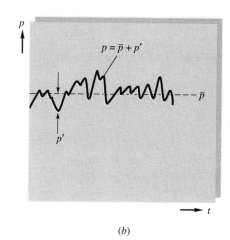

Fig. 6.7 Definition of mean and fluctuating turbulent variables: (*a*) velocity; (*b*) pressure.

(*a*)   (*b*)

However, the mean square of a fluctuation is not zero and is a measure of the *intensity* of the turbulence

$$\overline{u'^2} = \frac{1}{T} \int_0^T u'^2 \, dt \neq 0 \tag{6.11}$$

Nor in general are the mean fluctuation products such as $\overline{u'v'}$ and $\overline{u'p'}$ zero in a typical turbulent flow.

Reynolds' idea was to split each property into mean plus fluctuating variables

$$u = \bar{u} + u' \qquad v = \bar{v} + v' \qquad w = \bar{w} + w' \qquad p = \bar{p} + p' \tag{6.12}$$

Substitute these into Eqs. (6.7), and take the time mean of each equation. The continuity relation reduces to

$$\frac{\partial \bar{u}}{\partial x} + \frac{\partial \bar{v}}{\partial y} + \frac{\partial \bar{w}}{\partial z} = 0 \tag{6.13}$$

which is no different from a laminar continuity relation.

However, each component of the momentum equation (6.7*b*), after time averaging, will contain mean values plus three mean products, or *correlations*, of fluctuating velocities. The most important of these is the momentum relation in the mainstream, or *x*, direction, which takes the form

$$\rho \frac{d\bar{u}}{dt} = -\frac{\partial \bar{p}}{\partial x} + \rho g_x + \frac{\partial}{\partial x}\left(\mu \frac{\partial \bar{u}}{\partial x} - \rho \overline{u'^2}\right)$$

$$+ \frac{\partial}{\partial y}\left(\mu \frac{\partial \bar{u}}{\partial y} - \rho \overline{u'v'}\right) + \frac{\partial}{\partial z}\left(\mu \frac{\partial \bar{u}}{\partial z} - \rho \overline{u'w'}\right) \tag{6.14}$$

The three correlation terms $-\rho\overline{u'^2}$, $-\rho\overline{u'v'}$, and $-\rho\overline{u'w'}$ are called *turbulent stresses* because they have the same dimensions and occur right alongside the newtonian (laminar) stress terms $\mu(\partial \bar{u}/\partial x)$, etc. Actually, they are convective acceleration terms (which is why the density appears), not stresses, but they have the mathematical effect of stress and are so termed almost universally in the literature.

The turbulent stresses are unknown a priori and must be related by experiment to

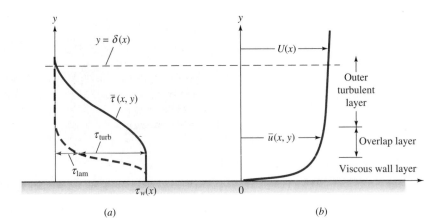

Fig. 6.8 Typical velocity and shear distributions in turbulent flow near a wall: (*a*) shear; (*b*) velocity.

geometry and flow conditions, as detailed in Refs. 1 to 3. Fortunately, in duct and boundary-layer flow, the stress $-\rho \overline{u'v'}$ associated with direction y normal to the wall is dominant, and we can approximate with excellent accuracy a simpler streamwise momentum equation

$$\rho \frac{d\bar{u}}{dt} \approx -\frac{\partial \bar{p}}{\partial x} + \rho g_x + \frac{\partial \tau}{\partial y} \tag{6.15}$$

where

$$\tau = \mu \frac{\partial \bar{u}}{\partial y} - \rho \overline{u'v'} = \tau_{\text{lam}} + \tau_{\text{turb}} \tag{6.16}$$

Figure 6.8 shows the distribution of τ_{lam} and τ_{turb} from typical measurements across a turbulent-shear layer near a wall. Laminar shear is dominant near the wall (the *wall layer*), and turbulent shear dominates in the *outer layer*. There is an intermediate region, called the *overlap layer*, where both laminar and turbulent shear are important. These three regions are labeled in Fig. 6.8.

In the outer layer τ_{turb} is two or three orders of magnitude greater than τ_{lam}, and vice versa in the wall layer. These experimental facts enable us to use a crude but very effective model for the velocity distribution $\bar{u}(y)$ across a turbulent wall layer.

The Logarithmic-Overlap Law

We have seen in Fig. 6.8 that there are three regions in turbulent flow near a wall:

1. Wall layer: Viscous shear dominates.
2. Outer layer: Turbulent shear dominates.
3. Overlap layer: Both types of shear are important.

From now on let us agree to drop the overbar from velocity $\bar{u}$. Let τ_w be the wall shear stress, and let δ and U represent the thickness and velocity at the edge of the outer layer, $y = \delta$.

For the wall layer, Prandtl deduced in 1930 that u must be independent of the shear-layer thickness

$$u = f(\mu, \tau_w, \rho, y) \tag{6.17}$$

By dimensional analysis, this is equivalent to

$$u^+ = \frac{u}{u^*} = F\left(\frac{yu^*}{\nu}\right) \qquad u^* = \left(\frac{\tau_w}{\rho}\right)^{1/2} \tag{6.18}$$

Equation (6.18) is called the *law of the wall*, and the quantity u^* is termed the *friction velocity* because it has dimensions $\{LT^{-1}\}$, although it is not actually a flow velocity.

Subsequently, Kármán in 1933 deduced that u in the outer layer is independent of molecular viscosity, but its deviation from the stream velocity U must depend on the layer thickness δ and the other properties

$$(U - u)_{\text{outer}} = g(\delta, \tau_w, \rho, y) \tag{6.19}$$

Again, by dimensional analysis we rewrite this as

$$\frac{U - u}{u^*} = G\left(\frac{y}{\delta}\right) \tag{6.20}$$

where u^* has the same meaning as in Eq. (6.18). Equation (6.20) is called the *velocity-defect law* for the outer layer.

Both the wall law (6.18) and the defect law (6.20) are found to be accurate for a wide variety of experimental turbulent duct and boundary-layer flows [1–3]. They are different in form, yet they must overlap smoothly in the intermediate layer. In 1937 C. B. Millikan showed that this can be true only if the overlap-layer velocity varies logarithmically with y:

$$\frac{u}{u^*} = \frac{1}{\kappa} \ln \frac{yu^*}{\nu} + B \qquad \text{overlap layer} \tag{6.21}$$

Over the full range of turbulent wall flows, the dimensionless constants κ and B are found to have the approximate values $\kappa \approx 0.41$ and $B \approx 5.0$. Equation (6.21) is called the *logarithmic-overlap layer*.

Thus by dimensional reasoning and physical insight we infer that a plot of u versus $\ln y$ in a turbulent-shear layer will show a curved wall region, a curved outer region, and a straight-line logarithmic overlap. Figure 6.9 shows that this is exactly the case. The four outer-law profiles shown all merge smoothly with the logarithmic-overlap law but have different magnitudes because they vary in external pressure gradient. The wall law is unique and follows the linear viscous relation

$$u^+ = \frac{u}{u^*} = \frac{yu^*}{\nu} = y^+ \tag{6.22}$$

from the wall to about $y^+ = 5$, thereafter curving over to merge with the logarithmic law at about $y^+ = 30$.

Believe it or not, Fig. 6.9, which is nothing more than a shrewd correlation of velocity profiles, is the basis for all existing "theory" of turbulent-shear flows. Notice that we have not solved any equations at all but have merely expressed the streamwise velocity in a neat form.

There is serendipity in Fig. 6.9: The logarithmic law (6.21), instead of just being a short overlapping link, actually approximates nearly the entire velocity profile, except for the outer law when the pressure is increasing strongly downstream (as in a diffuser). The inner-wall law typically extends over less than 2 percent of the profile and can be neglected. Thus we can use Eq. (6.21) as an excellent approximation to solve nearly

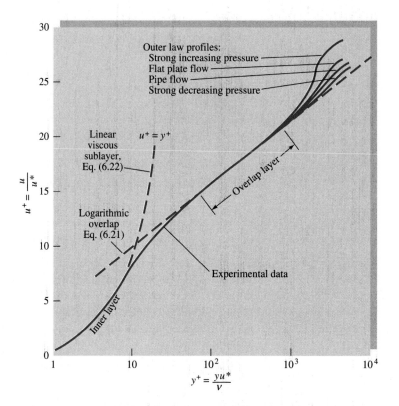

Fig. 6.9 Experimental verification of the inner-, outer-, and overlap-layer laws relating velocity profiles in turbulent wall flow.

every turbulent-flow problem presented in this and the next chapter. Many additional applications are given in Refs. 2 and 3.

EXAMPLE 6.3

Air at 20°C flows through a 14-cm-diameter tube under fully developed conditions. The centerline velocity is $u_0 = 5$ m/s. Estimate from Fig. 6.9 (a) the friction velocity u^*, (b) the wall shear stress τ_w, and (c) the average velocity $V = Q/A$.

Solution

Part (a) For pipe flow Fig. 6.9 shows that the logarithmic law, Eq. (6.21), is accurate all the way to the center of the tube. From Fig. E6.3 $y = R - r$ should go from the wall to the centerline as shown. At the center $u = u_0$, $y = R$, and Eq. (6.21) becomes

$$\frac{u_0}{u^*} = \frac{1}{0.41} \ln \frac{Ru^*}{\nu} + 5.0 \tag{1}$$

Since we know that $u_0 = 5$ m/s and $R = 0.07$ m, u^* is the only unknown in Eq. (1). Find the solution by trial and error

$$u^* = 0.228 \text{ m/s} = 22.8 \text{ cm/s} \qquad \qquad \textit{Ans. (a)}$$

where we have taken $\nu = 1.51 \times 10^{-5}$ m²/s for air from Table 1.4.

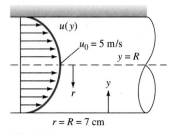

Fig. E6.3

Part (b)   Assuming a pressure of 1 atm, we have $\rho = p/(RT) = 1.205$ kg/m³. Since by definition $u^* = (\tau_w/\rho)^{1/2}$, we compute

$$\tau_w = \rho u^{*2} = (1.205 \text{ kg/m}^3)(0.228 \text{ m/s})^2 = 0.062 \text{ kg/(m} \cdot \text{s}^2) = 0.062 \text{ Pa} \qquad \textit{Ans. (b)}$$

This is a very small shear stress, but it will cause a large pressure drop in a long pipe (170 Pa for every 100 m of pipe).

Part (c)   The average velocity V is found by integrating the logarithmic-law velocity distribution

$$V = \frac{Q}{A} = \frac{1}{\pi R^2} \int_0^R u 2\pi r \, dr \qquad (2)$$

Introducing $u = u^*[(1/\kappa) \ln (yu^*/\nu) + B]$ from Eq. (6.21) and noting that $y = R - r$, we can carry out the integration of Eq. (2), which is rather laborious. The final result is

$$V = 0.835u_0 = 4.17 \text{ m/s} \qquad \textit{Ans. (c)}$$

We shall not bother showing the integration here because it is all worked out and a very neat formula is given in Eqs. (6.49) and (6.59).

Notice that we started from almost nothing (the pipe diameter and the centerline velocity) and found the answers without solving the differential equations of continuity and momentum. We just used the logarithmic law, Eq. (6.21), which makes the differential equations unnecessary for pipe flow. This is a powerful technique, but you should remember that all we are doing is using an experimental velocity correlation to approximate the actual solution to the problem.

We should check the Reynolds number to ensure turbulent flow

$$\text{Re}_d = \frac{Vd}{\nu} = \frac{(4.17 \text{ m/s})(0.14 \text{ m})}{1.51 \times 10^{-5} \text{ m}^2/\text{s}} = 38{,}700$$

Since this is greater than 4000, the flow is definitely turbulent.

6.4 Flow in a Circular Pipe

As our first example of a specific viscous-flow analysis, we take the classic problem of flow in a full pipe, driven by pressure or gravity or both. Figure 6.10 shows the geometry of the pipe of radius R. The x axis is taken in the flow direction and is inclined to the horizontal at an angle ϕ.

Before proceeding with a solution to the equations of motion, we can learn a lot by making a control-volume analysis of the flow between sections 1 and 2 in Fig. 6.10. The continuity relation, Eq. (3.23), reduces to

$$Q_1 = Q_2 = \text{const}$$

or $$V_1 = \frac{Q_1}{A_1} = V_2 = \frac{Q_2}{A_2} \qquad (6.23)$$

since the pipe is of constant area. The steady-flow energy equation (3.71) reduces to

$$\frac{p_1}{\rho} + \frac{1}{2} \alpha_1 V_1^2 + gz_1 = \frac{p_2}{\rho} + \frac{1}{2} \alpha_2 V_2^2 + gz_2 + gh_f \qquad (6.24)$$

since there are no shaft-work or heat-transfer effects. Now assume that the flow is fully

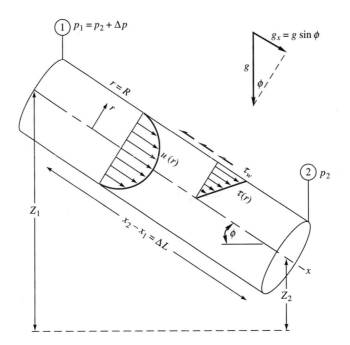

Fig. 6.10 Control volume of steady, fully developed flow between two sections in an inclined pipe.

developed (Fig. 6.6), and correct later for entrance effects. Then the kinetic-energy correction factor $\alpha_1 = \alpha_2$, and since $V_1 = V_2$ from (6.23), Eq. (6.24) now reduces to a simple expression for the friction-head loss h_f

$$h_f = \left(z_1 + \frac{p_1}{\rho g}\right) - \left(z_2 + \frac{p_2}{\rho g}\right) = \Delta\left(z + \frac{p}{\rho g}\right) = \Delta z + \frac{\Delta p}{\rho g} \qquad (6.25)$$

The pipe-head loss equals the change in the sum of pressure and gravity head, i.e., the change in height of the HGL. Since the velocity head is constant through the pipe, h_f also equals the height change of the EGL. Recall that the EGL decreases downstream in a flow with losses unless it passes through an energy source, e.g., as a pump or heat exchanger.

Finally apply the momentum relation (3.40) to the control volume in Fig. 6.10, accounting for applied forces due to pressure, gravity, and shear

$$\Delta p\ \pi R^2 + \rho g(\pi R^2)\ \Delta L \sin \phi - \tau_w(2\pi R)\ \Delta L = \dot{m}(V_1 - V_2) = 0 \qquad (6.26)$$

This equation relates h_f to the wall shear stress

$$\Delta z + \frac{\Delta p}{\rho g} = h_f = \frac{2\tau_w}{\rho g}\frac{\Delta L}{R} \qquad (6.27)$$

where we have substituted $\Delta z = \Delta L \sin \phi$ from Fig. 6.10.

So far we have not assumed either laminar or turbulent flow. If we can correlate τ_w with flow conditions, we have solved the problem of head loss in pipe flow. Functionally, we can assume that

$$\tau_w = F(\rho, V, \mu, d, \epsilon) \qquad (6.28)$$

where ϵ is the wall-roughness height. Then dimensional analysis tells us that

$$\frac{8\tau_w}{\rho V^2} = f = F\left(\text{Re}_d, \frac{\epsilon}{d}\right) \tag{6.29}$$

The dimensionless parameter f is called the *Darcy friction factor*, after Henry Darcy (1803–1858), a French engineer whose pipe-flow experiments in 1857 first established the effect of roughness on pipe resistance.

Combining Eqs. (6.27) and (6.29), we obtain the desired expression for finding pipe-head loss

$$h_f = f \frac{L}{d} \frac{V^2}{2g} \tag{6.30}$$

This is the *Darcy-Weisbach equation*, valid for duct flows of any cross section and for laminar and turbulent flow. It was proposed by Julius Weisbach, a German professor who in 1850 published the first modern textbook on hydrodynamics.

Our only remaining problem is to find the form of the function F in Eq. (6.29) and plot it in the Moody chart of Fig. 6.13.

Equations of Motion

For either laminar or turbulent flow, the continuity equation in cylindrical coordinates is given by (App. E)

$$\frac{1}{r} \frac{\partial}{\partial r} (rv_r) + \frac{1}{r} \frac{\partial}{\partial \theta} (v_\theta) + \frac{\partial u}{\partial x} = 0 \tag{6.31}$$

We assume that there is no swirl or circumferential variation, $v_\theta = \partial/\partial\theta = 0$, and fully developed flow: $u = u(r)$ only. Then Eq. (6.31) reduces to

$$\frac{1}{r} \frac{\partial}{\partial r} (rv_r) = 0$$

or
$$rv_r = \text{const} \tag{6.32}$$

But at the wall, $r = R, v_r = 0$ (no slip); therefore (6.32) implies that $v_r = 0$ everywhere. Thus in fully developed flow there is only one velocity component, $u = u(r)$.

The momentum differential equation in cylindrical coordinates now reduces to

$$\rho u \frac{\partial u}{\partial x} = -\frac{dp}{dx} + \rho g_x + \frac{1}{r} \frac{\partial}{\partial r} (r\tau) \tag{6.33}$$

where τ can represent either laminar or turbulent shear. But the left-hand side vanishes because $u = u(r)$ only. Rearrange, noting from Fig. 6.10 that $g_x = g \sin \phi$:

$$\frac{1}{r} \frac{\partial}{\partial r} (r\tau) = \frac{d}{dx} (p - \rho gx \sin \phi) = \frac{d}{dx} (p + \rho gz) \tag{6.34}$$

Since the left-hand side varies only with r and the right-hand side varies only with x, it follows that both sides must be equal to the same constant.[1] Therefore we can integrate Eq. (6.34) to find the shear distribution across the pipe, utilizing the fact that $\tau = 0$ at $r = 0$

$$\tau = \frac{1}{2} r \frac{d}{dx} (p + \rho gz) = (\text{const})(r) \tag{6.35}$$

---

[1] Ask your instructor to explain this to you if necessary.

Thus the shear varies linearly from the centerline to the wall, for either laminar or turbulent flow. This is also shown in Fig. 6.10. At $r = R$, we have the wall shear

$$\tau_w = \frac{1}{2} R \frac{\Delta p + \rho g \, \Delta z}{\Delta L} \tag{6.36}$$

which is identical with our momentum relation (6.27). We can now complete our study of pipe flow by applying either laminar or turbulent assumptions to fill out Eq. (6.35).

Laminar-Flow Solution

Note in Eq. (6.35) that the HGL slope $d(p + \rho g z)/dx$ is *negative* because both pressure and height drop with x. For laminar flow, $\tau = \mu \, du/dr$, which we substitute in Eq. (6.35)

$$\mu \frac{du}{dr} = \frac{1}{2} rK \qquad K = \frac{d}{dx} (p + \rho g z) \tag{6.37}$$

Integrate once

$$u = \frac{1}{4} r^2 \frac{K}{\mu} + C_1 \tag{6.38}$$

The constant C_1 is evaluated from the no-slip condition at the wall: $u = 0$ at $r = R$

$$0 = \frac{1}{4} R^2 \frac{K}{\mu} + C_1 \tag{6.39}$$

or $C_1 = -\frac{1}{4} R^2 K / \mu$. Introduce into Eq. (6.38) to obtain the exact solution for laminar fully developed pipe flow

$$u = \frac{1}{4\mu} \left[-\frac{d}{dx} (p + \rho g z) \right] (R^2 - r^2) \tag{6.40}$$

The laminar-flow profile is thus a paraboloid falling to zero at the wall and reaching a maximum at the axis

$$u_{max} = \frac{R^2}{4\mu} \left[-\frac{d}{dx} (p + \rho g z) \right] \tag{6.41}$$

It resembles the sketch of $u(r)$ given in Fig. 6.10.

The laminar distribution (6.40) is called *Hagen-Poiseuille flow* to commemorate the experimental work of G. Hagen in 1839 and J. L. Poiseuille in 1940, both of whom established the pressure-drop law, Eq. (6.1). The first theoretical derivation of Eq. (6.40) was given independently by E. Hagenbach and by F. Neumann around 1859.

Other pipe-flow results follow immediately from Eq. (6.40). The volume flow is

$$Q = \int u \, dA = \int_0^R u_{max} \left(1 - \frac{r^2}{R^2} \right) 2\pi r \, dr$$

$$= \frac{1}{2} u_{max} \pi R^2 = \frac{\pi R^4}{8\mu} \left[-\frac{d}{dx} (p + \rho g z) \right] \tag{6.42}$$

Thus the average velocity in laminar flow is one-half the maximum velocity

$$V = \frac{Q}{A} = \frac{Q}{\pi R^2} = \frac{1}{2} u_{max} \tag{6.43}$$

For a horizontal tube ($\Delta z = 0$), Eq. (6.42) is of the form predicted by Hagen's experiment, Eq. (6.1):

$$\Delta p = \frac{8\mu L Q}{\pi R^4} \tag{6.44}$$

The wall shear is computed from the wall velocity gradient

$$\tau_w = \left| \mu \frac{du}{dr} \right|_{r=R} = \frac{2\mu u_{max}}{R} = \frac{1}{2} R \left| \frac{d}{dx}(p + \rho g z) \right| \tag{6.45}$$

This gives an exact theory for laminar Darcy friction factor

$$f = \frac{8\tau_w}{\rho V^2} = \frac{8(8\mu V/d)}{\rho V^2} = \frac{64\mu}{\rho V d}$$

or

$$f_{lam} = \frac{64}{Re_d} \tag{6.46}$$

This is plotted in the Moody chart (Fig. 6.13). The fact that f drops off with increasing Re_d should not mislead us into thinking that shear decreases with velocity: Eq. (6.45) clearly shows that τ_w is proportional to u_{max}; it is interesting to note that τ_w is independent of density because the fluid acceleration is zero.

The laminar head loss follows from Eq. (6.30)

$$h_{f,lam} = \frac{64\mu}{\rho V d} \frac{L}{d} \frac{V^2}{2g} = \frac{32\mu L V}{\rho g d^2} = \frac{128\mu L Q}{\pi \rho g d^4} \qquad \frac{4\,Q}{\pi d^2} = V \tag{6.47}$$

We see that laminar head loss is proportional to V.

EXAMPLE 6.4

An oil with $\rho = 900$ kg/m^3 and $\nu = 0.0002$ m^2/s flows upward through an inclined pipe as shown in Fig. E6.4. The pressure and elevation are known at sections 1 and 2, 10 m

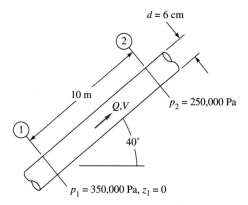

Fig. E6.4

apart. Assuming steady laminar flow, (*a*) verify that the flow is up, (*b*) compute h_f between 1 and 2, and compute (*c*) Q, (*d*) V, and (*e*) Re_d. Is the flow really laminar?

Solution

Part (a) For later use, calculate

$$\mu = \rho\nu = (900 \text{ kg/m}^3)(0.0002 \text{ m}^2/\text{s}) = 0.18 \text{ kg/(m} \cdot \text{s)}$$

$$z_2 = \Delta L \sin 40° = (10 \text{ m})(0.643) = 6.43 \text{ m}$$

The flow goes in the direction of falling HGL; therefore compute the grade-line height at each section

$$\text{HGL}_1 = z_1 + \frac{p_1}{\rho g} = 0 + \frac{350{,}000}{900(9.807)} = 39.65 \text{ m}$$

$$\text{HGL}_2 = z_2 + \frac{p_2}{\rho g} = 6.43 + \frac{250{,}000}{900(9.807)} = 34.75 \text{ m}$$

The HGL is lower at section 2; hence the flow is from 1 to 2 as assumed.   *Ans. (a)*

Part (b) The head loss is the change in HGL:

$$h_f = \text{HGL}_1 - \text{HGL}_2 = 39.65 \text{ m} - 34.75 \text{ m} = 4.9 \text{ m} \qquad \textit{Ans. (b)}$$

Half the length of the pipe is quite a large head loss.

Part (c) We can compute Q from the various laminar-flow formulas, notably Eq. (6.47)

$$Q = \frac{\pi \rho g d^4 h_f}{128 \mu L} = \frac{\pi(900)(9.807)(0.06)^4(4.9)}{128(0.18)(10)} = 0.0076 \text{ m}^3/\text{s} \qquad \textit{Ans. (c)}$$

Part (d) Divide Q by the pipe area to get the average velocity

$$V = \frac{Q}{\pi R^2} = \frac{0.0076}{\pi(0.03)^2} = 2.7 \text{ m/s} \qquad \textit{Ans. (d)}$$

Part (e) With V known, the Reynolds number is

$$\text{Re}_d = \frac{Vd}{\nu} = \frac{2.7(0.06)}{0.0002} = 810 \qquad \textit{Ans. (e)}$$

This is well below the transition value $\text{Re}_d = 2300$, and so we are fairly certain the flow is laminar.

Notice that by sticking entirely to consistent SI units (meters, seconds, kilograms, newtons) for all variables we avoid the need for any conversion factors in the calculations.

EXAMPLE 6.5

A liquid of specific weight $\rho g = 58 \text{ lb/ft}^3$ flows by gravity through a 1-ft tank and a 1-ft capillary tube at a rate of 0.15 ft³/h, as shown in Fig. E6.5. Sections 1 and 2 are at atmospheric pressure. Neglecting entrance effects, compute the viscosity of the liquid.

Solution

Apply the steady-flow energy equation (6.24), including the correction factor α:

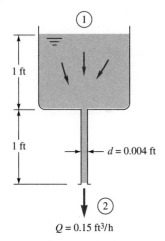

$Q = 0.15 \text{ ft}^3/\text{h}$

Fig. E6.5

$$\frac{p_1}{\rho g} + \frac{\alpha_1 V_1^2}{2g} + z_1 = \frac{p_2}{\rho g} + \frac{\alpha_2 V_2^2}{2g} + z_2 + h_f$$

The average exit velocity V_2 can be found from the volume flow and the pipe size:

$$V_2 = \frac{Q}{A_2} = \frac{Q}{\pi R^2} = \frac{(0.15/3600) \text{ ft}^3/\text{s}}{\pi (0.002 \text{ ft})^2} \approx 3.32 \text{ ft/s}$$

Meanwhile $p_1 = p_2 = p_a$, and $V_1 \approx 0$ in the large tank. Therefore, approximately,

$$h_f \approx z_1 - z_2 - \alpha_2 \frac{V_2^2}{2g} = 2.0 \text{ ft} - 2.0 \frac{(3.32 \text{ ft/s})^2}{2(32.2 \text{ ft/s}^2)} \approx 1.66 \text{ ft}$$

where we have introduced $\alpha_2 = 2.0$ for laminar pipe flow from Eq. (3.72). Note that h_f includes the entire 2-ft drop through the system and not just the 1-ft pipe length.

With the head loss known, the viscosity follows from our laminar-flow formula (6.47):

$$h_f = 1.66 \text{ ft} = \frac{32\mu LV}{\rho g d^2} = \frac{32\mu(1.0 \text{ ft})(3.32 \text{ ft/s})}{(58 \text{ lbf/ft}^3)(0.004 \text{ ft})^2} = 114{,}500 \, \mu$$

or

$$\mu = \frac{1.66}{114{,}500} = 1.45 \text{ E-5 slug}/(\text{ft} \cdot \text{s}) \qquad \qquad Ans.$$

Note that L in this formula is the *pipe* length of 1 ft. Finally, check the Reynolds number:

$$\text{Re}_d = \frac{\rho V d}{\mu} = \frac{(58/32.2 \text{ slug/ft}^3)(3.32 \text{ ft/s})(0.004 \text{ ft})}{1.45 \text{ E-5 slug}/(\text{ft} \cdot \text{s})} = 1650 \qquad \text{laminar}$$

Since this is less than 2300, we conclude that the flow is indeed laminar. Actually, for this head loss, there is a *second* (turbulent) solution, as we shall see in Example 6.8.

Turbulent-Flow Solution

For turbulent pipe flow we need not solve a differential equation but instead proceed with the logarithmic law, as in Example 6.3. Assume that Eq. (6.21) correlates the local mean velocity $u(r)$ all the way across the pipe

$$\frac{u(r)}{u^*} \approx \frac{1}{\kappa} \ln \frac{(R - r)u^*}{\nu} + B \qquad \qquad (6.48)$$

where we have replaced y by $R - r$. Compute the average velocity from this profile

$$V = \frac{Q}{A} = \frac{1}{\pi R^2} \int_0^R u^* \left[\frac{1}{\kappa} \ln \frac{(R - r)u^*}{\nu} + B \right] 2\pi r \, dr$$

$$= \frac{1}{2} u^* \left(\frac{2}{\kappa} \ln \frac{Ru^*}{\nu} + 2B - \frac{3}{\kappa} \right) \qquad \qquad (6.49)$$

Introducing $\kappa = 0.41$ and $B = 5.0$, we obtain, numerically,

$$\frac{V}{u^*} \approx 2.44 \ln \frac{Ru^*}{\nu} + 1.34 \qquad \qquad (6.50)$$

This looks only marginally interesting until we realize that V/u^* is directly related to the Darcy friction factor

$$\frac{V}{u^*} = \left(\frac{\rho V^2}{\tau_w}\right)^{1/2} = \left(\frac{8}{f}\right)^{1/2} \tag{6.51}$$

Moreover, the argument of the logarithm in (6.50) is equivalent to

$$\frac{Ru^*}{\nu} = \frac{\frac{1}{2}Vd}{\nu}\frac{u^*}{V} = \frac{1}{2}\,\mathrm{Re}_d\left(\frac{f}{8}\right)^{1/2} \tag{6.52}$$

Introducing (6.52) and (6.51) into Eq. (6.50), changing to a base-10 logarithm, and rearranging, we obtain

$$\frac{1}{f^{1/2}} \approx 1.99 \log\,(\mathrm{Re}_d f^{1/2}) - 1.02 \tag{6.53}$$

In other words, by simply computing the mean velocity from the logarithmic-law correlation, we obtain a relation between the friction factor and Reynolds number for turbulent pipe flow. Prandtl derived Eq. (6.53) in 1935 and then adjusted the constants slightly to fit friction data better

$$\frac{1}{f^{1/2}} = 2.0 \log\,(\mathrm{Re}_d f^{1/2}) - 0.8 \tag{6.54}$$

This is the accepted formula for a smooth-walled pipe. Some numerical values may be listed as follows:

Re_d	4000	10^4	10^5	10^6	10^7	10^8
f	0.0399	0.0309	0.0180	0.0116	0.0081	0.0059

Thus f drops by only a factor of 5 over a 10,000-fold increase in Reynolds number. Equation (6.54) is cumbersome to solve if Re_d is known and f is wanted. There are many alternate approximations in the literature from which f can be computed explicitly from Re_d

$$f = \begin{cases} 0.316\,\mathrm{Re}_d^{-1/4} & 4000 < \mathrm{Re}_d < 10^5 \quad \text{H. Blasius (1911)} \\[2mm] \left(1.8 \log \dfrac{\mathrm{Re}_d}{6.9}\right)^{-2} & \text{Ref. 9} \end{cases} \tag{6.55}$$

Blasius, a student of Prandtl, presented his formula in the first correlation ever made of pipe friction versus Reynolds number. Although his formula has a limited range, it illustrates what was happening to Hagen's 1839 pressure-drop data. For a horizontal pipe, from Eq. (6.55),

$$h_f = \frac{\Delta p}{\rho g} = f\,\frac{L}{d}\frac{V^2}{2g} \approx 0.316\left(\frac{\mu}{\rho Vd}\right)^{1/4}\frac{L}{d}\frac{V^2}{2g}$$

or

$$\Delta p \approx 0.158\,L\rho^{3/4}\mu^{1/4}d^{-5/4}V^{7/4} \tag{6.56}$$

at low turbulent Reynolds numbers. This explains why Hagen's data for pressure drop begin to increase as the 1.75 power of the velocity, in Fig. 6.4. Note that Δp varies only slightly with viscosity, which is characteristic of turbulent flow. Introducing $Q = \frac{1}{4}\pi d^2 V$ into Eq. (6.56), we obtain the alternate form

$$\Delta p \approx 0.241 L\rho^{3/4}\mu^{1/4}d^{-4.75}Q^{1.75} \tag{6.57}$$

For a given flow rate Q, the turbulent pressure drop decreases with diameter even more sharply than the laminar formula (6.47). Thus the quickest way to reduce required pumping pressure is to increase the pipe size, although, of course, the larger pipe is more expensive. Doubling the pipe size decreases Δp by a factor of about 27 for a given Q. Compare Eq. (6.56) with Example 5.7 and Fig. 5.10.

The maximum velocity in turbulent pipe flow is given by Eq. (6.48), evaluated at $r = 0$

$$\frac{u_{max}}{u^*} \approx \frac{1}{\kappa} \ln \frac{Ru^*}{\nu} + B \qquad (6.58)$$

Combining this with Eq. (6.49), we obtain the formula relating mean velocity to maximum velocity

$$\frac{V}{u_{max}} \approx (1 + 1.33\sqrt{f})^{-1} \qquad (6.59)$$

Some numerical values are

Re_d	4000	10^4	10^5	10^6	10^7	10^8
V/u_{max}	0.790	0.811	0.849	0.875	0.893	0.907

The ratio varies with the Reynolds number and is much larger than the value of 0.5 predicted for all laminar pipe flow in Eq. (6.43). Thus a turbulent velocity profile, as shown in Fig. 6.11, is very flat in the center and drops off sharply to zero at the wall.

Effect of Rough Walls

It was not known until experiments in 1800 by Coulomb [6] that surface roughness has an effect on friction resistance. It turns out that the effect is negligible for laminar pipe flow, and all the laminar formulas derived in this section are valid for rough walls also. But turbulent flow is strongly affected by roughness. In Fig. 6.9 the linear viscous sublayer only extends out to $y^+ = yu^*/\nu = 5$. Thus, compared with the diameter, the sublayer thickness y_s is only

$$\frac{y_s}{d} = \frac{5\nu/u^*}{d} = \frac{14.1}{Re_d f^{1/2}} \qquad (6.60)$$

Fig. 6.11 Comparison of laminar and turbulent pipe-flow velocity profiles for the same volume flow: (a) laminar flow; (b) turbulent flow.

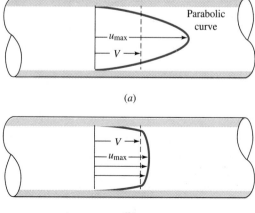

(a)

(b)

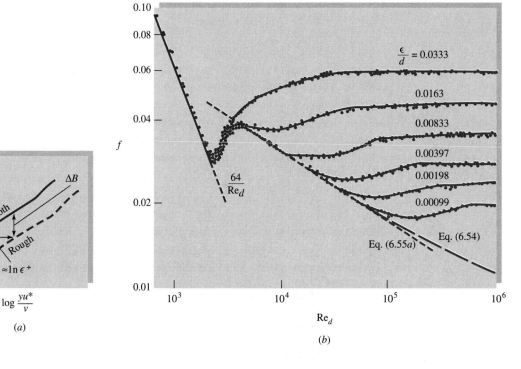

(a)

(b)

Fig. 6.12 Effect of wall roughness on turbulent pipe flow. (*a*) The logarithmic overlap-velocity profile shifts down and to the right; (*b*) experiments with sand-grain roughness by Nikuradse [7] shows a systematic increase of the turbulent friction factor with the roughness ratio.

For example, at $Re_d = 10^5$, $f = 0.0180$, $y_s/d = 0.001$. A wall roughness of about $0.001d$ will break up the sublayer and profoundly change the wall law in Fig. 6.9.

Measurements of $u(y)$ in turbulent rough-wall flow by Prandtl's student Nikuradse [7] show, as in Fig. 6.12a, that a roughness height ϵ will force the logarithm-law profile outward on the abscissa by an amount approximately equal to $\ln \epsilon^+$, where $\epsilon^+ = \epsilon u^*/\nu$. The slope of the logarithm law remains the same, $1/\kappa$, but the shift outward causes the constant B to be less by an amount $\Delta B \approx (1/\kappa) \ln \epsilon^+$.

Nikuradse [7] simulated roughness by gluing uniform sand grains onto the inner walls of the pipes. He then measured the pressure drops and flow rates and correlated friction factor versus Reynolds number in Fig. 6.12b. We see that laminar friction is unaffected, but turbulent friction, after an *onset* point, increases monotonically with the roughness ratio ϵ/d. For any given ϵ/d, the friction factor becomes constant (*fully rough*) at high Reynolds numbers. These points of change are certain values of $\epsilon^+ = \epsilon u^*/\nu$:

$$\frac{\epsilon u^*}{\nu} < 5: \quad \textit{hydraulically smooth} \text{ walls, no effect of roughness on friction}$$

$$5 < \frac{\epsilon u^*}{\nu} < 70: \quad \textit{transitional} \text{ roughness, moderate Reynolds-number effect}$$

$$\frac{\epsilon u^*}{\nu} > 70: \quad \textit{fully rough} \text{ flow, sublayer totally broken up and friction independent of Reynolds number}$$

For fully rough flow, $\epsilon^+ > 70$, the log-law downshift ΔB in Fig. 6.12a is

$$\Delta B \approx \frac{1}{\kappa} \ln \epsilon^+ - 3.5 \qquad (6.61)$$

and the logarithm law modified for roughness becomes

$$u^+ = \frac{1}{\kappa} \ln y^+ + B - \Delta B = \frac{1}{\kappa} \ln \frac{y}{\epsilon} + 8.5 \qquad (6.62)$$

The viscosity vanishes, and hence fully rough flow is independent of the Reynolds number. If we integrate Eq. (6.62) to obtain the average velocity in the pipe, we obtain

$$\frac{V}{u^*} = 2.44 \ln \frac{d}{\epsilon} + 3.2$$

or

$$\frac{1}{f^{1/2}} = -2.0 \log \frac{\epsilon/d}{3.7} \qquad \text{fully rough flow} \qquad (6.63)$$

There is no Reynolds-number effect; hence the head loss varies exactly as the square of the velocity in this case. Some numerical values of friction factor may be listed:

ϵ/d	0.00001	0.0001	0.001	0.01	0.05
f	0.00806	0.0120	0.0196	0.0379	0.0716

The friction factor increases by 9 times as the roughness increases by a factor of 5000. In the transitional-roughness region, sand grains behave somewhat differently from commercially rough pipes, so Fig. 6.12b has now been replaced by the Moody chart.

The Moody Chart

In 1939 to cover the transitionally rough range, Colebrook [9] combined the smooth-wall [Eq. (6.54)] and fully rough [Eq. (6.63)] relations into a clever interpolation formula

$$\frac{1}{f^{1/2}} = -2.0 \log \left(\frac{\epsilon/d}{3.7} + \frac{2.51}{\mathrm{Re}_d f^{1/2}} \right) \qquad (6.64)$$

This is the accepted design formula for turbulent friction. It was plotted in 1944 by Moody [8] into what is now called the *Moody chart* for pipe friction (Fig. 6.13). The Moody chart is probably the most famous and useful figure in fluid mechanics. It is accurate to ± 15 percent for design calculations over the full range shown in Fig. 6.13. It can be used for circular and noncircular (Sec. 6.6) pipe flows and for open-channel flows (Chap. 10). The data can even be adapted as an approximation to boundary-layer flows (Chap. 7).

Equation (6.64) is cumbersome to evaluate for f if Re_d is known. An alternate explicit formula given by Haaland [33] as

$$\frac{1}{f^{1/2}} \approx -1.8 \log \left[\frac{6.9}{\mathrm{Re}_d} + \left(\frac{\epsilon/d}{3.7} \right)^{1.11} \right] \qquad (6.64a)$$

varies less than 2 percent from Eq. (6.64).

The shaded area in the Moody chart indicates the range where transition from laminar to turbulent flow occurs. There are no reliable friction factors in this range, $2000 < \mathrm{Re}_d < 4000$. Notice that the roughness curves are nearly horizontal in the fully rough regime to the right of the dashed line.

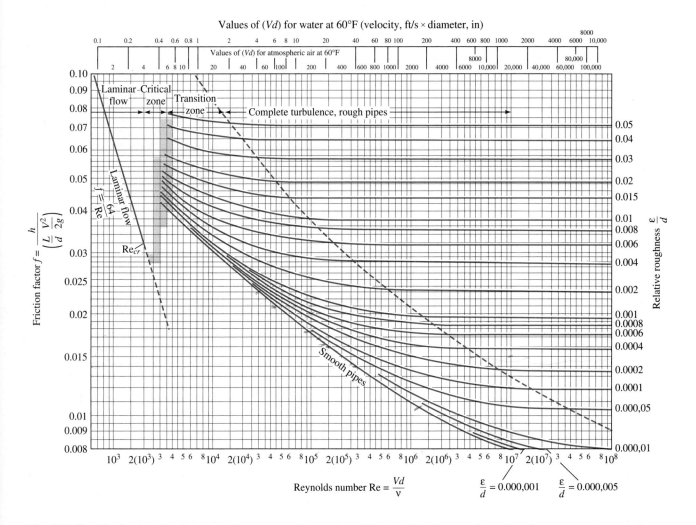

Fig. 6.13 The Moody chart for pipe friction with smooth and rough walls. This chart is identical to Eq. (6.64) for turbulent flow. (*From Ref. 8, by permission of the ASME.*)

From tests with commercial pipes Moody gave the values for average pipe roughness listed in Table 6.1.

Table 6.1 Average Roughness of Commercial Pipes

Material (new)	ϵ ft	ϵ mm
Riveted steel	0.003–0.03	0.9–9.0
Concrete	0.001–0.01	0.3–3.0
Wood stave	0.0006–0.003	0.18–0.9
Cast iron	0.00085	0.26
Galvanized iron	0.0005	0.15
Asphalted cast iron	0.0004	0.12
Commercial steel or wrought iron	0.00015	0.046
Drawn tubing	0.000005	0.0015
Glass	"Smooth"	"Smooth"

EXAMPLE 6.6[1]

Compute the loss of head and pressure drop in 200 ft of horizontal 6-in-diameter asphalted cast-iron pipe carrying water with a mean velocity of 6 ft/s.

Solution

One can estimate the Reynolds number of water and air from the Moody chart. Look across the top of the chart to V (ft/s) $\times$ d (in) $=$ 36, and then look directly down to the bottom abscissa to find that Re_d(water) $\approx 2.7 \times 10^5$. The roughness ratio for asphalted cast iron ($\epsilon = 0.0004$ ft) is

$$\frac{\epsilon}{d} = \frac{0.0004}{\frac{6}{12}} = 0.0008$$

Find the line on the right side for $\epsilon/d = 0.0008$, and follow it to the left until it intersects the vertical line for Re $= 2.7 \times 10^5$. Read, approximately, $f = 0.02$ [or compute $f = 0.0197$ from Eq. (6.64a)]. Then the head loss is

$$h_f = f \frac{L}{d} \frac{V^2}{2g} = (0.02) \frac{200}{0.5} \frac{(6 \text{ ft/s})^2}{2(32.2 \text{ ft/s}^2)} = 4.5 \text{ ft} \qquad Ans.$$

The pressure drop for a horizontal pipe ($z_1 = z_2$) is

$$\Delta p = \rho g h_f = (62.4 \text{ lbf/ft}^3)(4.5 \text{ ft}) = 280 \text{ lbf/ft}^2 \qquad Ans.$$

Moody points out that this computation, even for clean new pipe, can be considered accurately only to about ± 10 percent.

EXAMPLE 6.7

Oil, with $\rho = 900$ kg/m^3 and $\nu = 0.00001$ m^2/s, flows at 0.2 m^3/s through 500 m of 200-mm-diameter cast-iron pipe. Determine (*a*) the head loss and (*b*) the pressure drop if the pipe slopes down at 10° in the flow direction.

Solution

First compute the velocity from the known flow rate

$$V = \frac{Q}{\pi R^2} = \frac{0.2 \text{ m}^3/\text{s}}{\pi (0.1 \text{ m})^2} = 6.4 \text{ m/s}$$

Then the Reynolds number is

$$Re_d = \frac{Vd}{\nu} = \frac{(6.4 \text{ m/s})(0.2 \text{ m})}{0.00001 \text{ m}^2/\text{s}} = 128,000$$

From Table 6.1, $\epsilon = 0.26$ mm for cast-iron pipe. Then

$$\frac{\epsilon}{d} = \frac{0.26 \text{ mm}}{200 \text{ mm}} = 0.0013$$

[1] This example was given by Moody in his 1944 paper [8].

Enter the Moody chart on the right at $\epsilon/d = 0.0013$ (you will have to interpolate), and move to the left to intersect with Re $= 128,000$. Read $f \approx 0.0225$ [from Eq. (6.64) for these values we could compute $f = 0.0227$]. Then the head loss is

$$h_f = f\frac{L}{d}\frac{V^2}{2g} = (0.0225)\frac{500 \text{ m}}{0.2 \text{ m}}\frac{(6.4 \text{ m/s})^2}{2(9.81 \text{ m/s}^2)} = 117 \text{ m} \qquad Ans. (a)$$

From Eq. (6.25) for the inclined pipe,

$$h_f = \frac{\Delta p}{\rho g} + z_1 - z_2 = \frac{\Delta p}{\rho g} + L\sin 10°$$

or $\quad \Delta p = \rho g[h_f - (500 \text{ m})\sin 10°] = \rho g(117 \text{ m} - 87 \text{ m})$

$$= (900 \text{ kg/m}^3)(9.81 \text{ m/s}^2)(30 \text{ m}) = 265,000 \text{ kg/(m} \cdot \text{s}^2) = 265,000 \text{ Pa} \quad Ans. (b)$$

EXAMPLE 6.8

Repeat Example 6.5 to see whether there is any possible turbulent-flow solution for a smooth-walled pipe.

Solution

In Example 6.5 we estimated a head loss $h_f \approx 1.66$ ft, assuming laminar exit flow ($\alpha \approx 2.0$). For this condition the friction factor is

$$f = h_f\frac{d}{L}\frac{2g}{V^2} = (1.66 \text{ ft})\frac{(0.004 \text{ ft})(2)(32.2 \text{ ft/s}^2)}{(1.0 \text{ ft})(3.32 \text{ ft/s})^2} \approx 0.0388$$

For laminar flow, $\text{Re}_d = 64/f = 64/0.0388 \approx 1650$, as we showed in Example 6.5. However, from the Moody chart (Fig. 6.13), we see that $f = 0.0388$ also corresponds to a *turbulent* smooth-wall condition, at $\text{Re}_d \approx 4500$. If the flow actually were turbulent, we should change our kinetic-energy factor to $\alpha \approx 1.06$ [Eq. (3.73)], whence the corrected $h_f \approx 1.82$ ft and $f \approx 0.0425$. With f known, we can estimate the Reynolds number from our formulas:

$$\text{Re}_d \approx 3250 \quad [\text{Eq. (6.54)}] \qquad \text{or} \qquad \text{Re}_d \approx 3400 \quad [\text{Eq. (6.55b)}]$$

So the flow *might* have been turbulent, in which case the viscosity of the fluid would have been

$$\mu = \frac{\rho V d}{\text{Re}_d} = \frac{1.80(3.32)(0.004)}{3300} = 7.2 \times 10^{-6} \text{ slug/(ft} \cdot \text{s)} \qquad Ans.$$

This is about 55 percent less than our laminar estimate in Example 6.5. The moral is to keep the capillary-flow Reynolds number below about 1000 to avoid such duplicate solutions.

6.5 Three Types of Pipe-Flow Problems

The Moody chart (Fig. 6.13) can be used to solve almost any problem involving friction losses in long pipe flows. However, many such problems involve considerable iteration and repeated calculations using the chart because the standard Moody chart is essentially a *head-loss chart*. One is supposed to know all other variables, compute Re_d, enter the chart, find f, and hence compute h_f. This is one of three fundamental problems which are commonly encountered in pipe-flow calculations:

1. Given d, L, and V or Q, ρ, μ, and g, compute the head loss h_f (head-loss problem).
2. Given d, L, h_f, ρ, μ, and g, compute the velocity V or flow rate Q (flow-rate problem).
3. Given Q, L, h_f, ρ, μ, and g, compute the diameter d of the pipe (sizing problem).

Only problem 1 is well suited to the Moody chart. We have to iterate to compute velocity or diameter because both d and V are contained in the ordinate *and* the abscissa of the chart.

Type 2 Problem:
Find the Flow Rate

Even though velocity (or flow rate) appears in both the ordinate and the abscissa on the Moody chart, iteration for turbulent flow is nevertheless quite fast, because f varies so slowly with Re_d. Alternately, in the spirit of Example 5.7, we could change the scaling variables to (ρ, μ, d) and thus arrive at dimensionless head loss versus dimensionless *velocity*. The result is[1]

$$\zeta = \text{fcn}(Re_d) \qquad \text{where} \qquad \zeta = \frac{gd^3 h_f}{L\nu^2} = \frac{f\, Re_d^2}{2} \tag{6.65}$$

Example 5.7 did this and offered the simple correlation $\zeta \approx 0.155\, Re_d^{1.75}$, which is valid for turbulent flow with smooth walls and $Re_d \leq 1$ E5.

A formula valid for all turbulent pipe flows is found by simply rewriting the Colebrook interpolation, Eq. (6.64), in the form of Eq. (6.65):

$$Re_d = -(8\zeta)^{1/2} \log\left(\frac{\epsilon/d}{3.7} + \frac{1.775}{\sqrt{\zeta}}\right) \qquad \zeta = \frac{gd^3 h_f}{L\nu^2} \tag{6.66}$$

Given ζ, we compute Re_d (and hence velocity) directly. Let us illustrate these two approaches with the following example.

EXAMPLE 6.9

Oil, with $\rho = 950$ kg/m^3 and $\nu = 2$ E-5 m^2/s, flows through a 30-cm-diameter pipe 100 m long with a head loss of 8 m. The roughness ratio is $\epsilon/d = 0.0002$. Find the average velocity and flow rate.

Direct Solution

First calculate the dimensionless head-loss parameter:

$$\zeta = \frac{gd^3 h_f}{L\nu^2} = \frac{(9.81 \text{ m/s}^2)(0.3 \text{ m})^3(8.0 \text{ m})}{(100 \text{ m})(2 \text{ E-5 m}^2/\text{s})^2} = 5.30 \text{ E7}$$

Now enter Eq. (6.66) to find the Reynolds number:

$$Re_d = -[8(5.3 \text{ E7})]^{1/2} \log\left(\frac{0.0002}{3.7} + \frac{1.775}{\sqrt{5.3 \text{ E7}}}\right) = 72{,}600$$

---

[1] The parameter ζ was suggested by H. Rouse in 1942.

The velocity and flow rate follow from the Reynolds number:

$$V = \frac{\nu \, \text{Re}_d}{d} = \frac{(2 \text{ E-5 m}^2/\text{s})(72{,}600)}{0.3 \text{ m}} \approx 4.84 \text{ m/s}$$

$$Q = V \frac{\pi}{4} d^2 = \left(4.84 \, \frac{\text{m}}{\text{s}}\right) \frac{\pi}{4} (0.3 \text{ m})^2 \approx 0.342 \text{ m}^3/\text{s} \qquad \qquad \textit{Ans.}$$

No iteration is required, but this idea falters if additional losses are present.

Iterative Solution

By definition, the friction factor is known except for V:

$$f = h_f \frac{d}{L} \frac{2g}{V^2} = (8 \text{ m})\left(\frac{0.3 \text{ m}}{100 \text{ m}}\right)\left[\frac{2(9.81 \text{ m/s}^2)}{V^2}\right] \qquad \text{or} \qquad fV^2 \approx 0.471 \qquad \text{(SI units)}$$

To get started, we only need to guess f, compute $V = \sqrt{0.471/f}$, then get Re_d, compute a better f from the Moody chart, and repeat. The process converges fairly rapidly. A good first guess is the "fully rough" value for $\epsilon/d = 0.0002$, or $f \approx 0.014$ from Fig. 6.13. The iteration would be as follows:

Guess $f \approx 0.014$, then $V = \sqrt{0.471/0.014} = 5.80$ m/s and $\text{Re}_d = Vd/\nu \approx 87{,}000$. At $\text{Re}_d = 87{,}000$ and $\epsilon/d = 0.0002$, compute $f_{\text{new}} \approx 0.0195$ [Eq. (6.64)].

New $f \approx 0.0195$, $V = \sqrt{0.481/0.0195} = 4.91$ m/s, then $\text{Re}_d = Vd/\nu = 73{,}700$. At $\text{Re}_d = 73{,}700$ and $\epsilon/d = 0.0002$, compute $f_{\text{new}} \approx 0.0201$ [Eq. (6.54)].

Better $f \approx 0.0201$, $V = \sqrt{0.471/0.0201} = 4.84$ m/s and $\text{Re}_d \approx 72{,}600$. At $\text{Re}_d = 72{,}600$ and $\epsilon/d = 0.0002$, compute $f_{\text{new}} \approx 0.0201$ [Eq. (6.54)].

We have converged to three significant figures. Thus our iterative solution is

$$V = 4.84 \text{ m/s}$$

$$Q = V\left(\frac{\pi}{4}\right)d^2 = (4.84)\left(\frac{\pi}{4}\right)(0.3)^2 \approx 0.342 \text{ m}^3/\text{s} \qquad \qquad \textit{Ans.}$$

The iterative approach is straightforward and not too onerous, so it is routinely used by engineers. Obviously this repetitive procedure is ideal for a personal computer.

EXAMPLE 6.10

Work Moody's problem (Example 6.6) backward, assuming that the head loss of 4.5 ft is known and the velocity (6.0 ft/s) is unknown.

Direct Solution

Find the parameter ζ, and compute the Reynolds number from Eq. (6.66):

$$\zeta = \frac{gd^3 h_f}{L\nu^2} = \frac{(32.2 \text{ ft/s}^2)(0.5 \text{ ft})^3(4.5 \text{ ft})}{(200 \text{ ft})(1.1 \text{ E-5 ft}^2/\text{s})^2} = 7.48 \text{ E8}$$

Eq. (6.66): $\text{Re}_d = -[8(7.48\ \text{E8})]^{1/2}\ \log\left(\dfrac{0.0008}{3.7} + \dfrac{1.775}{\sqrt{7.48\ \text{E8})}}\right) \approx 274{,}800$

Then
$$V = \nu\,\frac{\text{Re}_d}{d} = \frac{(1.1\ \text{E-5})(274{,}800)}{0.5} \approx 6.05\ \text{ft/s} \qquad\qquad Ans.$$

We did not get 6.0 ft/s exactly because the 4.5-ft head loss was rounded off in Example 6.6.

Iterative Solution

As in Eq. (6.9) the friction factor is related to velocity:

$$f = h_f\,\frac{d}{L}\,\frac{2g}{V^2} = (4.5\ \text{ft})\left(\frac{0.5\ \text{ft}}{200\ \text{ft}}\right)\left[\frac{2(32.2\ \text{ft/s}^2)}{V^2}\right] \approx \frac{0.7245}{V^2}$$

or
$$V = \sqrt{0.7245/f}$$

Knowing $\epsilon/d = 0.0008$, we can guess f and iterate until the velocity converges. Begin with the fully rough estimate $f \approx 0.019$ from Fig. 6.13. The resulting iterates are

$f_1 = 0.019:$ $V_1 = \sqrt{0.7245/f_1} = 6.18\ \text{ft/s}$ $\text{Re}_{d1} = \dfrac{Vd}{\nu} = 280{,}700$

$f_2 = 0.0198:$ $V_2 = 6.05\ \text{ft/s}$ $\text{Re}_{d_2} = 274{,}900$

$f_3 = 0.01982:$ $V_3 = 6.046\ \text{ft/s}$ $\qquad\qquad\qquad\qquad\qquad Ans.$

The calculation converges rather quickly to the same result as that obtained through direct computation.

Type 3 Problem: Find the Pipe Diameter

The Moody chart is especially awkward for finding the pipe size, since d occurs in all three parameters f, Re_d, and ϵ/d. Further, it depends upon whether we know the velocity or the flow rate. We cannot know both, or else we could immediately compute $d = \sqrt{4Q/(\pi V)}$.

Let us assume that we know the flow rate Q. Note that this requires us to redefine the Reynolds number in terms of Q:

$$\text{Re}_d = \frac{Vd}{\nu} = \frac{4Q}{\pi d\nu} \tag{6.67}$$

Then, if we choose (Q, ρ, μ) as scaling parameters (to eliminate d), we obtain the functional relationship

$$\text{Re}_d = \frac{4Q}{\pi d\nu} = \text{fcn}\left(\frac{gh_f}{L\nu^5}, \frac{\epsilon\nu}{Q}\right) \tag{6.68}$$

and can thus solve d when the right-hand side is known. Unfortunately, the writer knows of no *formula* for this relation, nor is he able to rearrange Eq. (6.64) into the explicit form of Eq. (6.68). One could recalculate and *plot* the relation, and indeed an ingenious "pipe-sizing" plot is given in Ref. 13. Here it seems reasonable to forgo a plot or curve fitted formula and to simply set up the problem as an iteration in terms of the Moody-chart variables. In this case we also have to set up the friction factor in terms of the flow rate:

$$f = h_f \frac{d}{L} \frac{2g}{V^2} = \frac{\pi^2}{8} \frac{g h_f d^5}{L Q^2} \tag{6.69}$$

The following two examples illustrate the iteration.

EXAMPLE 6.11

Work Example 6.9 backward, assuming that $Q = 0.342$ m^3/s and $\epsilon = 0.06$ mm are known but that d (30 cm) is unknown. Recall $L = 100$ m, $\rho = 950$ kg/m^3, $\nu = 2$ E-5 m^2/s, and $h_f = 8$ m.

Iterative Solution

First write the diameter in terms of the friction factor:

$$f = \frac{\pi^2}{8} \frac{(9.81 \text{ m/s}^2)(8 \text{ m})d^5}{(100 \text{ m})(0.342 \text{ m}^3/\text{s})^2} = 8.28d^5 \qquad \text{or} \qquad d \approx 0.655f^{1/5} \tag{1}$$

in SI units. Also write the Reynolds number and roughness ratio in terms of the diameter:

$$\text{Re}_d = \frac{4(0.342 \text{ m}^3/\text{s})}{\pi(2 \text{ E-5 m}^2/\text{s})d} = \frac{21{,}800}{d} \tag{2}$$

$$\frac{\epsilon}{d} = \frac{6 \text{ E-5 m}}{d} \tag{3}$$

Guess f, compute d from (1), then compute Re_d from (2) and ϵ/d from (3), and compute a better f from the Moody chart or Eq. (6.64). Repeat until (fairly rapid) convergence. Having no initial estimate for f, the writer guesses $f \approx 0.03$ (about in the middle of the turbulent portion of the Moody chart). The following calculations result:

$$f \approx 0.03 \qquad d \approx 0.655(0.03)^{1/5} \approx 0.325 \text{ m}$$

$$\text{Re}_d \approx \frac{21{,}800}{0.325} \approx 67{,}000 \qquad \frac{\epsilon}{d} \approx 1.85 \text{ E-4}$$

Eq. (6.54): $\qquad f_{\text{new}} \approx 0.0203 \qquad \text{then} \qquad d_{\text{new}} \approx 0.301 \text{ m}$

$$\text{Re}_{d,\text{new}} \approx 72{,}500 \qquad \frac{\epsilon}{d} \approx 2.0 \text{ E-4}$$

Eq. (6.54): $\qquad f_{\text{better}} \approx 0.0201 \qquad \text{and} \qquad d = 0.300 \text{ m}$ *Ans.*

The procedure has converged to the correct diameter of 30 cm given in Example 6.9.

EXAMPLE 6.12

Work Moody's problem, Example 6.6, backward to find the unknown (6 in) diameter if the flow rate $Q = 1.18$ ft^3/s is known. Recall $L = 200$ ft, $\epsilon = 0.0004$ ft, and $\nu = 1.1$ E-5 ft^2/s.

Solution

Write f, Re_d, and ϵ/d in terms of the diameter:

$$f = \frac{\pi^2}{8} \frac{gh_f d^5}{LQ^2} = \frac{\pi^2}{8} \frac{(32.2 \text{ ft/s}^2)(4.5 \text{ ft})d^5}{(200 \text{ ft})(1.18 \text{ ft}^3/\text{s})^2} = 0.642d^5 \qquad \text{or} \qquad d \approx 1.093 f^{1/5} \qquad (1)$$

$$Re_d = \frac{4(1.18 \text{ ft}^3/\text{s})}{\pi(1.1 \text{ E-5 ft}^2/\text{s})\, d} = \frac{136{,}600}{d} \qquad (2)$$

$$\frac{\epsilon}{d} = \frac{0.0004 \text{ ft}}{d} \qquad (3)$$

with everything in BG units, of course. Guess f; compute d from (1), Re_d from (2), and ϵ/d from (3); and then compute a better f from the Moody chart. Repeat until convergence. The writer traditionally guesses an initial $f \approx 0.03$:

$$f \approx 0.03 \qquad d \approx 1.093(0.03)^{1/5} \approx 0.542 \text{ ft}$$

$$Re_d = \frac{136{,}600}{0.542} \approx 252{,}000 \qquad \frac{\epsilon}{d} \approx 7.38 \text{ E-4}$$

$$f_{\text{new}} \approx 0.0196 \qquad d_{\text{new}} \approx 0.498 \text{ ft} \qquad Re_d \approx 274{,}000 \qquad \frac{\epsilon}{d} \approx 8.03 \text{ E-4}$$

$$f_{\text{better}} \approx 0.0198 \qquad d \approx 0.499 \text{ ft} \qquad\qquad\qquad\qquad\qquad Ans.$$

Convergence is rapid, and the predicted diameter is correct, about 6 in. The slight discrepancy (0.499 rather than 0.500 ft) arises because h_f was rounded to 4.5 ft.

In discussing pipe-sizing problems, we should remark that commercial pipes are made only in certain sizes. Table 6.2 lists standard water-pipe sizes in the United States. If the sizing calculation gives an intermediate diameter, the next largest pipe size should be selected.

Table 6.2 Nominal and Actual Sizes of Schedule 40 Wrought-Steel Pipe*

Nominal size, in	Actual ID, in
$\frac{1}{8}$	0.269
$\frac{1}{4}$	0.364
$\frac{3}{8}$	0.493
$\frac{1}{2}$	0.622
$\frac{3}{4}$	0.824
1	1.049
$1\frac{1}{2}$	1.610
2	2.067
$2\frac{1}{2}$	2.469
3	3.068

* Nominal size within 1 percent for 4 in or larger.

6.6 Flow in Noncircular Ducts[1]

If the duct is noncircular, the analysis of full developed flow follows that of the circular pipe but is more complicated algebraically. For laminar flow, one can solve the exact equations of continuity and momentum. For turbulent flow, the logarithm-law velocity profile can be used, or (better and simpler) the hydraulic diameter is an excellent approximation.

The Hydraulic Diameter

For a noncircular duct, the control-volume concept of Fig. 6.10 is still valid, but the cross-sectional area A does not equal πR^2 and the cross-sectional perimeter wetted by the shear stress $\mathcal{P}$ does not equal $2\pi R$. The momentum equation (6.26) thus becomes

$$\Delta p\, A + \rho g A\, \Delta L \sin \phi - \bar{\tau}_w \mathcal{P}\, \Delta L = 0$$

[1] This section may be omitted without loss of continuity.

or

$$h_f = \frac{\Delta p}{\rho g} + \Delta z = \frac{\bar{\tau}_w}{\rho g}\frac{\Delta L}{A/\mathcal{P}} \tag{6.70}$$

This is identical to Eq. (6.27) except that (1) the shear stress is an average value integrated around the perimeter and (2) the length scale $A/\mathcal{P}$ takes the place of the pipe radius R. For this reason a noncircular duct is said to have a *hydraulic radius* R_h, defined by

$$R_h = \frac{A}{\mathcal{P}} = \frac{\text{cross-sectional area}}{\text{wetted perimeter}} \tag{6.71}$$

This concept receives constant use in open-channel flow (Chap. 10), where the channel cross section is almost never circular. If, by comparison to Eq. (6.29) for pipe flow, we define the friction factor in terms of average shear

$$f_{\text{NCD}} = \frac{8\bar{\tau}_w}{\rho V^2} \tag{6.72}$$

where NCD stands for noncircular duct and $V = Q/A$ as usual, Eq. (6.70) becomes

$$h_f = f\,\frac{L}{4R_h}\frac{V^2}{2g} \tag{6.73}$$

This is equivalent to Eq. (6.30) for pipe flow except that d is replaced by $4R_h$. Therefore we customarily define the *hydraulic diameter* as

$$D_h = \frac{4A}{\mathcal{P}} = \frac{4 \times \text{area}}{\text{wetted perimeter}} = 4R_h \tag{6.74}$$

We should stress that the wetted perimeter includes all surfaces acted upon by the shear stress. For example, in a circular annulus, both the outer and the inner perimeter should be added. The fact that D_h equals $4R_h$ is just one of those things: Chalk it up to an engineer's sense of humor. Note that for the degenerate case of a circular pipe, $D_h = 4\pi R^2/(2\pi R) = 2R$, as expected.

We would therefore expect by dimensional analysis that this friction factor f, based upon hydraulic diameter as in Eq. (6.72), would correlate with the Reynolds number and roughness ratio based upon the hydraulic diameter

$$f = F\left(\frac{VD_h}{\nu}, \frac{\epsilon}{D_h}\right) \tag{6.75}$$

and this is the way the data are correlated. But we should not necessarily expect the Moody chart (Fig. 6.13) to hold exactly in terms of this new length scale. And it does not, but it is surprisingly accurate:

$$f \approx \begin{cases} \dfrac{64}{\text{Re}_{D_h}} & \pm 40\% \quad \text{laminar flow} \\[2em] f_{\text{Moody}}\left(\text{Re}_{D_h}, \dfrac{\epsilon}{D_h}\right) & \pm 15\% \quad \text{turbulent flow} \end{cases} \tag{6.76}$$

Now let us look at some particular cases.

Flow between Parallel Plates

As shown in Fig. 6.14, flow between parallel plates a distance h apart is the limiting case of flow through a very wide rectangular channel. For fully developed flow, $u = u(y)$ only, which satisfies continuity identically. The momentum equation in cartesian coordinates reduces to

$$0 = -\frac{dp}{dx} + \rho g_x + \frac{d\tau}{dy} \qquad \tau_{\text{lam}} = \mu \frac{du}{dy} \tag{6.77}$$

subject to no-slip conditions: $u = 0$ at $y = \pm h$. The laminar-flow solution was given as an example in Eq. (4.143). Here we also allow for the possibility of a sloping channel, with a pressure gradient due to gravity. The solution is

$$u = \frac{1}{2\mu}\left[-\frac{d}{dx}(p + \rho g z)\right](h^2 - y^2) \tag{6.78}$$

If the channel has width b, the volume flow is

$$Q = \int_{-h}^{+h} u(y)b \, dy = \frac{bh^3}{3\mu}\left[-\frac{d}{dx}(p + \rho g z)\right]$$

or

$$V = \frac{Q}{bh} = \frac{h^2}{3\mu}\left[-\frac{d}{dx}(p + \rho g z)\right] = \frac{2}{3}u_{\text{max}} \tag{6.79}$$

Note the difference between a parabola [Eq. (6.79)] and a paraboloid [Eq. (6.43)]: the average is two-thirds of the maximum velocity in plane flow and one-half in axisymmetric flow.

The wall shear stress in developed channel flow is a constant:

$$\tau_w = \mu \left|\frac{du}{dy}\right|_{y=+h} = h\left[-\frac{d}{dx}(p + \rho g z)\right] \tag{6.80}$$

This may be nondimensionalized as a friction factor:

$$f = \frac{8\tau_w}{\rho V^2} = \frac{24\mu}{\rho V h} = \frac{24}{\text{Re}_h} \tag{6.81}$$

These are exact analytic laminar-flow results, so there is no reason to resort to the hydraulic-diameter concept. However, if we did use D_h, a discrepancy would arise. The hydraulic diameter of a wide channel is

Fig. 6.14 Fully developed flow between parallel plates.

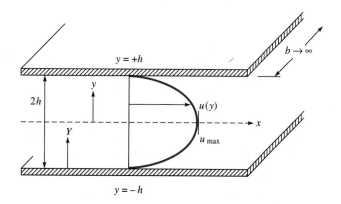

$$D_h = \frac{4A}{\mathcal{P}} = \lim_{b \to \infty} \frac{4(2bh)}{2b + 4h} = 4h \tag{6.82}$$

or twice the distance between the plates. Substituting into Eq. (6.81), we obtain the interesting result

Parallel plates:
$$f_{\text{lam}} = \frac{96\mu}{\rho V(4h)} = \frac{96}{\text{Re}_{D_h}} \tag{6.83}$$

Thus, if we could not work out the laminar theory and chose to use the approximation $f \approx 64/\text{Re}_{D_h}$, we would be 33 percent low. The hydraulic-diameter approximation is relatively crude in laminar flow, as Eq. (6.76) states.

Just as in circular-pipe flow, the laminar solution above becomes unstable at about $\text{Re}_{D_h} \approx 2000$; transition occurs and turbulent flow results.

For turbulent flow between parallel plates, we can again use the logarithm law, Eq. (6.21), as an approximation across the entire channel, using not y but a wall coordinate Y, as shown in Fig. 6.14:

$$\frac{u(Y)}{u^*} \approx \frac{1}{\kappa} \ln \frac{Y u^*}{\nu} + B \qquad 0 < Y < h \tag{6.84}$$

This distribution looks very much like the flat turbulent profile for pipe flow in Fig. 6.11b, and the mean velocity is

$$V = \frac{1}{h} \int_0^h u \, dY = u^* \left(\frac{1}{\kappa} \ln \frac{h u^*}{\nu} + B - \frac{1}{\kappa} \right) \tag{6.85}$$

Recalling that $V/u^* = (8/f)^{1/2}$, we see that Eq. (6.85) is equivalent to a parallel-plate friction law. Rearranging and cleaning up the constant terms, we obtain

$$\frac{1}{f^{1/2}} \approx 2.0 \log (\text{Re}_{D_h} f^{1/2}) - 1.19 \tag{6.86}$$

where we have introduced the hydraulic diameter $D_h = 4h$. This is remarkably close to the pipe-friction law, Eq. (6.54). Therefore we conclude that the use of the hydraulic diameter in this turbulent case is quite successful. That turns out to be true for other noncircular turbulent flows also.

Equation (6.86) can be brought into exact agreement with the pipe law by rewriting it in the form

$$\frac{1}{f^{1/2}} = 2.0 \log (0.64 \, \text{Re}_{D_h} f^{1/2}) - 0.8 \tag{6.87}$$

Thus the turbulent friction is predicted most accurately when we use an effective diameter D_{eff} equal to 0.64 times the hydraulic diameter. The effect on f itself is much less, about 10 percent at most. We can compare with Eq. (6.83) for laminar flow, which predicted

Parallel plates:
$$D_{\text{eff}} = \tfrac{64}{96} D_h = \tfrac{2}{3} D_h \tag{6.88}$$

This close resemblance ($0.64 D_h$ versis $0.667 D_h$) occurs so often in noncircular duct flow that we take it to be a general rule for computing turbulent friction in ducts:

$$D_{\text{eff}} = D_h = \frac{4A}{\mathcal{P}} \qquad \text{reasonable accuracy}$$

$$D_{\text{eff}}(\text{laminar theory}) \quad \text{extreme accuracy} \quad (6.89)$$

Jones [10] shows that the effective-laminar-diameter idea collapses all data for rectangular ducts of arbitrary height-to-width ratio onto the Moody chart for pipe flow. We recommend this idea for all noncircular ducts.

EXAMPLE 6.13

Fluid flows at an average velocity of 6 ft/s between horizontal parallel plates a distance of 2.4 in apart. Find the head loss and pressure drop for each 100 ft of length for $\rho = 1.9$ slugs/ft^3 and (a) $\nu = 0.00002$ ft^3/s and (b) $\nu = 0.002$ ft^3/s. Assume smooth walls.

Solution

Part (a)

The viscosity $\mu = \rho\nu = 3.8 \times 10^{-5}$ slug/(ft · s). The spacing is $2h = 2.4$ in $= 0.2$ ft, and $D_h = 4h = 0.4$ ft. The Reynolds number is

$$\text{Re}_{D_h} = \frac{VD_h}{\nu} = \frac{(6.0 \text{ ft/s})(0.4 \text{ ft})}{0.00002 \text{ ft}^2/\text{s}} = 120{,}000$$

The flow is therefore turbulent. For reasonable accuracy, simply look on the Moody chart (Fig. 6.13) for smooth walls

$$f \approx 0.0173 \qquad h_f \approx f\frac{L}{D_h}\frac{V^2}{2g} = 0.0173\frac{100}{0.4}\frac{(6.0)^2}{2(32.2)} \approx 2.42 \text{ ft} \qquad \textit{Ans. (a)}$$

Since there is no change in elevation,

$$\Delta p = \rho g h_f = 1.9(32.2)(2.42) = 148 \text{ lbf/ft}^2 \qquad \textit{Ans. (a)}$$

This is the head loss and pressure drop per 100 ft of channel. For more accuracy, take $D_{\text{eff}} = \frac{2}{3}D_h$ from laminar theory; then

$$\text{Re}_{\text{eff}} = \frac{2}{3}(120{,}000) = 80{,}000$$

and from the Moody chart read $f \approx 0.0189$ for smooth walls. Thus a better estimate is

$$h_f = 0.0189\frac{100}{0.4}\frac{(6.0)^2}{2(32.2)} = 2.64 \text{ ft}$$

and

$$\Delta p = 1.9(32.2)(2.64) = 161 \text{ lbf/ft}^2 \qquad \textit{Better ans. (a)}$$

The more accurate formula predicts friction about 9 percent higher.

Part (b)

Compute $\mu = \rho\nu = 0.0038$ slug/(ft · s). The Reynolds number is $6.0(0.4)/0.002 = 1200$; therefore the flow is laminar, since Re is less than 2300.

You could use the laminar-flow friction factor, Eq. (6.83)

$$f_{\text{lam}} = \frac{96}{\text{Re}_{D_h}} = \frac{96}{1200} = 0.08$$

from which

$$h_f = 0.08\frac{100}{0.4}\frac{(6.0)^2}{2(32.2)} = 11.2 \text{ ft}$$

and

$$\Delta p = 1.9(32.2)(11.2) = 684 \text{ lbf/ft}^2 \qquad \textit{Ans. (b)}$$

Alternative, you can finesse the Reynolds number and go directly to the appropriate laminar-flow formula, Eq. (6.79)

$$V = \frac{h^2}{3\mu} \frac{\Delta p}{L}$$

or $\Delta p = \dfrac{3(6.0 \text{ ft/s})[0.0038 \text{ slug/(ft} \cdot \text{s)}](100 \text{ ft})}{(0.1 \text{ ft})^2} = 684 \text{ slugs/(ft} \cdot \text{s}^2) = 684 \text{ lbf/ft}^2$

and $h_f = \dfrac{\Delta p}{\rho g} = \dfrac{684}{1.9(32.2)} = 11.2 \text{ ft}$

This is one of those—perhaps unexpected—problems where the laminar friction is greater than the turbulent friction.

**Flow through
a Concentric Annulus**

Consider steady axial laminar flow in the annular space between two concentric cylinders, as in Fig. 6.15. There is no slip at the inner ($r = b$) and outer radius ($r = a$). For $u = u(r)$ only, the governing relation is Eq. (6.34)

$$\frac{d}{dr}\left(r\mu \frac{du}{dr}\right) = Kr \qquad K = \frac{d}{dx}(p + \rho gz) \qquad (6.90)$$

Integrate this twice

$$u = \frac{1}{4}r^2 \frac{K}{\mu} + C_1 \ln r + C_2$$

The constants are found from the two no-slip conditions

$$u(r = a) = 0 = \frac{1}{4}a^2 \frac{K}{\mu} + C_1 \ln a + C_2$$

$$u(r = b) = 0 = \frac{1}{4}b^2 \frac{K}{\mu} + C_1 \ln b + C_2$$

The final solution for the velocity profile is

$$u = \frac{1}{4\mu}\left[-\frac{d}{dx}(p + \rho gz)\right]\left[a^2 - r^2 + \frac{a^2 - b^2}{\ln (b/a)} \ln \frac{a}{r}\right] \qquad (6.91)$$

Fig. 6.15 Fully developed flow through a concentric annulus.

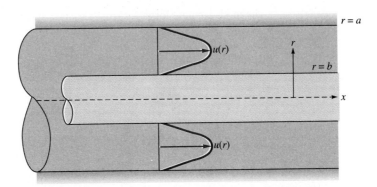

The volume flow is given by

$$Q = \int_b^a u2\pi r\, dr = \frac{\pi}{8\mu}\left[-\frac{d}{dx}(p + \rho gz)\right]\left[a^4 - b^4 - \frac{(a^2 - b^2)^2}{\ln\,(a/b)}\right] \qquad (6.92)$$

The velocity profile $u(r)$ resembles a parabola wrapped around in a circle to form a split doughnut, as in Fig. 6.15. The maximum velocity occurs at the radius

$$r' = \left[\frac{a^2 - b^2}{2\ln\,(a/b)}\right]^{1/2} \qquad u = u_{max} \qquad (6.93)$$

This maximum is closer to the inner radius but approaches the midpoint between cylinders as the clearance $a - b$ becomes small. Some numerical values are as follows:

$\dfrac{b}{a}$	0.01	0.1	0.2	0.5	0.8	0.9	0.99
$\dfrac{r' - b}{a - b}$	0.323	0.404	0.433	0.471	0.491	0.496	0.499

Also, as the clearance becomes small, the profile approaches a parabolic distribution, as if the flow were between two parallel plates. [Eq. (4.143)].

It is confusing to base the friction factor on the wall shear because there are two shear stresses, the inner stress being greater than the outer. It is better to define f with respect to the head loss, as in Eq. (6.73),

$$f = h_f \frac{D_h}{L}\frac{2g}{V^2} \qquad \text{where } V = \frac{Q}{\pi(a^2 - b^2)} \qquad (6.94)$$

The hydraulic diameter for an annulus is

$$D_h = \frac{4\pi(a^2 - b^2)}{2\pi(a + b)} = 2(a - b) \qquad (6.95)$$

It is twice the clearance, rather like the parallel-plate result of twice the distance between plates [Eq. (6.82)].

Substituting h_f, D_h, and V into Eq. (6.94), we find that the friction factor for laminar flow in a concentric annulus is of the form

$$f = \frac{64\zeta}{Re_{D_h}} \qquad \zeta = \frac{(a - b)^2(a^2 - b^2)}{a^4 - b^4 - (a^2 - b^2)^2/\ln\,(a/b)} \qquad (6.96)$$

The dimensionless term ζ is a sort of correction factor for the hydraulic diameter. We could rewrite Eq. (6.96) as

Concentric annulus: $\qquad f = \dfrac{64}{Re_{eff}} \qquad Re_{eff} = \dfrac{1}{\zeta}Re_{D_h} \qquad (6.97)$

Some numerical values of $f\,Re_{D_h}$ and $D_{eff}/D_h = 1/\zeta$ are given in Table 6.3.

For turbulent flow through a concentric annulus, the analysis might proceed by patching together two logarithmic-law profiles, one going out from the inner wall to meet the other coming in from the outer wall. We omit such a scheme here and proceed directly to the friction factor. According to the general rule proposed in Eq. (6.89), turbulent friction is predicted with excellent accuracy by replacing d in the Moody chart

Table 6.3 Laminar Friction Factors for a Concentric Annulus

b/a	$f\,Re_{D_h}$	$D_{eff}/D_h = 1/\zeta$
0.0	64.0	1.000
0.00001	70.09	0.913
0.0001	71.78	0.892
0.001	74.68	0.857
0.01	80.11	0.799
0.05	86.27	0.742
0.1	89.37	0.716
0.2	92.35	0.693
0.4	94.71	0.676
0.6	95.59	0.670
0.8	95.92	0.667
1.0	96.0	0.667

by $D_{eff} = 2(a - b)/\zeta$, with values listed in Table 6.3.[1] This idea includes roughness, also (replace ϵ/d in the chart by ϵ/D_{eff}). For a quick design number with about 10 percent accuracy, one can simply use the hydraulic diameter $D_h = 2(a - b)$.

EXAMPLE 6.14

What should the reservoir level h be to maintain a flow of 0.01 m³/s through the commercial steel annulus 30 m long shown in Fig. E6.14? Neglect entrance effects and take $\rho = 1000$ kg/m³ and $\nu = 1.02 \times 10^{-6}$ m²/s for water.

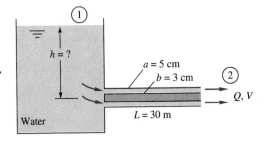

Fig. E6.14

Solution

Compute the average velocity and hydraulic diameter

$$V = \frac{Q}{A} = \frac{0.01 \text{ m}^3/\text{s}}{\pi[(0.05 \text{ m})^2 - (0.03 \text{ m})^2]} = 1.99 \text{ m/s}$$

$$D_h = 2(a - b) = 2(0.05 - 0.03) \text{ m} = 0.04 \text{ m}$$

Apply the steady-flow energy equation between sections 1 and 2:

$$\frac{p_1}{\rho} + \frac{1}{2} V_1^2 + gz_1 = \left(\frac{p_2}{\rho} + \frac{1}{2} V_2^2 + gz_2\right) + gh_f$$

But $p_1 = p_2 = p_a$, $V_1 \approx 0$, and $V_2 = V$ in the pipe. Therefore solve for

$$h_f = f\frac{L}{D_h}\frac{V^2}{2g} = z_1 - z_2 - \frac{V^2}{2g}$$

But $z_1 - z_2 = h$, the desired reservoir height. Thus, finally,

$$h = \frac{V^2}{2g}\left(1 + f\frac{L}{D_h}\right) \tag{1}$$

Since V, L, and D_h are known, our only remaining problem is to compute the annulus friction factor f. For a quick approximation, take $D_{eff} = D_h = 0.04$ m. Then

$$Re_{D_h} = \frac{VD_h}{\nu} = \frac{1.99(0.04)}{1.02 \times 10^{-6}} = 78,000$$

$$\frac{\epsilon}{D_h} = \frac{0.046 \text{ mm}}{40 \text{ mm}} = 0.00115$$

[1] Jones and Leung [44] show that data for annular flow also satisfy the effective-laminar-diameter idea.

where $\epsilon = 0.046$ mm has been read from Table 6.1 for commercial steel surfaces. From the Moody chart, read $f = 0.0232$. Then, from Eq. (1) above,

$$h \approx \frac{(1.99 \text{ m/s})^2}{2(9.81 \text{ m/s}^2)}\left(1 + 0.0232 \frac{30 \text{ m}}{0.04 \text{ m}}\right) = 3.71 \text{ m} \qquad \textit{Crude ans.}$$

For better accuracy, take $D_{\text{eff}} = D_h/\zeta = 0.670 D_h = 2.68$ cm, where the correction factor 0.670 has been read from Table 6.3 for $b/a = \frac{3}{5} = 0.6$. Then the corrected Reynolds number and roughness ratio are

$$\text{Re}_{\text{eff}} = \frac{V D_{\text{eff}}}{\nu} = 52,300 \qquad \frac{\epsilon}{D_{\text{eff}}} = 0.00172$$

From the Moody chart, read $f = 0.0257$. Then the improved computation for reservoir height is

$$h = \frac{(1.99 \text{ m/s})^2}{2(9.81 \text{ m/s}^2)}\left(1 + 0.0257 \frac{30 \text{ m}}{0.04 \text{ m}}\right) = 4.09 \text{ m} \qquad \textit{Better ans.}$$

The uncorrected hydraulic-diameter estimate is about 9 percent low. Note that we do *not* replace D_h by D_{eff} in the ratio L/D_h in Eq. (1) since this is implicit in the definition of friction factor.

Other Noncircular Cross Sections

In principle, any duct cross section can be solved analytically for the laminar-flow velocity distribution, volume flow, and friction factor. This is because any cross section can be mapped onto a circle by the methods of complex variables, and other powerful analytical techniques are also available. Many examples are given by White [3, pp. 119–122], Berker [11], and Olson and Wright [12, pp. 315–317]. Reference 34 is devoted entirely to laminar duct flow.

In general, however, most unusual duct sections have strictly academic and not commercial value. We list here only the rectangular and isosceles-triangular sections, in Table 6.4, leaving other cross sections for you to find in the references.

For turbulent flow in a duct of unusual cross section, one should replace d by D_h on the Moody chart if no laminar theory is available. If laminar results are known, such as Table 6.4, replace d by $D_{\text{eff}} = [64/(f\text{Re})]D_h$ for the particular geometry of the duct.

For laminar flow in rectangles and triangles, the wall friction varies greatly, being largest near the midpoints of the sides and zero in the corners. In turbulent flow through the same sections, the shear is nearly constant along the sides, dropping off sharply to zero in the corners. This is because of the phenomenon of turbulent *secondary flow*, in which there are nonzero mean velocities v and w in the plane of the cross section. Some measurements of axial velocity and secondary-flow patterns are shown in Fig. 6.16, as sketched by Nikuradse in his 1926 dissertation. The secondary-flow "cells" drive the mean flow toward the corners, so that the axial-velocity contours are similar to the cross section and the wall shear is nearly constant. This is why the hydraulic-diameter concept is so successful for turbulent flow. Laminar flow in a straight noncircular duct has no secondary flow. An accurate theoretical prediction of turbulent secondary flow has yet to be achieved, although numerical models are improving [36].

Table 6.4 Laminar Friction Constants $f\text{Re}$ for Rectangular and Triangular Ducts

Rectangular		Isosceles triangle	
b/a	$f\,\text{Re}_{D_h}$	θ, deg	$f\,\text{Re}_{D_h}$
0.0	96.00	0	48.0
0.05	89.91	10	51.6
0.1	84.68	20	52.9
0.125	82.34	30	53.3
0.167	78.81	40	52.9
0.25	72.93	50	52.0
0.4	65.47	60	51.1
0.5	62.19	70	49.5
0.75	57.89	80	48.3
1.0	56.91	90	48.0

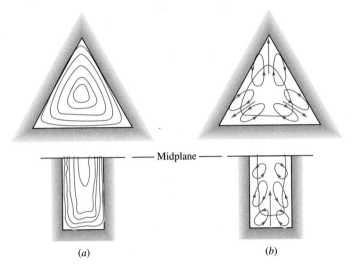

Fig. 6.16 Illustration of secondary turbulent flow in noncircular ducts: (*a*) axial mean-velocity contours; (*b*) secondary-flow cellular motions. (*After J. Nikuradse, dissertation, Göttingen, 1926.*)

Midplane

(*a*)   (*b*)

EXAMPLE 6.15

Air, with $\rho = 0.00237$ slug/ft^3 and $\nu = 0.000157$ ft^2/s, is forced through a horizontal square 9- by 9-in duct 100 ft long at 25 ft^3/s. Find the pressure drop if $\epsilon = 0.0003$ ft.

Solution

Compute the mean velocity and hydraulic diameter

$$V = \frac{25 \text{ ft}^3/\text{s}}{(0.75 \text{ ft})^2} = 44.4 \text{ ft/s}$$

$$D_h = \frac{4A}{\mathcal{P}} = \frac{4(81 \text{ in}^2)}{36 \text{ in}} = 9 \text{ in} = 0.75 \text{ ft}$$

From Table 6.4, for $b/a = 1.0$, the effective diameter is

$$D_{\text{eff}} = \frac{64}{56.91} D_h = 0.843 \text{ ft}$$

whence

$$\text{Re}_{\text{eff}} = \frac{VD_{\text{eff}}}{\nu} = \frac{44.4(0.843)}{0.000157} = 239{,}000$$

$$\frac{\epsilon}{D_{\text{eff}}} = \frac{0.0003}{0.843} = 0.000356$$

From the Moody chart, read $f = 0.0177$. Then the pressure drop is

$$\Delta p = \rho g h_f = \rho g \left(f \frac{L}{D_h} \frac{V^2}{2g} \right) = 0.00237(32.2) \left[0.0177 \frac{100}{0.75} \frac{44.4^2}{2(32.2)} \right]$$

or

$$\Delta p = 5.5 \text{ lbf/ft}^2 \qquad \qquad \textit{Ans.}$$

Pressure drop in air ducts is usually small because of the low density.

6.7 Minor Losses in Pipe Systems[1]

For any pipe system, in addition to the Moody-type friction loss computed for the length of pipe, there are additional so-called *minor losses* due to

1. Pipe entrance or exit
2. Sudden expansion or contraction
3. Bends, elbows, tees, and other fittings
4. Valves, open or partially closed
5. Gradual expansions or contractions

The losses may not be so minor; e.g., a partially closed valve can cause a greater pressure drop than a long pipe.

Since the flow pattern in fittings and valves is quite complex, the theory is very weak. The losses are commonly measured experimentally and correlated with the pipe-flow parameters. The data, especially for valves, are somewhat dependent upon the particular manufacturer's design, so that the values listed here must be taken as average design estimates [15, 16, 35, 43, 46].

The measured minor loss is usually given as a ratio of the head loss $h_m = \Delta p/(\rho g)$ through the device to the velocity head $V^2/(2g)$ of the associated piping system

$$\text{Loss coefficient } K = \frac{h_m}{V^2/(2g)} = \frac{\Delta p}{\frac{1}{2}\rho V^2} \tag{6.98}$$

Although K is dimensionless, it unfortunately is not correlated in the literature with the Reynolds number and roughness ratio but rather simply with the raw size of the pipe in, say, inches. Almost all data are reported for turbulent-flow conditions.

An alternate, and less desirable, procedure is to report the minor loss as if it were an *equivalent length* L_{eq} of pipe, satisfying the Darcy friction-factor relation

$$h_m = f\frac{L_{eq}}{d}\frac{V^2}{2g} = K\frac{V^2}{2g}$$

or

$$L_{eq} = \frac{Kd}{f} \tag{6.99}$$

Although the equivalent length should take some of the variability out of the loss data, it is an artificial concept and will not be pursued here.

A single pipe system may have many minor losses. Since all are correlated with $V^2/(2g)$, they can be summed into a single total system loss if the pipe has constant diameter

$$\Delta h_{tot} = h_f + \sum h_m = \frac{V^2}{2g}\left(\frac{fL}{d} + \sum K\right) \tag{6.100}$$

Note, however, that we must sum the losses separately if the pipe size changes so that V^2 changes. The length L in Eq. (6.100) is the total length of the pipe axis, including any bends.

There are many different valve designs in commercial use. Figure 6.17 shows five typical designs: (*a*) the *gate*, which slides down across the section; (*b*) the *globe*, which closes a hole in a special insert; (*c*) the *angle*, similar to a globe but with a 90° turn;

---

[1] This section may be omitted without loss of continuity.

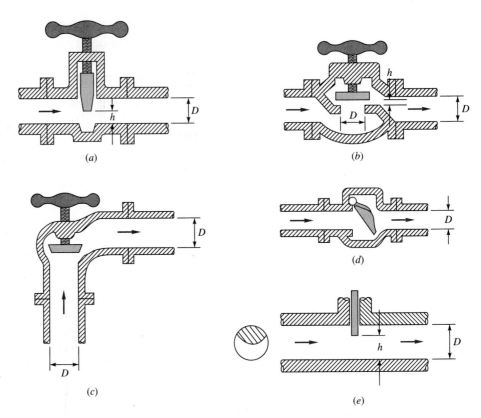

Fig. 6.17 Typical commercial valve geometries: (*a*) gate valve; (*b*) globe valve; (*c*) angle valve; (*d*) swing-check valve; (*e*) disk-type gate valve.

(*d*) the *swing-check* valve, which allows only one-way flow; and (*e*) the *disk*, which closes the section with a circular gate. The globe, with its tortuous flow path, has the highest losses when fully open. Many excellent details about these and other valves are given in the handbook by Lyons [35].

Table 6.5 lists loss coefficients K for four types of valve, three angles of elbow fitting,

Table 6.5 Resistance Coefficients $K = h_m/[V^2/(2g)]$ for Open Valves, Elbows, and Tees

	Nominal diameter, in								
	Screwed				Flanged				
	$\frac{1}{2}$	1	2	4	1	2	4	8	20
Valves (fully open):									
Globe	14	8.2	6.9	5.7	13	8.5	6.0	5.8	5.5
Gate	0.30	0.24	0.16	0.11	0.80	0.35	0.16	0.07	0.03
Swing check	5.1	2.9	2.1	2.0	2.0	2.0	2.0	2.0	2.0
Angle	9.0	4.7	2.0	1.0	4.5	2.4	2.0	2.0	2.0
Elbows:									
45° regular	0.39	0.32	0.30	0.29					
45° long radius					0.21	0.20	0.19	0.16	0.14
90° regular	2.0	1.5	0.95	0.64	0.50	0.39	0.30	0.26	0.21
90° long radius	1.0	0.72	0.41	0.23	0.40	0.30	0.19	0.15	0.10
180° regular	2.0	1.5	0.95	0.64	0.41	0.35	0.30	0.25	0.20
180° long radius					0.40	0.30	0.21	0.15	0.10
Tees:									
Line flow	0.90	0.90	0.90	0.90	0.24	0.19	0.14	0.10	0.07
Branch flow	2.4	1.8	1.4	1.1	1.0	0.80	0.64	0.58	0.41

and two tee connections. Fittings may be connected by either internal screws or flanges, hence the two listings. We see that K generally decreases with pipe size, which is consistent with the higher Reynolds number and decreased roughness ratio of large pipes. We stress that Table 6.5 represents losses *averaged among various manufacturers*, so there is an uncertainty as high as ± 50 percent.

The valve losses in Table 6.5 are for the fully open condition. Losses can be much higher for a partially open valve. Figure 6.18 gives average losses for three valves as a function of "percentage open," as defined by the opening-distance ratio h/D (see Fig. 6.17 for the geometries). Again we should warn of a possible uncertainty of ± 50 percent. Of all minor losses, valves, because of their complex geometry, are most sensitive to manufacturers' design details. For more accuracy, the particular design and manufacturer should be consulted [35].

The *butterfly* valve of Fig. 6.19a is a stem-mounted disk which, when closed, seats against an O-ring or compliant seal near the pipe surface. A single 90° turn opens the

Fig. 6.18 Average-loss coefficients for partially open valves (see sketches in Fig. 6.17).

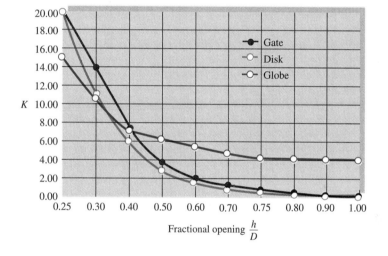

(a)

Fig. 6.19 Performance of butterfly valves: (a) typical geometry (*courtesy of Grinnell Corp., Cranston, R.I.*); (b) loss coefficients for three different manufacturers.

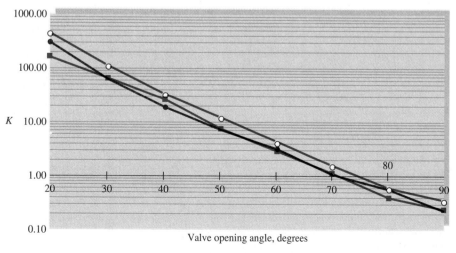

(b)

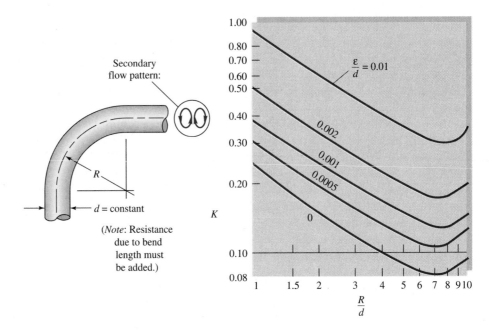

Fig. 6.20 Resistance coefficients for 90° bends.

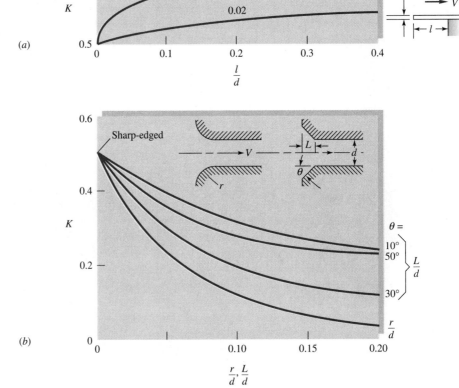

Fig. 6.21 Entrance and exit loss coefficients: (*a*) reentrant inlets; (*b*) rounded and beveled inlets. Exit losses are $K \approx 1.0$ for all shapes of exit (reentrant, sharp, beveled, or rounded). (*From Ref. 37.*)

valve completely, hence the design is ideal for controllable quick-opening and quick-closing situations such as occur in fire protection and the electric power industry. However, considerable dynamic torque is needed to close these valves, and losses are high when the valves are nearly closed.

Figure 6.19b shows butterfly-valve loss coefficients as a function of the opening angle θ for turbulent-flow conditions ($\theta = 0$ is closed). The losses are huge when the opening is small, and K drops off nearly exponentially with the opening angle. There is a factor of 2 spread among the various manufacturers. Note that K in Fig. 6.19b is, as usual, based on the average *pipe* velocity $V = Q/A$, not on the increased velocity of the flow as it passes through the narrow valve passage.

A bend or curve in a pipe, as in Fig. 6.20, always induces a loss larger than the simple Moody friction loss, due to flow separation at the walls and a swirling secondary flow arising from the centripetal acceleration. The loss coefficients K in Fig. 6.20 are for this additional bend loss. The Moody loss due to the axial length of the bend must be computed separately; i.e., the bend length should be added to the pipe length.

As shown in Fig. 6.21, entrance losses are highly dependent upon entrance geometry, but exit losses are not. Sharp edges or protrusions in the entrance cause large zones of flow separation and large losses. A little rounding goes a long way, and a well-rounded entrance ($r = 0.2d$) has a nearly negligible loss $K = 0.05$. At an exit, on the other hand, the flow simply passes out of the pipe into the large downstream reservoir and loses all its velocity head due to viscous dissipation. Therefore $K = 1.0$ for all submerged exits, no matter how well rounded.

If the entrance is from a finite reservoir, it is termed a *sudden contraction* (SC) between two sizes of pipe. If the exit is to finite-sized pipe, it is termed a *sudden expansion* (SE). The losses for both are graphed in Fig. 6.22. For the sudden expansion,

Fig. 6.22 Sudden expansion and contraction losses. Note that the loss is based on velocity head in the small pipe.

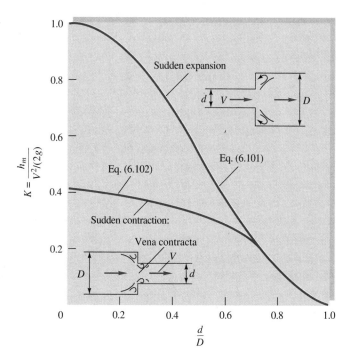

the shear stress in the corner separated flow, or deadwater region, is negligible, so that a control-volume analysis between the expansion section and the end of the separation zone gives a theoretical loss

$$K_{SE} = \left(1 - \frac{d^2}{D^2}\right)^2 = \frac{h_m}{V^2/(2g)} \qquad (6.101)$$

Note that K is based on the velocity head in the small pipe. Equation (6.101) is in excellent agreement with experiment.

For the sudden contraction, however, flow separation in the downstream pipe causes the main stream to contract through a minimum diameter d_{min}, called the *vena contracta*, as sketched in Fig. 6.22. Because the theory of the vena contracta is not well developed, the loss coefficient in the figure for sudden contraction is experimental. It fits the empirical formula

$$K_{SC} \approx 0.42\left(1 - \frac{d^2}{D^2}\right) \qquad (6.102)$$

up to the value $d/D = 0.76$, above which it merges into the sudden-expansion prediction, Eq. (6.101).

If the expansion or contraction is gradual, the losses are quite different. Figure 6.23 shows the loss through a gradual conical expansion, usually called a *diffuser* [14]. There is a spread in the data, depending upon the boundary-layer conditions in the upstream pipe. A thinner entrance boundary layer, like the entrance profile in Fig. 6.6, gives a smaller loss. Since a diffuser is intended to raise the static pressure of the flow, diffuser data list the pressure-recovery coefficient of the flow

Fig. 6.23 Flow losses in a gradual conical expansion region.

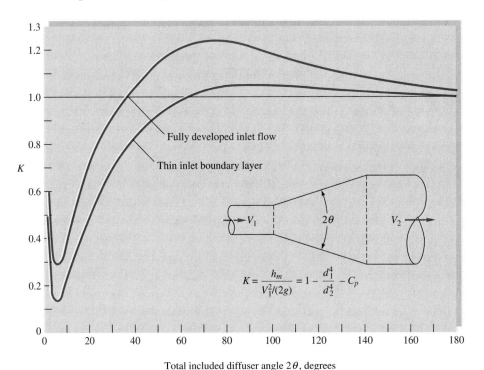

Total included diffuser angle 2θ, degrees

6.7 Minor Losses in Pipe Systems **341**

$$C_p = \frac{p_2 - p_1}{\frac{1}{2}\rho V_1^2} \tag{6.103}$$

The loss coefficient is related to this parameter by

$$K = \frac{h_m}{V^2/(2g)} = 1 - \frac{d_1^2}{d_2^4} - C_p \tag{6.104}$$

For a given area ratio, the higher the pressure recovery, the lower the loss; hence large C_p means a successful diffuser. From Fig. 6.23 the minimum loss (maximum recovery) occurs for a cone angle 2θ equal to about 5°. Angles smaller than this give a large Moody-type loss because of their excessive length. For cone angles greater than 40 to 60°, the loss is so excessive that it would actually be better to use a sudden expansion. This unexpected effect is due to gross flow separation in a wide-angle diffuser, as we shall see soon when we study boundary layers. Reference 14 has extensive data on diffusers.

For a gradual contraction, the loss is very small, as seen from the following experimental values [15]:

Contraction cone angle 2θ, deg	30	45	60
K for gradual contraction	0.02	0.04	0.07

References 15, 16, 43, and 46 contain additional data on minor losses.

EXAMPLE 6.16

Water, $\rho = 1.94$ slugs/ft^3 and $\nu = 0.000011$ ft^2/s, is pumped between two reservoirs at 0.2 ft^3/s through 400 ft of 2-in-diameter pipe and several minor losses, as shown in Fig. E6.16. The roughness ratio is $\epsilon/d = 0.001$. Compute the pump horsepower required.

Fig. E6.16

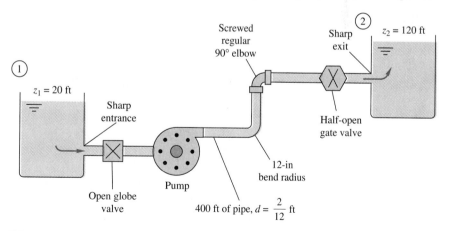

Solution

Write the steady-flow energy equation between sections 1 and 2, the two reservoir surfaces:

$$\frac{p_1}{\rho g} + \frac{V_1^2}{2g} + z_1 = \left(\frac{p_2}{\rho g} + \frac{V_2^2}{2g} + z_2\right) + h_f + \sum h_m - h_p$$

where h_p is the head increase across the pump. But since $p_1 = p_2$ and $V_1 = V_2 \approx 0$, solve for the pump head

$$h_p = z_2 - z_1 + h_f + \sum h_m = 120 \text{ ft} - 20 \text{ ft} + \frac{V^2}{2g}\left(\frac{fL}{d} + \sum K\right) \tag{1}$$

Now with the flow rate known, calculate

$$V = \frac{Q}{A} = \frac{0.2 \text{ ft}^3/\text{s}}{\frac{1}{4}\pi(\frac{2}{12} \text{ ft})^2} = 9.17 \text{ ft/s}$$

Now list and sum the minor loss coefficients:

Loss	K
Sharp entrance (Fig. 6.21)	0.5
Open globe valve (2 in, Table 6.5)	6.9
12-in bend (Fig. 6.20)	0.15
Regular 90° elbow (Table 6.5)	0.95
Half-closed gate valve (from Fig. 6.18)	2.7
Sharp exit (Fig. 6.21)	1.0
	$\sum K = 12.2$

Calculate the Reynolds number and pipe-friction factor

$$\text{Re}_d = \frac{Vd}{\nu} = \frac{9.17(\frac{2}{12})}{0.000011} = 139{,}000$$

For $\epsilon/d = 0.001$, from the Moody chart read $f = 0.0216$. Substitute into Eq. (1)

$$h_p = 100 \text{ ft} + \frac{(9.17 \text{ ft/s})^2}{2(32.2 \text{ ft/s}^2)}\left[\frac{0.0216(400)}{\frac{2}{12}} + 12.2\right]$$

$$= 100 \text{ ft} + 84 \text{ ft} = 184 \text{ ft} \qquad \text{pump head}$$

The pump must provide a power to the water of

$$P = \rho g Q h_p = [1.94(32.2) \text{ lbf/ft}^3](0.2 \text{ ft}^3/\text{s})(184 \text{ ft}) = 2300 \text{ ft} \cdot \text{lbf/s}$$

The conversion factor is $1 \text{ hp} = 550 \text{ ft} \cdot \text{lbf/s}$. Therefore

$$P = \frac{2300}{550} = 4.2 \text{ hp} \qquad\qquad\qquad Ans.$$

Allowing for an efficiency of 70 to 80 percent, a pump is needed with an input of about 6 hp.

6.8 Multiple-Pipe Systems[1]

If you can solve one pipe, you can solve them all; but when systems contain two or more pipes, certain basic rules make the calculations very smooth. Any resemblance between these rules and the rules for handling electric circuits is not coincidental.

Figure 6.24 shows three examples of multiple-pipe systems. The first is a set of three

---

[1] This section may be omitted without loss of continuity.

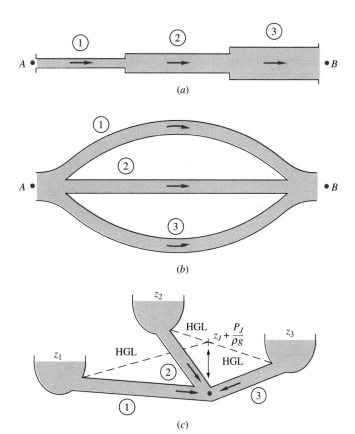

Fig. 6.24 Examples of multiple-pipe systems: (*a*) pipes in series; (*b*) pipes in parallel; (*c*) the three-reservoir junction problem.

(or more) pipes in series. Rule 1 is that the flow rate is the same in all pipes

$$Q_1 = Q_2 = Q_3 = \text{const}$$

or
$$V_1 d_1^2 = V_2 d_2^2 = V_3 d_3^2 \tag{6.105}$$

Rule 2 is that the total head loss through the system equals the sum of the head loss in each pipe

$$\Delta h_{A \to B} = \Delta h_1 + \Delta h_2 + \Delta h_3 \tag{6.106}$$

In terms of the friction and minor losses in each pipe, we could rewrite this as

$$\Delta h_{A \to B} = \frac{V_1^2}{2g}\left(\frac{f_1 L_1}{d_1} + \sum K_1\right) + \frac{V_2^2}{2g}\left(\frac{f_2 L_2}{d_2} + \sum K_2\right)$$
$$+ \frac{V_3^2}{2g}\left(\frac{f_3 L_3}{d_3} + \sum K_3\right) \tag{6.107}$$

and so on for any number of pipes in the series. Since V_2 and V_3 are proportional to V_1 from Eq. (6.105), Eq. (6.107) is of the form

$$\Delta h_{A \to B} = \frac{V_1^2}{2g}\left(\alpha_0 + \alpha_1 f_1 + \alpha_2 f_2 + \alpha_3 f_3\right) \tag{6.108}$$

where the α_i are dimensionless constants. If the flow rate is given, we can evaluate the right-hand side and hence the total head loss. If the head loss is given, a little iteration is needed, since f_1, f_2, and f_3 all depend upon V_1 through the Reynolds number. Begin by calculating f_1, f_2, and f_3, assuming fully rough flow, and the solution for V_1 will converge with one or two iterations.

EXAMPLE 6.17

Given is a three-pipe series system, as in Fig. 6.24a. The total pressure drop is $p_A - p_B = $ 150,000 Pa, and the elevation drop is $z_A - z_B = 5$ m. The pipe data are

Pipe	L, m	d, cm	ϵ, mm	ϵ/d
1	100	8	0.24	0.003
2	150	6	0.12	0.002
3	80	4	0.20	0.005

The fluid is water, $\rho = 1000$ kg/m^3 and $\nu = 1.02 \times 10^{-6}$ m^2/s. Calculate the flow rate Q in m^3/h through the system.

Solution

The total head loss across the system is

$$\Delta h_{A \to B} = \frac{p_A - p_B}{\rho g} + z_A - z_B = \frac{150{,}000}{1000(9.81)} + 5 \text{ m} = 20.3 \text{ m}$$

From the continuity relation (6.105) the velocities are

$$V_2 = \frac{d_1^2}{d_2^2} V_1 = \frac{16}{9} V_1 \qquad V_3 = \frac{d_1^2}{d_3^2} V_1 = 4V_1$$

and

$$\text{Re}_2 = \frac{V_2 d_2}{V_1 d_1} \text{Re}_1 = \frac{4}{3} \text{Re}_1 \qquad \text{Re}_3 = 2 \text{Re}_1$$

Neglecting minor losses and substituting into Eq. (6.107), we obtain

$$\Delta h_{A \to B} = \frac{V_1^2}{2g} [1250 f_1 + 2500 \left(\frac{16}{9} \right)^2 f_2 + 2000(4)^2 f_3]$$

or

$$20.3 \text{ m} = \frac{V_1^2}{2g} (1250 f_1 + 7900 f_2 + 32{,}000 f_3) \qquad (1)$$

This is the form which was hinted at in Eq. (6.108). It seems to be dominated by the third pipe loss $32{,}000 f_3$. Begin by estimating f_1, f_2, and f_3 from the Moody-chart fully rough regime

$$f_1 = 0.0262 \qquad f_2 = 0.0234 \qquad f_3 = 0.0304$$

Substitute in Eq. (1) to find $V_1^2 \approx 2g(20.3)/(33 + 185 + 973)$. The first estimate thus is $V_1 = 0.58$ m/s, from which

$$\text{Re}_1 \approx 45{,}400 \qquad \text{Re}_2 = 60{,}500 \qquad \text{Re}_3 = 90{,}800$$

Hence, from the Moody chart,

$$f_1 = 0.0288 \qquad f_2 = 0.0260 \qquad f_3 = 0.0314$$

Substitution into Eq. (1) gives the better estimate

$$V_1 = 0.565 \text{ m/s} \qquad Q = \tfrac{1}{4}\pi d_1^2 V_1 = 2.84 \times 10^{-3} \text{ m}^3/\text{s}$$

or $\qquad\qquad\qquad\qquad\qquad\qquad Q_1 = 10.2 \text{ m}^3/\text{h}$ *Ans.*

A second iteration gives $Q = 10.22 \text{ m}^3/\text{h}$, a negligible change.

The second multiple-pipe system is the *parallel*-flow case shown in Fig. 6.24*b*. Here the loss is the same in each pipe, and the total flow is the sum of the individual flows

$$\Delta h_{A \rightarrow B} = \Delta h_1 = \Delta h_2 = \Delta h_3 \qquad (6.109a)$$

$$Q = Q_1 + Q_2 + Q_3 \qquad (6.109b)$$

If the total head loss is known, it is relatively simple to solve for each Q_i and add. The reverse problem of known total flow rate Q requires quite a bit of iteration to determine how this flow splits up among the various pipes. The normal procedure is to guess, say, $Q_1 = Q/3$ and compute the head loss and hence Q_2 and Q_3 from Eq. (6.109a). Then, if the sum is incorrect, such as $Q_1 + Q_2 + Q_3 = 1.14Q$, then scale down the original guess to $Q_{1, \text{ new}} = Q_{1, \text{ old}}/1.14$, recompute Q_2 and Q_3, and test the sum again. Scale Q_1 up or down again if necessary. The process converges.

EXAMPLE 6.18

Assume that the same three pipes in Example 6.17 are now in parallel with the same total head loss of 20.3 m. Compute the total flow rate Q, neglecting minor losses.

Solution

From Eq. (6.109a) we can solve for each V separately

$$20.3 \text{ m} = \frac{V_1^2}{2g} 1250 f_1 = \frac{V_2^2}{2g} 2500 f_2 = \frac{V_3^2}{2g} 2000 f_3 \qquad (1)$$

Guess fully rough flow in pipe 1: $f_1 = 0.0262$, $V_1 = 3.49 \text{ m/s}$; hence $\text{Re}_1 = V_1 d_1/\nu = 273,000$. From the Moody chart read $f_1 = 0.0267$; recompute $V_1 = 3.46 \text{ m/s}$, $Q_1 = 62.5 \text{ m}^3/\text{h}$. [This problem can also be solved from Eq. (6.66).]

Next guess for pipe 2: $f_2 \approx 0.0234$, $V_2 \approx 2.61 \text{ m/s}$; then $\text{Re}_2 = 153,000$, and hence $f_2 = 0.0246$, $V_2 = 2.55 \text{ m/s}$, $Q_2 = 25.9 \text{ m}^3/\text{h}$.

Finally guess for pipe 3: $f_3 \approx 0.0304$, $V_3 \approx 2.56 \text{ m/s}$; then $\text{Re}_3 = 100,000$, and hence $f_3 = 0.0313$, $V_3 = 2.52 \text{ m/s}$, $Q_3 = 11.4 \text{ m}^3/\text{h}$.

This is satisfactory convergence. The total flow rate is

$$Q = Q_1 + Q_2 + Q_3 = 62.5 + 25.9 + 11.4 = 99.8 \text{ m}^3/\text{h} \qquad \textit{Ans.}$$

These three pipes carry 10 times more flow in parallel than they do in series.

Consider the third example of a *three-reservoir pipe junction*, as in Fig. 6.24c. If all flows are considered positive toward the junction, then

$$Q_1 + Q_2 + Q_3 = 0 \qquad (6.110)$$

which obviously implies that one or two of the flows must be away from the junction. The pressure must change through each pipe so as to give the same static pressure p_J at the junction. In other words, let the HGL at the junction have the elevation

$$h_J = z_J + \frac{p_J}{\rho g}$$

where p_J is in gage pressure for simplicity. Then the head loss through each, assuming $p_1 = p_2 = p_3 = 0$ (gage) at each reservoir surface, must be such that

$$\Delta h_1 = \frac{V_1^2}{2g} \frac{f_1 L_1}{d_1} = z_1 - h_J$$

$$\Delta h_2 = \frac{V_2^2}{2g} \frac{f_2 L_2}{d_2} = z_2 - h_J \qquad (6.111)$$

$$\Delta h_3 = \frac{V_3^2}{2g} \frac{f_3 L_3}{d_3} = z_3 - h_J$$

We guess the position h_J and solve Eqs. (6.111) for V_1, V_2, and V_3 and hence Q_1, Q_2, and Q_3, iterating until the flow rates balance at the junction according to Eq. (6.110). If we guess h_J too *high*, the sum $Q_1 + Q_2 + Q_3$ will be *negative* and the remedy is to reduce h_J, and vice versa.

EXAMPLE 6.19

Take the same three pipes as in Example 6.17, and assume that they connect three reservoirs at these surface elevations

$$z_1 = 20 \text{ m} \qquad z_2 = 100 \text{ m} \qquad z_3 = 40 \text{ m}$$

Find the resulting flow rates in each pipe, neglecting minor losses.

Solution

As a first guess, take h_J equal to the middle reservoir height, $z_3 = h_J = 40$ m. This saves one calculation ($Q_3 = 0$) and enables us to get the lay of the land:

Reservoir	h_J, m	$z_i - h_J$, m	f_i	V_i, m/s	Q_i, m³/h	L_i/d_i
1	40	−20	0.0267	−3.43	−62.1	1250
2	40	60	0.0241	4.42	45.0	2500
3	40	0		0	0	2000
					$\Sigma Q = -17.1$	

Since the sum of the flow rates toward the junction is negative, we guessed h_J too high. Reduce h_J to 30 m and repeat:

Reservoir	h_J, m	$z_i - h_J$, m	f_i	V_i, m/s	Q_i, m³/h
1	30	−10	0.0269	−2.42	−43.7
2	30	70	0.0241	4.78	48.6
3	30	10	0.0317	1.76	8.0
				$\sum Q =$	12.9

This is positive $\sum Q$, and so we can linearly interpolate to get an accurate guess: $h_J \approx$ 34.3 m. Make one final list:

Reservoir	h_J, m	$z_i - h_J$, m	f_i	V_i, m/s	Q_i, m³/h
1	34.3	−14.3	0.0268	−2.90	−52.4
2	34.3	65.7	0.0241	4.63	47.1
3	34.3	5.7	0.0321	1.32	6.0
				$\sum Q =$	0.7

This is close enough; hence we calculate that the flow rate is 52.4 m³/h toward reservoir 3, balanced by 47.1 m³/h away from reservoir 1 and 6.0 m³/h away from reservoir 3.

One further iteration with this problem would give $h_J = 34.53$ m, resulting in $Q_1 = -52.8$, $Q_2 = 47.0$, and $Q_3 = 5.8$ m³/h, so that $\sum Q = 0$ to three-place accuracy. Pedagogically speaking, we would then be exhausted.

The ultimate case of a multipipe system is the *piping network* illustrated in Fig. 6.25. This might represent a water supply system for an apartment or subdivision or even a city. This network is quite complex algebraically but follows the same basic rules:

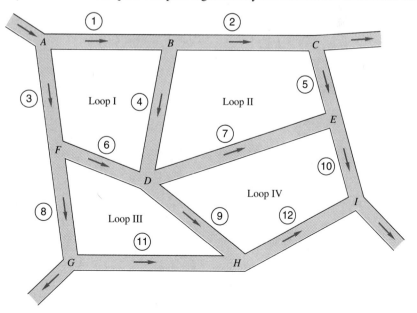

Fig. 6.25 Schematic of a piping network.

1. The net flow into any junction must be zero.
2. The net head loss around any closed loop must be zero. In other words, the HGL at each junction must have one and only one elevation.
3. All head losses must satisfy the Moody and minor-loss friction correlations.

By supplying these rules to each junction and independent loop in the network, one obtains a set of simultaneous equations for the flow rates in each pipe leg and the HGL (or pressure) at each junction. Solution may then be obtained by numerical iteration, as first developed in a hand-calculation technique by Prof. Hardy Cross in 1936 [17]. Computer solution of pipe-network problems is now quite common and covered in at least one specialized text [18]. Solution on microcomputers is also a reality. Some explicit numerical algorithms have been developed by Ormsbee and Wood [19]. Network analysis is quite useful for real water distribution systems if well calibrated with the actual system head-loss data.

6.9 Experimental Duct Flows: Diffuser Performance

The Moody chart is such a great correlation for tubes of any cross section with any roughness or flow rate that we may be deluded into thinking that the world of internal-flow prediction is at our feet. Not so. The theory is reliable only for ducts of constant cross section. As soon as the section varies, we must rely principally upon experiment to determine the flow properties. As mentioned many times before, experiment is a vital part of fluid mechanics.

Literally thousands of papers in the literature report experimental data for specific internal and external viscous flows. We have already seen several examples:

1. Vortex shedding from a cylinder (Fig. 5.2)
2. Drag of a sphere and a cylinder (Fig. 5.3)
3. Hydraulic model of an estuary (Fig. 5.9)
4. Rough-wall pipe flows (Fig. 6.12)
5. Secondary flow in ducts (Fig. 6.16)
6. Minor-duct-loss coefficients (Sec. 6.7)

Chapter 7 will treat a great many more external-flow experiments, especially in Sec. 7.5. Here we shall show data for one type of internal flow, the diffuser.

Diffuser Performance

A diffuser, shown in Fig. 6.26a and b, is an expansion or area increase intended to reduce velocity in order to recover the pressure head of the flow. Rouse and Ince [6] relate that it may have been invented by customers of the early Roman (about 100 A.D.) water supply system, where water flowed continuously and was billed according to pipe size. The ingenious customers discovered that they could increase the flow rate at no extra cost by flaring the outlet section of the pipe.

Engineers have always designed diffusers to increase pressure and reduce kinetic energy of ducted flows, but until about 1950, diffuser design was a combination of art, luck, and vast amounts of empiricism. Small changes in design parameters caused large changes in performance. The Bernoulli equation seemed highly suspect as a useful tool.

Neglecting losses and gravity effects, the incompressible Bernoulli equation predicts that

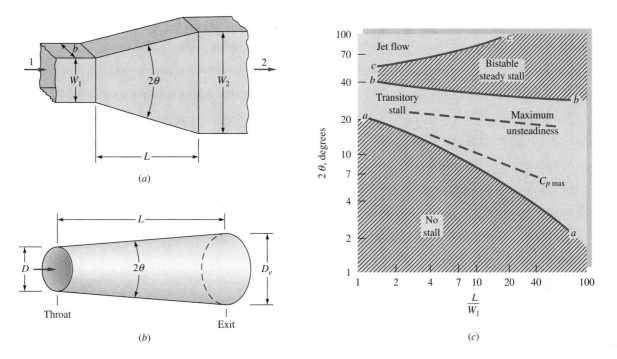

(a)

(b)

(c)

Fig. 6.26 Diffuser geometry and typical flow regimes: (a) geometry of a flat-walled diffuser; (b) geometry of a conical diffuser; (c) flat-diffuser stability map. (*From Ref. 14, by permission of Creare, Inc.*)

$$p + \tfrac{1}{2}\rho V^2 = p_0 = \text{const} \tag{6.112}$$

where p_0 is the stagnation pressure which the fluid would achieve if the fluid were slowed to rest ($V = 0$) without losses.

The basic output of a diffuser is the *pressure-recovery coefficient C_p*, defined as

$$C_p = \frac{p_e - p_t}{p_{0t} - p_t} \tag{6.113}$$

where subscripts e and t mean the exit and the throat (or inlet), respectively. Higher C_p means better performance.

Consider the flat-walled diffuser in Fig. 6.26a, where section 1 is the inlet and section 2 the exit. Application of Bernoulli's equation (6.112) to this diffuser predicts that

$$p_{01} = p_1 + \tfrac{1}{2}\rho V_1^2 = p_2 + \tfrac{1}{2}\rho V_2^2 = p_{02}$$

or

$$C_{p,\text{ frictionless}} = 1 - \left(\frac{V_2}{V_1}\right)^2 \tag{6.114}$$

Meanwhile, steady one-dimensional continuity would require that

$$Q = V_1 A_1 = V_2 A_2 \tag{6.115}$$

Combining (6.114) and (6.115), we can write the performance in terms of the *area ratio* $\text{AR} = A_2/A_1$, which is a basic parameter in diffuser design:

$$C_{p,\text{ frictionless}} = 1 - (\text{AR})^{-2} \tag{6.116}$$

A typical design would have $\text{AR} = 5:1$, for which Eq. (6.116) predicts $C_p = 0.96$, or nearly full recovery. But, in fact, measured values of C_p for this area ratio [14] are only as high as 0.86 and can be as low as 0.24.

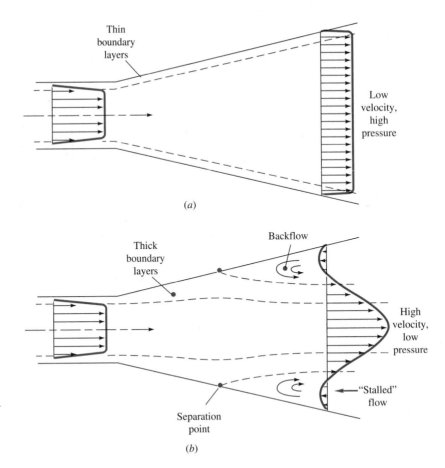

Fig. 6.27 Diffuser performance: (a) ideal pattern with good performance; (b) actual measured pattern with boundary-layer separation and resultant poor performance.

The basic reason for the discrepancy is flow separation, as sketched in Fig. 6.27. The increasing pressure in the diffuser is an unfavorable gradient (Sec. 7.4), which causes the viscous boundary layers to break away from the walls and greatly reduces the performance. Theories can now predict this behavior (see, e.g., Ref. 20).

As an added complication to boundary-layer separation, the flow patterns in a diffuser are highly variable and were considered mysterious and erratic until 1955, when Kline revealed the structure of these patterns with flow-visualization techniques in a simple water channel.

A complete *stability map* of diffuser flow patterns was published in 1962 by Fox and Kline [21], as shown in Fig. 6.26c. There are four basic regions. Below line *aa* there is steady viscous flow, no separation, and moderately good performance. Note that even a very short diffuser will separate, or stall, if its half-angle is greater than 10°.

Between lines *aa* and *bb* is a transitory stall pattern with strongly unsteady flow. Best performance, i.e., highest C_p, occurs in this region. The third pattern, between *bb* and *cc*, is steady bistable stall from one wall only. The stall pattern may flip-flop from one wall to the other, and performance is poor.

The fourth pattern, above line *cc*, is *jet flow*, where the wall separation is so gross and pervasive that the mainstream ignores the walls and simply passes on through at nearly constant area. Performance is extremely poor in this region.

Dimensional analysis of a flat-walled or conical diffuser shows that C_p should depend upon the following parameters:

1. Any two of the following geometric parameters:
   a. Area ratio AR $= A_2/A_1$ or $(D_e/D)^2$
   b. Divergence angle 2θ
   c. Slenderness L/W_1 or L/D
2. Inlet Reynolds number $Re_t = V_1 W_1/\nu$ or $Re_t = V_1 D/\nu$
3. Inlet Mach number $Ma_t = V_1/a_1$
4. Inlet boundary-layer *blockage factor* $B_t = A_{BL}/A_1$, where A_{BL} is the wall area blocked, or displaced, by the retarded boundary-layer flow in the inlet (typically B_t varies from 0.03 to 0.12)

A flat-walled diffuser would require an additional shape parameter to describe its cross section:

5. Aspect ratio AS $= b/W_1$

Even with this formidable list, we have omitted five possible important effects: inlet turbulence, inlet swirl, inlet profile vorticity, superimposed pulsations, and downstream obstruction, all of which occur in practical machinery applications.

The three most important parameters are AR, θ, and B. Typical performance maps for diffusers are shown in Fig. 6.28. For this case of 8 to 9 percent blockage, both the flat-walled and conical types give about the same maximum performance, $C_p = 0.70$, but at different divergence angles (9° flat versus 4.5° conical). Both types fall far short of the Bernoulli estimates of $C_p = 0.93$ (flat) and 0.99 (conical), primarily because of the blockage effect.

From the data of Ref. 14 we can determine that, in general, performance decreases with blockage and is approximately the same for both flat-walled and conical diffusers, as shown in Table 6.6. In all cases, the best conical diffuser is 10 to 80 percent longer than the best flat-walled design. Therefore, if length is limited in the design, the flat-walled design will give the better performance.

The experimental design of a diffuser is an excellent example of a successful attempt to minimize the undesirable effects of adverse pressure gradient and flow separation.

Table 6.6 Maximum Diffuser-Performance Data [14]

Inlet blockage B_t	Flat-walled		Conical	
	$C_{p,\max}$	L/W_1	$C_{p,\max}$	L/d
0.02	0.86	18	0.83	20
0.04	0.80	18	0.78	22
0.06	0.75	19	0.74	24
0.08	0.70	20	0.71	26
0.10	0.66	18	0.68	28
0.12	0.63	16	0.65	30

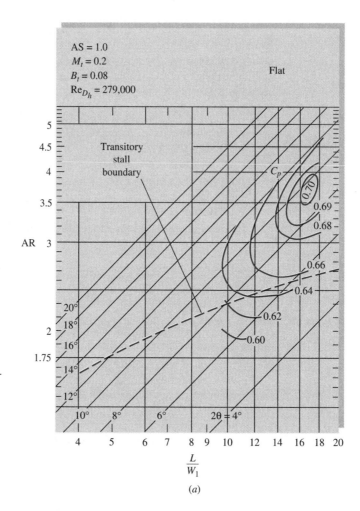

Fig. 6.28a Typical performance maps for flat-wall and conical diffusers at similar operating conditions: (a) flat wall. (*From Ref. 14, by permission of Creare, Inc.*)

6.10 Fluid Meters

Almost all practical fluids engineering problems are associated with the need for an accurate flow measurement. There is a need to measure *local* properties (velocity, pressure, temperature, density, viscosity, turbulent intensity), *integrated* properties (mass flow and volume flow), and *global* properties (visualization of the entire flow field). We shall concentrate in this section on velocity and volume-flow measurements.

We have discussed pressure measurement in Sec. 2.10. Measurement of other thermodynamic properties, such as density, temperature, and viscosity, is beyond the scope of this text and is treated in specialized books such as Refs. 22 and 23. Global visualization techniques were discussed in Sec. 1.7 for low-speed flows, and the special optical techniques used in high-speed flows are treated in Ref. 21 of Chap. 1. Flow-measurement schemes suitable for open-channel and other free-surface flows are treated in Chap. 10.

Local-Velocity Measurements

Velocity averaged over a small region, or point, can be measured by several different physical principles, listed in order of increasing complexity and sophistication:

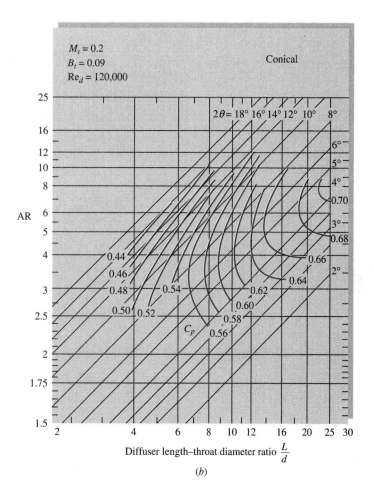

Fig. 6.28b Typical performance maps for flat-wall and conical diffusers at similar operating conditions: (b) conical wall. (*From Ref. 14, by permission of Creare, Inc.*)

1. Trajectory of floats or neutrally buoyant particles
2. Rotating mechanical devices
   a. Cup anemometer
   b. Savonius rotor
   c. Propeller meter
   d. Turbine meter
3. Pitot-static tube (Fig. 6.30)
4. Electromagnetic current meter
5. Hot wires and hot films
6. Laser-doppler anemometer (LDA)

Some of these meters are sketched in Fig. 6.29.

Floats or Buoyant Particles. A simple but effective estimate of flow velocity can be found from visible particles entrained in the flow. Examples include flakes on the surface of a channel flow, small neutrally buoyant spheres mixed with a liquid, or hydrogen bub-

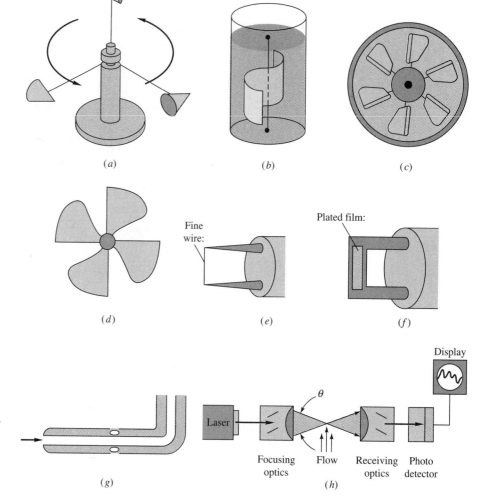

Fig. 6.29 Eight common velocity meters: (*a*) three-cup anemometer; (*b*) Savonius rotor; (*c*) turbine mounted in a duct; (*d*) free-propeller meter; (*e*) hot-wire anemometer; (*f*) hot-film anemometer; (*g*) pitot-static tube; (*h*) laser-doppler anemometer.

bles. Sometimes gas flows can be estimated from the motion of entrained dust particles. One must establish whether the particle motion truly simulates the fluid motion. Floats are commonly used to track the movement of ocean waters and can be designed to move at the surface, along the bottom, or at any given depth [24]. Many official tidal-current charts [25] were obtained by releasing and timing a floating spar attached to a length of string. One can release whole groups of spars to determine a flow pattern.

Rotating Sensors. The rotating devices of Fig. 6.29*a* to *d* can be used in either gases or liquids, and their rotation rate is approximately proportional to the flow velocity. The cup anemometer (Fig. 6.29*a*) and Savonius rotor (Fig. 6.29*b*) always rotate the same way, regardless of flow direction. They are popular in atmospheric and oceanographic applications and can be fitted with a direction vane to align themselves with the flow. The ducted-propeller (Fig. 6.29*c*) and free-propeller (Fig. 6.29*d*) meters must be aligned with the flow parallel to their axis of rotation. They can sense reverse flow because they will then rotate in the opposite direction. All these rotating sensors can be attached to counters or sensed by electromagnetic or slip-ring devices for either a continuous or a digital reading of flow velocity. All have the disadvantage of being relatively large and thus not representing a ''point.''

Pitot-Static Tube. A slender tube aligned with the flow (Figs. 6.29g and 6.30) can measure local velocity by means of a pressure difference. It has sidewall holes to measure the static pressure p_s in the moving stream and a hole in the front to measure the *stagnation* pressure p_0, where the stream is decelerated to zero velocity. Instead of measuring p_0 or p_s separately, it is customary to measure their difference with, say, a transducer, as in Fig. 6.30.

If $\mathrm{Re}_D > 1000$, where D is the probe diameter, the flow around the probe is nearly frictionless and Bernoulli's relation, Eq. (3.77), applies with good accuracy. For incompressible flow

$$p_s + \tfrac{1}{2}\rho V^2 + \rho g z_s \approx p_0 + \tfrac{1}{2}\rho(0)^2 + \rho g z_0$$

Assuming that the elevation pressure difference $\rho g(z_s - z_0)$ is negligible, this reduces to

$$V \approx \left[\frac{2(p_0 - p_s)}{\rho}\right]^{1/2} \tag{6.117}$$

This is the *Pitot formula*, named after the French engineer who designed the device in 1732.

The primary disadvantage of the pitot tube is that it must be aligned with the flow direction, which may be unknown. For yaw angles greater than 5°, there are substantial errors in both the p_0 and p_s measurements, as shown in Fig. 6.30. The pitot-static tube is useful in liquids and gases; for gases a compressibility correction is necessary if the stream Mach number is high (Chap. 9). Because of the slow response of the fluid-filled tubes leading to the pressure sensors, it is not useful for unsteady-flow measurements. It does resemble a point and can be made small enough to measure, e.g., blood flow in

Fig. 6.30 Pitot-static tube for combined measurement of static and stagnation pressure in a moving stream.

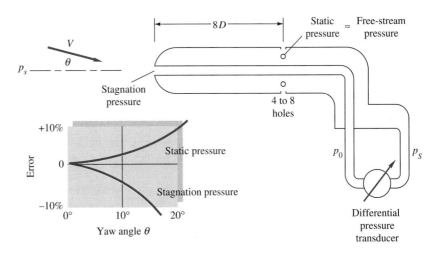

arteries and veins. It is not suitable for low-velocity measurement in gases because of the small pressure differences developed. For example, if $V = 1$ ft/s in standard air, from Eq. (6.117) we compute $p_0 - p$ equal to only 0.001 lbf/ft² (0.048 Pa). This is beyond the resolution of most pressure gages.

Electromagnetic Meter. If a magnetic field is applied across a conducting fluid, the fluid motion will induce a voltage across two electrodes placed in or near the flow. The electrodes can be streamlined or built into the wall, and they cause little or no flow resistance. The output is very strong for highly conducting fluids such as liquid metals. Seawater also gives good output, and electromagnetic current meters are in common use in oceanography. Even low-conductivity fresh water can be measured by amplifying the output and insulating the electrodes. Commercial instruments are available for most liquid flows but are relatively costly. Electromagnetic flowmeters are treated in Ref. 26.

Hot-Wire Anemometer. A very fine wire ($d = 0.01$ mm or less) heated between two small probes, as in Fig. 6.29e, is ideally suited to measure rapidly fluctuating flows such as the turbulent boundary layer. The idea dates back to work by L. V. King in 1914 on heat loss from long thin cylinders. If electric power is supplied to heat the cylinder, the loss varies with flow velocity across the cylinder according to *King's law*

$$q = I^2 R \approx a + b(\rho V)^n \tag{6.118}$$

where $n \approx \frac{1}{3}$ at very low Reynolds numbers and equals $\frac{1}{2}$ at high Reynolds numbers. The hot wire normally operates in the high-Reynolds-number range but should be calibrated in each situation to find the best-fit a, b, and n. The wire can be operated either at constant current I, so that resistance R is a measure of V, or at constant resistance R (constant temperature), with I a measure of velocity. In either case, the output is a nonlinear function of V, and the equipment should contain a *linearizer* to produce convenient velocity data. Many varieties of commercial hot-wire equipment are available, as are do-it-yourself designs [27]. Excellent detailed discussions of the hot wire are given in Refs. 1 and 28.

Because of its frailty, the hot wire is not suited to liquid flows, whose high density and entrained sediment will knock the wire right off. A more stable yet quite sensitive alternative for liquid-flow measurement is the hot-film anemometer (Fig. 6.29f). A thin metallic film, usually platinum, is plated onto a relatively thick support which can be a wedge, a cone, or a cylinder. The operation is similar to the hot wire. The cone gives best response but is liable to error when the flow is yawed to its axis.

Hot wires can easily be arranged in groups to measure two- and three-dimensional velocity components.

Laser-Doppler Anemometer. In the LDA a laser beam provides highly focused, coherent monochromatic light which is passed through the flow. When this light is scattered from a moving particle in the flow, a stationary observer can detect a change, or *doppler shift*, in the frequency of the scattered light. The shift Δf is proportional to the velocity of the particle. There is essentially zero disturbance of the flow by the laser.

Figure 6.29h shows the popular dual-beam mode of the LDA. A focusing device splits the laser into two beams, which cross the flow at an angle θ. Their intersection, which is the measuring volume or resolution of the measurement, resembles an ellipsoid about 0.5 mm wide and 0.1 mm in diameter. Particles passing through this measuring volume scatter the beams; they then pass through receiving optics to a photodetector which converts the light to an electric signal. A signal processor then converts electric frequency to a voltage which can be either displayed or stored. If λ is the wavelength of the laser light, the measured velocity is given by

$$V = \frac{\lambda \, \Delta f}{2 \sin (\theta/2)} \tag{6.119}$$

Multiple components of velocity can be detected by using more than one photodetector and other operating modes. Either liquids or gases can be measured as long as scattering particles are present. In liquids, normal impurities serve as scatterers, but gases may have to be seeded. The particles may be as small as the wavelength of the light. Although the measuring volume is not as small as with a hot wire, the LDA is capable of measuring turbulent fluctuations.

The advantages of the LDA are as follows:

1. No disturbance of the flow
2. High spatial resolution of the flow field
3. Velocity data that are independent of the fluid thermodynamic properties
4. An output voltage that is linear with velocity
5. No need for calibration

The disadvantages are that both the apparatus and the fluid must be transparent to light and that the cost is high (a basic system shown in Fig. 6.29h begins at about $40,000).

Once installed, an LDA can map the entire flow field in minutest detail. To truly appreciate the power of the LDA, one should examine, e.g., the amazingly detailed three-dimensional flow profiles measured by Eckardt [29] in a high-speed centrifugal compressor impeller. Extensive discussions of laser velocimetry are given in Refs. 38 and 39.

EXAMPLE 6.20

The pitot-static tube of Fig. 6.30 uses mercury as a manometer fluid. When it is placed in a water flow, the manometer height reading is $h = 8.4$ in. Neglecting yaw and other errors, what is the flow velocity V in ft/s?

Solution

From the two-fluid manometer relation (2.33), with $z_A = z_2$, the pressure difference is related to h by

$$p_0 - p_s = (\gamma_M - \gamma_w)h$$

Taking the specific weights of mercury and water from Table 2.1, we have

$$p_0 - p_s = (846 - 62.4 \text{ lbf/ft}^3) \frac{8.4}{12} \text{ ft} = 549 \text{ lbf/ft}^2$$

The density of water is $62.4/32.2 = 1.94$ slugs/ft^3. Introducing these values into the pitot-static formula (6.117), we obtain

$$V = \left[\frac{2(549 \ \text{lbf/ft}^2)}{1.94 \ \text{slugs/ft}^3}\right]^{1/2} = 23.8 \ \text{ft/s} \qquad \textit{Ans.}$$

Since this is a low-speed flow, no compressibility correction is needed.

Volume-Flow Measurements

It is often desirable to measure the integrated mass, or volume flow, passing through a duct. Accurate measurement of flow is vital in billing customers for a given amount of liquid or gas passing through a duct. The different devices available to make these measurements are discussed in great detail in the ASME text on fluid meters [30]. These devices split into two classes: mechanical instruments and head-loss instruments.

The mechanical instruments measure actual mass or volume of fluid by trapping it and counting it. The various types of measurement are

1. Mass measurement
   a. Weighing tanks
   b. Tilting traps

2. Volume measurement
   a. Volume tanks
   b. Reciprocating pistons
   c. Rotating slotted rings
   d. Nutating disk
   e. Sliding vanes
   f. Gear or lobed impellers
   g. Reciprocating bellows
   h. Sealed-drum compartments

The last three of these are suitable for gas flow measurement.

The head-loss devices obstruct the flow and cause a pressure drop which is a measure of flux:

1. Bernoulli-type devices
   a. Thin-plate orifice
   b. Flow nozzle
   c. Venturi tube

2. Friction-loss devices
   a. Capillary tube
   b. Porous plug

The friction-loss meters cause a large nonrecoverable head loss and obstruct the flow too much to be generally useful.

Four other widely used meters operate on different physical principles:

1. Turbine meter
2. Vortex meter
3. Ultrasonic flowmeter
4. Rotameter

Turbine Meter. The turbine meter, sometimes called a *propeller meter*, is a freely rotating propeller which can be installed in a pipeline. A typical design is shown in Fig. 6.31*a*. There are flow straighteners upstream of the rotor, and the rotation is measured by electric or magnetic pickup of pulses caused by passage of a point on the rotor. The rotor rotation is approximately proportional to the volume flow in the pipe.

A major advantage of the turbine meter is that each pulse corresponds to a finite incremental volume of fluid, and the pulses are digital and can be summed easily. Liquid-flow turbine meters have as few as two blades and produce a constant number of pulses per unit fluid volume over a 5:1 flow-rate range with ±0.25 percent accuracy. Gas meters need many blades to produce sufficient torque and are accurate to ±1 percent.

Fig. 6.31 The turbine meter widely used in the oil, gas, and water supply industries: (*a*) basic design; (*b*) typical calibration curve for a range of crude oils. (*Daniel Industries, Inc., Flow Products Division.*)

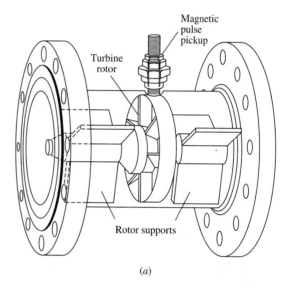

(*a*)

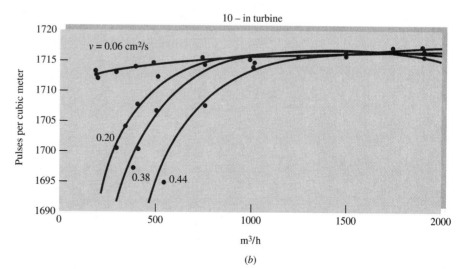

(*b*)

Since turbine meters are very individualistic, flow calibration is an absolute necessity. A typical liquid-meter calibration curve is shown in Fig. 6.31*b*. Researchers attempting to establish universal calibration curves have met with little practical success as a result of manufacturing variabilities.

Vortex Flowmeters. Recall from Fig. 5.2 that a bluff body placed in a uniform crossflow sheds alternating vortices at a nearly uniform Strouhal number $St = fL/U$, where U is the approach velocity and L is a characteristic body width. Since L and St are constant, this means that the shedding frequency is proportional to velocity

$$f = (\text{const})(LU) \tag{6.120}$$

The vortex meter introduces a shedding element across a pipe flow and picks up the shedding frequency downstream with a pressure, ultrasonic, or heat-transfer type of sensor. A typical design is shown in Fig. 6.32.

The advantages of a vortex meter are as follows:

1. Absence of moving parts
2. Accuracy to ± 1 percent over a wide flow-rate range (up to 100 : 1)
3. Ability to handle very hot or very cold fluids
4. Requirement of only a short pipe length
5. Calibration insensitive to fluid density or viscosity

For further details see Ref. 40.

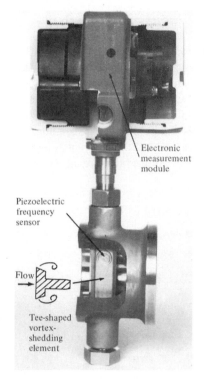

Fig. 6.32 A vortex flowmeter. (*The Foxboro Company.*)

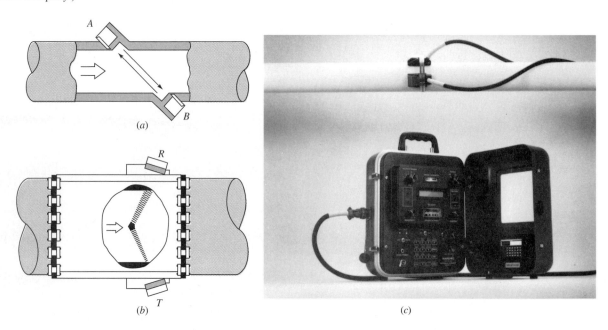

Fig. 6.33 Ultrasonic flowmeters: (*a*) pulse type; (*b*) doppler-shift type (*from Ref. 41*); (*c*) a portable noninvasive installation (*courtesy of Polysonics Inc., Houston, Tex.*)

Ultrasonic Flowmeters. The sound-wave analog of the laser velocimeter of Fig. 6.29h is the ultrasonic flowmeter. Two examples are shown in Fig. 6.33. The pulse-type flowmeter is shown in Fig. 6.33a. Upstream piezoelectric transducer A is excited with a short sonic pulse which propagates across the flow to downstream transducer B. The arrival at B triggers another pulse to be created at A, resulting in a regular pulse frequency f_A. The same process is duplicated in the reverse direction from B to A, creating frequency f_B. The difference $f_A - f_B$ is proportional to the flow rate. Figure 6.32b shows a doppler-type arrangement, where sound waves from transmitter T are scattered by particles or contaminants in the flow to receiver R. Comparison of the two signals reveals a doppler frequency shift which is proportional to the flow rate. Ultrasonic meters are nonintrusive and can be directly attached to pipe flows in the field (Fig. 6.33c). Their quoted uncertainty of ± 1 to 2 percent can rise to ± 5 percent or more due to irregularities in velocity profile, fluid temperature, or Reynolds number. For further details see Ref. 41.

Rotameter. The variable-area transparent *rotameter* of Fig. 6.34 has a float which, under the action of flow, rises in the vertical tapered tube and takes a certain equilibrium position for any given flow rate. A student exercise for the forces on the float would yield the approximate relation

$$Q = C_d A_a \left(\frac{2W_{\text{net}}}{A_{\text{float}}\rho_{\text{fluid}}} \right)^{1/2} \tag{6.121}$$

where W_{net} is the float's net weight in the fluid, $A_a = A_{\text{tube}} - A_{\text{float}}$ is the annular area between the float and the tube, and C_d is a dimensionless discharge coefficient of order unity, for the annular constricted flow. For slightly tapered tubes, A_a varies nearly linearly with the float position, and the tube may be calibrated and marked with a flow-rate scale, as in Fig. 6.34. The rotameter thus provides a readily visible measure of the flow rate. Capacity may be changed by using different-sized floats. Obviously the tube must be vertical, and the device does not give accurate readings for fluids containing high concentrations of bubbles or particles.

Bernoulli Obstruction Theory. Consider the generalized flow obstruction shown in Fig. 6.35. The flow in the basic duct of diameter D is forced through an obstruction of diameter d; the β ratio of the device is a key parameter

$$\beta = \frac{d}{D} \tag{6.122}$$

After leaving the obstruction, the flow may neck down even more through a vena contracta of diameter $D_2 < d$, as shown. Apply the Bernoulli and continuity equations for incompressible steady frictionless flow to estimate the pressure change:

Continuity: $\qquad\qquad Q = \frac{\pi}{4} D^2 V_1 = \frac{\pi}{4} D_2^2 V_2$

Bernoulli: $\qquad\qquad p_0 = p_1 + \frac{1}{2}\rho V_1^2 = p_2 + \frac{1}{2}\rho V_2^2$

Eliminating V_1, we solve these for V_2 or Q in terms of the pressure change $p_1 - p_2$:

$$\frac{Q}{A_2} = V_2 \approx \left[\frac{2(p_1 - p_2)}{\rho(1 - D_2^4/D^4)} \right]^{1/2} \tag{6.123}$$

Fig. 6.34 A commercial rotameter. The float rises in the tapered tube to an equilibrium position which is a measure of the fluid-flow rate. (*Courtesy of Blue White Industries, Westminster, Calif.*)

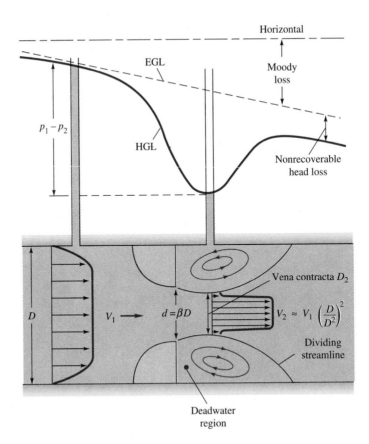

Fig. 6.35 Velocity and pressure change through a generalized Bernoulli obstruction meter.

But this is surely inaccurate because we have neglected friction in a duct flow, where we know friction will be very important. Nor do we want to get into the business of measuring vena contracta ratios D_2/d for use in (6.123). Therefore we assume that $D_2/D \approx \beta$ and then calibrate the device to fit the relation

$$Q = A_t V_t = C_d A_t \left[\frac{2(p_1 - p_2)/\rho}{1 - \beta^4} \right]^{1/2} \tag{6.124}$$

where subscript t denotes the throat of the obstruction. The dimensionless *discharge coefficient* C_d accounts for the discrepancies in the approximate analysis. By dimensional analysis for a given design we expect

$$C_d = f(\beta, \text{Re}_D) \qquad \text{where} \qquad \text{Re}_D = \frac{V_1 D}{\nu} \tag{6.125}$$

The geometric factor involving β in (6.124) is called the *velocity-of-approach factor*

$$E = (1 - \beta^4)^{-1/2} \tag{6.126}$$

One can also group C_d and E in Eq. (6.124) to form the dimensionless *flow coefficient* α

$$\alpha = C_d E = \frac{C_d}{(1 - \beta^4)^{1/2}} \tag{6.127}$$

Thus Eq. (6.124) can be written in the equivalent form

$$Q = \alpha A_t \left[\frac{2(p_1 - p_2)}{\rho} \right]^{1/2} \tag{6.128}$$

Obviously the flow coefficient is correlated in the same manner:

$$\alpha = f(\beta, \text{Re}_D) \tag{6.129}$$

Occasionally one uses the throat Reynolds number instead of the approach Reynolds number

$$\text{Re}_d = \frac{V_t d}{\nu} = \frac{\text{Re}_D}{\beta} \tag{6.130}$$

Since the design parameters are assumed known, the correlation of α from Eq. (6.129) or of C_d from Eq. (6.125) is the desired solution to the fluid-metering problem.

The mass flow is related to Q by

$$\dot{m} = \rho Q \tag{6.131}$$

and is thus correlated by exactly the same formulas.

Figure 6.36 shows the three basic devices recommended for use by the International Organization for Standardization (ISO) [31]: the orifice, nozzle, and venturi tube.

Fig. 6.36 International standard shapes for the three primary Bernoulli obstruction-type meters: (*a*) long radius nozzle; (*b*) thin-plate orifice; (*c*) venturi nozzle. (*From Ref. 31 by permission of the International Organization for Standardization.*)

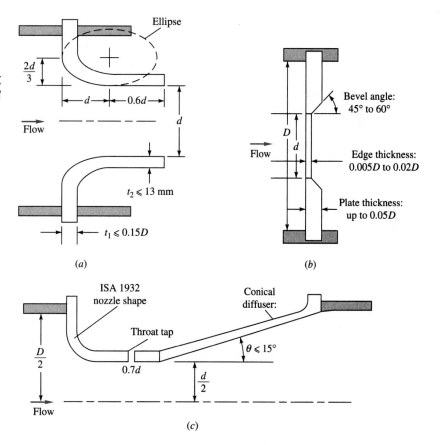

Thin-Plate Orifice. The thin-plate orifice, Fig. 6.36b, can be made with β in the range of 0.2 to 0.8, except that the hole diameter d should not be less than 12.5 mm. To measure p_1 and p_2, three types of tappings are commonly used:

1. Corner taps where the plate meets the pipe wall
2. $D: \frac{1}{2}D$ taps: pipe-wall taps at D upstream and $\frac{1}{2}D$ downstream
3. Flange taps: 1 in (25 mm) upstream and 1 in (25 mm) downstream of the plate, regardless of the size D

Types 1 and 2 approximate geometric similarity, but since the flange taps 3 do not, they must be correlated separately for every single size of pipe in which a flange-tap plate is used [30, 31].

Figure 6.37 shows the discharge coefficient of an orifice with $D : \frac{1}{2}D$ or type 2 taps in the Reynolds-number range $\text{Re}_D = 10^4$ to 10^7 of normal use. Although detailed charts such as Fig. 6.37 are available for designers [30], the ASME recommends use of the curve-fit formulas developed by the ISO [31]. The basic form of the curve fit is [42]

$$C_d = f(\beta) + 91.71\beta^{2.5}\text{Re}_D^{-0.75} + \frac{0.09\beta^4}{1 - \beta^4}F_1 - 0.0337\beta^3F_2 \qquad (6.132)$$

where

$$f(\beta) = 0.5959 + 0.0312\beta^{2.1} - 0.184\beta^8$$

Fig. 6.37 Discharge coefficient for a thin-plate orifice with $D: \frac{1}{2}D$ taps, plotted from Eqs. (6.132) and (6.133b).

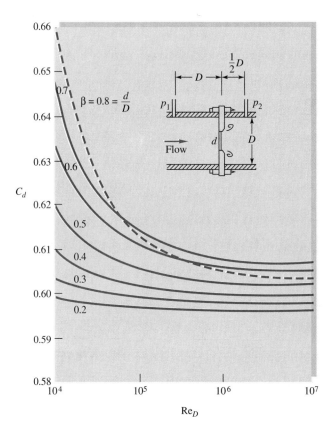

The correlation factors F_1 and F_2 vary with tap position:

Corner taps: $\qquad\qquad\qquad\qquad\qquad F_1 = 0 \qquad F_2 = 0$ (6.133a)

$D : \frac{1}{2}D$ taps: $\qquad\qquad\qquad\qquad F_1 = 0.4333 \qquad F_2 = 0.47$ (6.133b)

Flange taps: $\qquad F_2 = \dfrac{1}{D \text{ (in)}} \qquad F_1 = \begin{cases} \dfrac{1}{D \text{ (in)}} & D > 2.3 \text{ in} \\[2mm] 0.4333 & 2.0 \le D \le 2.3 \text{ in} \end{cases}$ (6.133c)

Note that the flange taps (6.133c), not being geometrically similar, use raw diameter in inches in the formula. The constants will change if other diameter units are used. We cautioned against such dimensional formulas in Example 1.4 and Eq. (5.17) and give Eq. (6.133c) only because flange taps are widely used in the United States.

Flow Nozzle. The flow nozzle comes in two types, a long-radius type shown in Fig. 6.36a and a short-radius type (not shown) called the ISA 1932 nozzle [30, 31]. The flow nozzle, with its smooth rounded entrance convergence, practically eliminates the vena contracta and gives discharge coefficients near unity. The nonrecoverable loss is still large because there is no diffuser provided for gradual expansion.

The ISO recommended correlation for long-radius-nozzle discharge coefficient is

$$C_d \approx 0.9965 - 0.00653\beta^{1/2}\left(\frac{10^6}{\text{Re}_D}\right)^{1/2} = 0.9965 - 0.00653\left(\frac{10^6}{\text{Re}_d}\right)^{1/2}$$ (6.134)

The second form is independent of the β ratio and is plotted in Fig. 6.38. A similar ISO correlation is recommended for the short-radius ISA 1932 flow nozzle

$$C_d \approx 0.9900 - 0.2262\beta^{4.1}$$
$$+ (0.000215 - 0.001125\beta + 0.00249\beta^{4.7})\left(\frac{10^6}{\text{Re}_D}\right)^{1.15}$$ (6.135)

Flow nozzles may have β values between 0.2 and 0.8.

Fig. 6.38 Discharge coefficient for long-radius nozzle and classical Herschel-type venturi.

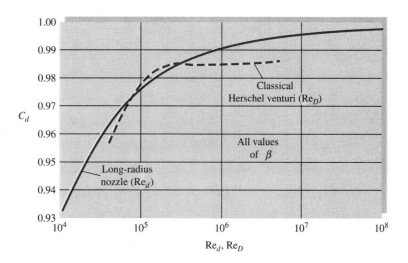

Venturi Meter. The third and final type of obstruction meter is the venturi, named in honor of Giovanni Venturi (1746–1822), an Italian physicist who first tested conical expansions and contractions. The original, or *classical*, venturi was invented by a U.S. engineer, Clemens Herschel, in 1898. It consisted of a 21° conical contraction, a straight throat of diameter d and length d, then a 7 to 15° conical expansion. The discharge coefficient is near unity, and the nonrecoverable loss is very small. Herschel venturis are seldom used now.

The modern venturi nozzle, Fig. 6.36c, consists of an ISA 1932 nozzle entrance and a conical expansion of half-angle no greater than 15°. It is intended to be operated in a narrow Reynolds-number range of 1.5×10^5 to 2×10^6. Its discharge coefficient, shown in Fig. 6.39, is given by the ISO correlation formula

$$C_d \approx 0.9858 - 0.196\beta^{4.5} \tag{6.136}$$

It is independent of Re_D within the given range. The Herschel venturi discharge varies with Re_D but not with β, as shown in Fig. 6.38. Both have very low net losses.

The choice of meter depends upon the loss and the cost and can be illustrated by the following table:

Type of meter	Net head loss	Cost
Orifice	Large	Small
Nozzle	Medium	Medium
Venturi	Small	Large

As so often happens, the product of inefficiency and initial cost is approximately constant.

The average nonrecoverable head losses for the three types of meters, expressed as a fraction of the throat velocity head $V_t^2/(2g)$, are shown in Fig. 6.40. The orifice has the greatest loss and the venturi the least, as discussed. The orifice and nozzle simulate partially closed valves as in Fig. 6.18, while the venturi is a very minor loss. When the

Fig. 6.39 Discharge coefficient for a venturi nozzle.

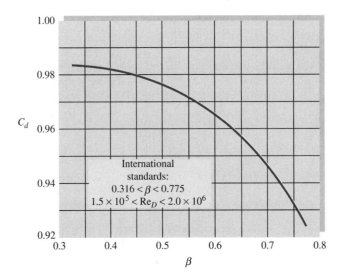

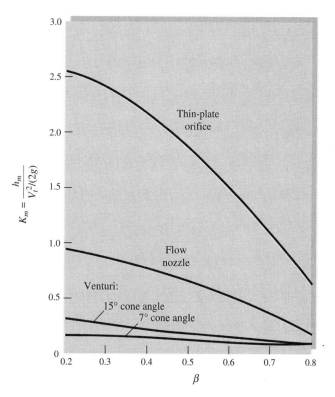

Fig. 6.40 Nonrecoverable head loss in Bernoulli obstruction meters. (*Adapted from Ref. 30.*)

loss is given as a fraction of the measured *pressure drop*, the orifice and nozzle have nearly equal losses, as Example 6.21 will illustrate.

The other types of instruments discussed earlier in this section can also serve as flowmeters if properly constructed. For example, a hot wire mounted in a tube can be calibrated to read volume flow rather than point velocity. Such hot-wire meters are commercially available, as are other meters modified to use velocity instruments. For further details see Ref. 30.

EXAMPLE 6.21

We want to meter the volume flow of water ($\rho = 1000$ kg/m^3, $\nu = 1.02 \times 10^{-6}$ m^2/s) moving through a 200-mm-diameter pipe at an average velocity of 2.0 m/s. If the differential pressure gage selected reads accurately at $p_1 - p_2 = 50{,}000$ Pa, what size meter should be selected for installing (*a*) an orifice with $D : \frac{1}{2}D$ taps, (*b*) a long-radius flow nozzle, or (*c*) a venturi nozzle? What would be the nonrecoverable head loss for each design?

Solution

Here the unknown is the β ratio of the meter. Since the discharge coefficient is a complicated function of β, iteration will be necessary. We are given $D = 0.2$ m and $V_1 = 2.0$ m/s. The pipe-approach Reynolds number is thus

$$\mathrm{Re}_D = \frac{V_1 D}{\nu} = \frac{(2.0)(0.2)}{1.02 \times 10^{-6}} = 392{,}000$$

The generalized formula (6.128) gives the throat velocity as

$$V_t = \frac{V_1}{\beta^2} = \alpha \left[\frac{2(p_1 - p_2)}{\rho} \right]^{1/2}$$

where everything is known except α and β. Solve for β^2

$$\beta^2 = \frac{1}{\alpha} \left(\frac{\rho V_1^2}{2 \, \Delta p} \right)^{1/2} \tag{1}$$

With $V_1 = 2.0$ m/s and $\Delta p = 50{,}000$ Pa, this should be valid for all three meters. Substitute in these numbers:

$$\beta^2 = \frac{1}{\alpha} \left[\frac{(1000)(2.0)^2}{2(50{,}000)} \right]^{1/2} = \frac{0.2}{\alpha}$$

or

$$\beta = \frac{0.447}{\alpha^{1/2}} \tag{2}$$

The solution depends only on getting the proper flow coefficient.

Part (a)   A good initial guess for an orifice is $\alpha \approx 0.62$. From Eq. (2) compute $\beta \approx 0.447/(0.62)^{1/2} = 0.568$. From Eq. (6.132) or Fig. 6.37 compute the discharge coefficient

$$C_d = 0.6064$$

for $\beta = 0.568$ and $\mathrm{Re}_D = 392{,}000$

Then $E = [1 - (0.568)^4]^{-1/2} = 1.0565$ $\alpha = C_d E = 0.6407$

Iterate Eq. (2) again

$$\beta = \frac{0.447}{(0.6407)^{1/2}} = 0.558 \qquad C_d = 0.6061 \qquad \alpha = 0.6378$$

Stop. We have converged satisfactorily to a design value

$$\beta \approx 0.56 \qquad d = \beta D = 112 \text{ mm} \qquad \qquad Ans. \ (a)$$

The throat velocity is $V_t = V_1/\beta^2 = 2.0/(0.56)^2 = 6.38$ m/s. The throat head is

$$\frac{V_t^2}{2g} = \frac{(6.38)^2}{2(9.81)} = 2.07 \text{ m}$$

From Fig. 6.40 for the orifice at $\beta = 0.56$, estimate $K_m \approx 1.7$. Then the nonrecoverable loss of the orifice will be

$$h_m = K_m \frac{V_t^2}{2g} \approx 1.7(2.07) = 3.5 \text{ m} \qquad \qquad Ans. \ (a)$$

Part (b)   A good guess for flow-nozzle design is $\alpha = 1.0$. Iterate Eq. (2) and list the results:

α	β, Eq. (2)	C_d, Fig. 6.38	E	$\alpha = EC_d$
1.0	0.447	0.9895	1.0206	1.0099
1.0099	0.445	0.9895	1.0202	1.0095
1.0095	0.445			

Convergence is rapid to

$$\beta = 0.445 \qquad d = \beta D = 89 \text{ mm} \qquad \qquad \textit{Ans. (b)}$$

The throat velocity is $2.0/(0.445)^2 = 10.1 \text{ m/s}$; the throat head is $(10.1)^2/[2(9.81)] = 5.2 \text{ m}$. From Fig. 6.40 for the nozzle read $K_m \approx 0.7$. Then the nozzle loss is

$$h_m = 0.7(5.2 \text{ m}) = 3.6 \text{ m} \qquad \qquad \textit{Ans. (b)}$$

This is the same as the orifice because of the higher throat head.

Part (c)   For the venturi guess $\alpha \approx 1.0$ and iterate Eq. (2):

$$\alpha = 1.0 \qquad \beta[\text{Eq. (2)}] = 0.447 \qquad C_d \text{ (Fig. 6.35)} = 0.9806$$
$$= 1.007 \qquad \qquad \qquad = 0.4468 \qquad \qquad \qquad = 0.9806$$

This rapidly converges to give

$$\beta = 0.4468 \qquad d = \beta D = 89 \text{ mm} \qquad \qquad \textit{Ans. (c)}$$

The throat velocity is $2.0/(0.4468)^2 = 10.0 \text{ m/s}$, and the throat head is $(10.0)^2/[2(9.81)] = 5.12 \text{ m}$. From Fig. 6.40 for the venturi estimate $K_m \approx 0.15$; hence

$$h_m = 0.15(5.12 \text{ m}) = 0.8 \text{ m} \qquad \qquad \textit{Ans. (c)}$$

This is only 22 percent of the orifice and nozzle losses.

Summary

This chapter is concerned with internal pipe and duct flows, which are probably the most common problems encountered in engineering fluid mechanics. Such flows are very sensitive to the Reynolds number and change from laminar to transitional to turbulent flow as the Reynolds number increases.

The various Reynolds-number regimes are outlined, and a semiempirical approach to turbulent-flow modeling is presented. The chapter then makes a detailed analysis of flow through a straight circular pipe, leading to the famous Moody chart (Fig. 6.13) for the friction factor. Possible uses of the Moody chart are discussed for flow-rate and sizing problems, as well as the application of the Moody chart to noncircular ducts using an equivalent duct "diameter." The addition of minor losses due to valves, elbows, fittings, and other devices is presented in the form of loss coefficients to be incorporated along with Moody-type friction losses. Multiple-pipe systems are discussed briefly and are seen to be quite complex algebraically and appropriate for computer solution.

Diffusers are added to ducts to increase pressure recovery at the exit of a system. Their behavior is presented as experimental data, since the theory of real diffusers is still not well developed. The chapter ends with a discussion of flowmeters, especially the pitot-static tube and the Bernoulli-obstruction type of meter. Flowmeters also require careful experimental calibration.

References

1. J. O. Hinze, *Turbulence*, 2d ed., McGraw-Hill, New York, 1975.
2. H. Schlichting, *Boundary Layer Theory*, 7th ed., McGraw-Hill, New York, 1979.
3. F. M. White, *Viscous Fluid Flow*, 2d ed., McGraw-Hill, New York, 1991.
4. O. Reynolds, "An Experimental Investigation of the Circumstances which Determine Whether the Motion of Water Shall Be Direct or Sinuous and of the Law of Resistance in Parallel Channels," *Phil. Trans. R. Soc.,* vol. 174, 1883, pp. 935–982.
5. P. G. Drazin and W. H. Reid, *Hydrodynamic Stability*, Cambridge University Press, London, 1981.
6. H. Rouse and S. Ince, *History of Hydraulics*, Iowa Institute of Hydraulic Research, State University of Iowa, Iowa City, 1957.
7. J. Nikuradse, "Strömungsgesetze in Rauhen Rohren," *VDI Forschungsh.* 361, 1933; English trans., *NACA Tech. Mem.* 1292.
8. L. F. Moody, "Friction Factors for Pipe Flow," *ASME Trans.,* vol. 66, pp. 671–684, 1944.
9. C. F. Colebrook, "Turbulent Flow in Pipes, with Particular Reference to the Transition between the Smooth and Rough Pipe Laws," *J. Inst. Civ. Eng. Lond.,* vol. 11, 1938–1939, pp. 133–156.
10. O. C. Jones, Jr., "An Improvement in the Calculations of Turbulent Friction in Rectangular Ducts," *J. Fluids Eng.*, June 1976, pp. 173–181.
11. R. Berker, *Handbuch der Physik*, vol. 7, no. 2, pp. 1–384, Springer-Verlag, Berlin, 1963.
12. R. M. Olson and S. J. Wright, *Essentials of Engineering Fluid Mechanics*, 5th ed., Harper & Row, New York, 1990.
13. D. Alciatore and W. S. Janna, "Modified Pipe Friction Diagrams That Eliminate Trial-and-Error Solutions," *Proc. 1st Natl. Fluid Dynamics Congress*, pt. 2, pp. 911–916, AIAA, Washington, 1988.
14. P. W. Runstadler, Jr., et al., "Diffuser Data Book," *Creare Inc. Tech. Note* 186, Hanover, N.H., 1975.
15. "Flow of Fluids through Valves, Fittings, and Pipe," *Crane Co. Tech. Pap.* 410, Chicago, 1957.
16. *Pipe Friction Manual*, 3d ed., The Hydraulic Institute, New York, 1961.
17. Hardy Cross, "Analysis of Flow in Networks of Conduits or Conductors," *Univ. Ill. Bull.* 286, November 1936.
18. R. W. Jepson, *Analysis of Flow in Pipe Networks*, Ann Arbor Pub., Ann Arbor, Mich., 1976.
19. L. E. Ormsbee and D. J. Wood, "Explicit Pipeline Network Calibration," *J. Water Resources Planning and Management*, vol. 112, no. 2, April 1986, pp. 166–182.
20. J. Bardina et al,. "A Prediction Method for Planar Diffuser Flows," *J. Fluids Eng.*, vol. 103, 1981, pp. 315–321.
21. R. W. Fox and S. J. Kline, "Flow Regime Data and Design Methods for Curved Subsonic Diffusers," *J. Basic Eng.*, vol. 84, 1962, pp. 303–312.
22. J. P. Holman, *Experimental Methods for Engineers*, 5th ed., McGraw-Hill, New York, 1989.
23. T. G. Beckwith and R. D. Marangoni, *Mechanical Measurements*, 4th ed., Addison-Wesley, Reading, Mass., 1990.
24. B. Warren and C. Wunsch (eds.), *Evolution of Physical Oceanography*, M.I.T. Press, Cambridge, Mass., 1981.
25. U.S. Department of Commerce, *Tidal Current Tables*, National Oceanographic and Atmospheric Administration, Washington, 1971.
26. J. A. Shercliff, *Electromagnetic Flow Measurement*, Cambridge University Press, New York, 1962.
27. J. A. Miller, "A Simple Linearized Hot-Wire Anemometer," *J. Fluids Eng.*, December 1976, pp. 749–752.

28. R. J. Goldstein (ed.), *Fluid Mechanics Measurements*, Hemisphere, New York, 1983.

29. D. Eckardt, "Detailed Flow Investigations within a High Speed Centrifugal Compressor Impeller," *J. Fluids Eng.*, September 1976, pp. 390–402.

30. H. S. Bean (ed.), *Fluid Meters: Their Theory and Application*, 6th ed., American Society of Mechanical Engineers, New York, 1971.

31. "Measurement of Fluid Flow by Means of Orifice Plates, Nozzles, and Venturi Tubes Inserted in Circular Cross Section Conduits Running Full," *Int. Organ. Stand. Rep.* DIS-5167, Geneva, April 1976.

32. P. Moin and P. R. Spalart, in *Advances in Turbulence*, W. K. George and R. Arndt (eds.), Hemisphere, New York, 1989, pp. 11–38.

33. S. E. Haaland, "Simple and Explicit Formulas for the Friction Factor in Turbulent Pipe Flow," *Fluids Eng.*, March 1983, pp. 89–90.

34. R. K. Shah and A. L. London, *Laminar Flow Forced Convection in Ducts*, Academic, New York, 1979.

35. J. L. Lyons, *Lyons' Valve Designers Handbook*, Van Nostrand Reinhold, New York, 1982.

36. A. O. Demuren and W. Rodi, "Calculations of Turbulence-Driven Secondary Motion in Non-circular Ducts," *J. Fluid Mech.*, vol. 140, 1984, pp. 189–222.

37. *ASHRAE Handbook of Fundamentals*, chap. 33, ASHRAE, Atlanta, 1981.

38. F. Durst, A. Melling, and J. H. Whitelaw, *Principles and Practice of Laser-Doppler Anemometry*, 2d ed., Academic, New York, 1981.

39. A. Dybbs and B. Ghorashi, *Laser Anemometry: Advances and Applications*, American Society of Mechanical Engineers, New York, 1991.

40. J. G. Kopp, "Vortex Flowmeters," *Meas. Control*, June 1983, pp. 280–284.

41. J. C. Graber, Jr., "Ultrasonic Flow," *Meas. Control*, October 1983, pp. 258–266.

42. ASME Fluid Meters Research Committee, "The ISO-ASME Orifice Coefficient Equation," *Mech. Eng.* July 1981, pp. 44–45.

43. R. D. Blevins, *Applied Fluid Dynamics Handbook*, Van Nostrand Reinhold, New York, 1984.

44. O. C. Jones, Jr., and J. C. M. Leung, "An Improvement in the Calculation of Turbulent Friction in Smooth Concentric Annuli," *J. Fluids Eng.*, December 1981, pp. 615–623.

45. P. R. Bandyopadhyay, "Aspects of the Equilibrium Puff in Transitional Pipe Flow, *J. Fluid Mech.*, vol. 163, 1986, pp. 439–458.

46. I. E. Idelchik, *Handbook of Hydraulic Resistance*, 2d ed., Hemisphere, New York, 1986.

Recommended Films
Films numbered 3, 4, 11, 12, 15, 23, 24, and 26 in App. C.

PROBLEMS

In addition to many traditional problems, categorized in the problem distribution list below, there are word problems, labeled W6.1 to W6.6 and a design project, D6.1.

Problem Distribution

6.1   In flow past a sphere, the boundary layer becomes turbulent at about $Re_D \approx 2.5$ E5. To what air speed in mi/h does this correspond for a golf ball whose diameter is 1.6 in? Do the pressure, temperature, and humidity of the air make any difference in your calculation?

6.2   For a thin wing moving parallel to its chord line, transition to a turbulent boundary layer normally occurs at $Re_x = 2.8 \times 10^6$, where x is the distance from the leading edge [2, 3]. If the wing is moving at 20 m/s, at what point on the wing will transition occur at 20°C for (a) air and (b) water?

6.3   If the wing of Prob. 6.2 is tested in a wind or water tunnel, it may undergo transition earlier than $Re_x = 2.8 \times 10^6$ if the test stream itself contains turbulent fluctuations. A semi-empirical correlation for this case [3, p. 383] is

$$Re_{x_{crit}}^{1/2} \approx \frac{-1 + (1 + 13.25\zeta^2)^{1/2}}{0.00392\zeta^2}$$

where ζ is the tunnel-turbulence intensity in percent. If $V = 20$ m/s in air at 20°C, use this formula to plot the transition position on the wing versus stream turbulence for ζ between 0 and 2 percent. At what value of ζ is x_{crit} decreased 50 percent from its value at $\zeta = 0$?

6.4   For flow of SAE 10 oil through a 5-cm-diameter pipe, from Fig. A.1, for what flow rate in m³/h would we expect transition to turbulence at (a) 20°C and (b) 100°C?

6.5   In flow past a body or wall, early transition to turbulence can be induced by placing a trip wire on the wall across the flow, as in Fig. P6.5. If the trip wire in Fig. P6.5 is placed where the local velocity is U, it will trigger turbulence if $Ud/\nu = 850$, where d is the wire diameter [3, p. 386]. If the sphere diameter is 20 cm and transition is observed at $Re_D = 90,000$, what is the diameter of the trip wire in mm?

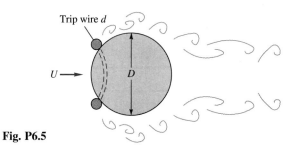

Fig. P6.5

6.6   A fluid at 20°C flows at 850 cm³/s through an 8-cm-diameter pipe. Determine whether the flow is laminar or turbulent if the fluid is (a) hydrogen, (b) air, (c) gasoline, (d) water, (e) mercury, or (f) glycerin.

6.7   Cola, approximated as pure water at 20°C, is to fill an 8-oz container (1 U.S. gal = 128 fl oz) through a 5-mm-diameter tube. Estimate the minimum filling time if the tube flow is to remain laminar. For what cola (water) temperature would this minimum time be 1 min?

6.8   SAE 10 oil at 20°C flows through a 3-cm-diameter tube. Estimate the entrance length in cm if Q is (a) 0.001 m³/s and (b) 0.03 m³/s.

6.9   A light liquid ($\rho \approx 950$ kg/m³) flows at an average velocity of 10 m/s through a horizontal smooth tube of diameter 5 cm. The fluid pressure is measured at 1-m intervals along the pipe, as follows:

x, m	0	1	2	3	4	5	6
p, kPa	304	273	255	240	226	213	200

Estimate (a) the average wall shear stress, in Pa, and (b) the wall shear stress in the fully developed region of the pipe.

6.10   SAE 10 oil at 20°C flows into a 1-cm-diameter smooth tube. The entrance length is found to be 15 cm. What is the oil flow rate in m³/h?

6.11   Derive the time-averaged x-momentum equation (6.14) by direct substitution of Eqs. (6.12) into the momentum equation (6.7). It is convenient to write the convective acceleration as

$$\frac{du}{dt} = \frac{\partial}{\partial x}(u^2) + \frac{\partial}{\partial y}(uv) + \frac{\partial}{\partial z}(uw)$$

which is valid because of the continuity relation, Eq. (6.7).

6.12 By analogy with Eq. (6.14) write the turbulent mean-momentum differential equation for (a) the y direction and (b) the z direction. How many turbulent stress terms appear in each equation? How many unique turbulent stresses are there for the total of three directions?

6.13 The following turbulent-flow velocity data $u(y)$, for air at 75°F and 1 atm near a smooth flat wall, were taken in the University of Rhode Island wind tunnel:

y, in	0.025	0.035	0.047	0.055	0.065
u, ft/s	51.2	54.2	56.8	57.6	59.1

Estimate (a) the wall shear stress and (b) the velocity u at $y = 0.22$ in.

6.14 Two infinite plates a distance h apart are parallel to the xz plane with the upper plate moving at speed V, as in Fig. P6.14. There is a fluid of viscosity μ and constant pressure between the plates. Neglecting gravity and assuming incompressible turbulent flow $u(y)$ between the plates, use the logarithmic law and appropriate boundary conditions to derive a formula for dimensionless wall shear stress versus dimensionless plate velocity. Sketch a typical shape of the profile $u(y)$.

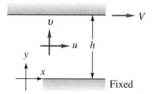

Fig. P6.14

6.15 For the turbulent flow defined by Prob. 6.14, evaluate the shear stress at the upper and lower walls if $V = 5$ m/s, $h = 2$ cm, and the fluid is water at 20°C.

6.16 By analogy with laminar shear, $\tau = \mu\,du/dy$, T. V. Boussinesq in 1877 postulated that turbulent shear could also be related to the mean-velocity gradient $\tau_{\text{turb}} = \epsilon\,du/dy$, where ϵ is called the *eddy viscosity* and is much larger than μ. If the logarithmic-overlap law, Eq. (6.21), is valid with $\tau \approx \tau_w$, show that $\epsilon \approx \kappa\rho u^* y$. Evaluate ϵ/μ at the centerline of the channel flow in Prob. 6.15.

6.17 Theodore von Kármán in 1930 theorized that turbulent shear could be represented by $\tau_{\text{turb}} = \epsilon\,du/dy$ where $\epsilon = \rho\kappa^2 y^2|du/dy|$ is called the *mixing-length eddy viscosity* and $\kappa \approx 0.41$ is Kármán's dimensionless *mixing-length constant* [2, 3]. Assuming that $\tau_{\text{turb}} \approx \tau_w$ near the wall, show that this expression can be integrated to yield the logarithmic-overlap law, Eq. (6.21).

6.18 Water at 20°C flows in a 9-cm-diameter pipe under fully developed conditions. The centerline velocity is 10 m/s. Compute (a) Q, (b) V, (c) τ_w, and (d) Δp for a 100-m pipe length.

In Probs. 6.19 to 6.99, neglect minor losses.

6.19 A 5-mm-diameter capillary tube is used as a viscometer for oils. When the flow rate is 0.071 m³/h, the measured pressure drop per unit length is 375 kPa/m. Estimate the viscosity of the fluid. Is the flow laminar? Can you also estimate the density of the fluid?

6.20 A soda straw is 20 cm long and 2 mm in diameter. It delivers cold cola, approximated as water at 10°C, at a rate of 3 cm³/s. (a) What is the head loss through the straw? What is the axial pressure gradient $\partial p/\partial x$ if the flow is (b) vertically up or (c) horizontal? Can the human lung deliver this much flow?

6.21 Water at 20°C is to be siphoned through a tube 1 m long and 2 mm in diameter, as in Fig. P6.21. Is there any height H for which the flow might not be laminar? What is the flow rate if $H = 50$ cm? Neglect the tube curvature.

Fig. P6.21

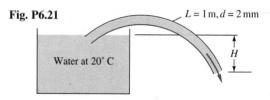

Water at 20° C $L = 1\,\text{m}, d = 2\,\text{mm}$ H

6.22 Determine the flow rate through the tank-tube system of Example 6.5 if the fluid is glycerin at 20°C.

6.23 Glycerin at 20°C is to be pumped through a horizontal smooth pipe at 3.1 m³/s. It is desired that (1) the flow be laminar and (2) the pressure drop be no more than 100 Pa/m. What is the minimum pipe diameter allowable?

6.24 The 6-cm-diameter pipe in Fig. P6.24 contains glycerin at 20°C flowing at a rate of 6 m³/h. Verify that the flow is laminar. For the pressure measurements shown, is the flow up or down? What is the indicated head loss for these pressures?

Fig. P6.24

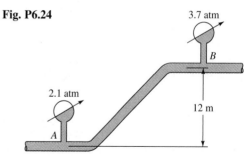

3.7 atm B 2.1 atm   12 m A

6.25 In Prob. 6.24, if bend losses are neglected, how long is the section of pipe between *A* and *B*?

6.26 In Example 6.5 let the tank diameter be 15 in, and let the fluid be kerosine at 20°C. Set up a differential equation, and integrate to find the time required to drain the entire tank. For simplicity, neglect the kinetic energy at the exit.

6.27 An oil (SG = 0.9) issues from the pipe in Fig. P6.27 at $Q = 35$ ft³/h. What is the kinematic viscosity of the oil in ft³/s? Is the flow laminar?

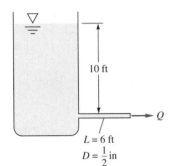

Fig. P6.27

10 ft

$L = 6$ ft

$D = \dfrac{1}{2}$ in

Q

6.28 In Prob. 6.27 what will the flow rate be, in m³/h, if the fluid is SAE 30 oil at 20°C?

6.29 Oil, with $\rho = 890$ kg/m³ and $\mu = 0.06$ kg/(m · s), is to be pumped through 1 km of straight horizontal pipe with a power input of 1 kW. What is the maximum possible mass flow rate, and corresponding pipe diameter, if laminar flow is to be maintained?

6.30 A steady push on the piston in Fig. P6.30 causes a flow rate $Q = 0.15$ cm³/s through the needle. The fluid has $\rho = 900$ kg/m³ and $\mu = 0.002$ kg/(m · s). What force *F* is required to maintain the flow?

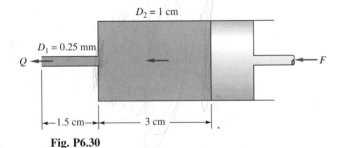

$D_2 = 1$ cm

$D_1 = 0.25$ mm

Q

F

1.5 cm — 3 cm

Fig. P6.30

6.31 SAE 10 oil at 20°C flows in a vertical pipe of diameter 2.5 cm. It is found that the pressure is constant throughout the fluid. What is the oil flow rate in m³/h? Is the flow up or down?

6.32 SAE 30 oil at 20°C flows at 0.001 m³/s through 100 m of 1-cm-diameter pipe and then for another 100 m at an increased $d = 2$ cm. The double-pipe system slopes upward

at 35° in the flow direction. Estimate (*a*) the total pressure change and (*b*) the power required to drive the flow.

6.33 For the configuration shown in Fig. P6.33, the fluid is ethyl alcohol at 20°C, and the tanks are very wide. Find the flow rate which occurs in m³/h. Is the flow laminar?

Fig. P6.33

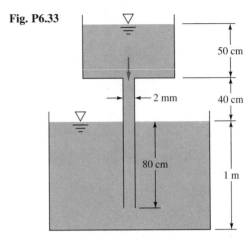

50 cm

2 mm

40 cm

80 cm

1 m

6.34 For the system in Fig. P6.33, if the fluid has density of 920 kg/m³ and the flow rate is unknown, for what value of viscosity will the capillary Reynolds number exactly equal the critical value of 2300?

6.35 Let us attack Prob. 6.33 in symbolic fashion, using Fig. P6.35. All parameters are constant except the upper tank depth *Z(t)*. Find an expression for the flow rate *Q(t)* as a function of *Z(t)*. Set up a differential equation, and solve for the time t_0 to drain the upper tank completely. Assume quasi-steady laminar flow.

Fig. P6.35

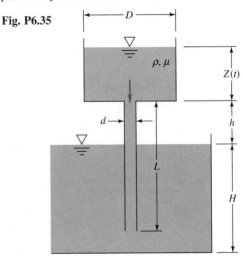

D

ρ, μ

Z(t)

d

h

L

H

6.36 For straightening and smoothing an airflow in a 50-cm-diameter duct, the duct is packed with a "honeycomb" of thin straws of length 30 cm and diameter 4 mm, as in Fig. P6.36. The inlet flow is air at 110 kPa and 20°C, moving at an average velocity of 6 m/s. Estimate the pressure drop across the honeycomb.

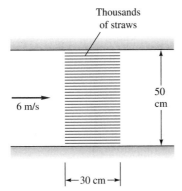

Fig. P6.36

6.37   Oil, with $\rho = 880 \text{ kg/m}^3$ and $\mu = 0.08 \text{ kg/(m} \cdot \text{s)}$, flows through a pipe with $d = 2$ cm and $L = 12$ m. The wall shear stress is 30 Pa. Estimate (a) the Reynolds number, (b) the total pressure drop, and (c) the power required to drive the fluid.

6.38   SAE 10 oil at 20°C flows through the 4-cm-diameter vertical pipe of Fig. P6.38. For the mercury manometer reading $h = 42$ cm shown, (a) calculate the volume flow rate in m^3/h, and (b) state the direction of flow.

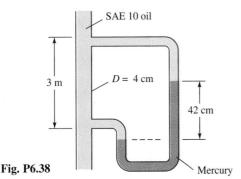

Fig. P6.38

6.39   Light oil, $\rho = 880 \text{ kg/m}^3$ and $\mu = 0.015 \text{ kg/(m} \cdot \text{s)}$, flows down a vertical 6-mm-diameter tube due to gravity only. Estimate the volume flow rate in m^3/h if (a) $L = 1$ m and (b) $L = 2$ m. (c) Verify that the flow is laminar.

6.40   SAE 30 oil at 20°C flows in the 3-cm-diameter pipe in Fig. P6.40, which slopes at 37°. For the pressure measurements shown, determine (a) whether the flow is up or down and (b) the flow rate in m^3/h.

6.41   Modify and repeat Prob. 6.40 if the pressures are the same but there is a pump between A and B which adds a 20-m

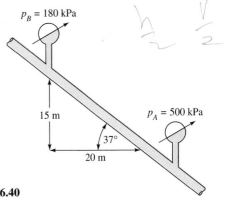

Fig. P6.40

head rise in the flow direction. Verify that the flow is laminar.

6.42   It is clear by comparing Figs. 6.12b and 6.13 that the effects of sand roughness and commercial (manufactured) roughness are not quite the same. Take the special case of commercial roughness ratio $\epsilon/d = 0.001$ in Fig. 6.13, and replot in the form of the wall-law shift ΔB (Fig. 6.12a) versus the logarithm of $\epsilon^+ = \epsilon u^*/\nu$. Compare your plot with Eq. (6.61).

6.43   Water at 20°C flows for 1 mi through a 3-in-diameter horizontal wrought-iron pipe at 250 gal/min. Estimate the head loss and the pressure drop in this length of pipe.

6.44   Mercury at 20°C flows through 4 m of 7-mm-diameter glass tubing at an average velocity of 3 m/s. Estimate the head loss in m and the pressure drop in kPa.

6.45   Oil, SG = 0.88 and $\nu = 4$ E-5 m^2/s, flows at 400 gal/min through a 6-in asphalted cast-iron pipe. The pipe is 0.5 mi long and slopes upward at 8° in the flow direction. Compute the head loss in ft and the pressure change.

6.46   Kerosine at 20°C is pumped at 0.15 m^3/s through 20 km of 16-cm-diameter cast-iron horizontal pipe. Compute the input power in kW required if the pumps are 85 percent efficient.

6.47   Derive Eq. (6.59), showing all steps. The constant 1.33 dates back to Prandtl's work in 1935 and may change slightly to 1.29 in your analysis.

6.48   Show that if Eq. (6.49) is accurate, the position in a turbulent pipe flow where local velocity u equals average velocity V occurs exactly at $r = 0.777R$, independent of the Reynolds number.

6.49   The tank-pipe system of Fig. P6.49 is to deliver at least 11 m^3/h of water at 20°C to the reservoir. What is the maximum roughness height ϵ allowable for the pipe?

6.50   Estimate the flow rate, in m^3/h, for the system of Fig. P6.49 if the pipe is made of cast iron.

6.51   The viscous sublayer (Fig. 6.9) is normally less than 1 percent of the pipe diameter and therefore very difficult to probe

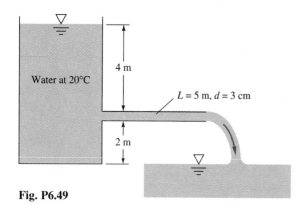

Fig. P6.49

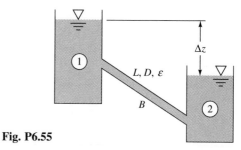

Fig. P6.55

with a finite-sized instrument. In an effort to generate a thick sublayer for probing, Pennsylvania State University in 1964 built a pipe with a flow of glycerin. Assume a smooth 12-in-diameter pipe with $V = 60$ ft/s and glycerin at 20°C. Compute the sublayer thickness in inches and the pumping horsepower required at 75 percent efficiency if $L = 40$ ft.

6.52 The pipe flow in Fig. P6.52 is driven by pressurized air in the tank. What gage pressure p_1 is needed to provide a 20°C water flow rate $Q = 60$ m³/h?

Fig. P6.52

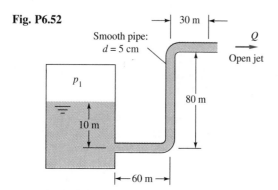

6.53 In Fig. P6.52 suppose that the fluid is gasoline at 20°C and $p_1 = 700$ kPa gage. What flow rate Q will result, in m³/h?

6.54 In Fig. P6.52 suppose that the fluid is carbon tetrachloride at 20°C and $p_1 = 1100$ kPa gage. What pipe diameter, in cm, is required to deliver a flow rate of 25 m³/h?

6.55 The reservoirs in Fig. P6.55 contain water at 20°C. If the pipe is smooth with $L = 4500$ m and $d = 4$ cm, what will the flow rate in m³/h be for $\Delta z = 100$ m?

6.56 Repeat Prob. 6.55 if the pipe is cast iron.

6.57 John Laufer (*NACA Tech. Rep.* 1174, 1954) gave velocity data for 20°C airflow in a smooth 24.7-cm-diameter pipe at Re $\approx$ 5 E5:

u/u_{CL}	1.0	0.997	0.988	0.959	0.908	0.847	0.818	0.771	0.690
r/R	0.0	0.102	0.206	0.412	0.617	0.784	0.846	0.907	0.963

The centerline velocity u_{CL} was 30.5 m/s. Determine (a) the average velocity by numerical integration and (b) the wall shear stress from the log-law approximation. Compare with the Moody chart and with Eq. (6.59).

6.58 In Fig. P6.55 assume that the pipe is cast iron with $L = 550$ m, $d = 7$ cm, and $\Delta z = 100$ m. If an 80 percent efficient pump is placed at point B, what input power is required to deliver 160 m³/h of water upward from reservoir 2 to 1?

6.59 Repeat Prob. 6.38 for a smooth pipe if the fluid is water at 20°C.

6.60 J. Nikuradse in 1932 suggested that smooth-wall turbulent pipe flow could be approximated by a power-law profile

$$u/u_{CL} \approx \left(\frac{y}{R}\right)^{1/N}$$

where y is distance from the wall and $N \approx 6$ to 9. Find the best value of N which fits Laufer's data in Prob. 6.57. Then use your formula to estimate the pipe volume flow, and compare with the measured value of 45 ft³/s.

6.61 A straight 10-cm commercial-steel pipe is 1 km long and is laid on a constant slope of 5°. Water at 20°C flows downward, due to gravity only. Estimate the flow rate in m³/h. What happens if the pipe length is 2 km?

6.62 Suppose that the pipe of Prob. 6.61 is asphalted cast iron and the desired flow rate is 50 m³/h. What is the proper pipe slope, in degrees?

6.63 A tank contains 1 m³ of water at 20°C and has a drawn-capillary outlet tube at the bottom, as in Fig. P6.63. Find the outlet volume flux Q in m³/h at this instant.

6.64 For the system in Fig. P6.63, solve for the flow rate in m³/h if the fluid is SAE 10 oil at 20°C. Is the flow laminar or turbulent?

6.65 In Prob. 6.63 the initial flow is turbulent. As the water drains out of the tank, will the flow revert to laminar motion as the tank becomes nearly empty? If so, at what tank depth? Estimate the time, in h, to drain the tank completely.

6.66 Ethyl alcohol at 20°C flows through a 10-cm horizontal drawn tube 100 m long. The fully developed wall shear stress is 14 Pa. Estimate (a) the pressure drop, (b) the volume flow rate, and (c) the velocity u at $r = 1$ cm.

6.67 What level h must be maintained in Fig. P6.67 to deliver a

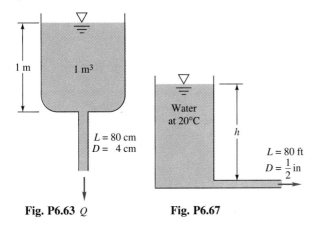

Fig. P6.63 *Q*   Fig. P6.67

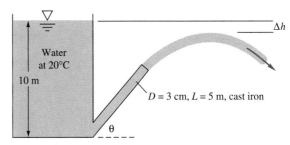

Fig. P6.72

flow rate of 0.015 ft³/s through the ½-in commercial-steel pipe?

6.68 Water at 20°C is to be pumped through 2000 ft of pipe from reservoir 1 to 2 at a rate of 3 ft³/s, as shown in Fig. P6.68. If the pipe is cast iron of diameter 6 in and the pump is 75 percent efficient, what horsepower pump is needed?

6.69 For Prob. 6.68 suppose the only pump available can deliver 80 hp to the fluid. What is the proper pipe size in inches to maintain the 3 ft³/s flow rate?

6.70 In Fig. P6.68 suppose the pipe is 6-in-diameter cast iron and the pump delivers 75 hp to the flow. What flow rate Q ft³/s results?

Fig. P6.68

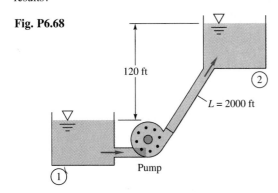

6.71 It is desired to solve Prob. 6.68 for the most economical pump and cast-iron pipe system. If the pump costs $125 per horsepower delivered to the fluid and the pipe costs $7000 per inch of diameter, what are the minimum cost and the pipe and pump size to maintain the 3 ft³/s flow rate? Make some simplifying assumptions.

6.72 The 5-m-long pipe in Fig. P6.72 may be oriented at any angle θ. If entrance losses are negligible for any θ (pure Moody friction loss), what is the optimum value of θ for which the jet height loss Δh is minimum?

6.73 Modify Prob. 6.67 so that the fluid is benzene at 20°C and

$h = 200$ ft, but the pipe roughness is unknown. If $Q = 10$ gal/min, estimate the average pipe roughness in inches.

6.74 In Fig. P6.67 suppose the fluid is gasoline at 20°C and $h = 90$ ft. What commercial-steel pipe diameter is required for the flow rate to be 0.015 ft³/s?

6.75 You wish to water your garden with 100 ft of ⅝-in-diameter hose whose roughness is 0.011 in. What will be the delivery, in ft³/s, if the gage pressure at the faucet is 60 lbf/in²? If there is no nozzle (just an open hose exit), what is the maximum horizontal distance the exit jet will carry?

6.76 The small turbine in Fig. P6.76 extracts 400 W of power from the water flow. Both pipes are wrought iron. Compute the flow rate Q m³/h. Sketch the EGL and HGL accurately.

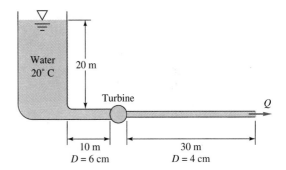

Fig. P6.76

6.77 Modify Prob. 6.76 into an economic analysis, as follows. Let the 40 m of wrought-iron pipe have a uniform diameter d. Let the steady water flow available be $Q = 30$ m³/h. The cost of the turbine is $4 per watt developed, and the cost of the piping is $75 per centimeter of diameter. The power generated may be sold for $0.08 per kilowatthour. Find the proper pipe diameter for minimum *payback time*, i.e., minimum time for which the power sales will equal the initial cost of the system.

6.78 In Fig. P6.78 the connecting pipe is commercial steel 6 cm in diameter. Estimate the flow rate, in m³/h, if the fluid is water at 20°C. Which way is the flow?

6.79 In Fig. P6.78, if the fluid is gasoline at 20°C, what should

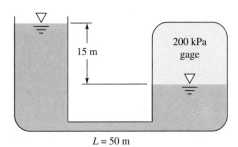

Fig. P6.78

the pipe diameter, in cm, be to maintain a flow rate of 25 m³/h?

6.80 The head-versus-flow-rate characteristics of a centrifugal pump are shown in Fig. P6.80. If this pump drives water at 20°C through 120 m of 30-cm-diameter cast-iron pipe, what will be the resulting flow rate, in m³/s?

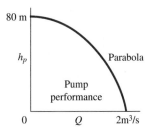

Fig. P6.80

6.81 The pump in Fig. P6.80 is used to deliver gasoline at 20°C through 350 m of 30-cm-diameter galvanized iron pipe. Estimate the resulting flow rate, in m³/s. (Note that the pump head is now in meters of gasoline.)

6.82 The pump in Fig. P6.80 has its maximum efficiency at a head of 45 m. If it is used to pump ethanol at 20°C through 200 m of commercial-steel pipe, what is the proper pipe diameter for maximum pump efficiency?

6.83 For the system of Fig. P6.55, let Δz = 80 m and L = 185 m of cast-iron pipe. What is the pipe diameter for which the flow rate will be 7 m³/h?

6.84 Modify the honeycomb problem of Fig. P6.36 so that the fluid is water at 20°C. Is the flow turbulent?

6.85 The pump of Fig. P6.80 is used to deliver 0.7 m³/s of methanol at 20°C through 95 m of cast-iron pipe. What is the proper pipe diameter?

6.86 SAE 10 oil at 20°C flows at an average velocity of 2 m/s between two smooth parallel horizontal plates 3 cm apart. Estimate (*a*) the centerline velocity, (*b*) the head loss per meter, and (*c*) the pressure drop per meter.

6.87 A commercial-steel annulus 40 ft long, with a = 1 in and $b = \frac{1}{2}$ in, connects two reservoirs which differ in surface height by 20 ft. Compute the flow rate in ft³/s through the annulus if the fluid is water at 20°C.

6.88 Show that for laminar flow through an annulus of very small clearance the flow rate Q is approximately proportional to the cube of the clearance $a − b$.

6.89 An annulus of narrow clearance causes a very large pressure drop and is useful as an accurate measurement of viscosity. If a smooth annulus 1 m long with a = 50 mm and b = 49 mm carries an oil flow at 0.001 m³/s, what is the oil viscosity if the pressure drop is 250 kPa?

6.90 A 90-ft-long sheet-steel duct carries air at approximately 20°C and 1 atm. The duct cross section is an equilateral triangle whose side measures 9 in. If a blower can supply 1 hp to the flow, what flow rate, in ft³/s, will result?

6.91 Heat exchangers often consist of many triangular passages. Typical is Fig. P6.91, with L = 60 cm and an isoceles-triangle cross section of side length a = 2 cm and included angle β = 80°. If the average velocity is V = 2 m/s and the fluid is SAE 10 oil at 20°C, estimate the pressure drop.

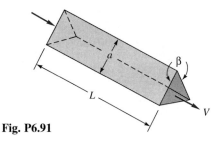

Fig. P6.91

6.92 Repeat Prob. 6.91 if the fluid is water at 20°C.

6.93 Modify Prob. 6.91 so that the angle β is unknown. For SAE 10 oil at 20°C, if the pressure drop is 120 kPa and the flow rate is 4 m³/h, what is the proper value of the angle β, in degrees?

6.94 As shown in Fig. P6.94, a multiduct cross section consists of seven 2-cm-diameter smooth thin tubes packed tightly in a hexagonal "bundle" within a single 6-cm-diameter tube. Air, at about 20°C and 1 atm, flows through this system at 150 m³/h. Estimate the pressure drop per meter.

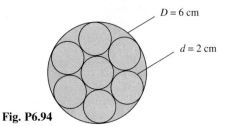

Fig. P6.94

6.95 Modify Prob. 6.94 as follows. Let the seven 2-cm tubes be solid rods, so that the air can only pass through the curved triangular cusped passages. Compute the pressure drop per meter of duct length.

6.96 Hydrogen, at 20°C and approximately 1 atm, is to be pumped through a smooth rectangular duct 85 m long of aspect ratio 5:1. If the flow rate is 0.7 m³/s and the pressure drop is 80 Pa, what should the width and height of the duct cross section be?

6.97 A wind tunnel has a wooden rectangular section 45 cm by 95 cm by 26 m long. It uses sea-level standard air at 31-m/s average velocity. Estimate the pressure drop and the power required if the fan efficiency is 75 percent.

6.98 A rectangular heat exchanger is to be divided into smaller sections using sheets of commercial steel 0.4 mm thick, as sketched in Fig. P6.98. The flow rate is 20 kg/s of water at 20°C. Basic dimensions are $L = 1$ m, $W = 20$ cm, and $H = 10$ cm. What is the proper number of *square* sections if the overall pressure drop is to be no more than 1600 Pa?

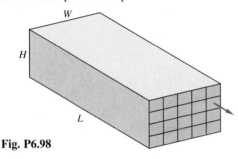

Fig. P6.98

6.99 Modify Prob. 6.98 as follows. Find the proper number of square sections to minimize the ratio of the pressure drop to the total amount of *wall area* between the various small ducts. Comment on your result.

6.100 Repeat Prob. 6.55 by including losses due to a sharp-edged entrance, the exit, and a fully open flanged globe valve. By what percentage is the flow rate decreased?

6.101 Repeat Prob. 6.67 by including losses due to a sharp entrance and a fully open screwed swing-check valve. By what percentage is the required tank level h increased?

6.102 A 70 percent efficient pump delivers water at 20°C from one reservoir to another 20 ft higher, as in Fig. P6.102. The piping system consists of 60 ft of galvanized-iron 2-in pipe, a reentrant entrance, two screwed 90° long-radius elbows, a screwed-open gate valve, and a sharp exit. What is the input power required in horsepower with and without a 6° well-designed conical expansion added to the exit? The flow rate is 0.4 ft³/s.

6.103 The reservoirs in Fig. P6.103 are connected by cast-iron pipes joined abruptly, with sharp-edged entrance and exit. Including minor losses, estimate the flow of water at 20°C if the surface of reservoir 1 is 45 ft higher than that of reservoir 2.

6.104 Two reservoirs containing water at 20°C are connected by 150 m of 10-cm-diameter cast-iron pipe, including a sharp entrance, a submerged exit, a half-closed gate valve, three

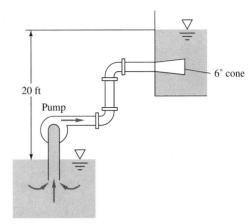

Fig. P6.102

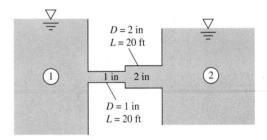

Fig. P6.103

30-cm-radius bends, and five regular 90° elbows. If the flow rate is 140 m³/h, what is the vertical difference in reservoir elevations?

6.105 The system in Fig. P6.105 consists of 1200 m of 5 cm cast-iron pipe, two 45° and four 90° flanged long-radius elbows, a fully open flanged globe valve, and a sharp exit into a reservoir. If the elevation at point 1 is 400 m, what gage pressure is required at point 1 to deliver 0.005 m³/s of water at 20°C into the reservoir?

Fig. P6.105

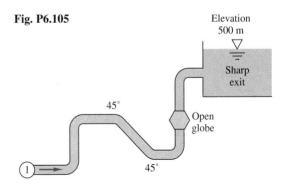

6.106 The water pipe in Fig. P6.106 slopes upward at 30°. The

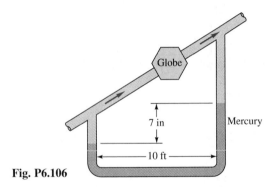

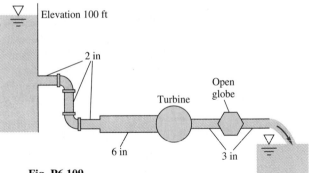

Fig. P6.106

Fig. P6.109

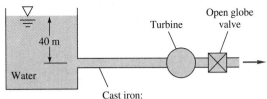

Fig. P6.110

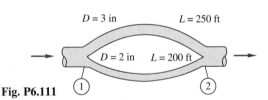

Fig. P6.111

pipe is 1-in-diameter and smooth. The flanged globe valve is fully open. If the mercury manometer shows a 7-in deflection, what is the flow rate in ft³/s?

6.107 In Fig. P6.107 the pipe is galvanized iron. Estimate the percentage increase in the flow rate (a) if the pipe entrance is cut off flush with the wall and (b) if the butterfly valve is opened wide.

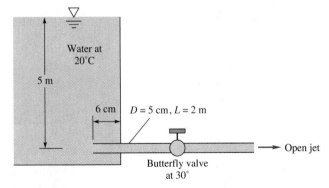

Fig. P6.107

6.108 Consider the flow system of Fig. P6.102, including the 6° cone diffuser. Suppose the pump head versus flow rate is approximated by

$$h_p \approx 45 - 125Q^2$$

with h_p in ft and Q in ft³/s. Estimate the resulting flow rate, in ft³/s.

6.109 In Fig. P6.109 there are 125 ft of 2-in pipe, 75 ft of 6-in pipe, and 150 ft of 3-in pipe, all cast iron. There are three 90° elbows and an open globe valve, all flanged. If the exit elevation is zero, what horsepower is extracted by the turbine when the flow rate is 0.16 ft³/s of water at 20°C?

6.110 In Fig. P6.110 the pipe entrance is sharp-edged. If the flow rate is 0.004 m³/s, what power, in W, is extracted by the turbine?

6.111 For the parallel-pipe system of Fig. P6.111, each pipe is cast

iron, and the pressure drop $p_1 - p_2 = 3$ lbf/in². Compute the total flow rate between 1 and 2 if the fluid is SAE 10 oil at 20°C.

6.112 If the two pipes in Fig. P6.111 are instead laid in series with the same total pressure drop of 3 lbf/in², what will the flow rate be? The fluid is SAE 10 oil at 20°C.

6.113 The parallel galvanized-iron pipe system of Fig. P6.113 delivers gasoline at 20°C with a total flow rate of 0.036 m³/s. If the pump is wide open and not running, with a loss coefficient $K = 1.5$, determine (a) the flow rate in each pipe and (b) the overall pressure drop.

$L_1 = 60$ m, $D_1 = 5$ cm

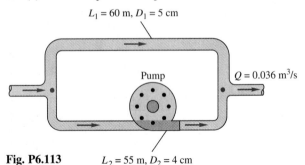

Fig. P6.113 $L_2 = 55$ m, $D_2 = 4$ cm

6.114 Modify Prob. 6.113 as follows. Let the pump be running and delivering 45 kW to the flow in pipe 2. The fluid is gasoline at 20°C. Determine (a) the flow rate in each pipe and (b) the overall pressure drop.

6.115 In Fig. P6.115 all pipes are 8-cm-diameter cast iron. Determine the flow rate from reservoir 1 if valve C is (a) closed and (b) open, $K = 0.5$.

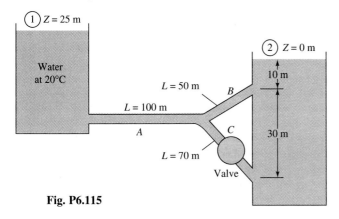

Fig. P6.115

6.116 For the series-parallel system of Fig. P6.116, all pipes are 8-cm-diameter asphalted cast iron. If the total pressure drop $p_1 - p_2 = 750$ kPa, find the resulting flow rate Q m³/h for water at 20°C. Neglect minor losses.

Fig. P6.116

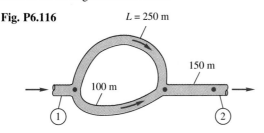

6.117 Modify Prob. 6.116 as follows. Let the flow rate be 45 m³/h of water at 20°C. Determine the overall pressure drop $p_1 - p_2$ in kPa. Neglect minor losses.

6.118 For the piping system of Fig. P6.118, all pipes are concrete with a roughness of 0.04 in. Neglecting minor losses, compute the overall pressure drop $p_1 - p_2$ in lbf/in². The fluid is water at 20°C. Let $Q = 20$ ft³/s.

Fig. P6.118

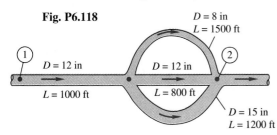

6.119 Modify Prob. 6.118 as follows. Let the pressure drop $p_1 - p_2$ be 98 lbf/in². Neglecting minor losses, determine the flow rate in m³/h.

6.120 Three cast-iron pipes are laid in parallel with these dimensions:

Pipe	Length, m	Diameter, cm
1	800	12
2	600	8
3	900	10

The total flow rate is 200 m³/h of water at 20°C. Determine (a) the flow rate in each pipe and (b) the pressure drop across the system.

6.121 Consider the three-reservoir system of Fig. P6.121 with the following data:

$$L_1 = 95 \text{ m} \qquad L_2 = 125 \text{ m} \qquad L_3 = 160 \text{ m}$$

$$z_1 = 25 \text{ m} \qquad z_2 = 115 \text{ m} \qquad z_3 = 85 \text{ m}$$

All pipes are 28-cm-diameter unfinished concrete ($\epsilon = 1$ mm). Compute the steady flow rate in all pipes for water at 20°C.

Fig. P6.121

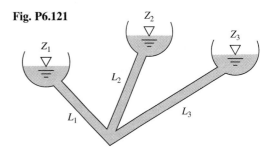

6.122 Modify Prob. 6.121 as follows. Reduce the diameter to 15 cm (with $\epsilon = 1$ mm), and compute the flow rates for water at 20°C. These flow rates distribute in nearly the same manner as in Prob. 6.121 but are about 5.2 times lower. Can you explain this difference?

6.123 Modify Prob. 6.121 as follows. All data are the same except that z_3 is unknown. Find the value of z_3 for which the flow rate in pipe 3 is 0.2 m³/s toward the junction. (This problem requires iteration and is best suited to a digital computer.)

6.124 The three-reservoir system in Fig. P6.124 delivers water at 20°C. The system data are as follows:

$$D_1 = 8 \text{ in} \qquad D_2 = 6 \text{ in} \qquad D_3 = 9 \text{ in}$$

$$L_1 = 1800 \text{ ft} \qquad L_2 = 1200 \text{ ft} \qquad L_3 = 1600 \text{ ft}$$

All pipes are galvanized iron. Compute the flow rate in all pipes.

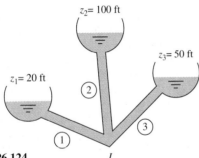

Fig. P6.124

6.125 Modify Prob. 6.124 as follows. Let all data be the same except z_3, which is unknown. What value of z_3 will cause the flow rate through pipe 3 to be 1.0 ft³/s toward the junction?

6.126 Modify Prob. 6.124 as follows. Let all data be the same except that pipe 1 is fitted with a butterfly valve (Fig. 6.19b). Estimate the proper valve opening angle (in degrees) for the flow rate through pipe 1 to be reduced to 1.5 ft³/s toward reservoir 1. (This problem requires iteration and is best suited to a digital computer.)

6.127 In the five-pipe horizontal network of Fig. P6.127, assume that all pipes have a friction factor $f = 0.025$. For the given inlet and exit flow rate of 2 ft³/s of water at 20°C, determine the flow rate and direction in all pipes. If $p_A = 120$ lbf/in² gage, determine the pressures at points B, C, and D.

Fig. P6.127

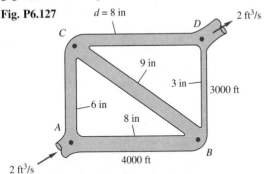

6.128 Modify Prob. 6.127 as follows. Let the inlet flow rate at A and the exit flow at D be unknown. Let $p_A - p_B = 100$ lbf/in². Compute the flow rate in all five pipes.

6.129 In Fig. P6.129 all four horizontal cast-iron pipes are 45 m long and 8 cm in diameter and meet at junction a, delivering water at 20°C. The pressures are known at four points as shown:

$$p_1 = 950 \text{ kPa} \qquad p_2 = 350 \text{ kPa}$$

$$p_3 = 675 \text{ kPa} \qquad p_4 = 100 \text{ kPa}$$

Neglecting minor losses, determine the flow rate in each pipe.

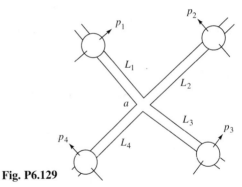

Fig. P6.129

6.130 In Fig. P6.130 lengths AB and BD are 2000 and 1500 ft, respectively. The friction factor is 0.022 everywhere, and $p_A = 90$ lbf/in² gage. All pipes have a diameter of 6 in. For water at 20°C, determine the flow rate in all pipes and the pressures at points B, C, and D.

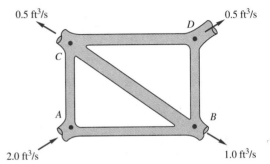

Fig. P6.130

6.131 A water-tunnel test section has a 1-m diameter and flow properties $V = 20$ m/s, $p = 100$ kPa, and $T = 20°C$. The boundary-layer blockage at the end of the section is 9 percent. If a conical diffuser is to be added at the end of the section to achieve maximum pressure recovery, what should its angle, length, exit diameter, and exit pressure be?

6.132 For Prob. 6.131 suppose we are limited by space to a total diffuser length of 10 m. What should the diffuser angle, exit diameter, and exit pressure be for maximum recovery?

6.133 A wind-tunnel test section is 3 ft square with flow properties $V = 150$ ft/s, $p = 15$ lbf/in² absolute, and $T = 68°F$. Boundary-layer blockage at the end of the test section is 8 percent. Find the angle, length, exit height, and exit pressure of a flat-walled diffuser added onto the section to achieve maximum pressure recovery.

6.134 For Prob. 6.133 supposes we are limited by space to a total diffuser length of 30 ft. What should the diffuser angle, exit height, and exit pressure be for maximum recovery?

6.135 A small airplane flying at 5000-m altitude uses a pitot stagnation probe without static holes. The measured stagnation pressure is 56.5 kPa. Estimate the airplane's speed in mi/h and its uncertainty. Is a compressibility correction needed?

6.136 For the pitot-static pressure arrangement of Fig. P6.136, the manometer fluid is (colored) water at 20°C. Estimate (*a*) the centerline velocity, (*b*) the pipe volume flow, and (*c*) the (smooth) wall shear stress.

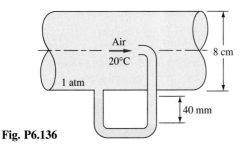

Fig. P6.136

6.137 For the 20°C water flow of Fig. P6.137, use the pitot-static arrangement to estimate (*a*) the centerline velocity and (*b*) the volume flow in the 5-in-diameter smooth pipe. (*c*) What error in flow rate is caused by neglecting the 1-ft elevation difference?

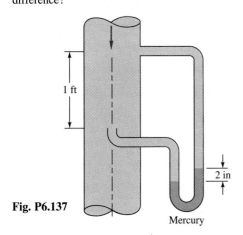

Fig. P6.137

6.138 An engineer who took college fluid mechanics on a pass-fail basis has placed the static pressure hole far upstream of the stagnation probe, as in Fig. P6.138, thus contaminating

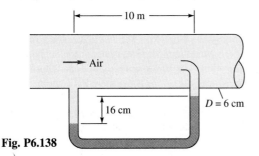

Fig. P6.138

the pitot measurement ridiculously with pipe friction losses. If the pipe flow is air at 20°C and 1 atm and the manometer fluid is Meriam red oil (SG = 0.827), estimate the air centerline velocity for the given manometer reading of 16 cm. Assume a smooth-walled tube.

6.139 Modify Prob. 6.138 as follows. Put the stagnation tube upstream and the static (smooth) wall hole 10 m downstream, with a volume flow rate of 400 m³/h. What will be the manometer reading now? (It will change drastically from that in Fig. P6.138.) Which leg will have the higher pressure?

6.140 Kerosine at 20°C flows at 18 m³/h in a 5-cm-diameter pipe. If a 2-cm-diameter thin-plate orifice with corner taps is installed, what will the measured pressure drop be, in Pa?

6.141 Gasoline at 20°C flows at 105 m³/h in a 10-cm-diameter pipe. We wish to meter the flow with a thin-plate orifice and a differential pressure transducer which reads best at about 55 kPa. What is the proper β ratio for the orifice?

6.142 The shower head in Fig. P6.142 delivers water at 50°C. An orifice-type flow reducer is to be installed. The upstream pressure is constant at 400 kPa. What flow rate, in gal/min, results without the reducer? What reducer orifice diameter would decrease the flow by 40 percent?

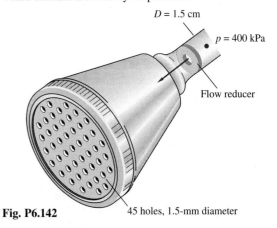

Fig. P6.142 45 holes, 1.5-mm diameter

6.143 A 10-cm-diameter smooth pipe contains an orifice plate with $D : \frac{1}{2}D$ taps and $\beta = 0.5$. The measured orifice pressure drop is 75 kPa for water flow at 20°C. Estimate the flow rate, in m³/h. What is the nonrecoverable head loss?

6.144 Accurate solution of Prob. 6.143, using Fig. 6.37, requires iteration because both the ordinate and the abscissa of this figure contain the unknown flow rate Q. In the spirit of Example 5.8, rescale the variables and construct a new plot in which Q may be read directly from the ordinate. Solve Prob. 6.143 with your new chart.

6.145 The 1-m-diameter tank in Fig. P6.145 is initially filled with gasoline at 20°C. There is a 2-cm-diameter orifice in the

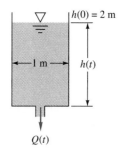

Fig. P6.145 $\qquad$ $Q(t)$

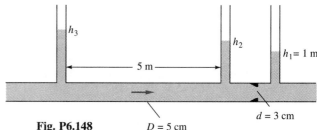

Fig. P6.148 $\qquad$ $D = 5$ cm

bottom. If the orifice is suddenly opened, estimate the time for the fluid level $h(t)$ to drop from 2.0 to 1.6 m.

6.146 A pipe connecting two reservoirs, as in Fig. P6.146, contains a thin-plate orifice. For water flow at 20°C, estimate (*a*) the volume flow through the pipe and (*b*) the pressure drop across the orifice plate.

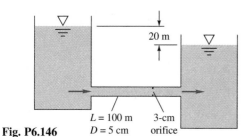

Fig. P6.146 $\qquad$ $D = 5$ cm $\qquad$ orifice

6.147 Air flows through a 6-cm-diameter smooth pipe which has a 2 m-long perforated section containing 500 holes (diameter 1 mm), as in Fig. P6.147. Pressure outside the pipe is sea-level standard air. If $p_1 = 105$ kPa and $Q_1 = 110$ m³/h, estimate p_2 and Q_2, assuming that the holes are approximated by thin-plate orifices. *Hint:* A momentum control volume may be very useful.

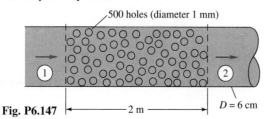

Fig. P6.147 $\qquad$ 2 m $\qquad$ $D = 6$ cm

6.148 A smooth pipe containing ethanol at 20°C flows at 7 m³/h through a Bernoulli obstruction, as in Fig. P6.148. Three piezometer tubes are installed, as shown. If the obstruction is a thin-plate orifice, estimate the piezometer levels (*a*) h_2 and (*b*) h_3.

6.149 Repeat Prob. 6.148 if the obstruction is a long-radius flow nozzle.

6.150 Gasoline at 20°C flows at 0.06 m³/s through a 15-cm pipe

and is metered by a 9-cm long-radius flow nozzle (Fig. 6.36*a*). What is the expected pressure drop across the nozzle?

6.151 Ethyl alcohol at 20°C flowing in a 6-cm-diameter pipe is metered through a 3-cm long-radius flow nozzle. If the measured pressure drop is 45 kPa, what is the estimated volume flow, in m³/h?

6.152 Kerosine at 20°C flows at 20 m³/h in an 8-cm-diameter pipe. The flow is to be metered by an ISA 1932 flow nozzle so that the pressure drop is 7000 Pa. What is the proper nozzle diameter?

6.153 Two water tanks, each with base area of 1 ft², are connected by a 0.5-in-diameter long-radius nozzle as in Fig. P6.153. If $h = 1$ ft as shown for $t = 0$, estimate the time for $h(t)$ to drop to 0.25 ft.

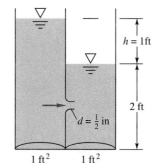

Fig. P6.153

6.154 Repeat Prob. 6.148 if the obstruction is a 7° cone venturi nozzle.

6.155 It is desired to meter a flow of 20°C gasoline in a 12-cm-diameter pipe, using a modern venturi nozzle. In order for international standards to be valid (Fig. 6.39), what is the permissible range of (*a*) flow rates, (*b*) nozzle diameters, and (*c*) pressure drops? (*d*) For the highest pressure-drop condition, would compressibility be a problem?

6.156 Ethanol at 20°C flows down through a modern venturi nozzle as in Fig. P6.156. If the mercury manometer reading is 4 in, as shown, estimate the flow rate, in gal/min.

6.157 Modify Prob. 6.156 if the fluid is air at 20°C, entering the venturi at a pressure of 18 lbf/in². Should a compressibility correction be used?

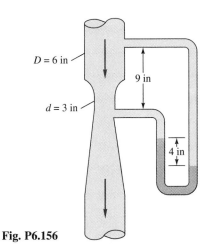

Fig. P6.156

6.158 Water at 20°C flows in a long horizontal commercial-steel 6-cm-diameter pipe which contains a classical Herschel venturi with a 4-cm throat. The venturi is connected to a mercury manometer whose reading is $h = 40$ cm. Estimate (*a*) the flow rate, in m^3/h, and (*b*) the total pressure difference between points 50 cm upstream and 50 cm downstream of the venturi.

6.159 A modern venturi nozzle is tested in a laboratory flow with water at 20°C. The pipe diameter is 5.5 cm, and the venturi throat diameter is 3.5 cm. The flow rate is measured by a weigh tank and the pressure drop by a water-mercury manometer. The mass flow rate and manometer readings are as follows:

$\dot{m}$, kg/s	0.95	1.98	2.99	5.06	8.15
h, mm	3.7	15.9	36.2	102.4	264.4

Use these data to plot a calibration curve of venturi discharge coefficient versus Reynolds number. Compare with the accepted correlation, Eq. (6.134).

6.160 The butterfly-valve losses in Fig. 6.19*b* may be viewed as a type of Bernoulli obstruction device, as in Fig. 6.35. The "throat area" A_t in Eq. (6.125) can be interpreted as the two slivers of opening around the butterfly disk when viewed from upstream. First fit the average loss K_{mean} versus the opening angle in Fig. 6.19*b* to an exponential curve. Then use your curve fit to compute the "discharge coefficient" of a butterfly valve as a function of the opening angle. Plot the results and compare them to those for a typical flowmeter.

Word Problems

W6.1 In fully developed straight-duct flow, the velocity profiles do not change (why?), but the pressure drops along the pipe axis. Thus there is pressure work done on the fluid. If, say, the pipe is insulated from heat loss, where does this energy go? Make a thermodynamic analysis of the pipe flow.

W6.2 From the Moody chart (Fig. 6.13), rough surfaces, such as sand grains or ragged machining, do not affect laminar flow. Can you explain why? They *do* affect turbulent flow. Can you develop, or suggest, an analytical-physical model of turbulent flow near a rough surface which might be used to predict the known increase in pressure drop?

W6.3 Differentiation of the laminar pipe-flow solution, Eq. (6.40), shows that the fluid shear stress $\tau(r)$ varies linearly from zero at the axis to τ_w at the wall. It is claimed that this is also true, at least in the time mean, for fully developed *turbulent* flow. Can you verify this claim analytically?

W6.4 A porous medium consists of many tiny tortuous passages, and Reynolds numbers based on pore size are usually very low, of order unity. In 1856 H. Darcy proposed that the pressure gradient in a porous medium was directly proportional to the volume-averaged velocity $\mathbf{V}$ of the fluid:

$$\nabla p = -\frac{\mu}{K}\mathbf{V}$$

where K is termed the *permeability* of the medium. This is now called *Darcy's law* of porous flow. Can you make a Poiseuille flow model of porous-media flow which verifies Darcy's law? Meanwhile, as the Reynolds number increases, so that $VK^{1/2}/\nu > 1$, the pressure drop becomes nonlinear, as was shown experimentally by P. H. Forscheimer as early as 1782. The flow is still decidedly laminar, yet the pressure gradient is quadratic:

$$\nabla p = -\frac{\mu}{K}\mathbf{V} - C|V|\mathbf{V} \qquad \text{Darcy-Forscheimer law}$$

where C is an empirical constant. Can you explain the reason for this nonlinear behavior?

W6.5 There are scores of flowmeter designs; we couldn't cover them all here. One of the most promising ideas is a *Coriolis flowmeter*. Look this up in the library, and explain in a brief report how it works and the advantages and disadvantages of typical designs.

W6.6 One flowmeter device, in wide use in the water supply and gasoline distribution industries, is the *nutating disk*. Look this up in the library, and explain in a brief report how it works and the advantages and disadvantages of typical designs.

Design Project

D6.1 A hydroponic garden uses the 10-m-long perforated-pipe system in Fig. D6.1 to deliver water at 20°C. The pipe is 5 cm in diameter and contains a circular hole every 20 cm. A pump delivers water at 75 kPa (gage) at the entrance, while the other end of the pipe is closed. If you attempted, e.g., Prob. 3.125, you know that the pressure near the closed end of a perforated "manifold" is surprisingly high, and there will be too much flow through the holes near that end. One remedy is to vary the hole size along the pipe axis. Make a design analysis, perhaps using a personal computer, to pick the optimum hole-size distribution that will make the discharge flow rate as uniform as possible along the pipe axis. You are constrained to pick hole sizes that correspond only to commercial (numbered) metric drill-bit sizes available to the typical machine shop.

Fig. D6.1

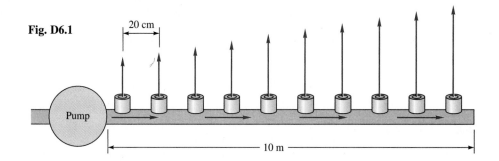

20 cm

Pump

10 m

Chapter 7
Boundary-Layer Flows

Motivation. This chapter is devoted to "external" flows around bodies immersed in a fluid stream. Such a flow will have viscous (shear and no-slip) effects near the body surfaces and in its wake, but will typically be nearly inviscid far from the body. These are unconfined *boundary-layer* flows.

Chapter 6 considered "internal" flows confined by the walls of a duct. In that case the viscous boundary layers grow from the sidewalls, meet downstream, and fill the entire duct. Viscous shear is the dominant effect. For example, the Moody chart of Fig. 6.13 is essentially a correlation of wall shear stress for long ducts of constant cross section.

External flows are unconfined, free to expand no matter how thick the viscous layers grow. Although boundary-layer theory (Sec. 7.3) is helpful in understanding external flows, complex body geometries usually require experimental data on the forces and moments caused by the flow. Such immersed-body flows are commonly encountered in engineering studies: *aerodynamics* (airplanes, rockets, projectiles), *hydrodynamics* (ships, submarines, torpedos), *transportation* (automobiles, trucks, cycles), *wind engineering* (buildings, bridges, water towers, wind turbines), and *ocean engineering* (buoys, breakwaters, pilings, cables, moored instruments). This chapter provides data and analysis to assist in such studies.

7.1 Reynolds-Number and Geometry Effects

The technique of boundary-layer (BL) analysis can be used to compute viscous effects near solid walls and to "patch" these onto the outer inviscid motion. This patching is more successful as the body Reynolds number becomes larger, as shown in Fig. 7.1.

In Fig. 7.1 a uniform stream U moves parallel to a sharp flat plate of length L. If the Reynolds number UL/ν is low (Fig. 7.1a), the viscous region is very broad and extends far ahead and to the sides of the plate. The plate retards the oncoming stream greatly, and small changes in flow parameters cause large changes in the pressure distribution along the plate. Thus, although in principle it should be possible to patch the viscous and inviscid layers in a mathematical analysis, their interaction is strong and nonlinear [1 to 3]. There is no existing simple theory for external-flow analysis at Reynolds numbers from 1 to about 1000. Such thick-shear-layer flows are typically studied by experiment or by numerical modeling of the flow field on a digital computer [4].

A high-Reynolds-number flow (Fig. 7.1b) is much more amenable to boundary-layer patching, as first pointed out by Prandtl in 1904. The viscous layers, either laminar or

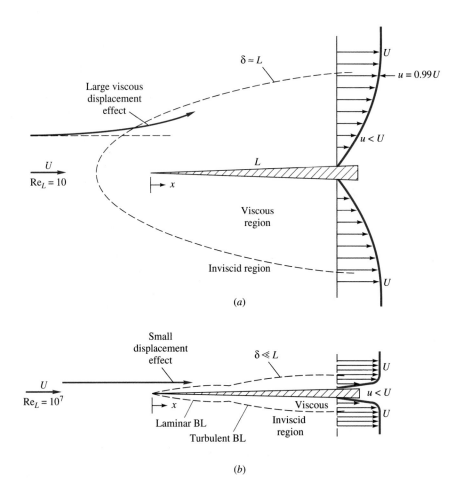

Fig. 7.1 Comparison of flow past a sharp flat plate at low and high Reynolds numbers: (*a*) laminar, low-Re flow; (*b*) high-Re flow.

turbulent, are very thin, thinner even than the drawing shows. We define the boundary-layer thickness δ as the locus of points where the velocity u parallel to the plate reaches 99 percent of the external velocity U. As we shall see in Sec. 7.4, the accepted formulas for flat-plate flow are

$$\frac{\delta}{x} \approx \begin{cases} \dfrac{5.0}{\mathrm{Re}_x^{1/2}} & \text{laminar} \quad (7.1a) \\[2mm] \dfrac{0.16}{\mathrm{Re}_x^{1/7}} & \text{turbulent} \quad (7.1b) \end{cases}$$

where $\mathrm{Re}_x = Ux/\nu$ is called the *local Reynolds number* of the flow along the plate surface. The turbulent-flow formula applies for Re_x greater than approximately 10^6.

Some computed values from Eq. (7.1) are

Re_x	10^4	10^5	10^6	10^7	10^8
$(\delta/x)_{\text{lam}}$	0.050	0.016	0.005		
$(\delta/x)_{\text{turb}}$			0.022	0.016	0.011

The blanks indicate that the formula is not applicable. In all cases these boundary layers are so thin that their displacement effect on the outer inviscid layer is negligible. Thus the pressure distribution along the plate can be computed from inviscid theory as if the boundary layer were not even there. This external pressure field then "drives" the boundary-layer flow, acting as a forcing function in the momentum equation along the surface. We shall explain this boundary-layer theory in Secs. 7.4 and 7.5.

For slender bodies, such as plates and airfoils parallel to the oncoming stream, we conclude that this assumption of negligible interaction between the boundary layer and the outer pressure distribution is an excellent approximation.

For a blunt-body flow, however, even at very high Reynolds numbers, there is a discrepancy in the viscous-inviscid patching concept. Figure 7.2 shows two sketches of flow past a two- or three-dimensional blunt body. In the idealized sketch (7.2a), there is a thin film of boundary layer about the body and a narrow sheet of viscous wake in the rear. The patching theory would be glorious for this picture, but it is false. In the actual flow (Fig. 7.2b), the boundary layer is thin on the front, or windward, side of the body, where the pressure decreases along the surface (*favorable* pressure gradient). But in the rear the boundary layer encounters increasing pressure (*adverse* pressure gradient) and breaks off, or separates, into a broad, pulsating wake. (See Fig. 5.2a for a photograph of a specific example.) The mainstream is deflected by this wake, so that the external flow is quite different from the prediction from inviscid theory with the addition of a thin boundary layer.

The theory of strong interaction between blunt-body viscous and inviscid layers is

Fig. 7.2 Illustration of the strong interaction between viscous and inviscid regions in the rear of blunt-body flow: (*a*) idealized and definitely false picture of blunt-body flow; (*b*) actual picture of blunt-body flow.

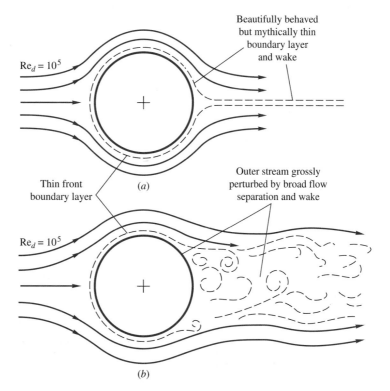

not well developed. Flows like Fig. 7.2b are normally studied experimentally. Reference 5 is an example of efforts to improve the theory of separated-boundary-layer flows. Reference 6 is a textbook devoted to separated flow.

EXAMPLE 7.1

A long, thin flat plate is placed parallel to a 20-ft/s stream of water at 20°C. At what distance x from the leading edge will the boundary-layer thickness be 1 in?

Solution

Since we do not know the Reynolds number, we must guess which of Eqs. (7.1) applies. From Table 1.4 for water, $\nu = 1.09 \times 10^{-5}$ ft²/s; hence

$$\frac{U}{\nu} = \frac{20 \text{ ft/s}}{1.09 \times 10^{-5} \text{ ft}^2/\text{s}} = 1.84 \times 10^6 \text{ ft}^{-1}$$

With $\delta = 1$ in $= \frac{1}{12}$ ft, try Eq. (7.1a):

Laminar flow: $$\frac{\delta}{x} = \frac{5}{(Ux/\nu)^{1/2}}$$

or $$x = \frac{\delta^2(U/\nu)}{5^2} = \frac{(\frac{1}{12} \text{ ft})^2(1.84 \times 10^6 \text{ ft}^{-1})}{25} = 511 \text{ ft}$$

Now we can test the Reynolds number to see whether the formula applied:

$$\text{Re}_x = \frac{Ux}{\nu} = \frac{(20 \text{ ft/s})(511 \text{ ft})}{1.09 \times 10^{-5} \text{ ft}^2/\text{s}} = 9.4 \times 10^8$$

This is impossible since the maximum Re_x for laminar flow past a flat plate is 3×10^6. So we try again with Eq. (7.1b):

Turbulent flow: $$\frac{\delta}{x} = \frac{0.16}{(Ux/\nu)^{1/7}}$$

or $$x = \left[\frac{\delta(U/\nu)^{1/7}}{0.16}\right]^{7/6} = \left[\frac{(\frac{1}{12} \text{ ft})(1.84 \times 10^6 \text{ ft}^{-1})^{1/7}}{0.16}\right]^{7/6} = (4.09)^{7/6} = 5.17 \text{ ft} \quad Ans.$$

Test $$\text{Re}_x = \frac{(20 \text{ ft/s})(5.17 \text{ ft})}{1.09 \times 10^{-5} \text{ ft}^2/\text{s}} = 9.5 \times 10^6$$

This is a perfectly proper turbulent-flow condition; hence we have found the correct position x on our second try.

7.2 Momentum-Integral Estimates

When we derived the momentum-integral relation, Eq. (3.37), and applied it to a flat-plate boundary layer in Example 3.11, we promised to consider it further in Chap. 7. Well, here we are! Let us review the problem, using Fig. 7.3.

A shear layer of unknown thickness grows along the sharp flat plate in Fig. 7.3. The no-slip wall condition retards the flow, making it into a rounded profile $u(y)$, which

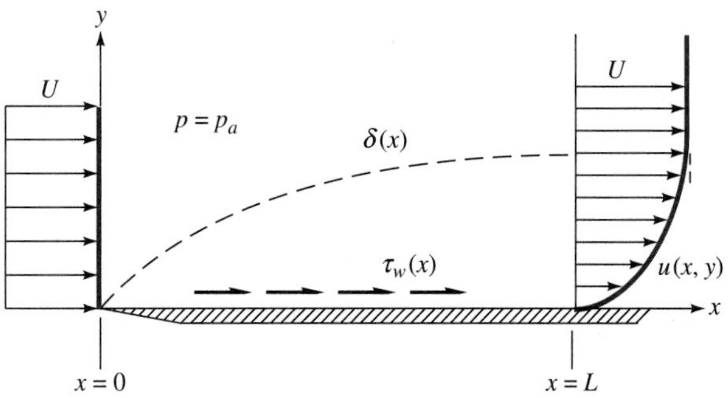

Fig. 7.3 Growth of a boundary layer on a flat plate.

merges into the external velocity U = constant at a "thickness" $y = \delta(x)$. By utilizing the control volume of Fig. 3.11, we found (without making any assumptions about laminar versus turbulent flow) in Example 3.11 that the drag force on the plate is given by the following momentum integral across the exit plane

$$D(x) = \rho b \int_0^{\delta(x)} u(U - u) \, dy \qquad (7.2)$$

where b is the plate width into the paper and the integration is carried out along a vertical plane x = constant. You should review the momentum-integral relation (3.37) and its use in Example 3.11.

Kármán's Analysis of the Flat Plate

Equation (7.2) was derived in 1921 by Kármán [7], who wrote it in the convenient form of the *momentum thickness* θ

$$D(x) = \rho b U^2 \theta \qquad \theta = \int_0^\delta \frac{u}{U}\left(1 - \frac{u}{U}\right) dy \qquad (7.3)$$

Momentum thickness is thus a measure of total plate drag. Kármán then noted that the drag also equals the integrated wall shear stress along the plate

$$D(x) = b \int_0^x \tau_w(x) \, dx$$

or

$$\frac{dD}{dx} = b\tau_w \qquad (7.4)$$

Meanwhile, the derivative of Eq. (7.3), with U = constant, is

$$\frac{dD}{dx} = \rho b U^2 \frac{d\theta}{dx}$$

By comparing this with Eq. (7.4) Kármán arrived at what is now called the *momentum-integral relation* for flat-plate boundary-layer flow

$$\tau_w = \rho U^2 \frac{d\theta}{dx} \qquad (7.5)$$

It is valid for either laminar or turbulent flow.

To get a numerical result for laminar flow, Kármán assumed that the velocity profiles had an approximately parabolic shape

$$u(x, y) \approx U\left(\frac{2y}{\delta} - \frac{y^2}{\delta^2}\right) \qquad 0 \le y \le \delta(x) \tag{7.6}$$

which makes it possible to estimate both momentum thickness and wall shear

$$\theta = \int_0^\delta \left(\frac{2y}{\delta} - \frac{y^2}{\delta^2}\right)\left(1 - \frac{2y}{\delta} + \frac{y^2}{\delta^2}\right) dy \approx \frac{2}{15}\,\delta$$

$$\tau_w = \mu \left.\frac{\partial u}{\partial y}\right|_{y=0} \approx \frac{2\mu U}{\delta} \tag{7.7}$$

By substituting (7.7) into (7.5) and rearranging we obtain

$$\delta \, d\delta \approx 15 \frac{\nu}{U}\, dx \tag{7.8}$$

where $\nu = \mu/\rho$. We can integrate from 0 to x, assuming that $\delta = 0$ at $x = 0$, the leading edge

$$\frac{1}{2}\,\delta^2 = \frac{15\nu x}{U}$$

or

$$\frac{\delta}{x} \approx 5.5\left(\frac{\nu}{Ux}\right)^{1/2} = \frac{5.5}{\mathrm{Re}_x^{1/2}} \tag{7.9}$$

This is the desired thickness estimate. It is all approximate, of course, part of Kármán's *momentum-integral theory* [7], but it is startlingly accurate, being only 10 percent higher than the known exact solution for laminar flat-plate flow, which we gave as Eq. (7.1a).

By combining Eqs. (7.9) and (7.7) we also obtain a shear-stress estimate along the plate

$$c_f = \frac{2\tau_w}{\rho U^2} \approx \left(\frac{\frac{8}{15}}{\mathrm{Re}_x}\right)^{1/2} = \frac{0.73}{\mathrm{Re}_x^{1/2}} \tag{7.10}$$

Again this estimate, in spite of the crudeness of the profile assumption (7.6) is only 10 percent higher than the known exact laminar-plate-flow solution $c_f = 0.664/\mathrm{Re}_x^{1/2}$, treated in Sec. 7.4. The dimensionless quantity c_f, called the *skin-friction coefficient*, is analogous to the friction factor f in ducts.

A boundary layer can be judged as "thin" if, say, the ratio δ/x is less than about 0.1. This occurs at $\delta/x = 0.1 = 5.0/\mathrm{Re}_x^{1/2}$ or at $\mathrm{Re}_x = 2500$. For Re_x less than 2500 we can estimate that boundary-layer theory fails because the thick layer has a significant effect on the outer inviscid flow. The upper limit on Re_x for laminar flow is about 3×10^6, where measurements on a smooth flat plate [8] show that the flow undergoes transition to a turbulent boundary layer. From 3×10^6 upward the turbulent Reynolds number may be arbitrarily large, and a practical limit at present is 5×10^9 for oil supertankers.

Displacement Thickness

Another interesting effect of a boundary layer is its small but finite displacement of the outer streamlines. As shown in Fig. 7.4, outer streamlines must deflect outward a dis-

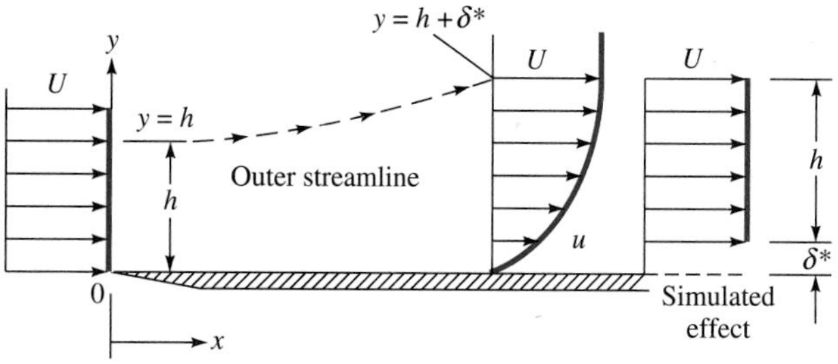

Fig. 7.4 Displacement effect of a boundary layer.

tance $\delta^*(x)$ to satisfy conservation of mass between the inlet and outlet

$$\int_0^h \rho U b \, dy = \int_0^\delta \rho u b \, dy \qquad \delta = h + \delta^* \qquad (7.11)$$

The quantity δ^* is called the *displacement thickness* of the boundary layer. To relate it to $u(y)$, cancel ρ and b from Eq. (7.11), evaluate the left integral, and slyly add and subtract U from the right integrand:

$$Uh = \int_0^\delta (U + u - U) \, dy = U(h + \delta^*) + \int_0^\delta (u - U) \, dy$$

or

$$\delta^* = \int_0^\delta \left(1 - \frac{u}{U}\right) dy \qquad (7.12)$$

Thus the ratio of δ^*/δ varies only with the dimensionless velocity-profile shape u/U.

Introducing our profile approximation (7.6) into (7.12), we obtain by integration the approximate result

$$\delta^* \approx \frac{1}{3} \delta \qquad \frac{\delta^*}{x} \approx \frac{1.83}{\mathrm{Re}_x^{1/2}} \qquad (7.13)$$

These estimates are only 6 percent away from the exact solutions for laminar flat-plate flow given in Sec. 7.4: $\delta^* = 0.344\delta = 1.721x/\mathrm{Re}_x^{1/2}$. Since δ^* is much smaller than x for large Re_x and the outer streamline slope V/U is proportional to δ^*, we conclude that the velocity normal to the wall is much smaller than the velocity parallel to the wall. This is a key assumption in boundary-layer theory (Sec. 7.3).

We also conclude from the success of these simple parabolic estimates that Kármán's momentum-integral theory is effective and useful. Many details of this theory are given in Refs. 1 to 3.

EXAMPLE 7.2

Are low-speed, small-scale air and water boundary layers really thin? Consider flow at $U = 1$ ft/s past a flat plate 1 ft long. Compute the boundary-layer thickness at the trailing edge for (*a*) air and (*b*) water at 20°C.

Solution

Part (a) From Table A.3, $\nu_{air} \approx 1.61$ E-4 ft^2/s. The trailing-edge Reynolds number thus is

$$\mathrm{Re}_L = \frac{UL}{\nu} = \frac{(1 \text{ ft/s})(1 \text{ ft})}{1.61 \text{ E-4 ft}^2/\text{s}} = 6200$$

Since this is less than 10^6, the flow is presumed laminar, and since it is greater than 2500, the boundary layer is reasonably thin. From Eq. (7.1a), the predicted laminar thickness is

$$\frac{\delta}{x} \approx \frac{5.0}{\sqrt{6200}} = 0.0634$$

or, at $x = 1$ ft, $\delta = 0.0634$ ft ≈ 0.76 in   *Ans. (a)*

Part (b)   From Table A.2 $\nu_{\text{water}} \approx 1.08$ E-5 ft^2/s. The trailing-edge Reynolds number is

$$\mathrm{Re}_L = \frac{(1 \text{ ft/s})(1 \text{ ft})}{1.08 \text{ E-5 ft}^2/\text{s}} \approx 92{,}600$$

This again satisfies the laminar and thinness conditions. The boundary-layer thickness is

$$\frac{\delta}{x} \approx \frac{5.0}{\sqrt{92{,}600}} = 0.0164$$

or, at $x = 1$ ft, $\delta = 0.0164$ ft ≈ 0.20 in   *Ans. (b)*

Thus, even at such low velocities and short lengths, both airflows and water flows satisfy the boundary-layer approximations.

7.3 The Boundary-Layer Equations

In Chaps. 4 and 6 we learned that there are several dozen known analytical laminar-flow solutions [1 to 3]. None are for external flow around immersed bodies, although this is one of the primary applications of fluid mechanics. No exact solutions are known for turbulent flow, whose analysis typically uses empirical modeling laws to relate time-mean variables.

There are presently three techniques used to study external flows: (1) numerical (digital-computer) solutions, (2) experimentaton, and (3) boundary-layer theory.

Computational fluid dynamics (CFD) is now well developed and described in advanced texts such as that by Anderson et al. [4]. Thousands of computer solutions and models have been published; execution times, mesh sizes, and graphical presentations are improving each year. Both laminar- and turbulent-flow solutions have been published, and turbulence modeling is a current research topic [9]. Except for a brief discussion of inviscid-flow computer analysis in Chap. 8, the topic of CFD is beyond our scope here.

Experimentation is the most common method of studying external flows. Chapter 5 outlined the technique of dimensional analysis, and we shall give many nondimensional experimental data for external flows in Sec. 7.6.

The third tool is boundary-layer theory, first formulated by Ludwig Prandtl in 1904. We shall follow Prandtl's ideas here and make certain order-of-magnitude assumptions to greatly simplify the Navier-Stokes equations (4.38) into boundary-layer equations which are solved relatively easily and patched onto the outer inviscid-flow field.

One of the great achievements of boundary-layer theory is its ability to predict the flow separation illustrated in Fig. 7.2b. Before 1904 no one realized that such thin shear layers could cause such a gross effect as flow separation. Unfortunately, even today theory cannot accurately predict the behavior of the separated-flow region and its interaction with the outer layer. This is the weakness of boundary-layer theory, which we hope will be overcome by intensive research into the dynamics of separated flows [6].

Derivation for Two-Dimensional Flow

We consider only steady two-dimensional incompressible viscous flow with the x direction along the wall and y normal to the wall, as in Fig. 7.3.[1] We neglect gravity, which is important only in boundary layers where fluid buoyancy is dominant [2, sec. 4.13]. From Chap. 4, the complete equations of motion consist of continuity and the x- and y-momentum relations

$$\frac{\partial u}{\partial x} + \frac{\partial v}{\partial y} = 0 \tag{7.14a}$$

$$\rho\left(u\,\frac{\partial u}{\partial x} + v\,\frac{\partial u}{\partial y}\right) = -\frac{\partial p}{\partial x} + \mu\left(\frac{\partial^2 u}{\partial x^2} + \frac{\partial^2 u}{\partial y^2}\right) \tag{7.14b}$$

$$\rho\left(u\,\frac{\partial v}{\partial x} + v\,\frac{\partial v}{\partial y}\right) = -\frac{\partial p}{\partial y} + \mu\left(\frac{\partial^2 v}{\partial x^2} + \frac{\partial^2 v}{\partial y^2}\right) \tag{7.14c}$$

These should be solved for u, v, and p subject to typical no-slip, inlet, and exit boundary conditions, but in fact they are too difficult to handle for most external flows.

In 1904 Prandtl correctly deduced that a shear layer must be very thin if the Reynolds number is large, so that the following approximations apply:

Velocities:
$$v \ll u \tag{7.15a}$$

Rates of change:
$$\frac{\partial}{\partial x} \ll \frac{\partial}{\partial y} \tag{7.15b}$$

Our discussion of displacement thickness in the previous section was intended to justify these assumptions.

Applying these approximations to Eq. (7.14c) results in a powerful simplification

$$\frac{\partial p}{\partial y} \approx 0 \quad \text{or} \quad p \approx p(x) \text{ only} \tag{7.16}$$

In other words, the y-momentum equation can be neglected entirely, and the pressure varies only *along* the boundary layer, not through it. The pressure-gradient term in Eq. (7.14b) is assumed to be known in advance from Bernoulli's equation applied to the outer inviscid flow

$$\frac{\partial p}{\partial x} = \frac{dp}{dx} = -\rho U\,\frac{dU}{dx} \tag{7.17}$$

Presumably we have already made the inviscid analysis and know the distribution of $U(x)$ along the wall (Chap. 8).

Meanwhile, one term in Eq. (7.14b) is negligible due to Eqs. (7.15)

---

[1] For a curved wall, x can represent the arc length along the wall and y can be everywhere normal to x with negligible change in the boundary-layer equations as long as the radius of curvature of the wall is large compared with the boundary-layer thickness [1 to 3].

$$\frac{\partial^2 u}{\partial x^2} \ll \frac{\partial^2 u}{\partial y^2} \tag{7.18}$$

However, neither term in the continuity relation (7.14a) can be neglected—another warning that continuity is always a vital part of any fluid-flow analysis.

The net result is that the three full equations of motion (7.14) are reduced to Prandtl's two boundary-layer equations

Continuity:
$$\frac{\partial u}{\partial x} + \frac{\partial v}{\partial y} = 0 \tag{7.19a}$$

Momentum along wall:
$$u\frac{\partial u}{\partial x} + v\frac{\partial u}{\partial y} \approx U\frac{dU}{dx} + \frac{1}{\rho}\frac{\partial \tau}{\partial y} \tag{7.19b}$$

where
$$\tau = \begin{cases} \mu\dfrac{\partial u}{\partial y} & \text{laminar flow} \\[2mm] \mu\dfrac{\partial u}{\partial y} - \rho\overline{u'v'} & \text{turbulent flow} \end{cases}$$

These are to be solved for $u(x, y)$ and $v(x, y)$, with $U(x)$ assumed to be a known function from the outer inviscid-flow analysis. There are two boundary conditions on u and one on v:

At $y = 0$ (wall): $u = v = 0$ (no slip)   (7.20a)

At $y = \delta(x)$ (outer stream): $u = U(x)$ (patching)   (7.20b)

Unlike the Navier-Stokes equations (7.14), which are mathematically elliptic and must be solved simultaneously over the entire flow field, the boundary-layer equations (7.19) are mathematically parabolic and are solved by beginning at the leading edge and marching downstream as far as you like, stopping at the separation point or earlier if you prefer.[1]

The boundary-layer equations have been solved for scores of interesting cases of internal and external flow for both laminar and turbulent flow, utilizing the inviscid distribution $U(x)$ appropriate to each flow. Full details of boundary-layer theory and results and comparison with experiment are given in Refs. 1 to 3. Here we shall confine ourselves primarily to flat-plate solutions (Sec. 7.4).

7.4 The Flat-Plate Boundary Layer

The classic and most often used solution of boundary-layer theory is for flat-plate flow, as in Fig. 7.3, which can represent either laminar or turbulent flow.

Laminar Flow

For laminar flow past the plate, the boundary-layer equations (7.19) can be solved exactly for u and v, assuming that the free-stream velocity U is constant ($dU/dx = 0$). The solution was given by Prandtl's student Blasius, in his 1908 dissertation from Göttingen. With an ingenious coordinate transformation, Blasius showed that the di-

---

[1] For further mathematical details, see Ref. 2, sec. 2.8.

mensionless velocity profile u/U is a function only of the single composite dimensionless variable $(y)[U/(\nu x)]^{1/2}$:

$$\frac{u}{U} = f'(\eta) \qquad \eta = y\left(\frac{U}{\nu x}\right)^{1/2} \tag{7.21}$$

where the prime denotes differentiation with respect to η. Substitution of (7.21) into the boundary-layer equations (7.19) reduces the problem, after much algebra, to a single third-order nonlinear ordinary differential equation for f

$$f''' + \tfrac{1}{2}ff'' = 0 \tag{7.22}$$

The boundary conditions (7.20) become

At $y = 0$: $\qquad\qquad\qquad\qquad f(0) = f'(0) = 0 \tag{7.23a}$

As $y \to \infty$: $\qquad\qquad\qquad\qquad f'(\infty) \to 1.0 \tag{7.23b}$

This is the *Blasius equation*, for which accurate solutions have been obtained only by numerical integration. Some tabulated values of the velocity-profile shape $f'(\eta) = u/U$ are given in Table 7.1.

   Since u/U approaches 1.0 only as $y \to \infty$, it is customary to select the boundary-layer thickness δ as that point where $u/U = 0.99$. From the table, this occurs at $\eta \approx 5.0$:

$$\delta_{99\%}\left(\frac{U}{\nu x}\right)^{1/2} \approx 5.0$$

or $\qquad\qquad\qquad \dfrac{\delta}{x} \approx \dfrac{5.0}{\mathrm{Re}_x^{1/2}} \qquad$ Blasius (1908) $\tag{7.24}$

With the profile known, Blasius, of course, could also compute the wall shear and displacement thickness

$$c_f = \frac{0.664}{\mathrm{Re}_x^{1/2}} \qquad \frac{\delta^*}{x} = \frac{1.721}{\mathrm{Re}_x^{1/2}} \tag{7.25}$$

Notice how close these are to our integral estimates, Eqs. (7.9), (7.10), and (7.13). When c_f is converted to dimensional form, we have

Table 7.1 The Blasius Velocity Profile [1–3]

$y[U/(\nu x)]^{1/2}$	u/U	$y[U/(\nu x)]^{1/2}$	u/U
0.0	0.0	2.8	0.81152
0.2	0.06641	3.0	0.84605
0.4	0.13277	3.2	0.87609
0.6	0.19894	3.4	0.90177
0.8	0.26471	3.6	0.92333
1.0	0.32979	3.8	0.94112
1.2	0.39378	4.0	0.95552
1.4	0.45627	4.2	0.96696
1.6	0.51676	4.4	0.97587
1.8	0.57477	4.6	0.98269
2.0	0.62977	4.8	0.98779
2.2	0.68132	5.0	0.99155
2.4	0.72899	∞	1.00000
2.6	0.77246		

$$\tau_w(x) = \frac{0.332\rho^{1/2}\mu^{1/2}U^{1.5}}{x^{1/2}}$$

The wall shear drops off with $x^{1/2}$ because of boundary-layer growth and varies as velocity to the 1.5 power. This is in contrast to laminar pipe flow, where $\tau_w \propto U$ and is independent of x.

If $\tau_w(x)$ is substituted into Eq. (7.4), we compute the total drag force

$$D(x) = b\int_0^x \tau_w(x)\, dx = 0.664b\rho^{1/2}\mu^{1/2}U^{1.5}x^{1/2} \tag{7.26}$$

The drag increases only as the square root of the plate length. The nondimensional *drag coefficient* is defined as

$$C_D = \frac{2D(L)}{\rho U^2 bL} = \frac{1.328}{\mathrm{Re}_L^{1/2}} = 2c_f(L) \tag{7.27}$$

Thus, for laminar plate flow, C_D equals twice the value of the skin-friction coefficient at the trailing edge. This is the drag on one side of the plate.

Kármán pointed out that the drag could also be computed from the momentum relation (7.2). In dimensionless form, Eq. (7.2) becomes

$$C_D = \frac{2}{L}\int_0^\delta \frac{u}{U}\left(1 - \frac{u}{U}\right) dy \tag{7.28}$$

This can be rewritten in terms of the momentum thickness at the trailing edge

$$C_D = \frac{2\theta(L)}{L} \tag{7.29}$$

Computation of θ from the profile u/U or from C_D gives

$$\frac{\theta}{x} = \frac{0.664}{\mathrm{Re}_x^{1/2}} \qquad \text{laminar flat plate} \tag{7.30}$$

Since δ is so ill defined, the momentum thickness, being definite, is often used to correlate data taken for a variety of boundary layers under differing conditions. The ratio of displacement to momentum thickness, called the dimensionless-profile *shape factor*, is also useful in integral theories. For laminar flat-plate flow

$$H = \frac{\delta^*}{\theta} = \frac{1.721}{0.664} = 2.59 \tag{7.31}$$

A large shape factor then implies that boundary-layer separation is about to occur.

If we plot the Blasius velocity profile from Table 7.1 in the form of u/U versus y/δ, we can see why the simple integral-theory guess, Eq. (7.6), was such a great success. This is done in Fig. 7.5. The simple parabolic approximation is not far from the true Blasius profile; hence its momentum thickness is within 10 percent of the true value. Also shown in Fig. 7.5 are three typical turbulent flat-plate velocity profiles. Notice how strikingly different in shape they are from the laminar profiles. Instead of decreasing monotonically to zero, the turbulent profiles are very flat and then drop off sharply at the wall. As you might guess, they follow the logarithmic-law shape and thus can be analyzed by momentum-integral theory if this shape is properly represented.

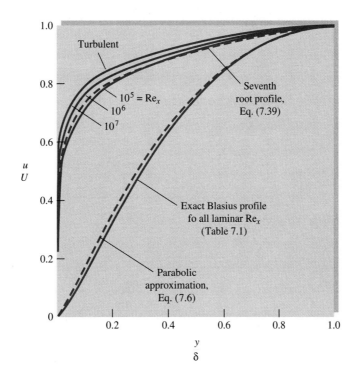

Fig. 7.5 Comparison of dimensionless laminar and turbulent flat-plate velocity profiles.

Transition to Turbulence

The laminar flat-plate boundary layer eventually becomes turbulent, but there is no unique value for this change to occur. With care in polishing the wall and keeping the free stream quiet, one can delay the transition Reynolds number to $Re_{x,tr} \approx 3$ E6 [8]. However, for typical commercial surfaces and gusty free streams, a more realistic value is $Re_{x,tr} \approx 5$ E5.

EXAMPLE 7.3

A sharp flat plate with $L = 1$ m and $b = 3$ m is immersed parallel to a stream of velocity 2 m/s. Find the drag on one side of the plate, and at the trailing edge find the thicknesses δ, δ^*, and θ for (a) air, $\rho = 1.23$ kg/m^3 and $\nu = 1.46 \times 10^{-5}$ m^2/s, and (b) water, $\rho = 1000$ kg/m^3 and $\nu = 1.02 \times 10^{-6}$ m^2/s.

Solution

Part (a)   The airflow Reynolds number is

$$\frac{VL}{\nu} = \frac{(2.0 \text{ m/s})(1.0 \text{ m})}{1.46 \times 10^{-5} \text{ m}^2/\text{s}} = 137,000$$

Since this is less than 3×10^6, we assume that the boundary layer is laminar. From Eq. (7.27), the drag coefficient is

$$C_D = \frac{1.328}{(137,000)^{1/2}} = 0.00359$$

Thus the drag on one side in the airflow is

$$D = C_D \tfrac{1}{2} \rho U^2 bL = 0.00359(\tfrac{1}{2})(1.23)(2.0)^2(3.0)(1.0) = 0.0265 \text{ N} \qquad Ans. (a)$$

The boundary-layer thickness at the end of the plate is

$$\frac{\delta}{L} = \frac{5.0}{\text{Re}_L^{1/2}} = \frac{5.0}{(137{,}000)^{1/2}} = 0.0135$$

or

$$\delta = 0.0135(1.0) = 0.0135 \text{ m} = 13.5 \text{ mm} \qquad Ans. (a)$$

We find the other two thicknesses simply by ratios:

$$\delta^* = \frac{1.721}{5.0}\,\delta = 4.65 \text{ mm} \qquad \theta = \frac{\delta^*}{2.59} = 1.79 \text{ mm} \qquad Ans. (a)$$

Notice that no conversion factors are needed with SI units.

Part (b) The water Reynolds number is

$$\text{Re}_L = \frac{2.0(1.0)}{1.02 \times 10^{-6}} = 1.96 \times 10^6$$

This is rather close to the critical value of 3×10^6, so that a rough surface or noisy free stream might trigger transition to turbulence; but let us assume that the flow is laminar. The water drag coefficient is

$$C_D = \frac{1.328}{(1.96 \times 10^6)^{1/2}} = 0.000949$$

and

$$D = 0.000949(\tfrac{1}{2})(1000)(2.0)^2(3.0)(1.0) = 5.70 \text{ N} \qquad Ans. (b)$$

The drag is 215 times more for water in spite of the higher Reynolds number and lower drag coefficient because water is 57 times more viscous and 813 times denser than air. From Eq. (7.26), in laminar flow, it should have $(57)^{1/2}(813)^{1/2} = 7.53(28.5) = 215$ times more drag.
  The boundary-layer thickness is given by

$$\frac{\delta}{L} = \frac{5.0}{(1.96 \times 10^6)^{1/2}} = 0.00357$$

or

$$\delta = 0.00357(1000 \text{ mm}) = 3.57 \text{ mm} \qquad Ans. (b)$$

By scaling down we have

$$\delta^* = \frac{1.721}{5.0}\,\delta = 1.23 \text{ mm} \qquad \theta = \frac{\delta^*}{2.59} = 0.48 \text{ mm} \qquad Ans. (b)$$

The water layer is 3.8 times thinner than the air layer, which reflects the square root of the 14.3 ratio of air to water kinematic viscosity.

Turbulent Flow

There is no exact theory for turbulent flat-plate flow, although there are many elegant computer solutions of the boundary-layer equations using various empirical models for the turbulent eddy viscosity [9]. The most widely accepted result is simply an integal analysis similar to our study of the laminar-profile approximation (7.6).

We begin with Eq. (7.5), which is valid for laminar or turbulent flow. We write it here for convenient reference:

$$\tau_w(x) = \rho U^2 \frac{d\theta}{dx} \tag{7.32}$$

From the definition of c_f, Eq. (7.10), this can be rewritten as

$$c_f = 2 \frac{d\theta}{dx} \tag{7.33}$$

Now recall from Fig. 7.5 that the turbulent profiles are nowhere near parabolic. Going back to Fig. 6.9, we see that flat-plate flow is very nearly logarithmic, with a slight outer wake and a thin viscous sublayer. Therefore, just as in turbulent pipe flow, we assume that the logarithmic law (6.21) holds all the way across the boundary layer

$$\frac{u}{u^*} \approx \frac{1}{\kappa} \ln \frac{yu^*}{\nu} + B \qquad u^* = \left(\frac{\tau_w}{\rho}\right)^{1/2} \tag{7.34}$$

with, as usual, $\kappa = 0.41$ and $B = 5.0$. At the outer edge of the boundary layer, $y = \delta$ and $u = U$, and Eq. (7.34) becomes

$$\frac{U}{u^*} = \frac{1}{\kappa} \ln \frac{\delta u^*}{\nu} + B \tag{7.35}$$

But the definition of the skin-friction coefficient, Eq. (7.10), is such that the following identities hold:

$$\frac{U}{u^*} \equiv \left(\frac{2}{c_f}\right)^{1/2} \qquad \frac{\delta u^*}{\nu} \equiv \text{Re}_\delta \left(\frac{c_f}{2}\right)^{1/2} \tag{7.36}$$

Therefore Eq. (7.35) is a *skin-friction law* for turbulent flat-plate flow

$$\left(\frac{2}{c_f}\right)^{1/2} \approx 2.44 \ln \left[\text{Re}_\delta \left(\frac{c_f}{2}\right)^{1/2}\right] + 5.0 \tag{7.37}$$

It is a complicated law, but we can at least solve for a few values and list them:

Re_δ	10^4	10^5	10^6	10^7
c_f	0.00493	0.00315	0.00217	0.00158

Following a suggestion of Prandtl, we can forget the complex log friction law (7.37) and simply fit the numbers in the table to a power-law approximation

$$c_f \approx 0.02 \, \text{Re}_\delta^{-1/6} \tag{7.38}$$

This we shall use as the left-hand side of Eq. (7.33). For the right-hand side, we need an estimate for $\theta(x)$ in terms of $\delta(x)$. If we use the logarithmic-law profile (7.34), we shall be up to our hips in logarithmic integrations for the momentum thickness. Instead we follow another suggestion of Prandtl, who pointed out that the turbulent profiles in Fig. 7.5 can be approximated by a one-seventh-power law

$$\left(\frac{u}{U}\right)_{\text{turb}} \approx \left(\frac{y}{\delta}\right)^{1/7} \tag{7.39}$$

This is shown as a dashed line in Fig. 7.5. It is an excellent fit to the low-Reynolds-number turbulent data, which were all that were available to Prandtl at the time. With this simple approximation, the momentum thickness (7.28) can easily be evaluated:

$$\theta \approx \int_0^\delta \left(\frac{y}{\delta}\right)^{1/7}\left[1 - \left(\frac{y}{\delta}\right)^{1/7}\right] dy = \frac{7}{72}\delta \tag{7.40}$$

We accept this result and substitute Eqs. (7.38) and (7.40) into Kármán's momentum law (7.33)

$$c_f = 0.02 \ \mathrm{Re}_\delta^{-1/6} = 2\frac{d}{dx}\left(\frac{7}{72}\delta\right)$$

or

$$\mathrm{Re}_\delta^{-1/6} = 9.72\frac{d\delta}{dx} = 9.72\frac{d(\mathrm{Re}_\delta)}{d(\mathrm{Re}_x)} \tag{7.41}$$

Separate the variables and integrate, assuming $\delta = 0$ at $x = 0$:

$$\mathrm{Re}_\delta \approx 0.16 \ \mathrm{Re}_x^{6/7} \qquad \text{or} \qquad \frac{\delta}{x} \approx \frac{0.16}{\mathrm{Re}_x^{1/7}} \tag{7.42}$$

Thus the thickness of a turbulent boundary layer increases as $x^{6/7}$, far more rapidly than the laminar increase $x^{1/2}$. Equation (7.42) is the solution to the problem, because all other parameters are now available. For example, combining Eqs. (7.42) and (7.38), we obtain the friction variation

$$c_f \approx \frac{0.027}{\mathrm{Re}_x^{1/7}} \tag{7.43}$$

Writing this out in dimensional form, we have

$$\tau_{w,\text{turb}} \approx \frac{0.0135\mu^{1/7}\rho^{6/7}U^{13/7}}{x^{1/7}} \tag{7.44}$$

Turbulent plate friction drops slowly with x, increases nearly as ρ and U^2, and is rather insensitive to viscosity.

We can evaluate the drag coefficient from Eq. (7.29)

$$C_D = \frac{0.031}{\mathrm{Re}_L^{1/7}} = \frac{7}{6}c_f(L) \tag{7.45}$$

Then C_D is only 16 percent greater than the trailing-edge skin friction [compare with Eq. (7.27) for laminar flow].

The displacement thickness can be estimated from the one-seventh-power law and Eq. (7.12):

$$\delta^* \approx \int_0^\delta \left[1 - \left(\frac{y}{\delta}\right)^{1/7}\right] dy = \frac{1}{8}\delta \tag{7.46}$$

The turbulent flat-plate shape factor is approximately

$$H = \frac{\delta^*}{\theta} = \frac{\frac{1}{8}}{\frac{7}{72}} = 1.3 \tag{7.47}$$

These are the basic results of turbulent flat-plate theory.

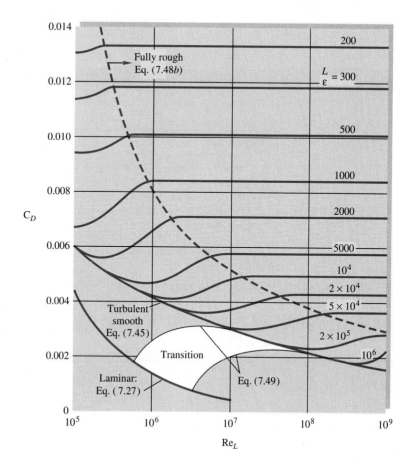

Fig. 7.6 Drag coefficient of laminar and turbulent boundary layer on smooth and rough flat plates. This chart is the flat-plate analog of the Moody diagram of Fig. 6.13.

Figure 7.6 shows flat-plate drag coefficients for both laminar- and turbulent-flow conditions. The smooth-wall relations (7.27) and (7.45) are shown, along with the effect of wall roughness, which is quite strong. The proper roughness parameter here is x/ϵ or L/ϵ, by analogy with the pipe parameter ϵ/d. In the fully rough regime, C_D is independent of the Reynolds number, so that the drag varies exactly as U^2 and is independent of μ. Reference 2 presents a theory of rough flat-plate flow, and Ref. 1 gives a curve fit for skin friction and drag in the fully rough regime:

$$c_f \approx \left(2.87 + 1.58 \log \frac{x}{\epsilon} \right)^{-2.5} \tag{7.48a}$$

$$C_D \approx \left(1.89 + 1.62 \log \frac{L}{\epsilon} \right)^{-2.5} \tag{7.48b}$$

Equation (7.48b) is plotted to the right of the dashed line in Fig. 7.6. The figure also shows the behavior of the drag coefficient in the transition region $5 \times 10^5 < \mathrm{Re}_L < 8 \times 10^7$, where the laminar drag at the leading edge is an appreciable fraction of the total drag. Schlichting [1] suggests the following curve fits for these transition drag curves depending upon the Reynolds number $\mathrm{Re}_{\mathrm{trans}}$ where transition begins:

$$C_D \approx \begin{cases} \dfrac{0.031}{\mathrm{Re}_L^{1/7}} - \dfrac{1440}{\mathrm{Re}_L} & \mathrm{Re}_{\mathrm{trans}} = 5 \times 10^5 & (7.49a) \\[3mm] \dfrac{0.031}{\mathrm{Re}_L^{1/7}} - \dfrac{8700}{\mathrm{Re}_L} & \mathrm{Re}_{\mathrm{trans}} = 3 \times 10^6 & (7.49b) \end{cases}$$

EXAMPLE 7.4

A hydrofoil 1.2 ft long and 6 ft wide is placed in a water flow of 40 ft/s, with $\rho = 1.99$ slugs/ft^3 and $\nu = 0.000011$ ft^2/s. (a) Estimate the boundary-layer thickness at the end of the plate. Estimate the friction drag for (b) turbulent smooth-wall flow from the leading edge, (c) laminar turbulent flow with $\mathrm{Re}_{\mathrm{trans}} = 5 \times 10^5$, and (d) turbulent rough-wall flow with $\epsilon = 0.0004$ ft.

Solution

Part (a)   The Reynolds number is

$$\mathrm{Re}_L = \frac{UL}{\nu} = \frac{(40 \text{ ft/s})(1.2 \text{ ft})}{0.000011 \text{ ft}^2/\text{s}} = 4.36 \times 10^6$$

Thus the trailing-edge flow is certainly turbulent. The maximum boundary-layer thickness would occur for turbulent flow starting at the leading edge. From Eq. (7.42),

$$\frac{\delta(L)}{L} = \frac{0.16}{(4.36 \times 10^6)^{1/7}} = 0.018$$

or $\qquad\qquad \delta = 0.018(1.2 \text{ ft}) = 0.0216 \text{ ft}$ *Ans. (a)*

This is 7.5 times thicker than a fully laminar boundary layer at the same Reynolds number.

Part (b)   For fully turbulent smooth-wall flow, the drag coefficient on one side of the plate is, from Eq. (7.45),

$$C_D = \frac{0.031}{(4.36 \times 10^6)^{1/7}} = 0.00349$$

Then the drag on both sides of the foil is approximately

$$D = 2C_D(\tfrac{1}{2}\rho U^2)bL = 2(0.00349)(\tfrac{1}{2})(1.99)(40)^2(6.0)(1.2) = 80 \text{ lb} \qquad \textit{Ans. (b)}$$

Part (c)   With a laminar leading edge and $\mathrm{Re}_{\mathrm{trans}} = 5 \times 10^5$, Eq. (7.49a) applies:

$$C_D = 0.00349 - \frac{1440}{4.36 \times 10^6} = 0.00316$$

The drag can be recomputed for this lower drag coefficient:

$$D = 2C_D(\tfrac{1}{2}\rho U^2)bL = 72 \text{ lbf} \qquad \textit{Ans. (c)}$$

Part (d)   Finally, for the rough wall, we calculate

$$\frac{L}{\epsilon} = \frac{1.2 \text{ ft}}{0.0004 \text{ ft}} = 3000$$

From Fig. 7.6 at $Re_L = 4.36 \times 10^6$, this condition is just inside the fully rough regime. Equation (7.48b) applies:

$$C_D = (1.89 + 1.62 \log 3000)^{-2.5} = 0.00644$$

and the drag estimate is

$$D = 2C_D(\tfrac{1}{2}\rho U^2)bL = 148 \text{ lbf} \qquad\qquad \textit{Ans. (d)}$$

This small roughness nearly doubles the drag. It is probable that the total hydrofoil drag is still another factor of 2 larger because of trailing-edge flow-separation effects.

7.5 Boundary Layers with Pressure Gradient[1]

The flat-plate analysis of the previous section should give us a good feeling for the behavior of both laminar and turbulent boundary layers, except for one important effect: flow separation. Prandtl showed that separation like that in Fig. 7.2b is caused by excessive momentum loss near the wall in a boundary layer trying to move downstream against increasing pressure, $dp/dx > 0$, which is called an *adverse pressure gradient*. The opposite case of decreasing pressure, $dp/dx < 0$, is called a *favorable gradient*, where flow separation can never occur. In a typical immersed-body flow, e.g., Fig. 7.2b, the favorable gradient is on the front of the body and the adverse gradient is in the rear, as discussed in detail in Chap. 8.

We can explain flow separation with a geometric argument about the second derivative of velocity u at the wall. From the momentum equation (7.19b) at the wall, where $u = v = 0$, we obtain

$$\left.\frac{\partial \tau}{\partial y}\right|_{\text{wall}} = \left.\mu \frac{\partial^2 u}{\partial y^2}\right|_{\text{wall}} = -\rho U \frac{dU}{dx} = \frac{dp}{dx}$$

or

$$\left.\frac{\partial^2 u}{\partial y^2}\right|_{\text{wall}} = \frac{1}{\mu}\frac{dp}{dx} \qquad\qquad (7.50)$$

for either laminar or turbulent flow. Thus in an adverse gradient the second derivative of velocity is positive at the wall; yet it must be negative at the outer layer ($y = \delta$) to merge smoothly with the mainstream flow $U(x)$. It follows that the second derivative must pass through zero somewhere in between, at a point of inflection, and any boundary-layer profile in an adverse gradient must exhibit a characteristic S shape.

Figure 7.7 illustrates the general case. In a favorable gradient (Fig. 7.7a) the profile is very rounded, there is no point of inflection, there can be no separation, and laminar profiles of this type are very resistant to a transition to turbulence [1 to 3].

In a zero pressure gradient (Fig. 7.7b), e.g., flat-plate flow, the point of inflection is at the wall itself. There can be no separation, and the flow will undergo transition at Re_x no greater than about 3×10^6, as discussed earlier.

In an adverse gradient (Fig. 7.7c to e), a point of inflection (PI) occurs in the boundary layer, its distance from the wall increasing with the strength of the adverse gradient. For a weak gradient (Fig. 7.7c) the flow does not actually separate, but it is vulnerable to transition to turbulence at Re_x as low as 10^5 [1, 2]. At a moderate gradient, a critical

[1] This section may be omitted without loss of continuity.

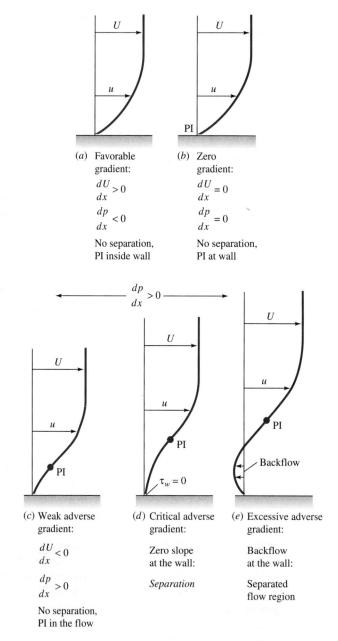

Fig. 7.7 Effect of pressure gradient on boundary-layer profiles; PI = point of inflection.

condition (Fig. 7.7d) is reached where the wall shear is exactly zero ($\partial u/\partial y = 0$). This is defined as the *separation point* ($\tau_w = 0$), because any stronger gradient will actually cause backflow at the wall (Fig. 7.7e): the boundary layer thickens greatly, and the main flow breaks away, or separates, from the wall (Fig. 7.2b).

The flow profiles of Fig. 7.7 usually occur in sequence as the boundary layer progresses along the wall of a body. For example, in Fig. 7.2a, a favorable gradient occurs on the front of the body, zero pressure gradient occurs just upstream of the shoulder, and an adverse gradient occurs successively as we move around the rear of the body.

  A second practical example is the flow in a duct consisting of a nozzle, throat, and diffuser, as in Fig. 7.8. The nozzle flow is a favorable gradient and never separates, nor does the throat flow where the pressure gradient is approximately zero. But the expanding-area diffuser produces low velocity and increasing pressure, an adverse gradient. If the diffuser angle is too large, the adverse gradient is excessive, and the boundary layer will separate at one or both walls, with backflow, increased losses, and poor pressure recovery. In the diffuser literature [10] this condition is called *diffuser stall*, a term used also in airfoil aerodynamics (Sec. 7.6) to denote airfoil boundary-layer separation. Thus the boundary-layer behavior explains why a large-angle diffuser has heavy flow losses (Fig. 6.23) and poor performance (Fig. 6.28).

  Presently boundary-layer theory can compute only up to the separation point, after which it is invalid. New techniques are now developed for analyzing the strong interaction effects caused by separated flows [5, 6].

Laminar Integral Theory

Both laminar and turbulent theories can be developed from Kármán's general two-dimensional boundary-layer integral relation [7], which extends Eq. (7.33) to variable $U(x)$

$$\frac{\tau_w}{\rho U^2} = \frac{1}{2} c_f = \frac{d\theta}{dx} + (2 + H) \frac{\theta}{U} \frac{dU}{dx} \qquad (7.51)$$

Fig. 7.8 Boundary-layer separation in a diffuser.

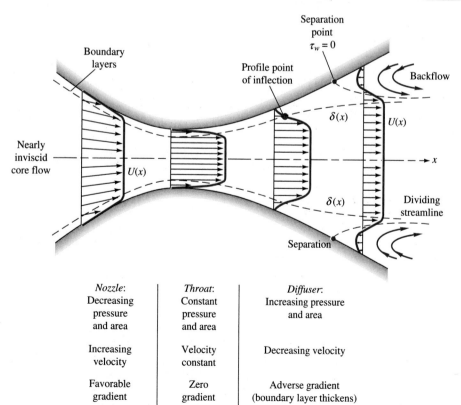

Nozzle:	Throat:	Diffuser:
Decreasing pressure and area	Constant pressure and area	Increasing pressure and area
Increasing velocity	Velocity constant	Decreasing velocity
Favorable gradient	Zero gradient	Adverse gradient (boundary layer thickens)

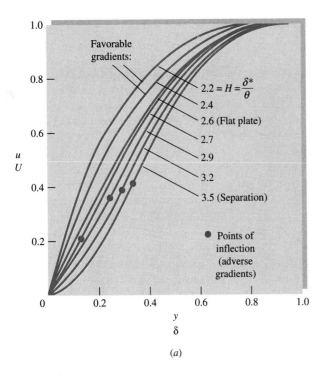

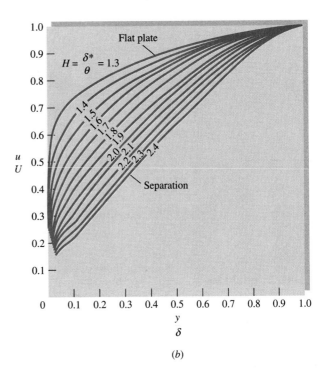

(a)

(b)

Fig. 7.9 Velocity profiles with pressure gradient: (a) laminar flow; (b) turbulent flow with adverse gradients.

where $\theta(x)$ is the momentum thickness and $H(x) = \delta^*(x)/\theta(x)$ is the shape factor. From Eq. (7.17) negative dU/dx is equivalent to positive dp/dx, that is, an adverse gradient.

We can integrate Eq. (7.51) to determine $\theta(x)$ for a given $U(x)$ if we correlate c_f and H with the momentum thickness. This has been done by examining typical velocity profiles of laminar and turbulent boundary-layer flows for various pressure gradients. Some examples are given in Fig. 7.9, showing that the shape factor H is a good indicator of the pressure gradient. The higher the H, the stronger the adverse gradient, and separation occurs approximately at

$$H \approx \begin{cases} 3.5 & \text{laminar flow} \\ 2.4 & \text{turbulent flow} \end{cases} \tag{7.52}$$

The laminar profiles (Fig. 7.9a) clearly exhibit the S shape and a point of inflection with an adverse gradient. But in the turbulent profiles (Fig. 7.9b) the points of inflection are typically buried deep within the thin viscous sublayer, which can hardly be seen on the scale of the figure.

There are scores of turbulent theories in the literature, but they are all complicated algebraically and will be omitted here. The reader is referred to advanced texts [1, 2, 9].

For laminar flow, a simple and effective method was developed by Thwaites [11], who found that Eq. (7.51) can be correlated by a single dimensionless momentum-thickness variable λ, defined as

$$\lambda = \frac{\theta^2}{\nu}\frac{dU}{dx} \tag{7.53}$$

Using a straight-line fit to his correlation, Thwaites was able to integrate Eq. (7.51) in closed form, with the result

$$\theta^2 = \theta_0^2 \left(\frac{U_0}{U}\right)^6 + \frac{0.45\nu}{U^6} \int_0^x U^5 \, dx \qquad (7.54)$$

where θ_0 is the momentum thickness at $x = 0$ (usually taken to be zero). Separation ($c_f = 0$) was found to occur at a particular value of λ

Separation: $\qquad\qquad\qquad\qquad \lambda = -0.09 \qquad\qquad\qquad\qquad (7.55)$

Finally, Thwaites correlated values of the dimensionless shear stress $S = \tau_w \theta/(\mu U)$ with λ, and his graphed result can be curve-fitted as follows:

$$S(\lambda) = \frac{\tau_w \theta}{\mu U} \approx (\lambda + 0.09)^{0.62} \qquad (7.56)$$

This parameter is related to the skin friction by the identity

$$S \equiv \tfrac{1}{2} c_f \, \mathrm{Re}_\theta \qquad (7.57)$$

Equations (7.54) to (7.56) constitute a complete theory for the laminar boundary layer with variable $U(x)$, with an accuracy of ± 10 percent compared with exact digital-computer solutions of the laminar-boundary-layer equations (7.19). Complete details of Thwaites' and other laminar theories are given in Refs. 2 and 3.

As a demonstration of Thwaites' method, take a flat plate, where $U = $ constant, $\lambda = 0$, and $\theta_0 = 0$. Equation (7.54) integrates to

$$\theta^2 = \frac{0.45\nu x}{U}$$

or $\qquad\qquad\qquad\qquad \dfrac{\theta}{x} = \dfrac{0.671}{\mathrm{Re}_x^{1/2}} \qquad\qquad\qquad\qquad (7.58)$

This is within 1 percent of Blasius' exact solution, Eq. (7.30).

With $\lambda = 0$, Eq. (7.56) predicts the flat-plate shear to be

$$\frac{\tau_w \theta}{\mu U} = (0.09)^{0.62} = 0.225$$

or $\qquad\qquad\qquad\qquad c_f = \dfrac{2\tau_w}{\rho U^2} = \dfrac{0.671}{\mathrm{Re}_x^{1/2}} \qquad\qquad\qquad\qquad (7.59)$

This is also within 1 percent of the Blasius result, Eq. (7.25). However, the general accuracy of this method is poorer than 1 percent because Thwaites actually "tuned" his correlation constants to make them agree with exact flat-plate theory.

We shall not compute any more boundary-layer details here, but as we go along, investigating various immersed-body flows, especially in Chap. 8, we shall use Thwaites' method to make qualitative assessments of the boundary-layer behavior.

EXAMPLE 7.5

In 1938 Howarth proposed a linearly decelerating external-velocity distribution

$$U(x) = U_0\left(1 - \frac{x}{L}\right) \tag{1}$$

as a theoretical model for laminar-boundary-layer study. (a) Use Thwaites' method to compute the separation point x_{sep} for $\theta_0 = 0$, and compare with the exact digital-computer solution $x_{sep}/L = 0.119863$ given by H. Wipperman in 1966. (b) Also compute the value of $c_f = 2\tau_w/(\rho U^2)$ at $x/L = 0.1$.

Solution

Part (a) First note that $dU/dx = -U_0/L = $ constant: Velocity decreases, pressure increases, and the pressure gradient is adverse throughout. Now integrate Eq. (7.54)

$$\theta^2 = \frac{0.45\nu}{U_0^6(1 - x/L)^6}\int_0^x U_0^5\left(1 - \frac{x}{L}\right)^5 dx = 0.075\frac{\nu L}{U_0}\left[\left(1 - \frac{x}{L}\right)^{-6} - 1\right] \tag{2}$$

Then the dimensionless factor λ is given by

$$\lambda = \frac{\theta^2}{\nu}\frac{dU}{dx} = -\frac{\theta^2 U_0}{\nu L} = -0.075\left[\left(1 - \frac{x}{L}\right)^{-6} - 1\right] \tag{3}$$

From Eq. (7.55) we set this equal to -0.09 for separation

$$\lambda_{sep} = -0.09 = -0.075\left[\left(1 - \frac{x_{sep}}{L}\right)^{-6} - 1\right]$$

or

$$\frac{x_{sep}}{L} = 1 - (2.2)^{-1/6} = 0.123 \qquad\qquad Ans.\ (a)$$

This is less than 3 percent higher than Wipperman's exact solution, and the computational effort is very modest.

Part (b) To compute c_f at $x/L = 0.1$ (just before separation), we first compute λ at this point, using Eq. (3)

$$\lambda(x = 0.1L) = -0.075[(1 - 0.1)^{-6} - 1] = -0.0661$$

Then from Eq. (7.56) the shear parameter is

$$S(x = 0.1L) = (-0.0661 + 0.09)^{0.62} = 0.099 = \tfrac{1}{2}c_f\ Re_\theta \tag{4}$$

We can compute Re_θ in terms of Re_L from Eq. (2) or (3)

$$\frac{\theta^2}{L^2} = \frac{0.0661}{UL/\nu} = \frac{0.0661}{Re_L}$$

or

$$Re_\theta = 0.257\ Re_L^{1/2} \qquad \text{at } \frac{x}{L} = 0.1$$

Substitute into Eq. (4):

$$0.099 = \tfrac{1}{2}c_f(0.257\ Re_L^{1/2})$$

or

$$c_f = \frac{0.77}{Re_L^{1/2}} \qquad Re_L = \frac{UL}{\nu} \qquad\qquad Ans.\ (b)$$

We cannot actually compute c_f without the value of, say, U_0L/ν.

7.6 Experimental External Flows

Boundary-layer theory is very interesting and illuminating and gives us a great qualitative grasp of viscous-flow behavior, but, because of flow separation, the theory does not generally allow a quantitative computation of the complete flow field. In particular, there is at present no satisfactory theory for the forces on an arbitrary body immersed in a stream flowing at an arbitrary Reynolds number. Therefore experimentation is the key to treating external flows.

Literally thousands of papers in the literature report experimental data on specific external viscous flows. This section gives a brief description of the following external-flow problems:

1. Drag of two- and three-dimensional bodies
   a. Blunt bodies
   b. Streamlined shapes
2. Performance of lifting bodies
   a. Airfoils and aircraft
   b. Projectiles and finned bodies
   c. Birds and insects

For further reading see the goldmine of data compiled in Hoerner [12]. In later chapters we shall study data on supersonic airfoils (Chap. 9), open-channel friction (Chap. 10), and turbomachinery performance (Chap. 11).

Drag of Immersed Bodies

Any body of any shape when immersed in a fluid stream will experience forces and moments from the flow. If the body has arbitrary shape and orientation, the flow will exert forces and moments about all three coordinate axes, as shown in Fig. 7.10. It is customary to choose one axis parallel to the free stream and positive downstream. The force on the body along this axis is called *drag*, and the moment about that axis the *rolling moment*. The drag is essentially a flow loss and must be overcome if the body is to move against the stream.

A second and very important force is perpendicular to the drag and usually performs a useful job, such as bearing the weight of the body. It is called the *lift*. The moment about the lift axis is called *yaw*.

The third component, neither a loss nor a gain, is the *side force*, and about this axis

Fig. 7.10 Definition of forces and moments on a body immersed in a uniform flow.

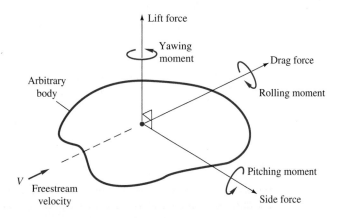

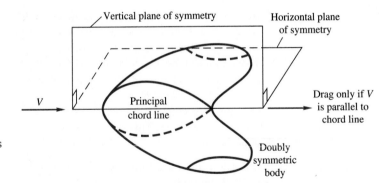

Fig. 7.11 Only the drag force occurs if the flow is parallel to both planes of symmetry.

is the *pitching moment*. To deal with this three-dimensional force-moment situation is more properly the role of a textbook on aerodynamics [for example, 13]. We shall limit the discussion here to lift and drag.

When the body has symmetry about the lift-drag axis, e.g., airplanes, ships, and cars moving directly into a stream, the side force, yaw, and roll vanish, and the problem reduces to a two-dimensional case: two forces, lift and drag, and one moment, pitch.

A final simplification often occurs when the body has two planes of symmetry, as in Fig. 7.11. A wide variety of shapes such as cylinders, wings, and all bodies of revolution satisfy this requirement. If the free stream is parallel to the intersection of these two planes, called the *principal chord line of the body*, the body experiences drag only, with no lift, side force, or moments.[1] This type of degenerate one-force drag data is what is most commonly reported in the literature, but if the free stream is not parallel to the chord line, the body will have an unsymmetric orientation and all three forces and three moments can arise in principle.

In low-speed flow past geometrically similar bodies with identical orientation and relative roughness, the drag coefficient should be a function of the body Reynolds number

$$C_D = f(\text{Re}) \tag{7.60}$$

The Reynolds number is based upon the free-stream velocity V and a characteristic length L of the body, usually the chord or body length parallel to the stream

$$\text{Re} = \frac{VL}{\nu} \tag{7.61}$$

For cylinders, spheres, and disks, the characteristic length is the diameter D.

Characteristic Area

Drag coefficients are defined by using a characteristic area A which may differ depending upon the body shape:

$$C_D = \frac{\text{drag}}{\frac{1}{2}\rho V^2 A} \tag{7.62}$$

The factor $\frac{1}{2}$ is our traditional tribute to Euler and Bernoulli. The area A is usually one of three types:

---

[1] In bodies with shed vortices, such as the cylinder in Fig. 5.2, there may be *oscillating* lift, side force, and moments, but their mean value is zero.

1. *Frontal area*, the body as seen from the stream; suitable for thick, stubby bodies, such as spheres, cylinders, cars, missiles, projectiles, and torpedoes
2. *Planform area*, the body area as seen from above; suitable for wide, flat bodies such as wings and hydrofoils.
3. *Wetted area*, customary for surface ships and barges

In using drag or other fluid-force data, it is important to note what length and area are being used to scale the measured coefficients.

Friction Drag and Pressure Drag

As we have mentioned, the theory of drag is weak and inadequate, except for the flat plate. This is because of flow separation. Boundary-layer theory can predict the separation point but cannot accurately estimate the (usually low) pressure distribution in the separated region. The difference between the high pressure in the front stagnation region and the low pressure in the rear separated region causes a large drag contribution called *pressure drag*. This is added to the integrated shear stress or *friction drag* of the body, which it often exceeds:

$$C_D = C_{D,\text{press}} + C_{D,\text{fric}} \tag{7.63}$$

The relative contribution of friction and pressure drag depends upon the body's shape, especially its thickness. Figure 7.12 shows drag data for a streamlined cylinder of very

Fig. 7.12 Drag of a streamlined two-dimensional cylinder at $\text{Re}_c = 10^6$: (*a*) effect of thickness ratio on percentage of friction drag; (*b*) total drag versus thickness when based upon two different areas.

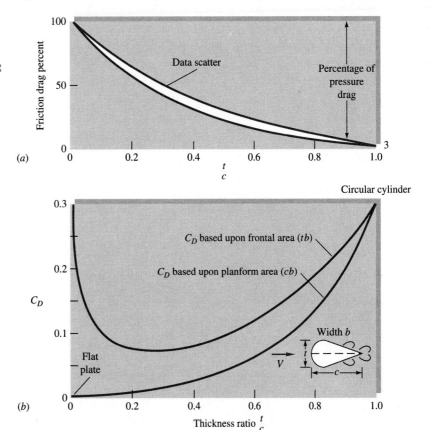

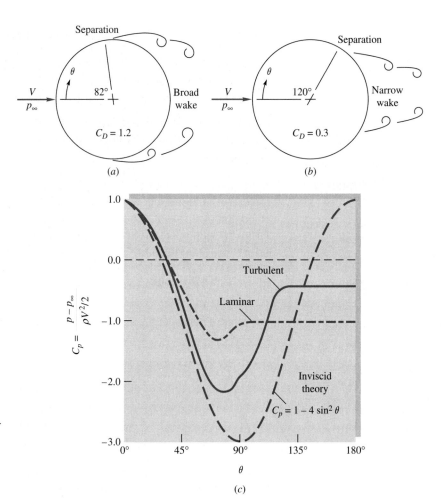

Fig. 7.13 Flow past a circular cylinder: (*a*) laminar separation; (*b*) turbulent separation; (*c*) theoretical and actual surface-pressure distributions.

large depth into the paper. At zero thickness the body is a flat plate and exhibits 100 percent friction drag. At thickness equal to the chord length, simulating a circular cylinder, the friction drag is only about 3 percent. Friction and pressure drag are about equal at thickness $t/c = 0.25$. Note that C_D in Fig. 7.12*b* looks quite different when based upon frontal area instead of planform area, planform being the usual choice for this body shape. The two curves in Fig. 7.12*b* represent exactly the same drag data.

Figure 7.13 illustrates the dramatic effect of separated flow and the subsequent failure of boundary-layer theory. The theoretical inviscid pressure distribution on a circular cylinder (Chap. 8) is shown as the dashed line in Fig. 7.13*c*:

$$C_p = \frac{p - p_\infty}{\frac{1}{2}\rho V^2} = 1 - 4 \sin^2 \theta \qquad (7.64)$$

where p_∞ and V are the pressure and velocity, respectively, in the free stream. The actual laminar and turbulent boundary-layer pressure distributions in Fig. 7.13*c* are startlingly different from those predicted by theory. Laminar flow is very vulnerable to the adverse gradient on the rear of the cylinder, and separation occurs at $\theta = 82°$, which certainly

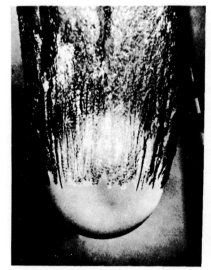 

Fig. 7.14 Strong differences in laminar and turbulent separation on an 8.5-in bowling ball entering water at 25 ft/s; (*a*) smooth ball, laminar boundary layer; (*b*) same entry, turbulent flow induced by patch of nose-sand roughness. (*U.S. Navy photograph, Ordnance Test Station, Pasadena Annex.*)

could not have been predicted from inviscid theory. The broad wake and very low pressure in the separated laminar region cause the large drag $C_D = 1.2$.

The turbulent boundary layer in Fig. 7.13*b* is more resistant, and separation is delayed until $\theta = 120°$, with a resulting smaller wake, higher pressure on the rear, and 75 percent less drag, $C_D = 0.3$. This explains the sharp drop in drag at transition in Fig. 5.3.

The same sharp difference between vulnerable laminar separation and resistant turbulent separation can be seen for a sphere in Fig. 7.14. The laminar flow (Fig. 7.14*a*) separates at about 80°, $C_D = 0.5$, while the turbulent flow (Fig. 7.14*b*) separates at 120°, $C_D = 0.2$. Here the Reynolds numbers are exactly the same, and the turbulent boundary layer is induced by a patch of sand roughness at the nose of the ball. Golf balls fly in this range of Reynolds numbers, which is why they are deliberately dimpled—to induce a turbulent boundary layer and lower drag. Again we would find the actual pressure distribution on the sphere to be quite different from that predicted by inviscid theory.

In general, we cannot overstress the importance of body streamlining to reduce drag at Reynolds numbers above about 100. This is illustrated in Fig. 7.15. The rectangular cylinder (Fig. 7.15*a*) has rampant separation at all sharp corners and very high drag.

Fig. 7.15 The importance of streamlining in reducing drag of a body (C_D based on frontal area): (*a*) rectangular cylinder; (*b*) rounded nose; (*c*) rounded nose and streamlined sharp trailing edge; (*d*) circular cylinder with the same drag as case (*c*).

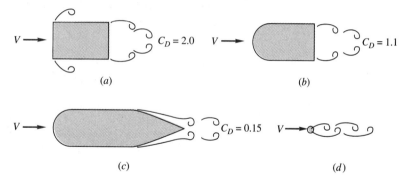

Rounding its nose (Fig. 7.15b) reduces drag by about 45 percent, but C_D is still high. Streamlining its rear to a sharp trailing edge (Fig. 7.15c) reduces its drag another 85 percent to a practical minimum for the given thickness. As a dramatic contrast, the circular cylinder (Fig. 7.15d) has one-eighth the thickness and one-three-hundredth the cross section (c) (Fig. 7.15c), yet it has the same drag. For high-performance vehicles and other moving bodies, the name of the game is drag reduction, for which intense research is now in progress for both aerodynamic and hydrodynamic applications [20].

The drag of some representative wide-span (nearly two-dimensional) bodies is shown versus the Reynolds number in Fig. 7.16a. All bodies have high C_D at very low (*creeping flow*) Re ≤ 1.0, while they spread apart at high Reynolds numbers according to their degree of streamlining. All values of C_D are based on the planform area except the plate normal to the flow. The birds and the sailplane are, of course, not very two-

Fig. 7.16 Drag coefficients of smooth bodies at low Mach numbers: (a) two-dimensional bodies; (b) three-dimensional bodies. Note the Reynolds-number independence of blunt bodies at high Re.

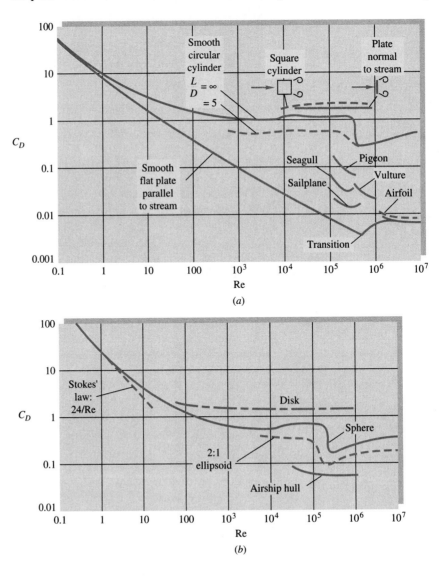

dimensional, having only modest span length. Note that birds are not nearly as efficient as modern sailplanes or airfoils [14].

Table 7.2 gives a few data on drag, based on frontal area, of two-dimensional bodies

Table 7.2 Drag of Two-Dimensional Bodies at Re $\geq 10^4$

Shape	C_D based on frontal area	Shape	C_D based on frontal area

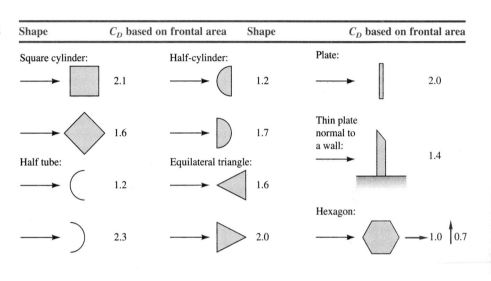

Square cylinder: 2.1

1.6

Half tube: 1.2

2.3

Half-cylinder: 1.2

1.7

Equilateral triangle: 1.6

2.0

Plate: 2.0

Thin plate normal to a wall: 1.4

Hexagon: 1.0 | 0.7

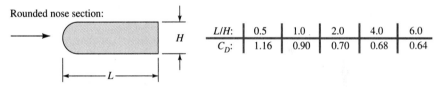

Rounded nose section:

L/H:	0.5	1.0	2.0	4.0	6.0
C_D:	1.16	0.90	0.70	0.68	0.64

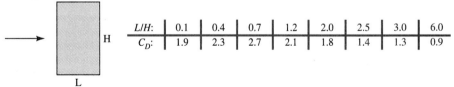

Rectangular section:

L/H:	0.1	0.4	0.7	1.2	2.0	2.5	3.0	6.0
C_D:	1.9	2.3	2.7	2.1	1.8	1.4	1.3	0.9

Elliptical cylinder:

	Laminar	Turbulent
1:1	1.2	0.3
2:1	0.6	0.2
4:1	0.35	0.15
8:1	0.25	0.1

of various cross section, at Re $\geq 10^4$. The sharp-edged bodies, which tend to cause flow separation regardless of the character of the boundary layer, are insensitive to the Reynolds number. The elliptic cylinders, being smoothly rounded, have the laminar-to-turbulent transition effect of Figs. 7.13 and 7.14 and are therefore quite sensitive to the character of the boundary layer.

EXAMPLE 7.6

A square 6-in piling is acted on by a water flow of 5 ft/s that is 20 ft deep, as shown in Fig. E7.6. Estimate the maximum bending exerted by the flow on the bottom of the piling.

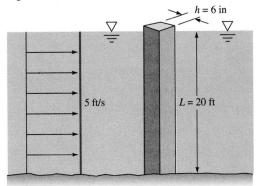

Fig. E7.6

Solution

Assume seawater with $\rho = 1.99$ slugs/ft^3 and kinematic viscosity $\nu = 0.000011$ ft^2/s. With a piling width of 0.5 ft, we have

$$Re_h = \frac{(5 \text{ ft/s})(0.5 \text{ ft})}{0.000011 \text{ ft}^2/\text{s}} = 2.3 \times 10^5$$

This is the range where Table 7.2 applies. The worst case occurs when the flow strikes the flat side of the piling, $C_D \approx 2.1$. The frontal area is $A = Lh = (20 \text{ ft})(0.5 \text{ ft}) = 10$ ft^2. The drag is estimated by

$$F = C_D(\tfrac{1}{2}\rho V^2 A) \approx 2.1(\tfrac{1}{2})(1.99 \text{ slugs/ft}^3)(5 \text{ ft/s})^2(10 \text{ ft}^2) = 522 \text{ lbf}$$

If the flow is uniform, the center of this force should be at approximately middepth. Therefore the bottom bending moment is

$$M_0 \approx \frac{FL}{2} = 522(10) = 5220 \text{ ft} \cdot \text{lbf} \qquad \qquad Ans.$$

According to the flexure formula from strength of materials, the bending stress at the bottom would be

$$S = \frac{M_0 y}{I} = \frac{(5220 \text{ ft} \cdot \text{lb})(0.25 \text{ ft})}{\tfrac{1}{12}(0.5 \text{ ft})^4} = 251,000 \text{ lbf/ft}^2 = 1740 \text{ lbf/in}^2$$

to be multiplied, of course, by the stress-concentration factor due to the built-in end conditions.

Some drag coefficients of three-dimensional bodies are listed in Table 7.3 and Fig. 7.16b. Again we can conclude that sharp edges always cause flow separation and high

Table 7.3 Drag of Three-Dimensional Bodies at Re $\geq 10^4$

Body	C_D based on frontal area	Body	C_D based on frontal area
Cube:	1.07	Cone:	θ: 10° 20° 30° 40° 60° 75° 90° C_D: 0.30 0.40 0.55 0.65 0.80 1.05 1.15
(diamond)	0.81	Short cylinder, laminar flow:	L/D: 1 2 3 5 10 20 40 ∞ C_D: 0.64 0.68 0.72 0.74 0.82 0.91 0.98 1.20
Cup:	1.4	Porous parabolic dish [23]:	Porosity: 0 0.1 0.2 0.3 0.4 0.5 ← C_D: 1.42 1.33 1.20 1.05 0.95 0.82 → C_D: 0.95 0.92 0.90 0.86 0.83 0.80
(cup)	0.4		
Disk:	1.17	Average person:	$C_D A \approx 9\ \text{ft}^2$ $\quad C_D A \approx 1.2\ \text{ft}^2$
Parachute (Low porosity):	1.2	Pine and spruce trees [24]:	U, m/s: 10 20 30 40 C_D: 1.2 ± 0.2 1.0 ± 0.2 0.7 ± 0.2 0.5 ± 0.2

Body	Ratio	C_D based on frontal area	Body	Ratio	C_D based on frontal area
Rectangular plate:	b/h 1 5 10 20 ∞	1.18 1.2 1.3 1.5 2.0	Flat-faced cylinder:	L/d 0.5 1 2 4 8	1.15 0.90 0.85 0.87 0.99

Body			Laminar	Turbulent
Ellipsoid:	L/d	0.75	0.5	0.2
		1	0.47	0.2
		2	0.27	0.13
		4	0.25	0.1
		8	0.2	0.08

drag which is insensitive to the Reynolds number. Rounded bodies like the ellipsoid have drag which depends upon the point of separation, so that both the Reynolds number and the character of the boundary layer are important. Body length will generally decrease pressure drag by making the body relatively more slender, but sooner or later the friction drag will catch up. For the flat-faced cylinder in Table 7.3, pressure drag decreases with L/d but friction increases, so that minimum drag occurs at about $L/d = 2$.

Aerodynamic Forces on Road Vehicles

Automobiles and trucks are now the subject of much research on aerodynamic forces, both lift and drag [21]. At least one textbook is devoted to the subject [22]. Consumer, manufacturer, and government interest has cycled between high speed/high horsepower and lower speeds/lower drag. Better streamlining of car shapes has resulted over the

Fig. 7.17 Aerodynamics of automobiles: (*a*) the historical trend for drag coefficients [21]; (*b*) effect of bottom rear upsweep angle on drag and downward lift force [25].

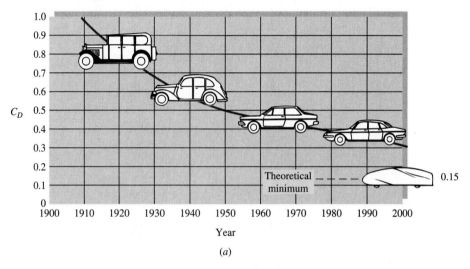

(*a*)

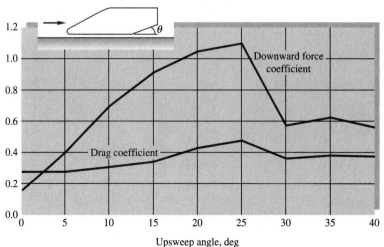

(*b*)

years in a large decrease in the automobile drag coefficient, as shown in Fig. 7.17a. Modern cars have an average drag coefficient of about 0.35, based upon the frontal area. Since the frontal area has also decreased sharply, the actual raw drag *force* on cars has dropped even more than indicated in Fig. 7.17a. The practical minimum, shown tentatively for the year 2000, is $C_D \approx 0.15$ for a tear-shaped vehicle, which can be achieved any time the public is willing to purchase such a shape. Note that basing C_D on the frontal area is awkward, since one would need an accurate drawing of the automobile to estimate its frontal area. For this reason, some technical articles simply report the raw drag in newtons or pound-force.

Many companies and laboratories have automotive wind tunnels, some full-scale and/ or with moving floors to approximate actual kinematic similarity. The blunt shapes of most automobiles, together with their proximity to the ground, cause a wide variety of flow and geometric effects. Simple changes in part of the shape can have a large influence on aerodynamic forces. Figure 7.17b shows force data by Bearman et al. [25] for an idealized smooth automobile shape with upsweep in the rear of the bottom section. We see that by simply adding an upsweep angle of 25°, we can quadruple the downward force, gaining tire traction at the expense of doubling the drag. For this study, the effect of a moving floor was small—about a 10 percent increase in both drag and lift compared to a fixed floor.

It is difficult to quantify the exact effect of geometric changes on automotive forces, since, e.g., changes in a windshield shape might interact with downstream flow over the roof and trunk. Nevertheless, based on correlation of many model and full-scale tests, Ref. 26 proposes a formula for automobile drag which adds separate effects such as front ends, cowls, fenders, windshield, roofs, and rear ends.

Figure 7.18 shows the horsepower required to drive a typical tractor-trailer truck at speeds up to 80 mi/h (117 ft/s or 36 m/s). The rolling resistance increases linearly and the air drag quadratically with speed ($C_D \approx 1.0$). The two are about equally important at 55 mi/h, which is the nominal speed limit in the United States. As shown in Fig. 7.18b, air drag can be reduced by attaching a deflector to the top of the tractor. If the angle of the deflector is adjusted to carry the flow smoothly over the top and around

Fig. 7.18 Drag reduction of a tractor-trailer truck: (*a*) horsepower required to overcome resistance; (*b*) deflector added to cab reduces air drag by 20 percent. (*Uniroyal Inc.*)

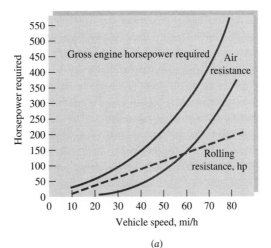

(*a*)   (*b*)

the sides of the trailer, the reduction in C_D is about 20 percent. Thus, at 55 mi/h the total resistance is reduced 10 percent, with a corresponding reduction in fuel costs and/ or trip time for the trucker. This type of applied fluids engineering can be a large factor in many of the conservation-oriented transportation problems of the future.

EXAMPLE 7.7

A high-speed car with $m = 2000$ kg, $C_D = 0.3$, and $A = 1$ m² deploys a 2-m parachute to slow down from an initial velocity of 100 m/s (Fig. E7.7). Assuming constant C_D, brakes free, and no rolling resistance, calculate the distance and velocity of the car after 1, 10, 100, and 1000 s. For air assume $\rho = 1.2$ kg/m³, and neglect interference between the wake of the car and the parachute.

Fig. E7.7

Solution

Newton's law applied in the direction of motion gives

$$F_x = m \frac{dV}{dt} = -F_c - F_p = -\frac{1}{2} \rho V^2 (C_{Dc}A_c + C_{Dp}A_p)$$

where subscript c denotes the car and subscript p the parachute. This is of the form

$$\frac{dV}{dt} = -\frac{K}{m} V^2 \qquad K = \sum C_D A \frac{\rho}{2}$$

Separate the variables and integrate

$$\int_{V_0}^{V} \frac{dV}{V^2} = -\frac{K}{m} \int_0^t dt$$

or

$$V_0^{-1} - V^{-1} = -\frac{K}{m} t$$

Rearrange and solve for the velocity V:

$$V = \frac{V_0}{1 + (K/m)V_0 t} \qquad K = \frac{(C_{Dc}A_c + C_{Dp}A_p)\rho}{2} \tag{1}$$

We can integrate this to find the distance traveled:

$$S = \frac{V_0}{\alpha} \ln (1 + \alpha t) \qquad \alpha = \frac{K}{m} V_0 \tag{2}$$

Now work out some numbers. From Table 7.3, $C_{Dp} \approx 1.2$; hence

$$C_{Dc}A_c + C_{Dp}A_p = 0.3(1 \text{ m}^2) + 1.2 \frac{\pi}{4} (2 \text{ m})^2 = 4.07 \text{ m}^2$$

Then $\qquad \dfrac{K}{m} V_0 = \dfrac{\frac{1}{2}(4.07 \text{ m}^2)(1.2 \text{ kg/m}^3)(100 \text{ m/s})}{2000 \text{ kg}} = 0.122 \text{ s}^{-1} = \alpha$

Now make a table of the results for V and S from Eqs. (1) and (2):

t, s	1	10	100	1000
V, m/s	89	45	7.6	0.8
S, m	94	654	2110	3940

Air resistance alone will not stop a body completely. If you don't apply the brakes, you'll be halfway to the Yukon Territory and still going.

Drag of Surface Ships

The drag data above, such as Tables 7.2 and 7.3, are for bodies "fully immersed" in a free stream, i.e., with no free surface. If, however, the body moves at or near a free liquid surface, *wave-making drag* becomes important and is dependent upon both the Reynolds number and the Froude number. To move through a water surface, a ship must create waves on both sides. This implies putting energy into the water surface and requires a finite drag force to keep the ship moving, even in a frictionless fluid. The total drag of a ship can then be approximated as the sum of friction drag and wave-making drag:

$$F \approx F_{\text{fric}} + F_{\text{wave}} \qquad \text{or} \qquad C_D \approx C_{D,\text{fric}} + C_{D,\text{wave}}$$

The friction drag can be estimated by the (turbulent) flat-plate formula, Eq. (7.45), based on the below-water or *wetted area* of the ship.

Reference 27 is an interesting review of both theory and experiment for wake-making surface ship drag. Generally speaking, the bow of the ship creates a wave system whose wavelength is related to the ship speed but not necessarily to the ship length. If the stern of the ship is a wave *trough*, the ship is essentially climbing uphill and has high wave drag. If the stern is a wave crest, the ship is nearly level and has lower drag. The criterion for these two conditions results in certain approximate Froude numbers [27]:

$$\text{Fr} = \dfrac{V}{\sqrt{gL}} \approx \dfrac{0.53}{\sqrt{N}} \qquad \begin{array}{l} \text{high drag if } N = 1, 3, 5, 7, \ldots; \\ \text{low drag if } N = 2, 4, 6, 8, \ldots \end{array} \qquad (7.65)$$

where V is the ship's speed, L is the ship's length along the centerline, and N is the number of half-lengths, from bow to stern, of the drag-making wave system. The wave drag will increase with the Froude number and oscillate between lower drag (Fr ≈ 0.38, 0.27, 0.22, ...) and higher drag (Fr ≈ 0.53, 0.31, 0.24, ...) with negligible variation for Fr < 0.2. Thus it is best to design a ship to cruise at $N = 2, 4, 6, 8$. Shaping the bow and stern can further reduce wave-making drag.

Figure 7.19 shows the data of Inui [27] for a model ship. The main hull, curve A, shows peaks and valleys in wave drag at the appropriate Froude numbers > 0.2. Introduction of a *bulb* protrusion on the bow, curve B, greatly reduces the drag. Adding a second bulb to the stern, curve C, is still better, and Inui recommends that the design speed of this two-bulb ship be at $N = 4$, Fr ≈ 0.27, which is a nearly "waveless" condition. In this figure $C_{D,\text{wave}}$ is defined as $2F_{\text{wave}}/(\rho V^2 L^2)$ instead of using the wetted area.

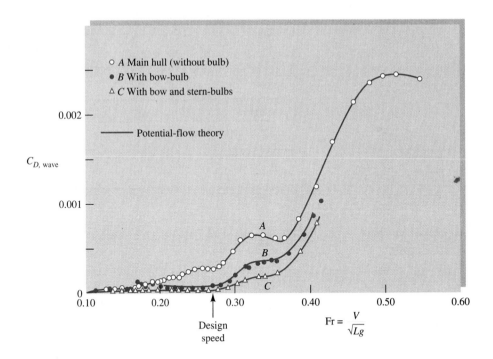

Fig. 7.19 Wave-making drag on a ship model (*after Inui* [27]). *Note:* The drag coefficient is defined as $C_{DW} = 2F/(\rho V^2 L^2)$.

The solid curves in Fig. 7.19 are based on potential-flow theory for the below-water hull shape. Chapter 8 is an introduction to potential-flow theory. Modern digital computers can be programmed for numerical CFD solutions of potential flow over the hulls of ships, submarines, yachts, and sailboats, including boundary-layer effects driven by the potential flow [28]. Thus theoretical prediction of flow past surface ships is now at a fairly high level.

Body Drag at High Mach Numbers

All the data presented above are for nearly incompressible flows, with Mach numbers assumed less than about 0.5. Beyond this value compressibility can be very important, with $C_D = \text{fcn}(\text{Re}, \text{Ma})$. As the stream Mach number increases, at some subsonic value $M_{\text{crit}} < 1$ which depends upon the body's bluntness and thickness, the local velocity at some point near the body surface will become sonic. If Ma increases beyond Ma_{crit}, shock waves form, intensify, and spread, raising surface pressures near the front of the body and therefore increasing the pressure drag. The effect can be dramatic with C_D increasing tenfold, and sixty years ago this sharp increase was called the *sonic barrier*, implying that it could not be surmounted. Of course, it can be—the rise in C_D is finite, as supersonic bullets have proved for centuries.

Figure 7.20 shows the effect of the Mach number on the drag coefficient of various body shapes tested in air.[1] We see that compressibility affects blunt bodies earlier, with Ma_{crit} equal to 0.4 for cylinders, 0.6 for spheres, and 0.7 for airfoils and pointed projectiles. Also the Reynolds number (laminar versus turbulent boundary-layer flow) has

---

[1] There is a slight effect of the specific-heat ratio k which would appear if other gases were tested.

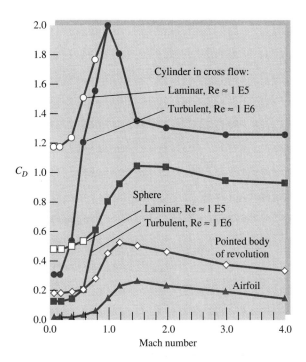

Fig. 7.20 Effect of the Mach number on the drag of various body shapes (data from Refs. 23 and 29).

a large effect below Ma_{crit} for spheres and cylinders but becomes unimportant above $Ma \approx 1$. In contrast, the effect of the Reynolds number is small for airfoils and projectiles and is not shown in Fig. 7.20. A general statement might divide Reynolds- and Mach-number effects as follows:

$$Ma \le 0.4: \quad \text{Reynolds number important, Mach number unimportant}$$
$$0.4 < Ma < 1: \quad \text{both Reynolds and Mach numbers important}$$
$$Ma > 1.0: \quad \text{Reynolds number unimportant, Mach number important}$$

At supersonic speeds, a broad *bow shock wave* forms in front of the body (see Figs. 9.10b and 9.19), and the drag is mainly due to high shock-induced pressures on the front. Making the bow a sharp point can sharply reduce the drag (Fig. 9.28) but does not eliminate the bow shock. Chapter 9 gives a brief treatment of compressibility. References 30 and 31 are more advanced textbooks devoted entirely to compressible flow.

Forces on Lifting Bodies

Lifting bodies (airfoil, hydrofoils, or vanes) are intended to provide a large force normal to the free stream and as little drag as possible. Conventional design practice has evolved a shape not unlike a bird's wing, i.e., relatively thin ($t/c \le 0/18$) with a rounded leading edge and a sharp trailing edge. A typical shape is sketched in Fig. 7.21.

For our purposes we consider the body to be symmetric, as in Fig. 7.11, with the free-stream velocity in the vertical plane. If the chord line between the leading and trailing edge is not a line of symmetry, the airfoil is said to be *cambered*. The camber line is the line midway between the upper and lower surfaces of the vane.

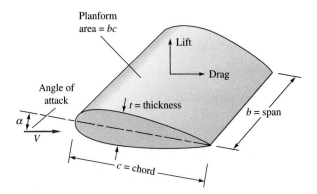

Fig. 7.21 Definition sketch for a lifting vane.

The angle between the free stream and the chord line is called the *angle of attack* α. The lift L and the drag D vary with this angle. The dimensionless forces are defined with respect to the planform area $A_p = bc$:

Lift coefficient:
$$C_L = \frac{L}{\frac{1}{2}\rho V^2 A_p} \tag{7.66a}$$

Drag coefficient:
$$C_D = \frac{D}{\frac{1}{2}\rho V^2 A_p} \tag{7.66b}$$

If the chord length is not constant, as in the tapered wings of modern aircraft, $A_p = \int c \, db$.

For low-speed flow with a given roughness ratio, C_L and C_D should vary with α and the chord Reynolds number

$$C_L = f(\alpha, \text{Re}_c) \quad \text{or} \quad C_D = f(\alpha, \text{Re}_c)$$

where $\text{Re}_c = Vc/\nu$. The Reynolds numbers are commonly in the turbulent-boundary-layer range and have a modest effect.

The rounded leading edge prevents flow separation there, but the sharp trailing edge causes a separation which generates the lift. Figure 7.22 shows what happens when a flow starts up past a lifting vane or an airfoil.

Just after start-up in Fig. 7.22a the streamline motion is irrotational and inviscid. The rear stagnation point, assuming a positive angle of attack, is on the upper surface, and there is no lift; but the flow cannot long negotiate the sharp turn at the trailing edge: it separates, and a *starting vortex* forms in Fig. 7.22b. This starting vortex is shed downstream in Fig. 7.22c and d, and a smooth streamline flow develops over the wing, leaving the foil in a direction approximately parallel to the chord line. Lift at this time is fully developed, and the starting vortex is gone. Should the flow now cease, a *stopping vortex* of opposite (clockwise) sense will form and be shed. During flight, increases or decreases in lift will cause incremental starting or stopping vortices, always with the effect of maintaining a smooth parallel flow at the trailing edge. We pursue this idea mathematically in Chap. 8. The details of start-up and stopping are clearly shown in the film on vorticity, listed as number 2 in App. C.

At a low angle of attack, the rear surfaces have an adverse pressure gradient but not enough to cause significant boundary-layer separation. The flow pattern is smooth, as in Fig. 7.22d, and drag is small and lift excellent. As the angle of attack is increased,

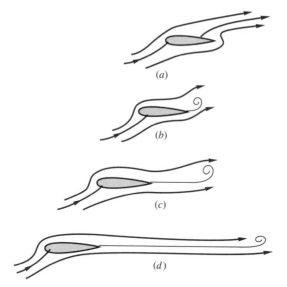

Fig. 7.22 Transient stages in the development of lift: (*a*) start-up: rear stagnation point on the upper surface: no lift; (*b*) sharp trailing edge induces separation, and a starting vortex forms: slight lift; (*c*) starting vortex is shed, and streamlines flow smoothly from trailing edge: lift is now 80 percent developed; (*d*) starting vortex now shed far behind, trailing edge now very smooth: lift fully developed.

the upper-surface adverse gradient becomes stronger, and generally a *separation bubble* begins to creep forward on the upper surface.[1] At a certain angle $\alpha = 15$ to $20°$, the flow is separated completely from the upper surface, as in Fig. 7.23. The airfoil is said

[1] For some airfoils the bubble leaps, not creeps, forward, and stall occurs rapidly and dangerously.

Fig. 7.23 At high angle of attack, smoke-flow visualization shows stalled flow on the upper surface of a lifting vane. [*From Ref. 19*, Illustrated Experiments in Fluid Mechanics (*The NCFMF Book of Film Notes*), *National Committee for Fluid Mechanics Films, Education Development Center, Inc., copyright 1972.*]

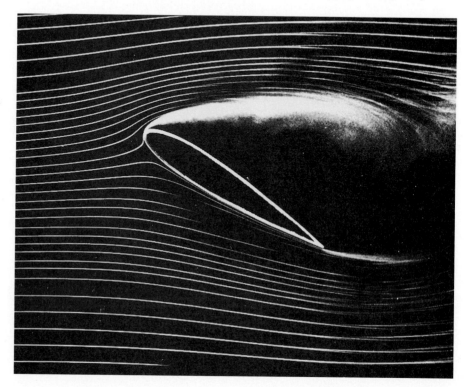

to be *stalled*: Lift drops off markedly, drag increases markedly, and the foil is no longer flyable.

Early airfoils were thin, modeled after birds' wings. The German engineer Otto Lilienthal (1848–1896) experimented with flat and cambered plates on a rotating arm. He and his brother Gustav flew the world's first glider in 1891. Horatio Frederick Phillips (1845–1912) built the first wind tunnel in 1884 and measured the lift and drag of cambered vanes. The first theory of lift was proposed by Frederick W. Lanchester shortly afterward. Modern airfoil theory dates from 1905, when the Russian hydrodynamicist N. E. Joukowsky (1847–1921) developed a circulation theorem (Chap. 8) for computing airfoil lift for arbitrary camber and thickness. With this basic theory, as extended and developed by Prandtl and Kármán and their students, it is now possible to design a low-speed airfoil to satisfy particular surface-pressure distributions and boundary-layer characteristics. There are whole families of airfoil designs, notably those developed in the United States under the sponsorship of the NACA (now NASA). Extensive theory and data on these airfoils are contained in Ref. 16. We shall discuss this further in Chap. 8.

Figure 7.24 shows the lift and drag on a symmetric airfoil denoted as the NACA 0009 foil, the last digit indicating the thickness of 9 percent. With no flap extended, this airfoil, as expected, has zero lift at zero angle of attack. Up to about 12° the lift coefficient increases linearly with a slope of 0.1 per degree, or 6.0 per radian. This is in agreement with the theory outlined in Chap. 8:

$$C_{L,\text{theory}} \approx 2\pi \sin\left(\alpha + \frac{2h}{c}\right) \tag{7.67}$$

where h/c is the maximum camber expressed as a fraction of the chord. The NACA 0009 has zero camber; hence $C_L = 2\pi \sin \alpha \approx 0.11\alpha$, where α is in degrees. This is excellent agreement.

Fig. 7.24 Lift and drag of a symmetric NACA 0009 airfoil of infinite span, including effect of a split-flap deflection. Note that roughness can increase C_D from 100 to 300 percent.

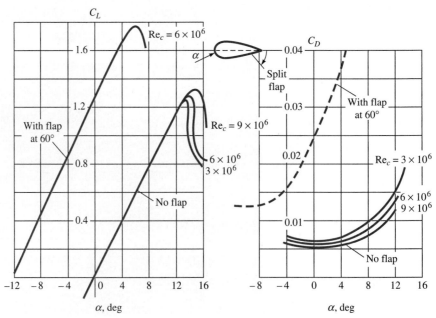

The drag coefficient of the smooth-model airfoils in Fig. 7.24 is as low as 0.005, which is actually lower than both sides of a flat plate in turbulent flow. This is misleading inasmuch as a commercial foil will have roughness effects; e.g., a paint job will double the drag coefficient.

The effect of increasing Reynolds number in Fig. 7.24 is to increase the maximum lift and stall angle (without changing the slope appreciably) and to reduce the drag coefficient. This is a salutary effect, since the prototype will probably be at a higher Reynolds number than the model (10^7 or more).

For takeoff and landing, the lift is greatly increased by deflecting a split flap, as shown in Fig. 7.24. This makes the airfoil unsymmetric (or effectively cambered) and changes the zero-lift point to $\alpha = -12°$. The drag is also greatly increased by the flap, but the reduction in takeoff and landing distance is worth the extra power needed.

A lifting craft cruises at low angle of attack, where the lift is much larger than the drag. Maximum lift-to-drag ratios for the common airfoils lie between 20 and 50.

Some airfoils, such as the NACA 6 series, are shaped to provide favorable gradients over much of the upper surface at low angles. Thus separation is small, and transition to turbulence is delayed; the airfoil retains a good length of laminar flow even at high Reynolds numbers. The lift-drag polar plot in Fig. 7.25 shows the NACA 0009 data from Fig. 7.24 and a laminar-flow airfoil, NACA 63–009, of the same thickness. The laminar-flow airfoil has a low-drag bucket at small angles but also suffers lower stall angle and lower maximum lift coefficient. The drag is 30 percent less in the bucket, but the bucket disappears if there is significant surface roughness.

All the data in Figs. 7.24 and 7.25 are for infinite span, i.e., a two-dimensional flow pattern about wings without tips. The effect of finite span can be correlated with the dimensionless slenderness, or *aspect ratio*, denoted (AR),

$$\text{AR} = \frac{b^2}{A_p} = \frac{b}{c} \tag{7.68}$$

Fig. 7.25 Lift-drag polar plot for standard (0009) and a laminar-flow (63-009) NACA airfoil.

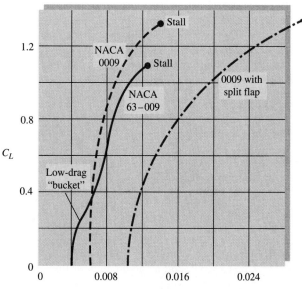

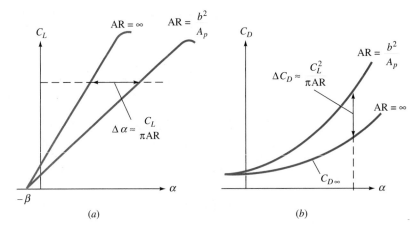

Fig. 7.26 Effect of finite aspect ratio on lift and drag of an airfoil: (*a*) effective angle increase; (*b*) induced drag increase.

where $\bar{c}$ is the average chord length. Finite-span effects are shown in Fig. 7.26. The lift slope decreases, but the zero-lift angle is the same; and the drag increases, but the zero-lift drag is the same. The theory of finite-span airfoils [16] predicts that the effective angle of attack increases, as in Fig. 7.26, by the amount

$$\Delta \alpha \approx \frac{C_L}{\pi AR} \tag{7.69}$$

When applied to Eq. (7.67), the finite-span lift becomes

$$C_L \approx \frac{2\pi \sin(\alpha + 2h/c)}{1 + 2/AR} \tag{7.70}$$

The associated drag increase is $\Delta C_D \approx C_L \sin \Delta \alpha \approx C_L \Delta \alpha$, or

$$C_D \approx C_{D\infty} + \frac{C_L^2}{\pi AR} \tag{7.71}$$

where $C_{D\infty}$ is the drag of the infinite-span airfoil, as sketched in Fig. 7.24. These correlations are in good agreement with experiments on finite-span wings [16].

The existence of a maximum lift coefficient implies the existence of a minimum speed, or *stall speed*, for a craft whose lift supports its weight

$$L = W = C_{L,\max}(\tfrac{1}{2}\rho V_s^2 A_p)$$

or

$$V_s = \left(\frac{2W}{C_{L,\max}\rho A_p}\right)^{1/2} \tag{7.72}$$

The stall speed of typical aircraft varies between 60 and 200 ft/s, depending upon the weight and value of $C_{L,\max}$. The pilot must hold the speed greater than about $1.2V_s$ to avoid the instability associated with complete stall.

The split flap in Fig. 7.24 is only one of many devices used to secure high lift at low speeds. Figure 7.27*a* shows six such devices whose lift performance is given in 7.27*b* along with a standard (*A*) and laminar-flow (*B*) airfoil. The double-slotted flap achieves $C_{L,\max} \approx 3.4$, and a combination of this plus a leading-edge slat can achieve $C_{L,\max} \approx 4.0$. These are not scientific curiosities; e.g., the Boeing 727 commercial jet aircraft uses a triple-slotted flap plus a leading-edge slat during landing.

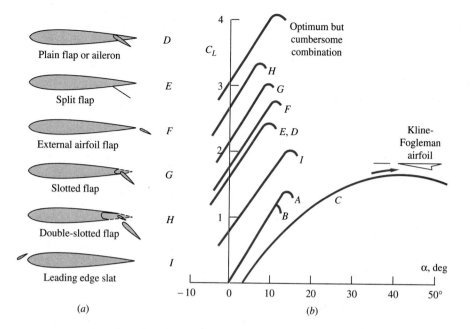

Fig. 7.27 Performance of airfoils with and without high-lift devices: A = NACA 0009; B = NACA 63-009; C = Kline-Fogleman airfoil (Ref. 17); D to I shown in (*a*): (*a*) types of high-lift devices; (*b*) lift coefficients for various devices.

Also shown as *C* in Fig. 7.27*b* is the Kline-Fogleman airfoil [17], not yet a reality. The designers are amateur model-plane enthusiasts who did not know that conventional aerodynamic wisdom forbids a sharp leading edge and a step cutout from the trailing edge. The Kline-Fogleman airfoil has relatively high drag but shows an amazing continual increase in lift out to $\alpha = 45°$. In fact, we may fairly say that this airfoil does not stall and provides smooth performance over a tremendous range of flight conditions. No explanation for this behavior has yet been published by any aerodynamicist. This airfoil is presently under study by NASA and may or may not have any commercial value.

Another violation of conventional aerodynamic wisdom is that military aircraft are beginning to fly, briefly, *above the stall point*. Fighter pilots are learning to make quick maneuvers in the stalled region as detailed in Ref. 32. Some planes can even *fly continuously* while stalled—the Grumman X-29 experimental aircraft recently set a record by flying at $\alpha = 67°$.

Further information on the performance of lifting craft can be found in Refs. 12, 13, and 16. We discuss this matter again briefly in Chap. 8.

EXAMPLE 7.8

An aircraft weighs 75,000 lb, has a planform area of 2500 ft^2, and can deliver constant thrust of 12,000 lb. It has an aspect ratio of 7, and $C_{D\infty} \approx 0.02$. Neglecting rolling resistance, estimate the takeoff distance at sea level if takeoff speed equals 1.2 times stall speed. Take $C_{L,\max} = 2.0$.

Solution

The stall speed from Eq. (7.72), with sea-level density $\rho = 0.00237$ slug/ft^3, is

$$V_s = \left(\frac{2W}{C_{L,\max}\rho A_p}\right)^{1/2} = \left[\frac{2(75,000)}{2.0(0.00237)(2500)}\right]^{1/2} = 112.5 \text{ ft/s}$$

Hence takeoff speed $V_0 = 1.2V_s = 135$ ft/s. The drag is estimated from Eq. (7.71) for $AR = 7$ as

$$C_D \approx 0.02 + \frac{C_L^2}{7\pi} = 0.02 + 0.0455C_L^2$$

A force balance in the direction of takeoff gives

$$F_s = m\frac{dV}{dt} = \text{thrust} - \text{drag} = T - kV^2 \qquad k = \tfrac{1}{2}C_D\rho A_p \tag{1}$$

Since we are looking for distance, not time, we introduce $dV/dt = V\,dV/ds$ into Eq. (1), separate variables, and integrate

$$\int_0^{S_0} dS = \frac{m}{2}\int_0^{V_0}\frac{d(V^2)}{T - kV^2} \qquad k \approx \text{const}$$

or

$$S_0 = \frac{m}{2k}\ln\frac{T}{T - kV_0^2} = \frac{m}{2k}\ln\frac{T}{T - D_0} \tag{2}$$

where $D_0 = kV_0^2$ is the takeoff drag. Equation (2) is the desired theoretical relation for takeoff distance. For the particular numerical values, take

$$m = \frac{75,000}{32.2} = 2329 \text{ slugs}$$

$$C_{L_0} = \frac{W}{\tfrac{1}{2}\rho V_0^2 A_p} = \frac{75,000}{\tfrac{1}{2}(0.00237)(135)^2(2500)} = 1.39$$

$$C_{D_0} = 0.02 + 0.0455(C_{L_0})^2 = 0.108$$

$$k \approx \tfrac{1}{2}C_{D_0}\rho A_p = (\tfrac{1}{2})(0.108)(0.00237)(2500) = 0.319 \text{ slug/ft}$$

$$D_0 = kV_0^2 = 5820 \text{ lb}$$

Then Eq. (2) predicts that

$$S_0 = \frac{2329 \text{ slugs}}{2(0.319 \text{ slug/ft})}\ln\frac{12,000}{12,000 - 5820} = 3650 \ln 1.94 = 2420 \text{ ft} \qquad Ans.$$

A more exact analysis accounting for variable k [13] gives the same result to within 1 percent.

Summary

This chapter has dealt with viscous effects in extenal flow past bodies immersed in a stream. When the Reynolds number is large, viscous forces are confined to a thin boundary layer and wake in the vicinity of the body. Flow outside these "shear layers" is essentially inviscid and can be predicted by potential theory and Bernoulli's equation.

The chapter begins with a discussion of the flat-plate boundary layer and the use of momentum-integral estimates to predict the wall shear, friction drag, and thickness of such layers. These approximations suggest how to eliminate certain small terms in the

Navier-Stokes equations, resulting in Prandtl's boundary-layer equations for laminar and turbulent flow. Section 7.4 then solves the boundary-layer equations to give very accurate formulas for flat-plate flow at high Reynolds numbers. Rough-wall effects are included, and Sec. 7.5 gives a brief introduction to pressure-gradient effects. An adverse (decelerating) gradient is seen to cause flow separation, where the boundary layer breaks away from the surface and forms a broad, low-pressure wake.

Boundary-layer theory fails in separated flows, which are commonly studied by experiment. Section 7.6 gives data on drag coefficients of various two- and three-dimensional body shapes. The chapter ends with a brief discussion of lift forces generated by lifting bodies such as airfoils and hydrofoils. Airfoils also suffer flow separation or *stall* at high angles of incidence.

References

1. H. Schlichting, *Boundary Layer Theory*, 7th ed., McGraw-Hill, New York, 1979.
2. F. M. White, *Viscous Fluid Flow*, 2d ed., McGraw-Hill, New York, 1991.
3. L. Rosenhead (ed.), *Laminar Boundary Layers*, Oxford University Press, London, 1963.
4. D. A. Anderson, J. C. Tannehill, and R. H. Pletcher, *Computational Fluid Mechanics and Heat Transfer*, Hemisphere, New York, 1984.
5. R. H. Pletcher and C. L. Dancey, ''A Direct Method of Calculating through Separated Regions in Boundary Layer Flow,'' *J. Fluids Eng.*, September 1976, pp. 568–572.
6. P. K. Chang, *Control of Flow Separation*, McGraw-Hill, New York, 1976. See also P. K. Chang, *Recent Development in Flow Separation*, Pang Han Pub. Co., Seoul, Korea, 1983.
7. T. von Kármán, ''On Laminar and Turbulent Friction,'' *Z. Angew. Math. Mech.,* vol. 1, 1921, pp. 235–236.
8. G. B. Schubauer and H. K. Skramstad, ''Laminar Boundary Layer Oscillations and Stability of Laminar Flow,'' *Natl. Bur. Stand. Res. Pap.* 1772, April 1943 (see also *J. Aero. Sci.,* vol. 14, 1947, pp. 69–78, and *NACA Rep.* 909, 1947).
9. W. Rodi, *Turbulence Models and Their Application in Hydraulics*, Brookfield Pub., Brookfield, Vt., 1984.
10. P. W. Runstadler, Jr., et al., ''Diffuser Data Book,'' Creare Inc., *Tech. Note* 186, Hanover, N.H., May 1975.
11. B. Thwaites, ''Approximate Calculation of the Laminar Boundary Layer,'' *Aeronaut. Q.,* vol. 1, 1949, pp. 245–280.
12. S. F. Hoerner, *Fluid Dynamic Drag*, published by the author, Midland Park, N.J., 1965.
13. J. D. Anderson, *Fundamentals of Aerodynamics*, McGraw-Hill, New York, 1984.
14. V. Tucker and G. C. Parrott, ''Aerodynamics of Gliding Flight of Falcons and Other Birds,'' *J. Exp. Biol.,* vol. 52, 1970, pp. 345–368.
15. J. P. Comstock (ed.), *Principles of Naval Architecture*, Society of Naval Architects and Marine Engineers, New York, 1967.
16. I. H. Abbott and A. E. von Doenhoff, *Theory of Wing Sections*, Dover, New York, 1959.
17. R. L. Kline and F. F. Fogleman, Airfoil for Aircraft, U.S. Patent 3,706,430 Dec. 19, 1972.
18. T. Y. Yu et al. (eds.), *Swimming and Flying in Nature: Proceedings of a Symposium*, Plenum, New York, 1975.
19. National Committee for Fluid Mechanics Films, *Illustrated Experiments in Fluid Mechanics*, M.I.T. Press, Cambridge, Mass., 1972.
20. E. M. Uram and H. E. Weber (eds.), ''Laminar and Turbulent Boundary Layers,'' *ASME Symp. Proc.,* vol. I00167, February 1984.
21. G. Sovran, T. Morel, and W. T. Mason, Jr. (eds.), *Aerodynamic Drag Mechanisms of Bluff Bodies and Road Vehicles*, Plenum, New York, 1978.
22. W. H. Hucho, *Aerodynamics of Road Vehicles*, Butterworth, Boston, 1986.

23. R. D. Blevins, *Applied Fluid Dynamics Handbook*, van Nostrand Reinhold, New York, 1984.

24. R. C. Johnson, Jr., G. E. Ramey, and D. S. O'Hagen, "Wind Induced Forces on Trees," *J. Fluids Eng.*, vol. 104, March 1982, pp. 25–30.

25. P. W. Bearman et al., "The Effect of a Moving Floor on Wind-Tunnel Simulation of Road Vehicles," Paper No. 880245, SAE Transactions, *J. Passenger Cars*, vol. 97, sec. 4, 1988, pp. 4.200–4.214.

26. *CRC Handbook of Tables for Applied Engineering Science*, 2d ed., CRC Press, Boca Raton, Florida, 1973.

27. T. Inui, "Wavemaking Resistance of Ships," *Trans. Soc. Nav. Arch. Marine Engrs.*, vol. 70, 1962, pp. 283–326.

28. L. Larsson et al., "A Method for Resistance and Flow Prediction in Ship Design," *Trans. Soc. Nav. Arch. Marine Engrs.*, vol. 98, 1990, pp. 495–535.

29. J. K. Vennard and R. L. Street, *Elementary Fluid Mechanics*, 6th ed., Wiley, New York, 1982.

30. J. D. Anderson, Jr., *Modern Compressible Flow, with Historical Perspective*, McGraw-Hill, New York, 1982.

31. J. D. Anderson, Jr., *Hypersonic and High Temperature Gas Dynamics*, McGraw-Hill, New York, 1989.

32. S. J. Mraz, "High Angle of Attack Flight," *Machine Design*, vol. 63, no. 25, Dec. 12, 1991, pp. 50–55.

Recommended Films

Films numbered 1, 2, 8, 9, 14, 15, and 26 in App. C.

PROBLEMS

In addition to many traditional problems, categorized in the problem distribution list below, there are word problems, labeled W7.1 to W7.12 and a design project, D7.1.

Problem Distribution

Section	Topic	Problems
7.1	Reynolds-number and geometry	7.1–7.5
7.2	Momentum-integral estimates	7.6–7.12
7.3	The boundary-layer equations	7.13–7.15
7.4	Laminar flat-plate flow	7.16–7.29
7.4	Turbulent flat-plate flow	7.30–7.46
7.5	Boundary layers with pressure gradient	7.47–7.52
7.6	Drag of two dimensional bodies	7.53–7.63
7.6	Drag of three-dimensional bodies	7.64–7.114
7.6	Lifting bodies—airfoils	7.115–7.124

7.1 Air at 20°C and 1 atm flows at 20 m/s past a thin flat plate. Estimate the distance x from the leading edge at which the boundary thickness will be (*a*) 1 mm and (*b*) 10 cm. Assume $\mathrm{Re}_{x,\mathrm{crit}} = 5 \ \mathrm{E5}$.

7.2 Repeat Prob. 7.1 if the fluid is water at 20°C.

7.3 Equation (7.1*b*) assumes that the boundary layer on the plate is turbulent from the leading edge onward. Devise a scheme for determining the boundary-layer thickness more accurately when the flow is laminar up to a point $\mathrm{Re}_{x,\mathrm{crit}}$ and turbulent thereafter. Apply this scheme to computation of the boundary-layer thickness at $x = 1.5$ m in 40 m/s flow of air at 20°C and 1 atm past a flat plate. Compare your result with Eq. (7.1*b*). Assume $\mathrm{Re}_{x,\mathrm{crit}} \approx 1.2 \ \mathrm{E6}$.

7.4 Air at 20°C and 1 atm flows at 15 m/s past a flat plate with $\mathrm{Re}_{x,\mathrm{crit}} \approx 1 \ \mathrm{E6}$. At what point x will the boundary-layer thickness be 8 mm? Why do Eqs. (7.1) seem to fail? Make a sketch illustrating the discrepancy, then use the ideas in Prob. 7.3 to complete this problem correctly.

7.5 SAE 30 oil at 20°C flows at 1.8 ft³/s from a reservoir into a 6-in-diameter pipe. Use flat-plate theory to estimate the position x where the pipe-wall boundary layers meet in the center. Compare with Eq. (6.5), and give some explanations for the discrepancy.

7.6 For the laminar parabolic boundary-layer profile of Eq. (7.6), compute the shape factor H and compare with the exact Blasius result, Eq. (7.31).

7.7 Air at 20°C and 1 atm enters a 40-cm-square duct as in Fig. P7.7. Using the "displacement thickness" concept of Fig. 7.4, estimate (*a*) the mean velocity and (*b*) the mean pressure in the core of the flow at the position $x = 3$ m. (*c*) What is the average gradient, in Pa/m, in this section?

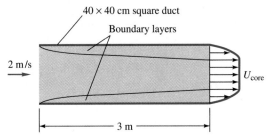

40 × 40 cm square duct

Boundary layers

2 m/s

U_{core}

3 m

Fig. P7.7

7.8 Repeat the flat-plate momentum-integral analysis of Sec. 7.2 by replacing the parabolic profile, Eq. (7.6), with the linear profile $u/U \approx y/\delta$. Compute c_f, θ/x, δ^*/x, and H.

7.9 Repeat prob. 7.8, but use instead the (extremely accurate) sinusoidal-velocity-profile assumption

$$\frac{u}{U} \approx \sin \frac{\pi y}{2\delta}$$

Compare this profile shape with the Blasius profile in Fig. 7.5.

7.10 Repeat Prob. 7.8, using the polynomial profile suggested by K. Pohlhausen in 1921:

$$\frac{u}{U} \approx 2\frac{y}{\delta} - 2\frac{y^3}{\delta^3} + \frac{y^4}{\delta^4}$$

Does this profile satisfy the boundary conditions of laminar flat-plate flow?

7.11 Find the correct form for a cubic velocity-profile polynomial

$$u = A + By + Cy^2 + Dy^3$$

to replace Eq. (7.6) in a flat-plate mometum analysis. Find the value of θ/δ for this profile, but do not pursue the analysis further.

7.12 The velocity profile shape $u/U \approx 1 - \exp(-4.605y/\delta)$ is a smooth curve with $u = 0$ at $y = 0$ and $u = 0.99U$ at $y = \delta$ and thus would seem to be a reasonable substitute for the parabolic flat-plate profile of Eq. (7.3). Yet when this new profile is used in the integral analysis of Sec. 7.3, we get the lousy result $\delta/x \approx 9.2/\text{Re}_x^{1/2}$, which is 80 percent high. What is the reason for the inaccuracy? [*Hint:* The answer lies in evaluating the laminar boundary-layer momentum equation (7.19b) at the wall, $y = 0$.]

7.13 Derive modified forms of the laminar boundary-layer equa-

tions (7.19) for the case of axisymmetric flow along the outside of a circular cylinder of constant radius R, as in Fig. P7.13. Consider the two special cases (*a*) $\delta \ll R$ and (*b*) $\delta \approx R$. What are the proper boundary conditions?

Fig. P7.13

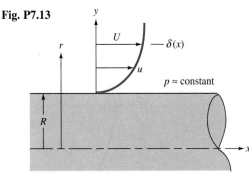

y

U

$\delta(x)$

r

u

$p \approx$ constant

R

x

7.14 Show that the two-dimensional laminar-flow pattern with $dp/dx = 0$

$$u = U_0(1 - e^{Cy}) \qquad v = v_0 < 0$$

is an exact solution to the boundary-layer equations (7.19). Find the value of the constant C in terms of the flow parameters. Are the boundary conditions satisfied? What might this flow represent?

7.15 Discuss whether fully developed laminar incompressible flow between parallel plates, Eq. (4.143) and Fig. 4.16*b*, represents an exact solution to the boundary-layer equations (7.19) and the boundary conditions (7.20). In what sense, if any, are duct flows also boundary-layer flows?

7.16 A thin flat plate 55 by 110 cm is immersed in a 6-m/s stream of SAE 10 oil at 20°C. Compute the total friction drag if the stream is parallel to (*a*) the long side and (*b*) the short side.

7.17 Helium at 20°C and low pressure flows past a thin flat plate 1 m long and 2 m wide. It is desired that the total friction drag of the plate be 0.5 N. What is the appropriate absolute pressure of the helium if U = 35 m/s?

7.18 In Prob. 7.7, when the duct is perfectly square, the core velocity speeds up. Suppose we wish to hold the core velocity constant by slanting the upper and lower walls while keeping the front and rear walls parallel. What angle of slant will be the best approximation? For this condition, what will be the total friction drag on the duct walls?

7.19 Program a method of numerical solution of the Blasius flat-plate relation, Eq. (7.22), subject to the conditions in (7.23). You will find that you cannot get started without knowing the initial second derivative $f''(0)$, which lies between 0.2 and 0.5. Devise an iteration scheme which starts at $f''(0) \approx 0.2$ and converges to the correct value. Print out $u/U = f'(\eta)$ and compare with Table 7.1.

7.20 Air at 20°C and 1 atm flows at 20 m/s past the flat plate in

Fig. P7.20. A pitot stagnation tube, placed 2 mm from the wall, develops a manometer head h = 16 mm of Meriam red oil, SG = 0.827. Use this information to estimate the downstream position x of the pitot tube. Assume laminar flow.

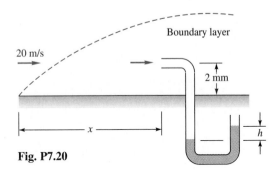

Fig. P7.20

7.21 For the data in Table 7.1, use any numerical or graphical method you think appropriate to evaluate the dimensionless laminar flat-plate momentum thickness $\theta\sqrt{U/(\nu x)}$. Compare your result with Eq. (7.30).

7.22 For the Blasius flat-plate problem, Eqs. (7.21) to (7.23), does a two-dimensional stream function $\psi(x, y)$ exist? If so, determine the correct *dimensionless* form for ψ, assuming that ψ = 0 at the wall, y = 0.

7.23 The similarity variable η in Eq. (7.21) was proposed by H. Blasius in 1908. Some modern textbooks modify this by inserting a factor of 2:

$$\eta^* = y\sqrt{\frac{U}{2\nu x}}$$

In terms of this new variable, the velocity components are as follows:

$$\frac{u}{U} = \frac{df}{d\eta^*} \qquad \frac{v}{U} = \left(\eta^*\frac{df}{d\eta^*} - f\right)\sqrt{\frac{\nu}{2Ux}}$$

Continuity, Eq. (7.19a), is satisfied identically by these variables. Now substitute these variables into the momentum equation (7.19b), assuming that dU/dx = 0, and determine the new form of the Blasius equation (7.22) and its new boundary conditions (7.23) on the function $f(\eta^*)$.

7.24 Air at 20°C and 1 atm flows past the flat plate in Fig. P7.24 under laminar conditions. There are two equally spaced pitot stagnation tubes, each placed 2 mm from the wall. The manometer fluid is water at 20°C. If U = 15 m/s and L = 50 cm, determine the values of the manometer readings h_1 and h_2, in mm.

7.25 Modify Prob. 7.24 to the following somewhat more difficult scenario. Let the known data be U = 15 m/s and h_1 =

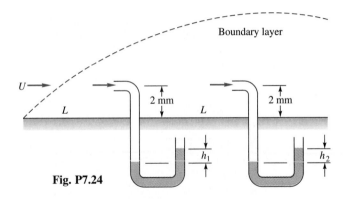

Fig. P7.24

8 mm of water. Use this information to determine (a) L, in cm, (b) h_2, in mm.

7.26 Modify Prob. 7.24 to the following definitely more difficult scenario. Let the known data be h_1 = 8 mm and h_2 = 5 mm of water. Use this information to determine (a) L, in cm, and (b) U, in m/s.

7.27 A thin smooth disk of diameter D is immersed parallel to a uniform stream of velocity U. Assuming laminar flow and using flat-plate theory as a guide, develop an approximate formula for the drag of the disk.

7.28 Flow straighteners are arrays of narrow ducts placed in wind tunnels to remove swirl and other in-plane secondary velocities. They can be idealized as square boxes constructed by vertical and horizontal plates, as in Fig. P7.28. The cross section is a by a, and the box length is L. Assuming laminar flat-plate flow and an array of $N \times N$ boxes, derive a formula for (a) the total drag on the bundle of boxes and (b) the effective pressure drop across the bundle.

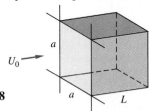

Fig. P7.28

7.29 Let the flow straighteners in Fig. P7.28 form an array of 20 × 20 boxes of size a = 4 cm and L = 25 cm. If the approach velocity is U_0 = 12 m/s and the fluid is sea-level standard air, estimate (a) the total array drag and (b) the pressure drop across the array. Compare with Sec. 6.6.

7.30 Repeat Prob. 7.16 if the fluid is water at 20°C and the plate surface is smooth.

7.31 Repeat Prob. 7.16 if the fluid is water at 20°C and the plate has an average roughness height of 1.5 mm.

7.32 A flat plate of length L and height δ is placed at a wall and is parallel to an approaching boundary layer, as in Fig.

P7.32. Assume that the flow over the plate is fully turbulent and that the approaching flow is a one-seventh-power law

$$u(y) = U_0\left(\frac{y}{\delta}\right)^{1/7}$$

Using strip theory, derive a formula for the drag coefficient of this plate. Compare this result with the drag of the same plate immersed in a uniform stream U_0.

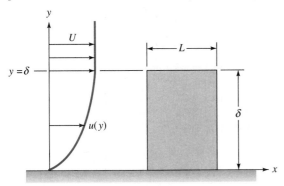

Fig. P7.32

7.33 An alternate analysis of turbulent flat-plate flow was given by Prandtl in 1927, using a wall shear-stress formula from pipe flow

$$\tau_w = 0.0225\rho U^2\left(\frac{\nu}{U\delta}\right)^{1/4}$$

Show that this formula can be combined with Eqs. (7.33) and (7.40) to derive the following relations for turbulent flat-plate flow:

$$\frac{\delta}{x} = \frac{0.37}{Re_x^{1/5}} \qquad c_f = \frac{0.0577}{Re_x^{1/5}} \qquad C_D = \frac{0.072}{Re_L^{1/5}}$$

These formulas are limited to Re_x between 5×10^5 and 10^7.

7.34 A thin equilateral-triangle plate is immersed parallel to a 12 m/s stream of water at 20°C, as in Fig. P7.34. Assuming $Re_{tr} = 5 \times 10^5$, estimate the drag of this plate.

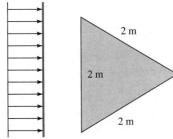

Fig. P7.34   12 m/s

7.35 Develop, using strip theory, an analytical formula for the drag of the triangular plate in Fig. P7.34 if the stream velocity is U, the side length is a, and the flow is completely turbulent.

7.36 A ship is 125 m long and has a wetted area of 3500 m². Its propellers can deliver a maximum power of 1.1 MW to seawater at 20°C. If all drag is due to friction, estimate the maximum ship speed, in kn.

7.37 A wind tunnel has a test section 1 m square and 6 m long with air at 20°C moving at an average velocity of 30 m/s. It is planned to slant the walls outward slightly to account for the growing boundary-layer displacement thickness on the four walls, thus keeping the test-section velocity constant. At what angle should they be slanted at to keep V constant between $x = 2$ m and $x = 4$ m?

7.38 Atmospheric boundary layers are very thick but follow formulas very similar to those of flat-plate theory. Consider wind blowing at 10 m/s at a height of 80 m above a smooth beach. Estimate the wind shear stress, in Pa, on the beach if the air is standard sea-level conditions. What will the wind velocity striking your nose be if (a) you are standing up and your nose is 170 cm off the ground; (b) you are lying on the beach and your nose is 17 cm off the ground?

7.39 A hydrofoil 50 cm long and 4 m wide moves at 28 kn in seawater at 20°C. Using flat-plate theory with $Re_{tr} = 5$ E5, estimate its drag, in N, for (a) a smooth wall and (b) a rough wall, $\epsilon = 0.3$ mm.

7.40 According to Hoerner [12, pp. 3–25], the drag of a flag 6 ft long and 3 ft high, fluttering in 50 mi/h sea-level-standard winds, is of the order of 13 lbf. How does this compare with flat-plate theory? What accounts for the discrepancy in this case?

7.41 Repeat Prob. 7.20 with the sole change that the pitot probe is now 20 mm from the wall (10 times higher). Show that the flow there cannot possibly be laminar, and use smooth-wall turbulent-flow theory to estimate the position x of the probe, in m.

7.42 A four-bladed helicopter rotor rotates at n r/min in air with properties (ρ, μ). Each blade has chord length C and extends from the center of rotation out to radius R (the hub size is neglected). Assuming turbulent flow from the leading edge, develop an analytical estimate for the power P required to drive this rotor.

7.43 In the flow of air at 20°C and 1 atm past a flat plate in Fig. P7.43, the wall shear is to be determined at position x by a *floating element* (a small area connected to a strain-gage force measurement). At $x = 2$ m, the element indicates a shear stress of 2.1 Pa. Assuming turbulent flow from the leading edge, estimate (a) the stream velocity U, (b) the boundary layer thickness δ at the element, and (c) the boundary-layer velocity u, in m/s, at 5 mm above the element.

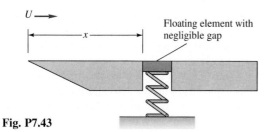

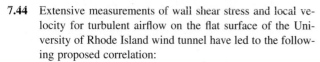

Fig. P7.43

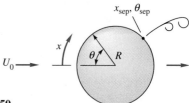

Fig. P7.50

7.44 Extensive measurements of wall shear stress and local velocity for turbulent airflow on the flat surface of the University of Rhode Island wind tunnel have led to the following proposed correlation:

$$\frac{\rho y^2 \tau_w}{\mu^2} \approx 0.0207 \left(\frac{uy}{\nu}\right)^{1.77}$$

Thus, if y and $u(y)$ are known at a point in a flat-plate boundary layer, the wall shear may be computed directly. If the answer to part (c) of Prob. 7.43 is $u \approx 27$ m/s, determine whether the correlation is accurate for this case.

7.45 Using the logarithmic law, Eq. (7.34), generate some numerical values for the two dimensionless parameters of Prob. 7.44, plot on log-log scales, and determine if the formula proposed in Prob. 7.44 is accurate. What are the limitations on the use of this correlation?

7.46 A ship is 150 m long and has a wetted area of 5000 m². If it is encrusted with barnacles, the ship requires 7000 hp to overcome friction drag when moving in seawater at 15 kn and 20°C. What is the average roughness of the barnacles? How fast would the ship move with the same power if the surface were smooth? Neglect wave drag.

7.47 As a case similar to Example 7.5, Howarth also proposed the adverse-gradient velocity distribution $U = U_0(1 - x^2/L^2)$ and computed separation at $x_{sep}/L = 0.271$ by a series-expansion method. Compute separation by Thwaites' method and compare.

7.48 In 1957 H. Görtler proposed the adverse-gradient test cases

$$U = \frac{U_0}{(1 + x/L)^n}$$

and computed separation for laminar flow at $n = 1$ to be $x_{sep}/L = 0.159$. Compare with Thwaites' method, assuming $\theta_0 = 0$.

7.49 Repeat Prob. 7.48 for $n = 2$ and compare with Görtler's series-expansion computation $x_{sep}/L = 0.078$.

7.50 For flow past a cylinder of radius R as in Fig. P7.50, the theoretical inviscid velocity distribution along the surface is $U = 2U_0 \sin(x/R)$, where U_0 is the oncoming stream velocity and x is the arc length measured from the nose (Chap. 8). Compute the laminar separation point x_{sep} and θ_{sep} by

Thwaites' method, and compare with the digital-computer solution $x_{sep}/R = 1.823$ ($\theta_{sep} = 104.5°$) given by R. M. Terrill in 1960.

7.51 Consider the flat-walled diffuser in Fig. P7.51, which is similar to that of Fig. 6.26a with constant width b. If x is measured from the inlet and the wall boundary layers are thin, show that the core velocity $U(x)$ in the diffuser is given approximately by

$$U = \frac{U_0}{1 + (2x \tan \theta)/W}$$

where W is the inlet height. Use this velocity distribution with Thwaites' method to compute the wall angle θ for which laminar separation will occur in the exit plane when diffuser length $L = 2W$. Note that the result is independent of the Reynolds number.

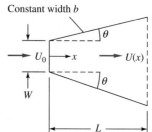

Fig. P7.51

7.52 In Fig. P7.52 a slanted upper wall creates a favorable pressure gradient on the upper surface of the flat plate. Use Thwaites' theory to estimate

$$C_D = \frac{F}{\frac{1}{2}\rho U_0^2 bL}$$

on the upper plate surface if $U_0 L/\nu = 10^5$. Compare with Eq. (7.27).

7.53 From Table 7.2, the drag coefficient of a wide plate normal to a stream is approximately 2.0. Let the stream conditions be U_∞ and p_∞. If the average pressure on the front of the plate is approximately equal to the free-stream stagnation pressure, what is the average pressure on the rear?

7.54 A chimney at sea level is 2 m in diameter and 40 m high. When it is subjected to 50 mi/h storm winds, what is the

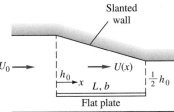

Fig. P7.52

estimated wind-induced bending moment about the bottom of the chimney?

7.55 A ship tows a submerged cylinder, which is 1.5 m in diameter and 22 m long, at 5 m/s in fresh water at 20°C. Estimate the towing power, in kW, required if the cylinder is (*a*) parallel and (*b*) normal to the tow direction.

7.56 A delivery vehicle carries a long sign on top, as in Fig. P7.56. If the sign is very thin and the vehicle moves at 55 mi/h, estimate the force on the sign (*a*) with no crosswind and (*b*) with a 10 mi/h crosswind.

Fig. P7.56

7.57 The main cross-cable between towers of a coastal suspension bridge is 60 cm in diameter and 90 m long. Estimate the total drag force on this cable in crosswinds of 50 mi/h. Are these laminar-flow conditions?

7.58 A long cylinder of rectangular cross section, 5 cm high and 30 cm long, is immersed in water at 20°C flowing at 12 m/s parallel to the long side of the rectangle. Estimate the drag force on the cylinder, per unit length, if the rectangle (*a*) has a flat face or (*b*) has a rounded nose.

7.59 Repeat Prob. 7.58 if the water flow is parallel to the short side.

7.60 A fishnet consists of 1-mm-diameter strings overlapped and knotted to form 1- by 1-cm squares. Estimate the drag of 1 m² of such a net when towed normal to its plane at 3 m/s in 20°C seawater. What horsepower is required to tow 400 ft² of this net?

7.61 A filter may be idealized as an array of cylindrical fibers normal to the flow, as in Fig. P7.61. Assuming that the fibers are uniformly distributed and have drag coefficients given

by Fig. 7.16*a*, derive an approximate expression for the pressure drop Δp through a filter of thickness *L*.

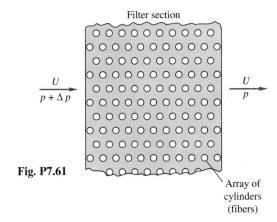

Fig. P7.61

7.62 A sea-level smokestack is 52 m high and has a square cross section. Its supports can withstand a maximum side force of 90 kN. If the stack is to survive 90 mi/h hurricane winds, what is its maximum possible width?

7.63 The cross section of a cylinder is shown in Fig. P7.63. Assume that on the front surface the velocity is given by potential theory (Sec. 8.4), $V = 2U_\infty \sin \theta$, from which the surface pressure is computed by Bernoulli's equation. In the separated flow on the rear, the pressure is assumed equal to its value at $\theta = 90°$. Compute the theoretical drag coefficient and compare with Table 7.2.

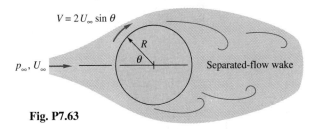

Fig. P7.63

7.64 A parachutist jumps from a plane, using an 8.5-m-diameter chute in the standard atmosphere. The total mass of the chutist and the chute is 90 kg. Assuming an open chute and quasisteady motion, estimate the time to fall from 2000- to 1000-m altitude.

7.65 The drag of a sphere at very low Reynolds numbers $Re_D \ll 1$ was given analytically by G. G. Stokes in 1851: $F = 3\pi\mu VD$ [2, pp. 175–178]. This formula is an example of Stokes' *law of creeping motion*, where inertia is negligible. Show that the drag coefficient in this region is $C_D = 24/Re_D$. A 1-mm-diameter sphere falls in 20°C glycerin at 2.5 mm/s. Is this a creeping motion? Compute (*a*) the Reynolds number, (b) the drag, and (c) the specific gravity of the sphere.

7.66 A sphere of density ρ_s and diameter D is dropped from rest in a fluid of density ρ and viscosity μ. Assuming a constant drag coefficient C_{d_0}, derive a differential equation for the fall velocity $V(t)$ and show that the solution is

$$V = \left[\frac{4gD(S-1)}{3C_{d_0}}\right]^{1/2} \tanh Ct$$

$$C = \left[\frac{3gC_{d_0}(S-1)}{4S^2D}\right]^{1/2}$$

where $S = \rho_s/\rho$ is the specific gravity of the sphere material.

7.67 Apply the theory of Prob. 7.66 to a steel sphere of diameter 2 cm, dropped from rest in water at 20°C. Estimate the time required for the sphere to reach 99 percent of its terminal (zero-acceleration) velocity.

7.68 A baseball weighs 145 g and is 7.35 cm in diameter. It is dropped from rest from a 35-m-high tower at approximately sea level. Assuming a laminar-flow drag coefficient, estimate (a) its terminal velocity and (b) whether it will reach 99 percent of its terminal velocity before it hits the ground.

7.69 Two baseballs from Prob. 7.68 are connected to a rod 7 mm in diameter and 56 cm long, as in Fig. P7.69. What power, in W, is required to keep the system spinning at 400 r/min? Include the drag of the rod, and assume sea-level standard air.

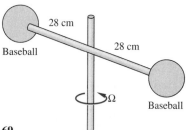

28 cm

Baseball

28 cm

Ω

Baseball

Fig. P7.69

7.70 A baseball from Prob. 7.68 is batted upward during a game at an angle of 45° and an initial velocity of 98 mi/h. Neglect spin and lift. Estimate the horizontal distance traveled, (a) neglecting drag and (b) accounting for drag in a numerical (computer) solution with a transition Reynolds number $Re_{D,\text{crit}} = 2.5$ E5.

7.71 A football weights 0.91 lbf and approximates an ellipsoid 6 in in diameter and 12 in long (Table 7.3). It is thrown upward at a 45° angle with an initial velocity of 80 ft/s. Neglect spin and lift. Assuming turbulent flow, estimate the horizontal distance traveled, (a) neglecting drag and (b) accounting for drag with a numerical (computer) model.

7.72 A settling tank for a municipal water supply is 2.5 m deep,

and 20°C water flows through continuously at 35 cm/s. Estimate the minimum length of the tank which will ensure that all sediment (SG = 2.55) will fall to the bottom for particle diameters greater than (a) 1 mm and (b) 100 μm.

7.73 A helium-filled balloon has a diameter of 4.3 m. The balloon material and payload weigh 240 N, not including the helium. The helium pressure is 115 kPa. Estimate the terminal ascent velocity in sea-level standard air.

7.74 Suppose that the balloon diameter in Prob. 7.73 is unknown. Estimate, at sea level, (a) the minimum diameter for which the balloon will rise and (b) the diameter for which the terminal ascent velocity is 4 m/s.

7.75 The helium-filled balloon in Fig. P7.75 is tethered at 20°C and 1 atm with a string of negligible weight and drag. The diameter is 50 cm, and the balloon material weighs 0.6 N, not including the helium. The helium pressure is 120 kPa. Estimate the tilt angle θ if the airstream velocity U is (a) 5 m/s or (b) 20 m/s.

Fig. P7.75

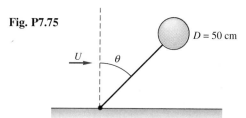

U θ $D = 50$ cm

7.76 Suppose that the balloon diameter in Prob. 7.75 is unknown. If $U = 5$ m/s, what is the proper diameter for which the tilt angle $\theta = 45°$?

7.77 Modify Prob. 7.75 as follows: Let the fluid be water at 20°C, and let the 50-cm-diameter sphere be solid cork (SG = 0.16). Estimate the tilt angle θ if the water velocity U is 3 m/s.

7.78 Apply Prob. 7.61 to a filter consisting of 300-μm-diameter fibers packed 250 per square centimeter in the plane of Fig. P7.61. For air at 20°C and 1 atm flowing at 1.5 m/s, estimate the pressure drop if the filter is 5 cm thick.

7.79 Assume that a radioactive dust particle approximates a sphere of density 2400 kg/m³. How long, in days, will it take such a particle to settle to sea level from an altitude of 12 km if the particle diameter is (a) 1 μm or (b) 20 μm?

7.80 A heavy sphere attached to a string should hang at an angle θ when immersed in a stream of velocity U, as in Fig. P7.80. Derive an expression for θ as a function of the sphere and flow properties. What is θ if the sphere is steel (SG = 7.86) of diameter 3 cm and the flow is sea-level standard air at $U = 40$ m/s? Neglect the string drag.

7.81 A parachutist is to land at sea level at a vertical velocity of 9 mi/h. Jumper and pack weigh 200 lbf. What should the diameter of the chute be?

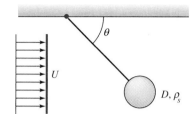

Fig. P7.80

7.82 The average skydiver with parachute unopened weighs 175 lbf and has a drag area $C_D A = 9$ ft^2 spread-eagled and 1.2 ft^2 falling feet first [12, p. 313]. What are the minimum and maximum terminal speeds that can be achieved by a sky-diver at 5000-ft standard altitude?

7.83 A high-speed car has a drag coefficient of 0.3 and a frontal area of 1 m^2. A parachute is to be used to slow this car from 80 to 40 m/s in 8 s. What should the chute diameter be? What distance will be traveled during this deceleration? Take $m = 2000$ kg.

7.84 A Ping-Pong ball weighs 2.6 g and has a diameter of 3.8 cm. It can be supported by an air jet from a vacuum cleaner outlet, as in Fig. P7.84. For sea-level standard air, what jet velocity is required?

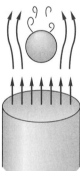

Fig. P7.84

7.85 Give a physical explanation of the fact, from Table 7.3, that the drag coefficient of a tree, based on nominal frontal area, drops off sharply as the wind velocity increases. See Ref. 24 for further details.

7.86 Hoerner [Ref. 12, pp. 3–25] states that the drag coefficient of a flag of 2 : 1 aspect ratio is 0.11 based on planform area. The University of Rhode Island has an aluminum flagpole 25 m high and 14 cm in diameter. It flies equal-sized na-tional and state flags together. If the fracture stress of alu-minum is 210 MPa, what is the maximum flag size that can be used yet avoids breaking the flagpole in hurricane (75 mi/h) winds?

7.87 A tractor-trailer truck has a drag-area $C_D A = 8$ m^2 bare and 6.7 m^2 with an aerodynamic deflector (Fig. 7.18b). Its rolling resistance is 50 N for each mile per hour of speed. Calculate the total horsepower required at sea level with and without

the deflector if the truck moves at (a) 55 mi/h and (b) 75 mi/h.

7.88 A pickup truck has a clean drag-area $C_D A$ of 35 ft^2. Estimate the horsepower required to drive the truck at 55 mi/h (a) clean and (b) with the 3- by 6-ft sign in Fig. P7.88 installed if the rolling resistance is 150 lbf at sea level.

Fig. P7.88

7.89 A water tower is approximated by a 15-m-diameter sphere mounted on a 1-m-diameter rod 20 m long. Estimate the bending moment at the root of the rod due to aerodynamic forces during hurricane winds of 40 m/s.

7.90 In the great hurricane of 1938, winds of 85 mi/h blew over a boxcar in Providence, Rhode Island. The boxcar was 10 ft high, 40 ft long, and 6 ft wide, with a 3-ft clearance above tracks 4.8 ft apart. What wind speed would topple a boxcar weighing 40,000 lbf?

7.91 A cup anemometer uses two 5-cm-diameter hollow hemi-spheres connected to 15-cm rods, as in Fig. P7.91. Rod drag

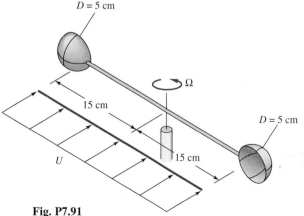

Fig. P7.91

is negligible, and the central bearing has a retarding torque of 0.004 N · m. Making simplifying assumptions to average out the time-varying geometry, estimate and plot the variation of anemometer rotation rate Ω with wind velocity U in the range $0 < U < 25$ m/s for sea-level standard air.

7.92 Repeat Prob. 7.91 if the anemometer consists of *four* cups placed at right angles to each other. Is the curve of Ω versus U linear?

7.93 A hot-film probe is mounted on a cone-and-rod system in a sea-level airstream of 45 m/s, as in Fig. P7.93. Estimate the maximum cone vertex angle allowable if the flow-induced bending moment at the root of the rod is not to exceed 30 N · cm.

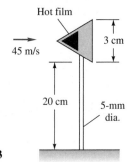

Fig. P7.93

7.94 A rotary mixer consists of two 1-m-long half-tubes rotating around a central arm, as in Fig. P7.94. Using the drag from Table 7.2, derive an expression for the torque T required to drive the mixer at angular velocity Ω in a fluid of density ρ. Suppose that the fluid is water at 20°C and the maximum driving power available is 20 kW. What is the maximum rotation speed Ω r/min?

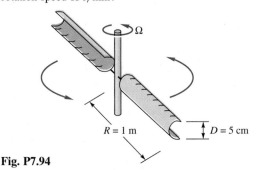

Fig. P7.94

7.95 An airplane weighing 12 kN, with a drag-area $C_D A \approx 15$ m², lands at sea level at 55 m/s and deploys a drag parachute 7 m in diameter. No other brakes are applied. (*a*) How long will it take the plane to slow down to 30 m/s? (*b*) How far will it have traveled in that time?

7.96 A Savonius rotor (Fig. 6.29*b*) can be approximated by the two open half-tubes in Fig. P7.96 mounted on a central axis.

If the drag of each tube is similar to that in Table 7.2, derive an approximate formula for the rotation rate Ω as a function of U, D, L, and the fluid properties (ρ, μ).

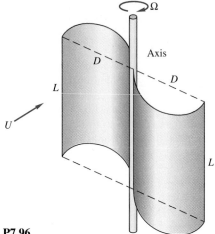

Fig. P7.96

7.97 A simple measurement of automobile drag can be found by an unpowered *coastdown* on a level road with no wind. Assume constant rolling resistance. For an automobile of mass 1500 kg and frontal area 2 m², the following velocity-versus-time data are obtained during a coastdown:

t, s	0	10	20	30	40
V, m/s	27.0	24.2	21.8	19.7	17.9

Estimate (*a*) the rolling resistance and (*b*) the drag coefficient. This problem is well suited for digital-computer analysis but can be done by hand also.

7.98 A buoyant ball of specific gravity SG < 1 dropped into water at inlet velocity V_0 will penetrate a distance h and then pop out again, as in Fig. P7.98. Make a dynamic analysis of this problem, assuming a constant drag coefficient, and derive an expression for h as a function of the system prop-

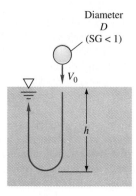

Fig. P7.98

erties. How far will a 5-cm-diameter ball with SG = 0.5 and $C_D \approx 0.47$ penetrate if it enters at 10 m/s?

7.99 Two steel balls (SG = 7.86) are connected by a thin hinged rod of negligible weight and drag, as in Fig. P7.99. A stop prevents the rod from rotating counterclockwise. Estimate the sea-level air velocity U for which the rod will first begin to rotate clockwise.

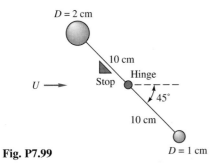

Fig. P7.99

7.100 Derive an analytical formula for the decelerating velocity $V(t)$ of the car coasting down in Prob. 7.97, assuming constant rolling resistance F, drag-area $C_D A$, mass m, and air density ρ. Apply your formula to check the data in Prob. 7.97, assuming $C_D = 0.4$ and $F = 100$ N.

7.101 Icebergs can be driven at substantial speeds by the wind. Let the iceberg be idealized as a large, flat cylinder, $D \gg L$, with one-eighth of its bulk exposed, as in Fig. P7.101. Let the seawater be at rest. If the upper and lower drag forces depend upon relative velocities between the berg and the fluid, derive an approximate expression for the steady iceberg speed V when driven by wind velocity U.

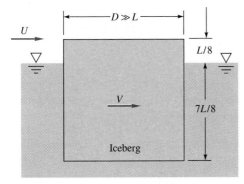

Fig. P7.101

7.102 Apply your theory of Prob. 7.101 to solve for V cm/s if $D = 700$ m, $L = 80$ m, and $U = 12$ m/s.

7.103 When immersed in a uniform stream V, a heavy rod hinged at A will hang at *Pode's angle* θ, after an analysis by L. Pode in 1951 (Fig. P7.103). Assume that the cylinder has

normal drag coefficient C_{DN} and tangential coefficient C_{DT} which relate the drag forces to V_N and V_T, respectively. Derive an expression for Pode's angle as a function of the flow and rod parameters. Find θ for a steel rod, $L = 40$ cm, $D = 1$ cm, hanging in sea-level air at $V = 35$ m/s.

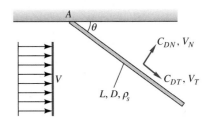

Fig. P7.103

7.104 Suppose that the body in Fig. P7.103 is a thin plate weighing 0.6 N, of length $L = 20$ cm and width $b = 4$ cm into the paper. For sea-level standard air, plot Pode's angle θ versus velocity V in the range $0 < V < 40$ m/s. Would this device make a good air-velocity meter (anemometer)?

7.105 A ship 50 m long, with a wetted area of 800 m², has the hull shape tested in Fig. 7.19. There are no bow or stern bulbs. The total propulsive power available is 1 MW. For seawater at 20°C, plot the ship's velocity V kn versus power P for $0 < P < 1$ MW. What is the most efficient setting?

7.106 A smooth steel 1-cm-diameter sphere ($W \approx 0.04$ N) is fired vertically at sea level at the initial supersonic velocity $V_0 = 1000$ m/s. Its drag coefficient is given by Fig. 7.20. Assuming that the speed of sound is constant at $a \approx 343$ m/s, compute the maximum altitude of the projectile (a) by a simple analytical estimate and (b) by a digital-computer program.

7.107 Repeat Prob. 7.106 if the body is a 9-mm steel bullet ($W \approx 0.07$ N) which approximates the "pointed body of revolution" in Fig. 7.20.

7.108 The data in Fig. P7.108 are for the lift and drag of a spinning sphere from Ref. 12, pp. 7–20. Suppose that a tennis ball ($W \approx 0.56$ N, $D \approx 6.35$ cm) is struck at sea level with initial velocity $V_0 = 30$ m/s and "topspin" (front of the ball rotating downward) of 120 r/s. If the initial height of the ball is 1.5 m, estimate the horizontal distance traveled before it strikes the ground.

7.109 Repeat Prob. 7.108 if the ball is struck with "underspin" (front of the ball rotating upward).

7.110 A baseball pitcher throws a curveball with an initial velocity of 65 mi/h and a spin of 6500 r/min about a vertical axis. A baseball weighs 0.32 lbf and has a diameter of 2.9 in. Using the data of Fig. P7.108 for turbulent flow, estimate how far such a curveball will have deviated from its straight-line path when it reaches home plate 60.5 ft away.

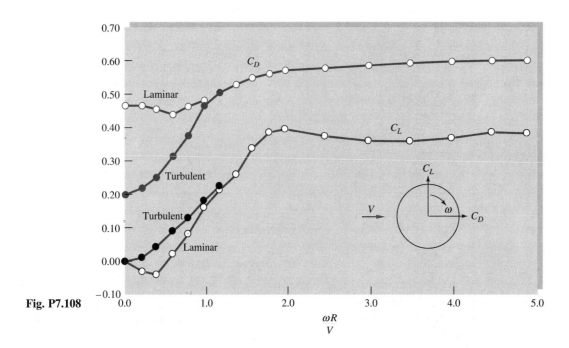

Fig. P7.108

7.111 A table tennis ball has a mass of 2.6 g and a diameter of 3.81 cm. It is struck horizontally at an initial velocity of 20 m/s while it is 50 cm above the table, as in Fig. P7.111. For sea-level air, what topspin (as shown), in r/min, will cause the ball to strike the opposite edge of the table, 4 m away? Make an analytical estimate, using Fig. P7.108, and account for the fact that the ball decelerates during flight.

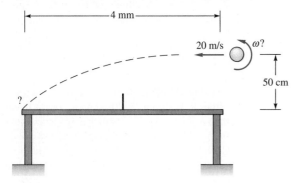

Fig. P7.111

7.112 Repeat Prob. 7.111 by making a detailed digital-computer solution for the flight path of the ball. Use Fig. P7.108 for lift and drag.

7.113 An automobile has a mass of 1000 kg and a drag-area $C_D A = 0.7$ m². The rolling resistance of 70 N is approximately constant. The car is coasting without brakes at 90 km/h as it begins to climb a hill of 10 percent grade (slope $= \tan^{-1} 0.1 = 5.71°$). How far up the hill will the car come to a stop?

7.114 Suppose that the car in Prob. 7.113 is placed at the top of the 10 percent grade hill and released from rest to coast down without brakes. What will be its speed, in km/h, after dropping a vertical distance of 20 m?

7.115 An airplane weighs 180 kN and has a wing area of 160 m² and a mean chord of 4 m. The airfoil properties are given by Fig. 7.24. If the airplane cruises at 250 mi/h at 3000-m standard altitude, what propulsive power is required to overcome wing drag?

7.116 The airplane of Prob. 7.115 is designed to land at $V_0 = 1.2V_{stall}$, using a split flap set at 60°. What is the proper landing speed in mi/h? What power is required for takeoff at the same speed?

7.117 Suppose that the airplane of Prob. 7.115 takes off at sea level without benefit of flaps, with C_L constant so that the takeoff speed is 100 mi/h. Estimate the takeoff distance if the thrust is 10 kN. How much thrust is needed to make the takeoff distance 1250 m?

7.118 Suppose that the airplane of Prob. 7.115 is fitted with all the best high-lift devices of Fig. 7.27. What is its minimum stall speed in mi/h? Estimate the stopping distance if the plane lands at $V_0 = 1.25V_{stall}$ with constant $C_L = 3.0$ and $C_D = 0.2$ and the braking force is 20 percent of the weight on the wheels.

7.119 An airplane has a mass of 5000 kg, a maximum thrust of

7000 N, and a rectangular wing with aspect ratio 6.0. It takes off at sea level with a 60° split flap whose two-dimensional properties are shown in Fig. 7.24. Assume all lift and all drag are due to the wing. What is the proper wing size if the takeoff distance is to be 1 km?

7.120 Show that if Eqs. (7.70) and (7.71) are valid, the maximum lift-to-drag ratio occurs when $C_D = 2C_{D\infty}$. What are $(L/D)_{max}$ and α for a symmetric wing when AR = 5 and $C_{D\infty} = 0.009$?

7.121 In gliding (unpowered) flight, the lift and drag are in equilibrium with the weight. Show that if there is no wind, the aircraft sinks at an angle

$$\tan \theta \approx \frac{\text{drag}}{\text{lift}}$$

For a sailplane of mass 200 kg, wing area 12 m², and aspect ratio 11, with an NACA 0009 airfoil, estimate (a) the stall speed, (b) the minimum gliding angle, and (c) the maximum distance it can glide in still air when it is 1200 m above level ground.

7.122 A boat of mass 2500 kg has two hydrofoils, each of chord 30 cm and span 1.5 m, with $C_{L,max} = 1.2$ and $C_{D\infty} = 0.08$. Its engine can deliver 130 kW to the water. For seawater at 20°C, estimate (a) the minimum speed for which the foils support the boat and (b) the maximum speed attainable.

7.123 In prewar days there was a controversy, perhaps apocryphal, about whether the bumblebee has a legitimate aerodynamic right to fly. The average bumblebee (*Bombus terrestris*) weighs 0.88 g, with a wing span of 1.73 cm and a wing area of 1.26 cm². It can indeed fly at 10 m/s. Using fixed-wing theory, what is the lift coefficient of the bee at this speed? Is this reasonable for typical airfoils?

7.124 The bumblebee can hover at zero speed by flapping its wings. Using the data of Prob. 7.123, devise a theory for flapping wings where the downstroke approximates a short flat plate normal to the flow (Table 7.3) and the upstroke is feathered at nearly zero drag. How many flaps per second of such a model wing are needed to support the bee's weight? (Actual measurements of bees show a flapping rate of 194 Hz.)

Word Problems

W7.1 How do you *recognize* a boundary layer? Cite some physical properties and some measurements which reveal appropriate characteristics.

W7.2 In Chap. 6 the Reynolds number for transition to turbulence in pipe flow was about $Re_{tr} \approx 2300$, whereas in flat-plate flow $Re_{tr} \approx 1\ E6$, nearly three orders of magnitude higher. What accounts for the difference?

W7.3 Without writing any equations, give a verbal description of boundary-layer displacement thickness.

W7.4 Describe, in words only, the basic ideas behind the "boundary-layer approximations."

W7.5 What is an *adverse* pressure gradient? Give three examples of flow regimes where such gradients occur.

W7.6 What is a *favorable* pressure gradient? Give three examples of flow regimes where such gradients occur.

W7.7 The drag of an airfoil (Fig. 7.12) increases considerably if you turn the sharp edge around 180° to face the stream. Can you explain this?

W7.8 In Table 7.3, the drag coefficient of a spruce tree decreases sharply with wind velocity. Can you explain this?

W7.9 Thrust is required to propel an airplane at a finite forward velocity. Does this imply an energy loss to the system? Explain the concepts of thrust and drag in terms of the first law of thermodynamics.

W7.10 How does the concept of *drafting*, in automobile and bicycle racing, apply to the material studied in this chapter?

W7.11 The circular cylinder of Fig. 7.13 is doubly symmetric and therefore should have no lift. Yet a lift sensor would definitely reveal a finite root-mean-square value of lift. Can you explain this behavior?

W7.12 Explain in words why a thrown spinning ball moves in a curved trajectory. Give some physical reasons why a side force is developed in addition to the drag.

Design Project

D7.1 It is desired to design a cup anemometer for wind speed, similar to Fig. P7.91, with a more sophisticated approach than the "average-torque" method of Prob. 7.91. The design should achieve an approximately linear relation between wind velocity and rotation rate in the range $20 < U < 40$ mi/h, and the anemometer should rotate at about 6 r/s at $U = 30$ mi/h. All specifications—cup diameter D, rod length L, rod diameter d, the bearing type, and all materials—are to be selected through your analysis. Make suitable assumptions about the instantaneous drag of the cups and rods at any given angle $\theta(t)$ of the system. Compute the instantaneous torque $T(t)$, and find and integrate the instantaneous angular acceleration of the device. Develop a complete theory for rotation rate versus wind speed in the range $0 < U < 50$ mi/h. Try to include actual commercial bearing-friction properties.

Chapter 8
Inviscid
Incompressible Flow

Motivation. In Chapter 4 we derived and discussed the basic differential equations of mass, momentum, and energy for a newtonian fluid. Then, in Sec. 4.11, we applied these equations to some illustrative incompressible viscous flows. Subsequently, viscous-flow analysis was extended in Chap. 6 to various duct (internal) flows and in Chap. 7 to some boundary-layer (external) flows.

Meanwhile, in Sec. 4.10, we also looked at some representative incompressible *inviscid* flows, which provide the outer or "driving" region for boundary-layer flows. The purpose of this chapter is to extend Sec. 4.10, inviscid-flow analysis, to a variety of geometries and conditions. The combination of all this gives us a good picture of incompressible-flow theory and its relation to experiment.

8.1 Introduction and Review

Figure 8.1 reminds us of the problems to be faced. A free stream approaches two closely spaced bodies, creating an "internal" flow between them and "external" flows above and below them. The fronts of the bodies are regions of favorable gradient (decreasing pressure along the surface), and the boundary layers will be attached and thin: Inviscid theory will give excellent results for the outer flow if $Re > 10^4$. For the internal flow

Fig. 8.1 Patching viscous- and inviscid-flow regions. The theory in this chapter does not apply to the boundary-layer regions.

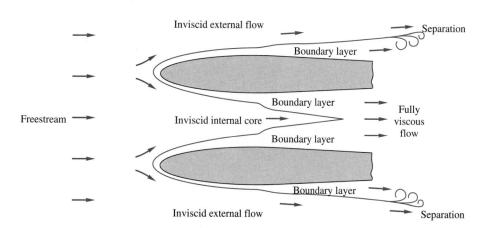

447

between bodies, the boundary layers will grow and eventually meet, and the inviscid core vanishes. Inviscid theory works well in a ''short'' duct $L/D < 10$, such as the nozzle of a wind tunnel. For longer ducts we must estimate boundary-layer growth and be cautious about using inviscid theory.

For the external flows above and below the bodies in Fig. 8.1, inviscid theory should work well for the outer flows, until the surface pressure gradient becomes adverse (increasing pressure) and the boundary layer separates or stalls. After the separation point, boundary-layer theory becomes inaccurate, and the outer flow streamlines are deflected and have a strong interaction with the viscous near-wall regions. The theoretical analysis of separated-flow regions is an active research area at present.

Review of Velocity-Potential Concepts

Recall from Sec. 4.9 that if viscous effects are neglected, low-speed flows are irrotational, $\nabla \times \mathbf{V} = 0$, and the velocity potential ϕ exists, such that

$$\mathbf{V} = \nabla\phi \quad \text{or} \quad u = \frac{\partial\phi}{\partial x} \quad v = \frac{\partial\phi}{\partial y} \quad w = \frac{\partial\phi}{\partial z} \tag{8.1}$$

The continuity equation (4.73), $\nabla \cdot \mathbf{V} = 0$, reduces to Laplace's equation for ϕ:

$$\nabla^2\phi = \frac{\partial^2\phi}{\partial x^2} + \frac{\partial^2\phi}{\partial y^2} + \frac{\partial^2\phi}{\partial z^2} = 0 \tag{8.2}$$

and the momentum equation (4.74) reduces to Bernoulli's equation:

$$\frac{\partial\phi}{\partial t} + \frac{p}{\rho} + \frac{1}{2}V^2 + gz = \text{const} \quad \text{where } V = |\nabla\phi| \tag{8.3}$$

Typical boundary conditions are known free-stream conditions

Outer boundaries: $\qquad\qquad \text{Known } \dfrac{\partial\phi}{\partial x}, \dfrac{\partial\phi}{\partial y}, \dfrac{\partial\phi}{\partial z} \tag{8.4}$

and no velocity normal to the boundary at the body surface:

Solid surfaces: $\qquad \dfrac{\partial\phi}{\partial n} = 0 \quad$ where n is perpendicular to body $\tag{8.5}$

Unlike the no-slip condition in viscous flow, here there is *no* condition on the tangential surface velocity $V_s = \partial\phi/\partial s$, where s is the coordinate along the surface. This velocity is determined as part of the solution to the problem.

Occasionally the problem involves a free surface, for which the boundary pressure is known and equal to p_a, usually a constant. The Bernoulli equation (8.3) then supplies a relation at the surface between V and the elevation z of the surface. For steady flow, e.g.,

Free surface: $\qquad\qquad V^2 = |\nabla\phi|^2 = \text{const} - 2gz_{\text{surf}} \tag{8.6}$

It should be clear to the reader that this use of Laplace's equation, with known values of the derivative of ϕ along the boundaries, is much easier than a direct attack using the fully viscous Navier-Stokes equations. The analysis of Laplace's equation is very well developed and is termed *potential theory*, with whole books written about the general theory [1] and its application to fluid mechanics [2 to 4]. There are many analytical techniques, including superposition of elementary functions, conformal mapping, numerical finite differences [5], numerical finite elements [6], numerical boundary elements [7], and electric or mechanical analogs [8] now outdated. Having found $\phi(x, y, z, t)$ from such an analysis, we then compute $\mathbf{V}$ by direct differentiation in Eq. (8.1), after which we compute p from Eq. (8.3). The procedure is quite straightforward, and many interesting albeit idealized results can be obtained.

Review of Stream Function Concepts

Recall from Sec. 4.7 that if a flow is described by only two coordinates, the stream function ψ also exists as an alternate approach. For plane incompressible flow in xy coordinates, the correct form is

$$u = \frac{\partial \psi}{\partial y} \qquad v = -\frac{\partial \psi}{\partial x} \tag{8.7}$$

The condition of irrotationality reduces to Laplace's equation for ψ also:

$$2\omega_z = 0 = \frac{\partial v}{\partial x} - \frac{\partial u}{\partial y} = \frac{\partial}{\partial x}\left(-\frac{\partial \psi}{\partial x}\right) - \frac{\partial}{\partial y}\left(\frac{\partial \psi}{\partial y}\right)$$

or

$$\frac{\partial^2 \psi}{\partial x^2} + \frac{\partial^2 \psi}{\partial y^2} = 0 \tag{8.8}$$

The boundary conditions again are known velocity in the stream and no flow through any solid surface:

Free stream: $\qquad\qquad$ Known $\dfrac{\partial \psi}{\partial x}, \dfrac{\partial \psi}{\partial y}$ $\qquad\qquad$ (8.9a)

Solid surface: $\qquad\qquad \psi_{body} = \text{const}$ $\qquad\qquad$ (8.9b)

Equation (8.9b) is particularly interesting because *any* line of constant ψ in a flow can therefore be interpreted as a body shape and may lead to interesting applications.

For the applications in this chapter, we may compute either ϕ or ψ or both, and the solution will be an *orthogonal flow net* as in Fig. 8.2. Once found, either set of lines may be considered the ϕ lines, and the other set will be the ψ lines. Both sets of lines are laplacian and could be useful.

Fig. 8.2 Streamlines and potential lines are orthogonal and may reverse roles if results are useful: (*a*) typical inviscid-flow pattern; (*b*) same as (*a*) with roles reversed.

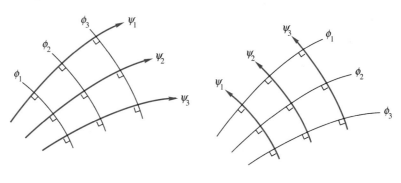

(*a*) $\qquad\qquad\qquad\qquad\qquad$ (*b*)

Plane Polar Coordinates

Many solutions in this chapter are conveniently expressed in polar coordinates (r, θ). Both the velocity components and the differential relations for ϕ and ψ are then changed, as follows:

$$v_r = \frac{\partial \phi}{\partial r} = \frac{1}{r}\frac{\partial \psi}{\partial \theta} \qquad v_\theta = \frac{1}{r}\frac{\partial \phi}{\partial \theta} = -\frac{\partial \psi}{\partial r} \tag{8.10}$$

Laplace's equation takes the form

$$\frac{1}{r}\frac{\partial}{\partial r}\left(r\frac{\partial \phi}{\partial r}\right) + \frac{1}{r^2}\frac{\partial^2 \phi}{\partial \theta^2} = 0 \tag{8.11}$$

Exactly the same equation holds for the polar-coordinate form of $\psi(r, \theta)$.

An intriguing facet of potential flow with no free surface is that the governing equations (8.2) and (8.8) contain no parameters, nor do the boundary conditions. Therefore the solutions are purely geometric, depending only upon the body shape, the free-stream orientation, and—surprisingly—the position of the rear stagnation point.[1] There is no Reynolds, Froude, or Mach number to complicate the dynamic similarity. Inviscid flows are kinematically similar without additional parameters—recall Fig. 5.6a.

8.2 Elementary Plane-Flow Solutions

Recall from Sec. 4.10 that we defined three elementary potential flows which are quite useful: (1) uniform stream in the x direction, (2) line source or sink at the origin, and (3) line vortex at the origin. (Recall Fig. 4.12 for these geometries.) Let us review these special cases here:

Uniform stream iU: $\qquad \psi = Uy \qquad\qquad \phi = Ux \qquad\qquad$ (8.12a)

Line source or sink: $\qquad \psi = m\theta \qquad\qquad \phi = m \ln r \qquad\qquad$ (8.12b)

Line vortex: $\qquad\qquad \psi = -K \ln r \qquad \phi = K\theta \qquad\qquad$ (8.12c)

The source "strength" m and the vortex "strength" K have the same dimensions, namely, velocity times length, or $\{L^2/T\}$.

If the uniform stream is written in plane polar coordinates, it becomes

Uniform stream iU: $\qquad \psi = Ur \sin \theta \qquad \phi = Ur \cos \theta \qquad$ (8.13)

This makes it easier to superimpose, say, a stream and a source or vortex by using the same coordinates. If the uniform stream is moving at angle α with respect to the x axis, i.e.,

$$u = U \cos \alpha = \frac{\partial \psi}{\partial y} = \frac{\partial \phi}{\partial x} \qquad v = U \sin \alpha = -\frac{\partial \psi}{\partial x} = \frac{\partial \phi}{\partial y}$$

then by integration we obtain the correct functions for flow at an angle:

$$\psi = U(y \cos \alpha - x \sin \alpha) \qquad \phi = U(x \cos \alpha + y \sin \alpha) \tag{8.14}$$

These expressions are useful in airfoil angle-of-attack problems (Sec. 8.7).

---

[1] The rear stagnation condition establishes the net amount of "circulation" about the body, giving rise to a lift force. Otherwise the solution could not be unique. See Sec. 8.4.

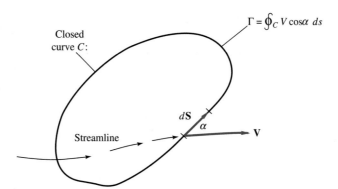

Fig. 8.3 Definition of the fluid circulation Γ.

Circulation

The line-vortex flow is irrotational everywhere except at the origin, where the vorticity $\nabla \times \mathbf{V}$ is infinite. This means that a certain line integral called the *fluid circulation* Γ does not vanish when taken around a vortex center.

With reference to Fig. 8.3, the circulation is defined as the counterclockwise line integral, around a closed curve C, of arc length ds times the velocity component tangent to the curve

$$\Gamma = \oint_C V \cos \alpha \, ds = \int_C \mathbf{V} \cdot d\mathbf{s} = \int_C (u \, dx + v \, dy + w \, dz) \qquad (8.15)$$

From the definition of ϕ, $\mathbf{V} \cdot d\mathbf{s} = \nabla \phi \cdot d\mathbf{s} = d\phi$ for an irrotational flow; hence normally Γ in an irrotational flow would equal the final value of ϕ minus the initial value of ϕ. Since we start and end at the same point, we compute $\Gamma = 0$, but not for vortex flow: With $\phi = K\theta$ from Eq. (8.12c) there is a change in ϕ of amount $2\pi K$ as we make one complete circle:

Path enclosing a vortex: $\qquad\qquad\qquad\qquad \Gamma = 2\pi K \qquad\qquad\qquad\qquad (8.16)$

Alternately the calculation can be made by defining a circular path of radius r around the vortex center, from Eq. (8.15)

$$\Gamma = \int_C v_\theta \, ds = \int_0^{2\pi} \frac{K}{r} r \, d\phi = 2\pi K \qquad (8.17)$$

In general, Γ denotes the net algebraic strength of all the vortex filaments contained within the closed curve. In the next section we shall see that a region of finite circulation within a flowing stream will be subjected to a lift force proportional to both U_∞ and Γ.

It is easy to show, by using Eq. (8.15), that a source or sink creates no circulation. If there are no vortices present, the circulation will be zero for any path enclosing any number of sources and sinks.

8.3 Superposition of Plane-Flow Solutions

We can now form a variety of interesting potential flows by summing the velocity-potential and stream functions of a uniform stream, source or sink, and vortex. Most of the results are classic, of course, needing only a brief treatment here.

**Graphical Method
of Superposition**

A simple means of accomplishing $\psi_{\text{tot}} = \sum \psi_i$ graphically is to plot the individual stream functions separately and then look at their intersections. The value of ψ_{tot} at each intersection is the sum of the individual values ψ_i which cross there. Connecting intersections with the same value of ψ_{tot} creates the desired superimposed flow streamlines.

A simple example is shown in Fig. 8.4, summing two families of streamlines ψ_a and ψ_b. The individual components are plotted separately, and four typical intersections are shown. Dashed lines are then drawn through intersections representing the same sum of $\psi_a + \psi_b$. These dashed lines are the desired solution. Often this graphical method is a quick means of evaluating the proposed superposition before a full-blown numerical plot routine is executed.

Some Examples from Chap. 4

In Sec. 4.10 we discussed a number of superposition examples.

1. Source m at $(-a, 0)$ plus an equal sink at $(\pm a, 0)$, Eq. (4.133), and Fig. 4.13:

$$\psi = -m \tan^{-1} \frac{2ay}{x^2 + y^2 - a^2} \qquad \phi = \frac{1}{2} m \ln \frac{(x + a)^2 + y^2}{(x - a)^2 + y^2} \quad (4.133)$$

The streamlines and potential lines are two families of orthogonal circles as plotted in Fig. 4.13. They resemble a magnet with poles at $(x, y) = (\pm a, 0)$.

2. Sink m plus a vortex K, both at the origin, Eq. (4.134), and Fig. 4.14:

$$\psi = m\theta - K \ln r \qquad \phi = m \ln r + K\theta \quad (4.134)$$

The streamlines are logarithmic spirals swirling into the origin, as in Fig. 4.14. They resemble a tornado or a bathtub vortex.

3. Uniform stream iU_∞ plus a source m at the origin, Eq. (4.135) and Fig. 4.15, the Rankine half-body:

$$\psi = U_\infty r \sin \theta + m\theta \qquad \phi = U_\infty r \cos \theta + m \ln r \quad (4.135)$$

If the origin contains a source, a plane half-body is formed with its nose to the left, as in Fig. 8.5a. If the origin is a *sink*, $m < 0$, the half-body nose is to the

Fig. 8.4 Intersections of elementary streamlines can be joined to form a combined streamline.

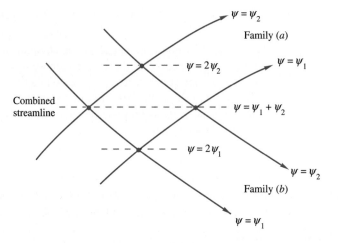

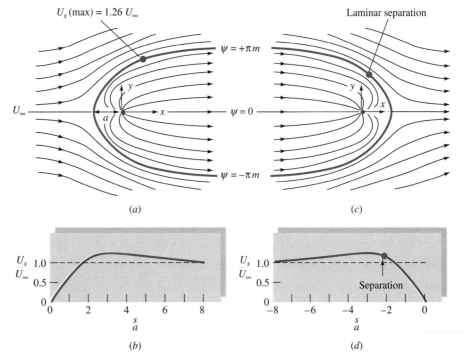

Fig. 8.5 The Rankine half-body; pattern (c) is not found in a real fluid because of boundary-layer separation: (a) uniform stream plus a source equals a half-body; stagnation point at $x = -a = -m/U_\infty$; (b) slight adverse gradient for s/a greater than 3.0: no separation; (c) uniform stream plus a sink equals the rear of a half-body; stagnation point at $x = a = m/U_\infty$; (d) strong adverse gradient for $s/a > -3.0$: separation.

right, as in Fig. 8.5c. In either case the stagnation point is at a position $a = m/U_\infty$ away from the origin.

Boundary-Layer Separation on a Half-Body

Although the inviscid-flow patterns, Fig. 8.5a and b, are mirror images, their viscous (boundary-layer) behavior is different. The body shape and the velocity along the surface are repeated here from Sec. 4.10:

$$V^2 = U_\infty^2\left(1 + \frac{a^2}{r^2} + \frac{2a}{r}\cos\theta\right) \quad \text{along} \quad r = \frac{m(\pi - \theta)}{U_\infty \sin\theta} \quad (8.18)$$

The computed surface velocities are plotted along the half-body contours in Fig. 8.5b and d as a function of arc length s/a measured from the stagnation point. These plots are also mirror images. However, if the nose is in front, Fig. 8.5b, the pressure gradient there is *favorable* (decreasing pressure along the surface). In contrast, the pressure gradient is *adverse* (increasing pressure along the surface) when the nose is in the rear, Fig. 8.5d, and boundary-layer separation may occur.

Application to Fig. 8.5b of Thwaites' laminar-boundary method from Eqs. (7.54) and (7.56) reveals that separation does not occur on the front nose of the half-body. Therefore Fig. 8.5a is a very realistic picture of streamlines past a half-body nose. In contrast, when applied to the tail, Fig. 8.5c, Thwaites' method predicts separation at about $s/a \approx -2.2$, or $\theta \approx 110°$. Thus, if a half-body is a solid surface, Fig. 8.5c is *not* realistic and a broad separated wake will form. However, if the half-body tail is a *fluid line* separating the sink-directed flow from the outer stream, as in Example 8.1, then

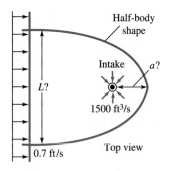

Half-body
shape

Intake   *a?*

L?

1500 ft³/s

Top view

0.7 ft/s

Fig. E8.1

Fig. 8.5c is quite realistic and useful. Computations for turbulent boundary-layer theory would be similar: separation on the tail, no separation on the nose.

EXAMPLE 8.1

An offshore power plant cooling-water intake sucks in 1500 ft³/s in water 30 ft deep, as in Fig. E8.1. If the tidal velocity approaching the intake is 0.7 ft/s, (a) how far downstream does the intake effect extend and (b) how much width L of tidal flow is entrained into the intake?

Solution

Recall from Eq. (4.131) that the sink strength m is related to the volume flow Q and the depth b into the paper

$$m = \frac{Q}{2\pi b} = \frac{1500 \text{ ft}^3/\text{s}}{2\pi(30 \text{ ft})} = 7.96 \text{ ft}^2/\text{s}$$

Therefore from Fig. 8.5 the desired lengths a and L are

$$a = \frac{m}{U_\infty} = \frac{7.96 \text{ ft}^2/\text{s}}{0.7 \text{ ft/s}} = 11.4 \text{ ft} \qquad \qquad Ans. (a)$$

$$L = 2\pi a = 2\pi(11.4 \text{ ft}) = 71 \text{ ft} \qquad \qquad Ans. (b)$$

Flow Past a Vortex

Consider a uniform stream U_∞ in the x direction flowing past a vortex of strength K with center at the origin. By superposition the combined stream function is

$$\psi = \psi_{\text{stream}} + \psi_{\text{vortex}} = U_\infty r \sin \theta - K \ln r \qquad (8.19)$$

The velocity components are given by

$$v_r = \frac{1}{r}\frac{\partial \psi}{\partial \theta} = U_\infty \cos \theta \qquad v_\theta = -\frac{\partial \psi}{\partial r} = -U_\infty \sin \theta + \frac{K}{r} \qquad (8.20)$$

The streamlines are plotted in Fig. 8.6 by the graphical method, intersecting the circular streamlines of the vortex with the horizontal lines of the uniform stream.

By setting $v_r = v_\theta = 0$ from (8.20) we find a stagnation point at $\theta = 90°$, $r = a = K/U_\infty$, or $(x, y) = (0, a)$. This is where the counterclockwise vortex velocity K/r exactly cancels the stream velocity U_∞.

Probably the most interesting thing about this example is that there is a nonzero lift force normal to the stream on the surface of any region enclosing the vortex, but we postpone this discussion until the next section.

An Infinite Row of Vortices

Consider an infinite row of vortices of equal strength K and equal spacing a, as in Fig. 8.7a. This case is included here to illustrate the interesting concept of a *vortex sheet*.

From Eq. (8.12c), the ith vortex in Fig. 8.7a has a stream function $\psi_i = -K \ln r_i$, so that the total infinite row has a combined stream function

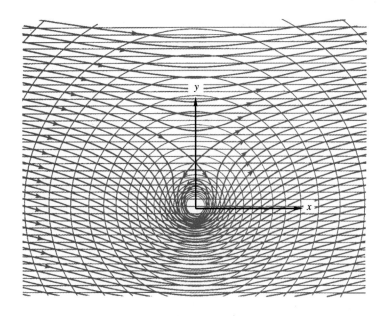

Fig. 8.6 Flow of a uniform stream past a vortex constructed by the graphical method.

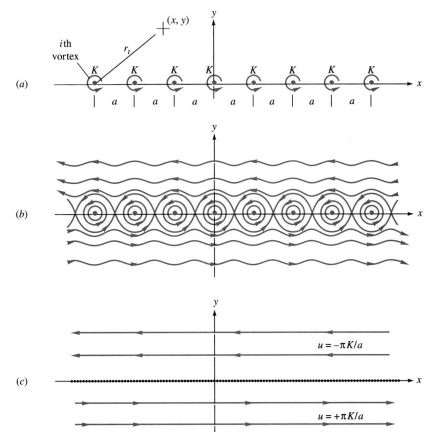

Fig. 8.7 Superposition of vortices: (*a*) an infinite row of equal strength; (*b*) streamline pattern for part (*a*); (*c*) vortex sheet: part (*b*) viewed from afar.

$$\psi = -K \sum_{i=1}^{\infty} \ln r_i \tag{8.21}$$

It can be shown [2, sec. 4.51] that this infinite sum of logarithms is equivalent to a closed-form function

$$\psi = -\tfrac{1}{2}K \ln \left[\frac{1}{2} \left(\cosh \frac{2\pi y}{a} - \cos \frac{2\pi x}{a} \right) \right] \tag{8.22}$$

Since the proof uses the complex variable $z = x + iy$, $i = (-1)^{1/2}$, we are not going to show the details here.

The streamlines from Eq. (8.22) are plotted in Fig. 8.7b, showing what is called a *cat's-eye* pattern of enclosed flow cells surrounding the individual vortices. Above the cat's eyes the flow is entirely to the left, and below the cat's eyes the flow is to the right. Moreover, these left and right flows are uniform if $|y| \gg a$, which follows by differentiating Eq. (8.22)

$$u = \frac{\partial \psi}{\partial y} \Big|_{|y| \gg a} = \pm \frac{\pi K}{a} \tag{8.23}$$

where the plus sign applies below the row and the minus sign above the row. This uniform left and right streaming is sketched in Fig. 8.7c. We stress that this effect is induced by the row of vortices: There is no uniform stream approaching the row in this example.

The Vortex Sheet

When Fig. 8.7b is viewed from afar, the streaming motion is uniform left above and uniform right below, as in Fig. 8.7c, and the vortices are packed so closely together that they are smudged into a continuous *vortex sheet*. The strength of the sheet is defined as

$$\gamma = \frac{2\pi K}{a} \tag{8.24}$$

and in the general case γ can vary with x. The circulation about any closed curve which encloses a short length dx of the sheet would be, from Eqs. (8.15) and (8.23),

$$d\Gamma = u_l\, dx - u_u\, dx = (u_l - u_u)\, dx = \frac{2\pi K}{a}\, dx = \gamma\, dx \tag{8.25}$$

where the subscripts l and u stand for lower and upper, respectively. Thus the sheet strength $\gamma = d\Gamma/dx$ is the circulation per unit length of the sheet. Thus when a vortex sheet is immersed in a uniform stream, γ is proportional to the lift per unit length of any surface enclosing the sheet.

Note that there is no velocity normal to the sheet at the sheet surface. Therefore a vortex sheet can simulate a thin-body shape, e.g., plate or thin airfoil. This is the basis of the thin-airfoil theory mentioned in Sec. 8.7.

The Doublet

As we move far away from the source-sink pair of Fig. 4.13, the flow pattern begins to resemble a family of circles tangent to the origin, as in Fig. 8.8. This limit of van-

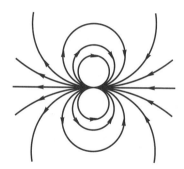

Fig. 8.8 A doublet, or source-sink pair, is the limiting case of Fig. 4.13 viewed from afar. Streamlines are circles tangent to the *x* axis at the origin.

ishingly small distance *a* is called a *doublet*. To keep the flow strength large enough to exhibit decent velocities as *a* becomes small, we specify that the product $2am$ remain constant. Let us call this constant λ. Then the stream function of a doublet is

$$\psi = \lim_{\substack{a \to 0 \\ 2am = \lambda}} \left(-m \tan^{-1} \frac{2ay}{x^2 + y^2 - a^2} \right) = -\frac{2amy}{x^2 + y^2} = -\frac{\lambda y}{x^2 + y^2} \qquad (8.26)$$

We have used the fact that $\tan^{-1} \alpha \approx \alpha$ as α becomes small. The quantity λ is called the *strength* of the doublet.

Equation (8.26) can be rearranged to yield

$$x^2 + \left(y + \frac{\lambda}{2\psi} \right)^2 = \left(\frac{\lambda}{2\psi} \right)^2$$

so that, as advertised, the streamlines are circles tangent to the origin with centers on the *y* axis. This pattern is sketched in Fig. 8.8.

In a similar manner the velocity potential of a doublet is found by taking the limit of Eq. (4.133) as $a \to 0$ and $2am = \lambda$

$$\phi_{\text{doublet}} = \frac{\lambda x}{x^2 + y^2}$$

or

$$\left(x - \frac{\lambda}{2\phi} \right)^2 + y^2 = \left(\frac{\lambda}{2\phi} \right)^2 \qquad (8.27)$$

The potential lines are circles tangent to the origin with centers on the *x* axis. Simply turn Fig. 8.8 clockwise 90° to visualize the ϕ lines, which are everywhere normal to the streamlines.

The doublet functions can also be written in polar coordinates

$$\psi = -\frac{\lambda \sin \theta}{r} \qquad \phi = \frac{\lambda \cos \theta}{r} \qquad (8.28)$$

These forms are convenient for the cylinder flows of the next section.

8.4 Plane Flow Past Closed-Body Shapes

A variety of closed-body external flows can be constructed by superimposing a uniform stream with sources, sinks, and vortices. The body shape will be closed only if the net source outflow equals the net sink inflow.

The Rankine Oval

A cylindrical shape called a *Rankine oval*, which is long compared with its height, is formed by a source-sink pair aligned parallel to a uniform stream, as in Fig. 8.9a.

From Eqs. (8.12a) and (4.133) the combined stream function is

$$\psi = U_\infty y - m \tan^{-1} \frac{2ay}{x^2 + y^2 - a^2} = U_\infty r \sin \theta + m(\theta_1 - \theta_2) \qquad (8.29)$$

When streamlines of constant ψ are plotted from Eq. (8.29), an oval body shape appears, as in Fig. (8.9b). The half-length *L* and half-height *h* of the oval depend upon the relative strength of source and stream, i.e., the ratio $m/(U_\infty a)$, which equals 1.0 in Fig. 8.9b.

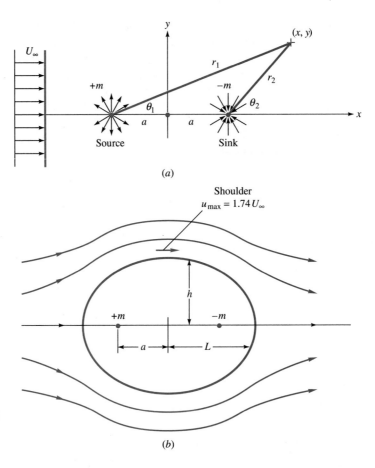

Fig. 8.9 Flow past a Rankine oval: (*a*) uniform stream plus a source-sink pair; (*b*) oval shape and streamlines for $m/(U_\infty a) = 1.0$.

The circulating streamlines inside the oval are uninteresting and not usually shown. The oval is the line $\psi = 0$.

There are stagnation points at the front and rear, $x = \pm L$, and points of maximum velocity and minimum pressure at the shoulders, $y = \pm h$, of the oval. All these parameters are a function of the basic dimensionless parameter $m/(U_\infty a)$, which we can determine from Eq. (8.29):

$$\frac{h}{a} = \cot \frac{h/a}{2m/(U_\infty a)} \qquad \frac{L}{a} = \left(1 + \frac{2m}{U_\infty a}\right)^{1/2}$$

$$\frac{u_{max}}{U_\infty} = 1 + \frac{2m/(U_\infty a)}{1 + h^2/a^2}$$

(8.30)

As we increase $m/(U_\infty a)$ from zero to large values, the oval shape increases in size and thickness from a flat plate of length $2a$ to a huge, nearly circular cylinder. This is shown in Table 8.1. In the limit as $m/(U_\infty a) \to \infty$, $L/h \to 1.0$ and $u_{max}/U_\infty \to 2.0$, which is equivalent to flow past a circular cylinder.

All the Rankine ovals except very thin ones have a large adverse pressure gradient on their leeward surface. Thus boundary-layer separation will occur in the rear with a broad wake flow, and the inviscid pattern is unrealistic in that region.

Flow Past a Circular Cylinder with Circulation

From Table 8.1 at large source strength the Rankine oval becomes a large circle, much greater in diameter than the source-sink spacing $2a$. Viewed on the scale of the cylinder, this is equivalent to a uniform stream plus a doublet. We also throw in a vortex at the doublet center, which does not change the shape of the cylinder.

Thus the stream function for flow past a circular cylinder with circulation, centered at the origin, is a uniform stream plus a doublet plus a vortex

$$\psi = U_\infty r \sin \theta - \frac{\lambda \sin \theta}{r} - K \ln r + \text{const} \tag{8.31}$$

The doublet strength λ has units of velocity times length squared. For convenience, let $\lambda = U_\infty a^2$, where a is a length, and let the arbitrary constant in Eq. (8.31) equal $K \ln a$. Then the stream function becomes

$$\psi = U_\infty \sin \theta \left(r - \frac{a^2}{r} \right) - K \ln \frac{r}{a} \tag{8.32}$$

The streamlines are plotted in Fig. 8.10 for four different values of the dimensionless

Table 8.1 Rankine-Oval Parameters from Eq. (8.30)

$m/(U_\infty a)$	h/a	L/a	L/h	u_{max}/U_∞
0.0	0.0	1.0	∞	1.0
0.01	0.031	1.010	32.79	1.020
0.1	0.263	1.095	4.169	1.187
1.0	1.307	1.732	1.326	1.739
10.0	4.435	4.583	1.033	1.968
100.0	14.130	14.177	1.003	1.997
∞	∞	∞	1.000	2.000

Fig. 8.10 Flow past a circular cylinder with circulation for values of $K/(U_\infty a)$ of (a) 0, (b) 1.0, (c) 2.0, and (d) 3.0.

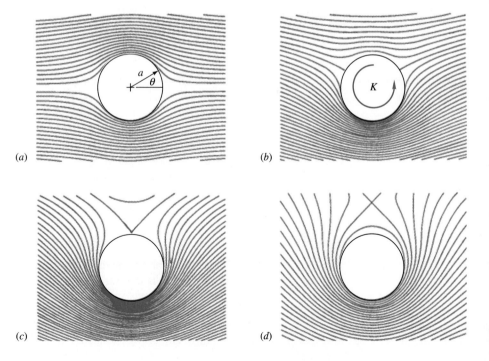

vortex strength $K/(U_\infty a)$. For all cases the line $\psi = 0$ corresponds to the circle $r = a$, that is, the shape of the cylindrical body. As circulation $\Gamma = 2\pi K$ increases, the velocity becomes faster and faster below the cylinder and slower and slower above it. The velocity components in the flow are given by

$$v_r = \frac{1}{r}\frac{\partial \psi}{\partial \theta} = U_\infty \cos \theta \left(1 - \frac{a^2}{r^2}\right)$$

$$v_\theta = -\frac{\partial \psi}{\partial r} = -U_\infty \sin \theta \left(1 + \frac{a^2}{r^2}\right) + \frac{K}{r}$$

(8.33)

The velocity at the cylinder surface $r = a$ is purely tangential, as expected

$$v_r(r = a) = 0 \qquad v_\theta(r = a) = -2U_\infty \sin \theta + \frac{K}{a}$$

(8.34)

For small K, two stagnation points appear on the surface at angles θ_s where $v_\theta = 0$, or, from Eq. (8.34),

$$\sin \theta_s = \frac{K}{2U_\infty a}$$

(8.35)

Figure 8.10a is for $K = 0$, $\theta_s = 0$ and 180°, or doubly symmetric inviscid flow past a cylinder with no circulation. Figure 8.10b is for $K/(U_\infty a) = 1$, $\theta_s = 30$ and 150°, and Fig. 8.10c is the limiting case where the two stagnation points meet at the top, $K/(U_\infty a) = 2$, $\theta_s = 90°$.

For $K > 2U_\infty a$, Eq. (8.35) is invalid, and the single stagnation point is above the cylinder, as in Fig. 8.10d, at a point $y = h$ given by

$$\frac{h}{a} = \frac{1}{2}[\beta + (\beta^2 - 4)^{1/2}] \qquad \beta = \frac{K}{U_\infty a} > 2$$

(8.36)

In Fig. 8.10d, $K/(U_\infty a) = 3.0$, and $h/a = 2.6$.

The Kutta-Joukowski Lift Theorem

For the cylinder flows of Fig. 8.10b to d there is a downward force, or negative lift, called the *Magnus effect*, which is proportional to stream velocity and vortex strength. We can see from the streamline pattern that the velocity on the top of the cylinder is less and therefore the pressure higher from Bernoulli's equation; this explains the force. There is no viscous force, of course, because our theory is inviscid.

The surface velocity is given by Eq. (8.34). From Bernoulli's equation (8.4), neglecting gravity, the surface pressure p_s is given by

$$p_\infty + \frac{1}{2}\rho U_\infty^2 = p_s + \frac{1}{2}\rho\left(-2U_\infty \sin \theta + \frac{K}{a}\right)^2$$

or

$$p_s = p_\infty = \tfrac{1}{2}\rho U_\infty^2(1 - 4\sin^2 \theta + 4\beta \sin \theta - \beta^2)$$

(8.37)

where $\beta = K/(U_\infty a)$ and p_∞ is the free-stream pressure. If b is the cylinder depth into the paper, the drag D is the integral over the surface of the horizontal component of pressure force

$$D = -\int_0^{2\pi} (p_s - p_\infty) \cos \theta \, ba \, d\theta$$

where $p_s - p_\infty$ is substituted from Eq. (8.37). But the integral of $\cos \theta$ times any power of $\sin \theta$ over a full cycle 2π is identically zero. Thus we obtain the (perhaps surprising) result

$$D(\text{cylinder with circulation}) = 0 \qquad (8.38)$$

This is a special case of d'Alembert's paradox, mentioned in Sec. 1.10:

> According to inviscid theory, the drag of any body of any shape immersed in a uniform stream is identically zero.

D'Alembert published this result in 1752 and pointed out himself that it did not square with the facts for real fluid flows. This unfortunate paradox caused everyone to overreact and reject all inviscid theory until 1904, when Prandtl first pointed out the profound effect of the thin viscous boundary layer on the flow pattern in the rear, as in Fig. 7.2b, for example.

The lift force L normal to the stream, taken positive upward, is given by summation of vertical pressure forces

$$L = -\int_0^{2\pi} (p_s - p_\infty) \sin \theta \, ba \, d\theta$$

Since the integral over 2π of any odd power of $\sin \theta$ is zero, only the third term in the parentheses in Eq. (8.37) contributes to the lift:

$$L = -\frac{1}{2} \rho U_\infty^2 \frac{4K}{aU_\infty} ba \int_0^{2\pi} \sin^2 \theta \, d\theta = -\rho U_\infty (2\pi K) b$$

or

$$\frac{L}{b} = -\rho U_\infty \Gamma \qquad (8.39)$$

Notice that the lift is independent of the radius a of the cylinder. Actually, though, as we shall see in Sec. 8.7, the circulation Γ depends upon the body size and orientation through a physical requirement.

Equation (8.39) was generalized by W. M. Kutta in 1902 and independently by N. Joukowski in 1906 as follows:

> According to inviscid theory, the lift per unit depth of any cylinder of any shape immersed in a uniform stream equals $\rho u_\infty \Gamma$, where Γ is the total net circulation contained within the body shape. The direction of the lift is 90° from the stream direction, rotating opposite to the circulation.

The problem in airfoil analysis, Sec. 8.7, is thus to determine the circulation Γ as a function of airfoil shape and orientation.

Experimental Lift and Drag of Rotating Cylinders

It is nearly impossible to test Fig. 8.10 by constructing a doublet and vortex with the same center and then letting a stream flow past them. But one physical realization would be a rotating cylinder in a stream. The viscous no-slip condition would cause the fluid in contact with the cylinder to move tangentially at the cylinder peripheral speed $v_\theta = a\omega$. A net circulation Γ would be set up by this no-slip mechanism, but it turns out to be less than 50 percent of the value expected from inviscid theory, primarily because of flow separation behind the cylinder.

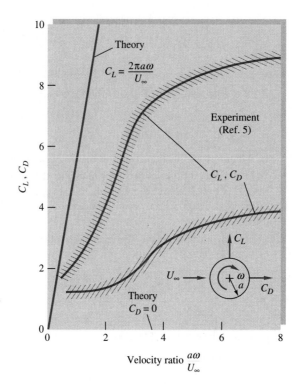

Fig. 8.11 Theoretical and experimental lift and drag of a rotating cylinder. (*From Ref. 22.*)

Figure 8.11 shows experimental lift and drag coefficients, based on planform area $2ba$, of rotating cylinders. From Eq. (8.38) the theoretical drag is zero, but the actual C_D is quite large, more even than the stationary cylinder of Fig. 5.3. The theoretical lift follows from Eq. (8.39)

$$C_L = \frac{L}{\frac{1}{2}\rho U_\infty^2(2ba)} = \frac{2\pi\rho U_\infty Kb}{\rho U_\infty^2 ba} = \frac{2\pi v_{\theta s}}{U_\infty} \tag{8.40}$$

where $v_{\theta s} = K/a$ is the peripheral speed of the cylinder.

Figure 8.11 shows that the theoretical lift from Eq. (8.40) is much too high, but the measured lift is quite respectable, much larger in fact than a typical airfoil of the same chord length, e.g., Fig. 7.24. Thus rotating cylinders have practical possibilities. The Flettner rotor ship built in Germany in 1924 employed rotating vertical cylinders which developed a thrust due to any winds blowing past the ship. The Flettner design did not gain any popularity, but such inventions may be more attractive in this era of high energy costs.

EXAMPLE 8.2

The experimental Flettner rotor sailboat at the University of Rhode Island is shown in Fig. E8.2. The rotor is 2.5 ft in diameter and 10 ft long and rotates at 220 r/min. It is driven by a small lawnmower engine. If the wind is a steady 10 kn and boat relative motion is neglected, what is the maximum thrust expected for the rotor? Assume standard air and water density.

Fig. E8.2

Solution

Convert the rotation rate to $\omega = 2\pi(220)/60 = 23.04$ rad/s. The wind velocity is 10 kn = 16.88 ft/s, so the velocity ratio is

$$\frac{a\omega}{U_\infty} = \frac{(1.25 \text{ ft})(23.04 \text{ rad/s})}{16.88 \text{ ft/s}} = 1.71$$

Entering Fig. 8.11, we read $C_L \approx 3.3$ and $C_D \approx 1.2$. From Table A.6, standard air density is 0.002377 slug/ft^3. Then the estimated rotor lift and drag are

$$L = C_L \tfrac{1}{2}\rho U_\infty^2 2ba = 3.3(\tfrac{1}{2})(0.002377)(16.88)^2(2)(10)(1.25)$$

$$= 27.9 \text{ lbf}$$

$$D = C_D \tfrac{1}{2}\rho U_\infty^2 2ba = L \frac{C_D}{C_L} = 27.9 \left(\frac{1.2}{3.3}\right) = 10.2 \text{ lbf}$$

The maximum thrust available is the resultant of these two

$$F = [(27.9)^2 + (10.2)^2]^{1/2} = 29 \text{ lbf} \qquad \qquad Ans.$$

If aligned along the boat's keel, this thrust will drive the boat at a speed of about 5 kn through the water.

The Kelvin Oval

A family of body shapes taller than they are wide can be formed by letting a uniform stream flow normal to a vortex pair. If U_∞ is to the right, the negative vortex $-K$ is placed at $y = +a$ and the counterclockwise vortex $+K$ placed at $y = -a$, as in Fig. 8.12. The combined stream function is

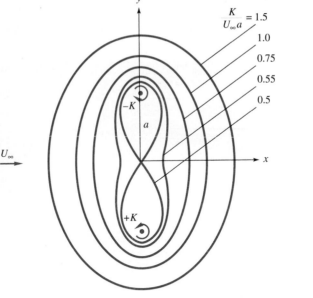

Fig. 8.12 Kelvin-oval body shapes as a function of the vortex-strength parameter $K/(U_\infty a)$; outer streamlines not shown.

$$\psi = U_\infty y - \frac{1}{2} K \ln \frac{x^2 + (y + a)^2}{x^2 + (y - a)^2} \tag{8.41}$$

The body shape is the line $\psi = 0$, and some of these shapes are shown in Fig. 8.12. For $K/(U_\infty a) > 10$ the shape is within 1 percent of a Rankine oval (Fig. 8.9) turned 90°, but for small $K/(U_\infty a)$ the waist becomes pinched in, and a figure-eight shape occurs at 0.5. For $K/(U_\infty a) < 0.5$ the stream blasts right between the vortices and isolates two more or less circular body shapes, one surrounding each vortex.

A closed body of practically any shape can be constructed by proper superposition of sources, sinks, and vortices. See the advanced work in Refs. 2 to 4 for further details.

A summary of elementary potential flows is given in Table 8.2.

Potential-Flow Analogs

For complicated potential-flow geometries, one can resort to other methods than superposition of sources, sinks, and vortices. There are a variety of devices which simulate solutions to Laplace's equation.

Table 8.2 Summary of Plane Incompressible Potential Flows

Type of Flow	Potential Functions		Remarks
Stream iU	$\psi = Uy$	$\phi = Ux$	See Fig. 4.12a
Line source ($m > 0$) or sink ($m < 0$)	$\psi = m\theta$	$\phi = m \ln r$	See Fig. 4.12b
Line vortex	$\psi = -K \ln r$	$\phi = K\theta$	See Fig. 4.12c
Half-body	$\psi = Ur \sin \theta + m\theta$ $\phi = Ur \cos \theta + m \ln r$		See Fig. 8.5
Doublet	$\psi = \dfrac{-\lambda \sin \theta}{r}$	$\phi = \dfrac{\lambda \cos \theta}{r}$	See Fig. 8.8
Rankine oval	$\psi = Ur \sin \theta + m(\theta_1 - \theta_2)$		See Fig. 8.9
Cylinder with circulation	$\psi = U \sin \theta \left(r - \dfrac{a^2}{r} \right) - K \ln \dfrac{r}{a}$		See Fig. 8.10

From 1897 to 1899 Hele-Shaw [9] developed a technique whereby laminar viscous flow between very closely spaced parallel plates simulated potential flow when viewed from above the plates. When obstructions are placed between the plates, the streamlines as visualized by dye streaks are identical to potential flow past the obstruction. Figure 8.13 illustrates Hele-Shaw flow past an array of cylinders. This pattern might be used to approximate the flow through rod banks in a heat exchanger. The Hele-Shaw apparatus makes an excellent laboratory demonstration of potential flow [10, pp. 8–10].

Other flow-mapping techniques are discussed in Ref. 8. Electromagnetic fields also satisfy Laplace's equation, with voltage analogous to velocity potential and current lines analogous to streamlines. At one time commercial analog field plotters were available, using thin conducting paper cut to the shape of the flow geometry. Potential lines (voltage contours) were plotted by probing the paper with a potentiometer pointer. Hand-sketching "curvilinear square" techniques were also popular. The availability and the simplicity of digital-computer potential-flow methods [5 to 7] have made analog models obsolete.

EXAMPLE 8.3

A Kelvin oval from Fig. 8.12 has $K/(U_\infty a) = 1.0$. Compute the velocity at the top shoulder of the oval in terms of U_∞.

Solution

We must locate the shoulder $y = h$ from Eq. (8.41) for $\psi = 0$ and then compute the velocity by differentiation. At $\psi = 0$ and $y = h$ and $x = 0$, Eq. (8.41) becomes

$$\frac{h}{a} = \frac{K}{U_\infty a} \ln \frac{h/a + 1}{h/a - 1}$$

With $K/(U_\infty a) = 1.0$ and the initial guess $h/a \approx 1.5$ from Fig. 8.12, we iterate and find the location $h/a = 1.5434$.

Fig. 8.13 Potential flow past an array of circular cylinders constrained between plane walls, visualized by the Hele-Shaw method. (*Tecquipment Ltd., Nottingham, England.*)

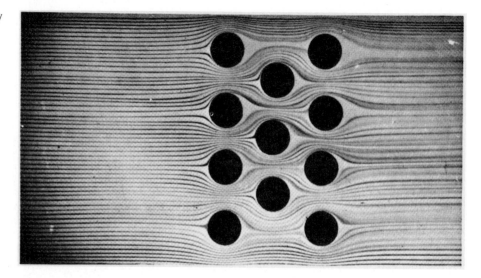

By inspection $v = 0$ at the shoulder because the streamline is horizontal. Therefore the shoulder velocity is, from Eq. (8.41),

$$u\bigg|_{y=h} = \frac{\partial \psi}{\partial y}\bigg|_{y=h} = U_\infty + \frac{K}{h-a} - \frac{K}{h+a}$$

Introducing $K = U_\infty a$ and $h = 1.5434a$, we obtain

$$u_{\text{shoulder}} = U_\infty(1.0 + 1.84 - 0.39) = 2.45U_\infty \qquad \textit{Ans.}$$

Because they are short-waisted compared with a circular cylinder, all the Kelvin ovals have shoulder velocity greater than the cylinder result $2.0U_\infty$ from Eq. (8.34).

8.5 Other Plane Potential Flows[1]

References 2 to 4 treat many other potential flows of interest in addition to the cases presented in Secs. 8.3 and 8.4. In principle, any plane potential flow can be solved by the method of *conformal mapping*, by using the complex variable

$$z = x + iy \qquad i = (-1)^{1/2}$$

It turns out that any arbitrary analytic function of this complex variable z has the remarkable property that both its real and its imaginary parts are solutions of Laplace's equation. If

$$f(z) = f(x + iy) = f_1(x, y) + if_2(x, y)$$

then
$$\frac{\partial^2 f_1}{\partial x^2} + \frac{\partial^2 f_1}{\partial y^2} = 0 = \frac{\partial^2 f_2}{\partial x^2} + \frac{\partial^2 f_2}{\partial y^2} \qquad (8.42)$$

We shall assign the proof of this as a problem. Even more remarkable if you have never seen it before is that lines of constant f_1 will be everywhere perpendicular to lines of constant f_2:

$$\left(\frac{dy}{dx}\right)_{f_1 = C} = -\frac{1}{(dy/dx)_{f_2 = C}} \qquad (8.43)$$

We also leave this proof as a problem exercise. This is true for totally arbitrary $f(z)$ as long as this function is analytic; i.e., it must have a unique derivative df/dz at every point in the region.

The net result of Eqs. (8.42) and (8.43) is that the functions f_1 and f_2 can be interpreted to be the potential lines and streamlines of an inviscid flow. By long custom we let the real part of $f(z)$ be the velocity potential and the imaginary part be the stream function

$$f(z) = \phi(x, y) + i\psi(x, y) \qquad (8.44)$$

We try various functions $f(z)$ and see whether any interesting flow pattern results. Of course, most of them have already been found, and we simply report on them here.

We shall not go into the details, but there are excellent treatments of this complex-variable technique on both an introductory [4, chap. 5; 10, chap. 5] and a more advanced [2, 3,] level. The method is less important now because of the popularity of digital-computer techniques.

---

[1] This section may be omitted without loss of continuity.

As a simple example, consider the linear function

$$f(z) = U_\infty z = U_\infty x + iU_\infty y$$

It follows from Eq. (8.44) that $\phi = U_\infty x$ and $\psi = U_\infty y$, which, we recall from Eq. (8.12a), represents a uniform stream in the x direction. Once you get used to the complex variable, the solution practically falls in your lap.

To find the velocities, you may either separate ϕ and ψ from $f(z)$ and differentiate or differentiate f directly

$$\frac{df}{dz} = \frac{\partial \phi}{\partial x} + i \frac{\partial \psi}{\partial x} = -i \frac{\partial \phi}{\partial y} + \frac{\partial \psi}{\partial y} = u - iv \tag{8.45}$$

Thus the real part of df/dz equals $u(x, y)$, and the imaginary part equals $-v(x, y)$. To get a practical result, the derivative df/dz must exist and be unique, hence the requirement that f be an analytic function. For Eq. (8.45), $df/dz = U_\infty = u$, since it is real, and $v = 0$, as expected.

Sometimes it is convenient to use the polar-coordinate form of the complex variable

$$z = x + iy = re^{i\theta} = r \cos \theta + ir \sin \theta$$

where

$$r = (x^2 + y^2)^{1/2} \qquad \theta = \tan^{-1} \frac{y}{x}$$

This form is especially convenient when powers of z occur.

Uniform Stream at an Angle of Attack

All the elementary plane flows of Sec. 8.2 have a complex-variable formulation. The uniform stream U_∞ at an angle of attack α has the complex potential

$$f(z) = U_\infty z e^{-i\alpha} \tag{8.46}$$

Compare this form with Eq. (8.14).

Line Source at a Point z_0

Consider a line source of strength m placed off the origin at a point $z_0 = x_0 + iy_0$. Its complex potential is

$$f(z) = m \ln (z - z_0) \tag{8.47}$$

This can be compared with Eq. (8.12b), which is valid only for the source at the origin. For a line sink, the strength m is negative.

Line Vortex at a Point z_0

If a line vortex of strength K is placed at point z_0, its complex potential is

$$f(z) = -iK \ln (z - z_0) \tag{8.48}$$

to be compared with Eq. (8.12c). Also compare to Eq. (8.47) to see that we reverse the meaning of ϕ and ψ simply by multiplying the complex potential by $-i$.

Flow around a Corner of Arbitrary Angle

Corner flow is an example of a pattern that cannot be conveniently produced by superimposing sources, sinks, and vortices. It has a strikingly simple complex representation

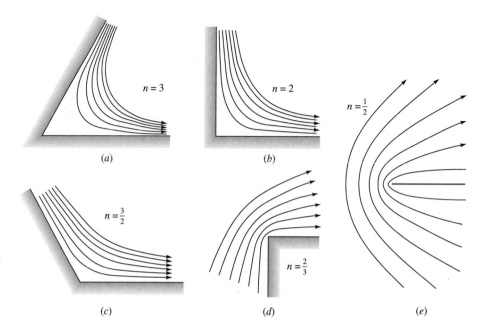

Fig. 8.14 Streamlines for corner flow, Eq. (8.49) for corner angle β of (*a*) 60°, (*b*) 90°, (*c*) 120°, (*d*) 270°, and (*e*) 360°.

$$f(z) = Az^n = Ar^n e^{in\theta} = Ar^n \cos n\theta + iAr^n \sin n\theta$$

where A and n are constants.

It follows from Eq. (8.44) that for this pattern

$$\phi = Ar^n \cos n\theta \qquad \psi = Ar^n \sin n\theta \qquad (8.49)$$

Streamlines from Eq. (8.49) are plotted in Fig. 8.14 for five different values of n. The flow is seen to represent a stream turning through an angle $\beta = \pi/n$. Patterns in Fig. 8.14*d* and *e* are not realistic on the downstream side of the corner, where separation will occur doe to the adverse pressure gradient and sudden change of direction. In general, separation always occurs downstream of salient, or protruding corners, except in creeping flows at low Reynolds number Re < 1.

Since $360° = 2\pi$ is the largest possible corner, the patterns for $n < \frac{1}{2}$ do not represent corner flow. They are peculiar-looking, and we ask you to plot one as a problem.

If we expand the plot of Fig. 8.14*a* to *c* to double size, we can represent stagnation flow toward a corner of angle $2\beta = 2\pi/n$. This is done in Fig. 8.15 for $n = 3, 2$, and 1.5. These are very realistic flows; although they slip at the wall, they can be patched to boundary-layer theories very successfully. We took a brief look at corner flows before, in Examples 4.5 and 4.9 and in Probs. 4.49 to 4.51.

Flow Normal to a Flat Plate

We treat this case separately because the Kelvin ovals of Fig. 8.12 failed to degenerate into a flat plate as K became small. The flat plate normal to a uniform stream is an extreme case worthy of our attention.

Although the result is quite simple, the derivation is very complicated and is given, e.g., in Ref. 2, sec. 9.3. There are three changes of complex variable, or *mappings*,

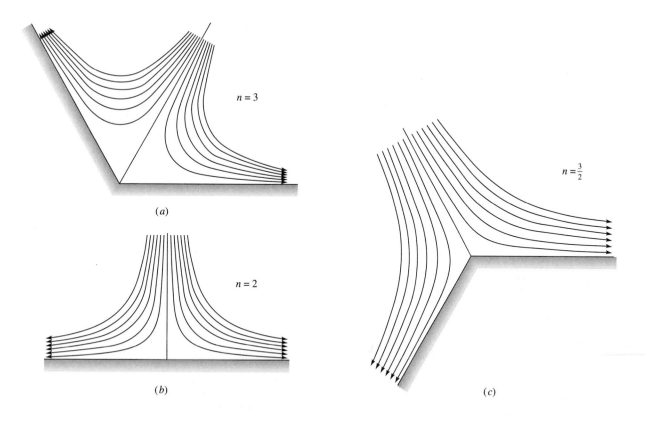

Fig. 8.15 Streamlines for stagnation flow from Eq. (8.49) for corner angle 2β of (a) 120°, (b) 180°, and (c) 240°.

beginning with the basic cylinder-flow solution of Fig. 8.10a. First the uniform stream is rotated to be vertical upward, then the cylinder is squeezed down into a plate shape, and finally the free stream is rotated back to the horizontal. The final result for complex potential is

$$f(z) = \phi + i\psi = U_\infty (z^2 + a^2)^{1/2} \tag{8.50}$$

where $2a$ is the height of the plate. To isolate ϕ or ψ, square both sides and separate real and imaginary parts

$$\phi^2 - \psi^2 = U_\infty^2 (x^2 - y^2 + a^2) \qquad \phi\psi = U_\infty^2 xy$$

We can solve for ψ to determine the streamlines

$$\psi^4 + \psi^2 U_\infty^2 (x^2 - y^2 + a^2) = U_\infty^4 x^2 y^2 \tag{8.51}$$

Equation (8.51) is plotted in Fig. 8.16a, revealing a doubly symmetric pattern of streamlines which approach very closely to the plate and then deflect up and over, with very high velocities and low pressures near the plate tips.

The velocity v_s along the plate surface is found by computing df/dz from Eq. (8.50) and isolating the imaginary part

$$\left.\frac{v_s}{U_\infty}\right|_{\text{plate surface}} = \frac{y/a}{(1 - y^2/a^2)^{1/2}} \tag{8.52}$$

Some values of surface velocity can be tabulated as follows:

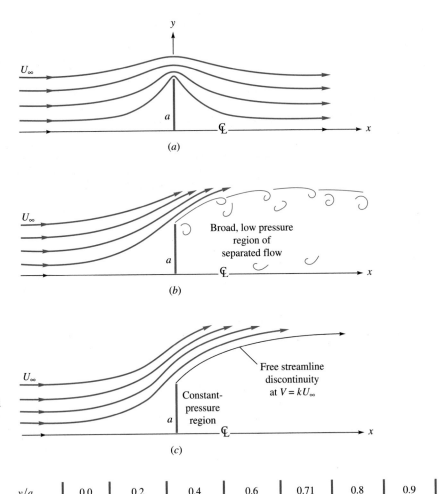

Fig. 8.16 Streamlines in upper half-plane for flow normal to a flat plate of height $2a$: (a) continuous potential-flow theory, Eq. (8.51); (b) actual measured flow pattern; (c) discontinuous potential theory with $k \approx 1.5$.

y/a	0.0	0.2	0.4	0.6	0.71	0.8	0.9	1.0
v_s/U_∞	0.0	0.204	0.436	0.750	1.00	1.33	2.07	∞

The origin is a stagnation point; then the velocity grows linearly at first and very rapidly near the tip, with both velocity and acceleration being infinite at the tip.

As you might guess, Fig. 8.16a is not realistic. In a real flow the sharp salient edge causes separation, and a broad, low-pressure wake forms in the lee, as in Fig. 8.16b. Instead of being zero, the drag coefficient is very large, $C_D \approx 2.0$ from Table 7.2.

A discontinuous-potential-flow theory which accounts for flow separation was devised by Helmholtz in 1868 and Kirchhoff in 1869. This free-streamline solution is shown in Fig. 8.16c, with the streamline which breaks away from the tip having a constant velocity $V = kU_\infty$. From Bernoulli's equation the pressure in the dead-water region behind the plate will equal $p_r = p_\infty + \frac{1}{2}\rho U_\infty^2(1 - k^2)$ to match the pressure along the free streamline. For $k = 1.5$ this Helmholtz-Kirchoff theory predicts $p_r = p_\infty - 0.625\rho U_\infty^2$ and an average pressure on the front $p_f = p_\infty + 0.375\rho U_\infty^2$, giving an overall drag coefficient of 2.0, in agreement with experiment. However, the coefficient k is a priori unknown and must be tuned to experimental data, so free-streamline theory can be considered only a qualified success. For further details see Ref. 2, sec. 11.2.

8.6 Images[1]

The previous solutions have all been for unbounded flows, such as a circular cylinder immersed in a broad expanse of uniformly streaming fluid, Fig. 8.10*a*. However, many practical problems involve a nearby rigid boundary constraining the flow, e.g., (1) groundwater flow near the bottom of a dam, (2) an airfoil near the ground, simulating landing or takeoff, or (3) a cylinder mounted in a wind tunnel with narrow walls. In such cases the basic unbounded-potential-flow solutions can be modified for wall effects by the method of *images*.

Consider a line source placed a distance *a* from a wall, as in Fig. 8.17*a*. To create the desired wall, an image source of identical strength is placed the same distance below the wall. By symmetry the two sources create a plane-surface streamline between them, which is taken to be the wall.

[1] This section may be omitted without loss of continuity.

Fig. 8.17 Constraining walls can be created by image flows: (*a*) source near a wall with identical image source; (*b*) vortex near a wall with image vortex of opposite sense; (*c*) airfoil in ground effect with image airfoil of opposite circulation; (*d*) source between two walls requiring an infinite row of images.

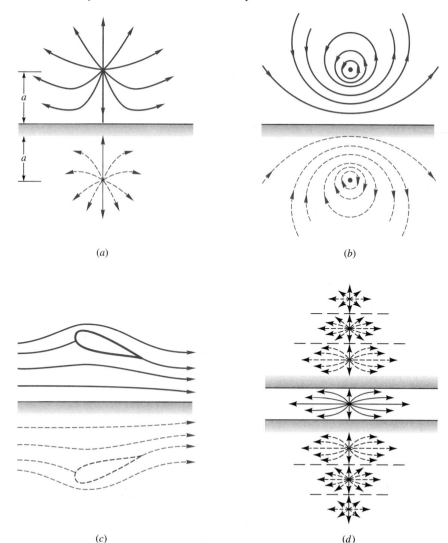

(*a*)

(*b*)

(*c*)

(*d*)

In Fig. 8.17b a vortex near a wall requires an image vortex the same distance below but of *opposite* rotation. We have shaded in the wall, but of course the pattern could also be interpreted as the flow near a vortex pair in an unbounded fluid.

In Fig. 8.17c an airfoil in a uniform stream near the ground is created by an image airfoil below the ground of opposite circulation and lift. This looks easy, but actually it is not because the airfoils are so close together that they interact and distort each other's shapes. A rule of thumb is that nonnegligible shape distortion occurs if the body shape is within two chord lengths of the wall. To eliminate distortion, a whole series of "corrective" images must be added to the flow to recapture the shape of the original isolated airfoil. Reference 2, sec. 7.75, has a good discussion of this procedure, which usually requires digital-computer summation of the multiple images needed.

Figure 8.17d shows a source constrained between two walls. One wall required only one image in Fig. 8.17a, but *two* walls require an infinite array of image sources above and below the desired pattern, as shown. Usually computer summation is necessary, but sometimes a closed-form summation can be achieved, as in the infinite vortex row of Eq. (8.22).

EXAMPLE 8.4

For the source near a wall as in Fig. 8.17a, the wall velocity is zero between the sources, rises to a maximum moving out along the wall, and then drops to zero far from the sources. If the source strength is 8 m²/s, how far from the wall should the source be to ensure that the maximum velocity along the wall will be 5 m/s?

Solution

At any point x along the wall, as in Fig. E8.4, each source induces a radial outward velocity $v_r = m/r$, which has a component $v_r \cos \theta$ along the wall. The total wall velocity is thus

$$u_{\text{wall}} = 2v_r \cos \theta$$

From the geometry of Fig. E8.4, $r = (x^2 + a^2)^{1/2}$ and $\cos \theta = x/r$. Then the total wall velocity can be expressed as

$$u = \frac{2mx}{x^2 + a^2}$$

This is zero at $x = 0$ and at $x \to \infty$. To find the maximum velocity, differentiate and set equal to zero

Fig. E8.4

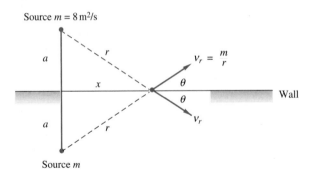

Source $m = 8\,\text{m}^2/\text{s}$

$v_r = \dfrac{m}{r}$

Wall

Source m

$$\frac{du}{dx} = 0 \quad \text{at} \quad x = a \quad \text{and} \quad u_{\max} = \frac{m}{a}$$

We have omitted a bit of algebra in giving these results. For the given source strength and maximum velocity, the proper distance a is

$$a = \frac{m}{u_{\max}} = \frac{8 \text{ m}^2/\text{s}}{5 \text{ m/s}} = 1.625 \text{ m} \qquad\qquad Ans.$$

For $x > a$, there is an adverse pressure gradient along the wall, and boundary-layer theory should be used to predict separation.

8.7 Airfoil Theory[1]

As mentioned in conjunction with the Kutta-Joukowski lift theorem, Eq. (8.39), the problem in airfoil theory is to determine the net circulation Γ as a function of airfoil shape and free-stream angle of attack α.

The Kutta Condition

Even if the airfoil shape and free-stream angle of attack are specified, the potential-flow-theory solution is nonunique: An infinite family of solutions can be found corresponding to different values of circulation Γ. Four examples of this nonuniqueness were shown for the cylinder flows in Fig. 8.10. The same is true of the airfoil, and Fig. 8.18

[1] This section may be omitted without loss of continuity.

Fig. 8.18 The Kutta condition properly simulates the flow about an airfoil; (a) too little circulation, stagnation point on rear upper surface; (b) too much, stagnation point on rear lower surface; (c) just right, Kutta condition requires smooth flow at trailing edge.

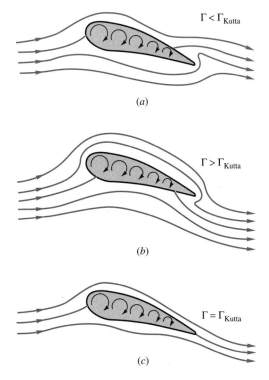

(a) $\quad \Gamma < \Gamma_{\text{Kutta}}$

(b) $\quad \Gamma > \Gamma_{\text{Kutta}}$

(c) $\quad \Gamma = \Gamma_{\text{Kutta}}$

shows three mathematically acceptable "solutions" to a given airfoil flow for small (Fig. 8.18a), large (Fig. 8.18b), and medium (Fig. 8.18c) net circulation. You can guess which case best simulates a real airfoil from the earlier discussion of transient-lift development in Fig. 7.22. It is the case (Fig. 8.18c) where the upper and lower flows meet and leave the trailing edge smoothly. If the trailing edge is rounded slightly, there will be a stagnation point there. If the trailing edge is sharp, approximating most airfoil designs, the upper- and lower-surface flow velocities will be equal as they meet and leave the airfoil.

This statement of the physically proper value of Γ is generally attributed to W. M. Kutta, hence the name *Kutta condition*, although some texts give credit to Joukowski and/or Chaplygin. All airfoil theories use the Kutta condition, which is in good agreement with experiment. It turns out that the correct circulation Γ_{Kutta} depends upon flow velocity, angle of attack, and airfoil shape.

Flat-Plate Airfoil Vortex-Sheet Theory

The flat plate is the simplest airfoil, having no thickness or "shape," but even its theory is not so simple. The problem can be solved by a complex-variable mapping [2, p. 480], but here we shall use a vortex-sheet approach. Figure 8.19a shows a flat plate of length C simulated by a vortex sheet of variable strength $\gamma(x)$. The free stream U_∞ is at an angle of attack α with respect to the plate chord line.

To make the lift "up" with flow from left to right as shown, we specify here that the circulation is positive clockwise. Recall from Fig. 8.7c that there is a jump in tangential velocity across a sheet equal to the local strength

$$u_u - u_l = \gamma(x) \tag{8.53}$$

If we omit the free stream, the sheet should cause a rightward flow $\delta u = +\frac{1}{2}\gamma$ on the upper surface and an equal and opposite leftward flow on the lower surface, as shown in Fig. 8.19a. The Kutta condition for this sharp trailing edge requires that this velocity difference vanish at the trailing edge to keep the exit flow smooth and parallel

$$\gamma(C) = 0 \tag{8.54}$$

The proper solution must satisfy this condition, after which the total lift can be computed by summing the sheet strength over the whole airfoil. From Eq. (8.39) for a foil of depth b

$$L = \rho U_\infty b\Gamma \qquad \Gamma = \int_0^C \gamma(x)\, dx \tag{8.55}$$

An alternate way to compute lift is from the dimensionless pressure coefficient C_p on the upper and lower surfaces

$$C_{pu,l} = \frac{p_{u,l} - p_\infty}{\frac{1}{2}\rho U_\infty^2} = 1 - \frac{U_{u,l}^2}{U_\infty^2} \tag{8.56}$$

where the last expression follows from Bernoulli's equation. The surface velocity squared is given by combining the uniform stream and the vortex-sheet velocity components from Fig. 8.19a:

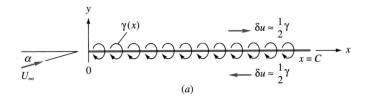

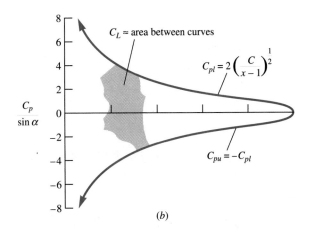

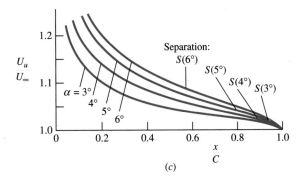

Fig. 8.19 Vortex-sheet solution for the flat-plate airfoil; (a) sheet geometry; (b) theoretical pressure coefficient on upper and lower surfaces; (c) upper-surface velocity with laminar separation points S.

$$U_{u,l}^2 = (U_\infty \cos \alpha \pm \delta u)^2 + (U_\infty \sin \alpha)^2$$

$$= U_\infty^2 \pm 2U_\infty \, \delta u \cos \alpha + \delta u^2 \approx U_\infty^2 \left(1 \pm \frac{2 \, \delta u}{U_\infty}\right) \tag{8.57}$$

where we have made the approximations $\delta u \ll U_\infty$ and $\cos \alpha \approx 1$ in the last expression, assuming a small angle of attack. Equations (8.56) and (8.57) combine to the first-order approximation

$$C_{p_{u,l}} = \mp\frac{2 \, \delta u}{U_\infty} = \mp\frac{\gamma}{U_\infty} \tag{8.58}$$

The lift force is the integral of the pressure difference over the length of the airfoil, assuming depth b

$$L = \int_0^C (p_l - p_u)b \, dx$$

or
$$C_L = \frac{L}{\frac{1}{2}\rho U_\infty^2 bC} = \int_0^1 (C_{p_l} - C_{p_u})\frac{dx}{C} = 2\int_0^2 \frac{\gamma}{U_\infty}\,d\!\left(\frac{x}{C}\right) \tag{8.59}$$

Equations (8.55) and (8.59) are entirely equivalent within the small-angle approximations.

The sheet strength $\gamma(x)$ is computed from the requirement that the net normal velocity $v(x)$ be zero at the sheet $(y = 0)$, since the sheet represents a solid plate or stream surface. Consider a small piece of sheet $\gamma\,dx$ located at position x_0. The velocity v at point x on the sheet is that of an infinitesimal line vortex of strength $d\Gamma = -\gamma\,dx$

$$dv\Big|_x = \frac{d\Gamma}{2\pi r}\Big|_{x_0 \to x} = \frac{-\gamma\,dx}{2\pi(x_0 - x)}$$

The total normal velocity induced by the entire sheet at point x is thus

$$v_{\text{sheet}} = -\int_0^C \frac{\gamma\,dx}{2\pi(x_0 - x)} \tag{8.60}$$

Meanwhile, from Fig. 8.19a, the uniform stream induces a constant normal velocity at every point on the sheet given by

$$v_{\text{stream}} = U_\infty \sin \alpha$$

Setting the sum of v_{sheet} and v_{stream} equal to zero gives the integral equation

$$\int_0^C \frac{\gamma\,dx}{x_0 - x} = 2\pi U_\infty \sin \alpha \tag{8.61}$$

to be solved for $\gamma(x)$ subject to the Kutta condition $\gamma(C) = 0$ from Eq. (8.54).

Although Eq. (8.61) is quite formidable (and not only for beginners), in fact it was solved long ago by using integral formulas developed by Poisson in the nineteenth century. The sheet strength which satisfies Eq. (8.61) is

$$\gamma(x) = 2U_\infty \sin \alpha \left(\frac{C}{x} - 1\right)^{1/2} \tag{8.62}$$

From Eq. (8.58) the surface-pressure coefficients are thus

$$c_{p_{u,l}} = \mp 2 \sin \alpha \left(\frac{C}{x} - 1\right)^{1/2} \tag{8.63}$$

Details of the calculations are given in advanced texts [for example, 11, chap. 5].

The pressure coefficients from Eq. (8.63) are plotted in Fig. 8.19b, showing that the upper surface has pressure continually increasing with x, that is, an adverse gradient. The upper-surface velocity $U_u \approx U_\infty + \delta u = U_\infty + \frac{1}{2}\gamma$ is plotted in Fig. 8.19c for various angles of attack. Above $\alpha = 5°$ the sheet contribution δu is about 20 percent of U_∞ so that the small-disturbance assumption is violated. Figure 8.19c also shows separation points computed by Thwaites' laminar-boundary-layer method, Eqs. (7.54) and (7.55). The prediction is that a flat plate would be extensively stalled on the upper surface for $\alpha > 6°$, which is approximately correct.

The lift coefficient of the airfoil is proportional to the area between c_{p_l} and c_{p_u} in Fig. 8.19b, from Eq. (8.59):

$$C_L = 2 \int_0^1 \frac{\gamma}{U} d\left(\frac{x}{C}\right) = 4 \sin\alpha \int_0^1 \left(\frac{C}{x} - 1\right)^{1/2} d\left(\frac{x}{C}\right) = 2\pi \sin\alpha \approx 2\pi\alpha \quad (8.64)$$

This is a classic result which was alluded to earlier in Eq. (7.70) without proof.

Also of interest is the moment coefficient about the leading edge (LE) of the airfoil, taken as positive counterclockwise

$$C_{M_{LE}} = \frac{M_{LE}}{\frac{1}{2}\rho U_\infty^2 bC^2} = \int_0^1 (C_{p_l} - C_{p_u})\frac{x}{C} d\left(\frac{x}{C}\right) = \frac{\pi}{2} \sin\alpha = \frac{1}{4} C_L \quad (8.65)$$

Thus the *center of pressure* (CP), or position of the resultant lift force, is at the one-quarter-chord point

$$\left(\frac{x}{C}\right)_{CP} = \frac{1}{4} \quad (8.66)$$

This theoretical result is independent of the angle of attack.

These results can be compared with experimental results for NACA airfoils in Fig. 8.20). The thinnest NACA airfoil is $t/C = 0.06$, and the thickest is 24 percent, or $t/C = 0.24$. The lift-curve slope $dC_L/d\alpha$ is within 9 percent of the theoretical value of 2π for all the various airfoil families at all thicknesses. Increasing thickness tends to increase both $C_{L,max}$ and the stall angle. The stall angle at $t/C = 0.06$ is about 8° and would be even less for a flat plate, verifying the boundary-layer separation estimates in Fig. 8.19c. Best performance is usually at about the 12 percent thickness point for any airfoil.

Potential Theory for Thick Cambered Airfoils

The theory of thick cambered airfoils is covered in advanced texts [for example, 2 to 4]; Ref. 13 has a thorough and comprehensive review of both inviscid and viscous aspects of airfoil behavior.

Basically the theory uses a complex-variable mapping which transforms the flow about a cylinder with circulation in Fig. 8.10 into flow about a foil shape with circulation. The circulation is then adjusted to match the Kutta condition of smooth exit flow from the trailing edge.

Regardless of the exact airfoil shape, the inviscid mapping theory predicts that the correct circulation for any thick cambered airfoil is

$$\Gamma_{Kutta} = \pi bCU_\infty\left(1 + 0.77\frac{t}{C}\right)\sin(\alpha + \beta) \quad (8.67)$$

where $\beta = \tan^{-1}(2h/C)$ and h is the maximum camber, or maximum deviation of the airfoil midline from its chord line, as in Fig. 8.21a.

The lift coefficient of the infinite-span airfoil is thus

$$C_L = \frac{\rho U_\infty \Gamma}{\frac{1}{2}\rho U_\infty^2 bC} = 2\pi\left(1 + 0.77\frac{t}{C}\right)\sin(\alpha + \beta) \quad (8.68)$$

This reduces to Eq. (8.64) when the thickness and camber are zero. Figure 8.20 shows that the thickness effect $1 + 0.77t/C$ is not verified by experiment. Some airfoils increase lift with thickness, others decrease, and none approach the theory very closely,

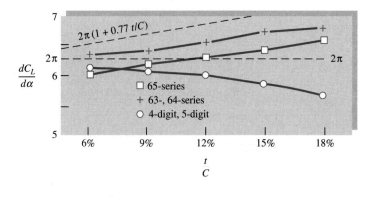

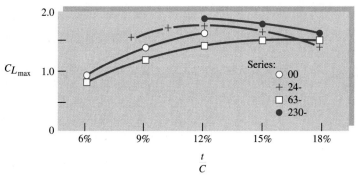

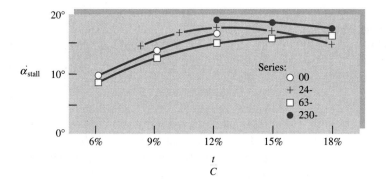

Fig. 8.20 Lift characteristics of smooth NACA airfoils as a function of thickness ratio, for infinite aspect ratio. (*From Ref. 12.*)

the primary reason being the boundary-layer growth on the upper surface affecting the airfoil "shape." Thus it is customary to drop the thickness effect from the theory

$$C_L \approx 2\pi \sin(\alpha + \beta) \qquad (8.69)$$

The theory correctly predicts that a cambered airfoil will have finite lift at zero angle of attack and zero lift (ZL) at an angle

$$\alpha_{ZL} = -\beta = -\tan^{-1}\frac{2h}{C} \qquad (8.70)$$

Equation (8.70) overpredicts the measured zero-lift angle by 1° or so, as shown in Table 8.3. The measured values are essentially independent of thickness. The designation XX

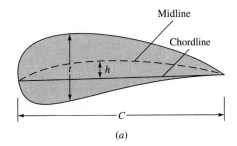

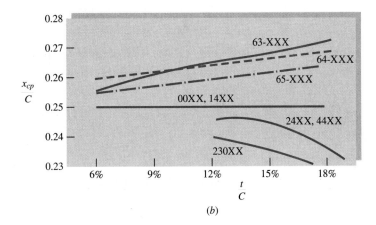

Fig. 8.21 Characteristics of NACA airfoils: (*a*) typical thick cambered airfoil; (*b*) center-of-pressure data; and (*c*) minimum drag coefficient.

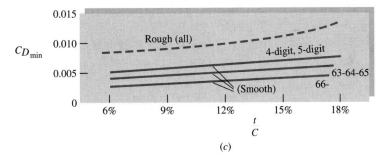

in the NACA series indicates the thickness in percent, and the other digits refer to camber and other details. For example, the 2415 airfoil has 2 percent maximum camber (the first digit) occurring at 40 percent chord (the second digit) with 15 percent maximum thickness (the last two digits). The maximum thickness need not occur at the same position as the maximum camber.

Table 8.3 Zero-Lift Angle of NACA Airfoils

Airfoil series	Camber h/C, %	Measured α_{ZL}, deg	Theory $-\beta$, deg
24XX	2.0	−2.1	−2.3
44XX	4.0	−4.0	−4.6
230XX	1.8	−1.3	−2.1
63-2XX	2.2	−1.8	−2.5
63-4XX	4.4	−3.1	−5.0
64-1XX	1.1	−0.8	−1.2

Figure 8.21*b* shows the measured position of the center of pressure of the various NACA airfoils, both symmetric and cambered. In all cases x_{CP} is within 0.02 chord length of the theoretical quarter-chord point predicted by Eq. (8.66). The standard cambered airfoils (24, 44, and 230 series) lie slightly forward of $x/C = 0.25$ and the low-drag (60 series) foils slightly aft. The symmetric airfoils are at 0.25.

Figure 8.21*c* shows the minimum drag coefficient of NACA airfoils as a function of thickness. As mentioned earlier in conjunction with Fig. 7.24, these foils when smooth actually have less drag than turbulent flow parallel to a flat plate, especially the low-drag 60 series. However, for standard surface roughness all foils have about the same minimum drag, roughly 30 percent greater than that for a smooth flat plate.

Wings of Finite Span

The results of airfoil theory and experiment in the previous subsection were for two-dimensional, or infinite-span, wings. But all real wings have tips and are therefore of finite span or finite aspect ratio AR, defined by

$$\text{AR} = \frac{b^2}{A_p} = \frac{b}{\overline{C}} \tag{8.71}$$

where b is the span length from tip to tip and A_p is the planform area of the wing as seen from above. The lift and drag coefficients of a finite-aspect-ratio wing depend strongly upon the aspect ratio and slightly upon the planform shape of the wing.

Vortices cannot end in a fluid; they must either extend to the boundary or form a closed loop. Figure 8.22*a* shows how the vortices which provide the wing circulation bend downstream at finite wing tips and extend far behind the wing to join the starting vortex (Fig. 7.22) downstream. The strongest vortices are shed from the tips, but some are shed from the body of the wing, as sketched schematically in Fig. 8.22*b*. The effective circulation $\Gamma(y)$ of these trailing shed vortices is zero at the tips and usually a maximum at the center plane, or root, of the wing. In 1918 Prandtl successfully modeled this flow by replacing the wing by a single lifting line and a continuous sheet of semi-infinite trailing vortices of strength $\gamma(y) = d\Gamma/dy$, as in Fig. 8.22*c*. Each elemental piece of trailing sheet $\gamma(\eta)\,d\eta$ induces a downwash, or downward velocity, $dw(y)$, given by

$$dw(y) = \frac{\gamma(\eta)\,d\eta}{4\pi(y - \eta)}$$

at position y on the lifting line. Note the denominator term 4π rather than 2π because the trailing vortex extends only from 0 to ∞ rather than from $-\infty$ to $+\infty$.

The total downwash $w(y)$ induced by the entire trailing vortex system is thus

$$w(y) = \frac{1}{4\pi}\int_{-(1/2)b}^{(1/2)b} \frac{\gamma(\eta)\,d\eta}{y - \eta} \tag{8.72}$$

When the downwash is vectorially added to the approaching free stream U_∞, the effective angle of attack at this section of the wing is reduced to

$$\alpha_{\text{eff}} = \alpha - \alpha_i \qquad \alpha_i = \tan^{-1}\frac{w}{U_\infty} \approx \frac{w}{U_\infty} \tag{8.73}$$

where we have used a small-amplitude approximation $w \ll U_\infty$.

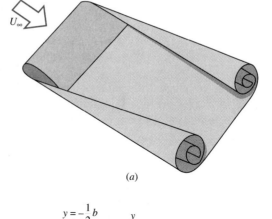

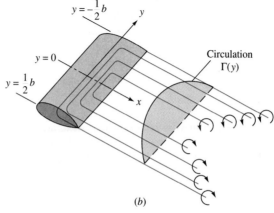

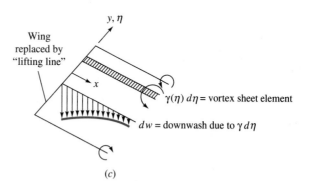

Fig. 8.22 Lifting-line theory for a finite wing: (*a*) actual trailing-vortex system behind a wing; (*b*) simulation by vortex system "bound" to the wing; (*c*) downwash on the wing due to an element of the trailing-vortex system.

The final step is to assume that the local circulation $\Gamma(y)$ is equal to that of a two-dimensional wing of the same shape and same effective angle of attack. From thin-airfoil theory, Eqs. (8.55) and (8.64), we have the estimate

$$C_L = \frac{\rho U_\infty \Gamma b}{\frac{1}{2}\rho U_\infty^2 bC} \approx 2\pi\alpha_{\text{eff}}$$

or

$$\Gamma \approx \pi C U_\infty \alpha_{\text{eff}} \qquad (8.74)$$

Combining Eqs. (8.72) and (8.74), we obtain Prandtl's lifting-line theory for a finite-span wing

$$\Gamma(y) = \pi C(y) U_\infty \left[\alpha(y) - \frac{1}{4\pi U_\infty} \int_{-(1/2)b}^{(1/2)b} \frac{(d\Gamma/d\eta)\,d\eta}{y - \eta} \right] \tag{8.75}$$

This is an integrodifferential equation to be solved for $\Gamma(y)$ subject to the conditions $\Gamma(\frac{1}{2}b) = \Gamma(-\frac{1}{2}b) = 0$. It is similar to the thin-airfoil integral equation (8.61) and even more formidable. Once it is solved, the total wing lift and induced drag are given by

$$L = \rho U_\infty \int_{-(1/2)b}^{(1/2)b} \Gamma(y)\,dy \qquad D_i = \rho U_\infty \int_{-(1/2)b}^{(1/2)b} \Gamma(y)\alpha_i(y)\,dy \tag{8.76}$$

Here is a case where the drag is not zero in a frictionless theory because the downwash causes the lift to slant backward by angle α_i so that it has a drag component parallel to the free-stream direction, $dD_i = dL \sin \alpha_i \approx dL\alpha_i$.

The complete solution to Eq. (8.75) for arbitrary wing planform $C(y)$ and arbitrary twist $\alpha(y)$ is treated in advanced texts [for example, 11]. It turns out that there is a simple representative solution for an untwisted wing of elliptical planform

$$C(y) = C_0 \left[1 - \left(\frac{2y}{b}\right)^2 \right]^{1/2} \tag{8.77}$$

The area and aspect ratio of this wing are

$$A_p = \int_{-(1/2)b}^{(1/2)b} C\,dy = \frac{1}{4}\pi b C_0 \qquad AR = \frac{2b}{\pi C_0} \tag{8.78}$$

The solution to Eq. (8.75) for this $C(y)$ is an elliptical circulation distribution of exactly similar shape

$$\Gamma(y) = \Gamma_0 \left[1 - \left(\frac{2y}{b}\right)^2 \right]^{1/2} \tag{8.79}$$

Substituting into Eq. (8.75) and integrating give a relation between Γ_0 and C_0

$$\Gamma_0 = \frac{\pi C_0 U_\infty \alpha}{1 + 2/AR} \tag{8.80}$$

where α is assumed constant across the untwisted wing.

Substitution into Eq. (8.76) gives the elliptical-wing lift

$$L = \tfrac{1}{4}\pi^2 b C_0 \rho U_\infty^2 \alpha$$

or

$$C_L = \frac{2\pi\alpha}{1 + 2/AR} \tag{8.81}$$

If we generalize this to a thick cambered finite wing of approximately elliptical planform, we obtain

$$C_L = \frac{2\pi \sin(\alpha + \beta)}{1 + 2/AR} \tag{8.82}$$

This result was given without proof as Eq. (7.70). From Eq. (8.72) the computed downwash for the elliptical wing is constant

$$w(y) = \frac{2U_\infty \alpha}{2 + AR} = const \qquad (8.83)$$

Finally, the induced drag coefficient from Eq. (8.76) is

$$C_{Di} = C_L \frac{w}{U_\infty} = \frac{C_L^2}{\pi\, AR} \qquad (8.84)$$

This was given without proof as Eq. (7.71).

Figure 8.23 shows the effectiveness of this theory when tested against a nonelliptical cambered wing by Prandtl in 1921 [14]. Figure 8.23a and b shows the measured lift curves and drag polars for five different aspect ratios. Note the increase in stall angle and drag and the decrease in lift slope as the aspect ratio decreases.

Figure 8.23c shows the lift data replotted against effective angle of attack $\alpha_{\mathrm{eff}} = (\alpha + \beta)/(1 + 2/AR)$, as predicted by Eq. (8.82). These curves should be equivalent to an infinite-aspect-ratio wing, and they do collapse together except near stall. Their common slope $dC_L/d\alpha$ is about 10 percent less than the theoretical value 2π, but this is consistent with the thickness and shape effects noted in Fig. 8.20.

Fig. 8.23 Comparison of theory and experiment for a finite wing: (a) measured lift [14]; (b) measured drag polar [14]; (c) lift reduced to infinite aspect ratio; (d) drag polar reduced to infinite aspect ratio.

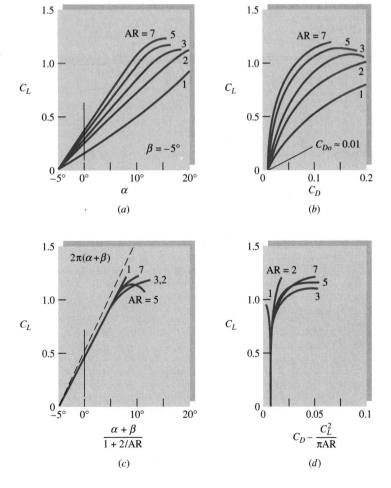

Figure 8.23*d* shows the drag data replotted with the theoretical induced drag $C_{Di} = C_L^2/(\pi AR)$ subtracted out. Again, except near stall, the data collapse onto a single line of nearly constant infinite-aspect-ratio drag $C_{D0} \approx 0.01$. We conclude that the finite-wing theory is very effective and may be used for design calculations.

8.8 Axisymmetric Potential Flow[1]

The same superposition technique which worked so well for plane flow in Sec. 8.3 is also successful for axisymmetric potential flow. We give some brief examples here.

Most of the basic results carry over from plane to axisymmetric flow with only slight changes owing to the geometric differences. Consider the following related flows:

Basic plane flow	Counterpart axisymmetric flow
Uniform stream	Uniform stream
Line source or sink	Point source or sink
Line doublet	Point doublet
Line vortex	No counterpart
Rankine half-body cylinder	Rankine half-body of revolution
Rankine-oval cylinder	Rankine oval of revolution
Circular cylinder	Sphere
Symmetric airfoil	Tear-shaped body

Since there is no such thing as a point vortex, we must forgo the pleasure of studying circulation effects in axisymmetric flow. However, as any smoker knows, there is an axisymmetric ring vortex, and there are also ring sources and ring sinks, which we leave to advanced texts [for example, 3].

Spherical Polar Coordinates

Axisymmetric potential flows are conveniently treated in the spherical polar coordinates of Fig. 8.24. There are only two coordinates (r, θ), and flow properties are constant on a circle of radius $r \sin \theta$ about the x axis.

The equation of continuity for incompressible flow in these coordinates is

$$\frac{\partial}{\partial r}(r^2 v_r \sin \theta) + \frac{\partial}{\partial \theta}(r v_\theta \sin \theta) = 0 \tag{8.85}$$

[1] This section may be omitted without loss of continuity.

Fig. 8.24 Spherical polar coordinates for axisymmetric flow.

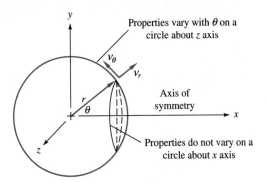

Properties vary with θ on a circle about z axis

Axis of symmetry

Properties do not vary on a circle about x axis

where v_r and v_θ are radial and tangential velocity as shown. Thus a spherical polar stream function[1] exists such that

$$v_r = -\frac{1}{r^2 \sin \theta} \frac{\partial \psi}{\partial \theta} \qquad v_\theta = \frac{1}{r \sin \theta} \frac{\partial \psi}{\partial r} \tag{8.86}$$

In like manner a velocity potential $\phi(r, \theta)$ exists such that

$$v_r = \frac{\partial \phi}{\partial r} \qquad v_\theta = \frac{1}{r} \frac{\partial \phi}{\partial \theta} \tag{8.87}$$

These formulas serve to deduce the ψ and ϕ functions for various elementary axisymmetric potential flows.

Uniform Stream in the x Direction

A stream U_∞ in the x direction has components

$$v_r = U_\infty \cos \theta \qquad v_\theta = -U_\infty \sin \theta$$

Substitution into Eqs. (8.86) and (8.87) and integrating give

Uniform stream: $\qquad \psi = -\frac{1}{2} U_\infty r^2 \sin^2 \theta \qquad \phi = U_\infty r \cos \theta \tag{8.88}$

As usual, arbitrary constants of integration have been neglected.

Point Source or Sink

Consider a volume flux Q issuing from a point source. The flow will spread out radially and at radius r will equal Q divided by the area $4\pi r^2$ of a sphere. Thus

$$v_r = \frac{Q}{4\pi r^2} = \frac{m}{r^2} \qquad v_\theta = 0 \tag{8.89}$$

with $m = Q/(4\pi)$ for convenience. Integrating (8.86) and (8.87) gives

Point source: $\qquad \psi = m \cos \theta \qquad \phi = -\frac{m}{r} \tag{8.90}$

For a point sink, change m to $-m$ in Eq. (8.90).

Point Doublet

Exactly as in Fig. 8.8, place a source at $(x, y) = (-a, 0)$ and an equal sink at $(+a, 0)$, taking the limit as a becomes small with the product $2am = \lambda$ held constant

$$\psi_{\text{doublet}} = \lim_{\substack{a \to 0 \\ 2am = \lambda}} (m \cos \theta_{\text{source}} - m \cos \theta_{\text{sink}}) = \frac{\lambda \sin^2 \theta}{r} \tag{8.91}$$

We leave the proof of this limit as a problem. The point-doublet velocity potential

$$\phi_{\text{doublet}} = \lim_{\substack{a \to 0 \\ 2am = \lambda}} \left(-\frac{m}{r_{\text{source}}} + \frac{m}{r_{\text{sink}}} \right) = \frac{\lambda \cos \theta}{r^2} \tag{8.92}$$

[1] It is often called *Stokes' stream function*, having been used in a paper Stokes wrote in 1851 on viscous sphere flow.

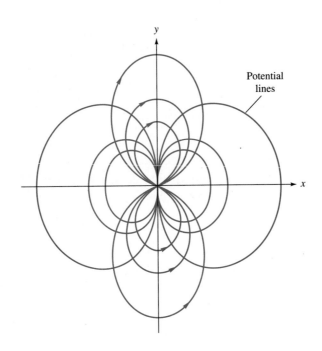

Fig. 8.25 Streamlines and potential lines due to a point doublet at the origin, from Eqs. (8.91) and (8.92).

The streamlines and potential lines are shown in Fig. 8.25. Unlike the plane doublet flow of Fig. 8.8, neither set of lines represents perfect circles.

Uniform Stream plus a Point Source

By combining Eqs. (8.88) and (8.90) we obtain the stream function for a uniform stream plus a point source at the origin

$$\psi = -\tfrac{1}{2}U_\infty r^2 \sin^2 \theta + m \cos \theta \tag{8.93}$$

From Eq. (8.86) the velocity components are, by differentiation,

$$v_r = U_\infty \cos \theta + \frac{m}{r^2} \qquad v_\theta = -U_\infty \sin \theta \tag{8.94}$$

Setting these equal to zero reveals a stagnation point at $\theta = 180°$ and $r = a = (m/U_\infty)^{1/2}$, as shown in Fig. 8.26. If we let $m = U_\infty a^2$, the stream function can be rewritten as

$$\frac{\psi}{U_\infty a^2} = \cos \theta - \frac{1}{2}\left(\frac{r}{a}\right)^2 \sin^2 \theta \tag{8.95}$$

The stream surface which passes through the stagnation point $(r, \theta) = (a, \pi)$ has the value $\psi = -U_\infty a^2$ and forms a half-body of revolution enclosing the point source, as shown in Fig. 8.26. This half-body can be used to simulate a pitot tube. Far downstream the half-body approaches the constant radius $R = 2a$ about the x axis. The maximum velocity and minimum pressure along the half-body surface occur at $\theta = 70.5°$, $r = a\sqrt{3}$, $V_s = 1.155U_\infty$. Downstream of this point there is an adverse gradient as V_s slowly decelerates to U_∞, but boundary-layer theory indicates no flow separation. Thus Eq. (8.95) is a very realistic simulation of a real half-body flow. But when the uniform

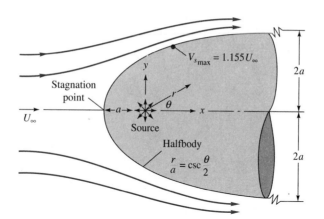

Fig. 8.26 Streamlines for a Rankine half-body of revolution.

stream is added to a sink to form a half-body rear surface, e.g., similar to Fig. 8.5c, separation is predicted and the inviscid pattern is not realistic.

Uniform Stream plus a Point Doublet

From Eqs. (8.88) and (8.91), combination of a uniform stream and a point doublet at the origin gives

$$\psi = -\frac{1}{2} U_\infty r^2 \sin^2 \theta + \frac{\lambda}{r} \sin^2 \theta \tag{8.96}$$

Examination of this relation reveals that the stream surface $\psi = 0$ corresponds to the sphere of radius

$$r = a = \left(\frac{2\lambda}{U_\infty}\right)^{1/3} \tag{8.97}$$

This is exactly analogous to the cylinder flow of Fig. 8.10a formed by combining a uniform stream and a line doublet.

Letting $\lambda = \frac{1}{2} U_\infty a^3$ for convenience, we rewrite Eq. (8.96) as

$$\frac{\psi}{\frac{1}{2} U_\infty a^2} = -\sin^2 \theta \left(\frac{r^2}{a^2} - \frac{a}{r}\right) \tag{8.98}$$

The streamlines for this sphere flow are plotted in Fig. 8.27. By differentiation from Eq. (8.86) the velocity components are

$$v_r = U_\infty \cos \theta \left(1 - \frac{a^3}{r^3}\right) \qquad v_\theta = -\frac{1}{2} U_\infty \sin \theta \left(2 + \frac{a^3}{r^3}\right) \tag{8.99}$$

We see that the radial velocity vanishes at the sphere surface $r = a$, as expected. There is a stagnation point at the front (a, π) and the rear $(a, 0)$ of the sphere. The maximum velocity occurs at the shoulder $(a, \pm \frac{1}{2}\pi)$, where $v_r = 0$ and $v_\theta = -1.5 U_\infty$. The surface-velocity distribution is

$$V_s = -v_\theta|_{r=a} = \frac{3}{2} U_\infty \sin \theta \tag{8.100}$$

Note the similarity to the cylinder surface velocity equal to $2U_\infty \sin \theta$ from Eq. (8.34) with zero circulation.

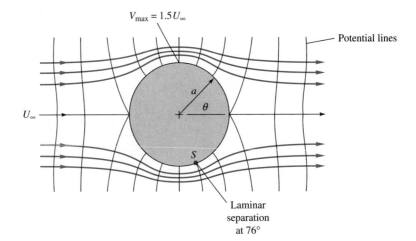

Fig. 8.27 Streamlines and potential lines for inviscid flow past a sphere.

Equation (8.100) predicts, as expected, an adverse pressure gradient on the rear ($\theta < 90°$) of the sphere. If we use this distribution with laminar-boundary-layer theory [for example, 15, p. 298], separation is computed to occur at about $\theta = 76°$, so that in the actual flow pattern of Fig. 7.14 a broad wake forms in the rear. This wake interacts with the free stream and causes Eq. (8.100) to be inaccurate even in the front of the sphere. The measured maximum surface velocity is equal only to about $1.3U_\infty$ and occurs at about $\theta = 107°$ (see Ref. 15, sec. 4.10.4, for further details).

The Concept of Hydrodynamic Mass

When a body moves through a fluid, it must push a finite mass of fluid out of the way. If the body is accelerated, the surrounding fluid must also be accelerated. The body behaves as if it were heavier by an amount called the *hydrodynamic mass* (also called the *added* or *virtual mass*) of the fluid. If the instantaneous body velocity is $U(t)$, the summation of forces must include this effect

$$\sum \mathbf{F} = (m + m_h) \frac{d\mathbf{U}}{dt} \tag{8.101}$$

where m_h, the hydrodynamic mass, is a function of body shape, the direction of motion, and (to a lesser extent) flow parameters such as the Reynolds number.

According to potential theory [2, sec. 6.4; 3, sec. 9.22], m_h depends only on the shape and direction of motion and can be computed by summing the total kinetic energy of the fluid relative to the body and setting this equal to an equivalent body energy

$$\text{KE}_{\text{fluid}} = \int \tfrac{1}{2} \, dm \, V_{\text{rel}}^2 = \tfrac{1}{2} m_h U^2 \tag{8.102}$$

The integration of fluid kinetic energy can also be accomplished by a body-surface integral involving the velocity potential [16, sec. 11].

Consider the previous example of a sphere immersed in a uniform stream. By subtracting out the stream velocity we can replot the flow as in Fig. 8.28, showing the streamlines relative to the moving sphere. Note the similarity to the doublet flow in

Fig. 8.25. The relative-velocity components are found by subtracting U from Eqs. (8.99)

$$v_r = -\frac{Ua^3 \cos\theta}{r^3} \qquad v_\theta = -\frac{Ua^3 \sin\theta}{2r^3}$$

The element of fluid mass, in spherical polar coordinates, is

$$dm = \rho(2\pi r \sin\theta)r\,dr\,d\theta$$

When dm and $V_{\text{rel}}^2 = v_r^2 + v_\theta^2$ are substituted into Eq. (8.102), the integral can be evaluated

$$\text{KE}_{\text{fluid}} = \tfrac{1}{3}\rho\pi a^3 U^2$$

or
$$m_h(\text{sphere}) = \tfrac{2}{3}\rho\pi a^3 \tag{8.103}$$

Thus, according to potential theory, the hydrodynamic mass of a sphere equals one-half of its displaced mass, independent of the direction of motion.

A similar result for a cylinder moving normal to its axis can be computed from Eqs. (8.33) after subtracting out the stream velocity. The result is

$$m_h(\text{cylinder}) = \rho\pi a^2 L \tag{8.104}$$

for a cylinder of length L, assuming two-dimensional motion. The cylinder's hydrodynamic mass equals its displaced mass.

Tables of hydrodynamic mass for various body shapes and directions of motion are given by Patton [17]. See also Ref. 21.

Fig. 8.28 Potential-flow streamlines relative to a moving sphere. Compare with Figs. 8.25 and 8.27.

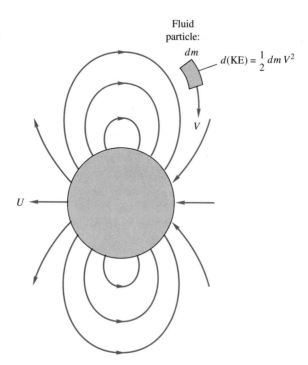

Fluid particle:

dm

$d(\text{KE}) = \dfrac{1}{2}\,dm\,V^2$

V

U

8.9 Numerical Analysis

When potential flow involves complicated geometries or unusual stream conditions, the classical superposition scheme of Secs. 8.3 and 8.4 becomes less attractive. Conformal mapping of body shapes, by using the complex-variable technique of Sec. 8.5, is no longer popular. Numerical analysis is the appropriate modern approach, and at least three different approaches are in use:

1. The finite-element method (FEM) [6, 19]
2. The finite-difference method (FDM) [5, 20]
3. *a.* Integral methods with distributed singularities [18]
   b. The boundary-element method [7]

Methods 3*a* and 3*b* are closely related, having first been developed on an ad hoc basis by aerodynamicists in the 1960s [18] and then generalized into a multipurpose applied-mechanics technique in the 1970s [7].

Methods 1 (or FEM) and 2 (or FDM), though strikingly different in concept, are comparable in scope, mesh size, and general accuracy. We concentrate here on the latter method for illustration purposes.

The Finite-Element Method

The finite-element method [19] is applicable to all types of linear and nonlinear partial differential equations in physics and engineering. The computational domain is divided into small regions, usually triangular or quadrilateral. These regions are delineated with a finite number of *nodes* where the field variable—temperature, velocity, pressure, stream function, etc.—is to be calculated. The solution in each region is approximated by an algebraic combination of local nodal values. Then the approximate functions are integrated over the region, and their error is minimized, often by using a weighting function. This process yields a set of N algebraic equations for the N unknown nodal values. The nodal equations are solved simultaneously, by matrix inversion or iteration. For further deails see Ref. 6 or 19.

The Finite-Difference Method

Although textbooks on numerical analysis [5, 20] apply finite-difference techniques to many different problems, here we concentrate on potential flow. The idea of FDM is to approximate the partial derivatives in a physical equation by "differences" between nodel values spaced a finite distance apart—a sort of numerical calculus. The basic partial differential equation is thus replaced by a set of algebraic equations for the nodal values. For potential (inviscid) flow, these algebraic equations are linear, but they are generally nonlinear for viscous flows. The solution for nodal values is obtained by iteration or matrix inversion. Nodal spacings need not be equal.

Here we illustrate the two-dimensional Laplace equation, choosing for convenience the stream-function form

$$\frac{\partial^2 \psi}{\partial x^2} + \frac{\partial^2 \psi}{\partial y^2} = 0 \tag{8.105}$$

subject to known values of ψ along any body surface and known values of $\partial\psi/\partial x$ and $\partial\psi/\partial y$ in the free stream.

Our finite-difference technique divides the flow field into equally spaced nodes, as shown in Fig. 8.29. To economize on the use of parentheses or functional notation,

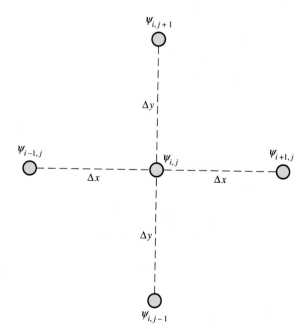

Fig. 8.29 Definition sketch for a two-dimensional rectangular finite-difference grid.

subscripts i and j denote the position of an arbitrary, equally spaced node, and $\psi_{i,j}$ denotes the value of the stream function at that node

$$\psi_{i,j} = \psi(x_0 + i\,\Delta x, \, y_0 + j\,\Delta y)$$

Thus, $\psi_{i+1,j}$ is just to the right of $\psi_{i,j}$, and $\psi_{i,j+1}$ is just above.

An algebraic approximation for the derivative $\partial\psi/\partial x$ is

$$\frac{\partial\psi}{\partial x} \approx \frac{\psi(x + \Delta x, y) - \psi(x, y)}{\Delta x}$$

A similar approximation for the second derivative is

$$\frac{\partial^2\psi}{\partial x^2} \approx \frac{1}{\Delta x}\left[\frac{\psi(x + \Delta x, y) - \psi(x, y)}{\Delta x} - \frac{\psi(x, y) - \psi(x - \Delta x, y)}{\Delta x}\right]$$

The subscript notation makes these expressions more compact

$$\frac{\partial\psi}{\partial x} \approx \frac{1}{\Delta x}(\psi_{i+1,j} - \psi_{i,j})$$

$$\frac{\partial^2\psi}{\partial x^2} \approx \frac{1}{\Delta x^2}(\psi_{i+1,j} - 2\psi_{i,j} + \psi_{i-1,j})$$

(8.106)

These formulas are exact in the calculus limit as $\Delta x \to 0$, but in numerical analysis we keep Δx and Δy finite, hence the term *finite differences*.

In an exactly similar manner we can derive the equivalent difference expressions for the y direction

$$\frac{\partial\psi}{\partial y} \approx \frac{1}{\Delta y}(\psi_{i,j+1} - \psi_{i,j})$$

$$\frac{\partial^2 \psi}{\partial y^2} \approx \frac{1}{\Delta y^2} (\psi,\ \text{yi}_{i,j+1} - 2\psi_{i,j} + \psi_{i,j-1})$$ (8.107)

The use of subscript notation allows these expressions to be programmed directly into a scientific computer language such as BASIC or FORTRAN.

When (8.106) and (8.107) are substituted into Laplace's equation (8.105), the result is the algebraic formula

$$2(1 + \beta)\psi_{i,j} \approx \psi_{i-1,j} + \psi_{i+1,j} + \beta(\psi_{i,j-1} + \psi_{i,j+1})$$ (8.108)

where $\beta = (\Delta x/\Delta y)^2$ depends upon the mesh size selected. This finite-difference model of Laplace's equation states that every nodal stream-function value $\psi_{i,j}$ is a linear combination of its four nearest neighbors.

The most commonly programmed case is a square mesh ($\beta = 1$), for which Eq. (8.108) reduces to

$$\psi_{i,j} \approx \tfrac{1}{4}(\psi_{i,j+1} + \psi_{i,j-1} + \psi_{i+1,j} + \psi_{i-1,j})$$ (8.109)

Thus, for a square mesh, each nodal value equals the arithmetic average of the four neighbors shown in Fig. 8.29. The formula is easily remembered and easily programmed. If P(I, J) is a subscripted variable stream function, the BASIC or FORTRAN statement of (8.109) is

$$P(I, J) = 0.25 * (P(I, J + 1) + P(I, J - 1) + P(I + 1, J) + P(I - 1, J))$$ (8.110)

This is applied in iterative fashion sweeping over each of the internal nodes (I, J), with known values of P specified at each of the surrounding boundary nodes. Any initial guesses can be specified for the internal nodes P(I, J), and the iteration process will converge to the final algebraic solution in a finite number of sweeps. The numerical error, compared with the exact solution of Laplace's equation, is proportional to the square of the mesh size.

Convergence can be speeded up by the *successive overrelaxation* (SOR) method, discussed by Patankar [5]. The modified SOR form of the iteration is

$$P(I, J) = P(I, J) + 0.25 * A * (P(I, J + 1) + P(I, J - 1)$$
$$+ P(I + 1, J) + P(I - 1, J) - 4 * P(I, J))$$ (8.111)

The recommended value of the SOR convergence factor A is about 1.7. Note that the value $A = 1.0$ reduces Eq. (8.111) to (8.110).

Let us illustrate the finite-difference method with an example.

EXAMPLE 8.5

Make a numerical analysis, using $\Delta x = \Delta y = 0.2$ m, of potential flow in the duct expansion shown in Fig. 8.30. The flow enters at a uniform 10 m/s, where the duct width is 1 m, and is assumed to leave at a uniform velocity of 5 m/s, where the duct width is 2 m. There is a straight section 1 m long, a 45° expansion section, and a final straight section 1 m long.

Solution

Using the mesh shown in Fig. 8.30 results in 45 boundary nodes and 91 internal nodes, with i varying from 1 to 16 and j varying from 1 to 11. The internal points are modeled by Eq.

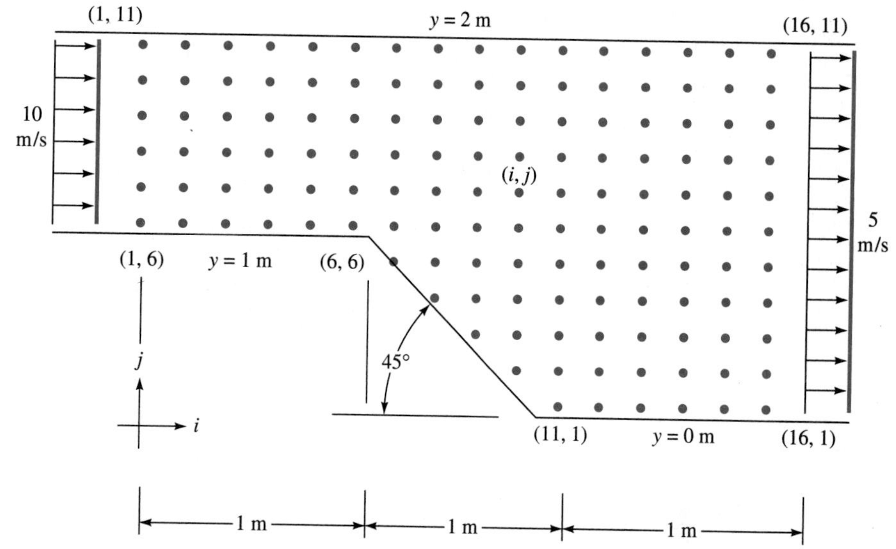

Fig. 8.30 Numerical model of potential flow through a two-dimensional 45° expansion. The nodal points shown are 20 cm apart. There are 45 boundary nodes and 91 internal nodes.

(8.110). For convenience, let the stream function be zero along the lower wall. Then since the volume flow is (10 m/s)(1 m) $=$ 10 m^2/s per unit depth, the stream function must equal 10 m^2/s along the upper wall. Over the entrance and exit planes, the stream function must vary linearly to give uniform velocities:

Inlet: $\qquad\qquad\qquad\qquad\qquad \psi(1, J) = 2 * (J - 6) \qquad$ for J $=$ 7 to 10

Exit: $\qquad\qquad\qquad\qquad\quad \psi(16, J) = J - 1 \qquad$ for J $=$ 2 to 10

All these boundary values must be input to the program and are shown printed in Fig. 8.31. Initial guesses are stored for the internal points, say, zero or an average value of 5.0 m^2/s. The program then starts at any convenient point, such as the upper left (2, 10), and evaluates Eq. (8.110) at every internal point, repeating this sweep iteratively until there are no further changes (within some selected maximum change) in the nodal values. The results are the finite-difference simulation of this potential flow for this mesh size; they are shown printed

$\psi=$ 10.00	10.00	10.00	10.00	10.00	10.00	10.00	10.00	10.00	10.00	10.00	10.00	10.00	10.00	10.00	10.00
8.00	8.02	8.04	8.07	8.12	8.20	8.30	8.41	8.52	8.62	8.71	8.79	8.85	8.91	8.95	9.00
6.00	6.03	6.06	6.12	6.22	6.37	6.58	6.82	7.05	7.26	7.44	7.59	7.71	7.82	7.91	8.00
4.00	4.03	4.07	4.13	4.26	4.48	4.84	5.24	5.61	5.93	6.19	6.41	6.59	6.74	6.88	7.00
2.00	2.02	2.05	2.09	2.20	2.44	3.08	3.69	4.22	4.65	5.00	5.28	5.50	5.69	5.85	6.00
$\psi=$ 0.00	0.00	0.00	0.00	0.00	0.00	1.33	2.22	2.92	3.45	3.87	4.19	4.45	4.66	4.84	5.00
						0.00	1.00	1.77	2.37	2.83	3.18	3.45	3.66	3.84	4.00
							0.00	0.80	1.42	1.90	2.24	2.50	2.70	2.86	3.00
								0.00	0.63	1.09	1.40	1.61	1.77	1.89	2.00
									0.00	0.44	0.66	0.79	0.87	0.94	1.00
										0.00	0.00	0.00	0.00	0.00	0.00

Fig. 8.31 Stream-function nodal values for the potential flow of Fig. 8.30. Boundary values are known inputs. Internal nodes are solutions to Eq. (8.110).

in Fig. 8.31 to three-digit accuracy. The reader should test a few nodes in Fig. 8.31 to verify that Eq. (8.110) is satisfied everywhere. The numerical accuracy of these printed values is difficult to estimate, since there is no known exact solution to this problem. In practice, one would keep decreasing the mesh size to see whether there were any significant changes in nodal values.

This problem is well within the capability of a small personal computer. The values shown in Fig. 8.31 were obtained after 100 iterations, or 6 min of execution time, on a Macintosh SE personal computer, using BASIC.

Although Fig. 8.31 is the computer solution to the problem, these numbers must be manipulated to yield practical engineering results. For example, one can interpolate these numbers to sketch various streamlines of the flow. This is done in Fig. 8.32a. We see that the streamlines are curved both upstream and downstream of the corner regions, especially near the lower wall. This indicates that the flow is not one-dimensional.

The velocities at any point in the flow can be computed from finite-difference formulas such as Eqs. (8.106) and (8.107). For example, at the point $(I, J) = (3, 6)$, from Eq. (8.107), the horizontal velocity is approximately

$$u(3, 6) \approx \frac{\psi(3, 7) - \psi(3, 6)}{\Delta y} = \frac{2.09 - 0.00}{0.2} = 10.45 \text{ m/s}$$

Fig. 8.32 Useful results computed from Fig. 8.31: (*a*) streamlines of the flow; (*b*) pressure-coefficient distribution along each wall.

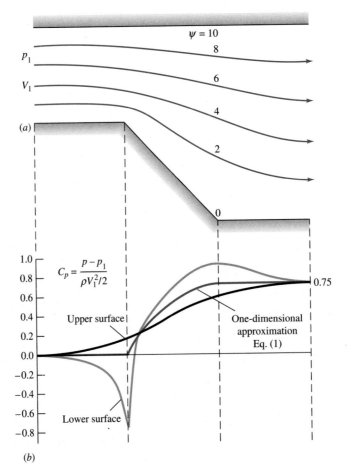

and the vertical velocity is zero from Eq. (8.106). Directly above this on the upper wall, we estimate

$$u(3, 11) \approx \frac{\psi(3, 11) - \psi(3,10)}{\Delta y} = \frac{10.00 - 8.07}{0.2} = 9.65 \text{ m/s}$$

The flow is not truly one-dimensional in the entrance duct. The lower wall, which contains the diverging section, accelerates the fluid, while the flat upper wall is actually decelerating the fluid.

Another output function, useful in making boundary-layer analyses of the wall regions, is the pressure distribution along the walls. If p_1 and V_1 are the pressure and velocity at the entrance ($I = 1$), conditions at any other point are computed from Bernoulli's equation (8.3), neglecting gravity

$$p + \tfrac{1}{2}\rho V^2 = p_1 + \tfrac{1}{2}\rho V_1^2$$

which can be rewritten as a dimensionless pressure coefficient

$$C_p = \frac{p - p_1}{\tfrac{1}{2}\rho V_1^2} = 1 - \left(\frac{V}{V_1}\right)^2$$

This determines p after V is computed from the stream-function differences in Fig. 8.31.

Figure 8.32b shows the computed wall-pressure distributions as compared with the one-dimensional continuity approximation $V_1 A_1 \approx V(x)A(x)$, or

$$C_p(\text{one-dim}) \approx 1 - \left(\frac{A_1}{A}\right)^2 \tag{1}$$

The one-dimensional approximation, which is rather crude for this large (45°) expansion, lies between the upper and lower wall pressures. One-dimensional theory would be much more accurate for a 10° expansion.

Analyzing Fig. 8.32b, we predict that boundary-layer separation will probably occur on the lower wall between the corners, where pressure is strongly rising (highly adverse gradient). Therefore potential theory is probably not too realistic for this flow, where viscous effects are strong. (Recall Figs. 6.27 and 7.8.)

Potential theory is *reversible*; i.e., when we reverse the flow arrows in Fig. 8.32a, then Fig. 8.32b is still valid and would represent a 45° *contraction* flow. The pressure would fall on both walls (no separation) from $x = 3$ m to $x = 1$ m. Between $x = 1$ m and $x = 0$, the pressure rises on the lower surface, indicating possible separation, probably just downstream of the corner.

This example should give the reader an idea of the usefulness and generality of numerical analysis of fluid flows.

The Boundary-Element Method

A relatively new technique for numerical solution of partial differential equations is the *boundary-element method*. Reference 7 is an introductory textbook outlining the concepts of BEM, including FORTRAN programs for potential theory and elastostatics. There are no interior elements. Rather, all nodes are placed on the boundary of the domain, as in Fig. 8.33. The "element" is a small piece of the boundary surrounding the node. The "strength" of the element can be either constant or variable.

For plane potential flow, the method takes advantage of the particular solution

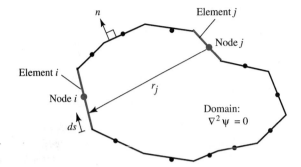

Fig. 8.33 Boundary elements of constant strength in plane potential flow.

$$\psi^* = \frac{1}{2\pi} \ln \frac{1}{r} \tag{8.112}$$

which satisfies Laplace's equation, $\nabla^2\psi = 0$. Each element i is assumed to have a different strength ψ_i. Then r represents the distance from that element to any other point in the flow field. Summing all these elemental effects, with proper boundary conditions, will give the total solution to the potential-flow problem.

At each element of the boundary, we typically know either the value of ψ or the value of $\partial\psi/\partial n$, where n is normal to the boundary. (Mixed combinations of ψ and $\partial\psi/\partial n$ are also possible but are not discussed here.) The correct strengths ψ_i are such that these boundary conditions are satisfied at every element. Summing these effects over N elements requires integration by parts plus a careful evaluation of the (singular) effect of element i upon itself. The mathematical details are given in Ref. 7. The result is a set of N algebraic equations for the unknown boundary values. In the case of elements of constant strength, the final expression is

$$\frac{1}{2}\psi_i + \sum_{j=1}^{N} \psi_j \left(\int_j \frac{\partial\psi^*}{\partial n} \, ds \right) = \sum_{j=1}^{N} \left(\frac{\partial\psi}{\partial n} \right)_j \left(\int_j \psi^* \, ds \right) \qquad i = 1 \text{ to } N \tag{8.113}$$

The integrals, which involve the logarithmic particular solution ψ^* from Eq. (8.112), are evaluated numerically for each element. Reference 7 recommends—and gives a program for—gaussian quadrature formulas.

Equations (8.113) contain $2N$ element values, ψ_i and $(\partial\psi/\partial n)_i$, of which N are known from the given boundary conditions. The remaining N are solved simultaneously from Eqs. (8.113). Generally this completes the analysis—only the boundary solution is computed, and interior points are not studied. In most cases, the boundary velocity and pressure are all that is needed.

We illustrated the method with stream function ψ. Naturally the entire technique also applies to velocity potential ϕ, if we are given proper conditions on ϕ or $\partial\phi/\partial n$ at each boundary element. The method is readily extended to three dimensions [7].

Reference 7 gives a complete FORTRAN listing for solving Eqs. (8.113) numerically for constant, linear, and quadratic element strength variations. We now use their constant-element-strength program, POCONBE [7], to take an alternate look at Example 8.5, which used the finite-difference method.

EXAMPLE 8.6

Solve the duct expansion problem, Example 8.5, using boundary elements. Use the same grid spacing $\Delta x = \Delta y = 0.2$ m for the element sizes.

Solution

The boundary nodes are equally spaced, as shown in Fig. 8.34. There are only 45 nodes, whereas there were 91 interior points for the FDM solution of Example 8.5. We expect the same accuracy for 50 percent fewer nodes. (Had we reduced the grid size to 0.1 m, there would be 90 nodes as opposed to 406 interior points—a savings of 78 percent.) The program POCONBE [7] asks you to input the location of these 45 nodes. The stream-function values are known all around the boundary: ψ equals 0 on the bottom and 10.0 on the top and is linearly increasing from 0 to 10.0 at entrance and exit. These values of ψ, shown on the outside in Fig. 8.34, are inputted into the program.

Once the input of nodes and element values is complete, the program immediately computes and displays or stores the 45 unknowns, which in this case are the values of $\partial\psi/\partial n$ all around the boundary. These values are shown on the inside of the top and bottom surfaces in Fig. 8.34 and represent the local surface velocity near each element, in m/s. The values of $\partial\psi/\partial n$ at entrance and exit, which are small fractions representing vertical velocity components, are not shown here.

Fig. 8.34 Boundary elements corresponding to the same grid size as Fig. 8.31. Nodal values of stream function and computed surface velocity are shown.

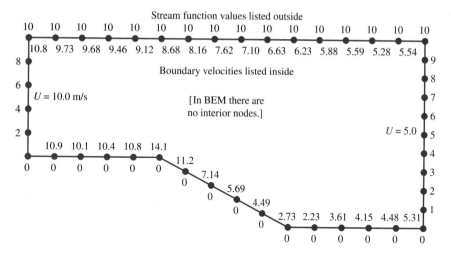

The reader may verify that use of the surface velocities in Fig. 8.34 to compute surface pressure coefficients, as in Example 8.5, leads to curves very similar to those shown in Fig. 8.32. The BEM approach, using the same boundary nodes, has accuracy comparable to that for an FDM computation. For further details see Ref. 7.

Summary

This chapter has analyzed a highly idealized but very useful type of flow: inviscid, incompressible, irrotational flow, for which Laplace's equation holds for the velocity potential (8.1) and for the plane stream function (8.7). The mathematics is well developed, and solutions of potential flows can be obtained for practically any body shape.

Some solution techniques outlined here are (1) superposition of elementary line or point solutions in both plane and axisymmetric flow, (2) the analytic functions of a complex variable, (3) use of variable-strength vortex sheets, and (4) numerical analysis on a digital computer. Potential theory is especially useful and accurate for thin bodies such as airfoils. The only requirement is that the boundary layer be thin, i.e., that the Reynolds number be large.

For blunt bodies or highly divergent flows, potential theory serves as a first approximation, to be used as input to a boundary-layer analysis. The reader should consult the advanced texts [for example, 2 to 4, 10 to 13] for further applications of potential theory.

References

1. O. D. Kellogg, *Foundations of Potential Theory*, Dover, New York, 1953.
2. J. M. Robertson, *Hydrodynamics in Theory and Application*, Prentice-Hall, Englewood Cliffs, N.J., 1965.
3. L. M. Milne-Thomson, *Theoretical Hydrodynamics*, 4th ed., Macmillan, New York, 1960.
4. H. R. Vallentine, *Applied Hydrodynamics*, 4th ed., Macmillan, New York, 1967.
5. S. V. Patankar, *Numerical Heat Transfer and Fluid Flow*, McGraw-Hill, New York, 1980.
6. G. F. Carey and J. T. Oden, *Finite Elements: Fluid Mechanics*, vol. 6, Prentice-Hall, Englewood Cliffs, N.J., 1986.
7. C. A. Brebbia and J. Dominquez, *Boundary Elements—An Introductory Course*, 2d ed., Computational Mechanics Publications, Southampton, England, and McGraw-Hill, New York, 1991.
8. A. D. Moore, "Fields from Fluid Flow Mappers," *J. Appl. Phys.,* vol. 20, 1949, pp. 790–804.
9. H. J. S. Hele-Shaw, "Investigation of the Nature of the Surface Resistance of Water and of Streamline Motion under Certain Experimental Conditions," *Trans. Inst. Nav. Archit.*, vol. 40, 1898, p. 25.
10. R. H. F. Pao, *Fluid Dynamics*, Merrill, Columbus, Ohio, 1967.
11. A. M. Kuethe and C.-Y. Chow, *Foundations of Aerodynamics*, 4th ed., Wiley, New York, 1986.
12. I. H. Abbott and A. E. von Doenhoff, *Theory of Wing Sections*, Dover, New York, 1959.
13. B. Thwaites (ed.), *Incompressible Aerodynamics*, Clarendon Press, Oxford, England, 1960.
14. L. Prandtl, "Applications of Modern Hydrodynamics to Aeronautics," *NACA Rep. 116*, 1921.
15. F. M. White, *Viscous Fluid Flow*, 2d ed., McGraw-Hill, New York, 1991.
16. C. S. Yih, *Fluid Mechanics*, McGraw-Hill, New York, 1969.
17. K. T. Patton, "Tables of Hydrodynamic Mass Factors for Translational Motion," *ASME Winter Annual Meeting*, Paper 65-WA/UNT-2, 1965.
18. J. L. Hess and A. M. O. Smith, "Calculation of Nonlifting Potential Flow about Arbitrary Three-Dimensional Bodies," *J. Ship Res.*, vol. 8, 1964, pp. 22–44.
19. K. H. Huebner and E. A. Thornton, *The Finite Element Method for Engineers*, 2d ed., Wiley, New York, 1983.
20. P. J. Roache, *Computational Fluid Dynamics*, Hermosa Press, Albuquerque, N. Mex., 1976.
21. J. N. Newman, *Marine Hydrodynamics*, M.I.T. Press, Cambridge, Mass., 1977.
22. H. Rouse, *Elementary Mechanics of Fluids*, Wiley, New York, 1946.

PROBLEMS

In addition to many traditional problems, categorized in the prob-lem distribution list below, there are word problems, labeled W8.1 to W8.7, and two design projects, D8.1 and D8.2.

Problem Distribution

Section	Topic	Problems
8.1	Introduction and review	8.1–8.7
8.2	Elementary plane-flow solutions	8.8–8.17
8.3	Superposition of plane flows	8.18–8.34
8.4	Plane flow past closed-body shapes	8.35–8.59
8.5	The complex potential	8.60–8.71
8.6	Images	8.72–8.79
8.7	Airfoil theory: Two-dimensional	8.80–8.84
8.7	Airfoil theory: Finite-span wings	8.85–8.90
8.8	Axisymmetric potential flow	8.91–8.103
8.8	Hydrodynamic mass	8.104–8.105
8.9	Finite-difference methods	8.106–8.111
8.9	Boundary-element methods	8.112–8.114

8.1 Prove that the streamlines $\psi(r, \theta)$ in polar coordinates from Eqs. (8.10) are orthogonal to the potential lines $\phi(r, \theta)$.

8.2 A uniform stream flows downward, $u = 0, v = -U_\infty$. Write the stream function and velocity potential for this flow in (*a*) cartesian coordinates and (*b*) polar coordinates.

8.3 Using cartesian coordinates, show that each velocity component (u, v, w) of a potential flow satisfies Laplace's equation separately.

8.4 Is the function $1/r$ a legitimate velocity potential in plane polar coordinates? if so, what is the associated stream function $\psi(r, \theta)$?

8.5 Consider the two-dimensional velocity distribution $u = -By, v = Bx$, where B is a constant. If this flow possesses a stream function, find its form. If it has a velocity potential, find that also. Compute the local angular velocity of the flow, if any, and describe what the flow might represent.

8.6 An incompressible flow has the velocity potential $\phi = 2Bxy$, where B is a constant. Find the stream function of this flow, sketch a few streamlines, and interpret the pattern.

8.7 Consider a flow with constant density and viscosity. If the flow possesses a velocity potential as defined by Eq. (8.1), show that it exactly satisfies the full Navier-Stokes equations (4.38). If this is so, why for inviscid theory do we back away from the full Navier-Stokes equations?

8.8 For the velocity distribution of Prob. 8.5, evaluate the circulation Γ around the rectangular closed curve defined by $(x, y) = (1, 1), (3, 1), (3, 2)$, and $(1, 2)$. Interpret your result, especially vis-à-vis the velocity potential.

8.9 Consider the two-dimensional flow $u = -Ax, v = Ay$, where A is a constant. Evaluate the circulation Γ around the rectangular closed curve defined by $(x, y) = (1, 1), (4, 1), (4, 3)$, and $(1, 3)$. Interpret your result, especially vis-à-vis the velocity potential.

8.10 A mathematical relation sometimes used in fluid mechanics is the theorem of Stokes [1]

$$\oint_C \mathbf{V} \cdot d\mathbf{s} = \iint_A (\nabla \times \mathbf{V}) \cdot \mathbf{n} \, dA$$

where A is any surface and C is the curve enclosing that surface. The vector $d\mathbf{s}$ is the differential arc length along C, and $\mathbf{n}$ is the unit outward normal vector to A. How does this relation simplify for irrotational flow, and how does the resulting line integral relate to velocity potential?

8.11 A power-plant discharges cooling water through the manifold in Fig. P8.11, which is 55 cm in diameter and 8 m high and is perforated with 25,000 holes 1 cm in diameter. Does this manifold simulate a line source? If so, what is the equivalent source strength m?

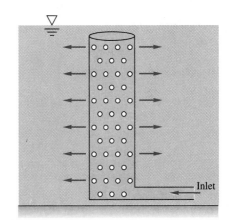

Fig. P8.11

8.12 Consider the flow due to a vortex of strength K at the origin. Evaluate the circulation from Eq. (8.15) about the clockwise path from $(r, \theta) = (a, 0)$ to $(2a, 0)$ to $(2a, 3\pi/2)$ to $(a, 3\pi/2)$ and back to $(a, 0)$. Interpret the result.

8.13 A well-known exact solution to the Navier-Stokes equations (4.38) is the unsteady circulating motion [15]

$$v_\theta = \frac{K}{2\pi r}\left[1 - \exp\left(-\frac{r^2}{4vt}\right)\right] \qquad v_r = v_z = 0$$

where K is a constant and ν is the kinematic viscosity. Does this flow have a polar-coordinate stream function and/or velocity potential? Explain. Evaluate the circulation Γ for this motion, plot it versus r for a given finite time, and interpret compared to ordinary line vortex motion.

8.14 A tornado may be modeled as the circulating flow shown in Fig. P8.14, with $v_r = v_z = 0$ and $v_\theta(r)$ such that

$$v_\theta = \begin{cases} \omega r & r \le R \\ \dfrac{\omega R^2}{r} & r > R \end{cases}$$

Determine whether this flow pattern is irrotational in either the inner or outer region. Using the r-momentum equation (E.5) of App. E, determine the pressure distribution $p(r)$ in the tornado, assuming $p = p_\infty$ as $r \to \infty$. Find the location and magnitude of the lowest pressure.

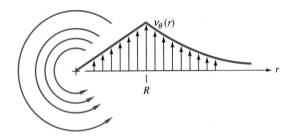

Fig. P8.14

8.15 Evaluate Prob. 8.14 for the particular case of a small-scale tornado, $R = 100$ m, $v_{\theta,\max} = 65$ m/s, with sea-level conditions at $r = \infty$. Plot $p(r)$ out to $r = 400$ m.

8.16 Evaluate Prob. 8.14 for the particular case of a large-scale hurricane, $R = 8$ km, $v_{\theta,\max} = 45$ m/s, with sea-level conditions at $r = \infty$. Plot $p(r)$ out to $r = 30$ km.

8.17 Examine the flow of Fig. 8.30 as an *analytical* (not a numerical) problem. Give the appropriate differential equation and the complete boundary conditions for both the stream function and the velocity potential. Is a Fourier-series solution possible?

8.18 Using the graphical method of Fig. 8.4, plot the streamlines and potential lines of the flow due to a line source of strength m at $(a, 0)$ plus a source $3m$ at $(-a, 0)$. What is the flow pattern viewed from afar?

8.19 Plot the streamlines and potential lines of the flow due to a line source of strength $3m$ at $(a, 0)$ plus a sink $-m$ at $(-a, 0)$. What is the pattern viewed from afar?

8.20 Plot the streamlines of the flow due to a line vortex $+K$ at $(0, +a)$ and a vortex $-K$ at $(0, -a)$. What is the pattern viewed from afar?

8.21 Plot the streamlines of the flow due to a line vortex $+K$ at

$(+a, 0)$ and a vortex $-2K$ at $(-a, 0)$. What is the pattern viewed from afar?

8.22 Plot the streamlines of a uniform stream $\mathbf{V} = \mathbf{i}U$ plus a clockwise line vortex $-K$ located at the origin. Are there any stagnation points?

8.23 Find the resultant velocity vector induced at point A in Fig. P8.23 by the uniform stream, vortex, and line source.

Fig. P8.23

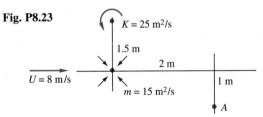

8.24 Line sources of equal strength $m = Ua$, where U is a reference velocity, are placed at $(x, y) = (0, a)$ and $(0, -a)$. Sketch the stream and potential lines in the upper half plane. Is $y = 0$ a "wall"? If so, sketch the pressure coefficient

$$C_p = \frac{p - p_0}{\frac{1}{2}\rho U^2}$$

along the wall, where p_0 is the pressure at $(0, 0)$. Find the minimum pressure point and indicate where flow separation might occur in the boundary layer.

8.25 Let the vortex/sink flow of Eq. (4.134) simulate a tornado as in Fig. P8.25. Suppose that the circulation about the tornado is $\Gamma = 8500$ m^2/s and that the pressure at $r = 40$ m is 2200 Pa less than the far-field pressure. Assuming inviscid flow at sea-level density, estimate (a) the appropriate sink strength $-m$, (b) the pressure at $r = 15$ m, and (c) the angle β at which the streamlines cross the circle at $r = 40$ m (see Fig. P8.25).

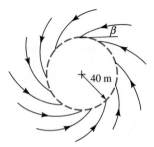

Fig. P8.25

8.26 Find the resultant velocity vector induced at point A in Fig. P8.26 by the uniform stream, line source, line sink, and vortex.

8.27 A counterclockwise line vortex of strength $3K$ at $(x, y) = (0, a)$ is combined with a clockwise vortex K at $(0, -a)$. Plot the streamline and potential-line pattern, and find the

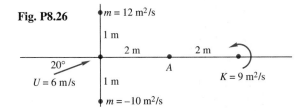

Fig. P8.26

point of minimum velocity between the two vortices.

8.28 Sources of equal strength m are placed at the four symmetric positions $(x, y) = (a, a), (-a, a), (-a, -a),$ and $(a, -a)$. Sketch the streamline and potential-line patterns. Do any plane "walls" appear?

8.29 A uniform water stream, $U_\infty = 20$ m/s and $\rho = 998$ kg/m^3, combines with a source at the origin to form a half-body. At $(x, y) = (0, 1.2$ m$)$, the pressure is 12.5 kPa less than p_∞. (a) Is this point outside the body? Estimate (b) the appropriate source strength m and (c) the pressure at the nose of the body.

8.30 Suppose that the total discharge from the manifold in Fig. P8.11 is 450 m^3/s and that there is a uniform ocean current of 60 cm/s to the right. Sketch the flow pattern from above, showing the dimensions and the region where the cooling-water discharge is confined.

8.31 A Rankine half-body is formed as shown in Fig. P8.31. For the stream velocity and body dimension shown, compute (a) the source strength m in m^2/s, (b) the distance a, (c) the distance h, and (d) the total velocity at point A.

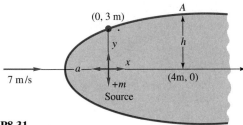

Fig. P8.31

8.32 Sketch the streamlines, especially the body shape, due to equal line sources $+m$ at $(-a, 0)$ and $(+a, 0)$ plus a uniform stream $U_\infty = ma$.

8.33 Sketch the streamlines, especially the body shape, due to equal line sources $+m$ at $(0, +a)$ and $(0, -a)$ plus a uniform stream $U_\infty = ma$.

8.34 Consider three equally spaced sources of strength m placed at $(x, y) = (0, +a), (0, 0),$ and $(0, -a)$. Sketch the resulting streamlines, noting the position of any stagnation points. What would the pattern look like from afar?

8.35 A Rankine oval is formed by a line source-sink pair with $m = 6$ m^2/s, $a = 2$ m, and $U_\infty = 6$ m/s. Find the length and width of the body and the velocity at the shoulder.

8.36 When a line source-sink pair with $m = 2$ m^2/s is combined with a uniform stream, it forms a Rankine oval whose minimum dimension is 40 cm. If $a = 15$ cm, what are the stream velocity and the velocity at the shoulder? What is the maximum dimension?

8.37 A Rankine oval 2 m long and 1 m high is immersed in a stream $U_\infty = 10$ m/s, as in Fig. P8.37. Estimate (a) the velocity at point A and (b) the location of point B where a particle approaching the stagnation point achieves its maximum deceleration.

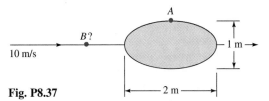

Fig. P8.37

8.38 A uniform stream U in the x direction combines with a source m at $(a, 0)$ and a sink $-m$ at $(-a, 0)$. Plot the resulting streamlines and note any stagnation points.

8.39 Sketch the streamlines of a uniform stream U_∞ past a line source-sink pair aligned vertically with the source at $+a$ and the sink at $-a$ on the y axis. Does a closed-body shape form?

8.40 Consider a uniform stream U_∞ plus line sources $+m$ at $(x, y) = (+a, 0)$ and $(-a, 0)$ and a single line sink $-2m$ at the origin. Does a closed-body shape appear? If so, plot its shape for $m/(U_\infty a)$ equal to (a) 1.0 and (b) 5.0.

8.41 A Kelvin oval is formed by a line-vortex pair with $K = 9$ m^2/s, $a = 1$ m, and $U = 10$ m/s. What are the height, width, and shoulder velocity of this oval?

8.42 For what value of $K/(U_\infty a)$ does the velocity at the shoulder of a Kelvin oval equal $4U_\infty$? What is the height h/a of this oval?

8.43 Consider water at 20°C flowing at 6 m/s past a 1-m-diameter circular cylinder. What doublet strength λ in m^3/s is required to simulate this flow? If the stream pressure is 200 kPa, use inviscid theory to estimate the surface pressure at θ equal to (a) 180°, (b) 135°, and (c) 90°.

8.44 Suppose that circulation is added to the cylinder flow of Prob. 8.43 sufficient to place the stagnation points at θ equal to 50° and 130°. What is the required vortex strength K in m^2/s? Compute the resulting pressure and surface velocity at (a) the stagnation points and (b) the upper and lower shoulders. What will the lift per meter of cylinder width be?

8.45 What circulation K must be added to the cylinder flow in Prob. 8.43 to place the stagnation point exactly at the upper shoulder? What will the velocity and pressure at the lower shoulder be then? What value of K causes the lower shoulder pressure to be 10 kPa?

8.46 A cylinder is formed by bolting two semicylindrical channels together on the inside, as shown in Fig. P8.46. There are 10 bolts per meter of width on each side, and the inside pressure is 50 kPa (gage). Using potential theory for the outside pressure, compute the tension force in each bolt if the fluid outside is sea-level air.

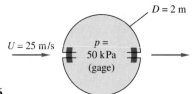

Fig. P8.46

8.47 A circular cylinder is fitted with two surface-mounted pressure sensors, to measure p_a at $\theta = 180°$ and p_b at $\theta = 105°$. The intention is to use the cylinder as a stream velocimeter. Using inviscid theory, derive a formula for estimating U_∞ in terms of p_a, p_b, ρ, and the cylinder radius a.

8.48 Wind at U_∞ and p_∞ flows past a Quonset hut which is a half-cylinder of radius a and length L (Fig. P8.48). The internal pressure is p_i. Using inviscid theory, derive an expression for the upward force on the hut due to the difference between p_i and p_s.

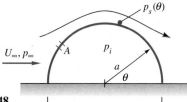

Fig. P8.48

8.49 In strong winds the force in Prob. 8.48 can be quite large. Suppose that a hole is introduced in the hut roof at point A to make p_i equal to the surface pressure there. At what angle θ should hole A be placed to make the net wind force zero?

8.50 It is desired to simulate flow past a two-dimensional ridge or bump by using a streamline which passes above the flow over a cylinder, as in Fig. P8.50. The bump is to be $a/2$

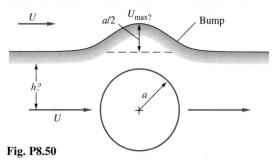

Fig. P8.50

high, where a is the cylinder radius. What is the elevation h of this streamline? What is U_{max} on the bump compared with stream velocity U?

8.51 Modify Prob. 8.50 as follows. Let the bump be such that $U_{max} = 1.5U$. Find (a) the upstream elevation h and (b) the height of the bump.

8.52 The Flettner rotor sailboat in Fig. E8.3 has a water drag coefficient of 0.006 based on a wetted area of 45 ft². If the rotor spins at 220 r/min, find the maximum boat velocity that can be achieved in a 15-mi/h wind. What is the optimum angle between the boat and the wind?

8.53 Modify Prob. 8.52 as follows. For the same sailboat data, find the wind velocity, in mi/h, which will drive the boat at an optimum speed of 10 kn parallel to its keel.

8.54 The original Flettner rotor ship was approximately 100 ft long, displaced 800 tons, and had a wetted area of 3500 ft². As sketched in Fig. P8.54, it had two rotors 50 ft high and 9 ft in diameter rotating at 750 r/min, which is far outside the range of Fig. 8.11. The measured lift and drag coefficients for each rotor were about 10 and 4, respectively. If the ship is moored and subjected to a crosswind of 25 ft/s, as in Fig. P8.54, what will the wind force parallel and normal to the ship centerline be? Estimate the power required to drive the rotors.

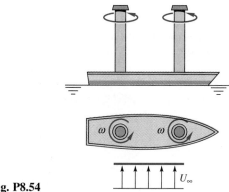

Fig. P8.54

8.55 Assume that the Flettner rotorship of Fig. P8.54 has a water resistance coefficient of 0.005. How fast will the ship sail in seawater at 20°C in a 20 ft/s wind if the keel aligns itself with the resultant force on the rotors? *Hint:* This is a problem in relative velocities.

8.56 The measured drag coefficient of a cylinder in crossflow, based on frontal area DL, is approximately 1.0 for the laminar-boundary-layer range (see Fig. 7.16a). Boundary-layer separation occurs near the shoulder (see Fig. 7.13a). This suggests an analytical model: the standard inviscid-flow solution on the front of the cylinder and constant pressure (equal to the shoulder value) on the rear. Use this model to predict the drag coefficient and comment on the results with reference to Fig. 7.13c.

8.57 In principle, it is possible to use rotating cylinders as aircraft wings. Consider a cylinder 30 cm in diameter, rotating at 2400 r/min. It is to lift a 55-kN airplane cruising at 100 m/s. What should the cylinder length be? How much power is required to maintain this speed? Neglect end effects on the rotating wing.

8.58 Plot the streamlines due to the combined flow of a line sink $-m$ at the origin plus line sources $+m$ at $(a, 0)$ and $(4a, 0)$. *Hint:* A cylinder of radius $2a$ will appear.

8.59 By analogy with Prob. 8.58 plot the streamlines due to counterclockwise line vortices $+K$ at $(0, 0)$ and $(4a, 0)$ plus a clockwise vortex $-K$ at $(a, 0)$. Again a cylinder appears.

8.60 One of the corner-flow patterns of Fig. 8.15 is given by the cartesian stream function $\psi = A(3yx^2 - y^3)$. Which one? Can the correspondence be proved from Eq. (8.49)?

8.61 Plot the streamlines of Eq. (8.49) in the upper right quadrant for $n = 4$. How does the velocity increase with x outward along the x axis from the origin? For what corner angle and value of n would this increase be linear in x? For what corner angle and n would the increase be as x^5?

8.62 Combine stagnation flow, Fig. 8.14b, with a source at the origin:

$$f(z) = Az^2 + m \ln z$$

Plot the streamlines for $m = AL^2$, where L is a length scale. Interpret.

8.63 The superposition in Prob. 8.62 leads to stagnation flow near a curved bump, in contrast to the flat wall of Fig. 8.14b. Determine the maximum height H of the bump as a function of the constants A and m.

8.64 Determine qualitatively from boundary-layer theory (Chap. 7) whether any of the three stagnation-flow patterns of Fig. 8.15 can suffer flow separation along the walls.

8.65 Potential flow past a wedge of half-angle θ leads to an important application of laminar-boundary-layer theory called the *Falkner-Skan flows* [15, pp. 242–247]. Let x denote distance along the wedge wall, as in Fig. P8.65, and let $\theta = 10°$. Use Eq. (8.49) to find the variation of surface velocity $U(x)$ along the wall. Is the pressure gradient adverse or favorable?

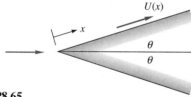

Fig. P8.65

8.66 The inviscid velocity along the wedge in Prob. 8.65 has the

analytic form $U(x) = Cx^m$, where $m = n - 1$ and n is the exponent in Eq. (8.49). Show that, for any C and n, computation of the boundary layer by Thwaites' method, Eqs. (7.53) and (7.54), leads to a unique value of the Thwaites parameter λ. Thus wedge flows are called *similar* [15, p. 244].

8.67 Investigate the complex potential function $f(z) = U_\infty(z + a^2/z)$ and interpret the flow pattern.

8.68 Investigate the complex potential function $f(z) = U_\infty z + m \ln [(z + a)/(z - a)]$ and interpret the flow pattern.

8.69 Investigate the complex potential $f(z) = A \cosh [\pi(z/a)]$, and plot the streamlines inside the region shown in Fig. P8.69. What hyphenated word (originally French) might describe such a flow pattern?

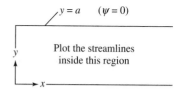

Fig. P8.69

8.70 Show that the complex potential $f = U_\infty\{z + \frac{1}{4}a \coth [\pi(z/a)]\}$ represents flow past an oval shape placed midway between two parallel walls $y = \pm\frac{1}{2}a$. What is a practical application?

8.71 Figure P8.71 shows the streamlines and potential lines of flow over a thin-plate weir as computed by the complex potential method. Compare qualitatively with Fig. 10.16a. State the proper boundary conditions at all boundaries. The velocity potential has equally spaced values. Why do the flow-net "squares" become smaller in the overflow jet?

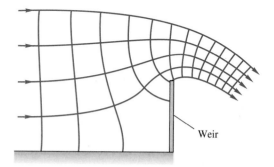

Fig. P8.71

8.72 Use the method of images to construct the flow pattern for a source $+m$ near two walls, as shown in Fig. P8.72. Sketch the velocity distribution along the lower wall $(y = 0)$. Is there any danger of flow separation along this wall?

8.73 Set up an image system to compute the flow of a source at

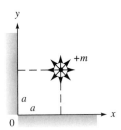

Fig. P8.72

unequal distances from two walls, as in Fig. P8.73. Find the point of maximum velocity on the y axis.

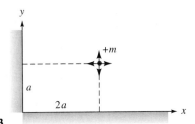

Fig. P8.73

8.74   A positive line vortex K is trapped in a corner, as in Fig. P8.74. Compute the total induced velocity vector at point B, $(x, y) = (2a, a)$, and compare with the induced velocity when no walls are present.

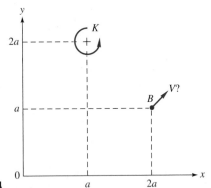

Fig. P8.74

8.75   The flow past a cylinder very near a wall might be simulated by doublet images, as in Fig. P8.75. Explain why the result is not very successful and the cylinder shape becomes badly distorted.

8.76   Use the method of images to approximate the flow pattern past a cylinder a distance $4a$ from a single wall, as in Fig. P8.76. To illustrate the effect of the wall, compute the velocities at corresponding points A, B and C, D, comparing with a cylinder flow in an infinite expanse of fluid.

8.77   Discuss how the flow pattern of Prob. 8.58 might be interpreted to be an image-system construction for circular walls.

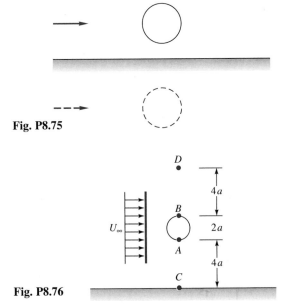

Fig. P8.75

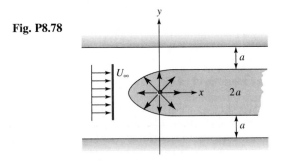

Fig. P8.76

Why are there two images instead of one?

8.78   Indicate the system of images needed to construct the flow of a uniform stream past a Rankine half-body constrained between two parallel walls, as in Fig. P8.78. For the particular dimensions shown in this figure, estimate the position of the nose of the resulting half-body.

Fig. P8.78

8.79   Explain the system of images needed to simulate the flow of a line source placed unsymmetrically between two parallel walls as in Fig. P8.79. Compute the velocity on the lower wall at $x = a$. How many images are needed to estimate this velocity within 1 percent?

8.80   The NACA 4412 airfoil has 4 percent camber and 12 percent thickness. For two-dimensional flow at an angle of attack of $5°$, estimate its theoretical lift coefficient and its moment coefficient about the leading edge.

8.81   A two-dimensional airfoil has 2 percent camber and 10 percent thickness. If $C = 1.75$ m, estimate its lift per meter

Fig. P8.79

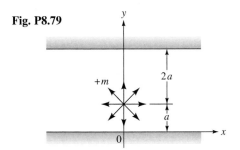

when immersed in 20°C water at $\alpha = 6°$ and $U = 18$ m/s.

8.82 The ultralight plane *Gossamer Condor* in 1977 was the first to complete the Kremer Prize figure-eight course under human power. Its wingspan was 29 m, with $C_{av} = 2.3$ m and a total mass of 95 kg. The drag coefficient was approximately 0.05. The pilot was able to deliver $\frac{1}{4}$ hp to propel the plane. Assuming two-dimensional flow at sea level, estimate (a) the cruise speed attained, (b) the lift coefficient, and (c) the horsepower required to achieve a speed of 15 kn.

8.83 Two-dimensional lift-drag data for the NACA 2412 airfoil with 2 percent camber (from Ref. 12) may be curve-fitted accurately as follows:

$$C_L \approx 0.178 + 0.109\alpha - 0.00109\alpha^2$$

$$C_D \approx 0.0089 + 1.97 \text{ E-4 } \alpha + 8.45 \text{ E-5 } \alpha^2$$

$$- 1.35 \text{ E-5 } \alpha^3 + 9.92 \text{ E-7 } \alpha^4$$

with α in degrees in the range $-4° < \alpha < +10°$. Compare (a) the lift-curve slope and (b) the angle of zero lift with theory, Eq. (8.69). (c) Prepare a polar lift-drag plot and compare with Fig. 7.25.

8.84 Reference 12 contains inviscid-theory calculations for the upper and lower surface velocity distributions $V(x)$ over an airfoil, where x is the chordwise coordinate. A typical result for small angle of attack is as follows:

x/c	V/U_∞(upper)	V/U_∞(lower)
0.0	0.0	0.0
0.025	0.97	0.82
0.05	1.23	0.98
0.1	1.28	1.05
0.2	1.29	1.13
0.3	1.29	1.16
0.4	1.24	1.16
0.6	1.14	1.08
0.8	0.99	0.95
1.0	0.82	0.82

Use these data, plus Bernoulli's equation, to estimate (a) the lift coefficient and (b) the angle of attack if the airfoil is symmetric.

8.85 A wing of 2 percent camber, 5-in chord, and 30-in span is tested at a certain angle of attack in a wind tunnel with sea-level standard air at 200 ft/s and is found to have lift of 30 lbf and drag of 1.5 lbf. Estimate from wing theory (a) the angle of attack, (b) the minimum drag of the wing and the angle of attack at which it occurs, and (c) the maximum lift-to-drag ratio.

8.86 An airplane has a mass of 20,000 kg and flies at 175 m/s at 5000-m standard altitude. Its rectangular wing has a 3-m chord and a symmetric airfoil at 2.5° angle of attack. Estimate (a) the wing span, (b) the aspect ratio, and (c) the induced drag.

8.87 A freshwater boat of mass 400 kg is supported by a rectangular hydrofoil of aspect ratio 8, 2 percent camber, and 12 percent thickness. If the boat travels at 8 m/s and $\alpha = 3.5°$, estimate (a) the chord length, (b) the power required if $C_{D_\infty} = 0.01$, and (c) the top speed if the boat is refitted with an engine which delivers 50 hp to the water.

8.88 The Boeing 727 airplane has a gross weight of 125,000 lbf, a wing area of 1200 ft², and an aspect ratio of 6. It is fitted with two turbofan engines and cruises at 532 mi/h at 30,000-ft standard altitude. Assume for this problem that its airfoil is the NACA 2412 section described in Prob. 8.83. If we neglect all drag except the wing, what thrust is required from each engine for these conditions?

8.89 The Beechcraft T-34C aircraft has a gross weight of 5500 lbf and a wing area of 60 ft² and flies at 322 mi/h at 10,000-ft standard altitude. It is driven by a propeller which delivers 300 hp to the air. Assume for this problem that its airfoil is the NACA 2412 section described in Prob. 8.83, and neglect all drag except the wing. What is the appropriate aspect ratio for the wing?

8.90 When moving at 15 m/s in seawater at its maximum lift-to-drag ratio of 18:1, a symmetric hydrofoil, of plan area 3 m², develops a lift of 120 kN. Estimate from wing theory (a) the aspect ratio and (b) the angle of attack in degrees.

8.91 If $\phi(r, \theta)$ in axisymmetric flow is defined by Eq. (8.85) and the coordinates are given in Fig. 8.24, determine what partial differential equation is satisfied by ϕ.

8.92 A point source with volume flow $Q = 30$ m³/s is immersed in a uniform stream of speed 4 m/s. A Rankine half-body of revolution results. Compute (a) the distance from source to the stagnation point and (b) the two points (r, θ) on the body surface where the local velocity equals 4.5 m/s.

8.93 The Rankine half-body of revolution (Fig. 8.26) could simulate the shape of a pitot-static tube (Fig. 6.30). According to inviscid theory, how far downstream from the nose should the static pressure holes be placed so that the local velocity is within ± 0.5 percent of U_∞? Compare your answer with the recommendation $x \approx 8D$ in Fig. 6.30.

8.94 Determine whether the Stokes streamlines from Eq. (8.86) are everywhere orthogonal to the Stokes potential lines from Eq. (8.87), as is the case for cartesian and plane polar coordinates.

8.95 Show that the axisymmetric potential flow formed by superposition of a point source $+m$ at $(x, y) = (-a, 0)$, a point sink $-m$ at $(+a, 0)$, and a stream U_∞ in the x direction forms a Rankine body of revolution as in Fig. P8.95. Find

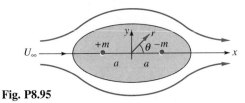

Fig. P8.95

analytic expressions for determining the length $2L$ and maximum diameter $2R$ of the body in terms of m, U_∞, and a.

8.96 For the Rankine body of P8.95, suppose that $a = 1$ m, $U_\infty = 12$ m/s, and $m = 30$ m³/s. Compute (a) the length, (b) the maximum diameter, and (c) the maximum surface velocity for the body.

8.97 The Rankine body of revolution in Fig. P8.97 is 60 cm long and 30 cm in diameter. When it is immersed in the low-pressure water tunnel as shown, cavitation may appear at point A. Compute the stream velocity U, neglecting surface wave formation, for which cavitation occurs.

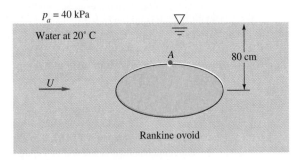

Fig. P8.97

8.98 We have studied the point source (sink) and the line source (sink) of infinite depth into the paper. Does it make any sense to define a finite-length line sink (source) as in Fig. P8.98? If so, how would you establish the mathematical properties of such a finite line sink? When combined with a uniform stream and a point source of equivalent strength

Fig. P8.98

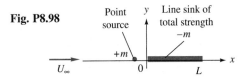

as in Fig. P8.98, should a closed-body shape be formed? Make a guess and sketch some of these possible shapes for various values of the dimensionless parameter $m/(U_\infty L^2)$.

8.99 Consider air flowing past a hemisphere resting on a flat surface, as in Fig. P8.99. If the internal pressure is p_i, find an expression for the pressure force on the hemisphere. By analogy with Prob. 8.49, at what point A on the hemisphere should a hole be cut so that the pressure force will be zero according to inviscid theory?

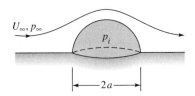

Fig. P8.99

8.100 A 1-m-diameter sphere is being towed at speed V in fresh water at 20°C as shown in Fig. P8.100. Assuming inviscid theory with an undistorted free surface, estimate the speed V in m/s at which cavitation will first appear on the sphere surface. Where will cavitation appear? For this condition, what will be the pressure at point A on the sphere which is 45° up from the direction of travel?

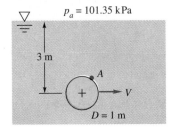

Fig. P8.100

8.101 Normally by its very nature inviscid theory is incapable of predicting body drag, but by analogy with Fig. 8.16c we can analyze flow approaching a hemisphere, as in Fig. P8.101. Assume that the flow on the front follows inviscid sphere theory, Eq. (8.96), and the pressure in the rear equals the shoulder pressure. Compute the drag coefficient and compare with experiment (Table 7.3). What are the defects and limitations of this analysis?

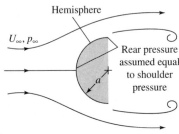

Fig. P8.101

8.102 A golf ball weighs 0.102 lbf and has a diameter of 1.7 in. A professional golfer strikes the ball at an initial velocity of 250 ft/s, an upward angle of 20°, and a backspin (front of the ball rotating upward). Assume that the lift coefficient on the ball (based on frontal area) follows Fig. P7.108. If the ground is level and drag is neglected, make a simple analysis to predict the impact point (*a*) without spin and (*b*) with backspin of 7500 r/min.

8.103 Modify Prob. 8.102 as follows. Golf balls are dimpled, not smooth, and have higher lift and lower drag ($C_L \approx 0.2$ and $C_D \approx 0.3$ for typical backspin). Using these values, make a computer analysis of the ball trajectory for the initial conditions of Prob. 8.102. If time permits, investigate the effect of initial angle for the range $10° < \theta_0 < 50°$.

8.104 Consider a cylinder of radius *a* moving at speed U_∞ through a still fluid, as in Fig. P8.104. Plot the streamlines relative to the cylinder by modifying Eq. (8.32) to give the relative flow with $K = 0$. Integrate to find the total relative kinetic energy, and verify the hydrodynamic mass of a cylinder from Eq. (8.104).

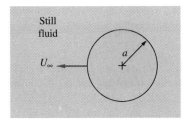

Fig. P8.104

8.105 In Table 7.2 the drag coefficient of a 4:1 elliptical cylinder in laminar-boundary-layer flow is 0.35. According to Patton [17], the hydrodynamic mass of this cylinder is $\pi \rho h b/4$, where *b* is width into the paper and *h* is the maximum thickness. Use these results to derive a formula from the time history *U(t)* of the cylinder if it is accelerated from rest in a still fluid by the sudden application of a constant force *F*.

8.106 Laplace's equation in plane polar coordinates, Eq. (8.11), is complicated by the variable radius. Consider the finite-difference mesh in Fig. P8.106, with nodes (*i*, *j*) equally spaced $\Delta\theta$ and Δr apart. Derive a finite-difference model for Eq. (8.11) similar to the cartesian expression (8.109).

8.107 Set up the numerical problem of Fig. 8.30 for an expansion of 30°. A new grid system and a nonsquare mesh may be needed. Give the proper nodal equation and boundary conditions. If possible, program this 30° expansion and solve on a digital computer.

8.108 Consider two-dimensional potential flow into a step contraction as in Fig. P8.108. The inlet velocity $U_1 = 7$ m/s, and the outlet velocity U_2 is uniform. The nodes (*i*, *j*) are

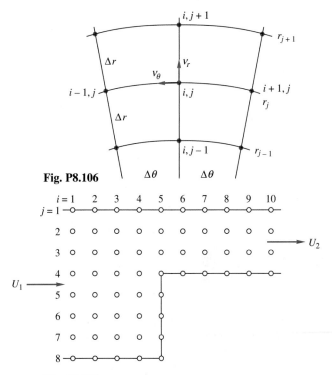

Fig. P8.106

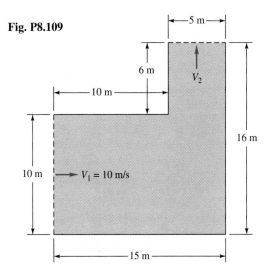

Fig. P8.108

labeled in the figure. Set up the complete finite-difference algebraic relations for all nodes. Solve, if possible, on a digital computer and plot the streamlines in the flow.

8.109 Consider inviscid flow through a two-dimensional 90° bend with a contraction, as in Fig. P8.109. Assume uniform flow at the entrance and exit. Make a finite-difference computer

Fig. P8.109

analysis for small grid size (at least 150 nodes), determine the dimensionless pressure distribution along the walls, and sketch the streamlines. (You may use either square or rectangular grids.)

8.110 For fully developed laminar incompressible flow through a straight noncircular duct, as in Sec. 6.6, the Navier-Stokes equations (4.38) reduce to

$$\frac{\partial^2 u}{\partial y^2} + \frac{\partial^2 u}{\partial z^2} = \frac{1}{\mu} \frac{dp}{dx} = \text{const} < 0$$

where (y, z) is the plane of the duct cross section and x is along the duct axis. Gravity is neglected. Using a nonsquare rectangular grid ($\Delta x, \Delta y$), develop a finite-difference model for this equation, and indicate how it may be applied to solve for flow in a rectangular duct of side lengths a and b.

8.111 Solve Prob. 8.110 numerically for a rectangular duct of side length b by $2b$, using at least 100 nodal points. Evaluate the volume flow rate and the friction factor, and compare with the results in Table 6.4:

$$Q \approx 0.1143 \frac{b^4}{\mu}\left(-\frac{dp}{dx}\right) \qquad f\,\text{Re}_{D_h} \approx 62.19$$

where $D_h = 4A/P = 4b/3$ for this case. Comment on the possible truncation errors of your model.

8.112 If your institution has an online potential-flow boundary-element computer code, use it to solve Prob. 8.108 for (a) the given mesh spacing and (b) one-half of the given spacing. Plot the velocity distribution along the duct walls, but do not attempt to find the internal streamlines.

8.113 By analogy with Prob. 8.112, solve Prob. 8.109, using an

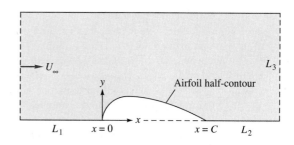

Fig. P8.114

online boundary-element computer code.

8.114 If your institution has an online potential-flow boundary-element computer code, consider flow past a symmetric airfoil, as in Fig. P8.114. The basic shape of an NACA symmetric airfoil is defined by the function [12]

$$\frac{2y}{t_{max}} \approx 1.4845\zeta^{1/2} - 0.63\zeta - 1.758\zeta^2$$
$$+ 1.4215\zeta^3 - 0.5075\zeta^4$$

where $\zeta = x/C$ and the maximum thickness t_{max} occurs at $\zeta = 0.3$. Use this shape as part of the lower boundary for zero angle of attack. Let the thickness be fairly large, say, $t_{max} = 0.12, 0.15,$ or 0.18. Choose a generous number of nodes (≥ 60), and calculate and plot the velocity distribution V/U_∞ along the airfoil surface. Compare with the theoretical results in Ref. 12 for NACA 0012, 0015, or 0018 airfoils. If time permits, investigate the effect of the boundary lengths L_1, L_2, and L_3, which can initially be set equal to the chord length C.

Word Problems

W8.1 What simplifications have been made, in the potential-flow theory of this chapter, which result in the elimination of the Reynolds number, Froude number, and Mach number as important parameters?

W8.2 In this chapter we superimpose many basic solutions, a concept associated with *linear* equations. Yet Bernoulli's equation (8.3) is *nonlinear*, being proportional to the square of the velocity. How, then, do we justify the use of superposition in inviscid-flow analysis?

W8.3 Give a physical explanation of circulation Γ as it relates to the lift force on an immersed body. If the line integral defined by Eq. (8.15) is zero, it means that the integrand is a perfect differential—but of what variable?

W8.4 Give a simple proof of Eq. (8.42), namely, that both the real and imaginary parts of a function $f(z)$ are laplacian if $z = x + iy$. What is the secret of this remarkable behavior?

W8.5 Figure 8.14 contains five body corners. Without carrying out any calculations, explain physically what the value of the inviscid fluid velocity must be at each of these five corners. Is any flow separation expected?

W8.6 Explain the Kutta condition physically. Why is it necessary?

W8.7 We have briefly outlined finite-difference and boundary-element methods for potential flow but have neglected the *finite-element* technique. Do some reading and write a brief essay on the use of the finite-element method for potential-flow problems.

Design Projects

D8.1 In 1927, Theodore von Kármán developed a scheme to use a uniform stream, plus a row of sources and sinks, to generate an arbitrary closed-body shape. A schematic of the idea is sketched in Fig. D8.1. The body is symmetric and at zero angle of attack. A total of N sources and sinks are distributed along the axis within the body, with strengths m_i at positions x_i, for $i = 1$ to N. The object is to find the correct distribution of strengths which approximates a given body shape $y(x)$ at a finite number of surface locations and then to compute the approximate surface velocity and pressure. The technique should work for either two-dimensional bodies (distributed line sources) or bodies of revolution (distributed point sources).

For our body shape let us select the NACA 0018 airfoil, given by the formula in Prob. 8.114 with $t_{max} = 0.18$. Develop the ideas stated above into N simultaneous algebraic equations which can be used to solve for the N unknown line source/sink strengths. Then program your equations for a computer, with $N \geq 20$, solve for m_i, compute the surface

velocities, and compare with the theoretical velocities for this shape in Ref. 12. Your goal should be to achieve accuracy within ± 1 percent of the classical results. If necessary, you should adjust N and the locations of the sources.

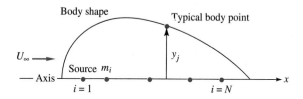

D8.2 Modify Prob. D8.1 to solve for the point-source distribution which approximates an "0018" body-of-revolution shape. Since no theoretical results are published, simply make sure that your results converge to ± 1 percent.

Chapter 9
Compressible Flow

Motivation. All eight of our previous chapters have been concerned with "low-speed" or "incompressible" flow, i.e., where the fluid velocity is much less than its speed of sound. In fact, we did not even develop an expression for the speed of sound of a fluid. That is done in this chapter.

When a fluid moves at speeds comparable to its speed of sound, density changes become significant and the flow is termed *compressible*. Such flows are difficult to obtain in liquids, since high pressures of order 1000 atm are needed to generate sonic velocities. In gases, however, a pressure ratio of only 2:1 will likely cause sonic flow. Thus compressible gas flow is quite common, and this subject is often called *gas dynamics*.

Probably the two most important and distinctive effects of compressibility on flow are (1) *choking*, wherein the duct flow rate is sharply limited by the sonic condition, and (2) *shock waves*, which are nearly discontinuous property changes in a supersonic flow. The purpose of this chapter is to explain such striking phenomena and to familiarize the reader with engineering calculations of compressible flow.

9.1 Introduction

We took a brief look in Chap. 4 [Eqs. (4.13) to (4.17)] to see when we might safely neglect the compressibility inherent in every real fluid. We found that the proper criterion for a nearly incompressible flow was a small Mach number

$$\text{Ma} = \frac{V}{a} \ll 1$$

where V is the flow velocity and a is the speed of sound of the fluid. Under small-Mach-number conditions, changes in fluid density are everywhere small in the flow field. The energy equation becomes uncoupled, and temperature effects can be either ignored or put aside for later study. The equation of state degenerates into the simple statement that density is nearly constant. This means that an incompressible flow requires only a momentum and continuity analysis, as we showed with many examples in Chaps. 7 and 8.

This chapter treats compressible flows, which have Mach numbers greater than about 0.3 and thus exhibit nonnegligible density changes. If the density change is significant, it follows from the equation of state that the temperature and pressure changes are also substantial. Large temperature changes imply that the energy equation can no longer be neglected. Therefore the work is doubled from two basic equations to four

1. Continuity equation
2. Momentum equation
3. Energy equation
4. Equation of state

to be solved simultaneously for four unknowns: pressure, density, temperature, and flow velocity (p, ρ, T, V). Thus the general theory of compressible flow is quite complicated, and we try here to make further simplifications, especially by assuming a reversible adiabatic or *isentropic* flow.

The Mach Number

The Mach number is the dominant parameter in compressible-flow analysis, with different effects depending upon its magnitude. Aerodynamicists especially make a distinction between the various ranges of Mach number, and the following rough classifications are commonly used:

Ma < 0.3: *incompressible flow*, where density effects are negligible.

0.3 < Ma < 0.8: *subsonic flow*, where density effects are important but no shock waves appear.

0.8 < Ma < 1.2: *transonic flow*, where shock waves first appear, dividing subsonic and supersonic regions of the flow. Powered flight in the transonic region is difficult because of the mixed character of the flow field.

1.2 < Ma < 3.0: *supersonic flow*, where shock waves are present but there are no subsonic regions.

3.0 < Ma: *hypersonic flow* [13], where shock waves and other flow changes are especially strong.

The numerical values listed above are only rough guides. These five categories of flow are appropriate to external high-speed aerodynamics. For internal (duct) flows, the most important question is simply whether the flow is subsonic (Ma < 1) or supersonic (Ma > 1), because the effect of area changes reverses, as we show in Sec. 9.4. Since supersonic-flow effects may go against intuition, you should study these differences carefully.

The Specific-Heat Ratio

In addition to geometry and Mach number, compressible-flow calculations also depend upon a second dimensionless parameter, the *specific-heat ratio* of the gas:

$$k = c_p/c_v \tag{9.1}$$

Earlier, in Chaps. 1 and 4, we used the same symbol k to denote the thermal conductivity of a fluid. We apologize for the duplication; thermal conductivity does not appear in these later chapters of the text.

Recall from Fig. 1.3 that k for the common gases decreases slowly with temperature and lies between 1.0 and 1.7. Variations in k have only a slight effect upon compressible-flow computations, and air, $k \approx 1.40$, is the dominant fluid of interest. Therefore, although we assign some problems involving, e.g., steam and CO_2 and helium, the compressible-flow tables in App. B are based solely upon the single value $k = 1.40$ for air.

This text contains only a single chapter on compressible flow, but, as usual, whole books have been written on the subject. References 1 to 6 and 26 are introductory, fairly elementary treatments, while Refs. 7 to 14 and 27 are advanced. From time to time we shall defer some specialized topic to these texts.

We note in passing that there are at least two flow patterns which depend strongly upon very small density differences, acoustics, and natural convection. Acoustics [9, 14] is the study of sound-wave propagation, which is accompanied by extremely small changes in density, pressure, and temperature. Natural convection is the gentle circulating pattern set up by buoyancy forces in a fluid stratified by uneven heating or uneven concentration of dissolved materials. Here we are concerned only with steady compressible flow where the fluid velocity is of magnitude comparable to that of the speed of sound.

The Perfect Gas

In principle, compressible-flow calculations can be made for any fluid equation of state, and we shall assign problems involving the steam tables [15], the gas tables [16], and liquids [Eq. (1.19)]. But in fact most elementary treatments are confined to the perfect gas with constant specific heats

$$p = \rho RT \qquad R = c_p - c_v = \text{const} \qquad k = \frac{c_p}{c_v} = \text{const} \qquad (9.2)$$

For all real gases, c_p, c_v, and k vary with temperature but only moderately; for example, c_p of air increases 30 percent as temperature increases from 0 to 5000°F. Since we rarely deal with such large temperature changes, it is quite reasonable to assume constant specific heats.

Recall from Sec. 1.6 that the gas constant is related to a universal constant Λ divided by the gas molecular weight

$$R_{\text{gas}} = \frac{\Lambda}{M_{\text{gas}}} \qquad (9.3)$$

where $\qquad \Lambda = 49{,}720 \text{ ft}^2/(\text{s}^2 \cdot °R) = 8314 \text{ m}^2/(\text{s}^2 \cdot \text{K})$

For air, $M = 28.97$, and we shall adopt the following property values for air throughout this chapter:

$$R = 1717 \text{ ft}^2/(\text{s}^2 \cdot °R) = 287 \text{ m}^2/(\text{s}^2 \cdot \text{K}) \qquad k = 1.400$$

$$c_v = \frac{R}{k-1} = 4293 \text{ ft}^2/(\text{s}^2 \cdot °R) = 718 \text{ m}^2/(\text{s}^2 \cdot \text{K}) \qquad (9.4)$$

$$c_p = \frac{kR}{k-1} = 6010 \text{ ft}^2/(\text{s}^2 \cdot °R) = 1005 \text{ m}^2/(\text{s}^2 \cdot \text{K})$$

Experimental values of k for eight common gases were shown in Fig. 1.3. From this figure and the molecular weight, the other properties can be computed, as in Eqs. (9.4).

The changes in the internal energy $\hat{u}$ and enthalpy h of a perfect gas are computed for constant specific heats as

$$\hat{u}_2 - \hat{u}_1 = c_v(T_2 - T_1) \qquad h_2 - h_1 = c_p(T_2 - T_1) \tag{9.5}$$

For variable specific heats one must integrate $\hat{u} = \int c_v \, dT$ and $h = \int c_p \, dT$ or use the gas tables [16]. Most modern thermodynamics texts now contain software for evaluating properties of nonideal gases [17].

Isentropic Process

The isentropic approximation is common in compressible-flow theory. We compute the entropy change from the first and second laws of thermodynamics for a pure substance [17 or 18]

$$T \, ds = dh - \frac{dp}{\rho} \tag{9.6}$$

Introducing $dh = c_p \, dT$ for a perfect gas and solving for ds, we substitute $\rho T = p/R$ from the perfect-gas law and obtain

$$\int_1^2 ds = \int_1^2 c_p \frac{dT}{T} - R \int_1^2 \frac{dp}{p} \tag{9.7}$$

If c_p is variable, the gas tables will be needed, but for constant c_p we obtain the analytic results

$$s_2 - s_1 = c_p \ln \frac{T_2}{T_1} - R \ln \frac{p_2}{p_1} = c_v \ln \frac{T_2}{T_1} - R \ln \frac{p_2}{p_1} \tag{9.8}$$

Equations (9.8) are used to compute the entropy change across a shock wave (Sec. 9.5), which is an irreversible process.

For isentropic flow, we set $s_2 = s_1$ and obtain the interesting power-law relations for an isentropic perfect gas

$$\frac{p_2}{p_1} = \left(\frac{T_2}{T_1}\right)^{k/(k-1)} = \left(\frac{\rho_2}{\rho_1}\right)^k \tag{9.9}$$

These relations are used in Sec. 9.3.

EXAMPLE 9.1

Argon flows through a tube such that its initial condition is $p_1 = 1.7$ MPa and $\rho_1 = 18$ kg/m^3 and its final condition is $p_2 = 248$ kPa and $T_2 = 400$ K. Estimate (a) the initial temperature, (b) the final density, (c) the change in enthalpy, and (d) the change in entropy of the gas.

Solution

From Table A.4 for argon, $R = 208$ m^2/(s$^2 \cdot$ K) and $k = 1.67$. Therefore estimate its specific heat at constant pressure from Eq. (9.4):

$$c_p = \frac{kR}{k-1} = \frac{1.67(208)}{1.67-1} \approx 519 \text{ m}^2/(\text{s}^2 \cdot \text{K})$$

The initial temperature and final density are estimated from the ideal gas law, Eq. (9.2):

$$T_1 = \frac{p_1}{\rho_1 R} = \frac{1.7 \text{ E6 N/m}^2}{(18 \text{ kg/m}^3)[208 \text{ m}^2/(\text{s}^2 \cdot \text{K})]} = 454 \text{ K} \qquad \text{Ans. } (a)$$

$$\rho_2 = \frac{p_2}{T_2 R} = \frac{248 \text{ E3 N/m}^2}{(400 \text{ K})[208 \text{ m}^2/(\text{s}^2 \cdot \text{K})]} = 2.98 \text{ kg/m}^3 \qquad \text{Ans. } (b)$$

From Eq. (9.5) the enthalpy change is

$$h_2 - h_1 = c_p(T_2 - T_1) = 519(400 - 454) \approx -28{,}000 \text{ J/kg (or m}^2/\text{s}^2) \qquad \text{Ans. } (c)$$

The argon temperature and enthalpy decrease as we move down the tube. Actually, there may not be any external cooling; i.e., the fluid enthalpy may be converted by friction to increased kinetic energy (Sec. 9.7).

Finally, the entropy change is computed from Eq. (9.8):

$$s_2 - s_1 = c_p \ln \frac{T_2}{T_1} - R \ln \frac{p_2}{p_1}$$

$$= 519 \ln \frac{400}{454} - 208 \ln \frac{0.248 \text{ E6}}{1.7 \text{ E6}}$$

$$= -66 + 400 \approx 334 \text{ m}^2/(\text{s}^2 \cdot \text{K}) \qquad \text{Ans. } (d)$$

The fluid entropy has increased. If there is no heat transfer, this indicates an irreversible process. Note that entropy has the same units as the gas constant and specific heat.

This problem is not just arbitrary numbers. It correctly simulates the behavior of argon moving subsonically through a tube with large frictional effects (Sec. 9.7).

9.2 The Speed of Sound

The so-called speed of sound is the rate of propagation of a pressure pulse of infinitesimal strength through a still fluid. It is a thermodynamic property of a fluid. Let us analyze it by first considering a pulse of finite strength, as in Fig. 9.1. In Fig. 9.1a the pulse, or pressure wave, moves at speed C toward the still fluid ($p, \rho, T, V = 0$) at the left, leaving behind at the right a fluid of increased properties ($p + \Delta p, \rho + \Delta \rho, T + \Delta T$) and a fluid velocity ΔV toward the left following the wave but much slower. We can determine these effects by making a control-volume analysis across the wave. To avoid the unsteady terms which would be necessary in Fig. 9.1a, we adopt instead the control volume of Fig. 9.1b, which moves at wave speed C to the left. The wave appears fixed from this viewpoint, and the fluid appears to have velocity C on the left and $C - \Delta V$ on the right. The thermodynamic properties $p, \rho,$ and T are not affected by this change of viewpoint.

The flow in Fig. 9.1b is steady and one-dimensional across the wave. The continuity equation is thus, from Eq. (3.24),

$$\rho A C = (\rho + \Delta \rho)(A)(C - \Delta V)$$

or

$$\Delta V = C \frac{\Delta \rho}{\rho + \Delta \rho} \qquad (9.10)$$

This proves our contention that the induced fluid velocity on the right is much smaller than the wave speed C. In the limit of infinitesimal wave strength (sound wave) this speed is itself infinitesimal.

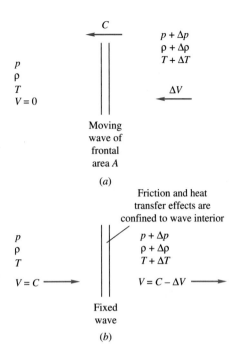

Fig. 9.1 Control-volume analysis of a finite-strength pressure wave: (a) control volume fixed to still fluid at left; (b) control volume moving left at wave speed C.

Notice that there are no velocity gradients on either side of the wave. Therefore, even if fluid viscosity is large, frictional effects are confined to the interior of the wave. Advanced texts [for example, 19, sec. 3-9.4] show that the thickness of pressure waves in gases is of order 10^{-6} ft at atmospheric pressure. Thus we can safely neglect friction and apply the one-dimensional momentum equation (3.40) across the wave

$$\Sigma F_{\text{right}} = \dot{m}(V_{\text{out}} - V_{\text{in}})$$

or

$$pA - (p + \Delta p)A = (\rho AC)(C - \Delta V - C) \tag{9.11}$$

Again the area cancels, and we can solve for the pressure change

$$\Delta p = \rho C\, \Delta V \tag{9.12}$$

If the wave strength is very small, the pressure change is small.

Finally combine Eqs. (9.10) and (9.12) to give an expression for the wave speed

$$C^2 = \frac{\Delta p}{\Delta \rho}\left(1 + \frac{\Delta \rho}{\rho}\right) \tag{9.13}$$

The larger the strength $\Delta \rho/\rho$ of the wave, the faster the wave speed; i.e., powerful explosion waves move much more quickly than sound waves. In the limit of infinitesimal strength $\Delta \rho \to 0$, we have what is defined to be the speed of sound a of a fluid:

$$a^2 = \frac{\partial p}{\partial \rho} \tag{9.14}$$

But the evaluation of the derivative requires knowledge of the thermodynamic process undergone by the fluid as the wave passes. Sir Isaac Newton in 1686 made a famous

Table 9.1 Sound Speed of Various Materials at 60°F (15.5°C) and 1 atm

Material	a, ft/s	a, m/s
Gases:		
H_2	4,246	1,294
He	3,281	1,000
Air	1,117	340
Ar	1,040	317
CO_2	873	266
CH_4	607	185
$^{238}UF_6$	297	91
Liquids:		
Glycerin	6,100	1,860
Water	4,890	1,490
Mercury	4,760	1,450
Ethyl alcohol	3,940	1,200
Solids:*		
Aluminum	16,900	5,150
Steel	16,600	5,060
Hickory	13,200	4,020
Ice	10,500	3,200

*Plane waves. Solids also have a *shear-wave speed*.

error by deriving a formula for sound speed which was equivalent to assuming an isothermal process, the result being 20 percent low for air, for example. He rationalized the discrepancy as being due to the "crassitude" (dust particles, etc.) in the air; the error is certainly understandable when we reflect that it was made 180 years before the proper basis was laid for the second law of thermodynamics.

We now see that the correct process must be *adiabatic* because there are no temperature gradients except inside the wave itself. For vanishing-strength sound waves we therefore have an infinitesimal adiabatic or isentropic process. The correct expression for the sound speed is

$$a = \left(\frac{\partial p}{\partial \rho}\Big|_s\right)^{1/2} = \left(k\frac{\partial p}{\partial \rho}\Big|_T\right)^{1/2} \tag{9.15}$$

for any fluid, gas or liquid. Even a solid has a sound speed.

For a perfect gas, From Eq. (9.2) or (9.9), we deduce that the speed of sound is

$$a = \left(\frac{kp}{\rho}\right)^{1/2} = (kRT)^{1/2} \tag{9.16}$$

The speed of sound increases as the square root of the absolute temperature. For air, with $k = 1.4$ and $R = 1717$, an easily memorized dimensional formula is

$$a(\text{ft/s}) \approx 49[T(°R)]^{1/2}$$
$$a(\text{m/s}) \approx 20[T(K)]^{1/2} \tag{9.17}$$

At sea-level standard temperature, 60°F = 520°R, $a = 1117$ ft/s. This decreases in the upper atmosphere, which is cooler; at 50,000-ft standard altitude, $T = -69.7°F = 389.9°R$ and $a = 49(389.9)^{1/2} = 968$ ft/s, or 13 percent less.

Some representative values of sound speed in various materials are given in Table 9.1. For liquids and solids it is common to define the *bulk modulus K* of the material

$$K = -\mathcal{V}\frac{\partial p}{\partial \mathcal{V}}\Big|_s = \rho\frac{\partial p}{\partial \rho}\Big|_s \tag{9.18}$$

For example, at standard conditions, the bulk modulus of carbon tetrachloride is 163,000 lbf/in² absolute, and its density is 3.09 slugs/ft³. Its speed of sound is therefore $[163,000(144)/3.09]^{1/2} = 2756$ ft/s, or 840 m/s. Steel has a bulk modulus of about 29×10^6 lbf/in² absolute and water about 320×10^3 lbf/in² absolute, or 90 times less.

For solids, it is sometimes assumed that the bulk modulus is approximately equivalent to Young's modulus of elasticity E, but in fact their ratio depends upon Poisson's ratio σ

$$\frac{E}{K} = 3(1 - 2\sigma) \tag{9.19}$$

The two are equal for $\sigma = \frac{1}{3}$, which is approximately the case for many common metals such as steel and aluminum.

EXAMPLE 9.2

Estimate the speed of sound of carbon monoxide at 200-kPa pressure and 300°C in m/s.

Solution

From Table A.4, for CO, the molecular weight is 28.01 and $k \approx 1.40$. Thus from Eq. (9.3) $R_{CO} = 8314/28.01 = 297 \text{ m}^2/(\text{s}^2 \cdot \text{K})$, and the given temperature is 300°C + 273 = 573 K. Thus from Eq. (9.16) we estimate

$$a_{CO} = (kRT)^{1/2} = [1.40(297)(573)]^{1/2} = 488 \text{ m/s} \qquad \textit{Ans.}$$

9.3 Adiabatic and Isentropic Steady Flow

As mentioned in Sec. 9.1, the isentropic approximation greatly simplifies a compressible-flow calculation. So does the assumption of adiabatic flow, even if nonisentropic.

Consider high-speed flow of a gas past an insulated wall, as in Fig. 9.2. There is no shaft work delivered to any part of the fluid. Therefore every streamtube in the flow satisfies the steady-flow energy equation in the form of Eq. (3.66)

$$h_1 + \tfrac{1}{2}V_1^2 + gz_1 = h_2 + \tfrac{1}{2}V_2^2 + gz_2 - q + w_v \qquad (9.20)$$

where point 1 is upstream of point 2. You may wish to review the details of Eq. (3.66) and its development. We saw in Example 3.16 that potential-energy changes of a gas are extremely small compared with kinetic-energy and enthalpy terms. We shall neglect the terms gz_1 and gz_2 in all gas-dynamic analyses.

Inside the thermal and velocity boundary layers in Fig. 9.2 the heat-transfer and viscous-work terms q and w_v are not zero. But outside the boundary layer q and w_v are zero by definition, so that the outer flow satisfies the simple relation

$$h_1 + \tfrac{1}{2}V_1^2 = h_2 + \tfrac{1}{2}V_2^2 = \text{const} \qquad (9.21)$$

The constant in Eq. (9.21) is equal to the maximum enthalpy which the fluid would achieve if brought to rest adiabatically. We call this value h_0, the *stagnation enthalpy* of the flow. Thus we rewrite Eq. (9.21) in the form

$$h + \tfrac{1}{2}V^2 = h_0 = \text{const} \qquad (9.22)$$

This should hold for steady adiabatic flow of any compressible fluid outside the boundary layer. The wall in Fig. 9.2 could be either the surface of an immersed body or the wall of a duct. We have shown the details of Fig. 9.2; typically the thermal-layer thickness δ_T is greater than the velocity-layer thickness δ_V because most gases have a

Fig. 9.2 Velocity and stagnation-enthalpy distributions near an insulated wall in a typical high-speed gas flow.

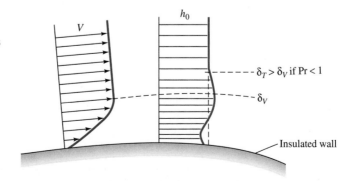

dimensionless Prandtl number Pr less than unity (see, e.g., Ref. 19, sec. 4-3.2). Note that the stagnation enthalpy varies inside the thermal boundary layer, but its average value is the same as that at the outer layer due to the insulated wall.

For nonperfect gases we may have to use the steam tables [15] or the gas tables [16] to implement Eq. (9.22). But for a perfect gas $h = c_p T$, and Eq. (9.22) becomes

$$c_p T + \tfrac{1}{2} V^2 = c_p T_0 \tag{9.23}$$

This establishes the stagnation temperature T_0 of an adiabatic perfect-gas flow, i.e., the temperature it achieves when decelerated to rest adiabatically.

An alternate interpretation of Eq. (9.22) occurs when the enthalpy and temperature drop to (absolute) zero, so that the velocity achieves a maximum value

$$V_{\max} = (2h_0)^{1/2} = (2c_p T_0)^{1/2} \tag{9.24}$$

No higher flow velocity can occur unless additional energy is added to the fluid through shaft work or heat transfer (Sec. 9.8).

Mach-Number Relations

The dimensionless form of Eq. (9.23) brings in the Mach number Ma as a parameter, by using Eq. (9.16) for the speed of sound of a perfect gas. Divide through by $c_p T$ to obtain

$$1 + \frac{V^2}{2c_p T} = \frac{T_0}{T} \tag{9.25}$$

But, from the perfect-gas law, $c_p T = [kR/(k-1)]T = a^2/(k-1)$, so that Eq. (9.25) becomes

$$1 + \frac{(k-1)V^2}{2a^2} = \frac{T_0}{T}$$

or

$$\frac{T_0}{T} = 1 + \frac{k-1}{2} \text{Ma}^2 \qquad \text{Ma} = \frac{V}{a} \tag{9.26}$$

This relation is plotted in Fig. 9.3 versus the Mach number for $k = 1.4$. At Ma $= 5$ the temperature has dropped to $\tfrac{1}{6} T_0$.

Since $a \propto T^{1/2}$, the ratio a_0/a is the square root of (9.26)

$$\frac{a_0}{a} = \left(\frac{T_0}{T}\right)^{1/2} = \left[1 + \frac{1}{2}(k-1)\text{Ma}^2\right]^{1/2} \tag{9.27}$$

Equation (9.27) is also plotted in Fig. 9.3. At Ma $= 5$ the speed of sound has dropped to 41 percent of the stagnation value.

Isentropic Pressure and Density Relations

Note that Eqs. (9.26) and (9.27) require only adiabatic flow and hold even in the presence of irreversibilities such as friction losses or shock waves.

If the flow is also *isentropic*, then for a perfect gas the pressure and density ratios can be computed from Eq. (9.9) as a power of the temperature ratio

$$\frac{p_0}{p} = \left(\frac{T_0}{T}\right)^{k/(k-1)} = \left[1 + \frac{1}{2}(k-1)\text{Ma}^2\right]^{k/(k-1)} \tag{9.28a}$$

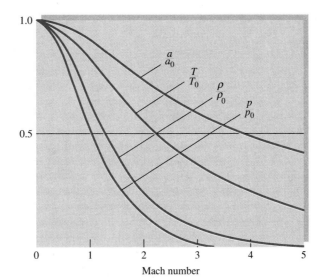

Fig. 9.3 Adiabatic (T/T_0 and a/a_0) and isentropic (p/p_0 and ρ/ρ_0) properties versus Mach number for $k = 1.4$.

$$\frac{\rho_0}{\rho} = \left(\frac{T_0}{T}\right)^{1/(k-1)} = \left[1 + \frac{1}{2}(k-1)\,\mathrm{Ma}^2\right]^{1/(k-1)} \qquad (9.28b)$$

These relations are also plotted in Fig. 9.3; at Ma = 5 the density is 1.13 percent of its stagnation value, and the pressure is only 0.19 percent of stagnation pressure.

The quantities p_0 and ρ_0 are the isentropic stagnation pressure and density, respectively, i.e., the pressure and density which the flow would achieve if brought isentropically to rest. In an adiabatic nonisentropic flow p_0 and ρ_0 retain their local meaning, but they vary throughout the flow as the entropy changes due to friction or shock waves. The quantities h_0, T_0, and a_0 are constant in an adiabatic nonisentropic flow (see Sec. 9.7 for further details).

Relationship to Bernoulli's Equation

The isentropic assumptions (9.28) are effective, but are they realistic? Yes. To see why, differentiate Eq. (9.22)

Adiabatic: $\qquad\qquad\qquad\qquad dh + V\,dV = 0 \qquad\qquad\qquad (9.29)$

Meanwhile, from Eq. (9.6), if $ds = 0$ (isentropic process),

$$dh = \frac{dp}{\rho} \qquad (9.30)$$

Combining (9.29) and (9.30), we find that an isentropic streamtube flow must be

$$\frac{dp}{\rho} + V\,dV = 0 \qquad (9.31)$$

But this is exactly the Bernoulli relation, Eq. (3.75), for steady frictionless flow with negligible gravity terms. Thus we see that the isentropic-flow assumption is equivalent to use of the Bernoulli or streamline form of the frictionless momentum equation.

Critical Values at the Sonic Point

The stagnation values (a_0, T_0, p_0, ρ_0) are useful reference conditions in a compressible flow, but of comparable usefulness are the conditions where the flow is sonic, Ma = 1.0. These sonic, or *critical*, properties are denoted by asterisks: p^*, ρ^*, a^*, and T^*. They are certain ratios of the stagnation properties as given by Eqs. (9.26) to (9.28) when Ma = 1.0; for k = 1.4

$$\frac{p^*}{p_0} = \left(\frac{2}{k+1}\right)^{k/(k-1)} = 0.5283 \qquad \frac{\rho^*}{\rho_0} = \left(\frac{2}{k+1}\right)^{1/(k-1)} = 0.6339$$

$$\frac{T^*}{T_0} = \frac{2}{k+1} = 0.8333 \qquad \frac{a^*}{a_0} = \left(\frac{2}{k+1}\right)^{1/2} = 0.9129$$

(9.32)

In all isentropic flow, all critical properties are constant; in adiabatic nonisentropic flow, a^* and T^* are constant, but p^* and ρ^* may vary.

The critical velocity V^* equals the sonic sound speed a^* by definition and is often used as a reference velocity in isentropic or adiabatic flow

$$V^* = a^* = (kRT^*)^{1/2} = \left(\frac{2k}{k+1}RT_0\right)^{1/2}$$

(9.33)

The usefulness of these critical values will become clearer as we study compressible duct flow with friction or heat transfer later in this chapter.

Some Useful Numbers for Air

Since the great bulk of our practical calculations are for air, k = 1.4, the stagnation-property ratios p/p_0, etc., from Eqs. (9.26) to (9.28), are tabulated for this value in Table B.1. The increments in Mach number are rather coarse in this table because the values are only meant as a guide; these equations are now a trivial matter to manipulate on a hand calculator. Thirty years ago every text had extensive compressible-flow tables with Mach-number spacings of about 0.01, so that accurate values could be interpolated.

For k = 1.4, the following numerical versions of the isentropic and adiabatic flow formulas are obtained:

$$\frac{T_0}{T} = 1 + 0.2 \text{ Ma}^2 \qquad \frac{\rho_0}{\rho} = (1 + 0.2 \text{ Ma}^2)^{2.5}$$

$$\frac{p_0}{p} = (1 + 0.2 \text{ Ma}^2)^{3.5}$$

(9.34)

Or, if we are given the properties, it is equally easy to solve for the Mach number (again with k = 1.4)

$$\text{Ma}^2 = 5\left(\frac{T_0}{T} - 1\right) = 5\left[\left(\frac{\rho_0}{\rho}\right)^{2/5} - 1\right] = 5\left[\left(\frac{p_0}{p}\right)^{2/7} - 1\right] \qquad (9.35)$$

Note that these isentropic-flow formulas serve as the equivalent of the frictionless adiabatic momentum and energy equations. They relate velocity to physical properties for a perfect gas, but they are *not* the "solution" to a gas-dynamics problem. The complete solution is not obtained until the continuity equation has also been satisfied, for either one-dimensional (Sec. 9.4) or multidimensional (Sec. 9.9) flow.

One final note: These isentropic-ratio–versus–Mach-number formulas are seductive, tempting one to solve all problems by jumping right into the tables. Actually, many problems involving (dimensional) velocity and temperature can be solved more easily from the original raw dimensional energy equation (9.23) plus the perfect-gas law (9.2), as the next example will illustrate.

EXAMPLE 9.3

Air flows adiabatically through a duct. At point 1 the velocity is 240 m/s, with $T_1 = 320$ K and $p_1 = 170$ kPa. Compute (a) T_0, (b) p_{01}, (c) ρ_0, (d) Ma, (e) V_{max}, and (f) V^*. At point 2 further downstream $V_2 = 290$ m/s and $p_2 = 135$ kPa. (g) What is the stagnation pressure p_{02}?

Solution

For air take $k = 1.4$, $c_p = 1005$ m^2/(s$^2 \cdot$ K), and $R = 287$ m^2/(s$^2 \cdot$ K). With V_1 and T_1 known, we can compute T_{01} from Eq. (9.23) without using the Mach number:

$$T_{01} = T_1 + \frac{V_1^2}{2c_p} = 320 + \frac{(240 \text{ m/s})^2}{2[1005 \text{ m}^2/(\text{s}^2 \cdot \text{K})]} = 320 + 29 = 349 \text{ K} \qquad Ans. \ (a)$$

Then compute Ma$_1$ from the known temperature ratio, using Eq. (9.35):

$$Ma_1^2 = 5\left(\frac{349}{320} - 1\right) = 0.453 \qquad Ma_1 = 0.67 \qquad Ans. \ (d)$$

Alternately compute $a_1 = \sqrt{kRT_1} = 359$ m/s, whence Ma$_1 = V_1/a_1 = 240/359 = 0.67$. The stagnation pressure at section 1 follows from Eq. (9.34):

$$p_{01} = p_1(1 + 0.2 \text{ Ma}_1^2)^{3.5} = (170 \text{ kPa})[1 + 0.2(0.67)^2]^{3.5} = 230 \text{ kPa} \qquad Ans. \ (b)$$

We need the density from the perfect-gas law before we can compute the stagnation density:

$$\rho_1 = \frac{p_1}{RT_1} = \frac{170,000}{(287)(320)} = 1.85 \text{ kg/m}^3$$

whence $\qquad \rho_0 = \rho_1(1 + 0.2 \text{ Ma}_1^2)^{2.5} = (1.85)[1 + 0.2(0.67)^2]^{2.5} = 2.29 \text{ kg/m}^3 \qquad Ans. \ (c)$

Alternately, we could have gone directly to $\rho_0 = p_0/(RT_0) = (230 \text{ E3})/[(287)(349)] = 2.29$ kg/m^3. Meanwhile, the maximum velocity follows from Eq. (9.24):

$$V_{max} = (2c_p T_0)^{1/2} = [2(1005)(349)]^{1/2} = 838 \text{ m/s} \qquad Ans. \ (e)$$

and the sonic velocity from Eq. (9.33) is

$$V^* = \left(\frac{2k}{k+1} RT_0\right)^{1/2} = \left[\frac{2(1.4)}{1.4 + 1} (287)(349)\right]^{1/2} = 342 \text{ m/s} \qquad Ans. \ (f)$$

At point 2, the temperature is not given, but since we know the flow is adiabatic, the stagnation temperature is constant: $T_{02} = T_{01} = 349$ K. Thus, from Eq. (9.23),

$$T_2 = T_{02} - \frac{V_2^2}{2c_p} = 349 - \frac{(290)^2}{2(1005)} = 307 \text{ K}$$

Then, although the flow itself is not isentropic, the local stagnation pressure is computed by the *local* isentropic condition

$$p_{02} = p_2 \left(\frac{T_{02}}{T_2} \right)^{k/(k-1)} = (135) \left(\frac{349}{307} \right)^{3.5} = 211 \text{ kPa} \qquad Ans. \ (g)$$

This is 8 percent less than the upstream stagnation pressure p_{01}. Notice that, in this last part, we took advantage of the given information (T_{02}, p_2, V_2) to obtain p_{02} in an efficient manner. You may verify by comparison that approaching this part through the (unknown) Mach number Ma_2 is more laborious.

9.4 Isentropic Flow with Area Changes

By combining the isentropic- and/or adiabatic-flow relations with the equation of continuity we can study practical compressible-flow problems. This section treats the one-dimensional flow approximation.

Figure 9.4 illustrates the one-dimensional flow assumption. A real flow, Fig. 9.4a, has no slip at the walls and a velocity profile $V(x, y)$ which varies across the duct section (compare with Fig. 7.8). If, however, the area change is small and the wall radius of curvature large

$$\frac{dh}{dx} \ll 1 \qquad h(x) \ll R(x) \tag{9.36}$$

then the flow is approximately one-dimensional, as in Fig. 9.4b, with $V \approx V(x)$ reacting to area change $A(x)$. Compressible-flow nozzles and diffusers do not always satisfy conditions (9.36), but we use the one-dimensional theory anyway because of its simplicity.

For steady one-dimensional flow the equation of continuity is, from Eq. (3.24),

$$\rho(x)V(x)A(x) = \dot{m} = \text{const} \tag{9.37}$$

Before applying this to duct theory, we can learn a lot from the differential form of Eq. (9.37)

$$\frac{d\rho}{\rho} + \frac{dV}{V} + \frac{dA}{A} = 0 \tag{9.38}$$

The differential forms of the frictionless momentum equation (9.31) and the sound-speed relation (9.15) are recalled here for convenience:

Fig. 9.4 Compressible flow through a duct: (a) real-fluid velocity profile; (b) one-dimensional approximation.

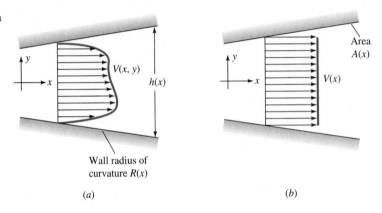

(a)

(b)

Duct geometry	Subsonic Ma < 1	Supersonic Ma > 1
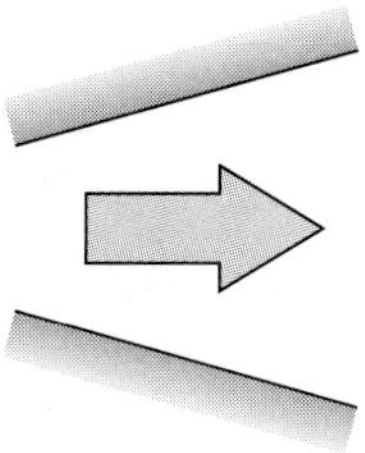 $dA > 0$	$dV < 0$ $dp > 0$ Subsonic diffuser	$dV > 0$ $dp < 0$ Supersonic nozzle
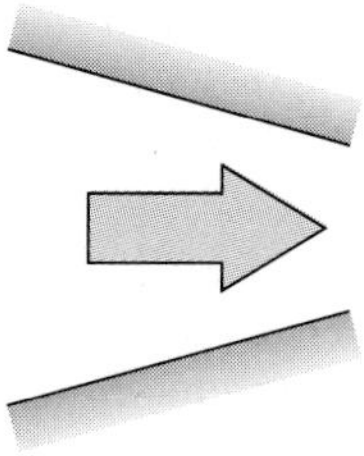 $dA < 0$	$dV > 0$ $dp < 0$ Subsonic nozzle	$dV < 0$ $dp > 0$ Supersonic diffuser

Fig. 9.5 Effect of Mach number on property changes with area change in duct flow.

Momentum
$$\frac{dp}{\rho} + V\,dV = 0$$

Sound speed:
$$dp = a^2\,d\rho$$
(9.39)

Now eliminate dp and $d\rho$ between Eqs. (9.38) and (9.39) to obtain the following relation between velocity change and area change in isentropic duct flow:

$$\frac{dV}{V} = \frac{dA}{A}\frac{1}{Ma^2 - 1} = -\frac{dp}{\rho V^2}$$
(9.40)

Inspection of this equation, without actually solving it, reveals a fascinating aspect of compressible flow: Property changes are of opposite sign for subsonic and supersonic flow because of the term $Ma^2 - 1$. There are four combinations of area change and Mach number, summarized in Fig. 9.5.

From earlier chapters we are used to subsonic behavior (Ma < 1): When area increases, velocity decreases and pressure increases, which is denoted a subsonic diffuser. But in supersonic flow (Ma > 1), the velocity actually increases when the area increases, a supersonic nozzle. The same opposing behavior occurs for an area decrease, which speeds up a subsonic flow and slows down a supersonic flow.

What about the sonic point Ma = 1? Since infinite acceleration is physically impossible, Eq. (9.40) indicates that dV can be finite only when $dA = 0$, that is, a minimum area (throat) or a maximum area (bulge). In Fig. 9.6 we patch together a throat section and a bulge section, using the rules from Fig. 9.5. The throat or converging-diverging section can smoothly accelerate a subsonic flow through sonic to supersonic flow, as in Fig. 9.6a. This is the only way a supersonic flow can be created by expanding the gas from a stagnant reservoir. The bulge section fails; the bulge Mach number moves away from a sonic condition rather than toward it.

Although supersonic flow downstream of a nozzle requires a sonic throat, the op-

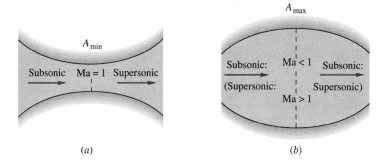

Fig. 9.6 From Eq. (9.40), in flow through a throat (*a*) the fluid can accelerate smoothly through sonic and supersonic flow. In flow through the bulge (*b*) the flow at the bulge cannot be sonic on physical grounds.

posite is not true: A compressible gas can pass through a throat section without becoming sonic.

Perfect-Gas Relations

We can use the perfect-gas and isentropic-flow relations to convert the continuity relation (9.37) into an algebraic expression involving only area and Mach number, as follows. Equate the mass flow at any section to the mass flow under sonic conditions (which may not actually occur in the duct)

$$\rho V A = \rho^* V^* A^*$$

or
$$\frac{A}{A^*} = \frac{\rho^*}{\rho} \frac{V^*}{V} \tag{9.41}$$

Both the terms on the right are functions only of Mach number for isentropic flow. From Eqs. (9.28) and (9.32)

$$\frac{\rho^*}{\rho} = \frac{\rho^*}{\rho_0} \frac{\rho_0}{\rho} = \left\{ \frac{2}{k+1} \left[1 + \frac{1}{2}(k-1)\,\text{Ma}^2 \right] \right\}^{1/(k-1)} \tag{9.42}$$

From Eqs. (9.26) and (9.32) we obtain

$$\frac{V^*}{V} = \frac{(kRT^*)^{1/2}}{V} = \frac{(kRT)^{1/2}}{V} \left(\frac{T^*}{T_0}\right)^{1/2} \left(\frac{T_0}{T}\right)^{1/2}$$

$$= \frac{1}{\text{Ma}} \left\{ \frac{2}{k+1} \left[1 + \frac{1}{2}(k-1)\,\text{Ma}^2 \right] \right\}^{1/2} \tag{9.43}$$

Combining Eqs. (9.41) to (9.43), we get the desired result

$$\frac{A}{A^*} = \frac{1}{\text{Ma}} \left[\frac{1 + \frac{1}{2}(k-1)\,\text{Ma}^2}{\frac{1}{2}(k+1)} \right]^{(1/2)(k+1)/(k-1)} \tag{9.44}$$

For $k = 1.4$, Eq. (9.44) takes the numerical form

$$\frac{A}{A^*} = \frac{1}{\text{Ma}} \frac{(1 + 0.2\,\text{Ma}^2)^3}{1.728} \tag{9.45}$$

which is plotted in Fig. 9.7. Equations (9.45) and (9.34) enable us to solve any one-dimensional isentropic-airflow problem given, say, the shape of the duct $A(x)$ and the stagnation conditions and assuming that there are no shock waves in the duct.

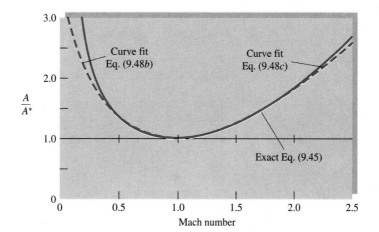

Fig. 9.7 Area ratio versus Mach number for isentropic flow of a perfect gas with $k = 1.4$.

Figure 9.7 shows that the minimum area which can occur in a given isentropic duct flow is the sonic, or critical, throat area. All other duct sections must have A greater than A^*. In many flows a critical sonic throat is not actually present, and the flow in the duct is either entirely subsonic or, more rarely, entirely supersonic.

Choking

From Eq. (9.41) the inverse ratio A^*/A equals $\rho V/(\rho^* V^*)$, the mass flow per unit area at any section compared with the critical mass flow per unit area. From Fig. 9.7 this inverse ratio rises from zero at Ma $= 0$ to unity at Ma $= 1$ and back down to zero at large Ma. Thus, for given stagnation conditions, the maximum possible mass flow passes through a duct when its throat is at the critical or sonic condition. The duct is then said to be *choked* and can carry no additional mass flow unless the throat is widened. If the throat is constricted further, the mass flow through the duct must decrease.

From Eqs. (9.32) and (9.33) the maximum mass flow is

$$\dot{m}_{max} = \rho^* A^* V^* = \rho_0 \left(\frac{2}{k+1}\right)^{1/(k-1)} A^* \left(\frac{2k}{k+1} R T_0\right)^{1/2}$$

$$= k^{1/2} \left(\frac{2}{k+1}\right)^{(1/2)(k+1)/(k-1)} A^* \rho_0 (R T_0)^{1/2} \tag{9.46}$$

For $k = 1.4$ this reduces to

$$\dot{m}_{max} = 0.6847 A^* \rho_0 (R T_0)^{1/2} = \frac{0.6847 p_0 A^*}{(R T_0)^{1/2}} \tag{9.47}$$

For isentropic flow through a duct, the maximum mass flow possible is proportional to the throat area and stagnation pressure and inversely proportional to the square root of the stagnation temperature. These are somewhat abstract facts, so let us illustrate with some examples.

The only cumbersome algebra in these problems is the inversion of Eq. (9.45) to compute the Mach number when A/A^* is known. The writer cannot do it without iteration, but maybe you can think of a way. Meanwhile the following curve-fitted formulas are suggested; they estimate the Mach number from $A/A*$ with ± 2 percent for $k = 1.4$ if you stay within the ranges listed for each formula:

$$
\text{Ma} \approx
\begin{cases}
\dfrac{1 + 0.27(A/A*)^{-2}}{1.728A/A*} & 1.34 < \dfrac{A}{A*} < \infty & (9.48a) \\[3ex]
1 - 0.88\left(\ln \dfrac{A}{A*}\right)^{0.45} & 1.0 < \dfrac{A}{A*} < 1.34 & (9.48b) \\[3ex]
1 + 1.2\left(\dfrac{A}{A*} - 1\right)^{1/2} & 1.0 < \dfrac{A}{A*} < 2.9 & (9.48c) \\[3ex]
\left[216\dfrac{A}{A*} - 254\left(\dfrac{A}{A*}\right)^{2/3}\right]^{1/5} & 2.9 < \dfrac{A}{A*} < \infty & (9.48d)
\end{cases}
$$

subsonic flow (9.48a), (9.48b)

supersonic flow (9.48d)

Formulas (9.48a) and (9.48d) are asymptotically correct as $A/A* \to \infty$, while (9.48b) and (9.48c) are just curve fits. However, formulas (9.48b) and (9.48c) are seen in Fig. 9.7 to be accurate within their recommended ranges.

Note that two solutions are possible for a given $A/A*$, one subsonic and one supersonic. The proper solution cannot be selected without further information, e.g., known pressure or temperature at the given duct section.

EXAMPLE 9.4

Air flows isentropically through a duct. At section 1 the area is 0.05 m² and $V_1 = 180$ m/s, $p_1 = 500$ kPa, and $T_1 = 470$ K. Compute (a) T_0, (b) Ma_1, (c) p_0, and (d) $A*$. If at section 2 the area is 0.036 m², compute Ma_2 and p_2 if the flow is (e) subsonic or (f) supersonic. Assume $k = 1.4$.

Solution

A general sketch of the problem is shown in Fig. E9.4. With V_1 and T_1 known, the energy equation (9.23) gives

$$
T_0 = T_1 + \frac{V_1^2}{2c_p} = 470 + \frac{(180)^2}{2(1005)} = 486 \text{ K} \qquad \text{Ans. (a)}
$$

The local sound speed $a_1 = \sqrt{kRT_1} = [(1.4)(287)(470)]^{1/2} = 435$ m/s. Hence

Fig. E9.4

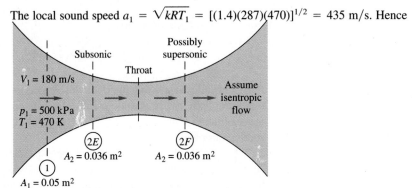

$$\text{Ma}_1 = \frac{V_1}{a_1} = \frac{180}{435} = 0.414 \qquad \textit{Ans. (b)}$$

With Ma_1 known, the stagnation pressure follows from Eq. (9.34):

$$p_0 = p_1(1 + 0.2\,\text{Ma}_1^2)^{3.5} = (500\text{ kPa})[1 + 0.2(0.414)^2]^{3.5} = 563\text{ kPa} \qquad \textit{Ans. (c)}$$

Similarly, from Eq. (9.45), the critical sonic-throat area is

$$\frac{A_1}{A^*} = \frac{(1 + 0.2\,\text{Ma}_1^2)^3}{1.728\,\text{Ma}_1} = \frac{[1 + 0.2(0.414)^2]^3}{1.728(0.414)} = 1.547$$

or

$$A^* = \frac{A_1}{1.547} = \frac{0.05\text{ m}^2}{1.547} = 0.0323\text{ m}^2 \qquad \textit{Ans. (d)}$$

This throat must *actually be present* in the duct if the flow is to become supersonic.

Part (e)

Given $A_2 = 0.036$ m^2, compute Ma_2 and p_2, assuming *subsonic* flow. This situation corresponds to section 2E in Fig. E9.4. The duct contracts to an area ratio $A_2/A^* = 0.036/0.0323 = 1.115$, which we should find on the *subsonic* portion of Table B.1 or the left side of Fig. 9.7. Equation (9.48b) gives a good estimate of the Mach number:

$$\text{Ma}_2 \approx 1 - 0.88 \ln (1.115)^{0.45} \approx 0.676 \qquad \text{(exact: 0.6735)} \qquad \textit{Ans. (e)}$$

whence

$$p_2 = \frac{p_0}{[1 + 0.2(0.676)^2]^{3.5}} = \frac{563\text{ kPa}}{1.358} \approx 415\text{ kPa} \qquad \textit{Ans. (e)}$$

The curve-fitted estimate of the Mach number is accurate here to less than 1 percent. Part (e) does *not* require a throat, sonic or otherwise; the flow could simply be contracting subsonically from A_1 to A_2.

Part (f)

Given $A_2 = 0.036$ m^2, compute Ma_2 and p_2, assuming *supersonic* flow. This situation corresponds to section 2F in Fig. E9.4. The sonic throat, $A^* = 0.0323$ m^2, *must* be present to develop supersonic flow. The area ratio is the same as in part (e) above, $A_2/A^* = 1.115$, but now we look in the *supersonic* portion of Table B.1 or at the right leg of Fig. 9.7. Equation (9.48c) provides a good estimate of the Mach number:

$$\text{Ma}_2(\text{supersonic}) \approx 1 + 1.2(1.115 - 1)^{1/2} \approx 1.407 \qquad \text{(exact: 1.400)} \qquad \textit{Ans. (f)}$$

whence

$$p_2 = \frac{p_0}{[1 + 0.2(1.407)^2]^{3.5}} = \frac{563\text{ kPa}}{3.214} = 175\text{ kPa} \qquad \textit{Ans. (f)}$$

Again the accuracy of the curve fit is less than 1 percent. Note that the supersonic-flow pressure level is much less than p_2 in part (e), and a sonic throat *must* have occurred between sections 1 and 2.

EXAMPLE 9.5

It is desired to expand air from $p_0 = 200$ kPa and $T_0 = 500$ K through a throat to an exit

Mach number of 2.5. If the desired mass flow is 3 kg/s, compute (a) the throat area and the exit (b) pressure, (c) temperature, (d) velocity, and (e) area, assuming isentropic flow, with $k = 1.4$.

Solution

The throat area follows from Eq. (9.47), because the throat flow must be sonic to produce a supersonic exit:

$$A^* = \frac{\dot{m}(RT_0)^{1/2}}{0.6847 p_0} = \frac{3.0[287(500)]^{1/2}}{0.6847(200,000)} = 0.00830 \text{ m}^2 = \frac{1}{4}\pi D^{*2}$$

or
$$D_{\text{throat}} = 10.3 \text{ cm} \qquad \text{Ans. (a)}$$

With the exit Mach number known, the isentropic-flow relations give the pressure and temperature:

$$p_e = \frac{p_0}{[1 + 0.2(2.5)^2]^{3.5}} = \frac{200,000}{17.08} = 11,700 \text{ Pa} \qquad \text{Ans. (b)}$$

$$T_e = \frac{T_0}{1 + 0.2(2.5)^2} = \frac{500}{2.25} = 222 \text{ K} \qquad \text{Ans. (c)}$$

The exit velocity follows from the known Mach number and temperature

$$V_e = \text{Ma}_e (kRT_e)^{1/2} = 2.5[1.4(287)(222)]^{1/2} = 2.5(299 \text{ m/s}) = 747 \text{ m/s} \qquad \text{Ans. (d)}$$

The exit area follows from the known throat area and exit Mach number and Eq. (9.45):

$$\frac{A_e}{A^*} = \frac{[1 + 0.2(2.5)^2]^3}{1.728(2.5)} = 2.64$$

or
$$A_e = 2.64 A^* = 2.64(0.0083 \text{ m}^2) = 0.0219 \text{ m}^2 = \tfrac{1}{4}\pi D_e^2$$

or
$$D_e = 16.7 \text{ cm} \qquad \text{Ans. (e)}$$

One point might be noted: The computation of the throat area A^* did not depend in any way on the numerical value of the exit Mach number. The exit was supersonic; therefore the throat is sonic and choked, and no further information is needed.

9.5 The Normal-Shock Wave

A common irreversibility occurring in supersonic internal or external flows is the normal-shock wave sketched in Fig. 9.8. Except at near-vacuum pressures such shock waves are very thin (a few micrometers thick) and approximate a discontinuous change in flow properties. We select a control volume just before and after the wave, as in Fig. 9.8.

The analysis is identical to that of Fig. 9.1; i.e., a shock wave is a fixed strong pressure wave. To compute all property changes rather than just the wave speed, we use all our basic one-dimensional steady-flow relations, letting section 1 be upstream and section 2 be downstream:

$$\rho_1 V_1 = \rho_2 V_2 = G = \text{const} \qquad (9.49a)$$

$$p_1 - p_2 = \rho_2 V_2^2 - \rho_1 V_1^2 \qquad (9.49b)$$

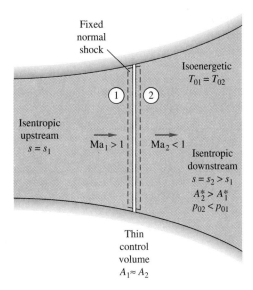

Fig. 9.8 Flow through a fixed normal-shock wave.

Energy:
$$h_1 + \tfrac{1}{2}V_1^2 = h_2 + \tfrac{1}{2}V_2^2 = h_0 = \text{const} \tag{9.49c}$$

Perfect gas:
$$\frac{p_1}{\rho_1 T_1} = \frac{p_2}{\rho_2 T_2} \tag{9.49d}$$

Constant c_p:
$$h = c_p T \qquad k = \text{const} \tag{9.49e}$$

Note that we have canceled out the areas $A_1 \approx A_2$, which is justified even in a variable duct section because of the thinness of the wave. The first successful analyses of these normal-shock relations are credited to W. J. M. Rankine (1870) and A. Hugoniot (1887), hence the modern term *Rankine-Hugoniot relations*. If we assume that the upstream conditions (p_1, V_1, ρ_1, h_1, T_1) are known, Eqs. (9.49) are five algebraic relations in the five unknowns (p_2, V_2, ρ_2, h_2, T_2). Because of the velocity-squared term, two solutions are found, and the correct one is determined from the second law of thermodynamics, which requires that $s_2 > s_1$.

The velocities V_1 and V_2 can be eliminated from Eqs. (9.49a) to (9.49c) to obtain the Rankine-Hugoniot relation

$$h_2 - h_1 = \frac{1}{2}(p_2 - p_1)\left(\frac{1}{\rho_2} + \frac{1}{\rho_1}\right) \tag{9.50}$$

This contains only thermodynamic properties and is independent of the equation of state. Introducing the perfect-gas law $h = c_p T = kp/[(k-1)\rho]$, we can rewrite this as

$$\frac{\rho_2}{\rho_1} = \frac{1 + \beta p_2/p_1}{\beta + p_2/p_1} \qquad \beta = \frac{k+1}{k-1} \tag{9.51}$$

We can compare this with the isentropic-flow relation for a very weak pressure wave in a perfect gas

$$\frac{\rho_2}{\rho_1} = \left(\frac{p_2}{p_1}\right)^{1/k} \tag{9.52}$$

Also, the actual change in entropy across the shock can be computed from the perfect-gas relation

$$\frac{s_2 - s_1}{c_v} = \ln\left[\frac{p_2}{p_1}\left(\frac{\rho_1}{\rho_2}\right)^k\right] \tag{9.53}$$

Assuming a given wave strength p_2/p_1, we can compute the density ratio and the entropy change and list them as follows for $k = 1.4$:

$\dfrac{p_2}{p_1}$	ρ_2/ρ_1		$\dfrac{s_2 - s_1}{c_v}$
	Eq. (9.51)	Isentropic	
0.5	0.6154	0.6095	−0.0134
0.9	0.9275	0.9275	−0.00005
1.0	1.0	1.0	0.0
1.1	1.00704	1.00705	0.00004
1.5	1.3333	1.3359	0.0027
2.0	1.6250	1.6407	0.0134

We see that the entropy change is negative if the pressure decreases across the shock, which violates the second law. Thus a rarefaction shock is impossible in a perfect gas.[1] We see also that weak-shock waves ($p_2/p_1 \leq 2.0$) are very nearly isentropic.

Mach-Number Relations

For a perfect gas all the property ratios across the normal shock are unique functions of k and the upstream Mach number Ma_1. For example, if we eliminate ρ_2 and V_2 from Eqs. (9.49a) to (9.49c) and introduce $h = kp/[(k - 1)\rho]$, we obtain

$$\frac{p_2}{p_1} = \frac{1}{k + 1}\left[\frac{2\rho_1 V_1^2}{p_1} - (k - 1)\right] \tag{9.54}$$

But for a perfect gas $\rho_1 V_1^2/p_1 = kV_1^2/(kRT_1) = k\,Ma_1^2$, so that Eq. (9.54) is equivalent to

$$\frac{p_2}{p_1} = \frac{1}{k + 1}[2k\,Ma_1^2 - (k - 1)] \tag{9.55}$$

From this equation we see that, for any k, $p_2 > p_1$ only if $Ma_1 > 1.0$. Thus for flow through a normal-shock wave, the upstream Mach number must be supersonic to satisfy the second law of thermodynamics.

What about the downstream Mach number? From the perfect-gas identity $\rho V^2 = kp\,Ma^2$, we can rewrite Eq. (9.49b) as

$$\frac{p_2}{p_1} = \frac{1 + k\,Ma_1^2}{1 + k\,Ma_2^2} \tag{9.56}$$

which relates the pressure ratio to both Mach numbers. By equating Eqs. (9.55) and (9.56) we can solve for

$$Ma_2^2 = \frac{(k - 1)\,Ma_1^2 + 2}{2k\,Ma_1^2 - (k - 1)} \tag{9.57}$$

---

[1] This is true also for most real gases; see Ref. 14, sec. 7.3.

Since Ma_1 must be supersonic, this equation predicts for all $k > 1$ that Ma_2 must be subsonic. Thus a normal-shock wave decelerates a flow almost discontinuously from supersonic to subsonic conditions.

Further manipulation of the basic relations (9.49) for a perfect gas gives additional equations relating the change in properties across a normal-shock wave in a perfect gas

$$\frac{\rho_2}{\rho_1} = \frac{(k + 1)\,Ma_1^2}{(k - 1)\,Ma_1^2 + 2} = \frac{V_1}{V_2}$$

$$\frac{T_2}{T_1} = [2 + (k - 1)\,Ma_1^2]\,\frac{2k\,Ma_1^2 - (k - 1)}{(k + 1)^2\,Ma_1^2} \qquad (9.58)$$

$$T_{02} = T_{01}$$

$$\frac{p_{02}}{p_{01}} = \frac{\rho_{02}}{\rho_{01}} = \left[\frac{(k + 1)\,Ma_1^2}{2 + (k - 1)\,Ma_1^2}\right]^{k/(k-1)}\left[\frac{k + 1}{2k\,Ma_1^2 - (k - 1)}\right]^{1/(k-1)}$$

Of additional interest is the fact that the critical, or sonic, throat area A^* in a duct increases across a normal shock

$$\frac{A_2^*}{A_1^*} = \frac{Ma_2}{Ma_1}\left[\frac{2 + (k - 1)\,Ma_1^2}{2 + (k - 1)\,Ma_2^2}\right]^{(1/2)(k+1)/(k-1)} \qquad (9.59)$$

All these relations are given in Table B.2 and plotted versus upstream Mach number Ma_1 in Fig. 9.9 for $k = 1.4$. We see that pressure increases greatly while temperature and density increase moderately. The effective throat area A^* increases slowly at first and then rapidly. The failure of students to account for this change in A^* is a common source of error in shock calculations.

The stagnation temperature remains the same, but the stagnation pressure and density decrease in the same ratio; i.e., the flow across the shock is adiabatic but nonisentropic.

Fig. 9.9 Change in flow properties across a normal-shock wave for $k = 1.4$.

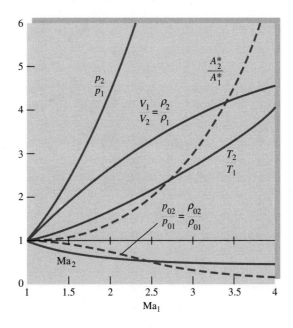

Other basic principles governing the behavior of shock waves can be summarized as follows:

1. The upstream flow is supersonic, and the downstream flow is subsonic.
2. For perfect gases (and also for real fluids except under bizarre thermodynamic conditions) rarefaction shocks are impossible, and only a compression shock can exist.
3. The entropy increases across a shock with consequent decreases in stagnation pressure and stagnation density and an increase in the effective sonic-throat area.
4. Weak shock waves are very nearly isentropic.

Normal-shock waves form in ducts under transient conditions, e.g., shock tubes, and in steady flow for certain ranges of the downstream pressure. Figure 9.10a shows a

Fig. 9.10 Normal shocks form in both internal and external flows: (*a*) Normal shock in a duct; note the Mach-wave pattern to the left (upstream), indicating supersonic flow (*courtesy of U.S. Air Force Arnold Engineering Development Center*). (*b*) Supersonic flow past a blunt body creates a normal shock at the nose; the apparent shock thickness and body-corner curvature are optical distortions (*courtesy of U.S. Army Ballistic Research Laboratory, Aberdeen Proving Ground*).

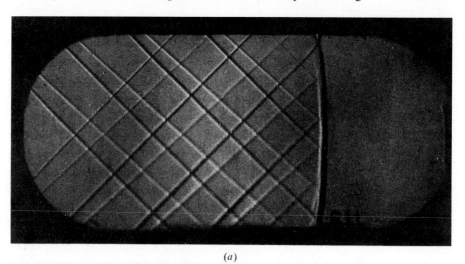

(*a*)

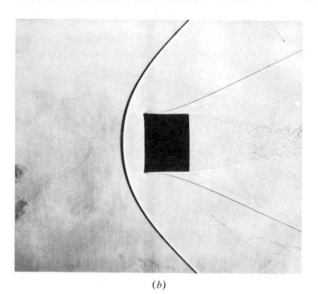

(*b*)

normal shock in a supersonic nozzle. Flow is from left to right. The oblique wave pattern to the left is formed by roughness elements on the nozzle walls and indicates that the upstream flow is supersonic. Note the absence of these Mach waves (see Sec. 9.10) in the subsonic flow downstream.

Normal-shock waves occur not only in supersonic duct flows but also in a variety of supersonic external flows. An example is the supersonic flow past a blunt body shown in Fig. 9.10b. The bow shock is curved, with a portion in front of the body which is essentially normal to the oncoming flow. This normal portion of the bow shock satisfies the property-change conditions just as outlined in this section. The flow inside the shock near the body nose is thus subsonic and at relatively high temperature $T_2 > T_1$, so that convective heat transfer is especially high in this region.

Each nonnormal portion of the bow shock in Fig. 9.10b satisfies the oblique-shock relations to be outlined in Sec. 9.9. Note also the oblique recompression shock on the sides of the body. What has happened is that the subsonic nose flow has accelerated around the corners back to supersonic flow at low pressure, which must then pass through the second shock to match the higher downstream pressure conditions.

Note the fine-grained turbulent wake structure in the rear of the body in Fig. 9.10b. The turbulent boundary layer along the sides of the body is also clearly visible.

The analysis of a complex multidimensional supersonic flow such as in Fig. 9.10 is beyond the scope of this book. For further information see, e.g., Ref. 14, chap. 9, or Ref. 8, chap. 16.

Moving Normal Shocks

The preceding analysis of the fixed shock applies equally well to the moving shock if we reverse the transformation used in Fig. 9.1. To make the upstream conditions simulate a still fluid, we move the shock of Fig. 9.8 to the left at speed V_1; that is, we fix our coordinates to a control volume moving with the shock. The downstream flow then appears to move to the left at a slower speed $V_1 - V_2$ following the shock. The thermodynamic properties are not changed by this transformation, so that all our Eqs. (9.50) to (9.59) are still valid.

EXAMPLE 9.6

Air flows from a reservoir where $p = 300$ kPa and $T = 500$ K through a throat to section 1 in Fig. E9.6, where there is a normal-shock wave. Compute (a) p_1, (b) p_2, (c) p_{02}, (d) A_2^*, (e) p_{03}, (f) A_3^*, (g) p_3, (h) T_{03}, and (i) T_3.

Solution

The reservoir conditions are the stagnation properties, which, for assumed one-dimensional adiabatic frictionless flow, hold through the throat up to section 1

$$p_{01} = 300 \text{ kPa} \qquad T_{01} = 500 \text{ K}$$

A shock wave cannot exist unless Ma_1 is supersonic; therefore the flow must have accelerated through a throat which is sonic

$$A_t = A_1^* = 1 \text{ m}^2$$

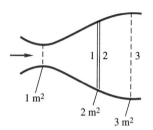

Fig. E9.6

We can now find the Mach number Ma_1 from the known isentropic area ratio

$$\frac{A_1}{A_1^*} = \frac{2 \text{ m}^2}{1 \text{ m}^2} = 2.0$$

From Eq. (9.48c)

$$\text{Ma}_1 \approx 1 + 1.2(2.0 - 1)^{1/2} = 2.20$$

Further iteration with Eq. (9.45) would give $\text{Ma}_1 = 2.1972$, showing that Eq. (9.48c) gives satisfactory accuracy. The pressure p_1 follows from the isentropic relation (9.28) (or Table B.1)

$$\frac{p_{01}}{p_1} = [1 + 0.2(2.20)^2]^{3.5} = 10.7$$

or

$$p_1 = \frac{300 \text{ kPa}}{10.7} = 28.06 \text{ kPa} \qquad\qquad Ans. (a)$$

The pressure p_2 is now obtained from Ma_1 and the normal-shock relation (9.55) or Table B.2

$$\frac{p_2}{p_1} = \frac{1}{2.4}[2.8(2.20)^2 - 0.4] = 5.48$$

or

$$p_2 = 5.48(28.06) = 154 \text{ kPa} \qquad\qquad Ans. (b)$$

In similar manner, for $\text{Ma}_1 = 2.20$, $p_{02}/p_{01} = 0.628$ from Eq. (9.58) and $A_2^*/A_1^* = 1.592$ from Eq. (9.59), or we can read Table B.2 for these values. Thus

$$p_{02} = 0.628(300 \text{ kPa}) = 188 \text{ kPa} \qquad\qquad Ans. (c)$$

$$A_2^* = 1.592(1 \text{ m}^2) = 1.592 \text{ m}^2 \qquad\qquad Ans. (d)$$

The flow from section 2 to 3 is isentropic (but at higher entropy than the flow upstream of the shock). Thus

$$p_{03} = p_{02} = 188 \text{ kPa} \qquad\qquad Ans. (e)$$

$$A_3^* = A_2^* = 1.592 \text{ m}^2 \qquad\qquad Ans. (f)$$

Knowing A_3^*, we can now compute p_3 by finding Ma_3 and without bothering to find Ma_2 (which happens to equal 0.547). The area ratio at section 3 is

$$\frac{A_3}{A_3^*} = \frac{3 \text{ m}^2}{1.592 \text{ m}^2} = 1.884$$

Then, since Ma_3 is known to be subsonic because it is downstream of a normal shock, we use Eq. (9.48a) to estimate

$$\text{Ma}_3 \approx \frac{1 + 0.27/(1.884)^2}{1.728(1.884)} = 0.330$$

The pressure p_3 then follows from the isentropic relation (9.28) or Table B.1

$$\frac{p_{03}}{p_3} = [1 + 0.2(0.330)^2]^{3.5} = 1.078$$

or
$$p_3 = \frac{188 \text{ kPa}}{1.078} = 174 \text{ kPa} \qquad \textit{Ans. (g)}$$

Meanwhile, the flow is adiabatic throughout the duct; thus

$$T_{01} = T_{02} = T_{03} = 500 \text{ K} \qquad \textit{Ans. (h)}$$

Therefore, finally, from the adiabatic relation (9.26)

$$\frac{T_{03}}{T_3} = 1 + 0.2(0.330)^2 = 1.022$$

or
$$T_3 = \frac{500 \text{ K}}{1.022} = 489 \text{ K} \qquad \textit{Ans. (i)}$$

Notice that this type of duct-flow problem, with or without a shock wave, requires straight-forward application of algebraic perfect-gas relations coupled with a little thought given to which formula is appropriate for the particular situation.

EXAMPLE 9.7

An explosion in air, $k = 1.4$, creates a spherical shock wave propagating radially into still air at standard conditions. At the instant shown in Fig. E9.7, the pressure just inside the shock is 200 lbf/in² absolute. Estimate (*a*) the shock speed C and (*b*) the air velocity V just inside the shock.

Fig. E9.7

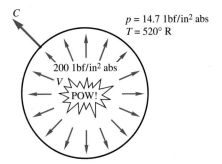

$p = 14.7$ 1bf/in² abs
$T = 520°$ R

200 1bf/in² abs
V
POW!

Solution

Part (a)   In spite of the spherical geometry the flow across the shock moves normal to the spherical wavefront; hence the normal-shock relations (9.50) to (9.59) apply. Fixing our control volume to the moving shock, we find that the proper conditions to use in Fig. 9.8 are

$$C = V_1 \qquad p_1 = 14.7 \text{ lbf/in}^2 \text{ absolute} \qquad T_1 = 520°\text{R}$$

$$V = V_1 - V_2 \qquad p_2 = 200 \text{ lbf/in}^2 \text{ absolute}$$

The speed of sound outside the shock is $a_1 \approx 49T_1^{1/2} = 1117$ ft/s. We can find Ma_1 from the known pressure ratio across the shock

$$\frac{p_2}{p_1} = \frac{200 \text{ lbf/in}^2 \text{ absolute}}{14.7 \text{ lbf/in}^2 \text{ absolute}} = 13.61$$

From Eq. (9.55) or Table B.2

$$13.61 = \frac{1}{2.4}(2.8\,\text{Ma}_1^2 - 0.4) \quad \text{or} \quad \text{Ma}_1 = 3.436$$

Then, by definition of the Mach number,

$$C = V_1 = \text{Ma}_1\,a_1 = 3.436(1117\ \text{ft/s}) = 3840\ \text{ft/s} \qquad \textit{Ans. (a)}$$

Part (b)   To find V_2, we need the temperature or sound speed inside the shock. Since Ma_1 is known, from Eq. (9.58) or Table B.2 for $\text{Ma}_1 = 3.436$ we compute $T_2/T_1 = 3.228$. Then

$$T_2 = 3.228 T_1 = 3.228(520°\text{R}) = 1679°\text{R}$$

At such a high temperature we should account for non-perfect-gas effects or at least use the gas tables [16], but we won't. Here just estimate from the perfect-gas energy equation (9.23) that

$$V_2^2 = 2c_p(T_1 - T_2) + V_1^2 = 2(6010)(520 - 1679) + (3840)^2 = 815,\!000$$

or
$$V_2 \approx 903\ \text{ft/s}$$

Notice that we did this without bothering to compute Ma_2, which equals 0.454, or $a_2 \approx 49T_2^{1/2} = 2000\ \text{ft/s}$.

Finally, the air velocity behind the shock is

$$V = V_1 - V_2 = 3840 - 903 \approx 2940\ \text{ft/s} \qquad \textit{Ans. (b)}$$

Thus a powerful explosion creates a brief but intense blast wind as it passes.[1]

9.6 Operation of Converging and Diverging Nozzles

By combining the isentropic-flow and normal-shock relations plus the concept of sonic throat choking, we can outline the characteristics of converging and diverging nozzles.

Converging Nozzle

First consider the converging nozzle sketched in Fig. 9.11a. There is an upstream reservoir at stagnation pressure p_0. The flow is induced by lowering the downstream outside, or *back*, pressure p_b below p_0, resulting in the sequence of states a to e shown in Fig. 9.11b and c.

For a moderate drop in p_b to states a and b, the throat pressure is higher than the critical value p^* which would make the throat sonic. The flow in the nozzle is subsonic throughout, and the jet exit pressure p_e equals the back pressure p_b. The mass flow is predicted by subsonic isentropic theory and is less than the critical value $\dot{m}_{\max}$, as shown in Fig. 9.11c.

For condition c, the back pressure exactly equals the critical pressure p^* of the throat. The throat becomes sonic, the jet exit flow is sonic, $p_e = p_b$, and the mass flow equals its maximum value from Eq. (9.46). The flow upstream of the throat is subsonic everywhere and predicted by isentropic theory based on the local area ratio $A(x)/A^*$ and Table B.1.

---

[1] This is the principle of the *shock-tube wind tunnel*, in which a controlled explosion creates a brief flow at very high Mach number, with data taken by fast-response instruments. See, e.g., Ref. 5, sec. 4.5.

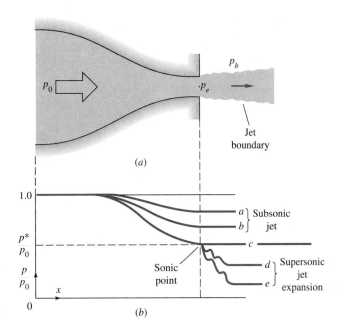

(a)

(b)

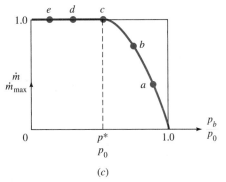

Fig. 9.11 Operation of a converging nozzle: (a) nozzle geometry showing characteristic pressures; (b) pressure distribution caused by various back pressures; (c) mass flow versus back pressure.

(c)

Finally, if p_b is lowered further to conditions d or e below p^*, the nozzle cannot respond further because it is choked at its maximum throat mass flow. The throat remains sonic with $p_e = p^*$, and the nozzle-pressure distribution is the same as in state c, as sketched in Fig. 9.11b. The exit jet expands supersonically so that the jet pressure can be reduced from p^* down to p_b. The jet structure is complex and multidimensional and is not shown here. Being supersonic, the jet cannot send any signal upstream to influence the choked flow conditions in the nozzle.

If the stagnation plenum chamber is large or supplemented by a compressor, and if the discharge chamber is larger or supplemented by a vacuum pump, the converging-nozzle flow will be steady or nearly so. Otherwise the nozzle will be blowing down, with p_0 decreasing and p_b increasing, and the flow states will be changing from, say, state e backward to state a. Blowdown calculations are usually made by a quasi-steady analysis based on isentropic steady-flow theory for the instantaneous pressures $p_0(t)$ and $p_b(t)$.

EXAMPLE 9.8

A converging nozzle has a throat area of 6 cm² and stagnation air conditions of 120 kPa and 400 K. Compute the exit pressure and mass flow if the back presure is (a) 90 kPa and (b) 45 kPa. Assume $k = 1.4$.

Solution

From Eq. (9.32) for $k = 1.4$ the critical (sonic) throat pressure is

$$\frac{p^*}{p_0} = 0.5283 \quad \text{or} \quad p^* = (0.5283)(120 \text{ kPa}) = 63.4 \text{ kPa}$$

If the back pressure is less than this amount, the nozzle flow is choked.

Part (a)   For $p_b = 90 \text{ kPa} > p^*$, the flow is subsonic, not choked. The exit pressure is $p_e = p_b$. The throat Mach number is found from the isentropic relation (9.35) or Table B.1:

$$\text{Ma}_e^2 = 5\left[\left(\frac{p_0}{p_e}\right)^{2/7} - 1\right] = 5\left[\left(\frac{120}{90}\right)^{2/7} - 1\right] = 0.4283 \qquad \text{Ma}_e = 0.654$$

The exit temperature is computed for this Mach number as

$$T_e = \frac{T_0}{1 + 0.2 \text{ Ma}_e^2} = \frac{400 \text{ K}}{1 + 0.2(0.654)^2} = 368 \text{ K}$$

whence

$$\rho_e = \frac{p_e}{RT_e} = \frac{90,000}{(287)(368)} = 0.851 \text{ kg/m}^3$$

The exit speed of sound is $a_e = \sqrt{kRT_e} = [(1.4)(287)(368)]^{1/2} = 385 \text{ m/s}$, so the exit velocity is $V_e = \text{Ma}_e\, a_e = (0.654)(385) = 251 \text{ m/s}$. The mass flow is thus

$$\dot{m} = \rho_e A_e V_e = (0.851 \text{ kg/m}^3)(0.0006 \text{ m}^2)(251 \text{ m/s}) \approx 0.128 \text{ kg/s} \qquad \textit{Ans. (a)}$$

for

$$p_e = p_b = 90 \text{ kPa} \qquad \textit{Ans. (a)}$$

Part (b)   For $p_b = 45 \text{ kPa} < p^*$, the flow is choked, similar to condition d in Fig. 9.11b. The exit pressure is sonic:

$$p_e = p^* = 63.4 \text{ kPa} \qquad \textit{Ans. (b)}$$

The (choked) mass flow is a maximum from Eq. (9.47):

$$\dot{m} = \dot{m}_{\max} = \frac{0.6847 p_0 A_e}{(RT_0)^{1/2}} = \frac{0.6847(120,000)(0.0006)}{[287(400)]^{1/2}} = 0.145 \text{ kg/s} \qquad \textit{Ans. (b)}$$

Any back pressure less than 63.4 kPa would cause this same choked mass flow. Note that the 50 percent increase in exit Mach number, from 0.654 to 1.0, has increased the mass flow only 12 percent, from 0.128 to 0.145 kg/s.

Converging-Diverging Nozzle

Now consider the converging-diverging nozzle sketched in Fig. 9.12a. If the back pressure p_b is low enough, there will be supersonic flow in the diverging portion and a

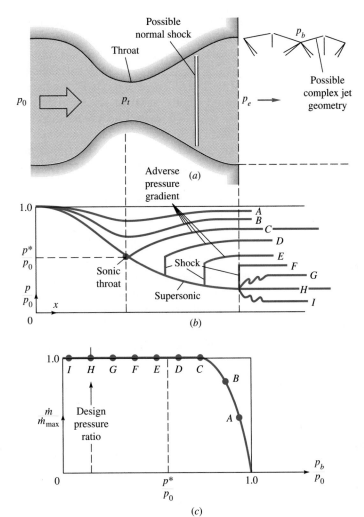

Fig. 9.12 Operation of a converging-diverging nozzle: (*a*) nozzle geometry with possible flow configurations; (*b*) pressure distribution caused by various back pressures; (*c*) mass flow versus back pressure.

variety of shock-wave conditions may occur, which are sketched in Fig. 9.12*b*. Let the back pressure be gradually decreased.

For curves *A* and *B* in Fig. 9.12*b* the back pressure is not low enough to induce sonic flow in the throat, and the flow in the nozzle is subsonic throughout. The pressure distribution is computed from subsonic isentropic area-change relations, e.g., Table B.1. The exit pressure $p_e = p_b$, and the jet is subsonic.

For curve *C* the area ratio A_e/A_t exactly equals the critical ratio A_e/A^* for a subsonic Ma_e in Table B.1. The throat becomes sonic, and the mass flux reaches a maximum in Fig. 9.12*c*. The remainder of the nozzle flow is subsonic, including the exit jet, and $p_e = p_b$.

Now jump for a moment to curve *H*. Here p_b is such that p_b/p_0 exactly corresponds to the critical-area ratio A_e/A^* for a *supersonic* Ma_e in Table B.1. The diverging flow is entirely supersonic, including the jet flow, and $p_e = p_b$. This is called the *design* *pressure ratio* of the nozzle and is the back pressure suitable for operating a supersonic wind tunnel or an efficient rocket exhaust.

Now back up and suppose that p_b lies between curves C and H, which is impossible according to purely isentropic-flow calculations. Then back pressures D to F occur in Fig. 9.12b. The throat remains choked at the sonic value, and we can match $p_e = p_b$ by placing a normal shock at just the right place in the diverging section to cause a *subsonic-diffuser* flow back to the back-pressure condition. The mass flow remains at maximum in Fig. 9.12c. At back pressure F the required normal shock stands in the duct exit. At back pressure G no single normal shock can do the job, and so the flow compresses outside the exit in a complex series of oblique shocks until it matches p_b.

Finally, at back pressure I, p_b is lower than the design pressure H, but the nozzle is choked and cannot respond. The exit flow expands in a complex series of supersonic wave motions until it matches the low back pressure. See, e.g., Ref. 9, sec. 5.4, for further details of these off-design jet-flow configurations.

Note that for p_b less than back pressure C, there is supersonic flow in the nozzle and the throat can receive no signal from the exit behavior. The flow remains choked, and the throat has no idea what the exit conditions are.

Note also that the normal shock-patching idea is idealized, Downstream of the shock the nozzle flow has an adverse pressure gradient, usually leading to wall boundary-layer separation. Blockage by the greatly thickened separated layer interacts strongly with the core flow (recall Fig. 6.27) and usually induces a series of weak two-dimensional compression shocks rather than a single one-dimensional normal shock (see, e.g., Ref. 14, pp. 292–293, for further details).

EXAMPLE 9.9

A converging-diverging nozzle (Fig. 9.12a) has a throat area of 0.002 m^2 and an exit area of 0.008 m^2. Air stagnation conditions are $p_0 = 1000$ kPa and $T_0 = 500$ K. Compute the exit pressure and mass flow for (a) design condition and the exit pressure and mass flow if (b) $p_b \approx 300$ kPa and (c) $p_b \approx 900$ kPa. Assume $k = 1.4$.

Solution

Part (a)

The design condition corresponds to supersonic isentropic flow at the given area ratio $A_e/A_t = 0.008/0.002 = 4.0$. We can find the design Mach number either by iteration of the area-ratio formula (9.45) or by the curve fit (9.48d)

$$\text{Ma}_{e,\text{design}} \approx [216(4.0) - 254(4.0)^{2/3}]^{1/5} \approx 2.95 \qquad (\text{exact} = 2.9402)$$

The accuracy of the curve fit is seen to be satisfactory. The design pressure ratio follows from Eq. (9.34)

$$\frac{p_0}{p_e} = [1 + 0.2(2.95)^2]^{3.5} = 34.1$$

or
$$p_{e,\text{design}} = \frac{1000 \text{ kPa}}{34.1} = 29.3 \text{ kPa} \qquad \qquad Ans. (a)$$

Since the throat is clearly sonic at design conditions, Eq. (9.47) applies

$$m_{design} = \dot{m}_{max} = \frac{0.6847 p_0 A_t}{(RT_0)^{1/2}} = \frac{0.6847(10^6 \text{ Pa})(0.002 \text{ m}^2)}{[287(500)]^{1/2}}$$

$$= 3.61 \text{ kg/s}$$

Ans. (a)

Part (b)   For $p_b = 300$ kPa we are definitely far below the subsonic isentropic condition C in Fig. 9.12b, but we may even be below condition F with a normal shock in the exit, i.e., in condition G, where oblique shocks occur outside the exit plane. If it is condition G, then $p_e = p_{e,design} = 29.3$ kPa because no shock has yet occurred. To find out, compute condition F by assuming an exit normal shock with $Ma_1 = 2.95$, that is, the design Mach number just upstream of the shock. From Eq. (9.55)

$$\frac{p_2}{p_1} = \frac{1}{2.4} [2.8(2.95)^2 - 0.4] = 9.99$$

or

$$p_2 = 9.99 p_1 = 9.99 p_{e,design} = 293 \text{ kPa}$$

Since this is less than the given $p_b = 300$ kPa, there is a normal shock just upstream of the exit plane (condition E). The exit flow is subsonic and equals the back pressure

$$p_e = p_b = 300 \text{ kPa}$$

Ans. (b)

Also

$$\dot{m} = \dot{m}_{max} = 3.61 \text{ kg/s}$$

Ans. (b)

The throat is still sonic and choked at its maximum mass flow.

Part (c)   Finally, for $p_b = 900$ kPa, which is up near condition C, we compute Ma_e and p_e for condition C as a comparison. Again $A_e/A_t = 4.0$ for this condition, with a subsonic Ma_e estimated from the curve-fitted Eq. (9.48a):

$$Ma_e(C) \approx \frac{1 + 0.27/(4.0)^2}{1.728(4.0)} = 0.147 \qquad (\text{exact} = 0.14655)$$

Then the isentropic exit-pressure ratio for this condition is

$$\frac{p_0}{p_e} = [1 + 0.2(0.147)^2]^{3.5} = 1.0152$$

or

$$p_e = \frac{1000}{1.0152} = 985 \text{ kPa}$$

The given back pressure of 900 kPa is less than this value, corresponding roughly to condition D in Fig. 9.12b. Thus for this case there is a normal shock just downstream of the throat, and the throat is choked

$$p_e = p_b = 900 \text{ kPa} \qquad \dot{m} = \dot{m}_{max} = 3.61 \text{ kg/s}$$

Ans. (c)

For this large exit-area ratio, the exit pressure would have to be larger than 985 kPa to cause a subsonic flow in the throat and a mass flow less than maximum.

9.7 Compressible Duct Flow with Friction[1]

Section 9.4 showed the effect of area change on a compressible flow while neglecting friction and heat transfer. We could now add friction and heat transfer to the area change

[1] This section may be omitted without loss of continuity.

and consider coupled effects, which is done in advanced texts [for example, 8, chap. 8]. Instead, as an elementary introduction, this section treats only the effect of friction, neglecting area change and heat transfer. The basic assumptions are

1. Steady one-dimensional adiabatic flow
2. Perfect gas with constant specific heats
3. Constant-area straight duct
4. Negligible shaft-work and potential-energy changes
5. Wall shear stress correlated by a Darcy friction factor

In effect, we are studying a Moody-type pipe-friction problem but with large changes in kinetic energy, enthalpy, and pressure in the flow.

Consider the elemental duct control volume of area A and length dx in Fig. 9.13. The area is constant, but other flow properties (p, ρ, T, h, V) may vary with x. Application of the three conservation laws to this control volume gives three differential equations

Continuity:
$$\rho V = \frac{\dot{m}}{A} = G = \text{const}$$

or
$$\frac{d\rho}{\rho} + \frac{dV}{V} = 0 \tag{9.60a}$$

x momentum:
$$pA - (p + dp)A - \tau_w \pi D \, dx = \dot{m}(V + dV - V)$$

or
$$dp + \frac{4\tau_w dx}{D} + \rho V \, dV = 0 \tag{9.60b}$$

Energy:
$$h + \tfrac{1}{2}V^2 = h_0 = c_p T_0 = c_p T + \tfrac{1}{2}V^2$$

or
$$c_p \, dT + V \, dV = 0 \tag{9.60c}$$

Since these three equations have five unknowns—p, ρ, T, V, and τ_w—we need two additional relations. One is the perfect-gas law

$$p = \rho RT \quad \text{or} \quad \frac{dp}{p} = \frac{d\rho}{\rho} + \frac{dT}{T} \tag{9.61}$$

To eliminate τ_w as an unknown, it is assumed that wall shear is correlated by a local Darcy friction factor f

Fig. 9.13 Elemental control volume for flow in a constant-area duct with friction.

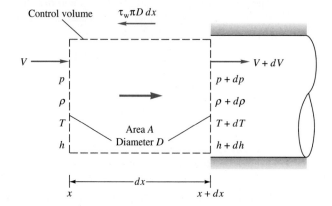

$$\tau_w = \tfrac{1}{8}f\rho V^2 = \tfrac{1}{8}fkp\ \mathrm{Ma}^2 \tag{9.62}$$

where the last form follows from the perfect-gas speed-of-sound expression $a^2 = kp/\rho$. In practice, f can be related to the local Reynolds number and wall roughness from, say, the Moody chart, Fig. 6.13.

Equations (9.60) and (9.61) are first-order differential equations and can be integrated, by using friction-factor data, from any inlet section 1, where p_1, T_1, V_1, etc., are known, to determine $p(x)$, $T(x)$, etc., along the duct. It is practically impossible to eliminate all but one variable to give, say, a single differential equation for $p(x)$, but all equations can be written in terms of the Mach number $\mathrm{Ma}(x)$ and the friction factor, by using the definition of Mach number

$$V^2 = \mathrm{Ma}^2\ kRT$$

or

$$\frac{2\ dV}{V} = \frac{2\ d\ \mathrm{Ma}}{\mathrm{Ma}} + \frac{dT}{T} \tag{9.63}$$

Adiabatic Flow

By eliminating variables between Eqs. (9.60) to (9.63), we obtain the working relations

$$\frac{dp}{p} = -k\ \mathrm{Ma}^2\ \frac{1 + (k - 1)\ \mathrm{Ma}^2}{2(1 - \mathrm{Ma}^2)}\ f\ \frac{dx}{D} \tag{9.64a}$$

$$\frac{d\rho}{\rho} = -\frac{k\ \mathrm{Ma}^2}{2(1 - \mathrm{Ma}^2)}\ f\ \frac{dx}{D} = -\frac{dV}{V} \tag{9.64b}$$

$$\frac{dp_0}{p_0} = \frac{d\rho_0}{\rho_0} = -\frac{1}{2}k\ \mathrm{Ma}^2 f\ \frac{dx}{D} \tag{9.64c}$$

$$\frac{dT}{T} = -\frac{k(k - 1)\ \mathrm{Ma}^4}{2(1 - \mathrm{Ma}^2)}\ f\ \frac{dx}{D} \tag{9.64d}$$

$$\frac{d\ \mathrm{Ma}^2}{\mathrm{Ma}^2} = k\ \mathrm{Ma}^2\ \frac{1 + \tfrac{1}{2}(k - 1)\ \mathrm{Ma}^2}{1 - \mathrm{Ma}^2}\ f\ \frac{dx}{D} \tag{9.64e}$$

All these except dp_0/p_0 have the factor $1 - \mathrm{Ma}^2$ in the denominator, so that, like the area-change formulas in Fig. 9.5, subsonic and supersonic flow have opposite effects:

Property	Subsonic	Supersonic
p	Decreases	Increases
ρ	Decreases	Increases
V	Increases	Decreases
$p_0,\ \rho_0$	Decreases	Decreases
T	Decreases	Increases
Ma	Increases	Decreases
Entropy	Increases	Increases

We have added to the list above that entropy must increase along the duct for either subsonic or supersonic flow as a consequence of the second law for adiabatic flow. For the same reason, stagnation pressure and density must both decrease.

The key parameter above is the Mach number. Whether the inlet flow is subsonic or supersonic, the duct Mach number always tends downstream toward Ma $= 1$ because this is the path along which the entropy increases. If the pressure and density are computed from Eqs. (9.64a) and (9.64b) and the entropy from Eq. (9.53), the result can be plotted in Fig. 9.14 versus Mach number for $k = 1.4$. The maximum entropy occurs at Ma $= 1$, so that the second law requires that the duct-flow properties continually approach the sonic point. Since p_0 and ρ_0 continually decrease along the duct due to the frictional (nonisentropic) losses, they are not useful as reference properties. Instead, the sonic properties p^*, ρ^*, T^*, p_0^*, and ρ_0^* are the appropriate constant reference quantities in adiabatic duct flow. The theory then computes the ratios p/p^*, T/T^*, etc., as a function of local Mach number and the integrated friction effect.

To derive working formulas, we first attack Eq. (9.64e), which relates the Mach number to friction. Separate the variables and integrate:

$$\int_0^{L^*} f \frac{dx}{D} = \int_{Ma^2}^{1.0} \frac{1 - Ma^2}{k\, Ma^4[1 + \frac{1}{2}(k - 1)\, Ma^2]} \, d\, Ma^2 \tag{9.65}$$

The upper limit is the sonic point, whether or not it is actually reached in the duct flow. The lower limit is arbitrarily placed at the position $x = 0$, where the Mach number is Ma. The result of the integration is

$$\frac{\overline{f}L^*}{D} = \frac{1 - Ma^2}{k\, Ma^2} + \frac{k + 1}{2k} \ln \frac{(k + 1)\, Ma^2}{2 + (k - 1)\, Ma^2} \tag{9.66}$$

where $\overline{f}$ is the average friction factor between 0 and L^*. In practice, an average f is always assumed, and no attempt is made to account for the slight changes in Reynolds number along the duct. For noncircular ducts, D is replaced by the hydraulic diameter $D_h = (4 \times \text{area})/\text{perimeter}$ as in Eq. (6.74).

Fig. 9.14 Adiabatic frictional flow in a constant-area duct always approaches Ma $= 1$ to satisfy the second law of thermodynamics. The computed curve is independent of the value of the friction factor.

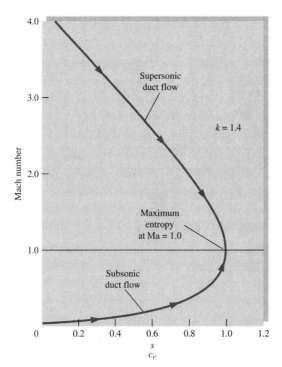

Equation (9.66) is tabulated versus Mach number in Table B.3. The length L^* is the length of duct required to develop a duct flow from Mach number Ma to the sonic point. Many problems involve short ducts which never become sonic, for which the solution uses the differences in the tabulated "maximum," or sonic, length. For example, the length ΔL required to develop from Ma_1 to Ma_2 is given by

$$\bar{f}\frac{\Delta L}{D} = \left(\frac{\bar{f}L^*}{D}\right)_1 - \left(\frac{\bar{f}L^*}{D}\right)_2 \qquad (9.67)$$

This avoids the need for separate tabulations for short ducts.

It is recommended that the friction factor $\bar{f}$ be estimated from the Moody chart (Fig. 6.13) for the average Reynolds number and wall-roughness ratio of the duct. Available data [20] on duct friction for compressible flow show good agreement with the Moody chart for subsonic flow, but the measured data in supersonic duct flow are up to 50 percent less than the equivalent Moody friction factor.

EXAMPLE 9.10

Air flows subsonically in an adiabatic 2-cm-diameter duct. The average friction factor is 0.024. What length of duct is necessary to accelerate the flow from $Ma_1 = 0.1$ to $Ma_2 = 0.5$? What additional length will accelerate it to $Ma_3 = 1.0$? Assume $k = 1.4$.

Solution

Equation (9.67) applies, with values of $\bar{f}L^*/D$ computed from Eq. (9.66) or read from Table B.3:

$$\bar{f}\frac{\Delta L}{D} = \frac{0.024\,\Delta L}{0.02\text{ m}} = \left(\frac{\bar{f}L^*}{D}\right)_{Ma=0.1} - \left(\frac{\bar{f}L^*}{D}\right)_{Ma=0.5}$$

$$= 66.9216 - 1.0691 = 65.8525$$

Thus
$$\Delta L = \frac{65.8525(0.02\text{ m})}{0.024} = 55\text{ m} \qquad \textit{Ans. (a)}$$

The additional length $\Delta L'$ to go from Ma $= 0.5$ to Ma $= 1.0$ is taken directly from Table B.2

$$f\frac{\Delta L'}{D} = \left(\frac{fL^*}{D}\right)_{Ma=0.5} = 1.0691$$

or
$$\Delta L' = L^*_{Ma=0.5} = \frac{1.0691(0.02\text{ m})}{0.024} = 0.9\text{ m} \qquad \textit{Ans. (b)}$$

This is typical of these calculations: It takes 55 m to accelerate up to Ma $= 0.5$ and then only 0.9 m more to get all the way up to the sonic point.

Formulas for other flow properties along the duct can be derived from Eqs. (9.64). Equation (9.64e) can be used to eliminate $f\,dx/D$ from each of the other relations, giving, for example, dp/p as a function only of Ma and $d\,Ma^2/Ma^2$. For convenience in tabulating the results, each expression is then integrated all the way from (p, Ma) to the sonic point (p^*, 1.0). The integrated results are

$$\frac{p}{p^*} = \frac{1}{Ma}\left[\frac{k+1}{2+(k-1)\,Ma^2}\right]^{1/2} \tag{9.68a}$$

$$\frac{\rho}{\rho^*} = \frac{V^*}{V} = \frac{1}{Ma}\left[\frac{2+(k-1)\,Ma^2}{k+1}\right]^{1/2} \tag{9.68b}$$

$$\frac{T}{T^*} = \frac{a^2}{a^{*2}} = \frac{k+1}{2+(k-1)\,Ma^2} \tag{9.68c}$$

$$\frac{p_0}{p_0^*} = \frac{p_0}{p_0^*} = \frac{1}{Ma}\left[\frac{2+(k-1)\,Ma^2}{k+1}\right]^{(1/2)(k+1)/(k-1)} \tag{9.68d}$$

All these ratios are also tabulated in Table B.3. For finding changes between points Ma_1 and Ma_2 which are not sonic, products of these ratios are used. For example,

$$\frac{p_2}{p_1} = \frac{p_2}{p^*}\frac{p^*}{p_1} \tag{9.69}$$

since p^* is a constant reference value for the flow.

EXAMPLE 9.11

For the duct flow of Example 9.10 assume that, at $Ma_1 = 0.1$, we have $p_1 = 600$ kPa and $T_1 = 450$ K. At section 2 farther downstream, $Ma_2 = 0.5$. Compute (a) p_2, (b) T_2, (c) V_2, and (d) p_{02}.

Solution

As preliminary information we can compute V_1 and p_{01} from the given data:

$$V_1 = Ma_1\,a_1 = 0.1[(1.4)(287)(450)]^{1/2} = 0.1(425 \text{ m/s}) = 42.5 \text{ m/s}$$

$$p_{01} = p_1(1 + 0.2\,Ma_1^2)^{3.5} = (600 \text{ kPa})[1 + 0.2(0.1)^2]^{3.5} = 604 \text{ kPa}$$

Now enter Table B.3 or Eqs. (9.68) to find the following property ratios:

Section	Ma	p/p^*	T/T^*	V/V^*	p_0/p_0^*
1	0.1	10.9435	1.1976	0.1094	5.8218
2	0.5	2.1381	1.1429	0.5345	1.3399

Use these ratios to compute all properties downstream:

$$p_2 = p_1\frac{p_2/p^*}{p_1/p^*} = (600 \text{ kPa})\frac{2.1381}{10.9435} = 117 \text{ kPa} \qquad \textit{Ans. (a)}$$

$$T_2 = T_1\frac{T_2/T^*}{T_1/T^*} = (450 \text{ K})\frac{1.1429}{1.1976} = 429 \text{ K} \qquad \textit{Ans. (b)}$$

$$V_2 = V_1\frac{V_2/V^*}{V_1/V^*} = (42.5 \text{ m/s})\frac{0.5345}{0.1094} = 208\,\frac{\text{m}}{\text{s}} \qquad \textit{Ans. (c)}$$

$$p_{02} = p_{01} \frac{p_{02}/p_0^*}{p_{01}/p_0^*} = (604 \text{ kPa}) \frac{1.3399}{5.8218} = 139 \text{ kPa} \qquad \textit{Ans. (d)}$$

Note the 77 percent reduction in stagnation pressure due to friction. The formulas are seductive, so check your work by other means. For example, check $p_{02} = p_2(1 + 0.2 \text{ Ma}_2^2)^{3.5}$.

Choking due to Friction

The theory here predicts that for adiabatic frictional flow in a constant-area duct, no matter what the inlet Mach number Ma_1 is, the flow downstream tends toward the sonic point. There is a certain duct length $L^*(\text{Ma}_1)$ for which the exit Mach number will be exactly unity. The duct is then choked.

But what if the actual length L is greater than the predicted ''maximum'' length L^*? Then the flow conditions must change, and there are two classifications.

Subsonic Inlet. If $L > L^*(\text{Ma}_1)$, the flow slows down until an inlet Mach number Ma_2 is reached such that $L = L^*(\text{Ma}_2)$. The exit flow is sonic, and the mass flow has been reduced by *frictional choking*. Further increases in duct length will continue to decrease the inlet Ma and mass flow.

Supersonic Inlet. From Table B.3 we see that friction has a very large effect on supersonic duct flow. Even an infinite inlet Mach number will be reduced to sonic conditions in only 41 diameters for $\bar{f} = 0.02$. Some typical numerical values are shown in Fig. 9.15, assuming an inlet Ma = 3.0 and $\bar{f} = 0.02$. For this condition $L^* = 26$ diameters. If

Fig. 9.15 Behavior of duct flow with a nominal supersonic inlet condition Ma = 3.0: (a) $L/D \leq 26$, flow is supersonic throughout duct; (b) $L/D = 40 > L^*/D$, normal shock at Ma = 2.0 with subsonic flow then accelerating to sonic exit point; (c) $L/D = 53$, shock must now occur at Ma = 2.5; (d) $L/D > 63$, flow must be entirely subsonic and choked at exit.

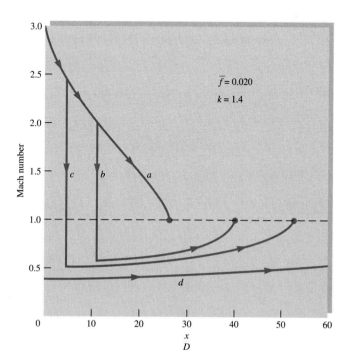

L is increased beyond 26*D*, the flow will not choke but a normal shock will form at just the right place for the subsequent subsonic frictional flow to become sonic exactly at the exit. Figure 9.15 shows two examples, for $L/D = 40$ and 53. As the length increases, the required normal shock moves upstream until, for Fig. 9.15, the shock is at the inlet for $L/D = 63$. Further increase in *L* causes the shock to move upstream of the inlet into the supersonic nozzle feeding the duct. Yet the mass flow is still the same as for the very short duct, because presumably the feed nozzle still has a sonic throat. Eventually, a very long duct will cause the feed-nozzle throat to become choked, thus reducing the duct mass flow. Thus supersonic friction changes the flow pattern if $L > L^*$ but does not choke the flow until *L* is much larger than L^*.

EXAMPLE 9.12

Air enters a 3-cm-diameter duct at $p_0 = 200$ kPa, $T_0 = 500$ K, and $V_1 = 100$ m/s. The friction factor is 0.02. Compute (*a*) the maximum duct length for these conditions, (*b*) the mass flow if the duct length is 15 m, and (*c*) the reduced mass flow if $L = 30$ m.

Solution

Part (a)   First compute

$$T_1 = T_0 - \frac{\frac{1}{2}V_1^2}{c_p} = 500 - \frac{\frac{1}{2}(100 \text{ m/s})^2}{1005 \text{ m}^2/(\text{s}^2 \cdot \text{K})} = 500 - 5 = 495 \text{ K}$$

$$a_1 = (kRT_1)^{1/2} \approx 20(495)^{1/2} = 445 \text{ m/s}$$

Thus

$$\text{Ma}_1 = \frac{V_1}{a_1} = \frac{100}{445} = 0.225$$

For this Ma_1, from Eq. (9.66) or interpolation in Table B.3,

$$\frac{\bar{f}L^*}{D} = 11.0$$

The maximum duct length possible for these inlet conditions is

$$L^* = \frac{(\bar{f}L^*/D)D}{\bar{f}} = \frac{11.0(0.03 \text{ m})}{0.02} = 16.5 \text{ m} \qquad \textit{Ans. (a)}$$

Part (b)   The given $L = 15$ m is less than L^*, and so the duct is not choked and the mass flow follows from inlet conditions

$$\rho_{01} = \frac{p_0}{RT_0} = \frac{200{,}000 \text{ Pa}}{287(500 \text{ K})} = 1.394 \text{ kg/m}^3$$

$$\rho_1 = \frac{\rho_{01}}{[1 + 0.2(0.225)^2]^{2.5}} = \frac{1.394}{1.0255} = 1.359 \text{ kg/m}^3$$

whence

$$\dot{m} = \rho_1 A V_1 = (1.359 \text{ kg/m}^3)\left[\frac{\pi}{4}(0.03 \text{ m})^2\right](100 \text{ m/s})$$

$$= 0.0961 \text{ kg/s} \qquad \textit{Ans. (b)}$$

Part (c)   Since $L = 30$ m is greater than L^*, the duct must choke back until $L = L^*$, corresponding to a lower inlet Ma_1:

$$L^* = L = 30 \text{ m}$$

$$\frac{\overline{f}L^*}{D} = \frac{0.02(30 \text{ m})}{0.03 \text{ m}} = 20.0$$

From Eq. (9.66) or interpolation in Table B.3 we find that this value of 20.0 corresponds to

$$Ma_{1,\text{choked}} = 0.174 \qquad (23\% \text{ less})$$

$$T_{1,\text{new}} = \frac{T_0}{1 + 0.2(0.174)^2} = 497 \text{ K}$$

$$a_{1,\text{new}} \approx 20(497 \text{ K})^{1/2} = 446 \text{ m/s}$$

$$V_{1,\text{new}} = Ma_1 a_1 = 0.174(446) = 77.6 \text{ m/s}$$

$$\rho_{1,\text{new}} = \frac{\rho_{01}}{[1 + 0.2(0.174)^2]^{2.5}} = 1.373 \text{ kg/m}^3$$

$$\dot{m}_{\text{new}} = \rho_1 A V_1 = 1.373 \left[\frac{\pi}{4}(0.03)^2 \right](77.6)$$

$$= 0.0753 \text{ kg/s} \qquad (22\% \text{ less}) \qquad \qquad \textit{Ans. (c)}$$

Isothermal Flow with Friction

The adiabatic frictional-flow assumption is appropriate to high-speed flow in short ducts. For flow in long ducts, e.g., natural-gas pipelines, the gas state more closely approximates an isothermal flow. The analysis is the same except that the isoenergetic energy equation (9.60c) is replaced by the simple relation

$$T = \text{const} \qquad dT = 0 \tag{9.70}$$

Again it is possible to write all property changes in terms of the Mach number. Integration of the Mach-number–friction relation yields

$$\frac{\overline{f}L_{\text{max}}}{D} = \frac{1 - k \, Ma^2}{k \, Ma^2} + \ln (k \, Ma^2) \tag{9.71}$$

which is the isothermal analog of Eq. (9.66) for adiabatic flow.

This friction relation has the interesting result that L_{max} becomes zero not at the sonic point but at $Ma_{\text{crit}} = 1/k^{1/2} = 0.845$ if $k = 1.4$. The inlet flow, whether subsonic or supersonic, tends downstream toward this limiting Mach number $1/k^{1/2}$. If the tube length L is greater than L_{max} from Eq. (9.71), a subsonic flow will choke back to a smaller Ma_1 and mass flow and a supersonic flow will experience a normal-shock adjustment similar to Fig. 9.15.

The exit isothermal choked flow is not sonic, and so the use of the asterisk is inappropriate. Let p', ρ', and V' represent properties at the choking point $L = L_{\text{max}}$. Then the isothermal analysis leads to the following Mach-number relations for the flow properties:

$$\frac{p}{p'} = \frac{1}{\text{Ma } k^{1/2}} \qquad \frac{V}{V'} = \frac{\rho'}{\rho} = \text{Ma } k^{1/2} \tag{9.72}$$

The complete analysis and some examples are given in advanced texts [for example, 8, sec. 6.4].

Mass Flow for a Given Pressure Drop

An interesting by-product of the isothermal analysis is an explicit relation between the pressure drop and duct mass flow. This is a common problem which requires numerical iteration for adiabatic flow, as outlined below. In isothermal flow, we may substitute $dV/V = -dp/p$ and $V^2 = G^2/[p/(RT)]^2$ in Eq. (9.73) to obtain

$$\frac{2p \, dp}{G^2 RT} + f\frac{dx}{D} - \frac{2 \, dp}{p} = 0$$

Since $G^2 RT$ is constant for isothermal flow, this may be integrated in closed form between $(x, p) = (0, p_1)$ and (L, p_2):

$$G^2 = \left(\frac{\dot{m}}{A}\right)^2 = \frac{p_1^2 - p_2^2}{RT[\bar{f}L/D + 2 \ln (p_1/p_2)]} \tag{9.73}$$

Thus mass flow follows directly from the known end pressures, without any use of Mach numbers or tables.

The writer does not know of any direct analogy to Eq. (9.73) for adiabatic flow. However, a useful adiabatic relation, involving velocities instead of pressures, is derived in several textbooks [5, p. 212; 34, p. 418]:

$$V_1^2 = \frac{a_0^2[1 - (V_1/V_2)^2]}{k\bar{f}L/D + (k + 1) \ln (V_2/V_1)} \tag{9.74}$$

where $a_0 = (kRT_0)^{1/2}$ is the stagnation speed of sound, constant for adiabatic flow. We assign the proof of this as a problem exercise. This may be combined with continuity for constant duct area $V_1/V_2 = \rho_2/\rho_1$, plus the following combination of adiabatic energy and the perfect-gas relation:

$$\frac{V_1}{V_2} = \frac{p_2}{p_1}\frac{T_1}{T_2} = \frac{p_2}{p_1}\left[\frac{2a_0^2 - (k - 1)V_1^2}{2a_0^2 - (k - 1)V_2^2}\right] \tag{9.75}$$

If we are given the end pressures, neither V_1 nor V_2 will likely be known in advance. By clever rearrangement of these relations, Haaland [35] develops an extremely fast-converging iteration scheme. Here we suggest only the following simple procedure. Begin with $a_0 \approx a_1$ and the bracketed term in Eq. (9.75) approximately equal to 1.0. Solve Eq. (9.75) for a first estimate of V_1/V_2, and use this value in Eq. (9.74) to get a better estimate of V_1. Use V_1 to improve your estimate of a_0, and repeat the procedure. The process should converge in a few iterations.

Equations (9.73) and (9.74) have one flaw: With the Mach number eliminated, the frictional choking phenomenon is not directly evident. Therefore, assuming a subsonic inlet flow, one should check the exit Mach number Ma_2 to ensure that it is not greater than $1/k^{1/2}$ for isothermal flow or greater than 1.0 for adiabatic flow. We illustrate both adiabatic and isothermal flow with the following example.

EXAMPLE 9.13

Air enters a pipe of 1-cm diameter and 1.2-m length at $p_1 = 220$ kPa and $T_1 = 300$ K. If $\bar{f} = 0.025$ and the exit pressure is $p_2 = 140$ kPa, estimate the mass flow for (a) isothermal flow and (b) adiabatic flow.

Solution

Part (a) For isothermal flow Eq. (9.73) applies without iteration:

$$\frac{\bar{f}L}{D} + 2 \ln \frac{p_1}{p_2} = \frac{(0.025)(1.2 \text{ m})}{0.01 \text{ m}} + 2 \ln \frac{220}{140} = 3.904$$

$$G^2 = \frac{(220{,}000 \text{ Pa})^2 - (140{,}000 \text{ Pa})^2}{[287 \text{ m}^2/(\text{s}^2 \cdot \text{K})](300 \text{ K})(3.904)} = 85{,}700 \quad \text{or} \quad G = 293 \text{ kg}/(\text{s} \cdot \text{m}^2)$$

Since $A = (\pi/4)(0.01 \text{ m})^2 = 7.85$ E-5 m², the isothermal mass flow estimate is

$$\dot{m} = GA = (293)(7.85 \text{ E-5}) \approx 0.0230 \text{ kg/s} \qquad \qquad \text{Ans. (a)}$$

Check that the exit Mach number is not choked:

$$\rho_2 = \frac{p_2}{RT} = \frac{140{,}000}{(287)(300)} = 1.626 \text{ kg/m}^3 \qquad V_2 = \frac{G}{\rho_2} = \frac{293}{1.626} = 180 \text{ m/s}$$

or $$\text{Ma}_2 = \frac{V_2}{\sqrt{kRT}} = \frac{180}{[1.4(287)(300)]^{1/2}} = \frac{180}{347} \approx 0.52$$

This is well below choking, and the isothermal solution is accurate.

Part (b) For adiabatic flow, iterate, using Eqs. (9.74) and (9.75) plus the definition of stagnation speed of sound. First guess $a_0 \approx a_1 \approx 347$ m/s. Our initial calculation assumes that the bracketed term in Eq. (9.75) is unity:

$$\frac{V_1}{V_2} = \frac{p_2}{p_1} (1.0) = \frac{140}{220} \approx 0.636$$

whence $$V_1^2 = \frac{(347)^2[1 - (0.636)^2]}{1.4(0.025)(1.2)/0.01 + (1.4 + 1) \ln (1/0.636)}$$
$$= 13{,}600 \quad \text{or} \quad V_1 \approx 117 \text{ m/s}$$

Finally estimate $V_2 \approx 117/0.636 \approx 183$ m/s, and use this to improve the estimate of a_0:

$$T_0 = T_1 + \frac{V_1^2}{2c_p} = 300 + \frac{(117)^2}{2(1005)} \approx 307 \text{ K} \qquad a_0 = \sqrt{kRT_0} \approx 351 \text{ m/s}$$

Now repeat the whole procedure, beginning with Eq. (9.75). The process converges rapidly:

Step 1: $a_0 \approx 347$ m/s $\dfrac{V_1}{V_2} \approx 0.636$ $V_1 \approx 117$ m/s $V_2 \approx 183$ m/s

Step 2: $a_0 \approx 351$ m/s $\dfrac{V_1}{V_2} \approx 0.658$ $V_1 \approx 116$ m/s $V_2 \approx 176$ m/s

Step 3: $\qquad a_0 \approx 351.04$ m/s $\qquad \dfrac{V_1}{V_2} \approx 0.6554 \qquad V_1 \approx 116.1$ m/s $\qquad V_2 \approx 177.2$ m/s

This looks like a good place to stop. Evaluate the density and the (adiabatic) mass flow:

$$\rho_1 = \frac{p_1}{RT} = \frac{220{,}000}{(287)(300)} = 2.555 \text{ kg/m}^3$$

$$\dot{m} = \rho_1 A V_1 = (2.555 \text{ kg/m}^3)\frac{\pi}{4}(0.01 \text{ m})^2(116.1 \text{ m/s}) = 0.0233 \text{ kg/s} \qquad \textit{Ans. (b)}$$

Finally check the exit Mach number: $T_2 = T_0 - V_2^2/(2c_p) = 291$ K, $a_2 = \sqrt{kRT_2} = 342$ m/s, and $\text{Ma}_2 = V_2/a_2 = 177.2/342 \approx 0.52$, or well below unity. The solution is correct. Note that, for low subsonic speeds, there is little difference between these two solutions.

9.8 Frictionless Duct Flow with Heat Transfer[1]

Heat addition or removal has an interesting effect on a compressible flow. Advanced texts [for example, 8, chap. 8] consider the combined effect of heat transfer coupled with friction and area change in a duct. Here we confine the analysis to heat transfer with no friction in a constant-area duct.

Consider the elemental duct control volume in Fig. 9.16. Between sections 1 and 2 an amount of heat δQ is added (or removed) to each incremental mass δm passing through. With no friction or area change, the control-volume conservation relations are quite simple:

Continuity: $\qquad\qquad\qquad \rho_1 V_1 = \rho_2 V_2 = G = \text{const} \qquad\qquad\qquad\qquad (9.76a)$

x momentum: $\qquad\qquad\qquad p_1 - p_2 = G(V_2 - V_1) \qquad\qquad\qquad\qquad\qquad (9.76b)$

Energy: $\qquad\qquad\qquad \dot{Q} = \dot{m}(h_2 + \tfrac{1}{2}V_2^2 - h_1 - \tfrac{1}{2}V_1^2)$

or $\qquad\qquad\qquad q = \dfrac{\dot{Q}}{\dot{m}} = \dfrac{\delta Q}{\delta m} = h_{02} - h_{01} \qquad\qquad\qquad\qquad\qquad (9.76c)$

---

[1] This section may be omitted without loss of continuity.

Fig. 9.16 Elemental control volume for frictionless flow in a constant-area duct with heat transfer. The length of the element is indeterminate in this simplified theory.

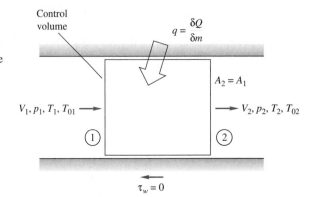

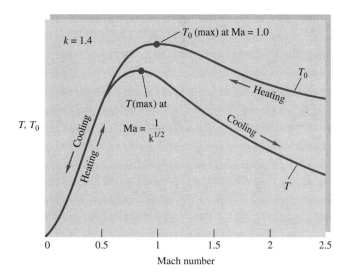

Fig. 9.17 Effect of heat transfer on Mach number.

The heat transfer results in a change in stagnation enthalpy of the flow. We shall not specify exactly how the heat is transferred—combustion, nuclear reaction, evaporation, condensation, or wall heat exchange—but simply that it happened in amount q between 1 and 2. We remark, however, that wall heat exchange is not a good candidate for the theory because wall convection is inevitably coupled with wall friction, which we neglected.

To complete the analysis, we use the perfect-gas and Mach-number relations

$$\frac{p_2}{\rho_2 T_2} = \frac{p_1}{\rho_1 T_1} \qquad h_{02} - h_{01} = c_p(T_{02} - T_{01})$$

$$\frac{V_2}{V_1} = \frac{Ma_2\, a_2}{Ma_1\, a_1} = \frac{Ma_2}{Ma_1}\left(\frac{T_2}{T_1}\right)^{1/2} \tag{9.77}$$

For a given heat transfer $q = \delta Q/\delta m$ or, equivalently, a given change $h_{02} - h_{01}$, Eqs. (9.76) and (9.77) can be solved algebraically for the property ratios p_2/p_1, Ma_2/Ma_1, etc., between inlet and outlet. Note that because the heat transfer allows the entropy to either increase or decrease, the second law imposes no restrictions on these solutions.

Before writing down these property-ratio functions, we illustrate the effect of heat transfer in Fig. 9.17, which shows T_0 and T versus Mach number in the duct. Heating increases T_0, and cooling decreases it. The maximum possible T_0 occurs at $Ma = 1.0$, and we see that heating, whether the inlet is subsonic or supersonic, drives the duct Mach number toward unity. This is analogous to the effect of friction in the previous section. The temperature of a perfect gas increases from $Ma = 0$ up to $Ma = 1/k^{1/2}$ and then decreases. Thus there is a peculiar—or at least unexpected—region where heating (increasing T_0) actually decreases the gas temperature, the difference being reflected in a large increase of the gas kinetic energy. For $k = 1.4$ this peculiar area lies between $Ma = 0.845$ and $Ma = 1.0$ (interesting but not very useful information).

The complete list of the effects of simple T_0 change on duct-flow properties is as follows:

	Heating		Cooling	
	Subsonic	Supersonic	Subsonic	Supersonic
T_0	Increases	Increases	Decreases	Decreases
Ma	Increases	Decreases	Decreases	Increases
p	Decreases	Increases	Increases	Decreases
ρ	Decreases	Increases	Increases	Decreases
V	Increases	Decreases	Decreases	Increases
p_0	Decreases	Decreases	Increases	Increases
s	Increases	Increases	Decreases	Decreases
T	*	Increases	†	Decreases

* Increases up to Ma $= 1/k^{1/2}$ and decreases thereafter.
† Decreases up to Ma $= 1/k^{1/2}$ and increases thereafter.

Probably the most significant item on this list is the stagnation pressure p_0, which always decreases during heating whether the flow is subsonic or supersonic. Thus heating does increase the Mach number of a flow but entails a loss in effective pressure recovery.

Mach-Number Relations

Equations (9.76) and (9.77) can be rearranged in terms of the Mach number and the results tabulated. For convenience, we specify that the outlet section is sonic, Ma $= 1$, with reference properties T_0^*, T^*, p^*, ρ^*, V^*, and p_0^*. The inlet is assumed to be at arbitrary Mach number Ma. Equations (9.76) and (9.77) then take the following form:

$$\frac{T_0}{T_0^*} = \frac{(k + 1) \, \text{Ma}^2 \, [2 + (k - 1) \, \text{Ma}^2]}{(1 + k \, \text{Ma}^2)^2} \tag{9.78a}$$

$$\frac{T}{T^*} = \frac{(k + 1)^2 \, \text{Ma}^2}{(1 + k \, \text{Ma}^2)^2} \tag{9.78b}$$

$$\frac{p}{p^*} = \frac{k + 1}{1 + k \, \text{Ma}^2} \tag{9.78c}$$

$$\frac{V}{V^*} = \frac{\rho^*}{\rho} = \frac{(k + 1) \, \text{Ma}^2}{1 + k \, \text{Ma}^2} \tag{9.78d}$$

$$\frac{p_0}{p_0^*} = \frac{k + 1}{1 + k \, \text{Ma}^2} \left[\frac{2 + (k - 1) \, \text{Ma}^2}{k + 1} \right]^{k/(k - 1)} \tag{9.78e}$$

These formulas are all tabulated versus Mach number in Table B.4. The tables are very convenient if inlet properties Ma_1, V_1, etc., are given but are somewhat cumbersome if the given information centers on T_{01} and T_{02}. Let us illustrate with an example.

EXAMPLE 9.14

A fuel-air mixture, approximated as air with $k = 1.4$, enters a duct combustion chamber at $V_1 = 75$ m/s, $p_1 = 150$ kPa, and $T_1 = 300$ K. The heat addition by combustion is 900 kJ/kg of mixture. Compute (a) the exit properties V_2, p_2, and T_2 and (b) the total heat addition which would have caused a sonic exit flow.

Solution

Part (a) First compute $T_{01} = T_1 + V_1^2/(2c_p) = 300 + (75)^2/[2(1005)] = 303$ K. Then compute the change in stagnation temperature of the gas:

$$q = c_p(T_{02} - T_{01}) \quad \text{or} \quad T_{02} = T_{01} + \frac{q}{c_p}$$

$$= 303 \text{ K} + \frac{900{,}000 \text{ J/kg}}{1005 \text{ J/(kg} \cdot \text{K)}} = 1199 \text{ K}$$

We have enough information to compute the initial Mach number:

$$a_1 = \sqrt{kRT_1} = [1.4(287)(300)]^{1/2} = 347 \text{ m/s} \qquad \text{Ma}_1 = \frac{V_1}{a_1} = \frac{75}{347} = 0.216$$

For this Mach number, use Eq. (9.78a) or Table B.4 to find the sonic value T_0^*:

$$\text{At Ma}_1 = 0.216: \quad \frac{T_{01}}{T_0^*} \approx 0.1992 \quad \text{or} \quad T_0^* = \frac{303 \text{ K}}{0.1992} \approx 1521 \text{ K}$$

Then the stagnation temperature ratio at section 2 is $T_{02}/T_0^* = 1199/1521 = 0.788$, which corresponds in Table B.4 to a Mach number $\text{Ma}_2 \approx 0.573$.

Now use Table B.4 at Ma_1 and Ma_2 to tabulate the desired property ratios.

Section	Ma	V/V^*	p/p^*	T/T^*
1	0.216	0.1051	2.2528	0.2368
2	0.573	0.5398	1.6442	0.8876

The exit properties are computed by using these ratios to find state 2 from state 1:

$$V_2 = V_1 \frac{V_2/V^*}{V_1/V^*} = (75 \text{ m/s}) \frac{0.5398}{0.1051} = 385 \text{ m/s} \qquad \textit{Ans. (a)}$$

$$p_2 = p_1 \frac{p_2/p^*}{p_1/p^*} = (150 \text{ kPa}) \frac{1.6442}{2.2528} = 109 \text{ kPa} \qquad \textit{Ans. (a)}$$

$$T_2 = T_1 \frac{T_2/T^*}{T_1/T^*} = (300 \text{ K}) \frac{0.8876}{0.2368} = 1124 \text{ K} \qquad \textit{Ans. (a)}$$

Part (b) The maximum allowable heat addition would drive the exit Mach number to unity:

$$T_{02} = T_0^* = 1521 \text{ K}$$

$$q_{max} = c_p(T_0^* - T_{01}) = [1005 \text{ J/(kg} \cdot \text{K)}](1521 - 303 \text{ K}) \approx 1.22 \text{ E6 J/kg} \qquad \textit{Ans. (b)}$$

Choking Effects due to Simple Heating

Equation (9.78a) and Table B.4 indicate that the maximum possible stagnation temperature in simple heating corresponds to T_0^*, or the sonic exit Mach number. Thus, for given inlet conditions, only a certain maximum amount of heat can be added to the flow, for example, 1.22 MJ/kg in Example 9.14. For a subsonic inlet there is no theoretical limit on heat addition: The flow chokes more and more as we add more heat, with the inlet velocity approaching zero. For supersonic flow, even if Ma_1 is infinite, there is a finite ratio $T_{01}/T_0^* = 0.4898$ for $k = 1.4$. Thus if heat is added without limit to a supersonic flow, a normal-shock-wave adjustment is required to accommodate the required property changes.

In subsonic flow there is no theoretical limit to the amount of cooling allowed: The exit flow just becomes slower and slower, and the temperature approaches zero. In supersonic flow only a finite amount of cooling can be allowed before the exit flow approaches infinite Mach number, with $T_{02}/T_0^* = 0.4898$ and the exit temperature equal to zero. There are very few practical applications for supersonic cooling.

EXAMPLE 9.15

What happens to the inlet flow in Example 9.14 if the heat addition is increased to 1400 kJ/kg and the inlet pressure and stagnation temperature are fixed? What will be the subsequent decrease in mass flow?

Solution

For $q = 1400$ kJ/kg, the exit will be choked at the stagnation temperature

$$T_0^* = T_{01} + \frac{q}{c_p} = 303 + \frac{1.4 \text{ E6 J/kg}}{1005 \text{ J/(kg} \cdot \text{K)}} \approx 1696 \text{ K}$$

This is higher than the value $T_0^* = 1521$ K in Example 9.14, so we know that condition 1 will have to choke down to a lower Mach number. The proper value is found from the ratio $T_{01}/T_0^* = 303/1696 = 0.1787$. From Table B.4 or Eq. (9.78a) for this condition, we read the new, lowered entrance Mach number: $Ma_{1,\text{new}} \approx 0.203$. With T_{01} and p_1 known, the other inlet properties follow from this Mach number:

$$T_1 = \frac{T_{01}}{1 + 0.2 \, Ma_1^2} = \frac{303}{1 + 0.2(0.203)^2} = 301 \text{ K}$$

$$a_1 = \sqrt{kRT_1} = [1.4(287)(301)]^{1/2} = 348 \text{ m/s}$$

$$V_1 = Ma_1 \, a_1 = (0.202)(348 \text{ m/s}) = 70 \text{ m/s}$$

$$\rho_1 = \frac{p_1}{RT_1} = \frac{150,000}{(287)(301)} = 1.74 \text{ kg/m}^3$$

Finally, the new lowered mass flow per unit area is

$$\frac{\dot{m}_{\text{new}}}{A} = \rho_1 V_1 = (1.74 \text{ kg/m}^3)(70 \text{ m/s}) = 122 \text{ kg/(s} \cdot \text{m}^2)$$

This is 7 percent less than in Example 9.14, due to choking by excess heat addition.

Relationship to the Normal-Shock Wave

The normal-shock-wave relations of Sec. 9.5 actually lurk within the simple heating relations as a special case. From Table B.4 or Fig. 9.17 we see that for a given stagnation temperature less than T_0^* there are two flow states which satisfy the simple heating relations, one subsonic and the other supersonic. These two states have (1) the same value of T_0, (2) the same mass flow per unit area, and (3) the same value of $p + \rho V^2$. Therefore these two states are exactly equivalent to the conditions on each side of a normal-shock wave. The second law would again require that the upstream flow Ma_1 be supersonic.

To illustrate this point, take $Ma_1 = 3.0$ and from Table B.4 read $T_{01}/T_0^* = 0.6540$ and $p_1/p^* = 0.1765$. Now, for the same value $T_{02}/T_0^* = 0.6540$, use Table B.4 or Eq. (9.78a) to compute $Ma_2 = 0.4752$ and $p_2/p^* = 1.8235$. The value of Ma_2 is exactly what we read in the shock table, Table B.2, as the downstream Mach number when $Ma_1 = 3.0$. The pressure ratio for these two states is $p_2/p_1 = (p_2/p^*)/(p_1/p^*) = 1.8235/0.1765 = 10.33$, which again is just what we read in Table B.2 for $Ma_1 = 3.0$. This illustration is meant only to show the physical background of the simple heating relations; it would be silly to make a practice of computing normal-shock waves in this manner.

9.9 Two-Dimensional Supersonic Flow

Up to this point we have considered only one-dimensional compressible-flow theories. This illustrated many important effects, but a one-dimensional world completely loses sight of the wave motions which are so characteristic of supersonic flow. The only "wave motion" we could muster in a one-dimensional theory was the normal-shock wave, which amounted only to a flow discontinuity in the duct.

Mach Waves

When we add a second dimension to the flow, wave motions immediately become apparent if the flow is supersonic. Figure 9.18 shows a celebrated graphical construction which appears in every fluid-mechanics textbook and was first presented by Ernst Mach in 1887. The figure shows the pattern of pressure disturbances (sound waves) sent out by a small particle moving at speed U through a still fluid whose sound velocity is a.

As the particle moves, it continually crashes against fluid particles and sends out spherical sound waves emanating from every point along its path. A few of these spherical disturbance fronts are shown in Fig. 9.18. The behavior of these fronts is quite different according as the particle speed is subsonic or supersonic.

In Fig. 9.18a, the particle moves subsonically, $U < a$, $Ma = U/a < 1$. The spherical disturbances move out in all directions and do not catch up with one another. They move well out in front of the particle also, because they travel a distance $a\,\delta t$ during the time interval δt in which the particle has moved only $U\,\delta t$. Therefore a subsonic body motion makes its presence felt everywhere in the flow field: You can "hear" or "feel" the pressure rise of an oncoming body before it reaches you. This is apparently why that pigeon in the road, without turning around to look at you, takes to the air and avoids being hit by your car.

At sonic speed, $U = a$, Fig. 9.18b, the pressure disturbances move at exactly the speed of the particle and thus pile up on the left at the position of the particle into a sort of "front locus," which is now called a *Mach wave*, after Ernst Mach. No disturbance reaches beyond the particle. If you are stationed to the left of the particle, you cannot "hear" the oncoming motion. If the particle blew its horn, you couldn't hear that either: A sonic car can sneak up on a pigeon.

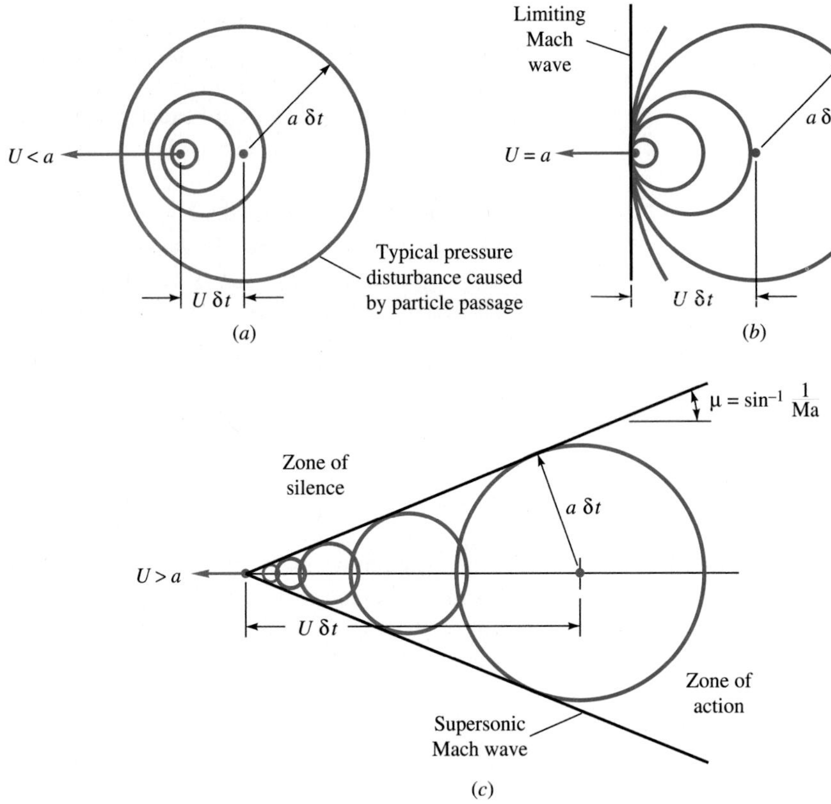

Fig. 9.18 Wave patterns set up by a particle moving at speed U into still fluid of sound velocity a: (a) subsonic, (b) sonic, and (c) supersonic motion.

In supersonic motion, $U > a$, the lack of advance warning is even more pronounced. The disturbance spheres cannot catch up with the fast-moving particle which created them. They all trail behind the particle and are tangent to a conical locus called the *Mach cone*. From the geometry of Fig. 9.18c the angle of the Mach cone is seen to be

$$\mu = \sin^{-1}\frac{a\,\delta t}{U\,\delta t} = \sin^{-1}\frac{a}{U} = \sin^{-1}\frac{1}{\mathrm{Ma}} \tag{9.79}$$

The higher the particle Mach number, the more slender the Mach cone; for example, μ is 30° at $\mathrm{Ma} = 2.0$ and 11.5° at $\mathrm{Ma} = 5.0$. For the limiting case of sonic flow, $\mathrm{Ma} = 1$, $\mu = 90°$; the Mach cone becomes a plane front moving with the particle, in agreement with Fig. 9.18b.

You cannot "hear" the disturbance caused by the supersonic particle in Fig. 9.18c until you are in the *zone of action* inside the Mach cone. No warning can reach your ears if you are in the *zone of silence* outside the cone. Thus an observer on the ground beneath a supersonic airplane does not hear the *sonic boom* of the passing cone until the plane is well past.

The Mach wave need not be a cone: Similar waves are formed by a small disturbance of any shape moving supersonically with respect to the ambient fluid. For example, the "particle" in Fig. 9.18c could be the leading edge of a sharp flat plate, which would form a Mach wedge of exactly the same angle μ. Mach waves are formed by small

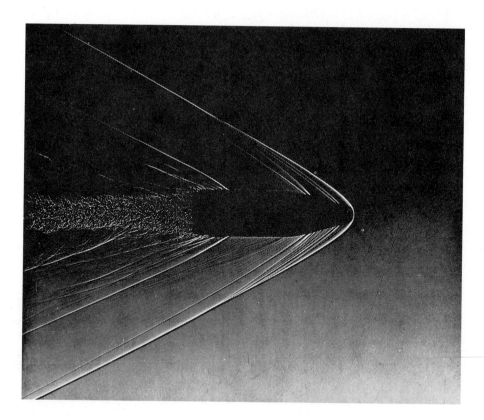

Fig. 9.19 Supersonic wave pattern emanating from a projectile moving at Ma $\approx$ 2.0. The heavy lines are oblique-shock waves and the light lines Mach waves (*courtesy of U.S. Army Ballistic Research Laboratory, Aberdeen Proving Ground.*)

roughnesses or boundary-layer irregularities in a supersonic wind tunnel or at the surface of a supersonic body. Look again at Fig. 9.10: Mach waves are clearly visible along the body surface downstream of the recompression shock, especially at the rear corner. Their angle is about 30°, indicating a Mach number of about 2.0 along this surface. A more complicated system of Mach waves emanates from the supersonic projectile in Fig. 9.19. The Mach angles change, indicating a variable supersonic Mach number along the body surface. There are also several stronger oblique-shock waves formed along the surface.

EXAMPLE 9.16

An observer on the ground does not hear the sonic boom caused by an airplane moving at 5-km altitude until it is 9 km past her. What is the approximate Mach number of the plane? Assume a small disturbance and neglect the variation of sound speed with altitude.

Solution

A finite disturbance like an airplane will create a finite-strength oblique-shock wave whose angle will be somewhat larger than the Mach-wave angle μ and will curve downward due to the variation in atmospheric sound speed. If we neglect these effects, the altitude and distance are a measure of μ, as seen in Fig. E9.16. Thus

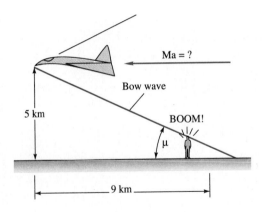

Fig. E9.16

$$\tan \mu = \frac{5 \text{ km}}{9 \text{ km}} = 0.5556 \quad \text{or} \quad \mu = 29.05°$$

Hence, from Eq. (9.79),

$$\text{Ma} = \csc \mu = 2.06 \qquad\qquad Ans.$$

The Oblique-Shock Wave

Figures 9.10 and 9.19 and our earlier discussion all indicate that a shock wave can form at an oblique angle to the oncoming supersonic stream. Such a wave will deflect the stream through an angle θ, unlike the normal-shock wave, for which the downstream flow is in the same direction. In essence, an oblique shock is caused by the necessity for a supersonic stream to turn through such an angle. Examples could be a finite wedge at the leading edge of a body and a ramp in the wall of a supersonic wind tunnel.

The flow geometry of an oblique shock is shown in Fig. 9.20. As for the normal shock of Fig. 9.8, state 1 denotes the upstream conditions and state 2 is downstream. The shock angle has an arbitrary value β, and the downstream flow V_2 turns at an angle θ which is a function of β and state 1 conditions. The upstream flow is always supersonic, but the downstream Mach number $\text{Ma}_2 = V_2/a_2$ may be subsonic, sonic, or supersonic, depending upon the conditions.

It is convenient to analyze the flow by breaking it up into normal and tangential

Fig. 9.20 Geometry of flow through an oblique-shock wave.

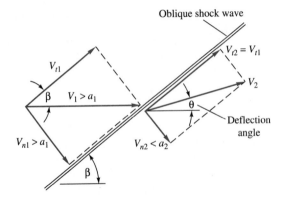

components with respect to the wave, as shown in Fig. 9.20. For a thin control volume just encompassing the wave, we can then derive the following integral relations, canceling out $A_1 = A_2$ on each side of the wave:

Continuity:
$$\rho_1 V_{n1} = \rho_2 V_{n2} \tag{9.80a}$$

Normal momentum:
$$p_1 - p_2 = \rho_2 V_{n2}^2 - \rho_1 V_{n1}^2 \tag{9.80b}$$

Tangential momentum:
$$0 = \rho_1 V_{n1}(V_{t2} - V_{t1}) \tag{9.80c}$$

Energy:
$$h_1 + \tfrac{1}{2}V_{n1}^2 + \tfrac{1}{2}V_{t1}^2 = h_2 + \tfrac{1}{2}V_{n2}^2 + \tfrac{1}{2}V_{t2}^2 = h_0 \tag{9.80d}$$

We see from Eq. (9.80c) that there is no change in tangential velocity across an oblique shock

$$V_{t2} = V_{t1} = V_t = \text{const} \tag{9.81}$$

Thus tangential velocity has as its only effect the addition of a constant kinetic energy $\tfrac{1}{2}V_t^2$ to each side of the energy equation (9.80d). We conclude that Eqs. (9.80) are identical to the normal-shock relations (9.49), with V_1 and V_2 replaced by the normal components V_{n1} and V_{n2}. All the various relations from Sec. 9.5 can be used to compute properties of an oblique-shock wave. The trick is to use the "normal" Mach numbers in place of Ma$_1$ and Ma$_2$:

$$\text{Ma}_{n1} = \frac{V_{n1}}{a_1} = \text{Ma}_1 \sin \beta$$

$$\tag{9.82}$$

$$\text{Ma}_{n2} = \frac{V_{n2}}{a_2} = \text{Ma}_2 \sin (\beta - \theta)$$

Then, for a perfect gas with constant specific heats, the property ratios across the oblique shock are the analogs of Eqs. (9.55) to (9.58) with Ma$_1$ replaced by Ma$_{n1}$:

$$\frac{p_2}{p_1} = \frac{1}{k + 1} [2k \, \text{Ma}_1^2 \sin^2 \beta - (k - 1)] \tag{9.83a}$$

$$\frac{\rho_2}{\rho_1} = \frac{\tan \beta}{\tan (\beta - \theta)} = \frac{(k + 1) \, \text{Ma}_1^2 \sin^2 \beta}{(k - 1) \, \text{Ma}_1^2 \sin^2 \beta + 2} = \frac{V_{n1}}{V_{n2}} \tag{9.83b}$$

$$\frac{T_2}{T_1} = [2 + (k - 1) \, \text{Ma}_1^2 \sin^2 \beta] \frac{2k \, \text{Ma}_1^2 \sin^2 \beta - (k - 1)}{(k + 1)^2 \, \text{Ma}_1^2 \sin^2 \beta} \tag{9.83c}$$

$$T_{02} = T_{01} \tag{9.83d}$$

$$\frac{p_{02}}{p_{01}} = \left[\frac{(k + 1) \, \text{Ma}_1^2 \sin^2 \beta}{2 + (k - 1) \, \text{Ma}_1^2 \sin^2 \beta} \right]^{k/(k-1)} \left[\frac{k + 1}{2k \, \text{Ma}_1^2 \sin^2 \beta - (k - 1)} \right]^{1/(k-1)} \tag{9.83e}$$

$$\text{Ma}_{n2}^2 = \frac{(k - 1) \, \text{Ma}_{n1}^2 + 2}{2k \, \text{Ma}_{n1}^2 - (k - 1)} \tag{9.83f}$$

All these are tabulated in the normal-shock Table B.2. If you wondered why that table listed the Mach numbers as Ma$_{n1}$ and Ma$_{n2}$, it should be clear now that the table is also valid for the oblique-shock wave.

Thinking all this over, we realize by hindsight that an oblique-shock wave is the flow pattern one would observe by running along a normal-shock wave (Fig. 9.8) at a constant tangential speed V_t. Thus the normal and oblique shocks are related by a galilean, or inertial, velocity transformation and therefore satisfy the same basic equations.

If we continue with this run-along-the-shock analogy, we find that the deflection angle θ increases with speed V_t up to a maximum and then decreases. From the geometry of Fig. 9.20 the deflection angle is given by

$$\theta = \tan^{-1}\frac{V_t}{V_{n2}} - \tan^{-1}\frac{V_t}{V_{n1}} \tag{9.84}$$

If we differentiate θ with respect to V_t and set the result equal to zero, we find that the maximum deflection occurs when $V_t/V_{n1} = (V_{n2}/V_{n1})^{1/2}$. We can substitute this back into Eq. (9.84) to compute

$$\theta_{max} = \tan^{-1} r^{1/2} - \tan^{-1} r^{-1/2} \qquad r = \frac{V_{n1}}{V_{n2}} \tag{9.85}$$

For example, if $\mathrm{Ma}_{n1} = 3.0$, from Table B.2 we find that $V_{n1}/V_{n2} = 3.8571$, the square root of which is 1.9640. Then Eq. (9.85) predicts a maximum deflection of $\tan^{-1} 1.9640 - \tan^{-1}(1/1.9640) = 36.03°$. The deflection is quite limited even for infinite Ma_{n1}: From Table B.2 for this case $V_{n1}/V_{n2} = 6.0$, and we compute from Eq. (9.85) that $\theta_{max} = 45.58°$.

This limited-deflection idea and other facts become more evident if we plot some of the solutions of Eqs. (9.83). For given values of V_1 and a_1, assuming as usual that $k = 1.4$, we can plot all possible solutions for V_2 downstream of the shock. Figure 9.21 does this in velocity-component coordinates V_x and V_y, with x parallel to V_1. Such a plot is called a *hodograph*. The heavy dark line which looks like a fat airfoil is the locus, or *shock polar*, of all physically possible solutions for the given Ma_1. The two dashed-line fishtails are solutions which increase V_2; they are physically impossible because they violate the second law.

Examining the shock polar in Fig. 9.21, we see that a given deflection line of small angle θ crosses the polar at two possible solutions: the *strong* shock, which greatly decelerates the flow, and the *weak* shock, which causes a much milder deceleration. The flow downstream of the strong shock is always subsonic, while that of the weak

Fig. 9.21 The oblique-shock polar hodograph, showing double solutions (strong and weak) for small deflection angle and no solutions at all for large deflection.

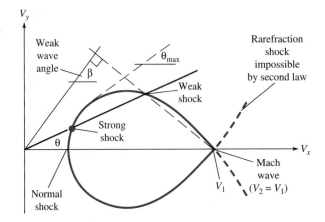

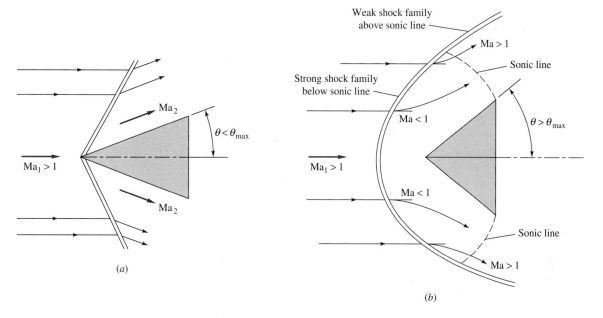

Fig. 9.22 Supersonic flow past a wedge: (*a*) small wedge angle, attached oblique shock forms; (*b*) large wedge angle, attached shock not possible, broad curved detached shock forms.

shock is usually supersonic but occasionally subsonic if the deflection is large. Both types of shock occur in practice. The weak shock is more prevalent, but the strong shock will occur if there is a blockage or high-pressure condition downstream.

Since the shock polar is only of finite size, there is a maximum deflection θ_{max}, shown in Fig. 9.21, which just grazes the upper edge of the polar curve. This verifies the kinematic discussion which led to Eq. (9.85). What happens if a supersonic flow is forced to deflect through an angle greater than θ_{max}? The answer is illustrated in Fig. 9.22 for flow past a wedge-shaped body.

In Fig. 9.22a the wedge half-angle θ is less than θ_{max}, and thus an oblique shock forms at the nose of wave angle β just sufficient to cause the oncoming supersonic stream to deflect through the wedge angle θ. Except for the usually small effect of boundary-layer growth (see, e.g., Ref. 19, sec. 7-5.2), the Mach number Ma_2 is constant along the wedge surface and is given by the solution of Eqs. (9.83). The pressure, density, and temperature along the surface are also nearly constant, as predicted by Eqs. (9.83). When the flow reaches the corner of the wedge, it expands to higher Mach number and forms a wake (not shown) similar to that in Fig. 9.10.

In Fig. 9.22b the wedge half-angle is greater than θ_{max}, and an attached oblique shock is impossible. The flow cannot deflect at once through the entire angle θ_{max}, yet somehow the flow must get around the wedge. A detached curve shock wave forms in front of the body, discontinuously deflecting the flow through angles smaller than θ_{max}. The flow then curves, expands, and deflects subsonically around the wedge, becoming sonic and then supersonic as it passes the corner region. The flow just inside each point on the curved shock exactly satisfies the oblique-shock relations (9.83) for that particular value of β and the given Ma_1. Every condition along the curved shock is a point on the shock polar of Fig. 9.21. Points near the front of the wedge are in the strong-shock family, and points aft of the sonic line are in the weak-shock family. The analysis of

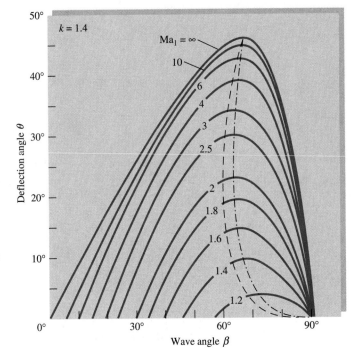

Fig. 9.23 Oblique-shock deflection versus wave angle for various upstream Mach numbers, $k = 1.4$: dash-dot curve, locus of θ_{max}, divides strong (right) from weak (left) shocks; dashed curve, locus of sonic points, divides subsonic Ma_2 (right) from supersonic Ma_2 (left).

detached shock waves is extremely complex, and experimentation is usually needed, e.g., the shadowgraph optical technique of Fig. 9.10.

The complete family of oblique-shock solutions can be plotted or computed from Eqs. (9.83). For a given k, the wave angle β varies with Ma_1 and θ, from Eq. (9.83b). By using a trigonometric identity for $\tan (\beta - \theta)$ this can be rewritten in the more convenient form

$$\tan \theta = \frac{2 \cot \beta \; (Ma_1^2 \sin^2 \beta - 1)}{Ma_1^2 \; (k + \cos 2\beta) + 2} \tag{9.86}$$

All possible solutions of Eq. (9.86) for $k = 1.4$ are shown in Fig. 9.23. For deflections $\theta < \theta_{max}$ there are two solutions: a weak shock (small β) and a strong shock (large β), as expected. All points along the dash-dot line for θ_{max} satisfy Eq. (9.85). A dashed line has been added to show where Ma_2 is exactly sonic. We see that there is a narrow region near maximum deflection where the weak-shock downstream flow is subsonic.

For zero deflections ($\theta = 0$) the weak-shock family satisfies the wave-angle relation

$$\beta = \mu = \sin^{-1} \frac{1}{Ma_1} \tag{9.87}$$

Thus weak shocks of vanishing deflection are equivalent to Mach waves. Meanwhile the strong shocks all converge at zero deflection to the normal-shock condition $\beta = 90°$.

Two additional oblique-shock charts are given in App. B, where Fig. B.1 gives the downstream Mach number Ma_2 and Fig. B.2 the pressure ratio p_2/p_1, each plotted as a function of Ma_1 and θ. Additional graphs, tables, and computer programs are given in Refs. 24 and 25.

Very Weak Shock Waves

For any finite θ the wave angle β for a weak shock is greater than the Mach angle μ. For small θ Eq. (9.86) can be expanded in a power series in $\tan \theta$ with the following linearized result for the wave angle:

$$\sin \beta = \sin \mu + \frac{k + 1}{4 \cos \mu} \tan \theta + \cdots \mathcal{O}(\tan^2 \theta) \cdots \qquad (9.88)$$

For Ma_1 between 1.4 and 20.0 and deflections less than 6° this relation predicts β to within 1° for a weak shock. For larger deflections it can be used as a useful initial guess for iterative solution of Eq. (9.86).

Other property changes across the oblique shock can also be expanded in a power series for small deflection angles. Of particular interest is the pressure change from Eq. (9.83a), for which the linearized result for a weak shock is

$$\frac{p_2 - p_1}{p_1} = \frac{k \, Ma_1^2}{(Ma_1^2 - 1)^{1/2}} \tan \theta + \cdots \mathcal{O}(\tan^2 \theta) \cdots \qquad (9.89)$$

The differential form of this relation is used in the next section to develop a theory for supersonic expansion turns. Figure 9.24 shows the exact weak-shock pressure jump computed from Eq. (9.83a). At very small deflections the curves are linear with slopes given by Eq. (9.89).

Finally, it is educational to examine the entropy change across a very weak shock. Using the same power-series expansion technique, we can obtain the following result for small flow deflections:

Fig. 9.24 Pressure jump across a weak oblique-shock wave from Eq. (9.83a) for $k = 1.4$. For very small deflections Eq. (9.89) applies.

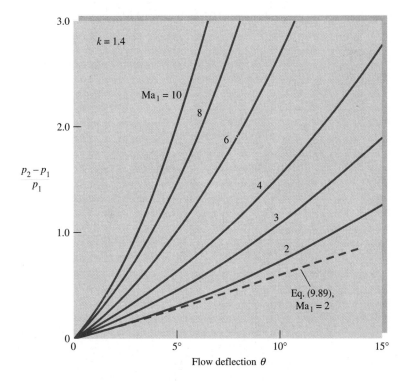

$$\frac{s_2 - s_1}{c_p} = \frac{(k^2 - 1)Ma_1^6}{12(Ma_1^2 - 1)^{3/2}} \tan^3 \theta + \cdots \mathcal{O}(\tan^4 \theta) \cdots \tag{9.90}$$

The entropy change is cubic in the deflection angle θ. Thus weak shock waves are very nearly isentropic, a fact which is also used in the next section.

EXAMPLE 9.17

Air at Ma $= 2.0$ and $p = 10$ lbf/in^2 absolute is forced to turn through $10°$ by a ramp at the body surface. A weak oblique shock forms as in Fig. E9.17. For $k = 1.4$ compute from exact oblique-shock theory (a) the wave angle β, (b) Ma$_2$, and (c) p_2. Also use the linearized theory to estimate (d) β and (e) p_2.

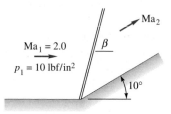

$Ma_1 = 2.0$
$p_1 = 10$ lbf/in^2

Fig. E9.17

Solution

With Ma$_1 = 2.0$ and $\theta = 10°$ known, we find β from Eq. (9.83b) or (9.86). From Fig. 9.23 we read $\beta \approx 39°$ within about $1°$. If we wish more accuracy, we can try 39 and $40°$ in Eq. (9.86) and see how close θ is to $10°$:

Eq. (9.86) (Ma$_1 = 2.0$): $\beta = 39°$ $\theta = 9.7102°$

$\beta = 40°$ $\theta = 10.6229°$

By interpolation we have the more accurate result

$$\beta = 39.32° \qquad\qquad Ans. (a)$$

The normal Mach number upstream is thus

$$Ma_{n1} = Ma_1 \sin \beta = 2.0 \sin 39.32° = 1.267$$

With Ma$_{n1}$ we can use the normal-shock relations (Table B.2) or Fig. 9.9 or Eqs. (9.56) to (9.58) to compute

$$Ma_{n2} = 0.8031 \qquad \frac{p_2}{p_1} = 1.707$$

Thus the downstream Mach number and pressure are

$$Ma_2 = \frac{Ma_{n2}}{\sin (\beta - \theta)} = \frac{0.8031}{\sin (39.32° - 10°)} = 1.64 \qquad Ans. (b)$$

$$p_2 = (10 \text{ lbf/in}^2 \text{ absolute})(1.707) = 17.07 \text{ lbf/in}^2 \text{ absolute} \qquad Ans. (c)$$

Notice that the computed pressure ratio agrees with Figs. 9.24 and B.2.

For the linearized theory the Mach angle is $\mu = \sin^{-1}(1/2.0) = 30°$. Equation (9.88) then estimates that

$$\sin \beta \approx \sin 30° + \frac{2.4 \tan 10°}{4 \cos 30°} = 0.622$$

or $\beta \approx 38.5° \qquad\qquad Ans. (d)$

Equation (9.89) estimates that

$$\frac{p_2}{p_1} \approx 1 + \frac{1.4(2)^2 \tan 10°}{(2^2 - 1)^{1/2}} = 1.57$$

or $\qquad\qquad p_2 \approx 1.57(10 \text{ lbf/in}^2 \text{ absolute}) \approx 15.7 \text{ lbf/in}^2 \text{ absolute}$ $\qquad$ *Ans. (e)*

These are reasonable estimates in spite of the fact that $10°$ is really not a "small" flow deflection.

9.10 Prandtl-Meyer Expansion Waves

The oblique-shock solution of Sec. 9.9 is for a finite compressive deflection θ which obstructs a supersonic flow and thus decreases its Mach number and velocity. The present section treats gradual changes in flow angle which are primarily *expansive*; i.e., they widen the flow area and increase the Mach number and velocity. The property changes accumulate in infinitesimal increments, and the linearized relations (9.88) and (9.89) are used. The local flow deflections are infinitesimal, so that the flow is nearly isentropic according to Eq. (9.90).

Figure 9.25 shows four examples, one of which (Fig. 9.25c) fails the test for gradual changes. The gradual compression of Fig. 9.25a is essentially isentropic, with a smooth increase in pressure along the surface, but the Mach angle decreases along the surface and the waves tend to coalesce farther out into an oblique-shock wave. The gradual expansion of Fig. 9.25b causes a smooth isentropic increase of Mach number and velocity along the surface, with diverging Mach waves formed.

The sudden compression of Fig. 9.25c cannot be accomplished by Mach waves: An oblique shock forms, and the flow is nonisentropic. This could be what you would see if you looked at Fig. 9.25a from far away. Finally, the sudden expansion of Fig. 9.25d is isentropic and forms a fan of centered Mach waves emanating from the corner. Note

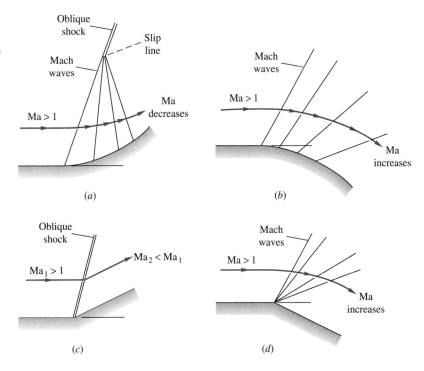

Fig. 9.25 Some examples of supersonic expansion and compression: (*a*) gradual isentropic compression on a concave surface, Mach waves coalesce farther out to form oblique shock; (*b*) gradual isentropic expansion on convex surface, Mach waves diverge; (*c*) sudden compression, nonisentropic shock forms; (*d*) sudden expansion, centered isentropic fan of Mach waves forms.

that the flow on any streamline passing through the fan changes smoothly to higher Mach number and velocity. In the limit as we near the corner the flow expands almost discontinuously at the surface. The cases in Fig. 9.25a, b, and d can all be handled by the Prandtl-Meyer supersonic-wave theory of this section, first formulated by Ludwig Prandtl and his student Theodor Meyer in 1907 to 1908.

Note that none of this discussion makes sense if the upstream Mach number is subsonic, since Mach wave and shock wave patterns cannot exist in subsonic flow.

The Prandtl-Meyer Perfect-Gas Function

Consider a small, nearly infinitesimal flow deflection $d\theta$ such as occurs between the first two Mach waves in Fig. 9.25a. From Eqs. (9.88) and (9.89) we have, in the limit,

$$\beta \approx \mu = \sin^{-1}\frac{1}{\text{Ma}} \tag{9.91a}$$

$$\frac{dp}{p} \approx \frac{k\ \text{Ma}^2}{(\text{Ma}^2 - 1)^{1/2}}\ d\theta \tag{9.91b}$$

Since the flow is nearly isentropic, we have the frictionless differential momentum equation for a perfect gas

$$dp = -\rho V\ dV = -kp\ \text{Ma}^2\ \frac{dV}{V} \tag{9.92}$$

Combining Eqs. (9.91a) and (9.92) to eliminate dp, we obtain a relation between turning angle and velocity change

$$d\theta = -(\text{Ma}^2 - 1)^{1/2}\ \frac{dV}{V} \tag{9.93}$$

This can be integrated into a functional relation for finite turning angles if we can relate V to Ma. We do this from the definition of Mach number

$$V = \text{Ma}\ a$$

or

$$\frac{dV}{V} = \frac{d\ \text{Ma}}{\text{Ma}} + \frac{da}{a} \tag{9.94}$$

Finally, we can eliminate da/a because the flow is isentropic and hence a_0 is constant for a perfect gas

$$a = a_0[1 + \tfrac{1}{2}(k - 1)\ \text{Ma}^2]^{-1/2}$$

or

$$\frac{da}{a} = \frac{-\tfrac{1}{2}(k - 1)\ \text{Ma}\ d\ \text{Ma}}{1 + \tfrac{1}{2}(k - 1)\ \text{Ma}^2} \tag{9.95}$$

Eliminating dV/V and da/a from Eqs. (9.93) to (9.95), we obtain a relation solely between turning angle and Mach number

$$d\theta = -\frac{(\text{Ma}^2 - 1)^{1/2}}{1 + \tfrac{1}{2}(k - 1)\ \text{Ma}^2}\ \frac{d\ \text{Ma}}{\text{Ma}} \tag{9.96}$$

Before integrating this expression, we note that the primary application is to expansions, i.e., increasing Ma and decreasing θ. Therefore, for convenience, we define the

Prandtl-Meyer angle $\omega(\text{Ma})$ which increases when θ decreases and is zero at the sonic point

$$d\omega = -d\theta \qquad \omega = 0 \quad \text{at} \quad \text{Ma} = 1 \tag{9.97}$$

Thus we integrate Eq. (9.96) from the sonic point to any value of Ma

$$\int_0^\omega d\omega = \int_1^{\text{Ma}} \frac{(\text{Ma}^2 - 1)^{1/2}}{1 + \frac{1}{2}(k - 1)\,\text{Ma}^2} \frac{d\,\text{Ma}}{\text{Ma}} \tag{9.98}$$

The integrals are evaluated in closed form, with the result, in radians,

$$\omega(\text{Ma}) = K^{1/2}\tan^{-1}\left(\frac{\text{Ma}^2 - 1}{K}\right)^{1/2} - \tan^{-1}(\text{Ma}^2 - 1)^{1/2} \tag{9.99}$$

where

$$K = \frac{k + 1}{k - 1}$$

This is the *Prandtl-Meyer supersonic expansion function*, which is plotted in Fig. 9.26 and tabulated in Table B.5 for $k = 1.4$. The angle ω changes rapidly at first and then levels off at high Mach number to a limiting value as $\text{Ma} \to \infty$:

$$\omega_{\text{max}} = \frac{\pi}{2}(K^{1/2} - 1) = 130.45° \qquad \text{if} \qquad k = 1.4 \tag{9.100}$$

Thus a supersonic flow can expand only through a finite turning angle before it reaches infinite Mach number, maximum velocity, and zero temperature.

Gradual expansion or compression between finite Mach numbers Ma_1 and Ma_2, nei-

Fig. 9.26 The Prandtl-Meyer super-sonic expansion from Eq. (9.99) for $k = 1.4$.

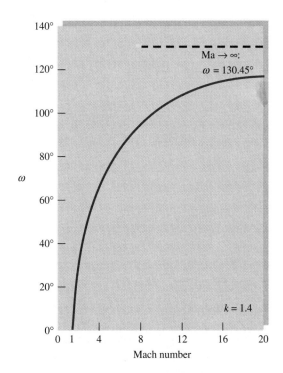

ther of which is unity, is computed by relating the turning angle $\Delta\omega$ to the difference in Prandtl-Meyer angles for the two conditions

$$\Delta\omega_{1\to2} = \omega(\text{Ma}_2) - \omega(\text{Ma}_1) \tag{9.101}$$

The change $\Delta\omega$ may be either positive (expansion) or negative (compression) as long as the end conditions lie in the supersonic range. Let us illustrate with an example.

EXAMPLE 9.18

Air ($k = 1.4$) flows at $\text{Ma}_1 = 3.0$ and $p_1 = 200$ kPa. Compute the final downstream Mach number and pressure for (*a*) an expansion turn of $20°$ and (*b*) a gradual compression turn of $20°$.

Solution

Part (*a*)   The isentropic stagnation pressure is

$$p_0 = p_1[1 + 0.2(3.0)^2]^{3.5} = 7347 \text{ kPa}$$

and this will be the same at the downstream point. For $\text{Ma}_1 = 3.0$ we find from Table B.5 or Eq. (9.99) that $\omega_1 = 49.757°$. The flow expands to a new condition such that

$$\omega_2 = \omega_1 + \Delta\omega = 49.757° + 20° = 69.757°$$

From Eq. (9.99) or interpolation in Table B.5 this corresponds to

$$\text{Ma}_2 = 4.32 \qquad\qquad Ans.\ (a)$$

The isentropic pressure at this new condition is

$$p_2 = \frac{p_0}{[1 + 0.2(4.32)^2]^{3.5}} = \frac{7347}{230.1} = 31.9 \text{ kPa} \qquad\qquad Ans.\ (a)$$

Part (*b*)   The flow compresses to a lower Prandtl-Meyer angle

$$\omega_2 = 49.757° - 20° = 29.757°$$

Again from Eq. (9.99) or Table B.5 we compute that

$$\text{Ma}_2 = 2.125 \qquad\qquad Ans.\ (b)$$

$$p_2 = \frac{p_0}{[1 + 0.2(2.125)^2]^{3.5}} = \frac{7347}{9.51} = 773 \text{ kPa} \qquad\qquad Ans.\ (b)$$

Similarly, density and temperature changes are computed by noticing that T_0 and ρ_0 are constant for isentropic flow.

Application to Supersonic Airfoils

The oblique-shock and Prandtl-Meyer expansion theories can be used to patch together a number of interesting and practical supersonic flow fields. This marriage, called *shock expansion theory*, is limited by two conditions: (1) Except in rare instances the flow must be supersonic throughout, and (2) the wave pattern must not suffer interference from waves formed in other parts of the flow field.

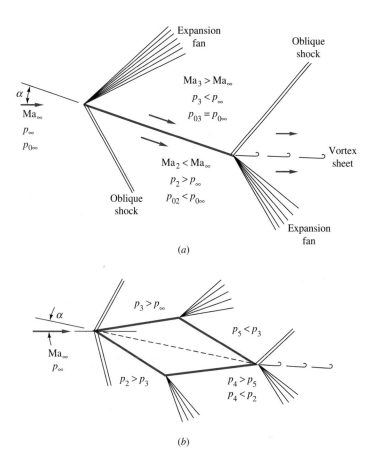

Fig. 9.27 Supersonic airfoils: (*a*) flat plate, higher pressure on lower surface, drag due to small downstream component of net pressure force; (*b*) diamond foil, higher pressures on both lower surfaces, additional drag due to body thickness.

A very successful application of shock expansion theory is to supersonic airfoils. Figure 9.27 shows two examples, a flat plate and a diamond-shaped foil. In contrast to subsonic-flow designs (Fig. 8.21), these airfoils must have sharp leading edges, which form attached oblique shocks or expansion fans. Rounded supersonic leading edges would cause detached bow shocks, as in Fig. 9.19 or 9.22*b*, greatly increasing the drag and lowering the lift.

In applying shock expansion theory, one examines each surface turning angle to see whether it is an expansion ("opening up") or compression (obstruction) to the surface flow. Figure 9.27*a* shows a flat-plate foil at an angle of attack. There is a leading-edge shock on the lower edge with flow deflection $\theta = \alpha$, while the upper edge has an expansion fan with increasing Prandtl-Meyer angle $\Delta\omega = \alpha$. We compute p_3 with expansion theory and p_2 with oblique-shock theory. The force on the plate is thus $F = (p_2 - p_3)Cb$, where C is the chord length and b the span width (assuming no wingtip effects). This force is normal to the plate, and thus the lift force normal to the stream is $L = F \cos \alpha$, and the drag parallel to the stream is $D = F \sin \alpha$. The dimensionless coefficients C_L and C_D have the same definitions as in low-speed flow, Eq. (7.66), except that the perfect-gas-law identity $\frac{1}{2}\rho V^2 \equiv \frac{1}{2}kp \, \text{Ma}^2$ is very useful here

$$C_L = \frac{L}{\frac{1}{2}kp_\infty \, \text{Ma}_\infty^2 \, bC} \qquad C_D = \frac{D}{\frac{1}{2}kp_\infty \, \text{Ma}_\infty^2 \, bC} \qquad (9.102)$$

The typical supersonic lift coefficient is much smaller than the subsonic value $C_L \approx 2\pi\alpha$, but the lift can be very large because of the large value of $\frac{1}{2}\rho V^2$ at supersonic speeds.

At the trailing edge in Fig. 9.27a, a shock and fan appear in reversed positions and bend the two flows back so that they are parallel in the wake and have the same pressure. They do not have quite the same velocity because of the unequal shock strengths on the upper and lower surfaces; hence a vortex sheet trails behind the wing. This is very interesting, but in the theory you ignore the trailing-edge pattern entirely, since it does not affect the surface pressures: The supersonic surface flow cannot "hear" the wake disturbances.

The diamond foil in Fig. 9.27b adds two more wave patterns to the flow. At this particular α less than the diamond half-angle, there are leading-edge shocks on both surfaces, the upper shock being much weaker. Then there are expansion fans on each shoulder of the diamond: The Prandtl-Meyer angle change $\Delta\omega$ equals the sum of the leading-edge and trailing-edge diamond half-angles. Finally, the trailing-edge pattern is similar to that of the flat plate (9.27a) and can be ignored in the calculation. Both lower-surface pressures p_2 and p_4 are greater than their upper counterparts, and the lift is nearly that of the flat plate. There is an additional drag due to thickness, because p_4 and p_5 on the trailing surfaces are lower than their counterparts p_2 and p_3. The diamond drag is greater than the flat-plate drag, but this must be endured in practice to achieve a wing structure strong enough to hold these forces.

The theory sketched in Fig. 9.27 is in good agreement with measured supersonic lift and drag as long as the Reynolds number is not too small (thick boundary layers) and the Mach number not too large (hypersonic flow). It turns out that for large Re_C and moderate supersonic Ma_∞ the boundary layers are thin and separation seldom occurs, so that the shock expansion theory, although frictionless, is quite successful. Let us look now at an example.

EXAMPLE 9.19

A flat-plate airfoil with $C = 2$ m is immersed at $\alpha = 8°$ in a stream with $\text{Ma}_\infty = 2.5$ and $p_\infty = 100$ kPa. Compute (a) C_L and (b) C_D, and compare with low-speed airfoils. Compute (c) lift and (d) drag in newtons per unit span width.

Solution

Instead of using a lot of space outlining the detailed oblique-shock and Prandtl-Meyer expansion computations, we list all pertinent results in Fig. E9.19 on the upper and lower surfaces. Using the theories of Secs. 9.9 and 9.10, you should verify every single one of the calculations in Fig. E9.19 to make sure that all details of shock expansion theory are well understood.

The important final results are p_2 and p_3, from which the total force per unit width on the plate is

$$F = (p_2 - p_3)bC = (165.7 - 56.85)(\text{kPa})(1 \text{ m})(2 \text{ m}) = 218 \text{ kN}$$

The lift and drag per meter width are thus

$$L = F \cos 8° = 216 \text{ kN} \qquad\qquad Ans. (c)$$

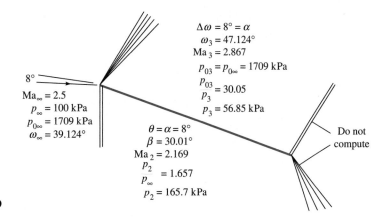

Fig. E9.19

$$D = F \sin 8° = 30 \text{ kN} \qquad \textit{Ans. (d)}$$

These are very large forces for only 2 m² of wing area.

From Eq. (9.102) the lift coefficient is

$$C_L = \frac{216 \text{ kN}}{\frac{1}{2}(1.4)(100 \text{ kPa})(2.5)^2(2 \text{ m}^2)} = 0.246 \qquad \textit{Ans. (a)}$$

The comparable low-speed coefficient from Eq. (8.64) is $C_L = 2\pi \sin 8° = 0.874$, which is 3.5 times larger.

From Eq. (9.102) the drag coefficient is

$$C_D = \frac{30 \text{ kN}}{\frac{1}{2}(1.4)(100 \text{ kPa})(2.5)^2(2 \text{ m}^2)} = 0.035 \qquad \textit{Ans. (b)}$$

From Fig. 7.24 for the NACA 0009 airfoil C_D at $\alpha = 8°$ is about 0.009, or about 4 times smaller.

Notice that this supersonic theory predicts a finite drag in spite of assuming frictionless flow with infinite wing aspect ratio. This is called *wave drag*, and we see that the d'Alembert paradox of zero body drag does not occur in supersonic flow.

Thin-Airfoil Theory

In spite of the simplicity of the flat-plate geometry, the calculations in Example 9.19 were laborious. In 1925 Ackeret [21] developed simple yet effective expressions for the lift, drag, and center of pressure of supersonic airfoils, assuming small thickness and angle of attack.

The theory is based on the linearized expression (9.89), where $\tan \theta \approx$ surface deflection relative to the free stream and condition 1 is the free stream, $\text{Ma}_1 = \text{Ma}_\infty$. For the flat-plate airfoil, the total force F is based on

$$\frac{p_2 - p_3}{p_\infty} = \frac{p_2 - p_\infty}{p_\infty} - \frac{p_3 - p_\infty}{p_\infty}$$

$$= \frac{k \text{ Ma}_\infty^2}{(\text{Ma}_\infty^2 - 1)^{1/2}} [\alpha - (-\alpha)] \qquad (9.103)$$

Substitution into Eq. (9.102) gives the linearized lift coefficient for a supersonic flat-plate airfoil

$$C_L \approx \frac{(p_2 - p_3)bC}{\frac{1}{2}kp_\infty \, \mathrm{Ma}_\infty^2 \, bC} \approx \frac{4\alpha}{(\mathrm{Ma}_\infty^2 - 1)^{1/2}} \tag{9.104}$$

Computations for diamond and other finite-thickness airfoils show no first-order effect of thickness on lift. Therefore Eq. (9.104) is valid for any sharp-edged supersonic thin airfoil at a small angle of attack.

The flat-plate drag coefficient is

$$C_D = C_L \tan \alpha \approx C_L \alpha \approx \frac{4\alpha^2}{(\mathrm{Ma}_\infty^2 - 1)^{1/2}} \tag{9.105}$$

However, the thicker airfoils have additional thickness drag. Let the chord line of the airfoil be the x axis, and let the upper-surface shape be denoted by $y_u(x)$ and the lower profile by $y_l(x)$. Then the complete Ackeret drag theory (see, e.g., Ref. 8, sec. 14.6, for details) shows that the additional drag depends on the mean square of the slopes of the upper and lower surfaces, defined by

$$\overline{y'^2} = \frac{1}{C} \int_0^C \left(\frac{dy}{dx}\right)^2 dx \tag{9.106}$$

The final expression for drag [8, p. 442] is

$$C_D \approx \frac{4}{(\mathrm{Ma}_\infty^2 - 1)^{1/2}} \left[\alpha^2 + \frac{1}{2}(\overline{y_u'^2} + \overline{y_l'^2})\right] \tag{9.107}$$

These are all in reasonable agreement with more exact computations, and their extreme simplicity makes them attractive alternatives to the laborious but accurate shock expansion theory. Consider the following example.

EXAMPLE 9.20

Repeat parts (a) and (b) of Example 9.19, using the linearized Ackeret theory.

Solution

From Eqs. (9.104) and (9.105) we have, for $\mathrm{Ma}_\infty = 2.5$ and $\alpha = 8° = 0.1396$ rad,

$$C_L \approx \frac{4(0.1396)}{(2.5^2 - 1)^{1/2}} = 0.244 \qquad C_D = \frac{4(0.1396)^2}{(2.5^2 - 1)^{1/2}} = 0.034 \qquad \textit{Ans.}$$

These are less than 3 percent lower than the more exact computations of Example 9.19.

A further result of the Ackeret linearized theory is an expression for the position x_{CP} of the center of pressure (CP) of the force distribution on the wing:

$$\frac{x_{\mathrm{CP}}}{C} = 0.5 + \frac{S_u - S_l}{2\alpha C^2} \tag{9.108}$$

where S_u is the cross-sectional area between the upper surface and the chord and S_l is the area between the chord and the lower surface. For a symmetric airfoil ($S_l = S_u$) we obtain x_{CP} at the half-chord point, in contrast with the low-speed airfoil result of Eq. (8.66), where x_{CP} is at the quarter-chord.

The difference in difficulty between the simple Ackeret theory and shock expansion theory is even greater for a thick airfoil, as the following example shows.

EXAMPLE 9.21

By analogy with Example 9.19 analyze a diamond, or double-wedge, airfoil of 2° half-angle and $C = 2$ m at $\alpha = 8°$ and $Ma_\infty = 2.5$. compute C_L and C_D by (a) shock expansion theory and (b) Ackeret theory. Pinpoint the difference from Example 9.19.

Solution

Part (a)

Again we omit the details of shock expansion theory and simply list the properties computed on each of the four airfoil surfaces in Fig. E9.21. Assume $p_\infty = 100$ kPa. There are both a force F normal to the chord line and a force P parallel to the chord. For the normal force the pressure difference on the front half is $p_2 - p_3 = 186.4 - 65.9 = 120.5$ kPa, and on the rear half it is $p_4 - p_5 = 146.9 - 48.1 = 98.1$ kPa. The average pressure difference is $\frac{1}{2}(120.5 + 98.1) = 109.3$ kPa, so that the normal force is

$$F = (109.3 \text{ kPa})(2 \text{ m}^2) = 218.6 \text{ kN}$$

For the chordwise force P the pressure difference on the top half is $p_3 - p_5 = 65.9 - 48.8 = 17.1$ kPa, and on the bottom half it is $p_2 - p_4 = 186.4 - 146.9 = 39.5$ kPa. The average difference is $\frac{1}{2}(17.1 + 39.5) = 28.3$ kPa, which when multiplied by the frontal area (maximum thickness times 1-m width) gives

$$P = (28.3 \text{ kPa})(0.07 \text{ m})(1 \text{ m}) = 2.0 \text{ kN}$$

Both F and P have components in the lift and drag directions. The lift force normal to the free stream is

$$L = F \cos 8° - P \sin 8° = 216.2 \text{ kN}$$

and

$$D = F \sin 8° + P \cos 8° = 32.4 \text{ kN}$$

Fig. E9.21

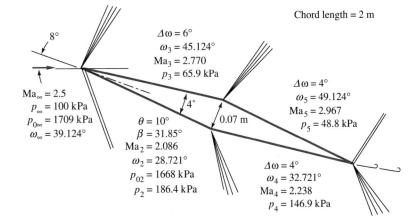

Chord length = 2 m

$Ma_\infty = 2.5$
$p_\infty = 100$ kPa
$p_{0\infty} = 1709$ kPa
$\omega_\infty = 39.124°$

$\theta = 10°$
$\beta = 31.85°$
$Ma_2 = 2.086$
$\omega_2 = 28.721°$
$p_{02} = 1668$ kPa
$p_2 = 186.4$ kPa

$\Delta\omega = 6°$
$\omega_3 = 45.124°$
$Ma_3 = 2.770$
$p_3 = 65.9$ kPa

$\Delta\omega = 4°$
$\omega_4 = 32.721°$
$Ma_4 = 2.238$
$p_4 = 146.9$ kPa

$\Delta\omega = 4°$
$\omega_5 = 49.124°$
$Ma_5 = 2.967$
$p_5 = 48.8$ kPa

For computing the coefficients, the denominator of Eq. (9.102) is the same as in Example 9.19: $\frac{1}{2}kp_\infty \text{Ma}_\infty^2 bC = \frac{1}{2}(1.4)(100 \text{ kPa})(2.5)^2(2 \text{ m}^2) = 875 \text{ kN}$. Thus, finally, shock expansion theory predicts

$$C_L = \frac{216.2 \text{ kN}}{875 \text{ kN}} = 0.247 \qquad C_D = \frac{32.4 \text{ kN}}{875 \text{ kN}} = 0.0370 \qquad \textit{Ans. (a)}$$

Part (b)   Meanwhile, by Ackeret theory, C_L is the same as in Example 9.20:

$$C_L = \frac{4(0.1396)}{(2.5^2 - 1)^{1/2}} = 0.244 \qquad \textit{Ans. (b)}$$

This is 1 percent less than the shock expansion result above. For the drag we need the mean-square slopes from Eq. (9.106)

$$\overline{y_u'^2} = \overline{y_l'^2} = \tan^2 2° = 0.00122$$

Then Eq. (9.107) predicts the linearized result

$$C_D = \frac{4}{(2.5^2 - 1)^{1/2}} [(0.1396)^2 + \frac{1}{2}(0.00122 + 0.00122)] = 0.0362 \qquad \textit{Ans. (b)}$$

This is 2 percent lower than shock expansion theory predicts. We could judge Ackeret theory to be "satisfactory." Ackeret theory predicts $p_2 = 167$ kPa (-11 percent), $p_3 = 60$ kPa (-9 percent), $p_4 = 140$ kPa (-5 percent), and $p_5 = 33$ kPa (-6 percent).

Three-Dimensional Supersonic Flow

We have gone about as far as we can go in an introductory treatment of compressible flow. Of course, there is much more, and you are invited to study further in the references at the end of the chapter.

Three-dimensional supersonic flows are highly complex, especially if they concern blunt bodies, which therefore contain embedded regions of subsonic and transonic flow, e.g., Fig. 9.10. Some flows, however, yield to accurate theoretical treatment such as flow past a cone at zero incidence, as shown in Fig. 9.28. The exact theory of cone flow is discussed in advanced texts [for example, 8, chap. 17], and extensive tables of such solutions have been published [22, 23]. There are similarities between cone flow and the wedge flows illustrated in Fig. 9.22: an attached oblique shock, a thin turbulent boundary layer, and an expansion fan at the rear corner. However, the conical shock deflects the flow through an angle less than the cone half-angle, unlike the wedge shock. As in the wedge flow, there is a maximum cone angle above which the shock must detach, as in Fig. 9.22b. For $k = 1.4$ and $\text{Ma}_\infty = \infty$, the maximum cone half-angle for an attached shock is about 57°, compared with the maximum wedge angle of 45.6° (see Ref. 23).

For more complicated body shapes one usually resorts to experimentation in a supersonic wind tunnel. Figure 9.29 shows a wind-tunnel study of supersonic flow past a model of an interceptor aircraft. The many junctions and wingtips and shape changes make theoretical analysis very difficult. Here the surface-flow patterns, which indicate boundary-layer development and regions of flow separation, have been visualized by the smearing of oil drops placed on the model surface before the test.

As we shall see in the next chapter, there is an interesting analogy between gas-dynamic shock waves and the surface water waves which form in an open-channel flow.

Fig. 9.28 Shadowgraph of flow past an 8° half-angle cone at $Ma_\infty = 2.0$. The turbulent boundary layer is clearly visible. The Mach lines curve slightly, and the Mach number varies from 1.98 just inside the shock to 1.90 at the surface. (*Courtesy of U.S. Army Ballistic Research Center, Aberdeen Proving Ground.*)

Fig. 9.29 Wind-tunnel test of the Cobra P-530 supersonic interceptor. The surface flow patterns are visualized by the smearing of oil droplets. (*Courtesy of Northrup Corporation.*)

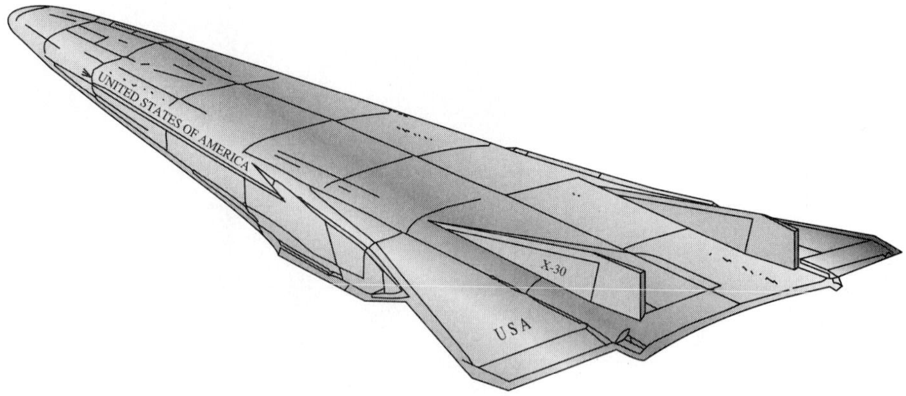

Fig. 9.30 The national aerospace plane (X-30). This air-breathing vehicle would take off and land horizontally and go into orbit above the atmosphere. (*Courtesy of NASA.*)

Chapter 11 of Ref. 14 explains how a water channel can be used in an inexpensive simulation of supersonic-flow experiments.

Like most other areas of fluid mechanics, the visual aspects of compressible flow are so striking and educational that they should not be missed. Films 47 to 51 on compressible flow in App. C are highly recommended and useful to both novices and experts.

The National Aerospace Plane

Supersonic fighters such as that in Fig. 9.29, are, of course, military aircraft, where performance is the primary consideration, not cost. For decades commercial transport aircraft have been subsonic, flying just below the critical Mach number where shock waves would appear. The United States dropped out of the supersonic transport competition, and the British/French *Concorde*, although technically satisfactory, is not financially successful.

Research in the United States centers now on a hypersonic (Ma ≈ 25) vehicle called the X-30, or *national aerospace plane*. The proposed configuration is shown in Fig. 9.30. The plane would take off normally, accelerate to orbital speed above the atmosphere, then reenter for a runway landing. It would use an air-breathing supersonic ramjet (''scramjet'') engine, and its structure would take advantage of new materials. Aerodynamic design would be accomplished by supercomputers. Flight control would be highly integrated by computers. Many government, industry, and university groups are working on the project.

It is not likely that the X-30 will lead to a financially viable commercial flight system, but it should lead the way to reduced-cost space flight and private-enterprise space ventures.

Summary

This chapter is a brief introduction to a very broad subject, compressible flow, sometimes called *gas dynamics*. The primary parameter is the Mach number Ma = V/a, which is large and causes the fluid density to vary significantly. This means that the continuity and momentum equations must be coupled to the energy relation and the equation of state to solve for the four unknowns ($p, \rho, T, \mathbf{V}$).

The chapter reviews the thermodynamic properties of an ideal gas and derives a formula for the speed of sound of a fluid. The analysis is then simplified to one-dimensional steady adiabatic flow without shaft work, for which the stagnation enthalpy of the gas is constant. A further simplification to isentropic flow enables formulas to be derived for high-speed gas flow in a variable-area duct. This reveals the phenomenon of sonic-flow *choking* (maximum mass flow) in the throat of a nozzle. At supersonic velocities there is the possibility of a normal-shock wave, where the gas discontinuously reverts to subsonic conditions. The normal shock explains the effect of back pressure on the performance of converging-diverging nozzles.

To illustrate nonisentropic flow conditions, there is a brief study of constant-area duct flow with friction and with heat transfer, both of which lead to choking of the exit flow.

The chapter ends with a discussion of two-dimensional supersonic flow, where oblique-shock waves and Prandtl-Meyer (isentropic) expansion waves appear. With a proper combination of shocks and expansions one can analyze supersonic airfoils.

References

1. A. Y. Pope, *Aerodynamics of Supersonic Flight*, 2d ed., Pitman, New York, 1958.
2. A. B. Cambel and B. H. Jennings, *Gas Dynamics*, McGraw-Hill, New York, 1958.
3. F. Cheers, *Elements of Compressible Flow*, Wiley, New York, 1963.
4. J. E. John, *Gas Dynamics*, 2d ed., Allyn & Bacon, Boston, 1984.
5. A. J. Chapman and W. F. Walker, *Introductory Gas Dynamics*, Holt, New York, 1971.
6. B. W. Imric, *Compressible Fluid Flow*, Halstead, New York, 1974.
7. R. Courant and K. O. Friedrichs, *Supersonic Flow and Shock Waves*, Interscience, New York, 1948; reprinted by Springer-Verlag, New York, 1977.
8. A. H. Shapiro, *The Dynamics and Thermodynamics of Compressible Fluid Flow*, Ronald, New York, 1953.
9. H. W. Liepmann and A. Roshko, *Elements of Gas Dynamics*, Wiley, New York, 1957.
10. R. von Mises, *Mathematical Theory of Compressible Fluid Flow*, Academic, New York, 1958.
11. J. A. Owczarek, *Gas Dynamics*, International Textbook, Scranton, Pa., 1964.
12. W. G. Vincenti and C. Kruger, *Introduction to Physical Gas Dynamics*, Wiley, New York, 1965.
13. J. D. Anderson, *Hypersonic and High-Temperature Gas Dynamics*, McGraw-Hill, New York, 1989.
14. P. A. Thompson, *Compressible Fluid Dynamics*, McGraw-Hill, New York, 1972.
15. J. H. Keenan et al., *Steam Tables: SI Version*, 2 vols., Wiley, New York, 1985.
16. J. H. Keenan et al., *Gas Tables*, 2d ed., Wiley-Interscience, New York, 1983.
17. W. C. Reynolds and H. C. Perkins, *Engineering Thermodynamics*, 2d ed., McGraw-Hill, New York, 1977.
18. K. Wark, *Thermodynamics*, 5th ed., McGraw-Hill, New York, 1988.
19. F. M. White, *Viscous Fluid Flow*, 2d ed., McGraw-Hill, New York, 1991.
20. J. H. Keenan and E. P. Neumann, "Measurements of Friction in a Pipe for Subsonic and Supersonic Flow of Air," *J. Appl. Mech.*, vol. 13, no. 2, 1946, p. A-91.
21. J. Ackeret, "Air Forces on Airfoils Moving Faster than Sound Velocity," *NACA Tech. Mem.* 317, 1925.
22. Z. Kopal, "Tables of Supersonic Flow around Cones," *M.I.T. Center Anal. Tech. Rep.* 1, 1947 (see also *Tech. Rep.* 3 and 5, 1947).
23. J. L. Sims, *Tables for Supersonic Flow around Right Circular Cones at Zero Angle of Attack*, NASA SP-3004, 1964 (see also NASA SP-3007).

24. J. Palmer et al., *Compressible Flow Tables for Engineers: With Appropriate Computer Programs*, Scholium Intl., Port Washington, N.Y., 1989.

25. S. M. Yahya (ed.), *Gas Tables for Compressible Flow Calculations*, Wiley Eastern, New Delhi, India, 1985.

26. S. M. Yahya, *Fundamentals of Compressible Flow*, Wiley Eastern, New Delhi, India, 1982.

27. S. Schreier, *Compressible Flow*, Wiley, New York, 1982.

28. M. A. Saad, *Compressible Fluid Flow*, Prentice-Hall, Englewood Cliffs, N.J., 1985.

29. A. Y. Pope and K. L. Goin, *High Speed Wind Tunnel Testing*, Wiley, New York, 1965.

30. W. Bober and R. A. Kenyon, *Fluid Mechanics*, Wiley, New York, 1980.

31. J. D. Anderson, *Modern Compressible Flow: With Historical Perspective*, McGraw-Hill, New York, 1982.

32. M. J. Zucrow and J. D. Hoffman, *Gas Dynamics*, Wiley, New York, 1976.

33. Z. Husain, *Gas Dynamics through Problems*, Halsted Press, New York, 1989.

34. J. E. Plapp, *Engineering Fluid Mechanics*, Prentice-Hall, Englewood Cliffs, N.J., 1968.

35. S. E. Haaland, "Adiabatic Flow of a Gas in a Pipe: Iterative Solution Methods Based on Efficient Fixed Point Relations," to appear in *J. Fluids Eng.* in 1993.

PROBLEMS

In addition to many traditional problems, categorized in the problem distribution list below, there are word problems, labeled W9.1 to W9.8, and a design project, D9.1.

Problem Distribution

Section	Topic	Problems
9.1	Introduction	9.1–9.9
9.2	The speed of sound	9.10–9.18
9.3	Adiabatic and isentropic flow	9.19–9.33
9.4	Isentropic flow with area changes	9.34–9.53
9.5	The normal-shock wave	9.54–9.62
9.6	Converging and diverging nozzles	9.63–9.85
9.7	Duct flow with friction	9.86–9.107
9.8	Frictionless duct flow with heat transfer	9.108–9.115
9.9	Mach waves	9.116–9.121
9.9	The oblique-shock wave	9.122–9.139
9.10	Prandtl-Meyer expansion waves	9.140–9.147
9.10	Supersonic airfoils	9.148–9.157

9.1 An ideal gas flows adiabatically through a duct. At section 1, $p_1 = 140$ kPa, $T_1 = 260°C$, and $V_1 = 75$ m/s. Farther downstream, $p_2 = 30$ kPa and $T_2 = 207°C$. Calculate V_2 in m/s and $s_2 - s_1$ in J/(kg · K) if the gas is (*a*) air, $k = 1.4$, and (*b*) argon, $k = 1.67$.

9.2 Solve Prob. 9.1 if the gas is steam. Use two approaches: (*a*) an ideal gas from Table A.4 and (*b*) real gas data from the steam tables [15].

9.3 If 8 kg of oxygen in a closed tank at 200°C and 300 kPa is heated until the pressure rises to 400 kPa, calculate (*a*) the new temperature, (*b*) the total heat transfer, and (*c*) the change in entropy.

9.4 Steam at 450°F and 75 lbf/in² absolute is compressed isentropically to 100 lb/in² absolute. What is the new temperature, in °F?

9.5 Steam enters a nozzle at 377°C, 1.6 MPa, and a steady speed of 200 m/s and accelerates isentropically until it exits at saturation conditions. Estimate the exit velocity and temperature.

9.6 Is it possible for the steam in Prob. 9.5 to continue accelerating until it exits with a moisture content of 12 percent? If so, estimate the new exit velocity and temperature.

9.7 Carbon dioxide ($k = 1.28$) enters a constant-area duct at 400°F, 100 lbf/in² absolute, and 500 ft/s. Farther downstream the properties are $V_2 = 1000$ ft/s and $T_2 = 900°F$. Compute (*a*) p_2, (*b*) the heat added between sections, (*c*) the entropy change between sections, and (*d*) the mass flow per unit area. *Hint:* This problem requires the continuity equation.

9.8 Atmospheric air at 20°C enters and fills an insulated tank which is initially evacuated. Using a control-volume analysis from Eq. (3.63), compute the tank air temperature when it is full.

9.9 Steam enters a duct at $p_1 = 50$ lbf/in² absolute, $T_1 = 360°F$, $V_1 = 200$ ft/s and leaves at $p_2 = 100$ lbf/in² absolute, $T_2 = 800°F$, and $V_2 = 1200$ ft/s. How much heat was added in Btu/lb?

9.10 A certain aircraft flies at the same Mach number regardless of its altitude. Compared to its speed at 12,000-m standard altitude, it flies 127 km/h faster at sea level. Determine its Mach number.

9.11 At 300°C and 1 atm, estimate the speed of sound of (a) nitrogen, (b) hydrogen, (c) helium, (d) steam, and (e) $^{238}UF_6$ ($k \approx 1.06$).

9.12 Assume that water follows Eq. (1.19) with $n \approx 7$ and $B \approx 3000$. Compute the bulk modulus (in kPa) and the speed of sound (in m/s) at (a) 1 atm and (b) 1100 atm (the deepest part of the ocean). (c) Compute the speed of sound at 20°C and 9000 atm and compare with the measured value of 2650 m/s (A. H. Smith and A. W. Lawson, *J. Chem. Phys.,* vol. 22, 1954, p. 351).

9.13 From Prob. 1.33, mercury data fit Eq. (1.19) with $n \approx 6$ and $B \approx 41,000$. Estimate (a) the bulk modulus and (b) the speed of sound of mercury at 2500 atm and compare with Table 9.1.

9.14 Assume steady adiabatic flow of a perfect gas. Show that the energy equation (9.21), when plotted as speed of sound versus velocity, forms an ellipse. Sketch this ellipse; label the intercepts and the regions of subsonic, sonic, and supersonic flow; and determine the ratio of the major and minor axes.

9.15 A weak pressure wave (sound wave) with a pressure change $\Delta p = 40$ Pa propagates through air at 20°C and 1 atm. Estimate (a) the density change, (b) the temperature change, and (c) the velocity change across the wave.

9.16 A weak pressure pulse Δp propagates through still air. Discuss the type of reflected pulse which occurs and the boundary conditions which must be satisfied when the wave strikes normal to, and is reflected from, (a) a solid wall and (b) a free liquid surface.

9.17 A submarine at a depth of 800 m sends a sonar signal and receives the reflected wave back from a similar submerged object in 15 s. Using Prob. 9.12 as a guide, estimate the distance to the other object.

9.18 The properties of a dense gas (high pressure and low temperature) are often approximated by van der Waals' equation of state [17, 18]:

$$p = \frac{\rho R T}{1 - b_1 \rho} - a_1 \rho^2$$

where constants a_1 and b_1 can be found from the critical temperature and pressure

$$a_1 = \frac{27 R^2 T_c^2}{64 p_c} = 9.0 \times 10^5 \text{ lbf} \cdot \text{ft}^4/\text{slug}^2$$

for air, and

$$b_1 = \frac{R T_c}{8 p_c} = 0.65 \text{ ft}^3/\text{slug}$$

for air. Find an analytic expression for the speed of sound

of a van der Waals gas. Assuming $k = 1.4$, compute the speed of sound of air in ft/s at $-100°F$ and 20 atm for (a) a perfect gas and (b) a van der Waals gas. What percentage higher density does the van der Waals relation predict?

9.19 The Concorde aircraft flies at Ma $\approx$ 2.3 at 11-km standard altitude. Estimate the temperature in °C at the front stagnation point. At what Mach number would it have a front stagnation-point temperature of 450°C?

9.20 A gas flows at $V = 200$ m/s, $p = 125$ kPa, and $T = 200°C$. For (a) air and (b) helium, compute the maximum pressure and the maximum velocity attainable by expansion or compression.

9.21 Air expands isentropically through a duct from $p_1 = 125$ kPa and $T_1 = 100°C$ to $p_2 = 80$ kPa and $V_2 = 325$ m/s. Compute (a) T_2, (b) Ma_2, (c) T_0, (d) p_0, (e) V_1, and (f) Ma_1.

9.22 Given the pitot stagnation temperature and pressure and the static-pressure measurements in Fig. P9.22, estimate the air velocity V, assuming (a) incompressible flow and (b) compressible flow.

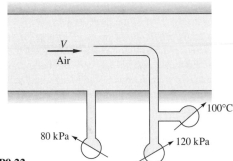

Fig. P9.22

9.23 Air flows isentropically in a duct. At section 1, $Ma_1 = 0.5$, $p_1 = 250$ kPa, and $T_1 = 300°C$. If, at section 2, $Ma_2 = 2.6$, calculate (a) T_2, (b) p_2, and (c) p_{02}.

9.24 For low-speed (nearly incompressible) gas flow, the stagnation pressure can be computed from Bernoulli's equation

$$p_0 = p + \frac{1}{2} \rho V^2$$

(a) For higher subsonic speeds, show that the isentropic relation (9.28a) can be expanded in a power series as follows:

$$p_0 \approx p + \frac{1}{2} \rho V^2 \left(1 + \frac{1}{4} Ma^2 + \frac{2-k}{24} Ma^4 + \cdots \right)$$

(b) Suppose that a pitot-static tube in air measures the pressure difference $p_0 - p$ and uses the Bernoulli relation, with stagnation density, to estimate the gas velocity. At what Mach number will the error be 4 percent?

9.25 If it is known that the air velocity in the duct is 750 ft/s, use the mercury-manometer measurement in Fig. P9.25 to

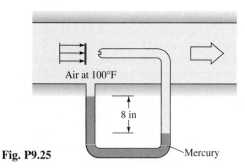

Fig. P9.25

estimate the static pressure in the duct in lbf/in^2 absolute.

9.26 Show that for isentropic flow of a perfect gas if a pitot-static probe measures p_0, p, and T_0, the gas velocity can be calculated from

$$V^2 = 2c_p T_0 \left[1 - \left(\frac{p}{p_0} \right)^{(k-1)/k} \right]$$

What would be a source of error if a shock wave were formed in front of the probe?

9.27 In many problems the sonic (*) properties are more useful reference values than the stagnation properties. For isentropic flow of a perfect gas, derive relations for p/p^*, T/T^*, and ρ/ρ^* as functions of the Mach number. Let us help by giving the density-ratio formula:

$$\rho/\rho^* = \left[\frac{k+1}{2 + (k-1)\,Ma^2} \right]^{1/(k-1)}$$

9.28 Some textbooks, e.g., Ref. 8, define and use an alternate Mach number related to the *sonic*, rather than local, speed of sound: $Ma^* = V/a^*$. (a) Show that it is related to the ordinary Mach number Ma by the relation

$$Ma^* = \left[\frac{(k+1)\,Ma^2}{2 + (k-1)\,Ma^2} \right]^{1/2}$$

(b) What is the limiting value of Ma^* when the local speed of sound drops to zero? (c) For small Ma, expand the formula above for Ma^* in a polynomial with terms up to Ma^3.

9.29 Steam from a large tank, where $T = 400°C$ and $p = 1$ MPa, expands isentropically through a nozzle until, at a section of 2-cm diameter, the pressure is 500 kPa. Using the steam tables [15], estimate (a) the temperature, (b) the velocity, and (c) the mass flow at this section. Is the flow subsonic?

9.30 Air flows in a duct of diameter 5 cm. At one section, $T_0 = 300°C$, $p = 120$ kPa, and $\dot{m} = 0.4$ kg/s. Estimate, at this section, (a) V, (b) Ma, and (c) ρ_0.

9.31 Air flows adiabatically through a duct. At one section $V_1 = 400$ ft/s, $T_1 = 200°F$, and $p_1 = 35$ lbf/in^2 absolute, while farther downstream $V_2 = 1100$ ft/s and $p_2 = 18$ lbf/in^2

absolute. Compute (a) Ma_2, (b) U_{max}, and (c) p_{02}/p_{01}.

9.32 The large compressed-air tank in Fig. P9.32 exhausts from a nozzle at an exit velocity of 235 m/s. The mercury manometer reads $h = 30$ cm. Assuming isentropic flow, compute the pressure (a) in the tank and (b) in the atmosphere. (c) What is the exit Mach number?

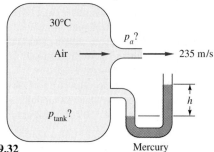

Fig. P9.32

9.33 Air flows isentropically from a reservoir, where $p = 300$ kPa and $T = 500$ K, to section 1 in a duct, where $A_1 = 0.2$ m^2 and $V_1 = 550$ m/s. Compute (a) Ma_1, (b) T_1, (c) p_1, (d) $\dot{m}$, and (e) A^*. Is the flow choked?

9.34 Steam in a tank at 450°F and 100 lbf/in^2 absolute exhausts through a converging nozzle of 0.1-in^2 throat area to a 1-atm environment. Compute the initial mass flow (a) for an ideal gas and (b) from the steam tables [15].

9.35 Air in a tank at 700 kPa and 20°C exhausts through a converging nozzle of throat area 0.65 cm^2 to 1-atm environment. Compute the initial mass flow in kg/s.

9.36 In Prob. 9.35, if the tank volume is 1.5 m^3, how long will it take the tank air pressure to blow down from 700 to 400 kPa absolute? Assume that the tank stagnation temperature is constant. How long will it blow down before the nozzle flow ceases being choked?

9.37 Make an exact control-volume analysis of the blowdown process in Fig. P9.37, assuming an insulated tank with neg-

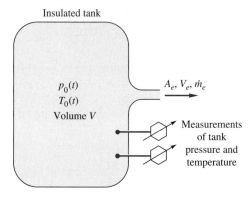

Fig. P9.37

ligible kinetic and potential energy within. Assume critical flow at the exit, and show that both p_0 and T_0 decrease during blowdown. Set up first-order differential equations for $p_0(t)$ and $T_0(t)$, and reduce and solve as far as you can.

9.38 Prob. 9.37 makes an ideal senior project or combined laboratory and computer problem, as described in Ref. 30, sec. 8.6. In Bober and Kenyon's lab experiment, the tank had a volume of 0.0352 ft³ and was initially filled with air at 50 lb/in² gage and 72°F. Atmospheric pressure was 14.5 lb/in² absolute, and the nozzle exit diameter was 0.05 in. After 2 s of blowdown, the measured tank pressure was 20 lb/in² gage and the tank temperature was −5°F. Compare these values with the theoretical analysis of Prob. 9.37.

9.39 Modify Prob. 9.32 so that the nozzle flow exits smoothly at critical flow, without further expansion, to an ambient pressure of 60 kPa. Estimate (a) the new exit velocity and (b) the manometer height h.

9.40 Air, with stagnation conditions of 800 kPa and 100°C, expands isentropically to a section of a duct where $A_1 = 20$ cm² and $p_1 = 47$ kPa. Compute (a) Ma_1, (b) the throat area, and (c) $\dot{m}$. At section 2 between the throat and section 1, the area is 9 cm². (d) Estimate the Mach number at section 2.

9.41 Air, with a stagnation pressure of 100 kPa, flows through the nozzle in Fig. P9.41, which is 2 m long and has an area variation approximated by

$$A \approx 20 - 20x + 10x^2$$

with A in cm² and x in m. It is desired to plot the complete family of isentropic pressures $p(x)$ in this nozzle, for the range of inlet pressures $1 < p(0) < 100$ kPa. Indicate those inlet pressures which are not physically possible and discuss briefly. If your computer has an online graphics routine, plot at least 15 pressure profiles; otherwise just hit the highlights and explain.

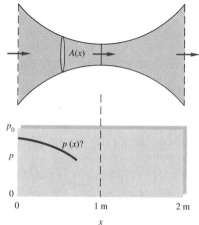

Fig. P9.41

9.42 Suppose that the duct of Prob. 9.41 has $T_0 = 300°C$ and $p(0) = 125$ kPa. If the flow is isentropic and the exit is supersonic, compute (a) $\dot{m}$ and (b) p_{exit}.

9.43 Air flows isentropically through a duct with $T_0 = 300°C$. At two sections with identical areas of 25 cm², the pressures are $p_1 = 120$ kPa and $p_2 = 60$ kPa. Determine (a) the mass flow, (b) the throat area, and (c) Ma_2.

9.44 In Prob. 3.34 we knew nothing about compressible flow at the time so merely assumed exit conditions p_2 and T_2 and computed V_2 as an application of the continuity equation. Suppose that the throat diameter is 3 in. For the given stagnation conditions in the rocket chamber in Fig. P3.34 and assuming $k = 1.4$ and a molecular weight of 26, compute the actual exit velocity, pressure, and temperature according to one-dimensional theory. If $p_a = 14.7$ lbf/in² absolute, compute the thrust from the analysis of Prob. 3.68. This thrust is entirely independent of the stagnation temperature (check this by changing T_0 to 2000°R if you like). Why?

9.45 At a point upstream of the throat of a converging-diverging nozzle the properties are $V_1 = 200$ m/s, $T_1 = 300$ K, and $p_1 = 125$ kPa. If the exit flow is supersonic, compute, from isentropic theory, (a) $\dot{m}$ and (b) A_1. The throat area is 35 cm².

9.46 If the writer did not falter, the results of Prob. 9.43 are (a) 0.671 kg/s, (b) 23.3 cm², and (c) 1.32. Do not tell your friends who are still working on Prob. 9.43. Consider a control volume which encloses the nozzle between these two 25-cm² sections. If the pressure outside the duct is 1 atm, determine the total force acting on this section of nozzle.

9.47 In wind-tunnel testing near Mach 1, a small area decrease caused by model blockage can be important. Suppose the test section area is 1 m², with unblocked test conditions $Ma = 1.10$ and $T = 20°C$. What model area will first cause the test section to choke? If the model cross section is 0.004 m² (0.4 percent blockage), what percentage change in test-section velocity results?

9.48 A force $F = 1100$ N pushes a piston of diameter 12 cm through an insulated cylinder containing air at 20°C, as in Fig. P9.48. The exit diameter is 3 mm, and $p_a = 1$ atm. Estimate (a) V_e, (b) V_p, and (c) $\dot{m}_e$.

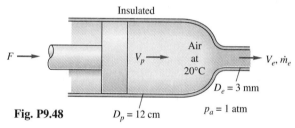

Fig. P9.48

9.49 Air expands through a nozzle and exits supersonically. The throat area is 10 cm², and the throat pressure is 100 kPa.

Find the pressure on either side of the throat where the duct area is 24 cm².

9.50 Air expands isentropically in a converging nozzle whose entrance conditions are $D_1 = 10$ cm, $p_1 = 150$ kPa, $T_1 = 100°C$, and $\dot{m} = 1$ kg/s. The flow discharges smoothly to an ambient pressure of 101 kPa. (a) What is the exit diameter of the nozzle? (b) How much further can the ambient pressure be reduced before it affects the inlet mass flow?

9.51 Repeat Prob. 9.50 if the gas is argon.

9.52 A converging-diverging nozzle exits smoothly to sea-level standard atmosphere. It is supplied by a 40-m³ tank initially at 800 kPa and 100°C. Assuming isentropic flow in the nozzle, estimate (a) the throat area and (b) the tank pressure after 10 s of operation. The exit area = 10 cm².

9.53 Air flows steadily from a reservoir at 20°C through a nozzle of exit area 20 cm² and strikes a vertical plate as in Fig. P9.53. The flow is subsonic throughout. A force of 135 N is required to hold the plate stationary. Compute (a) V_e, (b) Ma_e, and (c) p_0 if $p_a = 101$ kPa.

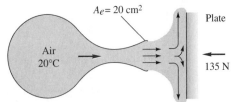

Fig. P9.53

9.54 For flow of air through a normal shock the upstream conditions are $V_1 = 600$ m/s, $T_{01} = 500$ K, and $p_{01} = 700$ kPa. Compute the downstream conditions Ma_2, V_2, T_2, p_2, and p_{02}.

9.55 Air, supplied by a reservoir at 450 kPa, flows through a converging-diverging nozzle whose throat area is 12 cm². A normal shock stands where $A_1 = 20$ cm². (a) Compute the pressure just downstream of this shock. Still farther downstream, at $A_3 = 30$ cm², estimate (b) p_3, (c) A_3^*, and (d) Ma_3.

9.56 Air from a reservoir at 20°C and 500 kPa flows through a duct and forms a normal shock downstream of a throat of area 10 cm². By an odd coincidence it is found that the stagnation pressure downstream of this shock exactly equals the throat pressure. What is the area where the shock wave stands?

9.57 Air flows from a tank through a nozzle into the standard atmosphere, as in Fig. P9.57. A normal shock stands in the exit of the nozzle, as shown. Estimate (a) the pressure in the tank and (b) the mass flow.

9.58 Argon (Table A.4) approaches a normal shock with $V_1 = 700$ m/s, $p_1 = 125$ kPa, and $T_1 = 350$ K. Estimate (a) V_2 and (b) p_2. (c) What pressure p_2 would result if the same

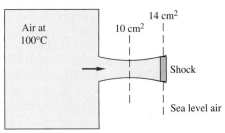

Fig. P9.57

velocity change V_1 to V_2 were accomplished isentropically?

9.59 An explosion in sea-level air spreads as a spherical wave. When the sphere diameter reaches 40 m, the pressure inside the wave is 600 kPa. Estimate the propagation speed of the wave at this instant.

9.60 When a pitot tube such as Fig. (6.30) is placed in a supersonic flow, a normal shock will stand in front of the probe. Suppose the probe reads $p_0 = 190$ kPa and $p = 150$ kPa. If the stagnation temperature is 400 K, estimate the (supersonic) Mach number and velocity upstream of the shock.

9.61 Repeat Prob. 9.56 except this time let the odd coincidence be that the *static* pressure downstream of the shock exactly equals the throat pressure. What is the area where the shock stands?

9.62 An atomic explosion propagates into still air at 14.7 lbf/in² absolute and 520°R. The pressure just inside the shock is 5000 lbf/in² absolute. Assuming $k = 1.4$, what are the speed C of the shock and the velocity V just inside the shock?

9.63 Sea-level standard air is sucked into a vacuum tank through a nozzle, as in Fig. P9.63. A normal shock stands where the nozzle area is 2 cm², as shown. Estimate (a) the pressure in the tank and (b) the mass flow.

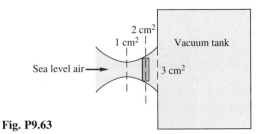

Fig. P9.63

9.64 Air in a large tank at 100°C and 150 kPa exhausts to the atmosphere through a converging nozzle with a 5-cm² throat area. Compute the exit mass flow if the atmospheric pressure is (a) 100 kPa, (b) 60 kPa, and (c) 30 kPa.

9.65 Air flows through a converging-diverging nozzle between two large reservoirs, as shown in Fig. P9.65. A mercury manometer between the throat and the downstream reservoir reads $h = 15$ cm. Estimate the downstream reservoir pressure. Is there a normal shock in the flow? If so, does it stand in the exit plane or farther upstream?

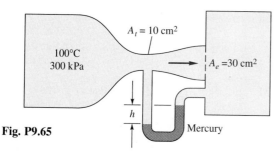

Fig. P9.65

9.66 In Prob. 9.65 what would be the mercury-manometer reading h if the nozzle were operating exactly at supersonic design conditions?

9.67 In Prob. 9.65 estimate the complete range of manometer readings h for which the flow through the nozzle is entirely isentropic, except possibly in the exit plane.

9.68 Air in a tank at 120 kPa and 300 K exhausts to the atmosphere through a 5-cm²-throat converging nozzle at a rate of 0.12 kg/s. What is the atmospheric pressure? What is the maximum mass flow possible at low atmospheric pressure?

9.69 With reference to Prob. 3.68, show that the thrust of a rocket engine exhausting into a vacuum is given by

$$F = \frac{p_0 A_e (1 + k\,\mathrm{Ma}_e^2)}{\left(1 + \dfrac{k-1}{2}\,\mathrm{Ma}_e^2\right)^{k/(k-1)}}$$

where A_e = exit area
Ma_e = exit Mach number
p_0 = stagnation pressure in combustion chamber

Note that stagnation temperature does not enter into the thrust.

9.70 Air, at stagnation temperature 100°C, expands isentropically through a nozzle of 6-cm² throat area and 18-cm² exit area. The mass flow is at its maximum value of 0.5 kg/s. Estimate the exit pressure for (a) subsonic and (b) supersonic exit flow.

9.71 For the nozzle of Prob. 9.70, allowing for nonisentropic flow, what is the range of exit tank pressures p_b for which (a) the diverging nozzle flow is fully supersonic, (b) the exit flow is subsonic, (c) the mass flow is independent of p_b, (d) the exit plane pressure p_e is independent of p_b, and (e) $p_e < p_b$?

9.72 Suppose the nozzle flow of Prob. 9.70 is not isentropic but instead has a normal shock at the position where area is 15 cm². Compute the resulting mass flow, exit pressure, and exit Mach number.

9.73 A supersonic nozzle with an exit area of 8 cm² discharges air at Ma = 2.5, p = 101 kPa, and T = 300 K. Compute (a) the exit velocity, (b) p_0, (c) T_0, (d) the throat area, and (e) the mass flow.

9.74 The perfect-gas assumption leads smoothly to Mach-number relations which are very convenient (and tabulated). This is not so for a real gas such as steam. To illustrate, let steam at T_0 = 500°C and p_0 = 2 MPa expand isentropically through a converging nozzle whose exit area is 10 cm². Using the steam tables, find (a) the exit pressure and (b) the mass flow when the flow is sonic, or choked. What complicates the analysis?

9.75 A double-tank system in Fig. P9.75 has two identical converging nozzles of 1-in² throat area. Tank 1 is very large, and tank 2 is small enough to be in steady-flow equilibrium with the jet from tank 1. Nozzle flow is isentropic, but entropy changes between 1 and 3 due to jet dissipation in tank 2. Compute the mass flow. (If you give up, Ref. 14, pp. 288–290, has a good discussion.)

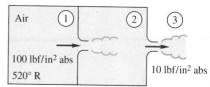

Fig. P9.75

9.76 A large reservoir at 20°C and 800 kPa is used to fill a small insulated tank through a converging-diverging nozzle with 1-cm² throat area and 1.66-cm² exit area. The small tank has a volume of 1 m³ and is initially at 20°C and 100 kPa. Estimate the elapsed time when (a) shock waves begin to appear inside the nozzle and (b) the mass flow begins to drop below its maximum value.

9.77 A perfect gas (not air) expands isentropically through a supersonic nozzle with an exit area 5 times its throat area. The exit Mach number is 3.8. What is the specific-heat ratio of the gas? What might this gas be? If p_0 = 300 kPa, what is the exit pressure of the gas?

9.78 The orientation of a hole can make a difference. Consider holes A and B in Fig. P9.78, which are identical but reversed.

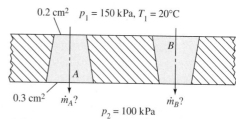

Fig. P9.78

For the given air properties on either side, compute the mass flow through each hole and explain why they are different.

9.79 Air with $p_0 = 300$ kPa and $T_0 = 500$ K flows through a converging-diverging nozzle with throat area of 1 cm² and exit area of 3 cm² into a receiver tank. The mass flow is 195.2 kg/h. For what range of receiver pressure is this mass flow possible?

9.80 A sea-level automobile tire is initially at 32 lbf/in² gage pressure and 75°F. When it is punctured with a hole which resembles a converging nozzle, its pressure drops to 15 lbf/in² gage in 12 min. Estimate the size of the hole, in thousandths of an inch. The tire volume = 2.5 ft³.

9.81 Helium, in a large tank at 100°C and 400 kPa, discharges to a receiver through a converging-diverging nozzle designed to exit at Ma = 2.5 with exit area 1.2 cm². Compute (a) the receiver pressure and (b) the mass flow at design conditions. (c) Also estimate the range of receiver pressures for which mass flow will be a maximum.

9.82 Air at 500 K flows through a converging-diverging nozzle with throat area of 1 cm² and exit area of 2.7 cm². When the mass flow is 182.2 kg/h, a pitot-static probe placed in the exit plane reads $p_0 = 250.6$ kPa and $p = 240.1$ kPa. Estimate the exit velocity. Is there a normal shock wave in the duct? If so, compute the Mach number just downstream of this shock.

9.83 When operating at design conditions (smooth exit to sea-level pressure), a rocket engine has a thrust of 1 million lbf. The chamber pressure and temperature are 600 lbf/in² absolute and 4000°R, respectively. The exhaust gases approximate $k = 1.38$ with a molecular weight of 26. Estimate (a) the exit Mach number and (b) the throat diameter.

9.84 Air flows through a duct as in Fig. P9.84, where $A_1 = 24$ cm², $A_2 = 18$ cm², and $A_3 = 32$ cm². A normal shock stands at section 2. Compute (a) the mass flow, (b) the Mach number, and (c) the stagnation pressure at section 3.

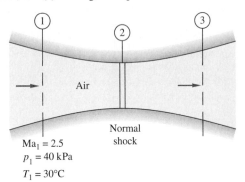

Ma$_1$ = 2.5
p_1 = 40 kPa
T_1 = 30°C

Fig. P9.84

9.85 A large tank delivers air through a nozzle of 1-cm² throat area and 2.7-cm² exit area. When the receiver pressure is

125 kPa, a normal shock stands in the exit plane. Estimate (a) the throat pressure and (b) the temperature in the upstream supply tank.

9.86 Air enters a 3-cm diameter pipe 15 m long at $V_1 = 73$ m/s, $p_1 = 550$ kPa, and $T_1 = 60$°C. The friction factor is 0.018. Compute V_2, p_2, T_2, and p_{02} at the end of the pipe. How much additional pipe length would cause the exit flow to be sonic?

9.87 Air enters a duct of $L/D = 40$ at $V_1 = 208$ m/s and $T_1 = 300$ K. The flow at the exit is choked. What is the average friction factor in the duct for adiabatic flow?

9.88 Air enters a 5- by 5-cm square duct at $V_1 = 900$ m/s and $T_1 = 300$ K. The friction factor is 0.02. For what length duct will the flow exactly decelerate to Ma = 1.0? If the duct length is 2 m, will there be a normal shock in the duct? If so, at what Mach number will it occur?

9.89 For most friction-flow problems here, the values of $\bar{f}$ have been set at arbitrary round numbers to simplify calculation. To make the analysis more realistic, repeat Prob. 9.86 by evaluating the friction factor from the smooth-wall Moody chart (Fig. 6.13).

9.90 Air, supplied at $p_0 = 700$ kPa and $T_0 = 330$ K, flows through a converging nozzle into a pipe of 2.5-cm diameter which exits to a near vacuum. If $\bar{f} = 0.022$, what will be the mass flow through the pipe if its length is (a) 0 m, (b) 1 m, and (c) 10 m?

9.91 Air flows steadily from a tank through the pipe in Fig. P9.91. There is a converging nozzle on the end. If the mass flow is 3 kg/s and the nozzle is choked, estimate (a) the Mach number at section 1 and (b) the pressure inside the tank.

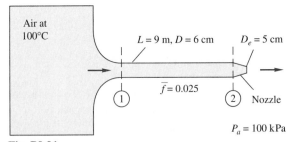

Air at 100°C

$L = 9$ m, $D = 6$ cm $D_e = 5$ cm

$\bar{f} = 0.025$ Nozzle

$P_a = 100$ kPa

Fig. P9.91

9.92 Modify Prob. 9.91 as follows. Let the pressure in the tank be 700 kPa, and let the nozzle be choked. Determine (a) Ma$_2$ and (b) the mass flow.

9.93 Modify Prob. 9.91 as follows. Remove the nozzle, so that the pipe exits to the atmosphere. If the tank pressure is 700 kPa, estimate the mass flow.

9.94 Compressible pipe flow with friction, Sec. 9.7, assumes constant stagnation enthalpy and mass flow but variable momentum. Such a flow is often called *Fanno flow*, and a line representing all possible property changes on a temperature-entropy chart is called a *Fanno line*. Assuming a perfect gas with $k = 1.4$ and the data of Prob. 9.86, draw a Fanno curve of the flow for a range of velocities from very low (Ma $\ll$ 1) to very high (Ma $\gg$ 1). Comment on the meaning of the maximum-entropy point on this curve.

9.95 Helium (Table A.4) enters a 5-cm-diameter pipe at $p_1 = 550$ kPa, $V_1 = 312$ m/s, and $T_1 = 40°C$. The friction factor is 0.025. If the flow is choked, determine (*a*) the length of the duct and (*b*) the exit pressure.

9.96 Derive and verify the adiabatic-pipe-flow velocity relation of Eq. (9.74), which is usually written in the form

$$\frac{\bar{f}L}{D} + \frac{k + 1}{k} \ln \frac{V_2}{V_1} = \frac{a_0^2}{k}\left(\frac{1}{V_1^2} - \frac{1}{V_2^2}\right)$$

9.97 By making a few algebraic substitutions, show that Eq. (9.74), or the relation in Prob. 9.96, may be written in the density form

$$\rho_1^2 = \rho_2^2 + \rho^{*2}\left(\frac{2k}{k + 1}\frac{\bar{f}L}{D} + 2\ln\frac{\rho_1}{\rho_2}\right)$$

Why is this formula awkward if one is trying to solve for the mass flow when the pressures are given at sections 1 and 2?

9.98 Compressible *laminar* flow, $f \approx 64/\text{Re}$, may occur in capillary tubes. Consider air, at stagnation conditions of 100°C and 200 kPa, entering a tube 3 cm long and 0.1 mm in diameter. If the receiver pressure is near vacuum, estimate (*a*) the average Reynolds number, (*b*) the Mach number at the entrance, and (*c*) the mass flow in kg/h.

9.99 A compressor forces air through a smooth pipe 20 m long and 4 cm in diameter, as in Fig. P9.99. The air leaves at 101 kPa and 200°C. The compressor data for pressure rise versus mass flow are shown in the figure. Using the Moody chart to estimate $\bar{f}$, compute the resulting mass flow.

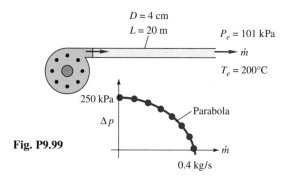

Fig. P9.99

9.100 Modify Prob. 9.99 as follows. Find the length of 4-cm-diameter pipe for which the pump pressure rise will be exactly 200 kPa.

9.101 How do the compressible-pipe-flow formulas behave for small pressure drops? Let air at 20°C enter a tube of diameter 1 cm and length 3 m. If $\bar{f} = 0.028$ with $p_1 = 102$ kPa and $p_2 = 100$ kPa, estimate the mass flow in kg/h for (*a*) isothermal flow, (*b*) adiabatic flow, and (*c*) incompressible flow (Chap. 6) at the entrance density.

9.102 Air at 550 kPa and 100°C enters a smooth 1-m-long pipe and then passes through a second smooth pipe to a 30-kPa reservoir, as in Fig. P9.102. Using the Moody chart to compute $\bar{f}$, estimate the mass flow through this system. Is the flow choked?

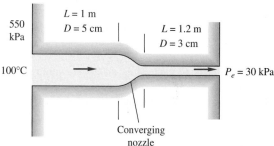

Fig. P9.102

9.103 Natural gas, with $k \approx 1.3$ and a molecular weight of 16, is to be pumped through 100 km of 81-cm-diameter pipeline. The downstream pressure is 150 kPa. If the gas enters at 60°C, the mass flow is 20 kg/s, and $\bar{f} = 0.024$, estimate the required entrance pressure for (*a*) isothermal flow and (*b*) adiabatic flow.

9.104 A tank of oxygen (Table A.4) at 20°C is to supply an astronaut through an umbilical tube 12 m long and 2 cm in diameter. The exit pressure in the tube is 40 kPa. If the desired mass flow is 90 kg/h and $\bar{f} = 0.025$, what should be the pressure in the tank?

9.105 Air enters a 0.5-in-diameter pipe subsonically at $p_1 = 60$ lbf/in² absolute and $T_1 = 600°R$. The pipe length is 20 ft, $\bar{f} = 0.018$, and the receiver pressure outside the pipe exit is 20 lbf/in² absolute. Compute the mass flow in the pipe, assuming (*a*) isothermal flow and (*b*) adiabatic flow.

9.106 Air at 300 K flows through a duct 50 m long with $\bar{f} = 0.019$. What is the minimum duct diameter which can carry the flow without choking if the entrance velocity is (*a*) 50 m/s, (*b*) 150 m/s, and (*c*) 420 m/s?

9.107 A fuel-air mixture, assumed equivalent to air, enters a duct combustion chamber at $V_1 = 104$ m/s and $T_1 = 300$ K. What amount of heat addition in kJ/kg will cause the exit flow to be choked? What will be the exit Mach number and temperature if 504 kJ/kg is added during combustion?

9.108 What happens to the inlet flow of Prob. 9.107 if the combustion yields 1500 kJ/kg heat addition and p_{01} and T_{01} remain the same? How much is the mass flow reduced?

9.109 A jet engine at 7000-m altitude takes in 45 kg/s of air and adds 550 kJ/kg in the combustion chamber. The chamber cross section is 0.5 m², and the air enters the chamber at 80 kPa and 5°C. After combustion the air expands through an isentropic converging nozzle to exit at atmospheric pressure. Estimate (a) the nozzle throat diameter, (b) the nozzle exit velocity, and (c) the thrust produced by the engine.

9.110 Compressible pipe flow with heat addition, Sec. 9.8, assumes constant momentum $(p + \rho V^2)$ and constant mass flow but variable stagnation enthalpy. Such a flow is often called *Rayleigh flow*, and a line representing all possible property changes on an temperature-entropy chart is called a *Rayleigh line*. Assuming air passing through the flow state $p_1 = 548$ kPa, $T_1 = 588$ K, $V_1 = 266$ m/s, and $A = 1$ m², draw a Rayleigh curve of the flow for a range of velocities from very low (Ma $\ll$ 1) to very high (Ma $\gg$ 1). Comment on the meaning of the maximum-entropy point on this curve.

9.111 Add to your Rayleigh line of Prob. 9.110 a Fanno line (see Prob. 9.94) for stagnation enthalpy equal to the value associated with state 1 in Prob. 9.110. The two curves will intersect at state 1, which is subsonic, and at a certain state 2, which is supersonic. Interpret these two states vis-à-vis Table B.2.

9.112 Air enters a duct subsonically at section 1 at 1.2 kg/s. When 650 kW of heat is added, the flow chokes at the exit at $p_2 = 95$ kPa and $T_2 = 700$ K. Assuming frictionless heat addition, estimate (a) the velocity and (b) the stagnation pressure at section 1.

9.113 Air enters a constant-area duct at $p_1 = 90$ kPa, $V_1 = 520$ m/s, and $T_1 = 558°C$. It is then cooled with negligible friction until it exits at $p_2 = 160$ kPa. Estimate (a) V_2, (b) T_2, and (c) the total amount of cooling in kJ/kg.

9.114 We have simplified things here by separating friction (Sec. 9.7) from heat addition (Sec. 9.8). Actually, they often occur together, and their effects must be evaluated simultaneously. Show that, for flow with friction *and* heat transfer in a constant-diameter pipe, the continuity, momentum, and energy equations may be combined into the following differential equation for Mach-number changes:

$$\frac{d\,\text{Ma}^2}{\text{Ma}^2} = \frac{1 + k\,\text{Ma}^2}{1 - \text{Ma}^2}\frac{dQ}{c_p T}$$
$$+ \frac{k\,\text{Ma}^2\,[2 + (k-1)\,\text{Ma}^2]}{2(1 - \text{Ma}^2)}\frac{f\,dx}{D}$$

where dQ is the heat added. A complete derivation, including many additional combined effects such as area change and mass addition, is given in chap. 8 of Ref. 8.

9.115 Air flows subsonically in a duct with $T_{01} = 305$ K. When heat is added in the amount of 948 kJ/kg, the pressure drops from $p_1 = 200$ to $p_2 = 106$ kPa. Using one-dimensional theory, estimate (a) Ma$_1$, (b) T_1, and (c) V_1.

9.116 An observer at sea level does not hear an aircraft flying at 12,000-ft standard altitude until it is 5 (statute) mi past her. Estimate the aircraft speed in ft/s.

9.117 An observer at sea level does not hear an aircraft flying at 6000-m standard altitude until 15 s after it has passed overhead. Estimate the aircraft speed in m/s.

9.118 A particle moving at uniform velocity in sea-level standard air creates the two disturbance spheres shown in Fig. P9.118. Compute the particle velocity and Mach number.

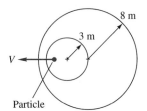

Fig. P9.118   Particle

9.119 The particle in Fig. P9.119 is moving supersonically in sea-level standard air. From the two given disturbance spheres, compute the particle Mach number, velocity, and Mach angle.

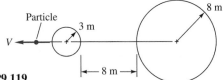

Fig. P9.119

9.120 The particle in Fig. P9.120 is moving in sea-level standard air. From the two disturbance spheres shown, estimate (a) the position of the particle at this instant and (b) the temperature in °C at the front stagnation point of the particle.

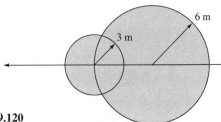

Fig. P9.120

9.121 A thermistor probe, in the shape of a needle parallel to the flow, reads a static temperature of $-25°C$ when inserted into a supersonic airstream. A conical disturbance cone of half-angle 17° is created. Estimate (a) the Mach number, (b) the velocity, and (c) the stagnation temperature of the stream.

9.122 Supersonic air takes a 5° compression turn, as in Fig. P9.122. Compute the downstream pressure and Mach number and the wave angle, and compare with small-disturbance theory.

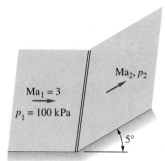

Fig. P9.122

9.123 Modify Prob. 9.122 as follows. Let the 5° total turn be in the form of five separate compression turns of 1° each. Compute the final Mach number and pressure, and compare the pressure with an isentropic expansion to the same final Mach number.

9.124 Determine the validity of the following alternate relation for the pressure ratio across an oblique shock wave:

$$\frac{p_2}{p_1} = \frac{\cot \theta \sin 2\beta - \cos 2\beta + k}{\cot \theta \sin 2\beta - \cos 2\beta - k}$$

If necessary, your proof (or disproof) may be somewhat tentative and heuristic.

9.125 Show that, as the upstream Mach number approaches infinity, the Mach number downstream of an attached oblique-shock wave will have the value

$$\text{Ma}_2 \approx \sqrt{\frac{k - 1}{2k \sin^2 (\beta - \theta)}}$$

9.126 Consider airflow at $\text{Ma}_1 = 2.2$. Calculate, to two decimal places, (a) the deflection angle for which the downstream flow is sonic and (b) the maximum deflection angle.

9.127 Do the Mach waves upstream of an oblique-shock wave intersect with the shock? Assuming supersonic downstream flow, do the downstream Mach waves intersect the shock? Show that for small deflections the shock-wave angle β lies halfway between μ_1 and $\mu_2 + \theta$ for any Mach number.

9.128 Air flows past a two-dimensional wedge-nosed body as in Fig. P9.128. Determine the wedge-half angle δ for which the horizontal component of the total pressure force on the nose is 35 kN/m of depth into the paper.

9.129 Air flows at supersonic speed toward a compression ramp, as in Fig. P9.129. A scratch on the wall at point a creates a wave of 30° angle, while the oblique shock created has a 50° angle. What is (a) the ramp angle θ and (b) the wave angle ϕ caused by a scratch at b?

9.130 Modify Prob. 9.129 as follows. If the wave angle ϕ is 42°,

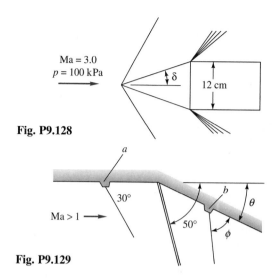

Fig. P9.128

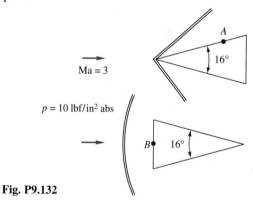

Fig. P9.129

determine (a) the shock-wave angle and (b) the deflection angle.

9.131 In Fig. P9.128, assume that the approach stream temperature is 20°C. For what wedge half-angle δ will the stream temperature along the wedge surface be 200°C?

9.132 Air flows at $\text{Ma} = 3$ and $p = 10$ lbf/in² absolute toward a wedge of 16° angle at zero incidence in Fig. P9.132. If the pointed edge is forward, what will be the pressure at point A? If the blunt edge is forward, what will be the pressure at point B?

Fig. P9.132

9.133 For the wedge with its pointed edge forward in the upper part of Fig. P9.132, let the base be 8 in high and have an average base pressure of 4.0 lbf/in². Compute the drag coefficient of this wedge and the drag force per foot of depth.

9.134 When an oblique shock strikes a solid wall, it reflects as a shock of sufficient strength to cause the exit flow Ma_3 to be parallel to the wall, as in Fig. P9.134. For airflow with $\text{Ma}_1 = 2.5$ and $p_1 = 100$ kPa, compute Ma_3, p_3, and the angle ϕ.

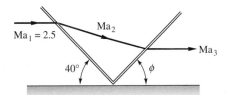

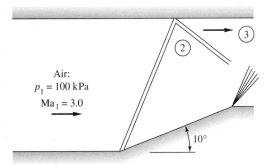

Fig. P9.134

9.135 A bend in the bottom of a supersonic duct flow induces a shock wave which reflects from the upper wall, as in Fig. P9.135. Compute the Mach number and pressure in region 3.

Fig. P9.135

9.136 Figure P9.136 is a special application of Prob. 9.135. With careful design, one can orient the bend on the lower wall so that the reflected wave is exactly canceled by the return bend, as shown. This is a method of reducing the Mach number in a channel (a supersonic diffuser). If the bend angle is $\phi = 10°$, find (a) the downstream width h and (b) the downstream Mach number. Assume a weak shock wave.

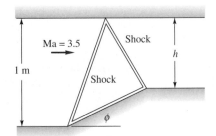

Fig. P9.136

9.137 Generalize Prob. 9.136 into a computer study as follows. Assuming weak shocks, find and plot all combinations of ϕ and h in Fig. P9.136 for which the canceled or "swallowed" reflected shock is possible.

9.138 The supersonic nozzle of Fig. P9.138 is overexpanded (case G of Fig. 9.12) with $A_e/A_t = 3.0$ and a stagnation pressure of 350 kPa. If the jet edge makes a 4° angle with the nozzle

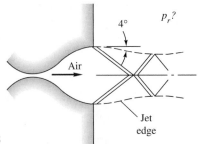

Fig. P9.138

centerline, what is the back pressure p_r in kPa?

9.139 Airflow at Ma = 2.2 takes a compression turn of 12° and then another turn of angle θ in Fig. P9.139. What is the maximum value of θ for the second shock to be attached? Will the two shocks intersect for any θ less than θ_{max}?

Fig. P9.139

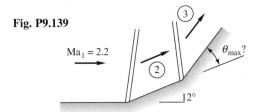

9.140 The solution to Prob. 9.122 is $Ma_2 = 2.750$, and $p_2 = 145.5$ kPa. Compare these results with an isentropic compression turn of 5°, using Prandtl-Meyer theory.

9.141 Supersonic airflow takes a 5° expansion turn, as in Fig. P9.141. Compute the downstream Mach number and pressure, and compare with small-disturbance theory.

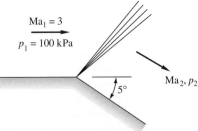

Fig. P9.141

9.142 A supersonic airflow at $Ma_1 = 3.2$ and $p_1 = 50$ kPa undergoes a compression shock followed by an isentropic expansion turn. The flow deflection is 30° for each turn. Compute Ma_2 and p_2 if (a) the shock is followed by the expansion and (b) the expansion is followed by the shock.

9.143 Airflow at $Ma_1 = 3.2$ passes through a 25° oblique-shock deflection. What isentropic expansion turn is required to bring the flow back to (a) Ma_1 and (b) p_1?

9.144 Consider a smooth isentropic compression turn of 20°, as shown in Fig. P9.144. The Mach waves thus generated will form a converging fan. Sketch this fan as accurately as possible, using at least five equally spaced waves, and demonstrate how the fan indicates the probable formation of an oblique-shock wave.

Fig. P9.144

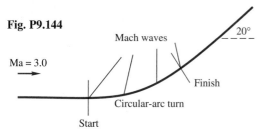

Mach waves

20°

Ma = 3.0

Finish

Circular-arc turn

Start

9.145 Air at $Ma_1 = 2.0$ and $p_1 = 100$ kPa undergoes an isentropic expansion to a downstream pressure of 50 kPa. What is the desired turn angle in degrees?

9.146 Helium, at 20°C and $V_1 = 2010$ m/s, undergoes a Prandtl-Meyer expansion until the temperature is -50°C. Estimate the turn angle in degrees.

9.147 A converging-diverging nozzle with a 4:1 exit-area ratio and $p_0 = 500$ kPa operates in an underexpanded condition (case I of Fig. 9.12) as in Fig. P9.147. The receiver pressure is $p_a = 10$ kPa, which is less than the exit pressure, so that expansion waves form outside the exit. For the given conditions, what will the Mach number Ma_2 and the angle ϕ of the edge of the jet be? Assume $k = 1.4$ as usual.

$p_a = 10$ kPa

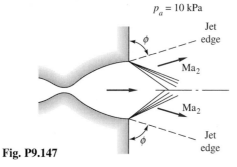

Jet edge

ϕ

Ma_2

Ma_2

Jet edge

ϕ

Fig. P9.147

9.148 Repeat Example 9.19 for an angle of attack of 6°. Is the lift coefficient linear with angle α in this range of $0° \leq \alpha \leq 8°$? Is the drag coefficient parabolic with α in this range?

9.149 Repeat Example 9.21 for an angle of attack of 2°. Is the lift coefficient linear with angle α in this range of $0° \leq \alpha \leq 8°$? Why does the drag coefficient not have the simple parabolic form $C_D \approx K\alpha^2$ in this range?

9.150 A flat-plate airfoil with $C = 1.2$ m is to have a lift of 30 kN/m when flying at 5000-m standard altitude with $U_\infty = 641$ m/s. Using Ackeret theory, estimate (*a*) the angle of attack and (*b*) the drag force in N/m.

9.151 Air flows at Ma = 2.5 past a half-wedge airfoil whose an-

gles are 4°, as in Fig. P9.151. Compute the lift and drag coefficient at α equal to (*a*) 0° and (*b*) 6°.

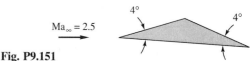

$Ma_\infty = 2.5$

4°

4°

Fig. P9.151

9.152 A supersonic airfoil has a parabolic symmetric shape for upper and lower surfaces

$$y_{u,l} = \pm 2t\left(\frac{x}{C} - \frac{x^2}{C^2}\right)$$

such that the maximum thickness is t at $x = \frac{1}{2}C$. Compute the drag coefficient at zero incidence by Ackeret theory, and compare with a symmetric double wedge of the same thickness.

9.153 Repeat Example 9.21, with $\alpha = 8°$, except that the airfoil is taken to be a diamond shape with a leading-edge included angle of 6° and a trailing-edge included angle of 2°.

9.154 A symmetric supersonic airfoil has its upper and lower surfaces defined by a sine waveshape:

$$y = \frac{t}{2} \sin \frac{\pi x}{C}$$

where t is the maximum thickness, which occurs at $x = C/2$. Use Ackeret theory to derive an expression for the drag coefficient at zero angle of attack. Compare your result with Ackeret theory for a symmetric double-wedge airfoil of the same thickness.

9.155 For the sine-wave airfoil shape of Prob. 9.154, with $Ma_\infty = 2.5$, $k = 1.4$, $t/C = 0.1$, and $\alpha = 0°$, plot (without computing the overall forces) the pressure distribution $p(x)/p_\infty$ along the upper surface for (*a*) Ackeret theory and (*b*) an oblique shock plus a continuous Prandtl-Meyer expansion.

9.156 A thin circular-arc airfoil is shown in Fig. P9.156. The leading edge is parallel to the free stream. Using linearized (small-turning-angle) supersonic-flow theory, derive a formula for the lift and drag coefficient for this orientation, and compare with Ackeret-theory results for an angle of attack $\alpha = \tan^{-1}(h/L)$.

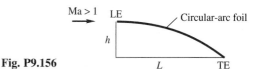

Ma > 1

LE

Circular-arc foil

h

L

TE

Fig. P9.156

9.157 Prove from Ackeret theory that for a given supersonic airfoil shape with sharp leading and trailing edges and a given thickness, the minimum-thickness drag occurs for a symmetric double-wedge shape.

WORD PROBLEMS

W9.1 Notice from Table 9.1 that (*a*) water and mercury and (*b*) aluminum and steel have nearly the same speeds of sound, yet the second of the two materials is much denser. Can you account for this oddity? Can molecular theory explain it?

W9.2 When an object approaches you at Ma = 0.8, you can hear it, according to Fig. 9.18*a*. But would there be a Doppler shift? For example, would a musical tone seem to you to have a higher or a lower pitch?

W9.3 The subject of this chapter is commonly called *gas dynamics*. But can liquids not perform in this manner? Using water as an example, make a rule-of-thumb estimate of the pressure level needed to drive a water flow at velocities comparable to the sound speed.

W9.4 Suppose a gas is driven at compressible subsonic speeds by a large pressure drop, p_1 to p_2. Describe its behavior on an appropriately labeled Mollier chart for (*a*) frictionless flow in a converging nozzle and (*b*) flow with friction in a long duct.

W9.5 Describe physically what the "speed of sound" represents. What kind of pressure changes occur in air sound waves during ordinary conversation?

W9.6 Give a physical description of the phenomenon of choking in a converging-nozzle gas flow. Could choking happen even if wall friction were not negligible?

W9.7 Shock waves are treated as discontinuities here, but they actually have a very small finite thickness. After giving it some thought, sketch your idea of the distribution of gas velocity, pressure, temperature, and entropy through the inside of a shock wave.

W9.8 Describe how an observer, running along a normal-shock wave at finite speed *V*, will see what appears to be an oblique-shock wave. Is there any limit to the running speed?

Design Project

D9.1 It is desired to select a rectangular wing for a fighter aircraft. The plane must be able (*a*) to take off and land on a 4500-ft-long sea-level runway and (*b*) to cruise supersonically at Ma = 2.3 at 28,000-ft altitude. For simplicity, assume a wing with zero sweepback. Let the aircraft maximum weight equal $(30 + n)(1000)$ lbf, where *n* is the number of letters in your surname. Let the available sea-level maximum thrust be one-third of the maximum weight, decreasing at altitude proportional to ambient density. Making suitable assumptions about the effect of finite aspect ratio on wing lift and drag for both subsonic and supersonic flight, select a wing of minimum area sufficient to perform these takeoff/landing and cruise requirements. Some thought should be given to analyzing the wingtips and wing roots in supersonic flight, where Mach cones form and the flow is not two-dimensional. If no satisfactory solution is possible, gradually increase the available thrust to converge to an acceptable design.

Chapter 10
Open-Channel Flow

Motivation. The duct flows of Chap. 6 were driven by a pressure difference between the ends of the duct. Such channels are closed and full of fluid, either gas or liquid. By contrast, an *open-channel flow* is liquid only and is *not* full; i.e., there is always a free surface exposed to ambient pressure. The basic balance of forces is between gravity (fluid weight) and friction.

Practical open-channel problems almost always concern *water* as the relevant fluid. The flow is generally turbulent, due to its large scale and small kinematic viscosity, and is three-dimensional, sometimes unsteady, and often surprisingly complex due to geometric effects. This chapter presents some simple engineering theories and correlations for steady flow in straight channels of simple geometry. Many of the concepts from steady duct flow—hydraulic diameter, friction factor, head losses—apply also to open channels.

10.1 Introduction

Simply stated, open-channel flow is the flow of a liquid in a conduit with a free surface. There are many practical examples, both artificial (flumes, spillways, canals, weirs, drainage ditches, culverts) and natural (streams, rivers, estuaries, floodplains). This chapter introduces the elementary analysis of such flows, which are dominated by the effects of gravity.

The presence of the free surface, which is essentially at atmospheric pressure, both helps and hurts the analysis. It helps because the pressure can be taken constant along the free surface, which therefore is equivalent to the *hydraulic grade line* (HGL) of the flow. Unlike flow in closed ducts, the pressure gradient is not a direct factor in open-channel flow, where the balance of forces is confined to gravity and friction.[1] But the free surface complicates the analysis because its shape is a priori unknown: The depth profile changes with conditions and must be computed as part of the problem, especially in unsteady problems involving wave motion.

Before proceeding, we remark, as usual, that whole books have been written on open-channel hydraulics [1 to 4]. There are also specialized texts devoted to wave motion [5 to 7] and to engineering aspects of coastal free-surface flows [8, 9]. This chapter is only an introduction to broader and more detailed treatments.

---

[1] Surface tension is rarely important because open channels are normally quite large and have a very large Weber number.

The One-Dimensional Approximation

An open channel always has two sides and a bottom, where the flow satisfies the no-slip condition. Therefore even a straight channel has a three-dimensional velocity distribution. Some measurements of straight-channel velocity contours are shown in Fig. 10.1. The profiles are quite complex, with maximum velocity typically occurring in the midplane about 20 percent below the surface. In very broad shallow channels the maximum velocity is near the surface, and the velocity profile is nearly logarithmic from the bottom to the free surface, as in Eq. (6.84). In noncircular channels there are also secondary motions similar to Fig. 6.16 for closed-duct flows. If the channel curves or meanders, the secondary motion intensifies due to centrifugal effects, with high velocity occurring near the outer radius of the bend. Curved natural channels are subject to strong bottom erosion and deposition effects.

Fig. 10.1 Measured isovelocity contours in typical straight open-channel flows. (*From Ref. 3.*)

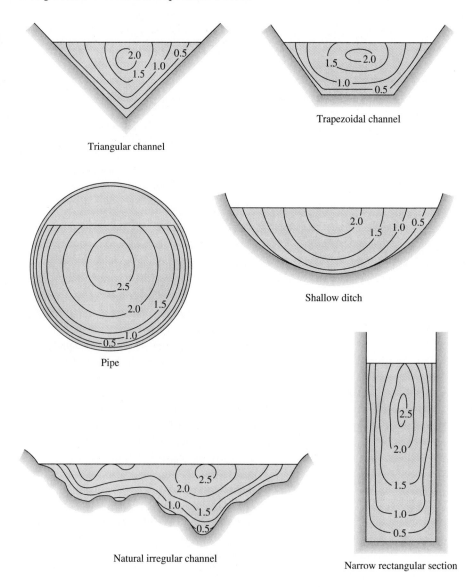

Triangular channel

Trapezoidal channel

Pipe

Shallow ditch

Natural irregular channel

Narrow rectangular section

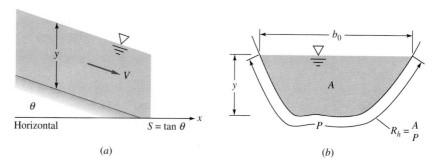

Fig. 10.2 Geometry and notation for open-channel flow: (*a*) side view; (*b*) cross section. All these parameters are constant in uniform flow.

(*a*)   (*b*)

With the advent of the supercomputer, it is possible to make numerical simulations of complex flow patterns such as in Fig. 10.1 [23]. However, the practical engineering approach, used here, is to make a one-dimensional-flow approximation, as in Fig. 10.2. Since the liquid density is nearly constant, the steady-flow continuity equation reduces to constant-volume flow Q along the channel

$$Q = V(x)A(x) = \text{const} \tag{10.1}$$

where V is average velocity and A the local cross-sectional area, as sketched in Fig. 10.2.

A second one-dimensional relation between velocity and channel geometry is the energy equation, including friction losses. If points 1 (upstream) and 2 (downstream) are on the free surface, $p_1 = p_2 = p_a$, and we have, for steady flow,

$$\frac{V_1^2}{2g} + z_1 = \frac{V_2^2}{2g} + z_2 + h_f \tag{10.2}$$

where z denotes the total elevation of the free surface, which includes the water depth y (see Fig. 10.2*a*) plus the height of the (sloping) bottom. The friction head loss h_f is analogous to head loss in duct flow from Eq. (6.30):

$$h_f \approx f \frac{x_2 - x_1}{D_h} \frac{V_{av}^2}{2g} \qquad D_h = \text{hydraulic diameter} = \frac{4A}{P} \tag{10.3}$$

where f is the average friction factor (Fig. 6.13) between sections 1 and 2. Since channels are irregular in shape, their "size" is taken to be the hydraulic diameter, with P the *wetted* perimeter—see Fig. 10.2*b*. Actually, open-channel formulas typically use the hydraulic *radius*

$$R_h = \frac{1}{4} D_h = \frac{A}{P} \tag{10.4}$$

The local Reynolds number of the channel would be $\text{Re} = VD_h/\nu$, which is usually highly turbulent (>1 E5). The only commonly occurring laminar channel flows are the thin sheets which form as rainwater drains from crowned streets and airport runways.

The wetted perimeter P (see Fig. 10.2*b*) includes the sides and bottom of the channel but not the free surface and, of course, not the parts of the sides above the water level. For example, if a rectangular channel is b wide and h high and contains water to depth y, its wetted perimeter is

$$P = b + 2y \tag{10.5}$$

not $2b + 2h$.

Although the Moody chart (Fig. 6.13) would give a good estimate of the friction factor in channel flow, in practice it is seldom used. An alternate correlation due to Robert Manning, discussed in Sec. 10.2, is the formula of choice in open-channel hydraulics.

Flow Classification by Depth Variation

The most common method of classifying open-channel flows is by the rate of change of the free-surface depth. The simplest and most widely analyzed case is *uniform flow*, where the depth (hence the velocity in steady flow) remains constant. Uniform-flow conditions are approximated by long straight runs of constant-slope and constant-area channel. A channel in uniform flow is said to be moving at its *normal depth* y_n, which is an important design parameter.

If the channel slope or cross section changes or there is an obstruction in the flow, then the depth changes and the flow is said to be *varied*. The flow is *gradually varying* if the one-dimensional approximation is valid and *rapidly varying* if not. Some examples of this method of classification are shown in Fig. 10.3. The classes can be summarized as follows:

1. Uniform flow (constant depth and slope)
2. Varied flow
   a. Gradually varied (one-dimensional)
   b. Rapidly varied (multidimensional)

Typically uniform flow is separated from rapidly varying flow by a region of gradually varied flow. Gradually varied flow can be analyzed by a first-order differential equation (Sec. 10.6), but rapidly varying flow usually requires experimentation or three-dimensional potential theory.

Flow Classification by Froude Number: Surface Wave Speed

A second and very interesting classification is by dimensionless Froude number, which for a rectangular or very wide channel takes the form $\mathrm{Fr} = V/(gy)^{1/2}$, where y is the water depth. The three flow regimes are

$$\mathrm{Fr} < 1.0 \qquad \text{subcritical flow}$$
$$\mathrm{Fr} = 1.0 \qquad \text{critical flow} \qquad\qquad (10.6)$$
$$\mathrm{Fr} > 1.0 \qquad \text{supercritical flow}$$

Fig. 10.3 Open-channel flow classified by regions of rapidly varying flow (RVF), gradually varying flow (GVF), and uniform-flow depth profiles.

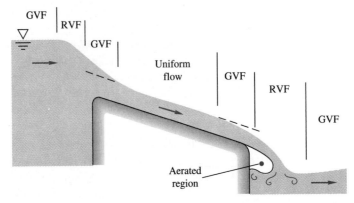

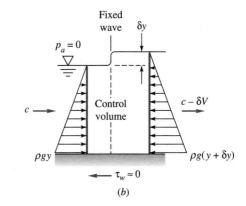

Fig. 10.4 Analysis of a small surface wave propagating into still shallow water; (*a*) moving wave, noninertial frame; (*b*) fixed wave, inertial frame of reference.

The Froude number for irregular channels is defined in Sec. 10.4. As mentioned in Sec. 9.10, there is a strong analogy here with the three compressible-flow regimes of the Mach number: subsonic (Ma < 1), sonic (Ma = 1), and supersonic (Ma > 1). We shall pursue the analogy in Sec. 10.4.

The Froude-number denominator $(gy)^{1/2}$ is the speed of an infinitesimal shallow-water surface wave. We can derive this with reference to Fig. 10.4*a*, which shows a wave of height δy propagating at speed c into still liquid. To achieve a steady-flow inertial frame of reference, we fix the coordinates on the waves as in Fig. 10.4*b*, so that the still water moves to the right at velocity c. Figure 10.4 is exactly analogous to Fig. 9.1, which analyzed the speed of sound in a fluid.

For the control volume of Fig. 10.4*b*, the one-dimensional continuity relation is, for channel width b,

$$\rho c y b = \rho(c - \delta V)(y + \delta y)b$$

or

$$\delta V = c\,\frac{\delta y}{y + \delta y} \tag{10.7}$$

This is analogous to Eq. (9.10); the velocity change δV induced by a surface wave is small if the wave is "weak," $\delta y \ll y$. If we neglect bottom friction in the short distance across the wave in Fig. 10.4*b*, the momentum relation is a balance between the net hydrostatic pressure force and momentum

$$-\tfrac{1}{2}\rho g b[(y + \delta y)^2 - y^2] = \rho c b y(c - \delta V - c)$$

or

$$g\left(1 + \frac{\tfrac{1}{2}\delta y}{y}\right)\delta y = c\,\delta V \tag{10.8}$$

This is analogous to Eq. (9.12). By eliminating δV between Eqs. (10.7) and (10.8) we obtain the desired expression for wave propagation speed

$$c^2 = gy\left(1 + \frac{\delta y}{y}\right)\left(1 + \frac{\tfrac{1}{2}\delta y}{y}\right) \tag{10.9}$$

The "stronger" the wave height δy, the faster the wave speed c, by analogy with Eq. (9.13). In the limit of an infinitesimal wave height $\delta y \to 0$, the speed becomes

$$c_0^2 = gy \tag{10.10}$$

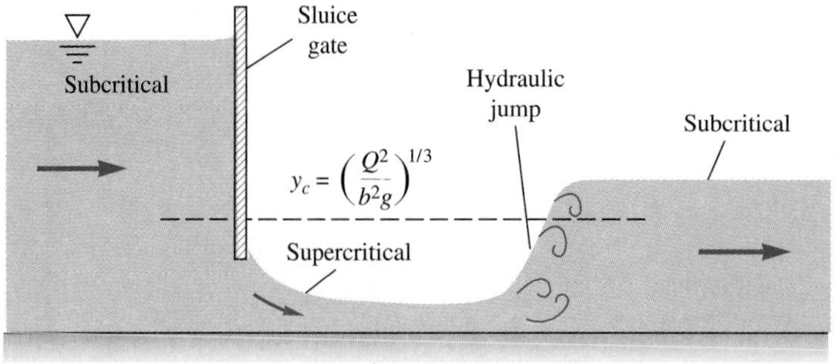

Fig. 10.5 Flow under a sluice gate accelerates from subcritical to critical to supercritical flow and then jumps back to subcritical flow.

This is the surface-wave equivalent of fluid sound speed a, and thus the Froude number in channel flow $\text{Fr} = V/c_0$ is the analog of the Mach number.

As in gas dynamics, a channel flow can accelerate from subcritical to critical to supercritical flow and then return to subcritical flow through a sort of normal shock called a *hydraulic jump* (Sec. 10.5). This is illustrated in Fig. 10.5. The flow upstream of the sluice gate is subcritical. It then accelerates to critical and supercritical flow as it passes under the gate, which serves as a sort of "nozzle." Further downstream the flow "shocks" back to subcritical flow because the downstream "receiver" height is too high to maintain supercritical flow. Note the similarity with the nozzle gas flows of Fig. 9.12.

The critical depth $y_c = [Q^2/(b^2 g)]^{1/3}$ is sketched as a dashed line in Fig. 10.5 for reference. Like the normal depth y_n, y_c is an important parameter in characterizing open-channel flow (see Sec. 10.4).

An excellent discussion of the various regimes of open-channel flow is given in Ref. 10.

10.2 Uniform Flow; the Chézy Formula

Uniform flow can occur in long straight runs of constant slope and constant channel cross section. The water depth is constant at $y = y_n$, and the velocity is constant at $V = V_0$. Let the slope be $S_0 = \tan\theta$, where θ is the angle the bottom makes with the horizontal, considered positive for downhill flow. Then Eq. (10.2), with $V_1 = V_2 = V_0$, becomes

$$h_f = z_1 - z_2 = S_0 L \tag{10.11}$$

where L is the channel length between sections 1 and 2. The head loss thus balances the loss in height of the channel. The flow is essentially fully developed, so that the Darcy-Weisbach relation, Eq. (6.30), holds

$$h_f = f \frac{L}{D_h} \frac{V_0^2}{2g} \qquad D_h = 4R_h \tag{10.12}$$

with $D_h = 4A/P$ used to accommodate noncircular channels. The geometry and notation for open-channel flow analysis are shown in Fig. 10.2.

By combining Eqs. (10.11) and (10.12) we obtain an expression for flow velocity in uniform channel flow

$$V_0 = \left(\frac{8g}{f}\right)^{1/2} R_h^{1/2} S_0^{1/2} \tag{10.13}$$

For a given channel shape and bottom roughness, the quantity $(8g/f)^{1/2}$ is constant and can be denoted by C. Equation (10.13) becomes

$$V_0 = C(R_h S_0)^{1/2} \qquad Q = CA(R_h S_0)^{1/2} \qquad (10.14)$$

These are called the *Chézy formulas*, first developed by the French engineer Antoine Chézy in conjunction with his experiments on the Seine River and the Courpalet Canal in 1769. The quantity C, called the *Chézy coefficient*, varies from about 60 ft$^{1/2}$/s for small rough channels to 160 ft$^{1/2}$/s for large smooth channels (30 to 90 m$^{1/2}$/s in SI units).

Over the past century a great deal of hydraulics research [11] has been devoted to the correlation of the Chézy coefficient with the roughness, shape, and slope of various open channels. Correlations are due to Ganguillet and Kutter in 1869, Manning in 1889, Bazin in 1897, and Powell in 1950 [11]. All these formulations are discussed in delicious detail in Ref. 3, chap. 5. Here we confine our treatment to Manning's correlation, the most popular.

The Manning Roughness Correlation

It is reasonably accurate, and physically correct, to attack the Chézy uniform-flow formula, Eq. (10.13), by using values of f from the Moody chart (Fig. 6.13). Since typical channels are large and rough, they are usually in the fully rough turbulent-flow regime, and Eq. (6.64) reduces to

Fully rough flow: $\qquad\qquad f \approx \left(2.0 \log \dfrac{3.7 D_h}{\epsilon}\right)^{-2} \qquad (10.15)$

where ϵ is the average wall roughness height. In practice, however, engineers prefer to use a simple correlation published in 1891 by Robert Manning [12], an Irish engineer. In tests with real channels, Manning found that the Chézy coefficient C increased approximately as the sixth root of the channel size. He proposed the simple formula

$$C = \left(\frac{8g}{f}\right)^{1/2} \approx \alpha \frac{R_h^{1/6}}{n} \qquad (10.16)$$

where n is a roughness parameter. Since the formula is clearly not dimensionally consistent, it requires a conversion factor α which changes with the system of units used:

$$\alpha = 1.0 \quad \text{SI units} \qquad \alpha = 1.486 \quad \text{BG units} \qquad (10.17)$$

Recall that we warned about this awkwardness in Example 1.4. You may verify that α is the cube root of the conversion factor between the meter and your chosen length scale: In BG units, $\alpha = (3.2808 \text{ ft/m})^{1/3} = 1.486$.*

The Manning formula for uniform-flow velocity is thus

$$V_0 \text{ (m/s)} \approx \frac{1.0}{n} [R_h(\text{m})]^{2/3} S_0^{1/2}$$

$$\qquad (10.18)$$

$$V_0 \text{ (ft/s)} \approx \frac{1.486}{n} [R_h(\text{ft})]^{2/3} S_0^{1/2}$$

---

* An interesting discussion of the history and "dimensionality" of Manning's formula is given in Ref. 3, pp. 98–99.

The channel slope S_0 is dimensionless, and n is taken to be the same in both systems. The volume flow rate simply multiplies this result by the area:

Uniform flow: $$Q = V_0 A \approx \frac{\alpha}{n} A R_h^{2/3} S_0^{1/2} \tag{10.19}$$

Experimental values of n (and the corresponding roughness height) are listed in Table 10.1 for various channel surfaces. There is a factor-of-15 variation from a smooth glass surface ($n \approx 0.01$) to a tree-lined floodplain ($n \approx 0.15$). Due to the irregularity of typical channel shapes and roughness, the scatter bands in Table 10.1 should be taken seriously.

Since Manning's sixth-root size variation is not exact, real channels can have a variable n depending upon the water depth. The Mississippi River near Memphis, Tennessee, has $n \approx 0.032$ at 40-ft flood depth, 0.030 at normal 20-ft depth, and 0.040 at 5-ft low-stage depth. Seasonal vegetative growth and factors such as bottom erosion can also affect the value of n.

Table 10.1 Experimental Values of Manning's n Factor*

	n	Average roughness height ϵ	
		ft	mm
Artificial lined channels:			
Glass	0.010 ± 0.002	0.0011	0.3
Brass	0.011 ± 0.002	0.0019	0.6
Steel, smooth	0.012 ± 0.002	0.0032	1.0
Painted	0.014 ± 0.003	0.0080	2.4
Riveted	0.015 ± 0.002	0.012	3.7
Cast iron	0.013 ± 0.003	0.0051	1.6
Cement, finished	0.012 ± 0.002	0.0032	1.0
Unfinished	0.014 ± 0.002	0.0080	2.4
Planed wood	0.012 ± 0.002	0.0032	1.0
Clay tile	0.014 ± 0.003	0.0080	2.4
Brickwork	0.015 ± 0.002	0.012	3.7
Asphalt	0.016 ± 0.003	0.018	5.4
Corrugated metal	0.022 ± 0.005	0.12	37
Rubble masonry	0.025 ± 0.005	0.26	80
Excavated earth channels:			
Clean	0.022 ± 0.004	0.12	37
Gravelly	0.025 ± 0.005	0.26	80
Weedy	0.030 ± 0.005	0.8	240
Stony, cobbles	0.035 ± 0.010	1.5	500
Natural channels:			
Clean and straight	0.030 ± 0.005	0.8	240
Sluggish, deep pools	0.040 ± 0.010	3	900
Major rivers	0.035 ± 0.010	1.5	500
Floodplains:			
Pasture, farmland	0.035 ± 0.010	1.5	500
Light brush	0.05 ± 0.02	6	2000
Heavy brush	0.075 ± 0.025	15	5000
Trees	0.15 ± 0.05	?	?

* A more complete list is given in Ref. 3, pp. 110–113.

EXAMPLE 10.1

A finished-concrete 8-ft-wide rectangular channel has a bed slope of 0.5° and a water depth of 4 ft. Predict the uniform flow rate in ft^3/s.

Solution

Part (a) From Table 10.1, for finished concrete, $n \approx 0.012$. The slope $S_0 = \tan 0.5° = 0.00873$. For depth $y = 4$ ft and width $b = 8$ ft, the geometric properties are

$$A = by = (8 \text{ ft})(4 \text{ ft}) = 32 \text{ ft}^2 \qquad P = b + 2y = 8 + 2(4) = 16 \text{ ft}$$

$$R_h = \frac{A}{P} = \frac{32 \text{ ft}^2}{16 \text{ ft}} = 2.0 \text{ ft} \qquad D_h = 4R_h = 8.0 \text{ ft}$$

From Manning's formula (10.19) in BG units, the estimated flow rate is

$$Q \approx \frac{1.486}{n} AR_h^{2/3}S_0^{1/2} = \frac{1.486}{0.012}(32 \text{ ft}^2)(2.0 \text{ ft})^{2/3}(0.00873)^{1/2} \approx 590 \text{ ft}^3/s \qquad Ans.$$

Considering the uncertainty in n (± 17 percent), it would be more realistic to report this estimate as $Q \approx 600 \pm 100$ ft^3/s. An alternate estimate, using the Moody formula (10.15) with $\epsilon = 0.0032$ ft from Table 10.1, would give $Q \approx 540$ ft^3/s.

Normal-Depth Estimates

With water depth y known, the computation of Q in Example 10.1 was quite straightforward. However, if Q is given, the computation of the normal depth y_n may require iteration or trial and error. Since the normal depth is a characteristic flow parameter, this is an important type of problem.

EXAMPLE 10.2

The asphalt-lined trapezoidal channel in Fig. E10.2 carries 300 ft^3/s of water under uniform-flow conditions when $S = 0.0015$. What is the normal depth y_n?

Fig. E10.2

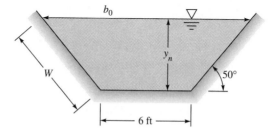

Solution

From Table 10.1, for asphalt, $n \approx 0.016$. The area and hydraulic radius are functions of y_n, which is unknown

$$b_0 = 6 \text{ ft} + 2y_n \cot 50° \qquad A = \tfrac{1}{2}(6 + b_0)y_n = 6y_n + y_n^2 \cot 50°$$

$$P = 6 + 2W = 6 + 2y_n \csc 50°$$

From Manning's formula (10.19) with a known $Q = 300$ ft^3/s, we have

$$300 = \frac{1.49}{0.016} (6y_n + y_n^2 \cot 50°)\left(\frac{6y_n + y_n^2 \cot 50°}{6 + 2y_n \csc 50°}\right)^{2/3} (0.0015)^{1/2}$$

or $$(6y_n + y_n^2 \cot 50°)^{5/3} = 83.2(6 + 2y_n \csc 50°)^{2/3}$$

This formula cannot be solved explicitly for y_n. Probably the simplest procedure is to guess a range of values of y_n, compute Q, and see whether it is near 300 ft^3/s. The following are some tabulated guesses:

y_n, ft	4.0	4.5	5.0	4.6
Q, ft^3/s	234	291	354	303

Then our Manning-formula estimate is that the normal depth is

$$y_n \approx 4.6 \text{ ft} \qquad\qquad Ans.$$

Obviously one could program computer algorithms to converge to this normal depth.

Uniform Flow in a Partly Full Circular Pipe

Consider the partially full pipe of Fig. 10.6a in uniform flow. The maximum velocity and flow rate actually occur before the pipe is completely full. In terms of the pipe radius R and the angle θ up to the free surface, the geometric properties are

Fig. 10.6 Uniform flow in a partly full circular channel: (*a*) geometry; (*b*) velocity and flow rate versus depth.

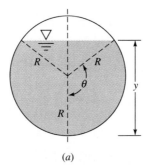

(a)

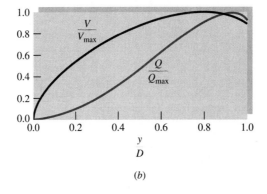

(b)

$$A = R^2\left(\theta - \frac{\sin 2\theta}{2}\right) \qquad P = 2R\theta \qquad R_h = \frac{R}{2}\left(1 - \frac{\sin 2\theta}{2\theta}\right)$$

The Manning formulas (10.19) predict a uniform flow as follows:

$$V_0 \approx \frac{\alpha}{n}\left[\frac{R}{2}\left(1 - \frac{\sin 2\theta}{2\theta}\right)\right]^{2/3} S_0^{1/2} \qquad Q = V_0 R^2\left(\theta - \frac{\sin 2\theta}{2}\right) \qquad (10.20)$$

For a given n and slope S_0, we may plot these two relations versus θ in Fig. 10.6b. There are two different maxima, as follows:

$$V_{\max} = 0.718\,\frac{\alpha}{n}\,R^{2/3}S_0^{1/2} \qquad \text{at} \quad \theta = 128.73° \quad \text{and} \quad y = 0.813D$$

$$\qquad (10.21)$$

$$Q_{\max} = 2.129\,\frac{\alpha}{n}\,R^{8/3}S_0^{1/2} \qquad \text{at} \quad \theta = 151.21° \quad \text{and} \quad y = 0.938D$$

As shown in Fig. 10.6b, the maximum velocity is 14 percent more than the velocity when running full, and similarly the maximum discharge is 8 percent more. Since real pipes running nearly full tend to have somewhat unstable flow, these differences are not that significant.

10.3 Efficient Uniform-Flow Channels

The simplicity of Manning's formulation (10.19) enables us to analyze channel flows to determine the most efficient low-resistance sections for given conditions. The most common problem is that of maximizing R_h for a given flow area and discharge. Since $R_h = A/P$, maximizing R_h for given A is the same as minimizing the wetted perimeter P. There is no general solution for arbitrary cross sections, but an analysis of the trapezoid section will show the basic results.

Consider the generalized trapezoid of angle θ in Fig. 10.7. For a given side angle θ, the flow area is

$$A = by + \alpha y^2 \qquad \alpha = \cot\theta \qquad (10.22)$$

The wetted perimeter is

$$P = b + 2W = b + 2y(1 + \alpha^2)^{1/2} \qquad (10.23)$$

Eliminating b between (10.22) and (10.23) gives

$$P = \frac{A}{y} - \alpha y + 2y(1 + \alpha^2)^{1/2} \qquad (10.24)$$

Fig. 10.7 Geometry of a trapezoidal channel section.

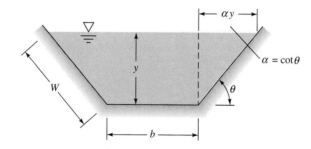

To minimize P, evaluate dP/dy for constant A and α and set equal to zero. The result is

$$A = y^2[2(1 + \alpha^2)^{1/2} - \alpha] \qquad P = 4y(1 + \alpha^2)^{1/2} - 2\alpha y \qquad R_h = \tfrac{1}{2}y \quad (10.25)$$

The last result is very interesting: For any angle θ, the most efficient cross section for uniform flow occurs when the hydraulic radius is half the depth.

Since a rectangle is a trapezoid with $\alpha = 0$, the most efficient rectangular section is such that

$$A = 2y^2 \qquad P = 4y \qquad R_h = \tfrac{1}{2}y \qquad b = 2y \qquad (10.26)$$

To find the correct depth y, these relations must be solved in conjunction with Manning's flow-rate formula (10.19) for the given discharge Q.

Best Trapezoid Angle

Equations (10.25) are valid for any value of α. What is the best value of α for a given depth and area? To answer this question, evaluate $dP/d\alpha$ from Eq. (10.24) with A and y held constant. The result is

$$2\alpha = (1 + \alpha^2)^{1/2} \qquad \alpha = \cot\theta = \frac{1}{3^{1/2}}$$

or $$\theta = 60° \qquad (10.27)$$

Thus the very best trapezoid section is half a hexagon.

Similar calculations with a circular channel section running partially full show best efficiency for a semicircle, $y = \tfrac{1}{2}D$. In fact, the semicircle is the best of all possible channel sections (minimum wetted perimeter for a given flow area). The percentage improvement over, say, half a hexagon is very slight, however.

EXAMPLE 10.3

What are the best dimensions for a rectangular brick channel designed to carry 5 m³/s of water in uniform flow with $S_0 = 0.001$?

Solution

From Eq. (10.26), $A = 2y^2$ and $R_h = \tfrac{1}{2}y$. Manning's formula (10.19) in SI units gives, with $n \approx 0.015$ from Table 10.1,

$$Q = \frac{1.0}{n} A R_h^{2/3} S_0^{1/2} \qquad \text{or} \qquad 5 \text{ m}^3/\text{s} = \frac{1.0}{0.015}(2y^2)\left(\frac{1}{2}y\right)^{2/3}(0.001)^{1/2}$$

which can be solved for

$$y^{8/3} = 1.882 \text{ m}^{8/3}$$

$$y = 1.27 \text{ m} \qquad \qquad Ans.$$

The proper area and width are

$$A = 2y^2 = 3.21 \text{ m}^2 \qquad b = \frac{A}{y} = 2.53 \text{ m} \qquad \qquad Ans.$$

It is constructive to see what flow rate a half-hexagon and semicircle would carry for the same area of 3.214 m².

For the half-hexagon (HH), with $\alpha = 1/3^{1/2} = 0.577$, Eq. (10.25) predicts

$$A = y_{HH}^2[2(1 + 0.577^2)^{1/2} - 0.577] = 1.732y_{HH}^2 = 3.214$$

or $y_{HH} = 1.362$ m, whence $R_h = \frac{1}{2}y = 0.681$ m. The half-hexagon flow rate is thus

$$Q = \frac{1.0}{0.015}(3.214)(0.681)^{2/3}(0.001)^{1/2} = 5.25 \text{ m}^3/\text{s}$$

or about 5 percent more than that for the rectangle.

For a semicircle, $A = 3.214 \text{ m}^2 = \pi D^2/8$, or $D = 2.861$ m, whence $P = \frac{1}{2}\pi D = 4.494$ m and $R_h = A/P = 3.214/4.484 = 0.715$ m. The semicircle flow rate will thus be

$$Q = \frac{1.0}{0.015}(3.214)(0.715)^{2/3}(0.001)^{1/2} = 5.42 \text{ m}^3/\text{s}$$

or about 8 percent more than that of the rectangle and 3 percent more than that of the half-hexagon.

10.4 Specific Energy; Critical Depth

As suggested by Bakhmeteff [13] in 1911, the specific energy E is a useful parameter in channel flow

$$E = y + \frac{V^2}{2g} \tag{10.28}$$

where y is the water depth. It is seen from Fig. 10.8a that E is the height of the *energy grade line* (EGL) above the channel bottom. For a given flow rate, there are usually two states possible for the same specific energy.

Rectangular Channels

Consider the possible states at a given location. Let $q = Q/b = Vy$ be the discharge per unit width of a rectangular channel. Then, with q constant, Eq. (10.28) becomes

$$E = y + \frac{q^2}{2gy^2} \qquad q = \frac{Q}{b} \tag{10.29}$$

Fig. 10.8 Specific-energy considerations: (a) illustration sketch; (b) depth versus E from Eq. (10.29), showing minimum specific energy occurring at critical depth.

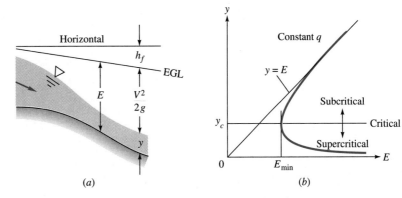

(a)   (b)

Figure 10.8b is a plot of y versus E for constant q from Eq. (10.29). There is a minimum value of E at a certain value of y called the *critical depth*. By setting $dE/dy = 0$ at constant q, we find that E_{min} occurs at

$$y = y_c = \left(\frac{q^2}{g}\right)^{1/3} = \left(\frac{Q^2}{b^2 g}\right)^{1/3} \tag{10.30}$$

The associated minimum energy is

$$E_{min} = E(y_c) = \tfrac{3}{2} y_c \tag{10.31}$$

The depth y_c corresponds to channel velocity equal to the shallow-water wave propagation speed C_0 from Eq. (10.10). To see this, rewrite Eq. (10.30) as

$$q^2 = g y_c^3 = (g y_c) y_c^2 = V_c^2 y_c^2 \tag{10.32}$$

By comparison it follows that the critical channel velocity is

$$V_c = (g y_c)^{1/2} = C_0 \qquad \mathrm{Fr} = 1 \tag{10.33}$$

For $E < E_{min}$ no solution exists in Fig. 10.8b, and thus such a flow is impossible physically. For $E > E_{min}$ two solutions are possible: (1) large depth with $V < V_c$, called *subcritical*, and (2) small depth with $V > V_c$, called *supercritical*. In subcritical flow, disturbances can propagate upstream because wave speed $C_0 > V$. In supercritical flow, waves are swept downstream: Upstream is a zone of silence, and a small obstruction in the flow will create a wedge-shaped wave exactly analogous to the Mach waves in Fig. 9.18c.[1] The angle of these waves must be

$$\mu = \sin^{-1} \frac{C_0}{V} = \sin^{-1} \frac{(gy)^{1/2}}{V} \tag{10.34}$$

The wave angle and the depth can thus be used as a simple measurement of supercritical-flow velocity.

Note from Fig. 10.8b that small changes in E near E_{min} cause a large change in the depth y, by analogy with small changes in duct area near the sonic point in Fig. 9.7. Thus critical flow is neutrally stable and is often accompanied by waves and undulations in the free surface. Channel designers should avoid long runs of near-critical flow.

EXAMPLE 10.4

A wide rectangular clean-earth channel has a flow rate $q = 50\ \mathrm{ft}^3/(\mathrm{s} \cdot \mathrm{ft})$. (a) What is the critical depth? (b) What type of flow exists if $y = 3$ ft?

Solution

Part (a) From Table 10.1, $n \approx 0.022$ and $\epsilon \approx 0.12$ ft. The critical depth follows from Eq. (10.30):

$$y_c = \left(\frac{q^2}{g}\right)^{1/3} = \left(\frac{50^2}{32.2}\right)^{1/3} = 4.27\ \mathrm{ft} \qquad \textit{Ans. (a)}$$

Part (b) If the actual depth is 3 ft, which is less than y_c, the flow must be *supercritical*. *Ans. (b)*

---

[1] This is the basis of the water-channel analogy for supersonic gas-dynamics experimentation [14, chap. 11].

Nonrectangular Channels

If the channel width varies with y, the specific energy must be written in the form

$$E = y + \frac{Q^2}{2gA^2} \tag{10.35}$$

The critical point of minimum energy occurs where $dE/dy = 0$ at constant Q. Since $A = A(y)$, Eq. (10.35) yields, for $E = E_{\min}$,

$$\frac{dA}{dy} = \frac{gA^3}{Q^2} \tag{10.36}$$

But $dA = b_0\,dy$, where b_0 is the channel width at the free surface. Therefore Eq. (10.36) is equivalent to

$$A_c = \left(\frac{b_0 Q^2}{g}\right)^{1/3} \tag{10.37a}$$

$$V_c = \frac{Q}{A_c} = \left(\frac{gA_c}{b_0}\right)^{1/2} \tag{10.37b}$$

For a given channel shape $A(y)$ and $b_0(y)$ and a given Q, Eq. (10.37) has to be solved by trial and error or by plotting to find the critical area A_c, from which V_c can be computed.

By comparing the actual depth and velocity with the critical values, we can determine the local flow condition

$$y > y_c,\ V < V_c: \quad \text{subcritical flow (Fr} < 1)$$

$$y < y_c,\ V > V_c: \quad \text{supercritical flow (Fr} > 1)$$

Critical Uniform Flow: The Critical Slope

If a critical channel flow is also moving uniformly (at constant depth), it must correspond to a *critical slope* S_c, with $y_n = y_c$. This condition is analyzed by equating Eq. (10.37a) to the Chézy (or Manning) formula:

$$Q^2 = \frac{gA_c^3}{b_0} = C^2 A_c^2 R_h S_c = \frac{\alpha^2}{n^2} A_c^2 R_h^{4/3} S_c$$

or

$$S_c = \frac{n^2 g A_c}{\alpha^2 b_0 R_{hc}^{4/3}} = \frac{n^2 g}{\alpha^2 R_{hc}^{1/3}} \frac{P}{b_0} = \frac{f}{8} \frac{P}{b_0} \tag{10.38}$$

where α^2 equals 1.0 for SI units and 2.208 for BG units. Equation (10.38) is valid for any channel shape. For a wide rectangular channel, $b_0 \gg y_c$, the formula reduces to

Wide rectangular channel:
$$S_c \approx \frac{n^2 g}{\alpha^2 y_c^{1/3}} \approx \frac{f}{8}$$

This is a special case, a reference point. In most channel flows $y_n \neq y_c$. For fully rough turbulent flow, the critical slope varies between 0.002 and 0.008.

EXAMPLE 10.5

The 50° triangular channel in Fig. E10.5 has a flow rate $Q = 16\ \text{m}^3/\text{s}$. Compute (a) y_c, (b) V_c, and (c) S_c if $n = 0.018$.

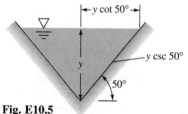

$-y\cot 50°-$

$-y\csc 50°$

y

$50°$

Fig. E10.5

Solution

Part (a) This is an easy cross section because all geometric quantities can be written directly in terms of depth y

$$P = 2y \csc 50° \qquad A = y^2 \cot 50°$$

$$R_h = \tfrac{1}{2}y \cos 50° \qquad b_0 = 2y \cot 50° \tag{1}$$

The critical-flow condition satisfies Eq. (10.37a)

$$gA_c^3 = b_0 Q^2$$

or

$$g(y_c^2 \cot 50°)^3 = (2y_c \cot 50°)Q^2$$

$$y_c = \left(\frac{2Q^2}{g \cot^2 50°}\right)^{1/5} = \left[\frac{2(16)^2}{9.81(0.839)^2}\right]^{1/5} = 2.37 \text{ m} \qquad Ans. \ (a)$$

Part (b) With y_c known, from Eqs. (1) we compute $P_c = 6.18$ m, $R_{hc} = 0.760$ m, $A_c = 4.70$ m^2, and $b_{0c} = 3.97$ m. The critical velocity from Eq. (10.37b) is

$$V_c = \frac{Q}{A} = \frac{16 \text{ m}^3/\text{s}}{4.70 \text{ m}^2} = 3.41 \text{ m/s} \qquad Ans. \ (b)$$

Part (c) With $n = 0.018$, we compute from Eq. (10.38) a critical slope

$$S_c = \frac{gn^2 P}{\alpha^2 R_h^{1/3} b_0} = \frac{9.81(0.018)^2(6.18)}{1.0(0.760)^{1/3}(3.97)} = 0.00542 \qquad Ans. \ (c)$$

Frictionless Flow over a Bump

A rough analogy to compressible gas flow in a nozzle (Fig. 9.12) is open-channel flow over a bump, as in Fig. 10.9a. The behavior of the free surface is sharply different according to whether the approach flow is subcritical or supercritical. The height of the bump also can change the character of the results. For frictionless two-dimensional flow, sections 1 and 2 in Fig. 10.9a are related by continuity and momentum:

$$V_1 y_1 = V_2 y_2 \qquad \frac{V_1^2}{2g} + y_1 = \frac{V_2^2}{2g} + y_2 + \Delta h$$

Eliminating V_2 between these two gives a cubic polynomial equation for the water depth y_2 over the bump:

$$y_2^3 - E_2 y_2^2 + \frac{V_1^2 y_1^2}{2g} = 0 \qquad \text{where } E_2 = \frac{V_1^2}{2g} + y_1 - \Delta h \tag{10.39}$$

This equation has one negative and two positive solutions if Δh is not too large. Its behavior is illustrated in Fig. 10.9b and depends upon whether condition 1 is on the upper or lower leg of the energy curve. The specific energy E_2 is exactly Δh less than the approach energy E_1, and point 2 will lie on the same leg of the curve as E_1. A subcritical approach, $\text{Fr}_1 < 1$, will cause the water level to decrease at the bump. Supercritical approach flow, $\text{Fr}_1 > 1$, causes a water-level increase over the bump.

If the bump height reaches $\Delta h_{max} = E_1 - E_c$, as illustrated in Fig. 10.9b, the flow at the crest will be exactly critical (Fr = 1). If $\Delta h > \Delta h_{max}$, there are no physically

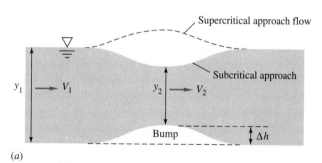

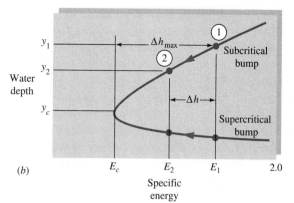

Fig. 10.9 Frictionless two-dimensional flow over a bump: (a) definition sketch showing Froude-number dependence; (b) specific-energy plot showing bump size and water depths.

correct solutions to Eq. (10.39). That is, a bump too large will "choke" the channel and cause frictional effects, typically a hydraulic jump (Sec. 10.5).

These bump arguments are reversed if the channel has a *depression* ($\Delta h < 0$): Subcritical approach flow will cause a water-level rise and supercritical flow a fall in depth. Point 2 will be $|\Delta h|$ to the right of point 1, and critical flow cannot occur.

EXAMPLE 10.6

Water flow in a wide channel approaches a 10-cm-high bump at 1.5 m/s and a depth of 1 m. Estimate (a) the water depth y_2 over the bump and (b) the bump height which will cause the crest flow to be critical.

Solution

Part (a)   First check the approach Froude number, assuming $C_0 = \sqrt{gy}$:

$$\mathrm{Fr}_1 = \frac{V_1}{\sqrt{gy_1}} = \frac{1.5 \text{ m/s}}{\sqrt{(9.81 \text{ m/s}^2)(1.0 \text{ m})}} = 0.479 \quad \text{(subcritical)}$$

For subcritical approach flow, if Δh is not too large, we expect a depression in the water level over the bump and a higher subcritical Froude number at the crest. With $\Delta h = 0.1$ m, the specific-energy levels must be

$$E_1 = \frac{V_1^2}{2g} + y_1 = \frac{(1.5)^2}{2(9.81)} + 1.0 = 1.115 \qquad E_2 = E_1 - \Delta h = 1.015 \text{ m}$$

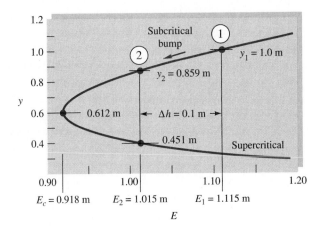

Fig. E10.6

This physical situation is shown on a specific-energy plot in Fig. E10.6. With y_1 in meters, Eq. (10.39) takes on the numerical values

$$y_2^3 - 1.015y_2^2 + 0.115 = 0$$

There are three real roots: $y_2 = +0.859$ m, $+0.451$ m, and -0.296 m. The third (negative) solution is physically impossible. The second (smaller) solution is the *supercritical* condition for E_2 and is not possible for this subcritical bump. The first solution is correct:

$$y_2(\text{subcritical}) \approx 0.859 \text{ m} \qquad\qquad\qquad Ans.~(a)$$

The surface level has dropped by $y_1 - y_2 - \Delta h = 1.0 - 0.859 - 0.1 = 0.041$ m. The crest velocity is $V_2 = V_1 y_1/y_2 = 1.745$ m/s. The Froude number at the crest is $\text{Fr}_2 = 0.601$. Flow downstream of the bump is subcritical. These flow conditions are shown in Fig. E10.6.

Part (b) For critical flow in a wide channel, with $q = Vy = 1.5$ m²/s, from Eq. (10.31),

$$E_{2,\min} = E_c = \frac{3}{2} y_c = \frac{3}{2} \left(\frac{q^2}{g}\right)^{1/3} = \frac{3}{2} \left[\frac{(1.5 \text{ m}^2/\text{s})^2}{9.81 \text{ m/s}^2}\right]^{1/3} = 0.918 \text{ m}$$

Therefore the maximum height for frictionless flow over this particular bump is

$$\Delta h_{\max} = E_1 - E_{2,\min} = 1.115 - 0.918 = 0.197 \text{ m} \qquad\qquad Ans.~(b)$$

For this bump, the solution of Eq. (10.39) is $y_2 = y_c = 0.612$ m, and the Froude number is unity at the crest. At critical flow the surface level has dropped by $y_1 - y_2 - \Delta h = 0.191$ m.

Flow under a Sluice Gate

A sluice gate is a bottom opening in a wall, as sketched in Fig. 10.10*a*, commonly used in control of rivers and channel flows. If the flow is allowed free discharge through the gap, as in Fig. 10.10*a*, the flow smoothly accelerates from subcritical (upstream) to critical (near the gap) to supercritical (downstream). The gate is then analogous to a converging-diverging nozzle in gas dynamics, as in Fig. 9.12, operating at its *design condition* (similar to point *H* in Fig. 9.12*b*).

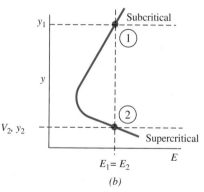
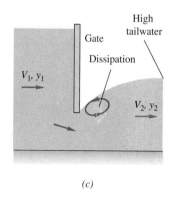

Fig. 10.10 Flow under a sluice gate passes through critical flow: (*a*) free discharge with vena contracta; (*b*) specific energy for free discharge; (*c*) dissipative flow under a drowned gate.

For free discharge, friction may be neglected, and since there is no bump ($\Delta h = 0$), Eq. (10.39) applies with $E_1 = E_2$:

$$y_2^3 - \left(\frac{V_1^2}{2g} + y_1\right)y_2^2 + \frac{V_1^2 y_1^2}{2g} = 0 \tag{10.40}$$

Given subcritical upstream flow (V_1, y_1), this cubic equation has only one real solution: supercritical flow at the same specific energy, as in Fig. 10.10*b*. The flow rate varies with the ratio y_2/y_1; we ask, as a problem exercise, to show that the flow rate is a maximum when $y_2/y_1 = \frac{2}{3}$.

The free discharge, Fig. 10.10*a*, contracts to a depth y_2 about 40 percent less than the gate's gap height, as shown. This is similar to a free *orifice* discharge, as in Fig. 6.35. If H is the height of the gate gap and b is the gap width into the paper, we can approximate the flow rate by orifice theory:

$$Q = C_d H b \sqrt{2gy_1} \qquad \text{where} \qquad C_d \approx \frac{0.61}{\sqrt{1 + 0.61H/y_1}} \tag{10.41}$$

in the range $H/y_1 < 0.5$. Thus a continuous variation in flow rate is accomplished by raising the gate.

If the tailwater is high, as in Fig. 10.10*c*, free discharge is not possible. The sluice gate is said to be *drowned* or partially drowned. There will be energy dissipation in the exit flow, probably in the form of a drowned hydraulic jump, and the downstream flow will return to subcritical. Equations (10.40) and (10.41) do not apply to this situation, and experimental discharge correlations are necessary [2, 15].

10.5 The Hydraulic Jump

In open-channel flow a supercritical flow can change quickly back to a subcritical flow by passing through a hydraulic jump, as in Fig. 10.5. The upstream flow is fast and shallow, and the downstream flow is slow and deep, analogous to the normal-shock wave of Fig. 9.8. Unlike the infinitesimally thin normal shock, the hydraulic jump is quite thick, ranging in length from 4 to 6 times the downstream depth y_2 [16].

Being extremely turbulent and agitated, the hydraulic jump is a very effective energy dissipator and is a feature of stilling-basin and spillway applications [17]. Figure 10.11 shows the jump formed at the bottom of a dam spillway in a model test. It is very

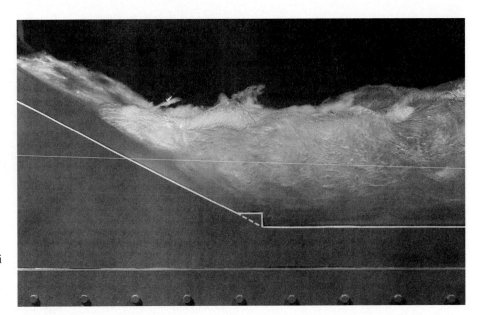

Fig. 10.11 Hydraulic jump formed on a spillway model for the Karnafuli Dam in East Pakistan. (*Courtesy of the St. Anthony Falls Hydraulic Laboratory, University of Minnesota.*)

important that such jumps be located on specially designed aprons; otherwise the channel bottom will be badly scoured by the agitation. Jumps also mix fluids very effectively and have application to sewage and water treatment designs.

Classification

The principal parameter affecting hydraulic-jump performance is the upstream Froude number $Fr_1 = V_1/(gy_1)^{1/2}$. The Reynolds number and channel geometry have only a secondary effect. As detailed in Ref. 16, the following ranges of operation can be outlined, as illustrated in Fig. 10.12:

$Fr_1 < 1.0$:	Jump impossible, violates second law of thermodynamics.
$Fr_1 = 1.0$ to 1.7:	Standing-wave, or *undular, jump* about $4y_2$ long; low dissipation, less than 5 percent.
$Fr_1 = 1.7$ to 2.5:	Smooth surface rise with small rollers, known as a *weak jump*; dissipation 5 to 15 percent.
$Fr_1 = 2.5$ to 4.5:	Unstable, *oscillating jump*; each irregular pulsation creates a large wave which can travel downstream for miles, damaging earth banks and other structures. Not recommended for design conditions. Dissipation 15 to 45 percent.
$Fr_1 = 4.5$ to 9.0:	Stable, well-balanced, *steady jump*; best performance and action, insensitive to downstream conditions. Best design range. Dissipation 45 to 70 percent.
$Fr_1 > 9.0$:	Rough, somewhat intermittent *strong jump*, but good performance. Dissipation 70 to 85 percent.

Further details can be found in Ref. 16 and Ref. 3, chap. 15.

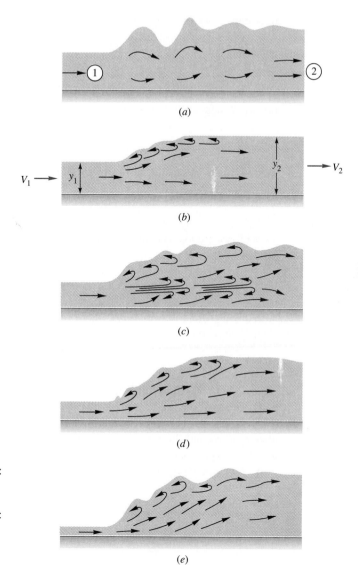

Fig. 10.12 Classification of hydraulic jumps: (*a*) Fr = 1.0 to 1.7: undular jumps; (*b*) Fr = 1.7 to 2.5: weak jump; (*c*) Fr = 2.5 to 4.5: oscillating jump; (*d*) Fr = 4.5 to 9.0: steady jump; (*e*) Fr > 9.0: strong jump. (*Adapted from Ref. 16.*)

Theory for a Horizontal Jump

A jump which occurs on a steep channel slope can be affected by the difference in water-weight components along the flow. The effect is small, however, so that the classic theory assumes that the jump occurs on a horizontal bottom.

You will be pleased to know that we have already analyzed this problem in Sec. 10.1. A hydraulic jump is exactly equivalent to the strong fixed wave in Fig. 10.4*b*, where the change in depth δy is not neglected. If V_1 and y_1 upstream are known, V_2 and y_2 are computed by applying continuity and momentum across the wave, as in Eqs. (10.7) and (10.8). Equation (10.9) is therefore the correct solution for a jump if we interpret C and y in Fig. 10.4b as upstream conditions V_1 and y_1, with $C - \delta V$ and $y + \delta y$ being the downstream conditions V_2 and y_2, as in Fig. 10.12b. Equation (10.9) becomes

$$V_1^2 = \tfrac{1}{2}gy_1\eta(\eta + 1) \tag{10.42}$$

where $\eta = y_2/y_1$. Introducing the Froude number $\mathrm{Fr}_1 = V_1/(gy_1)^{1/2}$ and solving this quadratic equation for η, we obtain

$$\frac{2y_2}{y_1} = -1 + (1 + 8\,\mathrm{Fr}_1^2)^{1/2} \tag{10.43}$$

With y_2 thus known, V_2 follows from the wide-channel continuity relation

$$V_2 = \frac{V_1 y_1}{y_2} \tag{10.44}$$

Finally, we can evaluate the dissipation head loss across the jump from the steady-flow energy equation

$$h_f = E_1 - E_2 = \left(y_1 + \frac{V_1^2}{2g}\right) - \left(y_2 + \frac{V_2^2}{2g}\right)$$

Introducing y_2 and V_2 from Eqs. (10.43) and (10.44), we find after considerable algebraic manipulation that

$$h_f = \frac{(y_2 - y_1)^3}{4y_1 y_2} \tag{10.45}$$

Equation (10.45) shows that the dissipation loss is positive only if $y_2 > y_1$, which is a requirement of the second law of thermodynamics. Equation (10.43) then requires that $\mathrm{Fr}_1 > 1.0$; that is, the upstream flow must be supercritical. Finally, Eq. (10.44) shows that $V_2 < V_1$ and the downstream flow is subcritical. All these results agree with our previous experience analyzing the normal-shock wave.

The present theory is for hydraulic jumps in wide horizontal channels. For the theory of prismatic or sloping channels see advanced texts [for example, 3, chaps. 15 and 16].

EXAMPLE 10.7

Water flows in a wide channel at $q = 10$ m³/(s · m) and $y_1 = 1.25$ m. If the flow undergoes a hydraulic jump, compute (a) y_2, (b) V_2, (c) Fr_2, (d) h_f, (e) the percentage dissipation, (f) the power dissipated per unit width, and (g) the temperature rise due to dissipation if $c_p = 4200$ J/(kg · K).

Solution

Part (a)   The upstream velocity is

$$V_1 = \frac{q}{y_1} = \frac{10 \text{ m}^3/(\text{s} \cdot \text{m})}{1.25 \text{ m}} = 8.0 \text{ m/s}$$

The upstream Froude number is therefore

$$\mathrm{Fr}_1 = \frac{V_1}{(gy_1)^{1/2}} = \frac{8.0}{[9.81(1.25)]^{1/2}} = 2.285$$

From Fig. 10.12 this is a weak jump. The depth y_2 is obtained from Eq. (10.43):

$$\frac{2y_2}{y_1} = -1 + [1 + 8(2.285)^2]^{1/2} = 5.54$$

or $\qquad y_2 = \frac{1}{2}y_1(5.54) = \frac{1}{2}(1.25)(5.54) = 3.46 \text{ m}$ $\qquad$ *Ans. (a)*

Part (b) From Eq. (10.44) the downstream velocity is

$$V_2 = \frac{V_1 y_1}{y_2} = \frac{8.0(1.25)}{3.46} = 2.89 \text{ m/s} \qquad \text{*Ans. (b)*}$$

Part (c) The downstream Froude number is

$$\text{Fr}_2 = \frac{V_2}{(gy_2)^{1/2}} = \frac{2.89}{[9.81(3.46)]^{1/2}} = 0.496 \qquad \text{*Ans. (c)*}$$

Part (d) As expected, Fr_2 is subcritical. From Eq. (10.45) the dissipation loss is

$$h_f = \frac{(3.46 - 1.25)^3}{4(3.46)(1.25)} = 0.625 \text{ m} \qquad \text{*Ans. (d)*}$$

Part (e) The percentage dissipation relates h_f to upstream energy

$$E_1 = y_1 + \frac{V_1^2}{2g} = 1.25 + \frac{(8.0)^2}{2(9.81)} = 4.51 \text{ m}$$

Hence $\qquad$ Percentage loss $= (100)\dfrac{h_f}{E_1} = \dfrac{100(0.625)}{4.51} = 14$ percent $\qquad$ *Ans. (e)*

Part (f) The power dissipated per unit width is

$$\text{Power} = \rho g q h_f = (9800 \text{ N/m}^3)[10 \text{ m}^3/(\text{s} \cdot \text{m})](0.625 \text{ m})$$

$$= 61.3 \text{ kW/m} \qquad \text{*Ans. (f)*}$$

Part (g) Finally the mass flow rate is $\dot{m} = \rho q = (1000 \text{ kg/m}^3)[10 \text{ m}^3/(\text{s} \cdot \text{m})] = 10{,}000$ kg/(s · m), and the temperature rise from the steady-flow energy equation is

$$\text{Power dissipated} = \dot{m} c_p \, \Delta T$$

or $\qquad 61{,}300 \text{ W/m} = [10{,}000 \text{ kg/(s} \cdot \text{m})][4200 \text{ J/(kg} \cdot \text{K)}] \, \Delta T$

from which

$$\Delta T = 0.0015 \text{ K} \qquad \text{*Ans. (g)*}$$

The dissipation is large, but the temperature rise is negligible.

10.6 Gradually Varied Flow[1]

In practical channel flows both the bottom slope and the water depth change with position, as in Fig. 10.3. An approximate analysis is possible if the flow is gradually varied, e.g., if the slopes are small and changes not too sudden. The basic assumptions are

[1] This section may be omitted without loss of continuity.

1. Slowly changing bottom slope
2. Slowly changing water depth (no hydraulic jumps)
3. Slowly changing cross section
4. One-dimensional velocity distribution
5. Pressure distribution approximately hydrostatic

The flow then satisfies the continuity relation (10.1) plus the energy equation with bottom friction losses included. The two unknowns for steady flow are velocity $V(x)$ and water depth $y(x)$, where x is distance along the channel.

Basic Differential Equation

Consider the length of channel dx illustrated in Fig. 10.13. All the terms which enter the steady-flow energy equation are shown, and the balance between x and $x + dx$ is

$$\frac{V^2}{2g} + y + S_0\,dx = S\,dx + \frac{V^2}{2g} + d\left(\frac{V^2}{2g}\right) + y + dy$$

or

$$\frac{dy}{dx} + \frac{d}{dx}\left(\frac{V^2}{2g}\right) = S_0 - S \tag{10.46}$$

where S_0 is the slope of the channel bottom (positive as shown in Fig. 10.13) and S is the slope of the EGL (which drops due to wall friction losses).

To eliminate the velocity derivative, differentiate the continuity relation

$$\frac{dQ}{dx} = 0 = A\,\frac{dV}{dx} + V\,\frac{dA}{dx} \tag{10.47}$$

But $dA = b_0\,dy$, where b_0 is the channel width at the surface. Eliminating dV/dx between Eqs. (10.46) and (10.47), we obtain

Fig. 10.13 Energy balance between two sections in a gradually varied open-channel flow.

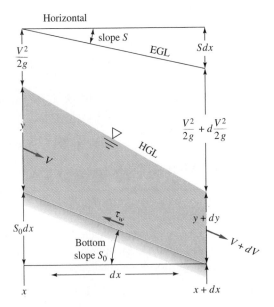

$$\frac{dy}{dx}\left(1 - \frac{V^2 b_0}{gA}\right) = S_0 - S \tag{10.48}$$

Finally, recall from Eq. (10.37) that $V^2 b_0/(gA)$ is the square of the Froude number of the local channel flow. The final desired form of the gradually varied flow equation is

$$\frac{dy}{dx} = \frac{S_0 - S}{1 - \mathrm{Fr}^2} \tag{10.49}$$

This equation changes sign according as the Froude number is subcritical or supercritical and is analogous to the one-dimensional gas-dynamic area-change formula (9.40).

The numerator of Eq. (10.49) changes sign according as S_0 is greater or less than S, which is the slope equivalent to uniform flow at the same discharge Q

$$S = S_{0n} = \frac{f}{D_h} \frac{V^2}{2g} = \frac{V^2}{R_h C^2} = \frac{n^2 V^2}{\alpha^2 R_h^{4/3}} \tag{10.50}$$

where C is the Chézy coefficient. The behavior of Eq. (10.49) thus depends upon the relative magnitude of the local bottom slope $S_0(x)$, compared with (1) uniform flow, $y = y_n$, and (2) critical flow, $y = y_c$. As in Eq. (10.38), the dimensional parameter α^2 equals 1.0 for SI units and 2.208 for BG units.

Classification of Solutions

It is customary to compare the actual channel slope S_0 with the critical slope S_c for the same Q from Eq. (10.38). There are five classes for S_0, giving rise to twelve distinct types of solution curves, all of which are illustrated in Fig. 10.14:

Slope class	Slope notation	Depth class	Solution curves
$S_0 > S_c$	Steep	$y_c > y_n$	S-1, S-2, S-3
$S_0 = S_c$	Critical	$y_c = y_n$	C-1, C-3
$S_0 < S_c$	Mild	$y_c < y_n$	M-1, M-2, M-3
$S_0 = 0$	Horizontal	$y_n = \infty$	H-2, H-3
$S_0 < 0$	Adverse	$y_n = $ imaginary	A-2, A-3

The solution letters S, C, M, H, and A obviously denote the names of the five types of slope. The numbers 1, 2, 3 relate to the position of the initial point on the solution curve with respect to the normal depth y_n and the critical depth y_c. In type 1 solutions, the initial point is above both y_n and y_c, and in all cases the water-depth solution $y(x)$ becomes even deeper and farther away from y_n and y_c. In type 2 solutions, the initial point lies between y_n and y_c, and if there is no change in S_0 or roughness, the solution tends asymptotically toward the lower of y_n or y_c. In type 3 cases, the initial point lies below both y_n and y_c, and the solution curve tends asymptotically toward the lower of these.

Figure 10.14 shows the basic character of the local solutions, but in practice, of course, S_0 varies with x and the overall solution patches together the various cases to form a continuous depth profile $y(x)$ compatible with a given initial condition and a given discharge Q. There is a fine discussion of various composite solutions in Ref. 3, chap. 9; see also Ref. 18, sec. 12.7.

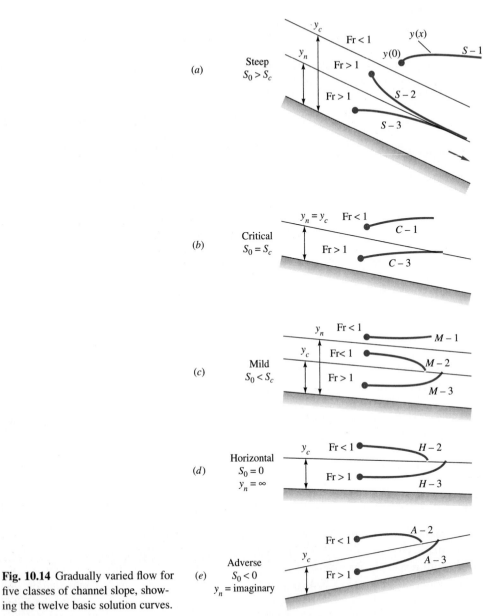

Fig. 10.14 Gradually varied flow for five classes of channel slope, showing the twelve basic solution curves.

Numerical Solution

The basic relation for gradually varied flow, Eq. (10.49), is a first-order ordinary differential equation which can be easily solved numerically. For a given constant-volume flow rate Q, it may be written in the form

$$\frac{dy}{dx} = \frac{S_0 - n^2 Q^2/(\alpha^2 A^2 R_h^{4/3})}{1 - Q^2 b_0/(gA^3)} \qquad (10.51)$$

subject to an initial condition $y = y_0$ at $x = x_0$. It is assumed that the bottom slope

$S_0(x)$ and the cross-sectional shape parameters (b_0, P, A) are known everywhere along the channel. Then one may solve Eq. (10.51) for local water depth $y(x)$ by any standard numerical method. The writer uses the Runge-Kutta method as implemented in BASIC for a personal computer. Step sizes Δx may be selected so that each change Δy is limited to no greater than, say, 1 percent. The solution curves are generally well behaved unless there are discontinuous changes in channel parameters. Note that if one approaches the critical depth y_c, the denominator of Eq. (10.51) approaches zero, so small step sizes are required. It helps physically to know what type solution curve (M-1, S-2, etc.) you are proceeding along, but this is not mathematically necessary.

EXAMPLE 10.8

Let us extend the data of Example 10.4 to compute a portion of the profile shape. Given is a wide channel with $n = 0.022$, $S_0 = 0.0048$, and $q = 50$ ft^3/(s · ft). If $y_0 = 3$ ft at $x = 0$, how far along the channel $x = L$ does it take the depth to rise to $y_L = 4$ ft? Is the 4-ft depth position upstream or downstream in Fig. E10.8a?

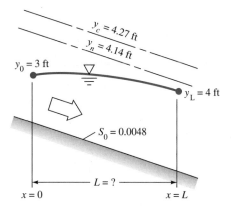

Fig. E10.8a

Solution

In Example 10.4 we computed $y_c = 4.27$ ft. Since our initial depth $y = 3$ ft is less than y_c, we know the flow is supercritical. Let us also compute the normal depth for the given slope S_0 by setting $q = 50$ ft^3/(s · ft) in the Chézy formula (10.19) with $R_h = y_n$:

$$q = \frac{\alpha}{n} A R_h^{2/3} S_0^{1/2} = \frac{1.486}{0.022} [y_n(1 \text{ ft})] y_n^{2/3} (0.0048)^{1/2} = 50 \text{ ft}^3/(\text{s} \cdot \text{ft})$$

Solve for: $\qquad\qquad\qquad\qquad y_n \approx 4.14$ ft

Thus both $y(0) = 3$ ft and $y(L) = 4$ ft are less than y_n, which is less than y_c, so we *must* be on an S-3 curve, as in Fig. 10.14a. For a wide channel, Eq. (10.51) reduces to

$$\frac{dy}{dx} = \frac{S_0 - n^2 q^2/(\alpha^2 y^{10/3})}{1 - q^2/(gy^3)}$$

$$\approx \frac{0.0048 - (0.022)^2 (50)^2/(2.208 y^{10/3})}{1 - (50)^2/(32.2 y^3)} \qquad \text{with } y(0) = 3 \text{ ft}$$

The initial slope is $y'(0) \approx 0.00494$, and a step size $\Delta x = 5$ ft would cause a change $\Delta y \approx (0.00494)(5$ ft$) \approx 0.025$ ft, less than 1 percent. We therefore integrate numerically with $\Delta x = 5$ ft to determine when the depth $y = 4$ ft is achieved. Tabulate some values:

x, ft	0	50	100	150	200	230
y, ft	3.00	3.25	3.48	3.70	3.90	4.00

The water depth, still supercritical, reaches $y = 4$ ft at

$$x \approx 230 \text{ ft } downstream. \qquad\qquad Ans.$$

We verify from Fig. 10.14a that water depth does increase downstream on an S-3 curve. The solution curve $y(x)$ is shown as the bold line in Fig. E10.8b.

For little extra effort we can investigate the entire family of S-3 solution curves for this problem. Figure E10.8b also shows what happens if the initial depth is varied from 0.5 to 3.5 ft in increments of 0.5 ft. All S-3 solutions smoothly rise and asymptotically approach the uniform-flow condition $y = y_n = 4.14$ ft.

Fig. E10.8b

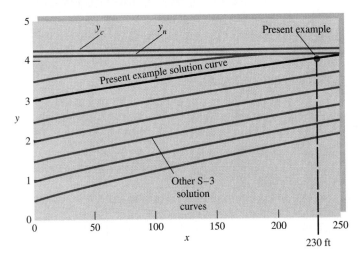

Some Illustrative Composite-Flow Profiles

The solution curves in Fig. 10.14 are somewhat simplistic, since they postulate constant bottom slopes. In practice, channel slopes can vary greatly, $S_0 = S_0(x)$, and the solution curves can cross between two regimes. Other parameter changes, such as $A(x)$, $b_0(x)$, and $n(x)$, can cause interesting composite-flow profiles. Some examples are shown in Fig. 10.15.

Figure 10.15a shows a change from a mild slope to a steep slope in a constant-width channel. The initial M-2 curve must change to an S-2 curve farther down the steep slope. The only way this can happen physically is for the solution curve to pass smoothly through the critical depth, as shown. The critical point is mathematically *singular* [3, sec. 9.6], and the flow near this point is generally *rapidly*, not gradually, varied. The flow pattern, accelerating from subcritical to supercritical, is similar to a converging-diverging nozzle in gas dynamics. Other scenarios for Fig. 10.15a are impossible. For example, the upstream curve cannot be M-1, for the break in slope would cause an S-1 curve which would move away from uniform steep flow.

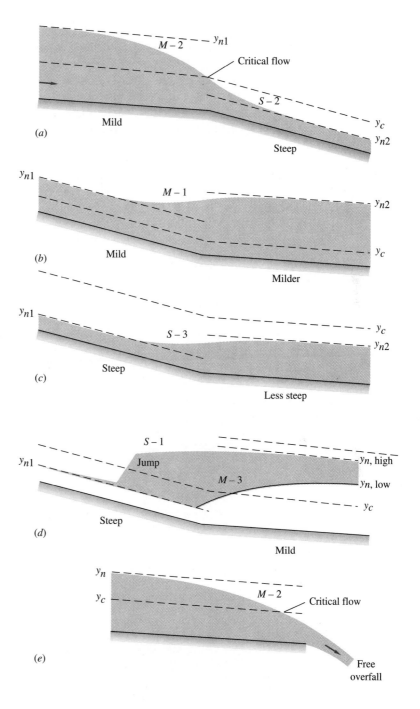

Fig. 10.15 Some examples of composite-flow profiles.

Figure 10.15*b* shows a mild slope which becomes even milder. The water depth moves smoothly along an M-1 curve to the new (higher) uniform flow. There is no singular point, so gradually varied theory is adequate.

Figure 10.15*c* illustrates a steep slope which becomes less steep. The depth will change smoothly along an S-3 curve to approach the new (higher) uniform flow. There is no singular point. Compare with Fig. 10.15*b*.

Figure 10.15*d* shows a steep slope which changes to mild. It is generally impossible to revert back smoothly from supercritical to subcritical flow without dissipation. A hydraulic jump will form whose position depends upon downstream conditions. Two cases are illustrated: (1) a jump to an S-1 curve to reach a high downstream normal depth and (2) a change to an M-3 curve and then a jump to a lower downstream depth.

Figure 10.15*e* illustrates a *free overfall* with a mild slope. This acts as a *control section* to the upstream flow, which then forms an M-2 curve and accelerates to critical flow near the overfall. The falling stream will be supercritical. The overfall "controls" the water depths upstream and can serve as an initial condition for computation of $y(x)$. This is the type of flow which occurs in a weir or waterfall, Sec. 10.7.

The examples in Fig. 10.15 show that changing conditions in open-channel flow can result in complex flow patterns. Many more examples of composite-flow profiles are given in Refs. 1, 3, and 18.

10.7 Flow Measurement and Control by Weirs

A *weir*, of which the ordinary dam is an example, is a channel obstruction over which the flow must deflect. For simple geometries the channel discharge Q correlates with gravity and with the blockage height H to which the upstream flow is backed up above the weir elevation (see Fig. 10.16). Thus a weir is a simple but effective open-channel flowmeter. We used a weir as an example of dimensional analysis in Prob. 5.32.

Fig. 10.16 Flow over wide, well-ventilated weirs: (*a*) sharp-crested; (*b*) broad-crested.

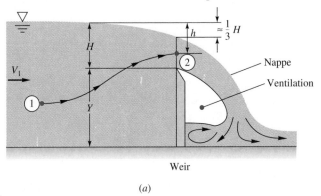

(*a*)

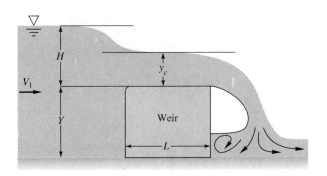

(*b*)

Figure 10.16 shows two common weirs, sharp-crested and broad-crested, assumed to be very wide. In both cases the flow upstream is subcritical, accelerates to critical near the top of the weir, and spills over into a supercritical *nappe*. For both weirs the discharge q per unit width is proportional to $g^{1/2}H^{3/2}$ but with somewhat different coefficients. The short-crested (or thin-plate) weir nappe should be *ventilated* to the atmosphere; i.e., it should spring clear of the weir crest. Unventilated or drowned nappes are more difficult to correlate and depend upon tailwater conditions. (The spillway of Fig. 10.11 is a sort of unventilated weir.)

A very complete discussion of weirs, including other designs such as the polygonal "Crump" weir and various contracting flumes, is given in the text by Ackers et al. [19].

Analysis of Sharp-Crested Weirs

It is possible to analyze weir flow by inviscid potential theory with an unknown (but solvable) free surface, as in Fig. P8.54. Here, however, we simply use one-dimensional-flow theory plus dimensional analysis to develop suitable weir flow-rate correlations.

A very early theoretical approach is credited to J. Weisbach in 1855. The velocity head at any point 2 above the weir crest is assumed to equal the total head upstream; i.e., Bernoulli's equation is used with no losses:

$$\frac{V_2^2}{2g} + H - h \approx \frac{V_1^2}{2g} + H \qquad \text{or} \qquad V_2(h) \approx \sqrt{2gh + V_1^2}$$

where h is the vertical distance down to point 2, as shown in Fig. 10.16a. If we accept for the moment, without proof, that the flow over the crest draws down to $h_{min} \approx H/3$, the volume flow $q = Q/b$ over the crest is approximately

$$q = \int_{crest} V_2 \, dh \approx \int_{H/3}^{H} (2gh + V_1^2)^{1/2} \, dh$$

$$= \frac{2}{3}\sqrt{2g}\left[\left(H + \frac{V_1^2}{2g}\right)^{3/2} - \left(\frac{H}{3} + \frac{V_1^2}{2g}\right)^{3/2}\right] \tag{10.52}$$

Normally the upstream velocity head $V_1^2/(2g)$ is neglected, so this expression reduces to

Sharp-crested theory: $\qquad q \approx 0.81(\tfrac{2}{3})(2g)^{1/2}H^{3/2}$ $\qquad\qquad$ (10.53)

This formula is functionally correct, but the coefficient 0.81 is too high and should be replaced by an experimentally determined discharge coefficient.

Analysis of Broad-Crested Weirs

The broad-crested weir of Fig. 10.16b can be analyzed more accurately because it creates a short run of nearly one-dimensional critical flow, as shown. Bernoulli's equation from upstream to the weir crest yields

$$\frac{V_1^2}{2g} + Y + H \approx \frac{V_c^2}{2g} + Y + y_c$$

If the crest is very wide into the paper, $V_c^2 = gy_c$ from Eq. (10.33). Thus we can solve for

$$y_c \approx \frac{2H}{3} + \frac{V_1^2}{3g} \approx \frac{2H}{3}$$

This result was used without proof to derive Eq. (10.53). Finally, the flow rate follows from wide-channel critical flow, Eq. (10.32):

Broad-crested theory: $\quad q = \sqrt{gy_c^3} \approx \frac{1}{\sqrt{3}} \left(\frac{2}{3}\right) \sqrt{2g} \left(H + \frac{V_1^2}{2g}\right)^{3/2}$ $\qquad$ (10.54)

Again we may usually neglect the upstream velocity head $V_1^2/(2g)$. The coefficient $1/\sqrt{3} \approx 0.577$ is about right, but experimental data are preferred.

Experimental Weir Discharge Coefficients

Theoretical weir-flow formulas may be modified experimentally as follows. Eliminate the numerical coefficients $\frac{2}{3}$ and $\sqrt{2}$, for which there is much sentimental attachment in the literature, and reduce the formula to

$$Q_{weir} = C_d b\sqrt{g} \left(H + \frac{V_1^2}{2g}\right)^{3/2} \approx C_d b\sqrt{g} H^{3/2} \qquad (10.55)$$

where b is the crest width and C_d is a dimensionless, experimentally determined *weir discharge coefficient* which may vary with the weir geometry, Reynolds number, and Weber number. Many data for many different weirs have been reported in the literature, as detailed in Ref. 19.

An accurate (± 2 percent) composite correlation for wide ventilated sharp crests is recommended as follows [19]:

Wide sharp-crested weir: $C_d \approx 0.564 + 0.0846 \dfrac{H}{Y} \quad$ for $\quad \dfrac{H}{Y} \le 2 \qquad (10.56)$

The Reynolds numbers $V_1 H/\nu$ for these data varied from 1 E4 to 2 E6, but the formula should apply to higher Re, such as large dams on rivers.

The broad-crested weir of Fig. 10.16b is considerably more sensitive to geometric parameters, including the surface roughness ϵ of the crest. If the leading-edge nose is rounded, $R/L \ge 0.05$, available data [19, chap. 7] may be correlated as follows:

Round-nosed broad-crested weir: $C_d \approx 0.544 \left(1 - \dfrac{\delta^*/L}{H/L}\right)^{3/2} \qquad (10.57)$

where $\qquad \dfrac{\delta^*}{L} \approx 0.001 + 0.2\sqrt{\epsilon/L}$

The chief effect is due to turbulent boundary-layer displacement-thickness growth δ^* on the crest as compared to upstream head H. The formula is limited to $H/L < 0.7$, $\epsilon/L \le 0.002$, and $V_1 H/\nu > 3$ E5. If the nose is round, there is no significant effect of weir height Y, at least if $H/Y < 2.4$.

If the broad-crested weir has a sharp leading edge, thus commonly called a *rectangular* weir, the discharge may depend upon the weir height Y. However, in a certain range of weir height and length, C_d is nearly constant:

Sharp-nosed
broad-crested weir:
$$C_d \approx 0.462 \quad \text{for} \quad 0.08 < \frac{H}{L} < 0.33$$

$$\quad (10.58)$$

$$0.22 < \frac{H}{Y} < 0.56$$

Surface roughness is not a significant factor here. For $H/L < 0.08$ there is large scatter (± 10 percent) in the data. For $H/L > 0.33$ and $H/Y > 0.56$, C_d increases up to 10 percent due to each parameter, and complex charts are needed for the discharge coefficient [19, chap. 6].

EXAMPLE 10.9

A weir in a horizontal channel is 1 m high and 4 m wide. The water depth upstream is 1.6 m. Estimate the discharge if the weir is (a) sharp-crested and (b) round-nosed with an unfinished cement broad crest 1.2 m long. Neglect $V_1^2/(2g)$.

Solution

Part (a)   We are given $Y = 1$ m and $H + Y \approx 1.6$ m, hence $H \approx 0.6$ m. Since $H \ll b$, we assume that the weir is "wide." For a sharp crest, Eq. (10.56) applies:

$$C_d \approx 0.564 + 0.0846 \frac{0.6 \text{ m}}{1 \text{ m}} \approx 0.615$$

Then the discharge is given by the basic correlation, Eq. (10.55):

$$Q = C_d b \sqrt{g} H^{3/2} = (0.615)(4 \text{ m})\sqrt{(9.81 \text{ m/s}^2)}(0.6 \text{ m})^{3/2} \approx 3.58 \text{ m}^3/\text{s} \quad \textit{Ans. (a)}$$

We check that $H/Y = 0.6 < 2.0$ for Eq. (10.56) to be valid. From continuity, $V_1 = Q/(by_1) = 3.58/[(4.0)(1.6)] = 0.56$ m/s, giving a Reynolds number $V_1 H/\nu \approx 3.4$ E5.

Part (b)   For a round-nosed broad-crested weir, Eq. (10.57) applies. For an unfinished cement surface, read $\epsilon \approx 2.4$ mm from Table 10.1. Then the displacement thickness is

$$\frac{\delta^*}{L} \approx 0.001 + 0.2\sqrt{\epsilon/L} = 0.001 + 0.2\left(\frac{0.0024 \text{ m}}{1.2 \text{ m}}\right)^{1/2} \approx 0.00994$$

Then Eq. (10.57) predicts the discharge coefficient:

$$C_d \approx 0.544\left(1 - \frac{0.00994}{0.6 \text{ m}/1.2 \text{ m}}\right)^{3/2} \approx 0.528$$

The estimated flow rate is thus

$$Q = C_d b \sqrt{g} H^{3/2} = 0.528(4 \text{ m})\sqrt{(9.81 \text{ m}^2/\text{s})}(0.6 \text{ m})^{3/2} \approx 3.07 \text{ m}^3/\text{s} \quad \textit{Ans. (b)}$$

Check that $H/L = 0.5 < 0.7$ as required. The approach Reynolds number is $V_1 H/\nu \approx 2.9$ E5, just barely below the recommended limit in Eq. (10.57).

Since $V_1 \approx 0.5$ m/s, $V_1^2/(2g) \approx 0.012$ m, so the error in taking total head equal to 0.6 m is about 2 percent. We could correct this for upstream velocity head if desired.

Other Thin-Plate Weir Designs

Weirs are often used for flow measurement and control of artificial channels. The two most common shapes are a rectangle and a V notch, as shown in Table 10.2. All should be fully ventilated and not drowned.

Table 10.2*a* shows a full-width rectangle, which will have slight end-boundary-layer effects but no end contractions. For a thin-plate design, the top is approximately sharp-crested, and Eq. (10.56) should give adequate accuracy, as shown in the table. Since the overfall spans the entire channel, artificial ventilation may be needed, such as holes in the channel walls.

Table 10.2*b* shows a partial-width rectangle, $b < L$, which will cause the sides of the overfall to contract inward and reduce the flow rate. An adequate contraction correction [19, 20] is to reduce the effective weir width by $0.1H$, as shown in the table. It seems, however, that this type of weir is rather sensitive to small effects, such as plate thickness and sidewall boundary-layer growth. Small heads ($H < 75$ mm) and small slot widths ($b < 30$ cm) are not recommended. See Refs. 19 and 20 for further details.

The V notch, in Table 10.2*c*, is intrinsically interesting in that its overfall has only one length scale, H—there is no separate "width." The discharge will thus be proportional to $H^{5/2}$, rather than a power of $\frac{3}{2}$. Application of Bernoulli's equation to the

Table 10.2 Thin-Plate Weirs for Flow Measurement

Thin-plate weir	Flow-rate correlation
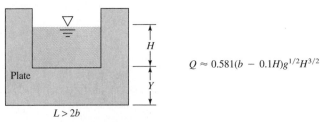 (a) Full-width rectangle.	$Q \approx \left(0.564 + 0.0846\dfrac{H}{Y}\right)bg^{1/2}H^{3/2}$
(b) Rectangle with side contractions. $L > 2b$	$Q \approx 0.581(b - 0.1H)g^{1/2}H^{3/2}$ $H < 0.5Y$
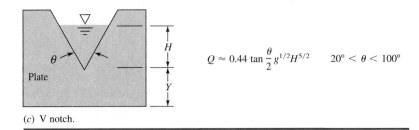 (c) V notch.	$Q \approx 0.44 \tan\dfrac{\theta}{2}g^{1/2}H^{5/2}$ $20° < \theta < 100°$

triangular opening, in the spirit of Eq. (10.52), leads to the following ideal flow rate for a V notch:

V notch:
$$Q_{\text{ideal}} = \frac{8\sqrt{2}}{15} \tan\frac{\theta}{2} g^{1/2}H^{5/2} \tag{10.59}$$

where θ is the total included angle of the notch. The actual measured flow is about 40 percent less than this, due to contraction similar to a thin-plate orifice. In terms of an experimental discharge coefficient, the recommended formula is

$$Q_{\text{V notch}} \approx C_d \tan\frac{\theta}{2} g^{1/2}H^{5/2} \qquad C_d \approx 0.44 \qquad \text{for} \qquad 20° < \theta < 100° \tag{10.60}$$

for heads $H > 50$ mm. For smaller heads, both Reynolds-number and Weber-number effects may be important, and a recommended correction [19] is

Low heads, $H < 50$ mm:
$$C_{d,\text{ V notch}} \approx 0.44 + \frac{0.9}{(\text{Re We})^{1/6}} \tag{10.61}$$

where $\text{Re} = \rho g^{1/2}H^{3/2}/\mu$ and $\text{We} = \rho gH^2/Y$, with Y being the coefficient of surface tension. Liquids other than water may be used with this formula, as long as $\text{Re} > 300/\tan(\theta/2)^{3/4}$ and $\text{We} > 300$.

A number of other thin-plate weir designs—trapezoidal, parabolic, circular arc, and U-shaped—are discussed in Ref. 21, which also contains considerable data on broad-crested weirs.

Backwater Curves

A weir is a flow barrier which not only alters the local flow over the weir but also modifies the flow-depth distribution far upstream. Any strong barrier in an open-channel flow creates a *backwater curve*, which can be computed by the gradually varied flow theory of Sec. 10.6. If Q is known, the weir formula, Eq. (10.55), determines H and hence the water depth just upstream of the weir, $y = H + Y$, where Y is the weir height. We then compute $y(x)$ upstream of the weir from Eq. (10.51), following in this case an M-1 curve (Fig. 10.14c). Such a barrier, where the water depth correlates with the flow rate, is called a channel *control point*. These are the starting points for numerical analysis of floodwater profiles in rivers as studied, e.g., by the U.S. Army Corps of Engineers [22].

EXAMPLE 10.10

A rectangular channel 8 m wide, with a flow rate of 30 m³/s, encounters a 4-m-high sharp-edged dam, as shown in Fig. E10.10a. Determine the water depth 2 km upstream if the channel slope is $S_0 = 0.0004$ and $n = 0.025$.

Solution

First determine the head H produced by the dam, using sharp-crested full-width weir theory, Eq. (10.56):

$$Q = 30 \text{ m}^3/\text{s} = C_d b g^{1/2}H^{3/2} = \left(0.564 + 0.0846\frac{H}{4\text{m}}\right)(8 \text{ m})(9.81 \text{ m/s}^2)^{1/2}H^{3/2}$$

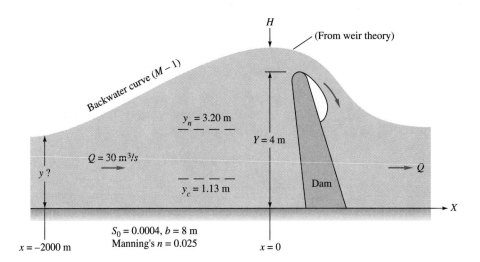

Fig. E10.10a

$x = -2000$ m

$S_0 = 0.0004$, $b = 8$ m
Manning's $n = 0.025$

$x = 0$

Since the term $0.0846H/4$ in parentheses is small, we may proceed by iteration to the solution $H \approx 1.59$ m. Then our initial condition at $x = 0$, just upstream of the dam, is $y(0) = Y + H = 4 + 1.59 = 5.59$ m. Compare this to the critical depth from Eq. (10.30):

$$y_c = \left(\frac{Q^2}{b^2 g}\right)^{1/3} = \left[\frac{(30 \text{ m}^3/\text{s})^2}{(8 \text{ m})^2 (9.81 \text{ m/s}^2)}\right]^{1/3} = 1.13 \text{ m}$$

Since $y(0)$ is greater than y_c, the flow upstream is subcritical. Finally, for reference purposes, estimate the normal depth from the Chézy equation (10.19):

$$Q = 30 \text{ m}^3/\text{s} = \frac{\alpha}{n} b y R_h^{2/3} S_0^{1/2} = \frac{1.0}{0.025} (8 \text{ m}) y_n \left(\frac{8 y_n}{8 + 2 y_n}\right) (0.0004)^{1/2}$$

By trial and error or iteration solve for $y_n \approx 3.20$ m. If there are no changes in channel width or slope, the water depth far upstream of the dam will approach this value. All these reference values $y(0)$, y_c, and y_n are shown in Fig. E10.10b.

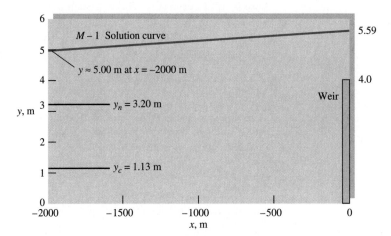

Fig. E10.10b

Since $y(0) > y_n > y_c$, the solution will be an M-1 curve as computed from gradually varied theory, Eq. (10.51), for a rectangular channel with the given input data:

$$\frac{dy}{dx} \approx \frac{S_0 - n^2Q^2/(\alpha^2 A^2 R_h^{4/3})}{1 - Q^2 b_0/(gA^3)} \qquad \alpha = 1.0 \qquad A = 8y \qquad n = 0.025 \qquad R_h = \frac{8y}{8 + 2y} \qquad b_0 = 8$$

Beginning with $y = 5.59$ m at $x = 0$, we integrate backward to $x = -2000$ m. For the Runge-Kutta method, four-figure accuracy is achieved for $\Delta x = -100$ m. The complete solution curve is shown in Fig. E10.10b. The desired solution value is

At $x = -2000$ m: $\hspace{4cm} y \approx 5.00$ m $\hspace{4cm}$ *Ans.*

Thus, even 2 km upstream, the dam has produced a ''backwater'' which is 1.8 m above the normal depth which would occur without a dam. For this example, a near-normal depth of, say, 10 cm greater than y_n, or $y \approx 3.3$ m, would not be achieved until $x = -13,400$ m. Backwater curves are quite far-reaching upstream, especially in flood stages.

Summary

This chapter is an introduction to open-channel flow analysis, limited to steady, one-dimensional-flow conditions. The basic analysis combines the continuity equation with the extended Bernoulli equation including friction losses.

Open-channel flows are classified either by depth variation or by Froude number, the latter being analogous to the Mach number in compressible duct flow (Chap. 9). Flow at constant slope and depth is called uniform flow and satisfies the classical Chézy equation (10.19). Straight prismatic channels can be optimized to find the cross section which gives maximum flow rate with minimum friction losses. As the slope and flow velocity increase, the channel reaches a *critical* condition of Froude number unity, where velocity equals the speed of a small-amplitude surface wave in the channel. Every channel has a critical slope which varies with the flow rate and roughness. If the flow becomes supercritical (Fr > 1), it may undergo a hydraulic jump to a greater depth and lower (subcritical) velocity, analogous to a normal-shock wave.

The analysis of gradually varied flow leads to a differential equation (10.51) which can be solved by finite-difference methods. The chapter ends with a discussion of the flow over a dam or weir, where the total flow rate can be correlated with upstream water depth.

Recommended Films

Films numbered 7, 12, 24, 25, 30 to 35, and 39 in App. C.

References

1. R. H. French, *Open-Channel Hydraulics*, McGraw-Hill, New York, 1985.
2. R. H. J. Sellin, *Flow in Channels*, Gordon & Breach, London, 1970.
3. Ven Te Chow, *Open Channel Hydraulics*, McGraw-Hill, New York, 1959.
4. F. M. Henderson, *Open Channel Flow*, Macmillan, New York, 1966.
5. B. Kinsman, *Wind Waves: Their Generation and Propagation on the Ocean Surface*, Prentice-Hall, Englewood Cliffs, N.J., 1964; Dover, New York, 1984.
6. M. J. Lighthill, *Waves in Fluids*, Cambridge University Press, London, 1978.
7. C. C. Mei, *The Applied Dynamics of Ocean Surface Waves*, Wiley, New York, 1983.
8. A. T. Ippen, *Estuary and Coastline Hydrodynamics*, McGraw-Hill, New York, 1966.
9. R. M. Sorenson, *Basic Coastal Engineering*, Wiley, New York, 1978.
10. J. M. Robertson and H. Rouse, ''The Four Regimes of Open Channel Flow,'' *Civ. Eng.*, vol. 11, no. 3, March 1941, pp. 169–171.

11. R. W. Powell, "Resistance to Flow in Rough Channels," *Trans. Am. Geophys. Union*, vol. 31, no. 4, August 1950, pp. 575–582.

12. R. Manning, "On the Flow of Water in Open Channels and Pipes," *Trans. I.C.E. Ireland*, vol. 20, 1891, pp. 161–207.

13. B. A. Bakhmeteff, *Hydraulics of Open Channels*, McGraw-Hill, New York, 1932.

14. P. A. Thompson, *Compressible-Fluid Dynamics*, McGraw-Hill, New York, 1972.

15. E. F. Brater, *Handbook of Hydraulics*, 6th ed., McGraw-Hill, New York, 1976.

16. U.S. Bureau of Reclamation," Research Studies on Stilling Basins, Energy Dissipators, and Associated Appurtenances," *Hydraulic Lab. Rep.* Hyd-399, June 1, 1955.

17. "Friction Factors in Open Channels, Report of the Committee on Hydromechanics," *ASCE J. Hydraul. Div.*, March 1963, pp. 97–143.

18. R. M. Olson and S. J. Wright, *Essentials of Engineering Fluid Mechanics*, 5th ed., Harper & Row, New York, 1990.

19. P. Ackers et al., *Weirs and Flumes for Flow Measurement*, Wiley, New York, 1978.

20. M. G. Bos, J. A. Replogle, and A. J. Clemmens, *Flow Measuring Flumes for Open Channel Systems*, Wiley, New York, 1984.

21. M. G. Bos, *Long-Throated Flumes and Broad-Crested Weirs*, Martinus Nijhoff (Kluwer), Dordrecht, The Netherlands, 1985.

22. U.S. Army Corps of Engineers, *HEC-2 Water Surface Profiles*, Hydrologic Engineering Center, 609 Second Street, Davis, CA.

23. W. Rodi, *Turbulence Models and Their Application in Hydraulics*, Brookfield Publishing, Brookfield, Vt., 1984.

PROBLEMS

In addition to many traditional problems, categorized in the problem distribution list below, there are word problems, labeled W10.1 to W10.13, and a design project, D10.1.

Problem Distribution

Section	Topic	Problems
10.1	Introduction: Froude number, wave speed	10.1–10.10
10.2	Uniform flow: The Chézy formula	10.11–10.36
10.3	Efficient uniform-flow channels	10.37–10.46
10.4	Specific energy: Critical depth	10.47–10.58
10.4	Flow over a bump	10.59–10.68
10.4	Sluice-gate flow	10.69–10.78
10.5	The hydraulic jump	10.79–10.96
10.6	Gradually varied flow	10.97–10.112
10.7	Weirs and flumes	10.113–10.123
10.7	Backwater curves	10.124–10.128

10.1 The formula for shallow-water wave propagation speed, Eq. (10.9) or (10.10), is independent of the physical properties of the liquid, i.e., density, viscosity, or surface tension. Does this mean that waves propagate at the same speed in water, mercury, gasoline, and glycerin? Explain.

10.2 A shallow-water wave 1 cm high propagates into still water of depth 1.1 m. Compute (*a*) the wave speed c and (*b*) the induced velocity δV.

10.3 Narragansett Bay is approximately 21 (statute) mi long and has an average depth of 42 ft. Tidal charts for the area indicate a time delay of 30 min between high tide at the mouth of the bay (Newport, Rhode Island) and its head (Providence, Rhode Island). Is this delay correlated with the propagation of a shallow-water tidal-crest wave through the bay? Explain.

10.4 The water-channel flow in Fig. P10.4 has a free surface in three places. Does it qualify as an open-channel flow? Explain. What does the dashed line represent?

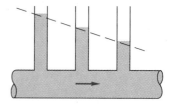

Fig. P10.4

10.5 Water flows rapidly in a channel 15 cm deep. Piercing the surface with a pencil point creates a wedgelike downstream wave of included angle 35°. Estimate the velocity V of the water.

10.6 Pebbles dropped successively at the same point, into a water channel flow of depth 42 cm, create two circular ripples, as in Fig. P10.6. From this information estimate (a) the Froude number and (b) the stream velocity.

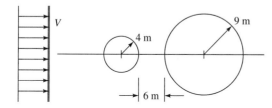

Fig. P10.6

10.7 Pebbles dropped successively at the same point, into a water channel flow of depth 65 cm, create two circular ripples, as in Fig. P10.7. From this information estimate (a) the Froude number and (b) the stream velocity.

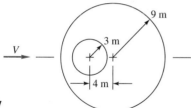

Fig. P10.7

10.8 An earthquake near the Kenai Peninsula, Alaska, creates a single "tidal" wave (called a *tsunami*) which propagates south across the Pacific Ocean. If the average ocean depth is 4 km and seawater density is 1025 kg/m³, estimate the time of arrival of this tsunami in Hilo, Hawaii.

10.9 Equation (10.10) is for a single disturbance wave. For *periodic* small-amplitude surface waves of wavelength λ and period T, inviscid theory [5 to 9] predicts a wave propagation speed

$$c_0^2 = \frac{g\lambda}{2\pi} \tanh \frac{2\pi y}{\lambda}$$

where y is the water depth and surface tension is neglected. (a) Determine if this expression is affected by the Reynolds number, Froude number, or Weber number. Derive the limiting values of this expression for (b) $y \ll \lambda$ and (c) $y \gg \lambda$. (d) Also for what ratio y/λ is the wave speed within 1 percent of limit (c)?

10.10 If surface tension Y is included in the analysis of Prob. 10.9, the resulting wave speed is [5 to 9]

$$c_0^2 = \left(\frac{g\lambda}{2\pi} + \frac{2\pi Y}{\rho\lambda} \right) \tanh \frac{2\pi y}{\lambda}$$

(a) Determine if this expression is affected by the Reynolds number, Froude number, or Weber number. Derive the limiting values of this expression for (b) $y \ll \lambda$ and (c) $y \gg \lambda$. (d) Finally determine the wavelength λ_{crit} for a minimum value of c_0, assuming that $y \gg \lambda$.

10.11 A rectangular channel is 2 m wide and contains water 3 m deep. If the slope is 0.85° and the lining is corrugated metal, estimate the discharge for uniform flow.

10.12 (a) For laminar draining of a wide thin sheet of water on pavement sloped at angle θ, as in Fig. P4.36, show that the flow rate is given by

$$Q = \frac{\rho g b h^3 \sin \theta}{3\mu}$$

where b is the sheet width and h its depth. (b) By (somewhat laborious) comparison with Eq. (10.13), show that this expression is compatible with a friction factor $f = 24/\text{Re}$, where $\text{Re} = V_{\text{av}} h / \nu$.

10.13 The laminar-draining flow from Prob. 10.12 may undergo transition to turbulence if $\text{Re} > 500$. If the pavement slope is 0.0045, what is the maximum sheet thickness, in mm, for which laminar flow is ensured?

10.14 The Chézy formula (10.18) is independent of fluid density and viscosity. Does this mean that water, mercury, alcohol, and SAE 30 oil will all flow down a given open channel at the same rate? Explain.

10.15 The finished-concrete channel of Fig. P10.15 is designed for a flow rate of 6 m³/s at a normal depth of 1 m. Determine (a) the design slope of the channel and (b) the percentage of reduction in flow if the surface is asphalt.

Fig. P10.15

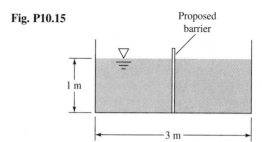

10.16 In Prob. 10.15, for finished concrete, determine the percentage of reduction in flow if the channel is divided in the center by the proposed barrier in Fig. P10.15. How does your estimate change if all surfaces are clay tile?

10.17 The trapezoidal channel of Fig. P10.17 is made of brickwork and slopes at 1:500. Determine the flow rate if the normal depth is 80 cm.

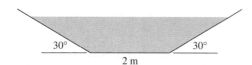

Fig. P10.17

10.18 Modify Prob. 10.17 as follows. Determine the normal depth for which the flow rate will be 8 m³/s.

10.19 Modify Prob. 10.17 as follows. Let the surface be clean earth, which erodes if V exceeds 1.5 m/s. What is the maximum depth to avoid erosion?

10.20 A circular corrugated-metal storm drain is flowing half full over a slope 4 ft/mi. Estimate the normal discharge if the drain diameter is 8 ft.

10.21 A sewer pipe has the shape of Fig. P10.21 and is constructed of unfinished concrete. The slope is 3 ft/mi. Plot the normal flow rate as a function of depth over the full range $0 < y < 7$ ft, and determine the maximum discharge and maximum velocity.

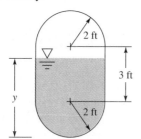

Fig. P10.21

10.22 A trapezoidal aqueduct (Fig. 10.7) has $b = 5$ m and $\theta = 40°$ and carries a normal flow of 60 m³/s of water when $y = 3.2$ m. For clay tile surfaces, estimate the required elevation drop in m/km.

10.23 For the aqueduct of Prob. 10.22, what will the normal depth be if the slope is 0.0003 and the discharge is 30 m³/s?

10.24 A riveted-steel channel slopes at 1:500 and has a V shape with an included angle of 80°. Find the normal depth if the flow rate is 900 m³/h.

10.25 The equilateral-triangle channel in Fig. P10.25 has constant

Fig. P10.25

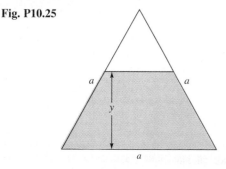

slope S_0 and constant Manning factor n. Find Q_{max} and V_{max}. Then, by analogy with Fig. 10.6b, plot the ratios Q/Q_{max} and V/V_{max} as a function of y/a for the complete range $0 < y/a < 0.866$.

10.26 For the channel of Fig. P10.25, determine the normal discharge for asphalt walls if $S_0 = 0.0022$, $a = 90$ cm, and the channel is 60 percent full of water.

10.27 A circular unfinished-cement water channel has a slope of 1:600 and a diameter of 5 ft. Estimate the normal discharge in gal/min for which the average wall shear stress is 0.15 lbf/ft², and compare your result to the maximum possible discharge for this channel.

10.28 Show that, for any straight prismatic channel in uniform flow, the average wall shear stress is given by

$$\tau_{av} \approx \rho g R_h S_0$$

If you happen to spot this result early, you can use it in solving Prob. 10.27.

10.29 Suppose that the trapezoidal channel of Fig. P10.17 contains sand and silt which we wish not to erode. According to an empirical correlation by A. Shields in 1936, the average wall shear stress τ_{crit} required to erode sand particles of diameter d_p is approximated by

$$\frac{\tau_{crit}}{(\rho_s - \rho)g \, d_p} \approx 0.5$$

where $\rho_s \approx 2400$ kg/m³ is the density of sand. If the slope of the channel in Fig. P10.17 is 1:900 and $n \approx 0.014$, determine the maximum water depth to keep from eroding particles of 1-mm diameter.

10.30 A clay tile V-shaped channel, with an included angle of 90°, is 1 km long and is laid out on a 1:400 slope. When running at a depth of 2 m, the upstream end is suddenly closed while the lower end continues to drain. Assuming quasi-steady normal discharge, find the time for the channel depth to drop to 20 cm.

10.31 A storm drain has the cross section shown in Fig. P10.31 and is laid on a slope of 1.5 m/km. If it is constructed of brickwork, find the normal discharge when it is exactly half full of water.

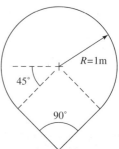

Fig. P10.31

10.32   A 2-m-diameter clay tile sewer pipe runs half full on a slope of 0.25°. Compute the normal flow rate in gal/min.

10.33   Five of the sewer pipes from Prob. 10.32 empty into a single asphalt pipe, also laid out at 0.25°. If the large pipe is also to run half full, what should be its diameter?

10.34   A brick rectangular channel with $S_0 = 0.002$ is designed to carry 230 ft^3/s of water in uniform flow. There is an argument over whether the channel width should be 4 or 8 ft. Which design needs fewer bricks? By what percentage?

10.35   In flood stage a natural channel often consists of a deep main channel plus two floodplains, as in Fig. P10.35. The floodplains are often shallow and rough. If the channel has the same slope everywhere, how would you analyze this situation for the discharge? Suppose that $y_1 = 20$ ft, $y_2 = 5$ ft, $b_1 = 40$ ft, $b_2 = 100$ ft, $n_1 = 0.020$, $n_2 = 0.040$, with a slope of 0.0002. Estimate the discharge in ft^3/s.

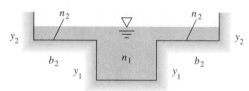

Fig. P10.35

10.36   The Blackstone River in northern Rhode Island normally flows at about 25 m^3/s and resembles Fig. P10.35 with a clean-earth center channel, $b_1 \approx 20$ m and $y_1 \approx 3$ m. The bed slope is about 2 ft/mi. The sides are heavy brush with $b_2 \approx 150$ m. During hurricane Carol in 1955, a record flow rate of 1000 m^3/s was estimated. Use this information to estimate the maximum flood depth y_2 during this event.

10.37   The answer to Prob. 10.34 is that the 8-ft width is 29 percent more efficient than the 4-ft width and is almost optimum. Verify this result, using the "best-efficiency" concepts of Sec. 10.3.

10.38   A rectangular channel has $b = 3$ m and $y = 1$ m. If n and S_0 are the same, what is the diameter of a semicircular channel that will have the same discharge? Compare the two wetted perimeters.

10.39   A trapezoidal channel has $n = 0.022$ and $S_0 = 0.0003$ and is made in the shape of a half-hexagon for maximum efficiency. What should the length of the side of the hexagon be if the channel is to carry 225 ft^3/s of water? What is the discharge of a semicircular channel of the same cross-sectional area and the same S_0 and n?

10.40   Using the geometry of Fig. 10.6a, prove that the most efficient circular open channel (maximum hydraulic radius for a given flow area) is a semicircle.

10.41   Determine the most efficient value of θ for the V-shaped channel of Fig. P10.41.

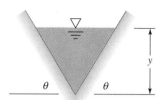

Fig. P10.41

10.42   Suppose that the side angles of the trapezoidal channel in Prob. 10.39 are reduced to 15° to avoid earth slides. If the bottom flat width is 8 ft, (a) determine the normal depth and (b) compare the resulting wetted perimeter with the solution $P = 24.1$ ft from Prob. 10.39. (Do not reveal this answer to friends still struggling with Prob. 10.39.)

10.43   What are the most efficient dimensions for a riveted-steel rectangular channel to carry 4.8 m^3/s at a slope of 1:900?

10.44   What are the most efficient dimensions for a half-hexagon cast-iron channel to carry 15,000 gal/min on a slope of 0.16°?

10.45   What is the most efficient depth for an asphalt trapezoidal channel, with sides sloping at 45°, to carry 3 m^3/s on a slope of 0.0008?

10.46   Sellin [2, p. 116] suggests that a channel which affords minimum erosion has a half-sine-wave shape, as in Fig. P10.46. The local depth takes the form $h(z) = h_0 \sin(\pi z/b)$. For uniform-flow conditions, determine the most efficient ratio h_0/b for this channel shape.

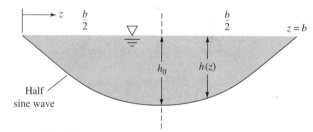

Fig. P10.46

10.47   Replot Fig. 10.8b in the form of q versus y for constant E. Does the maximum q occur at the critical depth?

10.48   A wide, clean-earth river has a flow rate $q = 150$ ft^3/(s · ft). What is the critical depth? If the actual depth is 12 ft, what is the Froude number of the river? Compute the critical slope by (a) Manning's formula and (b) the Moody chart.

10.49   Find the critical depth of the brick channel in Prob. 10.34 for both the 4- and 8-ft widths. Are the normal flows sub- or supercritical?

10.50   A pencil point piercing the surface of a rectangular channel flow creates a wedgelike 25° half-angle wave, as in Fig. P10.50. If the channel surface is painted steel and the depth is 35 cm, determine (*a*) the Froude number, (*b*) the critical depth, and (*c*) the critical slope for uniform flow.

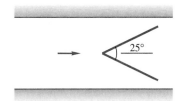

Fig. P10.50

10.51 Modify Prob. 10.50 as follows. Let the water be flowing in an unfinished-cement half-full circular channel of diameter 60 cm. Determine (*a*) the Froude number, (*b*) the flow velocity, and (*c*) the critical slope.

10.52 Modify Prob. 10.50 as follows. Let the water be flowing full in an asphalt half-hexagon channel of side length 40 cm. Determine (*a*) the Froude number, (*b*) the flow velocity, and (*c*) the critical slope.

10.53 For the river flow of Prob. 10.48, find the depth y_2 which has the same specific energy as the given depth $y_1 = 12$ ft. These are called *conjugate depths*. What is Fr_2?

10.54 A clay tile V-shaped channel has an included angle of 70° and carries 8.5 m³/s. Compute (*a*) the critical depth, (*b*) the critical velocity, and (*c*) the critical slope for uniform flow.

10.55 A trapezoidal channel resembles Fig. 10.7 with $b = 1$ m. The water depth is 2 m, and the flow rate is 32 m³/s. If you stick your fingernail in the surface, as in Fig. P10.50, what half-angle wave might appear?

10.56 A riveted-steel triangular duct flows partly full as in Fig. P10.56. If the critical depth is 50 cm, compute (*a*) the critical flow rate and (*b*) the critical slope.

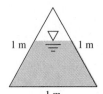

Fig. P10.56

10.57 For the triangular duct of Prob. 10.56, if the critical flow rate is 1.0 m³/s, compute (*a*) the critical depth and (*b*) the critical slope.

10.58 A circular corrugated-metal channel is half full and in uniform flow at a slope $S_0 = 0.0037$. Estimate the Froude number of the flow.

10.59 Uniform water flow in a wide brick channel of slope 0.02° moves over a 10-cm bump as in Fig. P10.59. A slight depression in the water surface results. if the minimum water depth over the bump is 50 cm, compute (*a*) the velocity over the bump and (*b*) the flow rate per meter of width.

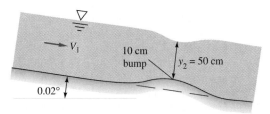

Fig. P10.59

10.60 Modify Prob. 10.59 as follows. Again assuming uniform subcritical approach flow (V_1, y_1), find (*a*) the flow rate and (*b*) y_2 for which the Froude number Fr_2 at the crest of the bump is exactly 0.8.

10.61 Modify Prob. 10.59 as follows. Again assuming uniform subcritical approach flow (V_1, y_1), find (*a*) the flow rate and (*b*) y_2 for which the flow at the crest of the bump is exactly critical ($Fr_2 = 1.0$).

10.62 Consider the flow in a wide channel over a bump, as in Fig. P10.62. One can estimate the water-depth change or *transition* with frictionless flow. Use continuity and the Bernoulli equation to show that

$$\frac{dy}{dx} = -\frac{dh/dx}{1 - V^2/(gy)}$$

Is the drawdown of the water surface realistic in Fig. P10.62? Explain under what conditions the surface might rise above its upstream position y_0.

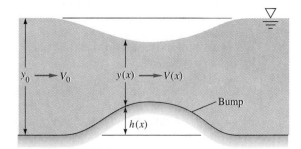

Fig. P10.62

10.63 In Fig. P10.62 let $V_0 = 1$ m/s and $y_0 = 1$ m. If the maximum bump height is 15 cm, estimate (*a*) the Froude number over the top of the bump and (*b*) the maximum depression in the water surface.

10.64 In Fig. P10.62 let $V_0 = 1$ m/s and $y_0 = 1$ m. If the flow over the top of the bump is exactly critical (Fr = 1.0), determine the bump height h_{max}.

10.65 Program and solve the differential equation of "frictionless flow over a bump," from Prob. 10.62, for entrance conditions $V_0 = 1$ m/s and $y_0 = 1$ m. Let the bump have the convenient shape $h = 0.5h_{max}[1 - \cos(2\pi x/L)]$, which simulates Fig. P10.62. Let $L = 3$ m, and generate a numerical solution for $y(x)$ in the bump region $0 < x < L$. If you have time for only one case, use $h_{max} = 15$ cm (Prob. 10.63), for which the maximum Froude number is 0.425. If more time is available, it is instructive to examine a complete family of surface profiles for $h_{max} \approx 1$ cm up to 35 cm (which is the solution of Prob. 10.64).

10.66 In Fig. P10.62 let $V_0 = 6$ m/s and $y_0 = 1$ m. If the maximum bump height is 35 cm, estimate (a) the Froude number over the top of the bump and (b) the maximum increase in the water-surface level.

10.67 In Fig. P10.62 let $V_0 = 6$ m/s and $y_0 = 1$ m. If the flow over the top of the bump is exactly critical (Fr = 1.0), determine the bump height h_{max}.

10.68 Modify Prob. 10.65 to have a supercritical approach condition $V_0 = 6$ m/s and $y_0 = 1$ m. If you have time for only one case, use $h_{max} = 35$ cm (Prob. 10.66), for which the maximum Froude number is 1.47. If more time is available, it is instructive to examine a complete family of surface profiles for 1 cm $< h_{max} <$ 52 cm (which is the solution to Prob. 10.67).

10.69 Given is the flow of a channel of large width b under a sluice gate, as in Fig. P10.69. Assuming frictionless steady flow with negligible upstream kinetic energy, derive a formula for the dimensionless flow ratio $Q^2/(y_1^3 b^2 g)$ as a function of the ratio y_2/y_1. Show by differentiation that the maximum flow rate occurs at $y_2 = 2y_1/3$.

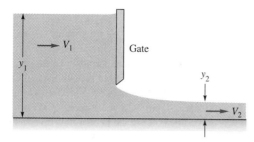

Fig. P10.69

10.70 In Fig. P10.69 let $y_1 = 90$ cm and $V_1 = 65$ cm/s. Estimate (a) y_2, (b) Fr_2, and (c) the flow rate per unit width.

10.71 In Fig. P10.69 let $y_1 = 95$ cm and $y_2 = 50$ cm. Estimate the flow rate per unit width if the upstream kinetic energy is (a) neglected and (b) included.

10.72 In Fig. P10.69 let $y_1 = 90$ cm and $y_2 = 15$ cm. Estimate (a) V_1, (b) Fr_2, and (c) the flow rate per unit width.

10.73 In Fig. P10.69 suppose that $y_1 = 1.2$ m and the gate is

raised so that its gap is 15 cm. Estimate the resulting flow rate per unit width.

10.74 With respect to Fig. P10.69, show that, for frictionless flow, the upstream velocity may be related to the water levels by

$$V_1 = \sqrt{\frac{2g(y_1 - y_2)}{K^2 - 1}}$$

where $K = y_1/y_2$.

10.75 A tank of water 1 m deep, 3 m long, and 4 m wide into the paper has a closed sluice gate on the right side, as in Fig. P10.75. At $t = 0$ the gate is opened to a gap of 10 cm. Assuming quasi-steady sluice-gate theory, estimate the time required for the water level to drop to 50 cm. Assume free outflow.

Fig. P10.75

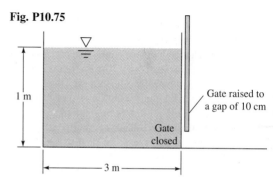

10.76 In Prob. 10.75 estimate what gap height would cause the tank level to drop from 1 m to 50 cm in exactly 1 min. Assume free outflow.

10.77 Equation (10.41) for the discharge coefficient is for free (nearly frictionless) outflow. If the outlet is *drowned*, as in Fig. 10.10c, there is dissipation and C_d drops sharply. Figure P10.77 shows data from Ref. 3 on drowned vertical

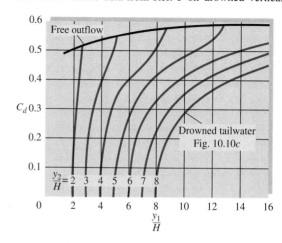

Fig. P10.77 (*from Ref. 3, p. 509*)

sluice gates. Use this chart to repeat Prob. 10.73, and plot the estimated flow rate versus y_2 in the range $0 < y_2 < 60$ cm.

10.78 Repeat Prob. 10.75 if the gate is drowned at $y_2 = 40$ cm.

10.79 Show that the Froude number downstream of a hydraulic jump will be given by $Fr_2 = 8^{1/2}Fr_1/[(1 + 8\ Fr_1^2)^{1/2} - 1]^{3/2}$. Does the formula remain correct if we reverse subscripts 1 and 2? Why?

10.80 For what Froude number Fr_1 is the energy dissipation in a hydraulic jump exactly 60 percent according to theory?

10.81 Water flows in a wide channel at $q = 25$ ft^3/(s · ft), $y_1 = 1$ ft, and then undergoes a hydraulic jump. Compute y_2, V_2, Fr_2, h_f, the percentage dissipation, and the horsepower dissipated per unit width. What is the critical depth?

10.82 The flow downstream of a wide hydraulic jump is 7 m deep and has a velocity of 2.2 m/s. Estimate the upstream (a) depth and (b) velocity and (c) the critical depth of the flow.

10.83 A wide-channel flow undergoes a hydraulic jump from 40 to 140 cm. Estimate (a) V_1, (b) V_2, (c) the critical depth, in cm, and (d) the percentage of dissipation.

10.84 Consider the flow under the sluice gate of Fig. P10.84. If $y_1 = 10$ ft and all losses are neglected except the dissipation in the jump, calculate y_2 and y_3 and the percentage of dissipation, and sketch the flow to scale with the EGL included. The channel is horizontal and wide.

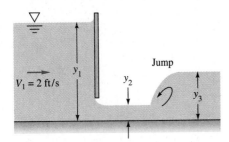

Fig. P10.84

10.85 Modify Prob. 10.84 as follows. Let $y_1 = 1$ m and $y_3 = 70$ cm, with V_1 unknown. Estimate the flow rate q in m^3/(s · m).

10.86 A *bore* is a hydraulic jump which propagates upstream into a still or slower-moving fluid, as in Fig. 10.4a. Suppose that the still water is 2 m deep and the water behind the bore is 3 m deep. Estimate (a) the propagation speed of the bore and (b) the induced water velocity.

10.87 A *tidal bore* may occur when the ocean tide enters an estuary against an oncoming river discharge, such as on the Severn River in England. Suppose that the tidal bore is 10 ft deep and propagates at 13 mi/h upstream into a river which is 7 ft deep. Estimate the river current in kn.

10.88 At one point in a rectangular channel 7 ft wide, the depth

is 2 ft and the flow rate is 200 ft^3/s. If a hydraulic jump occurs nearby, determine (a) whether it is upstream or downstream of this point and (b) the percentage of dissipation in the jump.

10.89 Water 30 cm deep is in uniform flow down a 1° unfinished-concrete slope when a hydraulic jump occurs, as in Fig. P10.89. If the channel is very wide, estimate the water depth y_2 downstream of the jump.

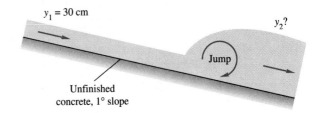

Fig. P10.89

10.90 Modify Prob. 10.89 as follows. Suppose that $y_2 = 1$ m and $y_1 = 30$ cm but the channel slope is not equal to 1°. Determine the proper slope for this condition.

10.91 No doubt you used the horizontal-jump formula (10.43) to solve Probs. 10.89 and 10.90, which is reasonable since the slope is so small. However, Chow [ref. 3, p. 425] points out that hydraulic jumps are *higher* on sloped channels, due to "the weight of the fluid in the jump." Make a control-volume sketch of a sloping jump to show why this is so. The sloped-jump chart given in Chow's figure 15-20 may be approximated by the following curve fit:

$$\frac{2y_2}{y_1} \approx [(1 + 8\ Fr_1^2)^{1/2} - 1]e^{3.5S_0}$$

where $0 < S_0 < 0.3$ are the channel slopes for which data are available. Use this correlation to modify your solution to Prob. 10.89. If time permits, make a graph of y_2/y_1 (≤ 20) versus Fr_1 (≤ 15) for various S_0 (≤ 0.3).

10.92 At the bottom of an 80-ft-wide spillway is a horizontal hydraulic jump with water depths 1 ft upstream and 10 ft downstream. Estimate (a) the flow rate and (b) the horsepower dissipated.

10.93 Water in a horizontal channel accelerates smoothly over a bump and then undergoes a hydraulic jump, as in Fig. P10.93. If $y_1 = 1$ m and $y_3 = 40$ cm, estimate (a) V_1, (b) V_3, (c) y_4, and (d) the bump height h.

10.94 Modify Prob. 10.93 as follows. Let the bump height be 20 cm and the subcritical approach velocity be $V_1 = 1.5$ m/s. Determine (a) y_2, (b) the supercritical flow V_3, and (c) y_4.

10.95 A 10-cm-high bump in a wide horizontal water channel creates a hydraulic jump just upstream and the flow pattern in Fig. P10.95. Neglecting losses except in the jump, for

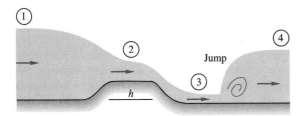

Fig. P10.93

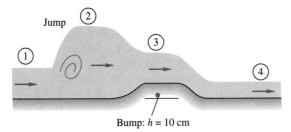

Fig. P10.95

the case $y_3 = 30$ cm, estimate (a) V_4, (b) y_4, (c) V_1, and (d) y_1.

10.96 Show that the Froude numbers on either side of a wide hydraulic jump are related by the simple relation $Fr_2 = Fr_1(y_1/y_2)^{3/2}$.

10.97 A brickwork rectangular channel 4 m wide is flowing at $8.0 \text{ m}^3/\text{s}$ on a slope of $0.1°$. Is this a mild, critical, or steep slope? What type of gradually varied solution curve are we on if the local water depth is (a) 1 m, (b) 1.5 m, and (c) 2 m?

10.98 A gravelly earth wide channel is flowing at $10 \text{ m}^3/\text{s}$ per meter of width on a slope of $0.75°$. Is this a mild, critical, or steep slope? What type of gradually varied solution curve are we on if the local water depth is (a) 1 m, (b) 2 m, and (c) 3 m?

10.99 A clay tile V-shaped channel of included angle $60°$ is flowing at $1.98 \text{ m}^3/\text{s}$ on a slope of $0.33°$. Is this a mild, critical, or steep slope? What type of gradually varied solution curve are we on if the local water depth is (a) 1 m, (b) 2 m, and (c) 3 m?

10.100 If bottom friction is included in the sluice-gate flow of Prob. 10.84, the depths (y_1, y_2, y_3) will vary with x. Sketch the type and shape of gradually varied solution curve in each region (1, 2, 3), and show the regions of rapidly varied flow.

10.101 Consider the gradual change from the profile beginning at point a in Fig. P10.101 on a mild slope S_{01} to a mild but steeper slope S_{02} downstream. Sketch and label the curve $y(x)$ expected.

10.102 The wide-channel flow in Fig. P10.102 changes from a

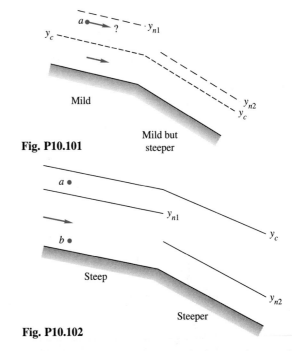

Fig. P10.101

Fig. P10.102

steep slope to one even steeper. Beginning at points a and b, sketch and label the water-surface profiles which are expected for gradually varied flow.

10.103 A circular painted-steel channel, $R = 50$ cm, runs half full at $1 \text{ m}^3/\text{s}$ on a slope of 5 m/km. Is this a mild or steep slope? Is the flow on a type 1, 2, or 3 curve?

10.104 The rectangular-channel flow in Fig. P10.104 expands to a cross section 50 percent wider. Beginning at points a and b, sketch and label the water-surface profiles which are expected for gradually varied flow.

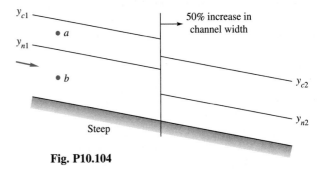

Fig. P10.104

10.105 In Prob. 10.84 the frictionless solution is $y_2 = 0.82$ ft, which we denote as $x = 0$ just downstream of the gate. If the channel is horizontal with $n = 0.018$ and there is no hydraulic jump, compute from gradually varied theory the downstream distance where $y = 2.0$ ft.

10.106 A rectangular channel with $n = 0.018$ and a constant slope of 0.0025 increases its width linearly from b to $2b$ over a distance L, as in Fig. P10.106. (a) Determine the variation $y(x)$ along the channel if $b = 4$ m, $L = 250$ m, the initial depth is $y(0) = 1.05$ m, and the flow rate is 7 m³/s. (b) Then, if your computer program is running well, determine the initial depth $y(0)$ for which the exit flow will be exactly critical.

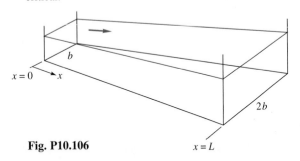

Fig. P10.106

10.107 A clean-earth wide-channel flow is flowing up an adverse slope with $S_0 = -0.002$. If the flow rate is $q = 4.5$ m³/(s · m), use gradually varied theory to compute the distance for the depth to drop from 3.0 to 2.0 m.

10.108 Illustrate Prob. 10.104 with a numerical example. Let the channel be rectangular with a width $b_1 = 10$ m for $0 < x < 100$ m, expanding to $b_2 = 15$ m for $100 < x < 250$ m. The flow rate is 27 m³/s, and $n = 0.012$. Compute the water depth at $x = 250$ m for initial depth $y(0)$ equal to (a) 75 cm and (b) 5 cm. Compare your results with the discussion in Prob. 10.104.

10.109 Figure P10.109 illustrates a free overfall or *dropdown* flow pattern, where a channel flow accelerates down a slope and falls freely over an abrupt edge. As shown, the flow reaches critical just before the overfall. Between y_c and the edge the flow is rapidly varied and does not satisfy gradually varied theory. Suppose that the flow rate is $q = 1.3$ m³/(s · m) and the surface is unfinished cement. Use Eq. (10.51) to estimate the water depth 300 m upstream as shown.

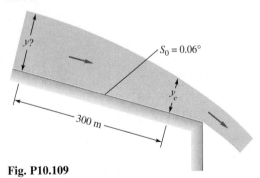

Fig. P10.109

10.110 We assumed frictionless flow in solving the bump case, Prob. 10.65, for which $V_2 = 1.21$ m/s and $y_2 = 0.826$ m over the crest when $h_{max} = 15$ cm, $V_1 = 1$ m/s, and $y_1 = 1$ m. However, if the bump is long and rough, friction may be important. Repeat Prob. 10.65 for the same bump shape, $h = 0.5h_{max}[1 - \cos(2\pi x/L)]$, to compute conditions (a) at the crest and (b) at the end of the bump, $x = L$. Let $h_{max} = 15$ cm and $L = 100$ m, and assume a clean-earth surface.

10.111 Modify Prob. 10.110 as follows. Keep all other data the same, and find the bump length L for which the flow first becomes critical somewhere along the bump surface.

10.112 The clean-earth channel in Fig. P10.112 is 6 m wide and slopes at 0.3°. Water flows at 30 m³/s in the channel and enters a reservoir so that the channel depth is 3 m just before the entry. Assuming gradually varied flow, how far is the distance L to a point in the channel where $y = 2$ m? What type of curve is the water surface?

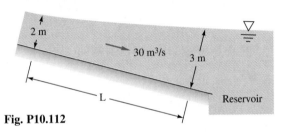

Fig. P10.112

10.113 Figure P10.113 shows a channel contraction section often called a *venturi flume* [19, p. 167], because measurements of y_1 and y_2 can be used to meter the flow rate. Show that if losses are neglected and the flow is one-dimensional and subcritical, the flow rate is given by

$$Q = \left[\frac{2g(y_1 - y_2)}{1/(b_2^2 y_2^2) - 1/(b_1^2 y_1^2)} \right]^{1/2}$$

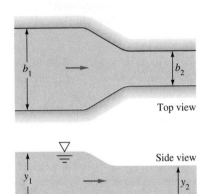

Fig. P10.113

Apply this to the special case $b_1 = 3$ m, $b_2 = 2$ m, and $y_1 = 1.9$ m. (*a*) Find the flow rate if $y_2 = 1.5$ m. (*b*) Also find the depth y_2 for which the flow becomes critical in the throat.

10.114 Investigate the possibility of *choking* in the venturi flume of Fig. P10.113. Let $b_1 = 4$ ft, $b_2 = 3$ ft, and $y_1 = 2$ ft. Compute the values of y_2 and V_1 for a flow rate of (*a*) 30 ft³/s and (*b*) 35 ft³/s. Explain your vexation.

10.115 Gradually varied theory, Eq. (10.49), neglects the effect of *width* changes, db/dx, assuming that they are small. But they are not small for a short, sharp contraction such as the venturi flume in Fig. P10.113. Show that, for a rectangular section with $b = b(x)$, Eq. (10.49) should be modified as follows:

$$\frac{dy}{dx} \approx \frac{S_0 - S + [V^2/(gb)](db/dx)}{1 - Fr^2}$$

Investigate a criterion for reducing this relation to Eq. (10.49).

10.116 Investigate the possibility of *frictional effects* in the venturi flume of Prob. 10.113, part (*a*), for which the frictionless solution is $Q = 9.88$ m³/s. Let the contraction be 3 m long and the measurements of y_1 and y_2 be at positions 3 m upstream and 3 m downstream of the contraction, respectively. Use the modified gradually varied theory of Prob. 10.115, with $n = 0.018$ to estimate the flow rate.

10.117 A full-width weir in a horizontal channel is 5 m wide and 80 cm high. The upstream depth is 1.5 m. Estimate the flow rate for (*a*) a sharp-crested weir and (*b*) a round-nosed broad-crested weir.

10.118 Using a Bernoulli-type analysis similar to Fig. 10.16*a*, show that the theoretical discharge of the V-shaped weir in Fig. P10.118 is given by

$$Q = 0.7542g^{1/2} \tan \alpha \, H^{5/2}$$

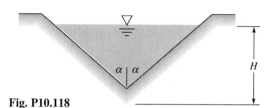

Fig. P10.118

10.119 Data by A. T. Lenz for water at 20°C (reported in Ref. 19) show a significant increase of discharge coefficient of V-notch weirs (Fig. P10.118) at low heads. For $\alpha = 20°$, some measured values are as follows:

H, ft	0.2	0.4	0.6	0.8	1.0
C_d	0.499	0.470	0.461	0.456	0.452

Determine if these data can be correlated with the Reynolds and Weber numbers vis-à-vis Eq. (10.61). If not, suggest another correlation.

10.120 The rectangular channel in Fig. P10.120 contains a V-notch weir as shown. The intent is to meter flow rates between 2.0 and 6.0 m³/s with an upstream hook gage set to measure water depths between 2.0 and 2.75 m. What are the most appropriate values for the notch height Y and the notch half-angle α?

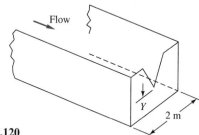

Fig. P10.120

10.121 Water flow in a rectangular channel is to be metered by a thin-plate weir with side contractions, as in Table 10.1*b*, with $L = 6$ ft and $Y = 1$ ft. It is desired to measure flow rates between 1500 and 3000 gal/min with only a 6-in change in upstream water depth. What is the most appropriate length for the weir width b?

10.122 In 1952 E. S Crump developed the triangular weir shape shown in Fig. P10.122 [Ref. 19, chap. 4]. The front slope is 1:2 to avoid sediment deposition, and the rear slope is 1:5 to maintain a stable tailwater flow. The beauty of the design is that it has a unique discharge correlation up to near-drowning conditions, $H_2/H_1 \leq 0.75$:

$$Q = C_d b g^{1/2} \left(H_1 + \frac{V_1^2}{2g} - k_h \right)^{3/2}$$

where $\quad C_d \approx 0.63 \quad$ and $\quad k_h \approx 0.3$ mm

The term k_h is a low-head loss factor. Suppose that the weir is 3 m wide and has a crest height $Y = 50$ cm. If the water depth upstream is 65 cm, estimate the flow rate in gal/min.

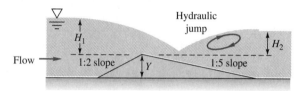

Fig. P10.122 The Crump weir [19, chap. 4]

10.123 The Crump weir calibration in Prob. 10.122 is for *modular* flow, i.e., when the flow rate is independent of downstream tailwater. When the weir becomes drowned, the flow rate decreases by the following factor:

$$Q = Q_{mod}f$$

where $\quad f \approx 1.035\left[0.817 - \left(\dfrac{H_2^*}{H_1^*}\right)^4\right]^{0.0647}$

for $0.70 \le H_2^*/H_1^* \le 0.93$, where H^* denotes $H_1 + V_1^2/(2g) - k_h$ for brevity. The weir is then *double-gaged* to measure both H_1 and H_2. Suppose that the weir crest is 1 m high and 2 m wide. If the measured upstream and downstream water depths are 2.0 and 1.9 m, respectively, estimate the flow rate in gal/min. Comment on the possible uncertainty of your estimate.

10.124 Water flows at 600 ft³/s in a rectangular channel 22 ft wide with $n \approx 0.024$ and a slope of 0.1°. A dam increases the depth to 15 ft, as in Fig. P10.124. Using gradually varied theory, estimate the distance L upstream at which the water depth will be 10 ft. What type of solution curve are we on? What should be the water depth asymptotically far upstream?

10.125 The Tupperware dam on the Blackstone River is 12 ft high, 100 ft wide, and sharp-edged. It creates a backwater similar to Fig. P10.124. Assume that the river is a weedy-earth rectangular channel 100 ft wide with a flow rate of 800 ft³/s. Estimate the water-depth 2 mi upstream of the dam if $S_0 = 0.001$.

10.126 Suppose that the rectangular channel of Fig. P10.120 is made of riveted steel and carries a flow of 8 m³/s on a slope of 0.15°. If the V-notch weir has $\alpha = 30°$ and $Y = 50$ cm, estimate, from gradually varied theory, the water depth 100 m upstream.

10.127 A horizontal gravelly earth channel 2 m wide contains a full-width Crump weir (Fig. P10.122) 1 m high. If the weir is not drowned, estimate, from gradually varied theory, the flow rate for which the water depth 100 m upstream will be 2 m.

10.128 A rectangular channel 4 m wide is blocked by a broad-crested weir 2 m high, as in Fig. P10.128. The channel is horizontal for 200 m upstream and then slopes at 0.7° as shown. The flow rate is 12 m³/s, and $n = 0.03$. Compute the water depth y at 300 m upstream from gradually varied theory.

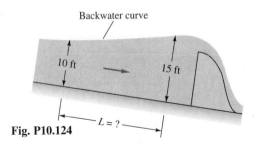

Backwater curve

10 ft

15 ft

$L = ?$

Fig. P10.124

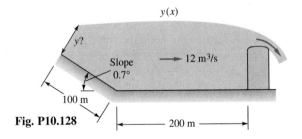

$y(x)$

$y?$

Slope 0.7°

12 m³/s

100 m

200 m

Fig. P10.128

WORD PROBLEMS

W10.1 Free-surface problems are driven by gravity. Why do so many of the formulas in this chapter contain the *square root* of the acceleration of gravity?

W10.2 Explain why the flow under a sluice gate, Fig. 10.10, either is or is not analogous to compressible gas flow through a converging-diverging nozzle, Fig. 9.12.

W10.3 In uniform open-channel flow, what is the balance of forces? Can you use such a force balance to derive the Chézy equation (10.13)?

W10.4 A shallow-water wave propagates at the speed $c_0 \approx (gy)^{1/2}$. What makes it propagate? That is, what is the balance of forces in such wave motion? In which direction

does such a wave propagate?

W10.5 Why is the Manning friction correlation, Eq. (10.16), used almost universally by hydraulics engineers, instead of the Moody friction factor?

W10.6 During horizontal channel flow over a bump, is the specific energy constant? Explain.

W10.7 Cite some similarities, and perhaps some dissimilarities, between a hydraulic jump and a gas-dynamic normal-shock wave.

W10.8 Give three examples of rapidly varied flow. For each case, cite reasons why it does not satisfy one or more of the five basic assumptions of gradually varied flow theory.

W10.9 Is a free overfall, Fig. 10.15*e*, similar to a weir? Could it be calibrated versus flow rate in the same manner as a weir? Explain.

W10.10 Cite some similarities, and perhaps some dissimilarities, between a weir and a Bernoulli obstruction flowmeter from Sec. 6.7.

W10.11 Is a bump, Fig. 10.9*a*, similar to a weir? If not, when does a bump become large enough, or sharp enough, to be a weir?

W10.12 After doing some reading and/or thinking, explain the design and operation of a *long-throated flume*.

W10.13 Describe the design and operation of a *critical-depth flume*. What are its advantages compared to the venturi flume of Prob. 10.113?

Design Project

D10.1 A straight weedy-earth channel has the trapezoidal shape of Fig. 10.7, with $b = 4$ m and $\theta = 35°$. The channel has a constant bottom slope of 0.001. The flow rate varies seasonally from 5 up to 10 m^3/s. It is desired to place a sharp-edged weir across the channel so that the water depth 1 km upstream remains at 2.0 m $\pm$ 10 percent throughout the year. Investigate the possibility of accomplishing this with a full-width weir; if successful, determine the proper weir height *Y*. If unsuccessful, try other alternatives, such as (*a*) a full-width broad crested weir or (*b*) a weir with side contractions or (*c*) a V-notch weir. Whatever your final design, cite the seasonal variation of normal depths and critical depths for comparison with the desired year-round depth of 2 m.

Chapter 11
Turbomachinery

Motivation. The most common practical engineering application for fluid mechanics is the design of fluid machinery. The most numerous types are machines which *add* energy to the fluid (the pump family), but also important are those which *extract* energy (turbines). Both types are usually connected to a rotating shaft, hence the name *turbomachinery*.

The purpose of this chapter is to make elementary engineering estimates of the performance of fluid machines. The emphasis will be upon nearly incompressible flow, i.e., liquids or low-velocity gases. Basic flow principles are discussed, but not the detailed construction of the machine.

11.1 Introduction and Classification

Turbomachines divide naturally into those which add energy (pumps) and extract energy (turbines). The prefix *turbo-* is a Latin word meaning ''spin'' or ''whirl,'' appropriate for rotating devices.

The pump is the oldest fluid-energy-transfer device known. At least two designs date before Christ: (1) the undershot-bucket waterwheels, or *norias*, used in Asia and Africa (1000 B.C.) and (2) Archimedes' screw pump (250 B.C.), still being manufactured today to handle solid-liquid mixtures. Paddlewheel turbines were used by the Romans in 70 B.C., and Babylonian windmills date back to 700 B.C.

Machines which deliver liquids are simply called *pumps*, but if gases are involved, three different terms are in use, depending upon the pressure rise achieved. If the pressure rise is very small (a few inches of water), a gas pump is called a *fan*; up to 1 atm, it is usually called a *blower*; and above 1 atm it is commonly termed a *compressor*.

Classification of Pumps

There are two basic types of pumps: positive-displacement and dynamic or momentum-change pumps. There are several billion of each type in use in the world today.

Positive-displacement pumps (PDPs) force the fluid along by volume changes. A cavity opens, and the fluid is admitted through an inlet. The cavity then closes, and the fluid is squeezed through an outlet. The mammalian heart is a good example, and many mechanical designs are in wide use. The text by Warring [14] gives an excellent summary of PDPs. A brief classification of PDP designs is as follows:

    A. Reciprocating
        1. Piston or plunger
        2. Diaphragm
    B. Rotary
        1. Single rotor
            a. Sliding vane
            b. Flexible tube or lining
            c. Screw
            d. Peristaltic (wave contraction)
        2. Multiple rotors
            a. Gear
            b. Lobe
            c. Screw
            d. Circumferential piston

All PDPs deliver a pulsating or periodic flow as the cavity volume opens, traps, and squeezes the fluid. Their great advantage is the delivery of any fluid regardless of its viscosity.

Figure 11.1 shows schematics of the operating principles of seven of these PDPs. It is rare for such devices to be run backward, so to speak, as turbines or energy extractors, the steam engine (reciprocating piston) being a classic exception.

Since PDPs compress mechanically against a cavity filled with liquid, a common feature is that they develop immense pressures if the outlet is shut down for any reason. Sturdy construction is required, and complete shutoff would cause damage if pressure-relief valves were not used.

Dynamic pumps simply add momentum to the fluid by means of fast-moving blades or vanes or certain special designs. There is no closed volume: The fluid increases momentum while moving through open passages and then converts its high velocity to a pressure increase by exiting into a diffuser section. Dynamic pumps can be classified as follows:

    A. Rotary
        1. Centrifugal or radial exit flow
        2. Axial flow
        3. Mixed flow (between radial and axial)
    B. Special designs
        1. Jet pump or ejector (see Fig. P3.36)
        2. Electromagnetic pumps for liquid metals
        3. Fluid-actuated: gas-lift or hydraulic-ram

We shall concentrate in this chapter on the rotary designs, sometimes called *rotodynamic pumps*. Other designs of both PDP and dynamic pumps are discussed in specialized texts [for example, 11, 14, 31].

Dynamic pumps generally provide a higher flow rate than PDPs and a much steadier discharge but are ineffective in handling high-viscosity liquids. Dynamic pumps also generally need *priming*; i.e., if they are filled with gas, they cannot suck up a liquid from below into their inlet. The PDP, on the other hand, is self-priming for most

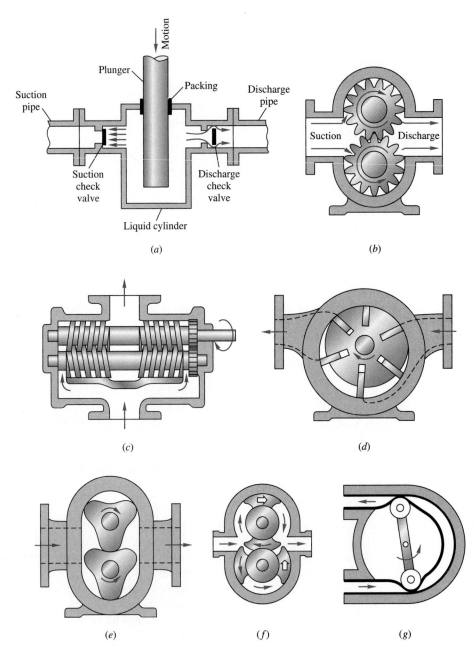

Fig. 11.1 Schematic design of positive-displacement pumps: (*a*) reciprocating piston or plunger, (*b*) external gear pump, (*c*) double-screw pump, (*d*) sliding vane, (*e*) three-lobe pump, (*f*) double circumferential piston, (*g*) flexible-tube squeegee.

applications. A dynamic pump can provide very high flow rates (up to 300,000 gal/min) but usually with moderate pressure rises (a few atmospheres). In contrast, a PDP can operate up to very high pressures (300 atm) but typically produces low flow rates (100 gal/min).

The relative *performance* (Δp versus Q) is quite different for the two types of pump, as shown in Fig. 11.2. At constant shaft rotation speed, the PDP produces nearly con-

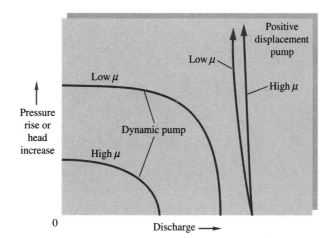

Fig. 11.2 Comparison of performance curves of typical dynamic and positive-displacement pumps at constant speed.

stant flow rate and virtually unlimited pressure rise, with little effect of viscosity. The flow rate of a PDP cannot be varied except by changing the displacement or the speed. The reliable constant-speed discharge from PDPs has led to their wide use in metering flows [35].

The dynamic pump, by contrast in Fig. 11.2, provides a continuous constant-speed variation of performance, from near-maximum Δp at zero flow (shutoff conditions) to zero Δp at maximum flow rate. High-viscosity fluids sharply degrade the performance of a dynamic pump.

As usual—and for the last time in this text—we remind the reader that this is merely an introductory chapter. Many books are devoted solely to turbomachines: generalized treatments [2 to 7], texts specializing in pumps [8 to 16], fans [17 to 20], compressors [21 to 23], turbines [24 to 28], and PDPs [35, 36]. There are several useful handbooks [29 to 32], and at least two elementary textbooks [33, 34] have a comprehensive discussion of turbomachines. The reader is referred to these sources for further details.

11.2 The Centrifugal Pump

Let us begin our brief look at rotodynamic machines by examining the characteristics of the centrifugal pump. As sketched in Fig. 11.3, this pump consists of an impeller rotating within a casing. Fluid enters axially through the *eye* of the casing, is caught up in the impeller blades, and is whirled tangentially and radially outward until it leaves

Fig. 11.3 Cutaway schematic of a typical centrifugal pump.

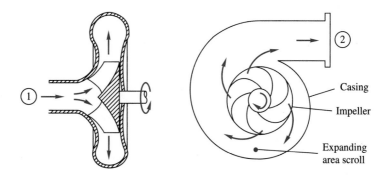

through all circumferential parts of the impeller into the diffuser part of the casing. The fluid gains both velocity and pressure while passing through the impeller. The doughnut-shaped diffuser, or *scroll*, section of the casing decelerates the flow and further increases the pressure.

The impeller blades are usually *backward-curved*, as in Fig. 11.3, but there are also radial and forward-curved blade designs, which slightly change the output pressure. The blades may be *open*, i.e., separated from the front casing only by a narrow clearance, or *closed*, i.e., shrouded from the casing on both sides by an impeller wall. The diffuser may be *vaneless*, as in Fig. 11.3, or fitted with fixed vanes to help guide the flow toward the exit.

Basic Output Parameters

Assuming steady flow, the pump basically increases the Bernoulli head of the flow between point 1, the eye, and point 2, the exit. From Eq. (3.67), neglecting viscous work and heat transfer, this change is denoted by H:

$$H = \left(\frac{p}{\rho g} + \frac{V^2}{2g} + z\right)_2 - \left(\frac{p}{\rho g} + \frac{V^2}{2g} + z\right)_1 = h_s - h_f \tag{11.1}$$

where h_s is the pump head supplied and h_f the losses. The net head H is a primary output parameter for any turbomachine. Since Eq. (11.1) is for incompressible flow, it must be modified for gas compressors with large density changes.

Usually V_2 and V_1 are about the same, $z_2 - z_1$ is no more than a meter or so, and the net pump head is essentially equal to the change in pressure head

$$H \approx \frac{p_2 - p_1}{\rho g} = \frac{\Delta p}{\rho g} \tag{11.2}$$

The power delivered to the fluid simply equals the specific weight times the discharge times the net head change

$$P_w = \rho g Q H \tag{11.3}$$

This is traditionally called the *water horsepower*. The power required to drive the pump is the *brake horsepower*[1]

$$\text{bhp} = \omega T \tag{11.4}$$

where ω is the shaft angular velocity and T the shaft torque. If there were no losses, P_w and brake horsepower would be equal, but of course P_w is actually less, and the *efficiency* η of the pump is defined as

$$\eta = \frac{P_w}{\text{bhp}} = \frac{\rho g Q H}{\omega T} \tag{11.5}$$

The chief aim of the pump designer is to make η as high as possible over as broad a range of discharge Q as possible.

The efficiency is basically composed of three parts: volumetric, hydraulic, and mechanical. The *volumetric efficiency* is

---

[1] Conversion factors may be needed: 1 hp $= 550$ ft $\cdot$ lbf/s.

$$\eta_v = \frac{Q}{Q + Q_L} \tag{11.6}$$

where Q_L is the loss of fluid due to leakage in the impeller-casing clearances. The *hydraulic efficiency* is

$$\eta_h = 1 - \frac{h_f}{h_s} \tag{11.7}$$

where h_f has three parts: (1) *shock* loss at the eye due to imperfect match between inlet flow and the blade entrances, (2) *friction* losses in the blade passages, and (3) *circulation* loss due to imperfect match at the exit side of the blades.

Finally, the *mechanical efficiency* is

$$\eta_m = 1 - \frac{P_f}{\text{bhp}} \tag{11.8}$$

where P_f is the power loss due to mechanical friction in the bearings, packing glands, and other contact points in the machine.

By definition, the total efficiency is simply the product of its three parts

$$\eta \equiv \eta_v \eta_h \eta_m \tag{11.9}$$

The designer has to work in all three areas to improve the pump.

Elementary Pump Theory

You may have thought that Eqs. (11.1) to (11.9) were formulas from pump *theory*. Not so; they are merely definitions of performance parameters and cannot be used in any predictive mode. To actually *predict* the head, power, efficiency, and flow rate of a pump, two theoretical approaches are possible: (1) simple one-dimensional-flow formulas and (2) complex digital-computer models which account for viscosity and three-dimensionality. Many of the best design improvements still come from testing and experience, and pump research remains a very active field [39]. The last ten years have seen considerable advances in *computational fluid-dynamics* (CFD) modeling of flow in turbomachines [42], and at least four commercial turbulent-flow three-dimensional CFD codes are now available.

To construct an elementary theory of pump performance, we assume one-dimensional flow and combine idealized fluid-velocity vectors through the impeller with the angular-momentum theorem for a control volume, Eq. (3.55).

The idealized velocity diagrams are shown in Fig. 11.4. The fluid is assumed to enter the impeller at $r = r_1$ with velocity component w_1 tangent to the blade angle β_1 plus circumferential speed $u_1 = \omega r_1$ matching the tip speed of the impeller. Its absolute entrance velocity is thus the vector sum of w_1 and u_1, shown as V_1. Similarly, the flow exits at $r = r_2$ with component w_2 parallel to the blade angle β_2 plus tip speed $u_2 = \omega r_2$, with resultant velocity V_2.

We applied the angular-momentum theorem to a turbomachine in Example 3.14 (Fig. 3.13) and arrived at a result for the applied torque T

$$T = \rho Q (r_2 V_{t2} - r_1 V_{t1}) \tag{11.10}$$

where V_{t1} and V_{t2} are the absolute circumferential velocity components of the flow. The

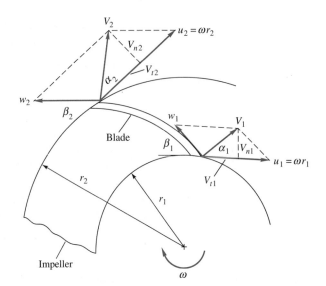

Fig. 11.4 Inlet and exit velocity diagrams for an idealized pump impeller.

power delivered to the fluid is thus

$$P_w = \omega T = \rho Q(u_2 V_{t2} - u_1 V_{t1})$$

$$\text{or} \qquad H = \frac{P_w}{\rho g Q} = \frac{1}{g}(u_2 V_{t2} - u_1 V_{t1})$$

(11.11)

These are the *Euler turbomachine equations*, showing that the torque, power, and ideal head are functions only of the rotor-tip velocities $u_{1,2}$ and the absolute fluid tangential velocities $V_{t1,2}$, independent of the axial velocities (if any) through the machine.

Additional insight is gained by rewriting these relations in another form. From the geometry of Fig. 11.4

$$V^2 = u^2 + w^2 - 2uw \cos \beta \qquad w \cos \beta = u - V_t$$

$$\text{or} \qquad uV_t = \tfrac{1}{2}(V^2 + u^2 - w^2)$$

(11.12)

Substituting this into Eq. (11.11) gives

$$H = \frac{1}{2g}[(V_2^2 - V_1^2) + (u_2^2 - u_1^2) - (w_2^2 - w_1^2)]$$

(11.13)

Thus the ideal head relates to the absolute plus the relative kinetic-energy change of the fluid minus the rotor-tip kinetic-energy change. Finally, substituting for H from its definition in Eq. (11.1) and rearranging, we obtain the classic relation

$$\frac{p}{\rho g} + z + \frac{w^2}{2g} - \frac{r^2 \omega^2}{2g} = \text{const}$$

(11.14)

This is the *Bernoulli equation in rotating coordinates* and applies to either two- or three-dimensional ideal incompressible flow.

For a centrifugal pump, the power can be related to the radial velocity $V_n = V_t \tan \alpha$ and the continuity relation

$$P_w = \rho Q(u_2 V_{n2} \cot \alpha_2 - u_1 V_{n1} \cot \alpha_1) \qquad (11.15)$$

where

$$V_{n2} = \frac{Q}{2\pi r_2 b_2} \quad \text{and} \quad V_{n1} = \frac{Q}{2\pi r_1 b_1}$$

and where b_1 and b_2 are the blade widths at inlet and exit. With the pump parameters r_1, r_2, β_1, β_2, and ω known, Eqs. (11.11) or Eq. (11.15) is used to compute idealized power and head versus discharge. The "design" flow rate Q^* is commonly estimated by assuming that the flow enters exactly normal to the impeller

$$\alpha_1 = 90° \qquad V_{n1} = V_1 \qquad (11.16)$$

We can expect this simple analysis to yield estimates within ± 25 percent for the head, water horsepower, and discharge of a pump. Let us illustrate with an example.

EXAMPLE 11.1

Given are the following data for a commercial centrifugal water pump: $r_1 = 4$ in, $r_2 = 7$ in, $\beta_1 = 30°$, $\beta_2 = 20°$, speed $= 1440$ r/min. Estimate (a) the design-point discharge, (b) the water horsepower, and (c) the head if $b_1 = b_2 = 1.75$ in.

Solution

Part (a) The angular velocity is $\omega = 2\pi$ r/s $= 2\pi(1440/60) = 150.8$ rad/s. Thus the tip speeds are $u_1 = \omega r_1 = 150.8(4/12) = 50.3$ ft/s and $u_2 = \omega r_2 = 150.8(7/12) = 88.0$ ft/s. From the inlet-velocity diagram, Fig. E11.1a, with $\alpha_1 = 90°$ for design point, we compute

$$V_{n1} = u_1 \tan 30° = 29.0 \text{ ft/s}$$

whence the discharge is

$$Q = 2\pi r_1 b_1 V_{n1} = (2\pi)\left(\frac{4}{12}\right)\left(\frac{1.75}{12}\right)(29.0)$$

$$= (8.87 \text{ ft}^3/\text{s})(60 \text{ s/min})\left(\frac{1728}{231} \text{ gal/ft}^3\right)$$

$$= 3980 \text{ gal/min} \qquad \qquad Ans. (a)$$

(The actual pump produces about 3500 gal/min.)

Part (b) The outlet radial velocity follows from Q

$$V_{n2} = \frac{Q}{2\pi r_2 b_2} = \frac{8.87}{2\pi(\frac{7}{12})(1.75/12)} = 16.6 \text{ ft/s}$$

This enables us to construct the outlet-velocity diagram as in Fig. E11.1b, given $\beta_2 = 20°$. The tangential component is

$$V_{t2} = u_2 - V_{n2} \cot \beta_2 = 88.0 - 16.6 \cot 20° = 42.4 \text{ ft/s}$$

$$\alpha_2 = \tan^{-1}\frac{16.6}{42.4} = 21.4°$$

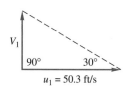

Fig. E11.1a

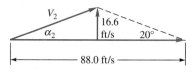

Fig. E11.1b

The power is then computed from Eq. (11.11) with $V_{t1} = 0$ at the design point

$$P_w = \rho Q u_2 V_{t2} = (1.94 \text{ slugs/ft}^3)(8.87 \text{ ft}^3/\text{s})(88.0 \text{ ft/s})(42.4 \text{ ft/s})$$

$$= \frac{64{,}100 \text{ ft} \cdot \text{lbf/s}}{550} = 117 \text{ hp} \qquad\qquad Ans. \ (b)$$

(The actual pump delivers about 125 water horsepower, requiring 147 bhp at 85 percent efficiency.)

Part (c) Finally, the head is estimated from Eq. (11.11)

$$H \approx \frac{P_w}{\rho g Q} = \frac{64{,}100 \text{ ft} \cdot \text{lbf/s}}{(62.4 \text{ lbf/ft}^3)(8.87 \text{ ft}^3/\text{s})} = 116 \text{ ft} \qquad Ans. \ (c)$$

(The actual pump develops about 140-ft head.) Improved methods for obtaining closer estimates are given in advanced references [for example, 6, 8, and 31].

Effect of Blade Angle on Pump Head

The simple theory above can be used to predict an important blade-angle effect. If we neglect inlet angular momentum, the theoretical water horsepower is

$$P_w = \rho Q u_2 V_{t2} \qquad\qquad (11.17)$$

where
$$V_{t2} = u_2 - V_{n2} \cot \beta_2 \qquad V_{n2} = \frac{Q}{2\pi r_2 b_2}$$

Then the theoretical head from Eq. (11.11) becomes

$$H \approx \frac{u_1^2}{g} - \frac{u_2 \cot \beta_2}{2\pi r_2 b_2 g} Q \qquad\qquad (11.18)$$

The head varies linearly with discharge Q, having a shutoff value u_2^2/g, where u_2 is the exit blade-tip speed. The slope is negative if $\beta_2 < 90°$ (backward-curved blades) and positive for $\beta_2 > 90°$ (forward-curved blades). This effect is shown in Fig. 11.5 and is accurate only at low flow rates.

The measured shutoff head of centrifugal pumps is only about 60 percent of the

Fig. 11.5 Theoretical effect of blade exit angle on pump head versus discharge.

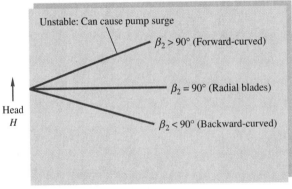

Unstable: Can cause pump surge

$\beta_2 > 90°$ (Forward-curved)

$\beta_2 = 90°$ (Radial blades)

$\beta_2 < 90°$ (Backward-curved)

Head
H

Discharge $Q \longrightarrow$

theoretical value $H_0 = \omega^2 r_2^2/g$. With the advent of the laser-doppler anemometer, researchers can now make detailed three-dimensional flow measurements inside pumps and can even animate the data into a movie [40].

The positive-slope condition in Fig. 11.5 can be unstable and can cause pump *surge*, an oscillatory condition where the pump "hunts" for the proper operating point. Surge may cause only rough operation in a liquid pump, but it can be a major problem in gas-compressor operation. For this reason a backward-curved or radial blade design is generally preferred. A survey of the problem of pump stability is given by Greitzer [41].

11.3 Pump Performance Curves and Similarity Rules

Since the theory of the previous section is rather qualitative, the only solid indicator of a pump's performance lies in extensive testing. For the moment let us discuss the centrifugal pump in particular. The general principles and the presentation of data are exactly the same for mixed-flow and axial-flow pumps and compressors.

Performance charts are almost always plotted for constant shaft-rotation speed n (in r/min usually). The basic independent variable is taken to be discharge Q (in gal/min usually for liquids and ft^3/min for gases). The dependent variables, or "output," are taken to be head H (pressure rise Δp for gases), brake horsepower (bhp), and efficiency η.

Figure 11.6 shows typical performance curves for a centrifugal pump. The head is approximately constant at low discharge and then drops to zero at $Q = Q_{max}$. At this speed and impeller size, the pump cannot deliver any more fluid than Q_{max}. The positive-slope part of the head is shown dashed; as mentioned earlier, this region can be unstable and can cause hunting for the operating point.

The efficiency η is always zero at no flow and at Q_{max}, and it reaches a maximum,

Fig. 11.6 Typical centrifugal pump performance curves at constant impeller-rotation speed. The units are arbitrary.

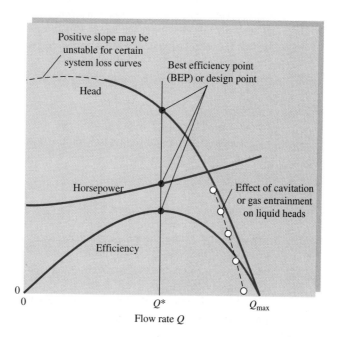

perhaps 80 to 90 percent, at about $0.6Q_{max}$. This is the *design flow rate Q** or *best efficiency point* (BEP), $\eta = \eta_{max}$. The head and horsepower at BEP will be termed H^* and P^* (or bhp*), respectively. It is desirable that the efficiency curve be flat near η_{max}, so that a wide range of efficient operation is achieved. However, some designs simply do not achieve flat efficiency curves. Note that η is not independent of H and P but rather is calculated from the relation in Eq. (11.5), $\eta = \rho gQH/P$.

As shown in Fig. 11.6, the horsepower required to drive the pump typically rises monotonically with the flow rate. Sometimes there is a large power rise beyond the BEP, especially for radial-tipped and forward-curved blades. This is considered undesirable because a much larger motor is then needed to provide high flow rates. Backward-curved blades typically have their horsepower level off above BEP ("nonoverloading" type of curve).

Measured Performance Curves

Figure 11.7 shows actual performance data for a commercial centrifugal pump. Figure 11.7a is for a basic casing size with three different impeller diameters. The head curves $H(Q)$ are shown, but the horsepower and efficiency curves have to be inferred from the contour plots. Maximum discharges are not shown, being far outside the normal operating range near the BEP. Everything is plotted raw, of course [feet, horsepower, gallons per minute (1 U.S. gal = 231 in^3)] since it is to be used directly by designers. Figure 11.7b is the same pump design with a 20 percent larger casing, a lower speed, and three larger impeller diameters. Comparing the two pumps may be a little confusing: The larger pump produces exactly the same discharge but only half the horsepower and half the head. This will be readily understood from the scaling or similarity laws we are about to formulate.

A point often overlooked is that raw curves like Fig. 11.7 are strictly applicable to a fluid of a certain density and viscosity, in this case water. If the pump were used to deliver, say, mercury, the brake horsepower would be about 13 times higher while Q, H, and η would be about the same. But in that case H should be interpreted as feet of *mercury*, not feet of water. If the pump were used for SAE 30 oil, *all* data would change (brake horsepower, Q, H, and η) due to the large change in viscosity (Reynolds number). Again this should become clear with the similarity rules.

Net Positive-Suction Head

In the top of Fig. 11.7 is plotted the *net positive-suction head* (NPSH), which is the head required at the pump inlet to keep the liquid from cavitating or boiling. The pump inlet or suction side is the low-pressure point where cavitation will first occur. The NPSH is defined as

$$\text{NPSH} = \frac{p_i}{\rho g} + \frac{V_i^2}{2g} - \frac{p_v}{\rho g} \qquad (11.19)$$

where p_i and V_i are the pressure and velocity at the pump inlet and p_v is the vapor pressure of the liquid. Given the left-hand side, NPSH, from the pump performance curve, we must ensure that the right-hand side is equal or greater in the actual system to avoid cavitation.

If the pump inlet is placed at a height Z_i above a reservoir whose free surface is at pressure p_a, we can use Bernoulli's equations to rewrite NPSH as

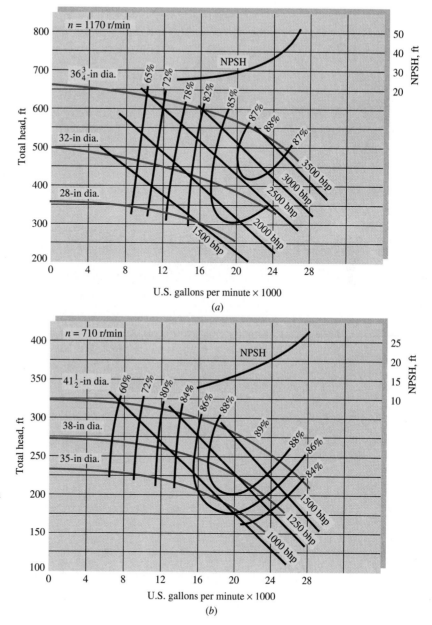

Fig. 11.7 Measured-performance curves for two models of a centrifugal water pump: (*a*) basic casing with three impeller sizes; (*b*) 20 percent larger casing with three larger impellers at slower speed. (*Ingersoll-Rand Corporation, Cameron Pump Division.*)

$$\text{NPSH} = \frac{p_a}{\rho g} - Z_i - h_{fi} - \frac{p_v}{\rho g} \qquad (11.20)$$

where h_{fi} is the friction-head loss between the reservoir and the pump inlet. Knowing p_a and h_{fi}, we can set the pump at a height Z_i which will keep the right-hand side greater than the "required" NPSH plotted in Fig. 11.7.

If cavitation does occur, there will be pump noise and vibration, pitting damage to the impeller, and a sharp dropoff in pump head and discharge. In some liquids this deterioration starts before actual boiling, as dissolved gases and light hydrocarbons are liberated.

Deviations from Ideal Pump Theory

The actual pump head data in Fig. 11.7 differ considerably from ideal theory, Eq. (11.18). Take, e.g., the 36.75-in-diameter pump at 1170 r/min in Fig. 11.7a. The theoretical shutoff head is

$$H_0(\text{ideal}) = \frac{\omega^2 r_2^2}{g} = \frac{[1170(2\pi/60) \text{ rad/s}]^2[(36.75/2)/(12) \text{ ft}]^2}{32.2 \text{ ft/s}^2} = 1093 \text{ ft}$$

From Fig. 11.7a, at $Q = 0$, we read the actual shutoff head to be only 670 ft, or 61 percent of the theoretical value. This is a sharp dropoff and is indicative of nonrecoverable losses of three types:

1. *Impeller recirculation loss,* significant only at low flow rates
2. *Friction losses* on the blade and passage surfaces, which increase monotonically with the flow rate
3. *"Shock" loss* due to mismatch between the blade angles and the inlet flow direction, especially significant at high flow rates

These are complicated three-dimensional-flow effects and hence are difficult to predict. Although, as mentioned, numerical (CFD) techniques are becoming more important [42], modern performance prediction is still a blend of experience, empirical correlations, idealized theory, and CFD modifications, as shown in a recent symposium concerning pump prediction schemes [39].

EXAMPLE 11.2

The 32-in pump of Fig. 11.7a is to pump 24,000 gal/min of water at 1170 r/min from a reservoir whose surface is at 14.7 lbf/in² absolute. If head loss from reservoir to pump inlet is 6 ft, where should the pump inlet be placed to avoid cavitation for water at (a) 60°F, p_v = 0.26 lbf/in² absolute, SG = 1.0 and (b) 200°F, p_v = 11.52 lbf/in² absolute, SG = 0.9635?

Solution

Part (a)

For either case read from Fig. 11.7a at 24,000 gal/min that the required NPSH is 40 ft. For this case ρg = 62.4 lbf/ft³. From Eq. (11.20) it is necessary that

$$\text{NPSH} \leq \frac{p_a - p_v}{\rho g} - Z_i - h_{fi}$$

or

$$40 \text{ ft} \leq \frac{(14.7 - 0.26)(144)}{62.4} - Z_i - 6.0$$

or

$$Z_i \leq 27.3 - 40 = -12.7 \text{ ft} \qquad\qquad Ans. (a)$$

The pump must be placed at least 12.7 ft *below* the reservoir surface to avoid cavitation.

Part (b)

For this case ρg = 62.4(0.9635) = 60.1 lbf/ft³. Equation (11.20) applies again with the higher p_v

$$40 \text{ ft} \le \frac{(14.7 - 11.52)(144)}{60.1} - Z_i - 6.0$$

or $$Z_i \le 1.6 - 40 = -38.4 \text{ ft} \qquad \qquad Ans. \ (b)$$

The pump must now be placed at least 38.4 ft below the reservoir surface. These are unusually stringent conditions because a large, high-discharge pump requires a large NPSH.

Dimensionless Pump Performance

For a given pump design, the output variables H and brake horsepower should be dependent upon discharge Q, impeller diameter D, and shaft speed n, at least. Other possible parameters are the fluid density ρ, viscosity μ, and surface roughness ϵ. Thus the performance curves in Fig. 11.7 are equivalent to the following assumed functional relations:[1]

$$gH = f_1(Q, D, n, \rho, \mu, \epsilon) \qquad \text{bhp} = f_2(Q, D, n, \rho, \mu, \epsilon) \qquad (11.21)$$

This is a straightforward application of dimensional-analysis principles from Chap. 5. As a matter of fact, it was given as an exercise (Prob. 5.20). For each function in Eq. (11.21) there are seven variables and three primary dimensions (M, L, and T); hence we expect $7 - 3 = 4$ dimensionless pis, and that is what we get. You can verify as an exercise that appropriate dimensionless forms for Eqs. (11.21) are

$$\frac{gH}{n^2D^2} = g_1\left(\frac{Q}{nD^3}, \frac{\rho nD^2}{\mu}, \frac{\epsilon}{D}\right)$$

$$(11.22)$$

$$\frac{\text{bhp}}{\rho n^3 D^5} = g_2\left(\frac{Q}{nD^3}, \frac{\rho nD^2}{\mu}, \frac{\epsilon}{D}\right)$$

The quantities $\rho nD^2/\mu$ and ϵ/D are recognized as the Reynolds number and roughness ratio, respectively. Three new pump parameters have arisen:

$$\text{Capacity coefficient } C_Q = \frac{Q}{nD^3}$$

$$\text{Head coefficient } C_H = \frac{gH}{n^2D^2} \qquad (11.23)$$

$$\text{Power coefficient } C_P = \frac{\text{bhp}}{\rho n^3 D^5}$$

Note that only the power coefficient contains fluid density, the parameters C_Q and C_H being kinematic types.

Figure 11.7 gives no warning of viscous or roughness effects. The Reynolds numbers are from 0.8 to 1.5×10^7, or fully turbulent flow in all passages probably. The roughness is not given and varies greatly among commercial pumps. But at such high Reynolds numbers we expect more or less the same percentage effect on all these pumps. Therefore it is common to assume that the Reynolds number and the roughness ratio have a constant effect, so that Eqs. (11.23) reduce to, approximately,

[1] We adopt gH as a variable instead of H for dimensional reasons.

$$C_H \approx C_H(C_Q) \qquad C_P \approx C_P(C_Q) \tag{11.24}$$

For geometrically similar pumps, we expect head and power coefficients to be (nearly) unique functions of the capacity coefficient. We have to watch out that the pumps are geometrically similar or nearly so because (1) manufacturers put different-sized impellers in the same casing, thus violating geometric similarity, and (2) large pumps have smaller ratios of roughness and clearances to impeller diameter than small pumps. In addition, the more viscous liquids will have significant Reynolds-number effects; e.g., a factor-of-3 or more viscosity increase causes a clearly visible effect on C_H and C_P.

The efficiency η is already dimensionless and is uniquely related to the other three. It varies with C_Q also

$$\eta \equiv \frac{C_H C_Q}{C_P} = \eta(C_Q) \tag{11.25}$$

We can test Eqs. (11.24) and (11.25) from the data of Fig. 11.7. The impeller diameters of 32 and 38 in are approximately 20 percent different in size, and so their ratio of impeller to casing size is the same. The parameters C_Q, C_H, and C_P are computed with n in r/s, Q in ft^3/s (gal/min $\times$ 2.23 $\times$ 10^{-3}), H and D in ft, $g = 32.2$ ft/s^2, and brake horsepower in horsepower times 550 ft $\cdot$ lbf/(s $\cdot$ hp). The nondimensional data are then plotted in Fig. 11.8. A dimensionless suction-head coefficient is also defined

$$C_{HS} = \frac{g(\text{NPSH})}{n^2 D^2} = C_{HS}(C_Q) \tag{11.26}$$

Fig. 11.8 Nondimensional plot of the pump performance data from Fig. 11.7. These numbers are not representative of other pump designs.

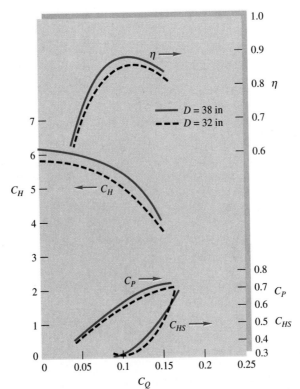

The coefficients C_P and C_{HS} are seen to correlate almost perfectly into a single function of C_Q, while η and C_H data deviate by a few percent. The last two parameters are more sensitive to slight discrepancies in model similarity; since the larger pump has smaller roughness and clearance ratios and a 40 percent larger Reynolds number, it develops slightly more head and is more efficient. The overall effect is a resounding victory for dimensional analysis.

The best-efficiency point in Fig. 11.8 is approximately

$$\eta_{max} \approx 0.88: \qquad \begin{matrix} C_{Q*} \approx 0.115 & C_{P*} \approx 0.65 \\ \\ C_{H*} \approx 5.0 & C_{HS*} \approx 0.37 \end{matrix} \qquad (11.27)$$

These values can be used to estimate the BEP performance of any size pump in this geometrically similar family. In like manner, the shutoff head is $C_H(0) \approx 6.0$, and by extrapolation the shutoff power is $C_P(0) \approx 0.25$ and the maximum discharge is $C_{Q,\,max} \approx 0.23$. Note, however, that Fig. 11.8 gives no reliable information about, say, the 28- or 35-in impellers in Fig. 11.7, which have a different impeller-to-casing-size ratio and thus must be correlated separately.

By comparing values of n^2D^2, nD^3, and n^3D^5 for two pumps in Fig. 11.7 we can see readily why the large pump had the same discharge but less power and head:

	D, ft	n, r/s	Discharge nD^3, ft³/s	Head n^2D^2/g, ft	Power $\rho n^3D^5/550$, hp
Fig. 11.7*a*	32/12	1170/60	370	84	3527
Fig. 11.7*b*	38/12	710/60	376	44	1861
Ratio	—	—	1.02	0.52	0.53

Discharge goes as nD^3, which is about the same for both pumps. Head goes as n^2D^2 and power as n^3D^5 for the same ρ (water), and these are about half as much for the larger pump. The NPSH goes as n^2D^2 and is also half as much for the 38-in pump.

EXAMPLE 11.3

A pump from the family of Fig. 11.8 has $D = 21$ in and $n = 1500$ r/min. Estimate (*a*) discharge, (*b*) head, (*c*) pressure rise, and (*d*) brake horsepower of this pump for water at 60°F and best efficiency.

Solution

Part (a) In BG units take $D = 21/12 = 1.75$ ft and $n = 1500/60 = 25$ r/s. At 60°F, ρ of water is 1.94 slugs/ft³. The BEP parameters are known from Fig. 11.8 or Eqs. (11.27). The BEP discharge is thus

$$Q* = C_{Q*}nD^3 = 0.115(25)(1.75)^3 = (15.4 \text{ ft}^3/\text{s})(448.8) = 6900 \text{ gal/min} \qquad Ans. (a)$$

Part (b) Similarly, the BEP head is

$$H* = \frac{C_{H*}n^2D^2}{g} = \frac{5.0(25)^2(1.75)^2}{32.2} = 300\text{-ft water} \qquad Ans. (b)$$

Part (c) Since we are not given elevation or velocity-head changes across the pump, we neglect them and estimate

$$\Delta p \approx \rho g H = 1.94(32.2)(300) = 18{,}600 \text{ lbf/ft}^2 = 129 \text{ lbf/in}^2 \qquad \text{Ans. (c)}$$

Part (d) Finally, the BEP power is

$$P^* = C_{P*}\rho n^3 D^5 = 0.65(1.94)(25)^3(1.75)^5$$

$$= \frac{323{,}000 \text{ ft} \cdot \text{lbf/s}}{550} = 590 \text{ hp} \qquad \text{Ans. (d)}$$

EXAMPLE 11.4

We want to build a pump from the family of Fig. 11.8, which delivers 3000 gal/min water at 1200 r/min at best efficiency. Estimate (*a*) the impeller diameter, (*b*) the maximum discharge, (*c*) the shutoff head, and (*d*) the NPSH at best efficiency.

Solution

Part (a) 3000 gal/min $= 6.68 \text{ ft}^3/\text{s}$ and 1200 r/min $= 20 \text{ r/s}$. At BEP we have

$$Q^* = C_{Q*}nD^3 = 6.68 \text{ ft}^3/\text{s} = (0.115)(20)D^3$$

or
$$D = \left[\frac{6.68}{0.115(20)}\right]^{1/3} = 1.43 \text{ ft} = 17.1 \text{ in} \qquad \text{Ans. (a)}$$

Part (b) The maximum Q is related to Q^* by a ratio of capacity coefficients

$$Q_{\max} = \frac{Q^* C_{Q,\max}}{C_{Q*}} \approx \frac{3000(0.23)}{0.115} = 6000 \text{ gal/min} \qquad \text{Ans. (b)}$$

Part (c) From Fig. 11.8 we estimated the shutoff head coefficient to be 6.0. Thus

$$H(0) \approx \frac{C_H(0)n^2 D^2}{g} = \frac{6.0(20)^2(1.43)^2}{32.2} = 152 \text{ ft} \qquad \text{Ans. (c)}$$

Part (d) Finally, from Eq. (11.27), the NPSH at BEP is approximately

$$\text{NPSH}^* = \frac{C_{HS*}n^2 D^2}{g} = \frac{0.37(20)^2(1.43)^2}{32.2} = 9.4 \text{ ft} \qquad \text{Ans. (d)}$$

Since this a small pump, it will be less efficient than the pumps in Fig. 11.8, probably about 85 percent maximum.

Similarity Rules

The success of Fig. 11.8 in correlating pump data leads to simple rules for comparing pump performance. If pump 1 and pump 2 are from the same geometric family and are operating at homologous points (the same dimensionless position on a chart such as Fig. 11.8), their flow rates, heads, and powers will be related as follows:

$$\frac{Q_2}{Q_1} = \frac{n_2}{n_1}\left(\frac{D_2}{D_1}\right)^3 \qquad \frac{H_2}{H_1} = \left(\frac{n_2}{n_1}\right)^2\left(\frac{D_2}{D_1}\right)^2$$

$$\frac{P_2}{P_1} = \frac{\rho_2}{\rho_1} \left(\frac{n_2}{n_1}\right)^3 \left(\frac{D_2}{D_1}\right)^5 \qquad (11.28)$$

These are the *similarity rules*, which can be used to estimate the effect of changing the fluid, speed, or size on any dynamic turbomachine—pump or turbine—within a geometrically similar family. A graphic display of these rules is given in Fig. 11.9, showing the effect of speed and diameter changes on pump performance. In Fig. 11.9a the size is held constant and the speed is varied 20 percent, while Fig. 11.9b shows a 20 percent size change at constant speed. The curves are plotted to scale but with arbitrary units. The speed effect (Fig. 11.9a) is substantial, but the size effect (Fig. 11.9b) is even more dramatic, especially for power, which varies as D^5. Generally we see that a given pump family can be adjusted in size and speed to fit a variety of system characteristics.

Strictly speaking, we would expect for perfect similarity that $\eta_1 = \eta_2$, but we have seen that larger pumps are more efficient, having a higher Reynolds number and lower roughness and clearance ratios. Two empirical correlations are recommended for maximum efficiency. One, developed by Moody [43] for turbines but also used for pumps, is a size effect. The other, suggested by Anderson [44] from thousands of pump tests, is a flow-rate effect:

Size changes [43]:
$$\frac{1 - \eta_2}{1 - \eta_1} \approx \left(\frac{D_1}{D_2}\right)^{1/4} \qquad (11.29a)$$

Flow-rate changes [44]:
$$\frac{0.94 - \eta_2}{0.94 - \eta_1} \approx \left(\frac{Q_1}{Q_2}\right)^{0.32} \qquad (11.29b)$$

Anderson's formula (11.29b) makes the practical observation that even an infinitely large pump will have losses. He thus proposes a maximum possible efficiency of 94 percent, rather than 100 percent. Anderson recommends that the same formula be used

Fig. 11.9 Effect of changes in size and speed on homologous pump performance: (*a*) 20 percent change in speed at constant size; (*b*) 20 percent change in size at constant speed.

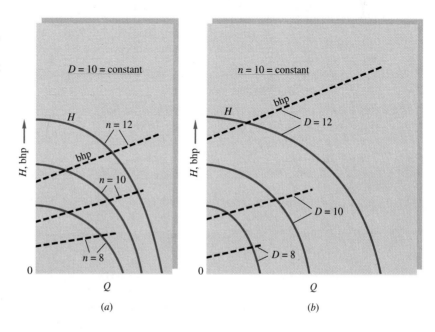

for turbines if the constant 0.94 is replaced by 0.95. The formulas in Eq. (11.29) assume the same value of surface roughness for both machines—one could micropolish a small pump and achieve the efficiency of a larger machine.

Effect of Viscosity

Centrifugal pumps are often used to pump oils and other viscous liquids up to 1000 times the viscosity of water. But the Reynolds numbers become low turbulent or even laminar, with a strong effect on performance. Figure 11.10 shows typical test curves of head and brake horsepower versus discharge. High viscosity causes a dramatic drop in head and discharge and increases in power requirements. The efficiency also drops substantially according to the following typical results:

μ/μ_{water}	1.0	10.0	100	1000
η_{max}, %	85	76	52	11

Beyond about $300\mu_{water}$ the deterioration in performance is so great that a positive-displacement pump is recommended.

11.4 Mixed- and Axial-Flow Pumps: The Specific Speed

We have seen from the previous section that the modern centrifugal pump is a formidable device, able to deliver very high heads and reasonable flow rates with excellent efficiency. It can match many system requirements. But basically the centrifugal pump is a high-head, low-flow machine, whereas there are many applications requiring low head and high discharge. To see that the centrifugal design is not convenient for such systems, consider the following example.

EXAMPLE 11.5

We want to use a centrifugal pump from the family of Fig. 11.8 to deliver 100,000 gal/min of water at 60°F with a head of 25 ft. What should be (a) the pump size and speed and (b) brake horsepower, assuming operation at best efficiency?

Solution

Part (a) Enter the known head and discharge into the BEP parameters from Eq. (11.27):

$$H^* = 25 \text{ ft} = \frac{C_{H*}n^2D^2}{g} = \frac{5.0n^2D^2}{32.2}$$

$$Q^* = 100,000 \text{ gal/min} = 222.8 \text{ ft}^3/\text{s} = C_{Q*}nD^3 = 0.115nD^3$$

The two unknowns are n and D. Solve simultaneously for

$$D = 12.4 \text{ ft} \qquad n = 1.03 \text{ r/s} = 62 \text{ r/min} \qquad \textit{Ans. (a)}$$

Part (b) The most efficient horsepower is then, from Eq. (11.27),

$$\text{bhp}^* \approx C_{P*}\rho n^3D^5 = \frac{0.65(1.94)(1.03)^3(12.4)^5}{550} = 720 \text{ hp} \qquad \textit{Ans. (b)}$$

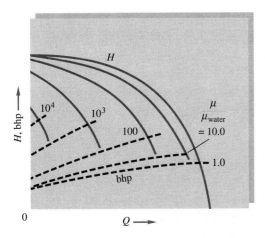

Fig. 11.10 Effect of viscosity on centrifugal pump performance.

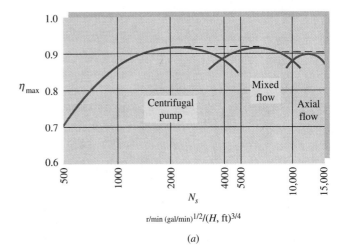

(a)

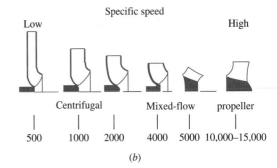

(b)

Fig. 11.11 (a) Optimum efficiency and (b) vane design of dynamic-pump families as a function of specific speed.

The solution to Example 11.5 is mathematically correct but results in a grotesque pump: an impeller more than 12 ft in diameter, rotating so slowly one can visualize oxen walking in a circle turning the shaft.

There are other dynamic-pump designs which do provide low head and high discharge. For example, there is a type of 38-in, 710 r/min pump, e.g., with the same input parameters as Fig. 11.7b, which will deliver the 25-ft head and 100,000 gal/min flow rate called for in Example 11.5. This is done by allowing the flow to pass through the impeller with an axial-flow component and less centrifugal component. The passages can be opened up to the increased flow rate with very little size increase, but the drop in radial outlet velocity decreases the head produced. These are the mixed-flow (part radial, part axial) and axial-flow (propeller-type) families of dynamic pump. Some vane designs are sketched in Fig. 11.11, which introduces an interesting new ''design'' parameter, the specific speed N_s or N_s'.

The Specific Speed

Most pump applications involve a known head and discharge for the particular system, plus a speed range dictated by electric motor speeds or cavitation requirements. The designer then selects the best size and shape (centrifugal, mixed, axial) for the pump. To help this selection, we need a dimensionless parameter involving speed, discharge, and head but not size. This is accomplished by eliminating the diameter between C_Q

and C_H, applying the result only to the BEP. This ratio is called the *specific speed* and has both a dimensionless form and a somewhat lazy, practical form:

Rigorous form:

$$N_s' = \frac{C_{Q*}^{1/2}}{C_{H*}^{3/4}} = \frac{n(Q*)^{1/2}}{(gH*)^{3/4}} \tag{11.30a}$$

Lazy but common:

$$N_s = \frac{(r/min)(gal/min)^{1/2}}{[H \ (ft)]^{3/4}} \tag{11.30b}$$

In other words, practicing engineers do not bother to change n to revolutions per second or $Q*$ to cubic feet per second or to include gravity with head, although the latter would be necessary for, say, a pump on the moon. The conversion factor is

$$N_s = 17182N_s'$$

Note that N_s is applied only to BEP; thus a single number characterizes an entire family of pumps. For example, the family of Fig. 11.8 has $N_s' \approx (0.115)^{1/2}/(5.0)^{3/4} = 0.1014$, $N_s = 1740$, regardless of size or speed.

It turns out that the specific speed is directly related to the most efficient pump design, as shown in Fig. 11.11. Low N_s means low Q and high H, hence a centrifugal pump, and large N_s implies an axial pump. The centrifugal pump is best for N_s between 500 and 4000, the mixed-flow pump for N_s between 4000 and 10,000, and the axial-flow pump for N_s above 10,000. Note the changes in impeller shape as N_s increases.

Suction Specific Speed

If we use NPSH rather than H in Eq. (11.30), the result is called *suction specific speed*

Rigorous

$$N_{ss}' = \frac{nQ^{1/2}}{(g \ NPSH)^{3/4}} \tag{11.31a}$$

Lazy:

$$N_{ss} = \frac{(r/min)(gal/min)^{1/2}}{[NPSH \ (ft)]^{3/4}} \tag{11.31b}$$

where NPSH denotes the available suction head of the system. Data from Wislicenus [4] show that a given pump is in danger of inlet cavitation if

$$N_{ss}' \geq 0.47 \qquad N_{ss} \geq 8100$$

In the absence of test data, this relation can be used, given n and Q, to estimate the minimum required NPSH.

Axial-Flow Pump Theory

A multistage axial-flow geometry is shown in Fig. 11.12a. The fluid essentially passes almost axially through alternate rows of fixed *stator* blades and moving *rotor* blades. The incompressible-flow assumption is frequently used even for gases, because the pressure rise per stage is usually small.

The simplified vector-diagram analysis assumes that the flow is one-dimensional and leaves each blade row at a relative velocity exactly parallel to the exit blade angle. Figure 11.12b shows the stator blades and their exit-velocity diagram. Since the stator is fixed, ideally the absolute velocity V_1 is parallel to the trailing edge of the blade. After vectorially subtracting the rotor tangential velocity u from V_1, we obtain the

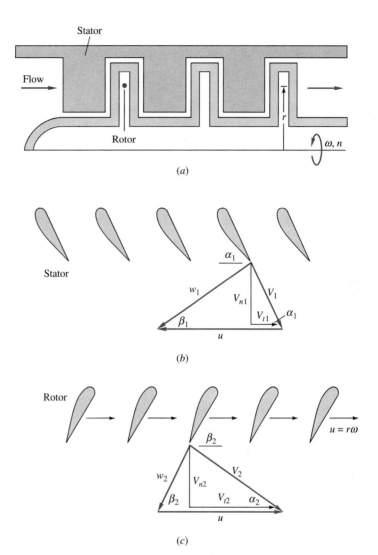

Fig. 11.12 Analysis of an axial-flow pump: (*a*) basic geometry; (*b*) stator blades and exit-velocity diagram; (*c*) rotor blades and exit-velocity diagram.

velocity w_1 relative to the rotor, which ideally should be parallel to the rotor leading edge.

Figure 11.12*c* shows the rotor blades and their exit-velocity diagram. Here the relative velocity w_2 is parallel to the blade trailing edge, while the absolute velocity V_2 should be designed to enter smoothly the next row of stator blades.

The theoretical power and head are given by Euler's turbine relation (11.11). Since there is no radial flow, the inlet and exit rotor speeds are equal, $u_1 = u_2$, and one-dimensional continuity requires that the axial-velocity component remain constant

$$V_{n1} = V_{n2} = V_n = \frac{Q}{A} = \text{const}$$

From the geometry of the velocity diagrams, the normal velocity (or volume flow) can be directly related to the blade rotational speed u:

$$u = \omega r_{av} = V_{n1}(\cot \alpha_1 + \cot \beta_1) = V_{n2}(\cot \alpha_2 + \cot \beta_2) \tag{11.32}$$

Thus the flow rate can be predicted from the rotational speed and the blade angles. Meanwhile, since $V_{t1} = V_{n1} \cot \alpha_1$ and $V_{t2} = u - V_{n2} \cot \alpha_2$, Euler's relation (11.11) for the pump head becomes

$$gH = uV_n(\cot \alpha_2 - \cot \alpha_1)$$

$$= u^2 - uV_n(\cot \alpha_1 + \cot \beta_2) \tag{11.33}$$

the preferred form because it relates to the blade angles α_1 and β_2. The shutoff or no-flow head is seen to be $H_0 = u^2/g$, just as in Eq. (11.18) for a centrifugal pump. The blade-angle parameter $\cot \alpha_1 + \cot \beta_2$ can be designed to be negative, zero, or positive, corresponding to a rising, flat, or falling head curve, as in Fig. 11.5.

Strictly speaking, Eq. (11.33) applies only to a single streamtube of radius r, but it is a good approximation for very short blades if r denotes the average radius. For long blades it is customary to sum Eq. (11.33) in radial strips over the blade area. Such complexity may not be warranted since theory, being idealized, neglects losses and usually predicts the head and power larger than those in actual pump performance.

Performance of an Axial-Flow Pump

At high specific speeds, the most efficient choice is an axial-flow, or propeller, pump, which develops high flow rate and low head. A typical dimensionless chart for a propeller pump is shown in Fig. 11.13. Note, as expected, the higher C_Q and lower C_H compared with Fig. 11.8. The head curve drops sharply with discharge, so that a large system-head change will cause a mild flow change. The power curve drops with head also, which means a possible overloading condition if the system discharge should

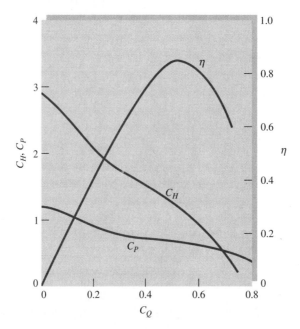

Fig. 11.13 Dimensionless performance curves for a typical axial-flow pump, $N_s = 12,000$. Constructed from data given by Stepanoff [8] for a 14-in pump at 690 r/min.

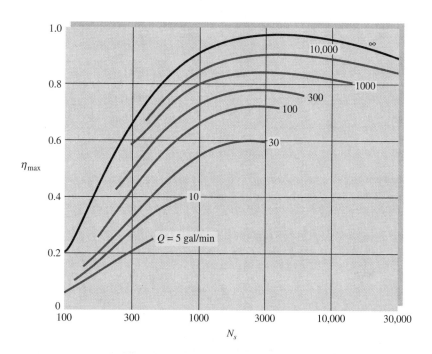

Fig. 11.14 Optimum efficiency of pumps versus capacity and specific speed. (*Adapted from Refs. 4 and 31.*)

suddenly decrease. Finally, the efficiency curve is rather narrow and triangular, as opposed to the broad, parabolic-shaped centrifugal pump efficiency (Fig. 11.8).

By inspection of Fig. 11.13, $C_{Q*} \approx 0.55$, $C_{H*} \approx 1.07$, $C_{P*} \approx 0.70$, and $\eta_{max} \approx 0.84$. From this we compute $N_s' \approx (0.55)^{1/2}/(1.07)^{3/4} = 0.705$, $N_s = 12{,}000$. The relatively low efficiency is due to small pump size: $d = 14$ in, $n = 690$ r/min, $Q* = 4400$ gal/min.

A repetition of Example 11.5 using Fig. 11.13 would show that this propeller pump family can provide a 25-ft head and 100,000 gal/min discharge if $D = 46$ in and $n = 430$ r/min, with bhp = 750; this is a much more reasonable design solution, with improvements still possible at larger-N_s conditions.

Pump Performance versus Specific Speed

Specific speed is such an effective parameter that it is used as an indicator of both performance and efficiency. Figure 11.14 shows a correlation of the optimum efficiency of a pump as a function of the specific speed and capacity. Because the dimensional parameter Q is a rough measure of both size and Reynolds number, η increases with Q. When this type of correlation was first published by Wislicenus [4] in 1947, it became known as *the* pump curve, a challenge to all manufacturers. We can check that the pumps of Figs. 11.7 and 11.13 fit the correlation very well.

Figure 11.15 shows the effect of specific speed on the shape of the pump performance curves, normalized with respect to the BEP point. The numerical values shown are representative but somewhat qualitative. The high-specific-speed pumps ($N_s \approx 10{,}000$) have head and power curves which drop sharply with discharge, implying overload or start-up problems at low flow. Their efficiency curve is very narrow.

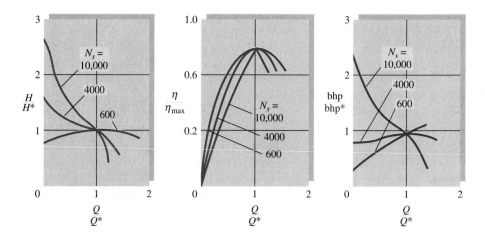

Fig. 11.15 Effect of specific speed on pump performance curves.

A low-specific-speed pump ($N_s = 600$) has a broad efficiency curve, a rising power curve, and a head curve which "droops" at shutoff, implying possible surge or hunting problems.

Although turbomachinery designs traditionally have been accomplished through extensive experimental programs, the theoretical techniques are catching up. Modern turbomachine design is a combination of sophisticated measurements [45] and theories which make use of boundary-layer theory (Sec. 7.5), numerical analysis (Sec. 8.9), compressible-flow analysis (Chap. 9), and dimensionless parameters (Chap. 5). Computer graphics help visualize the complex three-dimensional geometrics. These modern concepts are illustrated in Fig. 11.16. A recent international symposium [39] was devoted entirely to the performance of pumping machinery.

11.5 Matching Pumps to System Characteristics

The ultimate test of a pump is its match with the operating-system characteristics. Physically, the system head must match the head produced by the pump, and this intersection should occur in the region of best efficiency.

The system head will probably contain a static-elevation change $z_2 - z_1$ plus friction losses in pipes and fittings

$$H_{\text{sys}} = (z_2 - z_1) + \frac{V^2}{2g}\left(\sum \frac{fL}{D} + \sum K\right) \qquad (11.34)$$

where $\sum K$ denotes minor losses and V is the flow velocity in the principal pipe. Since V is proportional to the pump discharge Q, Eq. (11.34) represents a system-head curve $H_s(Q)$. Three examples are shown in Fig. 11.17: a static head $H_s = a$, static head plus laminar friction $H_s = a + bQ$, and static head plus turbulent friction $H_s = a + cQ^2$. The intersection of the system curve with the pump performance curve $H(Q)$ defines the operating point. In Fig. 11.17 the laminar-friction operating point is at maximum efficiency while the turbulent and static curves are off design. This may be unavoidable if system variables change, but the pump should be changed in size or speed if its operating point is consistently off design. Of course, a perfect match may not be possible

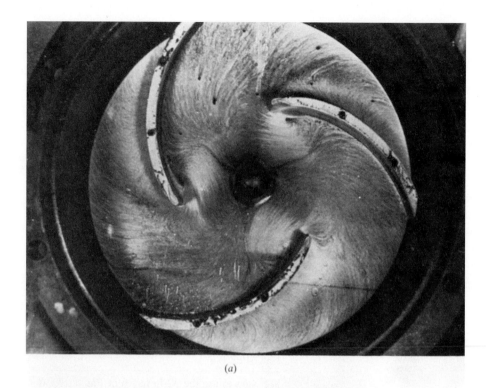

(a)

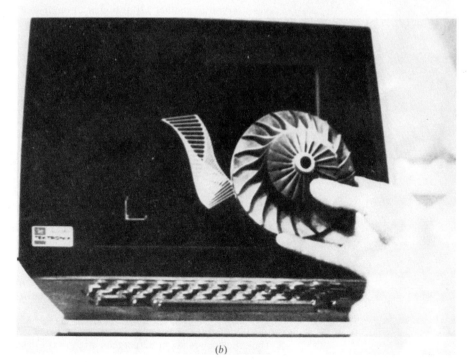

Fig. 11.16 Modern turbomachinery analysis uses a variety of techniques: (a) oil surface-flow pattern, showing inlet section blockage, on a three-bladed impeller (*from Ref. 46*); (b) impeller design curves visualized on a personal computer (*Concepts ETI Inc.*).

(b)

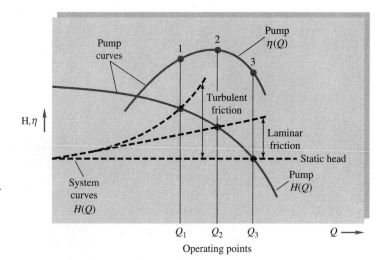

Fig. 11.17 Illustration of pump operating points for three types of system-head curves.

because commercial pumps have only certain discrete sizes and speeds. Let us illustrate these concepts with an example.

EXAMPLE 11.6

We want to use the 32-in pump of Fig. 11.7a at 1170 r/min to pump water at 60°F from one reservoir to another 120 ft higher through 1500 ft of 16-in-ID pipe with friction factor $f = 0.030$. (a) What will the operating point and efficiency be? (b) To what speed should the pump be changed to operate at the BEP?

Solution

Part (a) For reservoirs the initial and final velocities are zero; thus the system head is

$$H_s = z_2 - z_1 + \frac{V^2}{2g}\frac{fL}{D} = 120 \text{ ft} + \frac{V^2}{2g}\frac{0.030(1500 \text{ ft})}{\frac{16}{12} \text{ ft}}$$

From continuity in the pipe, $V = Q/A = Q/[\frac{1}{4}\pi(\frac{16}{12} \text{ ft})^2]$, and so we substitute for V above to get

$$H_s = 120 + 0.269Q^2 \qquad Q \text{ in ft}^3/\text{s} \tag{1}$$

Since Fig. 11.7a uses thousands of gallons per minute for the abscissa, we convert Q in Eq. (1) to this unit:

$$H_s = 120 + 1.335Q^2 \qquad Q \text{ in } 10^3 \text{ gal/min} \tag{2}$$

We can plot Eq. (2) on Fig. 11.7a and see where it intersects the 32-in pump-head curve, as in Fig. E11.6. A graphical solution gives approximately

$$H \approx 430 \text{ ft} \qquad Q \approx 15,000 \text{ gal/min}$$

The efficiency is about 82 percent, slightly off design.

An analytic solution is possible if we fit the pump-head curve to a parabola, which is very accurate

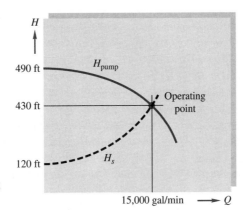

Fig. E11.6

$$H_{\text{pump}} \approx 490 - 0.26Q^2 \qquad Q \text{ in } 10^3 \text{ gal/min} \tag{3}$$

Equations (2) and (3) must match at the operating point:

$$490 - 0.26Q^2 = 120 + 1.335Q^2$$

or

$$Q^2 = \frac{490 - 120}{0.26 + 1.335} = 232$$

$$Q = 15.2 \times 10^3 \text{ gal/min} = 15,200 \text{ gal/min} \qquad \textit{Ans. (a)}$$

$$H = 490 - 0.26(15.2)^2 = 430 \text{ ft} \qquad \textit{Ans. (a)}$$

Part (b)   To move the operating point to BEP, we change n, which changes both $Q \propto n$ and $H \propto n^2$. From Fig. 11.7a, at BEP, $H^* \approx 386$ ft; thus for any n, $H^* = 386(n/1170)^2$. Also read $Q^* \approx 20 \times 10^3$ gal/min; thus for any n, $Q^* = 20(n/1170)$. Match H^* to the system characteristics, Eq. (2),

$$H^* = 386\left(\frac{n}{1170}\right)^2 \approx 120 + 1.335\left(20\,\frac{n}{1170}\right)^2 \qquad \textit{Ans. (b)}$$

which gives $n^2 < 0$. Thus it is impossible to operate at maximum efficiency with this particular system and pump.

Pumps Combined in Parallel

If a pump provides the right head but too little discharge, a possible remedy is to combine two similar pumps in parallel, i.e., sharing the same suction and inlet conditions. A parallel arrangement is also used if delivery demand varies, so that one pump is used at low flow and the second pump started up for higher discharges. Both pumps should have check valves to avoid backflow when one is shut down.

The two pumps in parallel need not be identical. Physically, their flow rates will sum for the same head, as illustrated in Fig. 11.18. If pump A has more head than pump B, pump B cannot be added in until the operating head is below the shutoff head of pump B. Since the system curve rises with Q, the combined delivery Q_{A+B} will be less than the separate operating discharges $Q_A + Q_B$ but certainly greater than either one. For a very flat (static) curve two similar pumps in parallel will deliver nearly twice the flow.

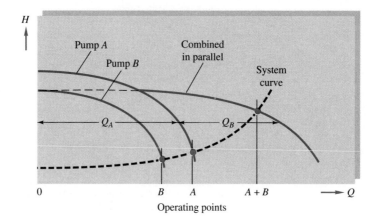

Fig. 11.18 Performance and operating points of two pumps operating singly and combined in parallel.

The combined brake horsepower is found by adding brake horsepower for each of pumps A and B at the same head as the operating point. The combined efficiency equals $\rho g(Q_{A+B})(H_{A+B})/(550\ \text{bhp}_{A+B})$.

If pumps A and B are not identical, as in Fig. 11.18, pump B should not be run and cannot even be started up if the operating point is above its shutoff head.

Pumps Combined in Series

If a pump provides the right discharge but too little head, consider adding a similar pump in series, with the output of pump B fed directly into the suction side of pump A. As sketched in Fig. 11.19, the physical principle for summing in series is that the two heads add at the same flow rate to give the combined-performance curve. The two need not be identical at all, since they merely handle the same discharge; they may even have different speeds although normally both are driven by the same shaft.

Fig. 11.19 Performance of two pumps combined in series.

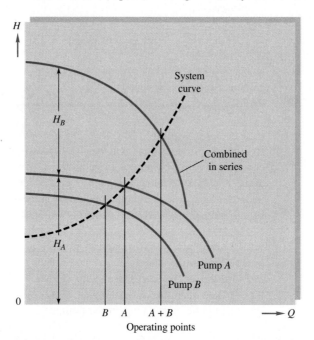

The need for a series arrangement implies that the system curve is steep, i.e., requires higher head than either pump A or B can provide. The combined operating-point head will be more than either A or B separately but not as great as their sum. The combined power is the sum of brake horsepower for A and B at the operating point flow rate. The combined efficiency is

$$\rho g(Q_{A+B})(H_{A+B})/550 \; \text{bhp}_{A+B}$$

similar to parallel pumps.

Whether pumps are used in series or in parallel, the arrangement will be uneconomical unless both pumps are operating near their best efficiency.

Multistage Pumps

For very high heads in continuous operation, the solution is a multistage pump, with the exit of one impeller feeding directly into the eye of the next. Centrifugal, mixed-flow, and axial-flow pumps have all been grouped in as many as 50 stages, with heads up to 8000 ft of water and pressure rises up to 5000 lbf/in^2 absolute. Figure 11.20 shows a section of a seven-stage centrifugal propane compressor which develops 300 lbf/in^2 rise at 40,000 ft^3/min and 35,000 bhp.

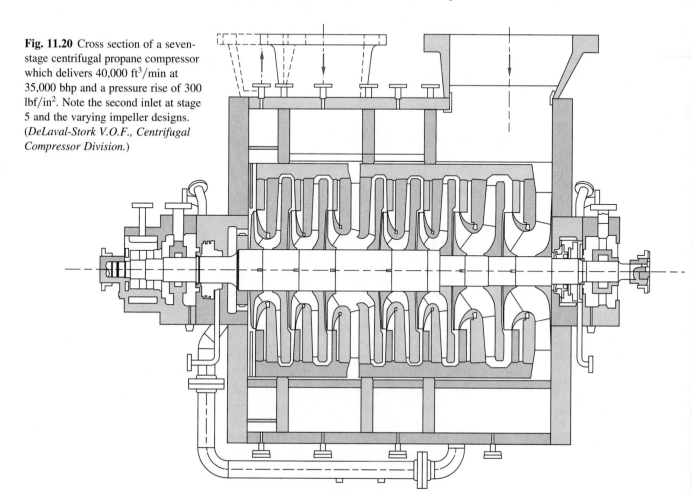

Fig. 11.20 Cross section of a seven-stage centrifugal propane compressor which delivers 40,000 ft^3/min at 35,000 bhp and a pressure rise of 300 lbf/in^2. Note the second inlet at stage 5 and the varying impeller designs. (*DeLaval-Stork V.O.F., Centrifugal Compressor Division.*)

EXAMPLE 11.7

Investigate extending Example 11.6 by using two 32-in pumps in parallel to deliver more flow. Is this efficient?

Solution

Since the pumps are identical, each delivers $\frac{1}{2}Q$ at the same 1170 r/min speed. The system curve is the same, and the balance-of-head relation becomes

$$H = 490 - 0.26(\tfrac{1}{2}Q)^2 = 120 + 1.335Q^2$$

or

$$Q^2 = \frac{490 - 120}{1.335 + 0.065} \qquad Q = 16{,}300 \text{ gal/min} \qquad\qquad Ans.$$

This is only 7 percent more than a single pump. Each pump delivers $\frac{1}{2}Q = 8130$ gal/min, for which the efficiency is only 60 percent. The total brake horsepower required is 3200, whereas a single pump used only 2000 bhp. This is a poor design.

EXAMPLE 11.8

Suppose the elevation change in Example 11.6 is raised from 120 to 500 ft, greater than a single 32-in pump can supply. Investigate using 32-in pumps in series at 1170 r/min.

Solution

Since the pumps are identical, the total head is twice as much and the constant 120 in the system-head curve is replaced by 500. The balance of heads becomes

$$H = 2(490 - 0.26Q^2) = 500 + 1.335Q^2$$

or

$$Q^2 = \frac{980 - 500}{1.335 + 0.52} \qquad Q = 16.1 \times 10^3 \text{ gal/min} \qquad\qquad Ans.$$

The operating head is $500 + 1.335(16.1)^2 = 845$ ft, or 97 percent more than that for a single pump in Example 11.5. Each pump is operating at 16.1×10^3 gal/min, which from Fig. 11.7a is 83 percent efficient, a pretty good match to the system. To pump at this operating point requires 4100 bhp, or about 2050 bhp for each pump.

11.6 Turbines

A turbine extracts energy from a fluid which possesses high head, but it is fatuous to say a turbine is a pump run backward. Basically there are two types, reaction and impulse, the difference lying in the manner of head conversion. In the reaction turbine, the fluid fills the blade passages, and the head change or pressure drop occurs within the impeller. Reaction designs are of the radial-flow, mixed-flow, and axial-flow types and are essentially dynamic devices designed to admit the high-energy fluid and extract its momentum. An impulse turbine first converts the high head through a nozzle into a high-velocity jet, which then strikes the blades at one position as they pass by. The impeller passages are not fluid-filled, and the jet flow past the blades is essentially at constant pressure. Reaction turbines are smaller because fluid fills all the blades at one time.

Reaction Turbines

Reaction turbines are low-head, high-flow devices. The flow is opposite that in a pump, entering at the larger-diameter section and discharging through the eye after giving up most of its energy to the impeller. Early designs were very inefficient because they lacked stationary guide vanes at the entrance to direct the flow smoothly into the impeller passages. The first efficient inward-flow turbine was built in 1849 by James B. Francis, a U.S. engineer, and all radial- or mixed-flow designs are now called *Francis turbines*. At still lower heads, a turbine can be designed more compactly with purely axial flow and is termed a *propeller turbine*. The propeller may be either fixed-blade or adjustable (Kaplan type), the latter being complicated mechanically but much more efficient at low-power settings. Figure 11.21 shows sketches of runner designs for Francis radial, Francis mixed-flow, and propeller-type turbines.

Idealized Radial Turbine Theory

The Euler turbomachine formulas (11.11) also apply to energy-extracting machines if we reverse the flow dirction and reshape the blades. Figure 11.22 shows a radial turbine runner. Again assume one-dimensional frictionless flow through the blades. Adjustable inlet guide vanes are absolutely necessary for good efficiency. They bring the inlet flow to the blades at angle α_2 and absolute velocity V_2 for minimum "shock" or directional-mismatch loss. After vectorially adding in the runner tip speed $u_2 = \omega r_2$, the outer blade angle should be set at angle β_2 to accommodate the relative velocity w_2, as shown in the figure. (See Fig. 11.4 for the analogous radial-pump velocity diagrams.)

Application of the angular-momentum control-volume theorem, Eq. (3.55), to Fig. 11.22 (see Example 3.14 for a similar case) yields an idealized formula for the power P extracted by the runner:

Fig. 11.21 Reaction turbines: (*a*) Francis, radial type; (*b*) Francis mixed-flow; (*c*) propeller axial-flow; (*d*) performance curves for a Francis turbine, $n = 600$ r/min, $D = 2.25$ ft, $N_{sp} = 29$.

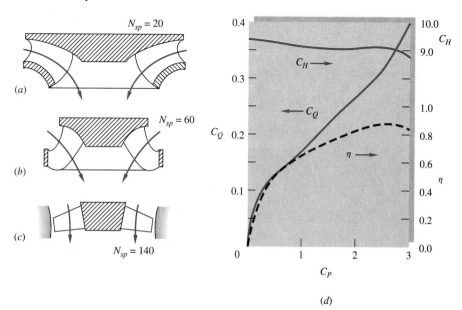

(*a*)

(*b*)

(*c*)

(*d*)

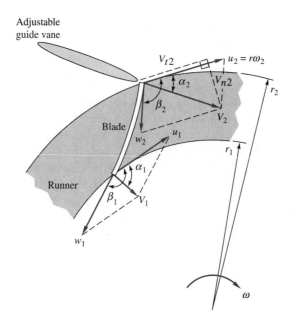

Fig. 11.22 Inlet- and outlet-velocity profiles for an idealized radial-flow reaction turbine runner.

$$P = \omega T = \rho \omega Q(r_2 V_{t2} - r_1 V_{t1}) = \rho Q(u_2 V_2 \cos \alpha_2 - u_1 V_1 \cos \alpha_1) \qquad (11.35)$$

where V_{t2} and V_{t1} are the absolute inlet and outlet circumferential velocity components of the flow. Note that Eq. (11.35) is identical to Eq. (11.11) for a radial pump, except that the blade shapes are different.

The absolute inlet normal velocity $V_{n2} = V_2 \sin \alpha_2$ is proportional to the flow rate Q. If the flow rate changes and the runner speed u_2 is constant, the vanes must be adjusted to a new angle α_2 so that w_2 still follows the blade surface. Thus adjustable inlet vanes are very important to avoid shock loss.

Power Specific Speed

Turbine parameters are similar to those of a pump, but the dependent variable is the output brake horsepower, which depends upon the inlet flow rate Q, available head H, impeller speed n, and diameter D. The efficiency is the output brake horsepower divided by the available water horsepower ρgQH. The dimensionless forms are C_Q, C_H, and C_P, defined just as for a pump, Eqs. (11.23). If we neglect Reynolds-number and roughness effects, the functional relationships are written with C_P as the independent variable:

$$C_H = C_H(C_P) \qquad C_Q = C_Q(C_P) \qquad \eta = \frac{\text{bhp}}{\rho gQH} = \eta(C_P) \qquad (11.36)$$

Figure 11.21d shows typical performance curves for a small Francis radial turbine. The maximum efficiency point is called the *normal power*, and the values for this particular turbine are

$$\eta_{\text{max}} = 0.89 \qquad C_{P*} = 2.70 \qquad C_{Q*} = 0.34 \qquad C_{H*} = 9.03$$

A parameter which compares the output power with the available head, independent of size, is found by eliminating the diameter between C_H and C_P. It is called the *power specific speed:*

Rigorous form:
$$N'_{sp} = \frac{C_P^{*1/2}}{C_H^{*5/4}} = \frac{n(\text{bhp})^{1/2}}{\rho^{1/2}(gH)^{5/4}}$$
(11.37a)

Lazy but common:
$$N_{sp} = \frac{(\text{r/min})(\text{bhp})^{1/2}}{[H\ (\text{ft})]^{5/4}}$$
(11.37b)

For water, $\rho = 1.94$ slugs/ft^3 and $N_{sp} = 273.3N'_{sp}$. The various turbine designs divide up nicely according to the range of power specific speed, as follows:

Turbine type	N_{sp} range	C_H range
Impulse	1–10	15–50
Francis	10–110	5–25
Propeller:		
Water	100–250	1–4
Gas, steam	25–300	10–80

Note that N_{sp}, like N_s for pumps, is defined only with respect to the BEP and has a single value for a given turbine family. In Fig. 11.21d, $N_{sp} = 273.3(2.70)^{1/2}/(9.03)^{5/4} = 29$, regardless of size.

Like pumps, turbines of large size are generally more efficient, and Eqs. (11.29) can be used as an estimate when data are lacking.

The design of a complete large-scale power-generating turbine system is a major engineering project, involving inlet and outlet ducts, trash racks, guide vanes, wicket gates, spiral cases, generator with cooling coils, bearings and transmission gears, runner blades, draft tubes, and automatic controls. Some typical large-scale reaction turbine designs are shown in Fig. 11.23. The reversible pump-and-turbine design of Fig. 11.23d requires special care for adjustable guide vanes to be efficient for flow in either direction.

The largest (1000-MW) hydropower designs are awesome when viewed on a human scale, as shown in Fig. 11.24. The economic advantages of small-scale model testing are evident from this photograph of the Francis turbine units at Grand Coulee Dam.

Impulse Turbines

For high head and relatively low power, i.e., low N_{sp}, not only would a reaction turbine require too high a speed but also the high pressure in the runner would require a massive casing thickness. The impulse turbine of Fig. 11.25 is ideal for this situation. Since N_{sp} is low, n will be low and the high pressure is confined to the small nozzle, which converts the head to an atmospheric pressure jet of high velocity V_j. The jet strikes the buckets and imparts a momentum change similar to that in our control-volume analysis for a moving vane in Example 3.10 or Prob. 3.51. The buckets have an elliptical split-cup shape, as in Fig. 11.25b. They are named *Pelton wheels*, after Lester A. Pelton (1829–1908), who produced the first efficient design.

From Example 3.10 the force and power delivered to a Pelton wheel are theoretically

$$F = \rho Q(V_j - u)(1 - \cos \beta)$$
$$P = Fu = \rho Qu(V_j - u)(1 - \cos \beta)$$
(11.38)

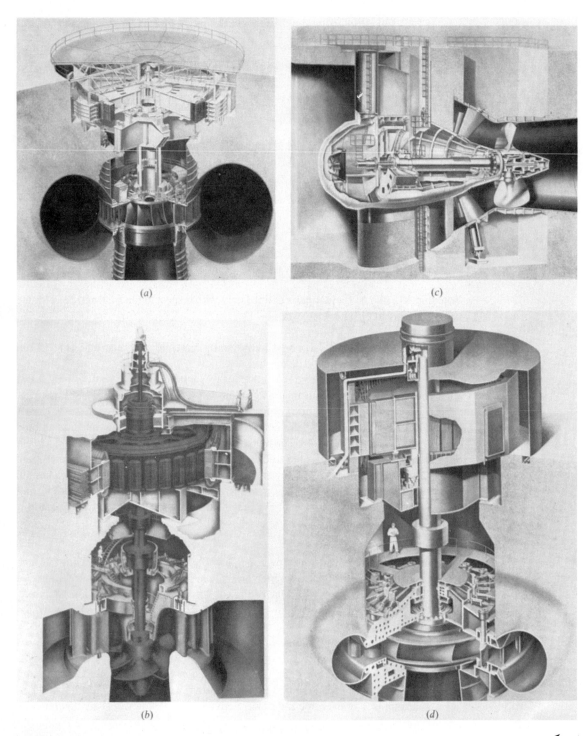

Fig. 11.23 Large-scale turbine designs depend upon available head and flow rate and operating conditions: (*a*) Francis (radial); (*b*) Kaplan (propeller); (*c*) bulb mounting with propeller runner; (*d*) reversible pump turbine with radial runner. (*Allis-Chalmers Fluid Products Company.*)

Fig. 11.24 Interior view of the 1.1-million hp (820-MW) turbine units on the Grand Coulee Dam of the Columbia River, showing the spiral case, the outer fixed vanes ("stay ring"), and the inner adjustable vanes ("wicket gates"). (*Allis-Chalmers Fluid Products Company.*)

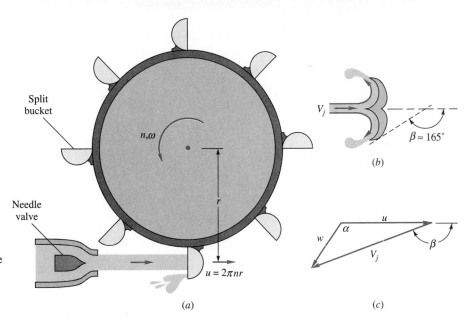

Fig. 11.25 Impulse turbine: (*a*) side view of wheel and jet; (*b*) top view of bucket; (*c*) typical velocity diagram.

where $u = 2\pi nr$ is the bucket linear velocity and r is the *pitch radius*, or distance to the jet centerline. A bucket angle $\beta = 180°$ gives maximum power but is physically impractical. In practice, $\beta \approx 165°$, or $1 - \cos\beta \approx 1.966$ or only 2 percent less than maximum power.

From Eq. (11.38) the theoretical power of an impulse turbine is parabolic in bucket speed u and is maximum when $dP/du = 0$, or

$$u^* = 2\pi n^* r = \tfrac{1}{2}V_j \qquad (11.39)$$

For a perfect nozzle, the entire available head would be converted to jet velocity $V_j = (2gH)^{1/2}$. Actually, since there are 2 to 8 percent nozzle losses, a velocity coefficient C_v is used

$$V_j = C_v(2gH)^{1/2} \qquad 0.92 \le C_v \le 0.98 \qquad (11.40)$$

By combining Eqs. (11.36) and (11.40), the theoretical impulse turbine efficiency becomes

$$\eta = 2(1 - \cos \beta)\phi(C_v - \phi) \qquad (11.41)$$

where
$$\phi = \frac{u}{(2gH)^{1/2}} = \text{peripheral-velocity factor}$$

Maximum efficiency occurs at $\phi = \tfrac{1}{2}C_v \approx 0.47$.

Figure 11.26 shows Eq. (11.41) plotted for an ideal turbine ($\beta = 180°$, $C_v = 1.0$) and for typical working conditions ($\beta = 160°$, $C_v = 0.94$). The latter case predicts $\eta_{max} = 85$ percent at $\phi = 0.47$, but the actual data for a 24-in Pelton wheel test are somewhat less efficient due to windage, mechanical friction, backsplashing, and non-uniform bucket flow. For this test $\eta_{max} = 80$ percent, and, generally speaking, an impulse turbine is not quite as efficient as the Francis or propeller turbines at their BEPs.

Figure 11.27 shows the optimum efficiency of the three turbine types, showing the importance of the power specific speed N_{sp} as a selection tool for the designer. These efficiencies are optimum and are obtained in careful design of large machines.

The water power available to a turbine may vary due to either net-head or flow-rate changes, both of which are common in field installations such as hydroelectric plants.

Fig. 11.26 Efficiency of an impulse turbine calculated from Eq. (11.41): solid curve = ideal, $\beta = 180°$, $C_v = 1.0$; dashed curve = actual, $\beta = 160°$, $C_v = 0.94$; open circles = data, Pelton wheel, diameter = 2 ft.

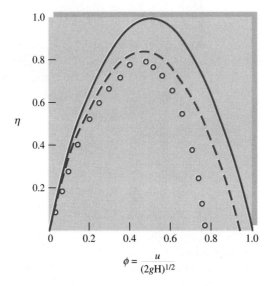

$$\phi = \frac{u}{(2gH)^{1/2}}$$

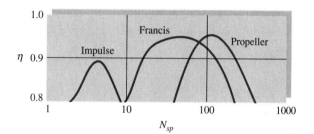

Fig. 11.27 Optimum efficiency of turbine designs.

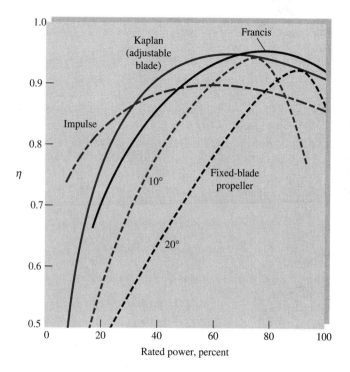

Fig. 11.28 Efficiency versus power level for various turbine designs at constant speed and head.

The demand for turbine power also varies from light to heavy, and the operating response is a change in the flow rate by adjustment of a gate valve or needle valve (Fig. 11.25a). As shown in Fig. 11.28, all three turbine types achieve fairly uniform efficiency as a function of the level of power being extracted. Especially effective is the adjustable-blade (Kaplan-type) propeller turbine, while the poorest is a fixed-blade propeller. The term *rated power* in Fig. 11.28 is the largest power delivery guaranteed by the manufacturer, as opposed to *normal power*, which is delivered at maximum efficiency.

For further details of design and operation of turbomachinery, the readable and interesting treatment in Ref. 33 is especially recommended. The feasibility of micro-hydropower is discussed in [26]. See also Refs. 27 to 29.

EXAMPLE 11.9

Investigate the possibility of using (*a*) a Pelton wheel similar to Fig. 11.26 or (*b*) the Francis turbine family of Fig. 11.21*d* to deliver 30,000 bhp from a net head of 1200 ft.

Solution

Part (a) From Fig. 11.27, the most efficient Pelton wheel occurs at about

$$N_{sp} \approx 4.5 = \frac{(r/min)(30{,}000 \text{ bhp})^{1/2}}{(1200 \text{ ft})^{1.25}}$$

or

$$n = 183 \text{ r/min} = 3.06 \text{ r/s}$$

From Fig. 11.26 the best operating point is

$$\phi \approx 0.47 = \frac{\pi D(3.06 \text{ r/s})}{[2(32.2)(1200)]^{1/2}}$$

or

$$D = 13.6 \text{ ft} \qquad \qquad Ans. (a)$$

This Pelton wheel is perhaps a little slow and a trifle large. You could reduce D and increase n by increasing N_{sp} to, say, 6 or 7 and accepting the slight reduction in efficiency. Or you could use a double-hung, two-wheel configuration, each delivering 15,000 bhp, which changes D and n by the factor $2^{1/2}$:

Double wheel: $n = (183)2^{1/2} = 260 \text{ r/min}$ $D = \dfrac{13.6}{2^{1/2}} = 9.6 \text{ ft}$ *Ans. (a)*

Part (b) The Francis wheel of Fig. 11.21d must have

$$N_{sp} = 29 = \frac{(r/min)(30{,}000 \text{ bhp})^{1/2}}{(1200 \text{ ft})^{1.25}}$$

or

$$n = 1183 \text{ r/min} = 19.7 \text{ r/s}$$

Then the optimum power coefficient is

$$C_{P*} = 2.70 = \frac{P}{\rho n^3 D^5} = \frac{30{,}000(550)}{(1.94)(19.7)^3 D^5}$$

or

$$D^5 = 412 \qquad D = 3.33 \text{ ft} = 40 \text{ in} \qquad \qquad Ans. (b)$$

This is a faster speed than normal practice, and the casing would have to withstand 1200 ft of water or about 520 lbf/in^2 internal pressure, but the 40-in size is extremely attractive. Francis turbines are now being operated at heads up to 1500 ft.

Wind Turbines

Wind energy has long been used as a source of mechanical power. The familiar four-bladed windmills of Holland, England, and the Greek islands have been used for centuries to pump water, grind grain, and saw wood. Modern research concentrates on the ability of wind turbines to generate electric power. Koeppl [47] stresses the potential for propeller-type machines, while Inglis [48] gives a more general analysis of wind turbines compared with alternative energy sources. Jarass [49] gives a detailed discussion of the technical and economic feasibility of large-scale electric power generation by wind. See also Refs. 50 to 52.

Some examples of wind turbine designs are shown in Fig. 11.29. The familiar American multiblade farm windmill (Fig. 11.29a) is of low efficiency, but thousands are in

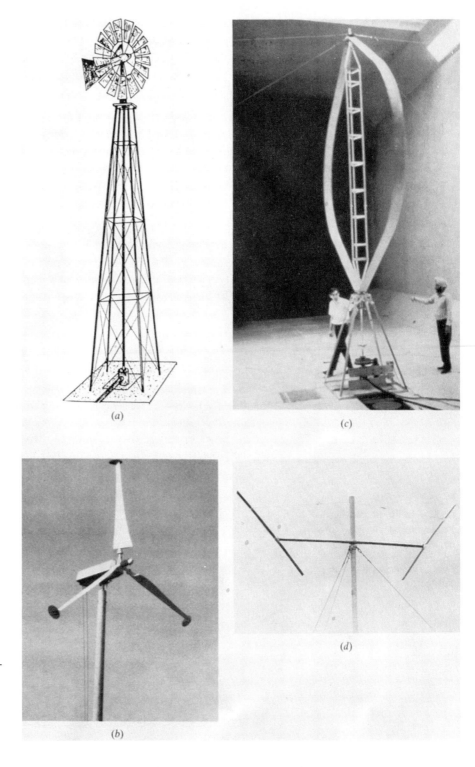

Fig. 11.29 Wind turbine designs: (*a*) the American multiblade farm HAWT; (*b*) propeller HAWT (*Grumman Aerospace Corp.*); (*c*) the Darrieus VAWT (*National Research Council, Canada*); (*d*) modified straight-blade Darrieus VAWT (*Reading University*).

use as a rugged, reliable, and inexpensive way to pump water. A more efficient design is the propeller mill in Fig. 11.29*b*, similar to the pioneering Smith-Putnam 1250-kW two-bladed system which operated on Grampa's Knob, 12 mi west of Rutland, Vermont, during 1941 to 1945. The Smith-Putnam design broke because of inadequate blade strength, but it withstood winds up to 115 mi/h and its efficiency was amply demonstrated [47].

The Dutch, American multiblade, and propeller mills are examples of *horizontal-axis wind turbines* (HAWTs), which are efficient but somewhat awkward in that they require extensive bracing and gear systems when combined with an electric generator. Thus a competing family of *vertical-axis wind turbines* (VAWTs) has been proposed which simplifies gearing and strength requirements. Figure 11.29*c* shows the "egg-beater" VAWT invented by G. J. M. Darrieus in 1925, now used in several government-sponsored demonstration systems. To minimize centrifugal stresses, the twisted blades of the Darrieus turbine follow a *troposkien* curve formed by a chain anchored at two points on a spinning vertical rod.

An alternative VAWT, simpler to construct than the troposkien, is the straight-bladed Darrieus-type turbine in Fig. 11.29*d*. This design, proposed by Reading University in England, has blades which pivot due to centrifugal action as wind speeds increase, thus limiting bending stresses.

Idealized Wind Turbine Theory

The ideal, frictionless efficiency of a propeller windmill was predicted by A. Betz in 1920, using the simulation shown in Fig. 11.30. The propeller is represented by an *actuator disk* which creates across the propeller plane a pressure discontinuity of area A and local velocity V. The wind is represented by a streamtube of approach velocity V_1 and a slower downstream wake velocity V_2. The pressure rises to p_b just before the disk and drops to p_a just after, returning to free-stream pressure in the far wake. To hold the propeller rigid when it is extracting energy from the wind, there must be a leftward force F on its support, as shown.

Fig. 11.30 Idealized actuator-disk and streamtube analysis of flow through a windmill.

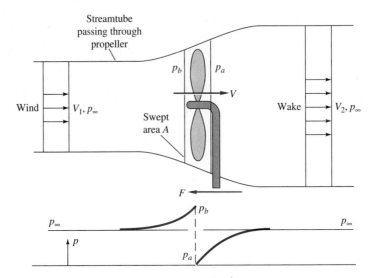

A control-volume–horizontal-momentum relation applied between sections 1 and 2 gives

$$\sum F_x = -F = \dot{m}(V_2 - V_1)$$

A similar relation for a control volume just before and after the disk gives

$$\sum F_x = -F + (p_b - p_a)A = \dot{m}(V_a - V_b) = 0$$

Equating these two yields the propeller force

$$F = (p_b - p_a)A = \dot{m}(V_1 - V_2) \tag{11.42}$$

Assuming ideal flow, the pressures can be found by applying the incompressible Bernoulli relation up to the disk

From 1 to b:
$$p_\infty + \tfrac{1}{2}\rho V_1^2 = p_b + \tfrac{1}{2}\rho V^2$$

From a to 2:
$$p_a + \tfrac{1}{2}\rho V^2 = p_\infty + \tfrac{1}{2}\rho V_2^2$$

Subtracting these and noting that $\dot{m} = \rho A V$ through the propeller, we can substitute for $p_b - p_a$ in Eq. (11.42) to obtain

$$p_b - p_a = \tfrac{1}{2}\rho(V_1^2 - V_2^2) = \rho V(V_1 - V_2)$$

or
$$V = \tfrac{1}{2}(V_1 + V_2) \tag{11.43}$$

Continuity and momentum thus require that the velocity V through the disk equal the average of the wind and far-wake speeds.

Finally, the power extracted by the disk can be written in terms of V_1 and V_2 by combining Eqs. (11.42) and (11.43)

$$P = FV = \rho A V^2(V_1 - V_2) = \tfrac{1}{4}\rho A(V_1^2 - V_2^2)(V_1 + V_2) \tag{11.44}$$

For a given wind speed V_1, we can find the maximum possible power by differentiating P with respect to V_2 and setting equal to zero. The result is

$$P = P_{\max} = \tfrac{8}{27}\rho A V_1^3 \qquad \text{at } V_2 = \tfrac{1}{3}V_1 \tag{11.45}$$

which corresponds to $V = 2V_1/3$ through the disk.

The maximum available power to the propeller is the mass flow through the propeller times the total kinetic energy of the wind

$$P_{\text{avail}} = \tfrac{1}{2}\dot{m}V_1^2 = \tfrac{1}{2}\rho A V_1^3$$

Thus the maximum possible efficiency of an ideal frictionless wind turbine is usually stated in terms of the *power coefficient*

$$C_P = \frac{P}{\tfrac{1}{2}\rho A V_1^3} \tag{11.46}$$

Equation (11.45) states that the total power coefficient is

$$C_{p,\max} = \tfrac{16}{27} = 0.593 \tag{11.47}$$

This is called the *Betz number* and serves as an ideal with which to compare the actual performance of real windmills.

Figure 11.31 shows the measured power coefficients of various wind turbine designs.

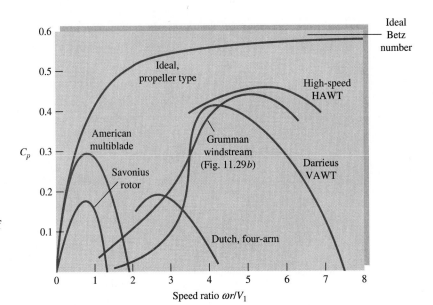

Fig. 11.31 Estimated performance of various wind turbine designs as a function of blade-tip speed ratio. (*From Ref. 53.*)

The independent variable is not V_2/V_1 (which is artificial and convenient only in the ideal theory) but the ratio of blade-tip speed ωr to wind speed. Note that the tip can move much faster than the wind, a fact disturbing to the laity but familiar to engineers in the behavior of iceboats and sailing vessels. The Darrieus has the many advantages of a vertical axis but has little torque at low speeds and also rotates more slowly at maximum power than a propeller, thus requiring a higher gear ratio for the generator. The Savonius rotor (Fig. 6.29b) has been suggested as a VAWT design [48] because it produces power at very low wind speeds, but it is inefficient and susceptible to storm damage because it cannot be feathered in high winds.

As shown in Fig. 11.32, there are many areas of the world where wind energy is an attractive alternative. Greenland, Newfoundland, Argentina, Chile, New Zealand, Iceland, Ireland, and the United Kingdom have the highest prevailing winds, but Australia, e.g., with only moderate winds, has the potential to generate half its electricity with wind turbines [53]. In addition, since the ocean is generally even windier than the land, there are many island areas of high potential for wind power. There have also been proposals [47] for ocean-based floating windmill farms. The inexhaustible availability of the winds, coupled with improved low-cost turbine designs, indicates a bright future for this alternative.

Summary

Turbomachinery design is perhaps the most practical and most active application of the principles of fluid mechanics. There are billions of pumps and turbines in use in the world, and thousands of companies are seeking improvements. This chapter discusses both positive-displacement devices and, more extensively, rotodynamic machines. With the centrifugal pump as an example, the basic concepts of torque, power, head, flow rate, and efficiency are developed for a turbomachine. Nondimensionalization leads to the pump similarity rules and some typical dimensionless performance curves for axial and centrifugal machines. The single most useful pump parameter is found to be the

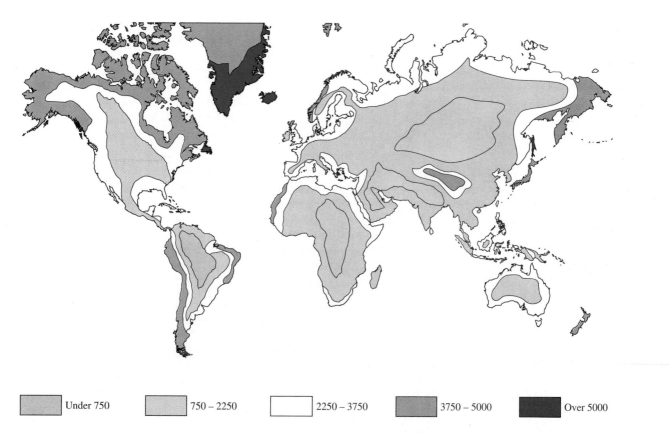

| | Under 750 | | 750 – 2250 | | 2250 – 3750 | | 3750 – 5000 | | Over 5000 |

Fig. 11.32 World availability of land-based wind energy: estimated annual electric output in kWh/kW of a wind turbine rated at 11.2 m/s (25 mi/h). (*From Ref. 54.*)

specific speed, which delineates the type of design needed. An interesting design application is the theory of pumps combined in series and in parallel.

Turbines extract energy from flowing fluids and are of two types: impulse turbines, which convert the momentum of a high-speed stream, and reaction turbines, where the pressure drop occurs within the blade passages in an internal flow. By analogy with pumps, the power specific speed is important for turbines and is used to classify them into impulse, Francis, and propeller-type designs. A special case of reaction turbine with unconfined flow is the wind turbine. Several types of windmills are discussed and their relative performances compared.

References

1. D. G. Wilson, ''Turbomachinery—From Paddle Wheels to Turbojets,'' *Mech. Eng.*, vol. 104, Oct. 1982, pp. 28–40.
2. D. G. Shepherd, *Principles of Turbomachinery*, Macmillan, New York, 1956.
3. G. T. Csanady, *Theory of Turbomachines*, McGraw-Hill, New York, 1964.
4. G. F. Wislicenus, *Fluid Mechanics of Turbomachinery*, 2d ed., McGraw-Hill, New York, 1965.
5. A. Betz, *Introduction to the Theory of Flow Machines*, Pergamon, New York, 1966.
6. O. E. Balje, *Turbomachines: A Guide to Design, Selection, and Theory*, Wiley, New York, 1981.
7. E. S. Logan, Jr., *Turbomachinery: Basic Theory and Applications*, Marcel Dekker, New York, 1981.

8. A. J. Stepanoff, *Centrifugal and Axial Flow Pumps*, 2d ed., Wiley, New York, 1957.

9. I. J. Karassik and R. Carter, *Centrifugal Pumps*, Dodge, New York, 1960.

10. A. J. Stepanoff, *Pumps and Blowers: Two-Phase Flow*, Wiley, New York, 1965.

11. T. G. Hicks and T. W. Edwards, *Pump Application Engineering*, McGraw-Hill, New York, 1971.

12. *Pump Selector for Industry*, Worthington Pump, Mountainside, N.J., 1977.

13. R. Walker, *Pump Selection*, 2d ed., Butterworth, London, 1979.

14. R. H. Warring, *Pumps: Selection, Systems, and Applications*, 2d ed., Gulf Pub., Houston, 1984.

15. V. L. Lobanoff and R. R. Ross, *Centrifugal Pumps, Design and Application*, Gulf Pub., Houston, 1985.

16. H. L. Stewart, *Pumps*, 5th ed., Macmillan, New York, 1991.

17. C. H. Berry, *Flow and Fan: Principles of Moving Air through Ducts*, 2d ed., Industrial Press, New York, 1963.

18. W. C. Osborne, *Fans*, 2d ed., Pergamon, London, 1977.

19. R. Jorgensen (ed.), *Fan Engineering*, Buffalo Forge, Buffalo, N.Y., 1983.

20. R. A. Wallis, *Axial Flow Fans and Ducts*, Wiley, New York, 1983.

21. J. H. Horlock, *Axial Flow Compressors*, Butterworth, London, 1958.

22. R. N. Brown, *Compressors*, Gulf Pub., Houston, 1986.

23. N. A. Cumpsty, *Compressor Aerodynamics*, Longmans, London, 1989.

24. J. H. Horlock, *Axial Flow Turbines*, Butterworth, London, 1966.

25. W. W. Bathe, *Fundamentals of Gas Turbines*, Wiley, New York, 1984.

26. D. McGuigan, *Small Scale Water Power*, Prism Press, Dorchester, Mass., 1978.

27. C. C. Warnick, *Hydropower Engineering*, Prentice-Hall, Englewood Cliffs, N.J., 1984.

28. J. J. Fritz, *Small and Mini Hydropower Systems*, McGraw-Hill, New York, 1984.

29. R. H. Warring (ed.), *Hydraulic Handbook*, 8th ed., Gulf Pub., Houston, 1983.

30. Hydraulic Institute, *Hydraulic Institute Standards for Centrifugal, Rotating, and Reciprocal Pumps*, New York, 1983.

31. I. J. Karassik, W. C. Krutzsch, W. H. Fraser, and J. P. Messina, *Pump Handbook*, 2d ed., McGraw-Hill, New York, 1985.

32. J. S. Gulliver and R. E. A. Arndt, *Hydropower Engineering Handbook*, McGraw-Hill, New York, 1990.

33. R. L. Daugherty, J. B. Franzini, and E. J. Finnemore, *Fluid Mechanics with Engineering Applications*, 8th ed., McGraw-Hill, New York, 1985.

34. R. H. Sabersky, A. J. Acosta, and E. G. Hauptmann, *Fluid Flow: A First Course in Fluid Mechanics*, 3d ed., Macmillan, New York, 1989.

35. J. P. Poynton, *Metering Pumps*, Marcel Dekker, New York, 1983.

36. R. P. Lambeck, *Hydraulic Pumps and Motors: Selection and Application for Hydraulic Power Control Systems*, Marcel Dekker, New York, 1983.

37. T. L. Henshaw, *Reciprocating Pumps*, Van Nostrand Reinhold, New York, 1987.

38. J. L. Miller, *The Reciprocating Pump: Theory, Design and Use,* Wiley, New York, 1987.

39. P. Cooper (ed.), ''Pumping Machinery—1989,'' *Proc. ASME Symp. FED*, vol. 81, American Society of Mechanical Engineers, New York, 1989.

40. M. C. Roco, P. Hamelin, T. Cader, and G. Davidson, ''Animation of LDV Measurements in a Centrifugal Pump,'' in *Fluid Machinery Forum—1990*, U.S. Rohatgi (ed.), FED, vol. 96, American Society of Mechanical Engineers, New York, 1990.

41. E. M. Greitzer, ''The Stability of Pumping Systems: The 1980 Freeman Scholar Lecture,'' *J. Fluids Eng.*, vol. 103, June 1981, pp. 193–242.

42. B. Lakshminarayana, ''An Assessment of Computational Fluid Dynamic Techniques in the Analysis and Design of Turbomachinery: The 1990 Freeman Scholar Lecture,'' *J. Fluids Eng.*, vol. 113, September 1991, pp. 315–352.

44. H. ...
    Principle," in ...

45. B. ... Symp., New York, ... Type Turbine," *ASCE Trans.*, vol. 89, 1926, p. 628.
    ponents of ... Quantity, and Efficiency in Pumps—The Area-Ratio
    ... ana and ... *ifugal Pumps and Compressors*, vol. 100127,

46. M. Murakami, K. ... inery," *ASME Symp.* ... 130, 19 ... Methods in Rotating Com-
    Impeller Passages of Centr ... and E. Asakura, "Velocity and Pres ... utions in the
    420–426. ... Pumps." *J. Fluids Eng.*, vol. 102, December 1980, pp.

47. G. W. Koeppl, *Putnam's Power fro* ... ..., 2d ed., Van Nostrand Reinhold, New York,
    1982.

48. D. R. Inglis, *Wind Power*, University of Michigan Pre ... n Arbor, 1978.

49. L. Jarass, *Wind Energy: An Assessment of the Technical and Econ ... mic Potential*, Springer-
    Verlag, Berlin, 1981.

50. A. J. Wortman, *Introduction to Wind Turbine Engineering*, Butterworth, Woburn, Mass.,
    1983.

51. F. R. Eldridge, *Wind Machines*, 2d ed., Van Nostrand Reinhold, New York, 1980.

52. D. M. Eggleston and F. S. Stoddard, *Wind Turbine Engineering Design*, Van Nostrand, New
    York, 1987.

53. M. L. Robinson, "The Darrieus Wind Turbine for Electrical Power Generation," *Aeronaut.
    J.,* June 1981, pp. 244–255.

54. D. F. Warne and P. G. Calnan, "Generation of Electricity from the Wind," *IEE Rev.*, vol.
    124, no. 11R, November 1977, pp. 963–985.

55. L. A. Haimerl, "The Crossflow Turbine," *Waterpower*, January 1960, pp. 5–13; see also
    ASME Symp. Small Hydropower Fluid Mach., vol. 1, 1980, and vol. 2, 1982.

PROBLEMS

In addition to many traditional problems, categorized in the problem distribution list below, there are word problems, labeled W11.1 to W11.10, and a design project, D11.1.

Problem Distribution

Section	Topic	Problems
11.1	Introduction and classification	11.1–11.14
11.2	Centrifugal pump theory	11.15–11.21
11.3	Pump performance and similarity rules	11.22–11.41
11.3	Net positive-suction head	11.42–11.44
11.4	Specific speed: Mixed- and axial-flow pumps	11.45–11.62
11.5	Matching pumps to system characteristics	11.63–11.73
11.5	Pumps in parallel or series	11.74–11.81
11.5	Pump instability	11.82–11.83
11.6	Reaction and impulse turbines	11.84–11.99
11.6	Wind turbines	11.100–11.103

11.1 Describe the geometry and operation of a peristaltic positive-displacement pump which occurs in nature.

11.2 What would be the technical classification of the following turbomachines: (*a*) a household fan, (*b*) a windmill, (*c*) an aircraft propeller, (*d*) a fuel pump in a car, (*e*) an eductor, (*f*) a fluid-coupling transmission, and (*g*) a power plant steam turbine?

11.3 A PDP can deliver almost any fluid, but there is always a limiting very high viscosity for which performance will deteriorate. Can you explain the probable reason?

11.4 Figure 11.2*c* shows a double-screw pump. Sketch a single-screw-pump and explain its operation. How did Archimedes' screw pump operate?

11.5 What type of pump is shown in Fig. P11.5? How does it operate?

11.6 Figure P11.6 shows two points a half-period apart in the operation of a pump. What type of pump is this? How does it work? Sketch your best guess of flow rate versus time for a few cycles.

11.7 A piston PDP has a 5-in diameter and a 2-in stroke and operates at 750 r/min with 92 percent volumetric effi-

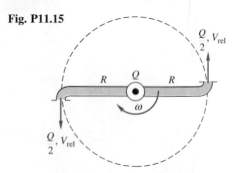

Fig. P11.5

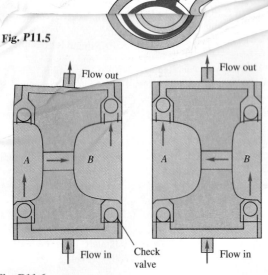

Fig. P11.6

11.12 Which is better, a PDP or a centrifugal pump, for (a) high flow rate, (b) high pressure rise, (c) self-priming, (d) low wear on parts, (e) steady outlet stream, (f) delivering high-viscosity fluids?

11.13 A 20-hp pump delivers 400 gal/min of gasoline at 20°C with 80 percent efficiency. What head and pressure rise result across the pump?

11.14 A pump delivers gasoline at 20°C and 12 m^3/h. At the inlet p_1 = 100 kPa, z_1 = 1 m, and V_1 = 2 m/s. At the exit p_2 = 500 kPa, z_2 = 4 m, and V_2 = 3 m/s. How much power is required if the motor efficiency is 80 percent?

11.15 A lawn sprinkler can be used as a simple turbine. As shown in Fig. P11.15, flow enters normal to the paper in the center and splits evenly into $Q/2$ and V_{rel} leaving each nozzle. The arms rotate at angular velocity ω and do work on a shaft. Draw the velocity diagram for this turbine. Neglecting friction, find an expression for the power delivered to the shaft. Find the rotation rate for which the power is a maximum.

Fig. P11.15

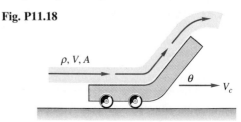

ciency. (a) What is its delivery, in gal/min? (b) If the pump delivers SAE 10W oil at 20°C against a head of 50 ft, what horsepower is required when the overall efficiency is 84 percent?

11.8 A centrifugal pump delivers 550 gal/min of water at 20°C when the brake horsepower is 22 and the efficiency is 71 percent. (a) Estimate the head rise in ft and the pressure rise in lbf/in². (b) Also estimate the head rise and horsepower if instead the delivery is 550 gal/min of gasoline at 20°C.

11.9 Figure P11.9 shows the measured performance of the Vickers model PVQ40 piston pump when delivering SAE 10W oil at 180°F ($\rho \approx 910$ kg/m^3). Make some general observations about these data vis-à-vis Fig. 11.2 and your intuition about the behavior of piston pumps.

11.10 Suppose that the piston pump of Fig. P11.9 is used to deliver 15 gal/min of water at 20°C using 20 brake horsepower. Neglecting Reynolds-number effects, use the figure to estimate (a) the speed in r/min and (b) the pressure rise in lbf/in².

11.11 A pump delivers 1500 L/min of water at 20°C against a pressure rise of 300 kPa. Kinetic- and potential-energy changes are negligible. If the driving motor supplies 9 kW, what is the overall efficiency?

11.16 For the "sprinkler turbine" of Fig. P11.15, let R = 18 cm, with total flow rate of 14 m^3/h of water at 20°C. If the nozzle exit diameter is 8 mm, estimate (a) the maximum power delivered in W and (b) the appropriate rotation rate in r/min.

11.17 A centrifugal pump has d_1 = 7 in, d_2 = 13 in, b_1 = 4 in, b_2 = 3 in, β_1 = 25°, and β_2 = 40° and rotates at 1160 r/min. If the fluid is gasoline at 20°C and the flow enters the blades radially, estimate the theoretical (a) flow rate in gal/min, (b) horsepower, and (c) head in ft.

11.18 A jet of velocity V strikes a vane which moves to the right at speed V_c, as in Fig. P11.18. The vane has a turning angle

Fig. P11.18

Fig. P11.9 Performance of the model PVQ40 piston pump delivering SAE 10W oil at 180°F. (*Courtesy of Vickers Inc., PDN/PACE Division.*)

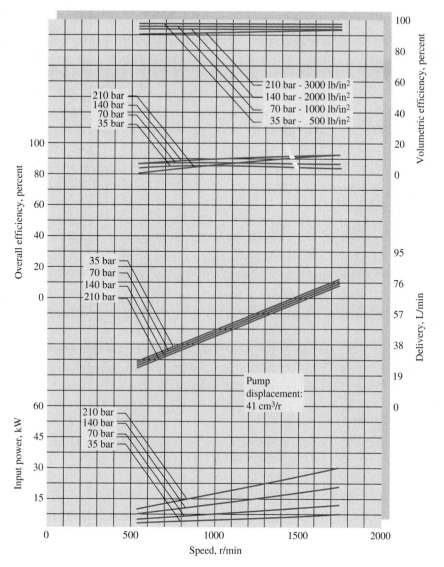

θ. Derive an expression for the power delivered to the vane by the jet. For what vane speed is the power maximum?

11.19 A centrifugal pump has $r_2 = 9$ in, $b_2 = 2$ in, and $\beta_2 = 35°$ and rotates at 1060 r/min. If it generates a head of 180 ft, determine the theoretical (*a*) flow rate in gal/min and (*b*) horsepower. Assume near-radial entry flow.

11.20 Suppose that Prob. 11.19 is reversed into a statement of the theoretical power $P_w \approx 153$ hp. Can you then compute the theoretical (*a*) flow rate and (*b*) head? Explain and resolve the difficulty which arises.

11.21 The centrifugal pump of Fig. P11.21 develops a flow rate

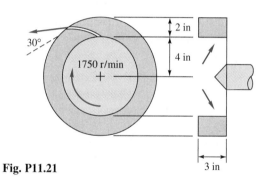

Fig. P11.21

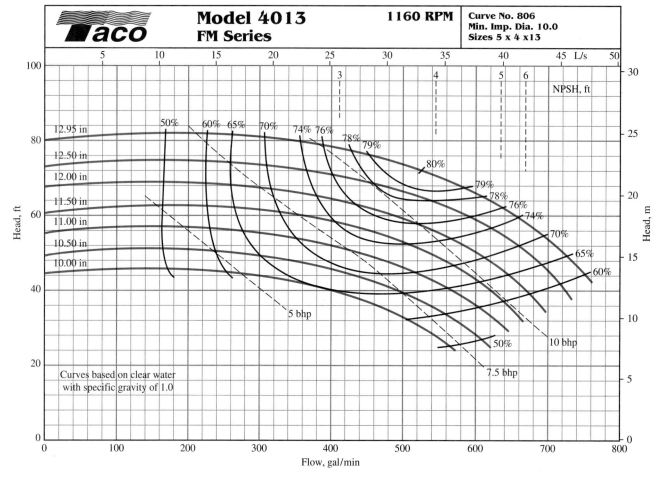

Fig. P11.24 Performance data for a centrifugal pump. (*Courtesy of Taco, Inc., Cranston, Rhode Island.*)

of 4200 gal/min of gasoline at 20°C with near-radial absolute inflow. Estimate the theoretical (*a*) horsepower, (*b*) head rise, and (*c*) appropriate blade angle at the inner radius.

11.22 If the 35-in water pump from Fig. 11.7*a* is run at 1000 r/min, what (*a*) head and (*b*) brake horsepower will result when the discharge is 14,000 gal/min?

11.23 If the 38-in-diameter pump of Fig. 11.7*b* is used to deliver 20°C kerosine at 850 r/min and 22,000 gal/min, what (*a*) head and (*b*) brake horsepower will result?

11.24 Figure P11.24 shows performance data for the Taco, Inc., model 4013 pump. Compute the ratios of measured shutoff head to the ideal value U^2/g for all seven impeller sizes. Determine the average and standard deviation of this ratio and compare it to the average for the six impellers in Fig. 11.7.

11.25 At what speed in r/min should the 35-in-diameter pump of Fig. 11.7*b* be run to produce a head of 400 ft at a discharge of 20,000 gal/min? What brake horsepower will be required? *Hint:* Fit $H(Q)$ to a formula.

11.26 Determine if the seven Taco, Inc., pump sizes in Fig. P11.24 can be collapsed into a single dimensionless chart of C_H, C_P, and η versus C_Q, as in Fig. 11.8. Comment on the results.

11.27 The 12-in pump of Fig. P11.24 is to be scaled up in size to provide a head of 90 ft and a flow rate of 1000 gal/min at BEP. Determine the correct (*a*) impeller diameter, (*b*) speed in r/min, and (*c*) horsepower required.

11.28 Tests by the Byron Jackson Co. of a 14.62-in-diameter centrifugal water pump at 2134 r/min yield the following data:

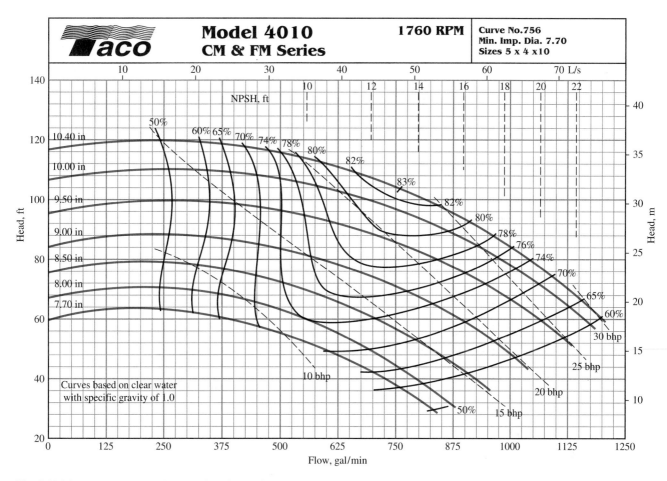

Fig. P11.31 Performance data for a family of centrifugal pump impellers. (*Courtesy of Taco, Inc., Cranston, Rhode Island.*)

Q, ft³/s	0	2	4	6	8	10
H, ft	340	340	340	330	300	220
bhp	135	160	205	255	330	330

What is the BEP? What is the specific speed? Estimate the maximum discharge possible.

11.29 If the scaling laws are applied to the pump of Prob. 11.28 for the same impeller diameter, determine (*a*) the speed for which the shutoff head will be 280 ft, (*b*) the speed for which the BEP flow rate will be 8.0 ft³/s, and (*c*) the speed for which the BEP conditions will require 80 hp.

11.30 A pump from the same family as Prob. 11.28 is built with $D = 18$ in and a BEP power of 250 hp for *gasoline* (not water). Using the scaling laws, estimate the resulting (*a*)

speed in r/min, (*b*) flow rate at BEP, and (*c*) shutoff head.

11.31 Figure P11.31 shows performance data for the Taco, Inc., model 4010 pump. Compute the ratios of measured shutoff head to the ideal value U^2/g for all seven impeller sizes. Determine the average and standard deviation of this ratio, and compare it to the average of 0.58 ± 0.02 for the seven impellers in Fig. P11.24. Comment on your results.

11.32 Determine if the seven Taco, Inc., impeller sizes in Fig. P11.31 can be collapsed into a single dimensionless chart of C_H, C_P, and η versus C_Q, as in Fig. 11.8. Comment on the results.

11.33 Clearly the maximum efficiencies of the pumps in Figs. P11.24 and P11.31 decrease with impeller size. Compare η_{max} for these two pump families with both the Moody and the Anderson correlations, Eqs. (11.29). Use the central impeller size as a comparison point.

11.34 You are asked to consider a pump geometrically similar to the 9-in-diameter pump of Fig. P11.31 to deliver 1200 gal/min at 1500 r/min. Determine the appropriate (a) impeller diameter, (b) BEP horsepower, (c) shutoff head, and (d) maximum efficiency. The fluid is kerosine, not water.

11.35 A 5-in-diameter centrifugal water pump, running at 1800 r/min, yields the following performance data:

Q, ft^3/min	1	3	5	7	9
H, ft	35	39	40	36	25
η, %	17	64	82	81	30

When it runs at 2400 r/min and 6 ft^3/min, the measured head is 66 ft. Compare this with the similarity-rule estimate, and compute the horsepower required at this new point.

11.36 Plot the dimensionless performance curves for the pump of Prob. 11.35 and compare with Fig. 11.8. Find the appropriate diameter in inches and speed in r/min for a geometrically similar pump to deliver 400 gal/min against a head of 200 ft. What brake horsepower would be required?

11.37 The efficiency of a centrifugal pump can be approximated by the curve fit $\eta \approx aQ - bQ^3$, where a and b are constants. For this approximation, (a) what is the ratio of Q^* at BEP to Q_{max}? If the maximum efficiency is 88 percent, what is the efficiency at (b) $\frac{1}{3}Q_{max}$ and (c) $\frac{4}{3}Q^*$?

11.38 A 6.85-in pump, running at 3500 r/min, has the following measured performance for water at 20°C:

Q, gal/min	50	100	150	200	250	300	350	400	450
H, ft	201	200	198	194	189	181	169	156	139
η, %	29	50	64	72	77	80	81	79	74

(a) Estimate the horsepower at BEP. If this pump is rescaled in water to provide 20 bhp at 3000 r/min, determine the appropriate (b) impeller diameter, (c) flow rate, and (d) efficiency for this new condition.

11.39 The Allis-Chalmers D30LR centrifugal compressor delivers 33,000 ft^3/min of SO_2 with a pressure change from 14.0 to 18.0 lbf/in^2 absolute using an 800-hp motor at 3550 r/min. What is the overall efficiency? What will the flow rate and Δp be at 3000 r/min? Estimate the diameter of the impeller.

11.40 Suppose that the 32-in pump of Fig. 11.7a is used to deliver air with inlet conditions of 14.7 lbf/in^2 absolute and 60°F. What pressure rise, discharge in ft^3/min, and brake horsepower will result if the pump is run at 1800 r/min?

11.41 It is desired to build a centrifugal pump geometrically similar to that of Prob. 11.28 to deliver 6500 gal/min of

gasoline at 20°C at 1060 r/min. Estimate the resulting (a) impeller diameter, (b) head, (c) brake horsepower, and (d) maximum efficiency.

11.42 An 8-in model pump delivering 180°F water at 800 gal/min and 2400 r/min begins to cavitate when the inlet pressure and velocity are 12 lbf/in^2 absolute and 20 ft/s, respectively. Find the required NPSH of a prototype which is 4 times larger and runs at 1000 r/min.

11.43 The 28-in-diameter pump in Fig. 11.7a at 1170 r/min is used to pump water at 20°C through a piping system at 14,000 gal/min. (a) Determine the required brake horsepower. The average friction factor is 0.018. (b) If there is 65 ft of 12-in-diameter pipe upstream of the pump, how far below the surface should the pump inlet be placed to avoid cavitation?

11.44 The pump of Prob. 11.28 is scaled up to an 18-in diameter, operating in water at best efficiency at 1760 r/min. The measured NPSH is 16 ft, and the friction loss between the inlet and the pump is 22 ft. Will it be sufficient to avoid cavitation if the pump inlet is placed 9 ft below the surface of a sea-level reservoir?

11.45 Determine the specific speeds of the seven Taco, Inc., pump impellers in Fig. P11.24. Are they appropriate for centrifugal designs? Are they approximately equal within experimental uncertainty? If not, why not?

11.46 Determine the specific speeds of the seven Taco, Inc., pump impellers in Fig. P11.31. Are they appropriate for centrifugal designs? Are they approximately equal within experimental uncertainty? If not, why not?

11.47 A typical household basement sump pump provides a discharge of 5 gal/min against a head of 15 ft. Estimate (a) the maximum efficiency and (b) the minimum horsepower required to drive such a pump.

11.48 Compute the specific speeds for the pumps in Probs. 11.28, 11.35, and 11.38 plus the median sizes in Figs. P11.24 and P11.31. Then determine if their maximum efficiencies match the values predicted in Fig. 11.14.

11.49 Data collected by the writer for flow coefficient at BEP for 30 different pumps are plotted versus specific speed in Fig. P11.49. Determine if the values of C_Q^* for the five pumps in Prob. 11.48 also fit on this correlation. If so, suggest a curve-fitted formula for the data.

11.50 Data collected by the writer for power coefficient at BEP for 30 different pumps are plotted versus specific speed in Fig. P11.50. Determine if the values of C_P^* for the five pumps in Prob. 11.48 also fit on this correlation. If so, suggest a curve-fitted formula for the data.

11.51 An axial-flow pump delivers 40 ft^3/s of air which enters at 20°C and 1 atm. The flow passage has a 10-in outer radius and an 8-in inner radius. Blade angles are $\alpha_1 = 60°$ and $\beta_2 = 70°$, and the rotor runs at 1800 r/min. For the

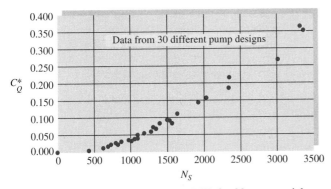

Fig. P11.49 Flow coefficient at BEP for 30 commercial pumps.

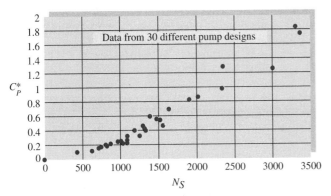

Fig. P11.50 Power coefficient at BEP for 30 commercial pumps.

first stage compute (a) the head rise and (b) the power required.

11.52 An axial-flow fan operates in sea-level air at 1200 r/min and has a blade-tip diameter of 1 m and a root diameter of 80 cm. The inlet angles are $\alpha_1 = 55°$ and $\beta_1 = 30°$, while at the outlet $\beta_2 = 60°$. Estimate the theoretical values of the (a) flow rate, (b) horsepower, and (c) outlet angle α_2.

11.53 If the axial-flow pump of Fig. 11.13 is used to deliver 70,000 gal/min of 20°C water at 1170 r/min, estimate (a) the proper impeller diameter, (b) the shutoff head, (c) the shutoff horsepower, and (d) Δp at best efficiency.

11.54 The Colorado River Aqueduct uses Worthington Corp. pumps which deliver 200 ft³/s at 450 r/min against a head of 440 ft. What types of pump are these? Estimate the impeller diameter.

11.55 We want to pump 70°C water at 20,000 gal/min and 1800 r/min. Estimate the type of pump, the horsepower required, and the impeller diameter if the required pressure rise for one stage is (a) 170 kPa and (b) 1350 kpa.

11.56 A pump is needed to deliver 40,000 gal/min of gasoline at 20°C against a head of 90 ft. Find the impeller size, speed, and brake horsepower needed to use the pump families of (a) Fig. 11.8 and (b) Fig. 11.13. Which is the better design?

11.57 Performance data for a 21-in-diameter air blower running at 3550 r/min are as follows:

Δp, inH$_2$O	29	30	28	21	10
Q, ft³/min	500	1000	2000	3000	4000
bhp	6	8	12	18	25

Note the fictitious expression of pressure rise in terms of water rather than air. What is the specific speed? How does the performance compare with Fig. 11.8? What are C_Q^*, C_H^*, and C_P^*?

11.58 The Worthington Corp. model A-12251 water pump, operating at maximum efficiency, produces 53 ft of head at 3500 r/min, 1.1 bhp at 3200 r/min, and 60 gal/min at 2940 r/min. What type of pump is this? What is its efficiency, and how does this compare with Fig. 11.14? Estimate the impeller diameter.

11.59 Suppose it is desired to deliver 700 ft³/min of propane gas (molecular weight = 44.06) at 1 atm and 20°C with a single-stage pressure rise of 8.0 inH$_2$O. Determine the appropriate size and speed for using the pump families of (a) Prob. 11.57 and (b) Fig. 11.13. Which is the better design?

11.60 A 45-hp pump is desired to generate a head of 200 ft when running at BEP with 20°C gasoline at 1200 r/min. Using the correlations in Figs. P11.49 and P11.50, determine the appropriate (a) specific speed, (b) flow rate, and (c) impeller diameter.

11.61 A mine ventilation fan, running at 295 r/min, delivers 500 m³/s of sea-level air with a pressure rise of 1100 Pa. Is this fan axial, centrifugal, or mixed? Estimate its diameter in ft. If the flow rate is increased 50 percent for the same diameter, by what percentage will the pressure rise change?

11.62 The actual mine ventilation fan discussed in Prob. 11.61 had a diameter of 20 ft [20, p. 339]. What would be the proper diameter for the pump family of Fig. 11.14 to provide 500 m³/s at 295 r/min and BEP? What would be the resulting pressure rise in Pa?

11.63 The 36.75-in pump in Fig. 11.7a at 1170 r/min is used to pump water at 60°F from a reservoir through 1000 ft of 12-in-ID galvanized-iron pipe to a point 200 ft above the reservoir surface. What flow rate and brake horsepower will result? If there is 40 ft of pipe upstream of the pump, how far below the surface should the pump inlet be placed to avoid cavitation?

11.64 In Prob. 11.63 the operating point is off design at an efficiency of only 77 percent. Is it possible, with the similarity rules, to change the pump rotation speed to deliver the water near BEP? Explain your results.

11.65 The 38-in pump of Fig. 11.7b is used in series to lift 20°C water 3000 ft through 4000 ft of 18-in-ID cast-iron pipe. For most efficient operation, how many pumps in series are needed if the rotation speed is (a) 710 r/min and (b) 1200 r/min?

11.66 It is proposed to run the pump of Prob. 11.35 at 1800 r/min to pump water at 20°C through the system in Fig. P11.66. The pipe is 3-cm-diameter commercial steel. What flow rate in ft³/min will result? Is this an efficient application?

Fig. P11.66

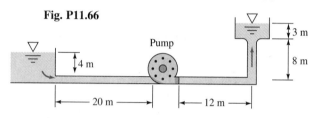

11.67 The pump of Prob. 11.28 is to deliver water at 20°C through 75 m of 10-cm-diameter galvanized-iron pipe. All other system losses are neglected. Determine the flow rate and brake horsepower for (a) 2134 r/min and (b) the rotation speed which gives best efficiency.

11.68 A 24-in pump is homologous to the 32-in pump in Fig. 11.7a. At 1400 r/min this pump delivers 12,000 gal/min of water from one reservoir through a long pipe to another 50 ft higher. What will the flow rate be if the pump speed is increased to 1750 r/min? Assume no change in pipe friction factor or efficiency.

11.69 The pump of Prob. 11.38, running at 3500 r/min, is used to deliver water at 20°C through 600 ft of cast-iron pipe to an elevation 100 ft higher. Determine (a) the proper pipe diameter for BEP operation and (b) the flow rate which results if the pipe diameter is 3 in.

11.70 The pump of Prob. 11.28, operating at 2134 r/min, is used with 20°C water in the system of Fig. P11.70. (a) If it is operating at BEP, what is the proper elevation z_2? (b) If $z_2 = 225$ ft, what is the flow rate? Let $D_{pipe} = 8$ in.

Fig. P11.70

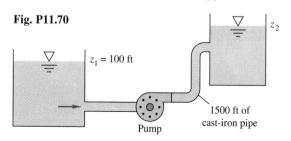

11.71 The pump of Prob. 11.38, running at 3500 r/min, delivers water at 20°C through 7200 ft of horizontal 5-in-diameter commercial-steel pipe. There are a sharp entrance, sharp exit, four 90° elbows, and a gate valve. Estimate (a) the flow rate if the valve is wide open and (b) the valve closing percentage which causes the pump to operate at BEP. (c) If the latter condition holds continuously for 1 year, estimate the energy cost at 10 ¢/kWh.

11.72 Performance data for a small commercial pump are as follows:

Q, gal/min	0	10	20	30	40	50	60	70
H, ft	75	75	74	72	68	62	47	24

This pump supplies 20°C water to a horizontal $\frac{5}{8}$-in-diameter garden hose ($\epsilon \approx 0.01$ in) which is 50 ft long. Estimate (a) the flow rate and (b) the hose diameter which would cause the pump to operate at BEP.

11.73 The piston pump of Fig. P11.9 is run at 1500 r/min to deliver SAE 10W oil through 100 m of vertical 2-cm-diameter wrought-iron pipe. If other system losses are neglected, estimate (a) the flow rate, (b) the pressure rise, and (c) the power required.

11.74 The 32-in pump in Fig. 11.7a is used at 1170 r/min in a system whose head curve is H_s (ft) $= 100 + 1.5Q^2$, with Q in thousands of gallons per minute. Find the discharge and brake horsepower required for (a) one pump, (b) two pumps in parallel, and (c) two pumps in series. Which configuration is best?

11.75 Two 35-in pumps from Fig. 11.7b are installed in parallel for the system of Fig. P11.75. Neglect minor losses. For water at 20°C, estimate the flow rate and power required if (a) both pumps are running and (b) one pump is shut off and isolated.

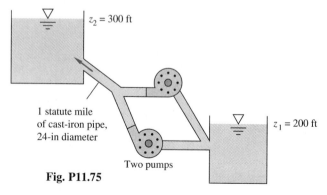

Fig. P11.75

11.76 Two 32-in pumps from Fig. 11.7a are combined in parallel to deliver water at 60°F through 1500 ft of horizontal pipe. If $f = 0.025$, what pipe diameter will ensure a flow rate of 35,000 gal/min for $n = 1170$ r/min?

11.77 Two pumps of the type tested in Prob. 11.35 are to be used at 1800 r/min to pump water at 20°C vertically through 60 ft of commercial-steel pipe. Should they be in series or in parallel? What is the proper pipe diameter for most efficient operation?

11.78 Suppose that the two pumps in Fig. P11.75 are modified to be in series, still at 710 r/min. What pipe diameter is required for BEP operation?

11.79 Two 32-in pumps from Fig. 11.7a are to be used in series at 1170 r/min to lift water through 500 ft of vertical cast-iron pipe. What should the pipe diameter be for most efficient operation? Neglect minor losses.

11.80 It is proposed to use one 32- and one 28-in pump from Fig. 11.7a in parallel to deliver water at 60°F. The system-head curve is $H_s = 50 + 0.3Q^2$, with Q in thousands of gallons per minute. What will the head and delivery be if both pumps run at 1170 r/min? If the 28-in pump is reduced below 1170 r/min, at what speed will it cease to deliver?

11.81 Show that if the net head H is varied for a turbine operating at a given valve opening and efficiency, the speed will vary as $H^{1/2}$ and the output power as $H^{3/2}$.

11.82 The S-shaped head-versus-flow curve in Fig. P11.82 occurs in some axial-flow pumps. Explain how a fairly flat system-loss curve might cause instabilities in the operation of the pump. How might we avoid instability?

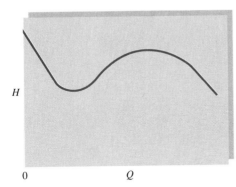

Fig. P11.82

11.83 The low-shutoff head-versus-flow curve in Fig. P11.83 occurs in some centrifugal pumps. Explain how a fairly flat system-loss curve might cause instabilities in the operation of the pump. What additional vexation occurs when two of these pumps are in parallel? How might we avoid instability?

11.84 Turbines are to be installed where the net head is 400 ft and the flow rate 250,000 gal/min. Discuss the type, number, and size of turbine which might be selected if the generator selected is (*a*) 48-pole, 60-cycle ($n = 150$ r/min) and (*b*) 8-pole ($n = 900$ r/min). Why are at least two

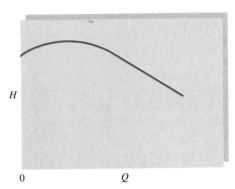

Fig. P11.83

turbines desirable from a planning point of view?

11.85 Turbines at the Conowingo Plant on the Susquehanna River each develop 54,000 bhp at 82 r/min under a head of 89 ft. What type of turbines are these? Estimate the flow rate and impeller diameter.

11.86 The Tupperware hydroelectric plant on the Blackstone River has four 36-in-diameter turbines, each providing 447 kW at 200 r/min and 205 ft³/s for a head of 30 ft. What type of turbines are these? How does their performance compare with Fig. 11.21?

11.87 An idealized radial turbine is shown in Fig. P11.87. The absolute flow enters at 30° and leaves radially inward. The flow rate is 3.5 m³/s of water at 20°C. The blade thickness is constant at 10 cm. Compute the theoretical power developed at 100 percent efficiency.

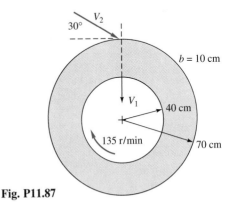

Fig. P11.87

11.88 A certain turbine in Switzerland delivers 25,000 bhp at 500 r/min under a net head of 5330 ft. What type of turbine is this? Estimate the approximate discharge and size.

11.89 A Pelton wheel of 12-ft pitch diameter operates under a net head of 2000 ft. Estimate the speed, power output, and flow rate for best efficiency if the nozzle exit diameter is 4 in.

11.90 An idealized radial turbine is shown in Fig. P11.90. The absolute flow enters at 25° with the blade angles as shown. The flow rate is 8 m³/s of water at 20°C. The blade thickness is constant at 20 cm. Compute the theoretical power developed at 100 percent efficiency.

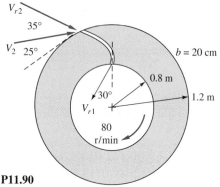

Fig. P11.90

11.91 The flow through an axial-flow *turbine* can be idealized by modifying the stator-rotor diagrams of Fig. 11.12 for energy absorption. Sketch a suitable blade and flow arrangement and the associated velocity vector diagrams. For further details see chap. 8 of Ref. 25.

11.92 At a proposed turbine installation the available head is 800 ft, and the water flow rate is 40,000 gal/min. Discuss the size, speed, and number of turbines which might be suitable for this purpose while using (*a*) a Pelton wheel and (*b*) a Francis wheel.

11.93 Figure P11.93 shows a cutaway of a *cross-flow* or "Banki"

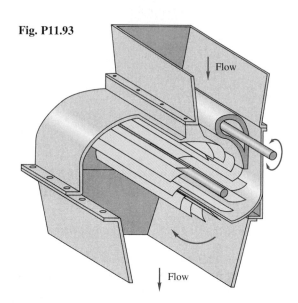

Fig. P11.93

turbine [55], which resembles a squirrel cage with slotted curved blades. The flow enters at about 2 o'clock, passes through the center and then again through the blades, leaving at about 8 o'clock. Report to the class on the operation and advantages of this design, including idealized velocity vector diagrams.

11.94 A simple cross-flow turbine, Fig. P11.93, was constructed and tested at the University of Rhode Island. The blades were made of PVC pipe cut lengthwise into three 120°-arc pieces. When it was tested in water at a head of 5.3 ft and a flow rate of 630 gal/min, the measured power output was 0.6 hp. Estimate (*a*) the efficiency and (*b*) the power specific speed. Let $n = 200$ r/min.

11.95 One can make a theoretical estimate of the proper diameter for a penstock in an impulse turbine installation, as in Fig. P11.95. Let L and H be known, and let the turbine performance be idealized by Eqs. (11.38) and (11.39). Account for friction loss h_f in the penstock, but neglect minor losses. Show that (*a*) the maximum power is generated when $h_f = H/3$, (*b*) the optimum jet velocity is $(4gH/3)^{1/2}$, and (*c*) the best nozzle diameter is $D_j = [D^5/(2fL)]^{1/4}$, where f is the pipe-friction factor.

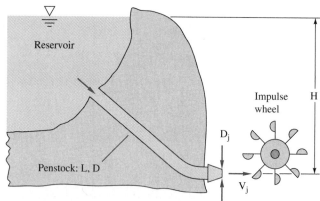

Fig. P11.95

11.96 Apply the results of Prob. 11.95 to determining the optimum (*a*) penstock diameter and (*b*) nozzle diameter for the data of Prob. 11.92 with a commercial-steel penstock of length 1500 ft.

11.97 It is planned to use the Francis turbine family of Fig. 11.21*d* at an installation with a head of 600 ft and a flow rate of 200 ft³/s. What are the proper impeller diameter and the optimum speed and power produced?

11.98 Francis and Kaplan turbines are often provided with *draft tubes*, which lead the exit flow into the tailwater region, as in Fig. P11.98. Explain at least two advantages in using a draft tube.

11.99 Turbines can also cavitate when the pressure at point 1 in

Fig. P11.98

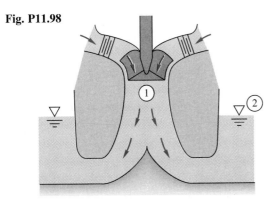

Fig. P11.98 drops too low. With NPSH defined by Eq. (11.20), the empirical criterion given by Wislicensus [4] for cavitation is

$$N_{ss} = \frac{(r/min)(gal/min)^{1/2}}{[NPSH\ (ft)]^{3/4}} \geq 11{,}000$$

Use this criterion to compute how high $z_1 - z_2$, the impeller eye in Fig. P11.98, can be placed for a Francis turbine with a head of 300 ft, $N_{sp} = 40$, and $p_a = 14\ lbf/in^2$ absolute before cavitation occurs in 60°F water.

11.100 One of the largest wind generators in operation today is the ERDA/NASA two-blade propeller HAWT in Sandusky, Ohio. The blades are 125 ft in diameter and reach maximum power in 19 mi/h winds. For this condition estimate (a) the power generated in kW, (b) the rotor speed in r/min, and (c) the velocity V_2 behind the rotor.

11.101 A Darrieus VAWT in operation in Lumsden, Saskatchewan, that is 32 ft high and 20 ft in diameter sweeps out an area of 432 ft². Estimate (a) the maximum power and (b) the rotor speed if it is operating in 16 mi/h winds.

11.102 An American 6-ft diameter multiblade HAWT is used to pump water to a height of 10 ft through 3-in-diameter cast-iron pipe. If the winds are 12 mi/h, estimate the rate of water flow in gal/min.

11.103 A very large Darrieus VAWT was constructed by the U.S. Department of Energy near Sandia, New Mexico. It is 60 ft high and 30 ft in diameter, with a swept area of 1200 ft². If the turbine is constrained to rotate at 90 r/min, use Fig. 11.31 to plot the predicted power output in kW versus wind speed in the range $V = 5$ to 40 mi/h.

Word Problems

W11.1 We know that an enclosed rotating bladed impeller will impart energy to a fluid, usually in the form of a pressure rise, but how does it actually happen? Discuss, with sketches, the physical mechanisms through which an impeller actually transfers energy to a fluid.

W11.2 Dynamic pumps (as opposed to PDPs) have difficulty moving highly viscous fluids. Lobanoff and Ross [15] suggest the following rule of thumb: D (in) $> 0.015\nu/\nu_{water}$, where D is the diameter of the discharge pipe. For example, SAE 30W oil ($\approx 300\nu_{water}$) should require at least a 4.5-in outlet. Can you explain some reasons for this limitation?

W11.3 The concept of NPSH dictates that liquid dynamic pumps should generally be immersed below the surface. Can you explain this? What is the effect of increasing the liquid temperature?

W11.4 For nondimensional fan performance, Wallis [20] suggests that the head coefficient should be replaced by FTP/($\rho n^2 D^2$), where FTP is the fan total pressure change. Explain the usefulness of this modification.

W11.5 Performance data for centrifugal pumps, even if well scaled geometrically, show a decrease in efficiency with decreasing impeller size. Discuss some physical reasons why this is so.

W11.6 Consider a dimensionless pump performance chart such as Fig. 11.8. What additional dimensionless parameters might modify or even destroy the similarity indicated in such data?

W11.7 One parameter not discussed in this text is the *number of blades* on an impeller. Do some reading on this subject, and report to the class about its effect on pump performance.

W11.8 Explain why some pump performance curves may lead to unstable operating conditions.

W11.9 Why are Francis and Kaplan turbines generally considered unsuitable for hydropower sites where the available head exceeds 1000 ft?

W11.10 Do some reading on the performance of the *free propeller* that is used on small, low-speed aircraft. What dimensionless parameters are typically reported for the data? How do the performance and efficiency compare with those for the axial-flow pump?

Design Project

P11.1 To save on electricity costs, a town water supply system uses gravity-driven flow from five large storage tanks during the day and then refills these tanks from 10 p.m. to 6 a.m. at a cheaper night rate of 7 ¢/kWh. The total resupply needed each night varies from 5 E5 to 2 E6 gal, with no more than 5 E6 gallons to any one tank. Tank elevations vary from 40 to 100 ft. A single constant-speed pump, drawing from a large groundwater aquifer and valved into five different cast-iron tank supply lines, does this job. Distances from the pump to the five tanks vary more or less evenly from 1 to 3 mi. Each line averages one elbow every 100 ft and has four butterfly valves which can be controlled at any desirable angle. Select a suitable pump family from one of the six data sets in this chapter: Figs. 11.8, P11.24, and P11.31 plus Probs. 11.28, 11.35, and 11.38. Assume ideal similarity (no Reynolds-number or pump roughness effects). The goal is to determine pump and pipeline sizes which achieve minimum total cost over a 5-year period. Some suggested cost data are

1. Pump and motor: $2500 plus $1500 per inch of pipe size
2. Valves: $100 plus $100 per inch of pipe size
3. Pipelines: 50¢ per inch of diameter per foot of length

Since the flow and elevation parameters vary considerably, a random daily variation within the specified ranges might give a realistic approach.

Appendix A
Physical Properties of Fluids

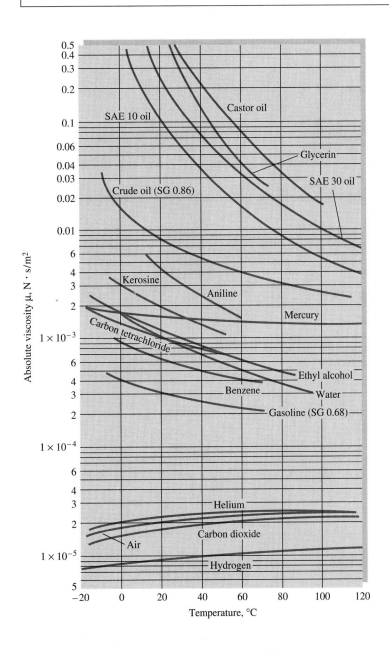

Fig. A.1 Absolute viscosity of common fluids at 1 atm.

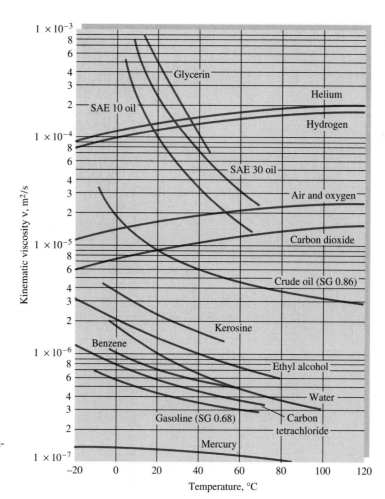

Fig. A.2 Kinematic viscosity of common fluids at 1 atm.

Table A.1 Viscosity and Density of Water at 1 atm

T, °C	ρ, kg/m³	μ, N·s/m²	ν, m²/s	T, °F	ρ, slug/ft³	μ, lb·s/ft²	ν, ft²/s
0	1000	1.788 E-3	1.788 E-6	32	1.940	3.73 E-5	1.925 E-5
10	1000	1.307 E-3	1.307 E-6	50	1.940	2.73 E-5	1.407 E-5
20	998	1.003 E-3	1.005 E-6	68	1.937	2.09 E-5	1.082 E-5
30	996	0.799 E-3	0.802 E-6	86	1.932	1.67 E-5	0.864 E-5
40	992	0.657 E-3	0.662 E-6	104	1.925	1.37 E-5	0.713 E-5
50	988	0.548 E-3	0.555 E-6	122	1.917	1.14 E-5	0.597 E-5
60	983	0.467 E-3	0.475 E-6	140	1.908	0.975 E-5	0.511 E-5
70	978	0.405 E-3	0.414 E-6	158	1.897	0.846 E-5	0.446 E-5
80	972	0.355 E-3	0.365 E-6	176	1.886	0.741 E-5	0.393 E-5
90	965	0.316 E-3	0.327 E-6	194	1.873	0.660 E-5	0.352 E-5
100	958	0.283 E-3	0.295 E-6	212	1.859	0.591 E-5	0.318 E-5

Suggested curve fits for water in the range $0 \leq T \leq 100°C$:

$$\rho\,(\text{kg/m}^3) \approx 1000 - 0.0178|T°C - 4°C|^{1.7} \pm 0.2\%$$

$$\ln \frac{\mu}{\mu_0} \approx -1.704 - 5.306z + 7.003z^2$$

$$z = \frac{273\text{ K}}{T\text{ K}} \qquad \mu_0 = 1.788\text{ E-3 kg/(m}\cdot\text{s)}$$

Table A.2 Viscosity and Density of Air at 1 atm

T, °C	ρ, kg/m³	μ, N·s/m²	ν, m²/s	T, °F	ρ, slug/ft³	μ, lb·s/ft²	ν, ft²/s
−40	1.52	1.51 E-5	0.99 E-5	−40	2.94 E-3	3.16 E-7	1.07 E-4
0	1.29	1.71 E-5	1.33 E-5	32	2.51 E-3	3.58 E-7	1.43 E-4
20	1.20	1.80 E-5	1.50 E-5	68	2.34 E-3	3.76 E-7	1.61 E-4
50	1.09	1.95 E-5	1.79 E-5	122	2.12 E-3	4.08 E-7	1.93 E-4
100	0.946	2.17 E-5	2.30 E-5	212	1.84 E-3	4.54 E-7	2.47 E-4
150	0.835	2.38 E-5	2.85 E-5	302	1.62 E-3	4.97 E-7	3.07 E-4
200	0.746	2.57 E-5	3.45 E-5	392	1.45 E-3	5.37 E-7	3.71 E-4
250	0.675	2.75 E-5	4.08 E-5	482	1.31 E-3	5.75 E-7	4.39 E-4
300	0.616	2.93 E-5	4.75 E-5	572	1.20 E-3	6.11 E-7	5.12 E-4
400	0.525	3.25 E-5	6.20 E-5	752	1.02 E-3	6.79 E-7	6.67 E-4
500	0.457	3.55 E-5	7.77 E-5	932	0.89 E-3	7.41 E-7	8.37 E-4

Suggested curve fits for air:

$$\rho = \frac{p}{RT} \qquad R_{\text{air}} \approx 287\text{ J/(kg}\cdot\text{K)}$$

Power law:
$$\frac{\mu}{\mu_0} \approx \left(\frac{T}{T_0}\right)^{0.7}$$

Sutherland law:
$$\frac{\mu}{\mu_0} \approx \left(\frac{T}{T_0}\right)^{3/2}\left(\frac{T_0 + S}{T + S}\right) \qquad S_{\text{air}} \approx 110.4\text{ K}$$

with $T_0 = 273$ K, $\mu_0 = 1.71$ E-5 kg/(m·s), and T in kelvins.

Table A.3 Properties of Common Liquids at 1 atm and 20°C (68°F)

Liquid	ρ, kg/m³	μ, kg/(m · s)	Y, N/m*	p_v, N/m²	Bulk modulus, N/m²	Viscosity parameter $C^\dagger$
Ammonia	608	2.20 E-4	2.13 E-2	9.10 E+5	—	1.05
Benzene	881	6.51 E-4	2.88 E-2	1.01 E+4	1.4 E+9	4.34
Carbon tetrachloride	1,590	9.67 E-4	2.70 E-2	1.20 E+4	9.65 E+8	4.45
Ethanol	789	1.20 E-3	2.28 E-2	5.7 E+3	9.0 E+8	5.72
Ethylene glycol	1,117	2.14 E-2	4.84 E-2	1.2 E+1	—	11.7
Freon 12	1,327	2.62 E-4	—	—	—	1.76
Gasoline	680	2.92 E-4	2.16 E-2	5.51 E+4	9.58 E+8	3.68
Glycerin	1,260	1.49	6.33 E-2	1.4 E-2	4.34 E+9	28.0
Kerosine	804	1.92 E-3	2.8 E-2	3.11 E+3	1.6 E+9	5.56
Mercury	13,550	1.56 E-3	4.84 E-1	1.1 E-3	2.55 E+10	1.07
Methanol	791	5.98 E-4	2.25 E-2	1.34 E+4	8.3 E+8	4.63
SAE 10W oil	870	1.04 E-1‡	3.6 E-2	—	1.31 E+9	15.7
SAE 10W30 oil	876	1.7 E-1‡	—	—	—	14.0
SAE 30W oil	891	2.9 E-1‡	3.5 E-2	—	1.38 E+9	18.3
SAE 50W oil	902	8.6 E-1‡	—	—	—	20.2
Water	998	1.00 E-3	7.28 E-2	2.34 E+3	2.19 E+9	Table A.1
Seawater (30‰)	1,025	1.07 E-3	7.28 E-2	2.34 E+3	2.33 E+9	7.28

* In contact with air.

† The viscosity-temperature variation of these liquids may be fitted to the empirical expression

$$\frac{\mu}{\mu_{20°C}} \approx \exp\left[C\left(\frac{293\ \text{K}}{T\ \text{K}} - 1\right)\right]$$

with accuracy of ±6 percent in the range $0 \leq T \leq 100°C$.

‡ Representative values. The SAE oil classifications allow a viscosity variation of up to ±50 percent, especially at lower temperatures.

Table A.4 Properties of Common Gases at 1 atm and 20°C (68°F)

Gas	Molecular weight	R, m²/(s² · K)	ρg, N/m³	μ, N · s/m²	Specific-heat ratio	Power-law exponent $n^\dagger$
H_2	2.016	4124	0.822	9.05 E-6	1.41	0.68
He	4.003	2077	1.63	1.97 E-5	1.66	0.67
H_2O	18.02	461	7.35	1.02 E-5	1.33	1.15
Ar	39.944	208	16.3	2.24 E-5	1.67	0.72
Dry air	28.96	287	11.8	1.80 E-5	1.40	0.67
CO_2	44.01	189	17.9	1.48 E-5	1.30	0.79
CO	28.01	297	11.4	1.82 E-5	1.40	0.71
N_2	28.02	297	11.4	1.76 E-5	1.40	0.67
O_2	32.00	260	13.1	2.00 E-5	1.40	0.69
NO	30.01	277	12.1	1.90 E-5	1.40	0.78
N_2O	44.02	189	17.9	1.45 E-5	1.31	0.89
Cl_2	70.91	117	28.9	1.03 E-5	1.34	1.00
CH_4	16.04	518	6.54	1.34 E-5	1.32	0.87

† The power-law curve fit, Eq. (1.27), $\mu/\mu_{293\,\text{K}} \approx (T/293)^n$, fits these gases to within ±4 percent in the range $250 \leq T \leq 1000$ K. The temperature must be in kelvins.

Table A.5 Surface Tension, Vapor Pressure, and Sound Speed of Water

T, °C	Y, N/m	p_v, kPa	a, m/s
0	0.0756	0.611	1402
10	0.0742	1.227	1447
20	0.0728	2.337	1482
30	0.0712	4.242	1509
40	0.0696	7.375	1529
50	0.0679	12.34	1542
60	0.0662	19.92	1551
70	0.0644	31.16	1553
80	0.0626	47.35	1554
90	0.0608	70.11	1550
100	0.0589	101.3	1543
120	0.0550	198.5	1518
140	0.0509	361.3	1483
160	0.0466	617.8	1440
180	0.0422	1,002	1389
200	0.0377	1,554	1334
220	0.0331	2,318	1268
240	0.0284	3,344	1192
260	0.0237	4,688	1110
280	0.0190	6,412	1022
300	0.0144	8,581	920
320	0.0099	11,274	800
340	0.0056	14,586	630
360	0.0019	18,651	370
374*	0.0*	22,090*	0*

* Critical point.

Table A.6 Properties of the Standard Atmosphere

z, m	T, K	p, Pa	ρ, kg/m³
−500	291.41	107,508	1.2854
0	288.16	101,350	1.2255
500	284.91	95,480	1.1677
1,000	281.66	89,889	1.1120
1,500	278.41	84,565	1.0583
2,000	275.16	79,500	1.0067
2,500	271.91	74,684	0.9570
3,000	268.66	70,107	0.9092
3,500	265.41	65,759	0.8633
4,000	262.16	61,633	0.8191
4,500	258.91	57,718	0.7768
5,000	255.66	54,008	0.7361
5,500	252.41	50,493	0.6970
6,000	249.16	47,166	0.6596
6,500	245.91	44,018	0.6237
7,000	242.66	41,043	0.5893
7,500	239.41	38,233	0.5564
8,000	236.16	35,581	0.5250
8,500	232.91	33,080	0.4949
9,000	229.66	30,723	0.4661
9,500	226.41	28,504	0.4387
10,000	223.16	26,416	0.4125
10,500	219.91	24,455	0.3875
11,000	216.66	22,612	0.3637
11,500	216.66	20,897	0.3361
12,000	216.66	19,312	0.3106
12,500	216.66	17,847	0.2870
13,000	216.66	16,494	0.2652
13,500	216.66	15,243	0.2451
14,000	216.66	14,087	0.2265
14,500	216.66	13,018	0.2094
15,000	216.66	12,031	0.1935
15,500	216.66	11,118	0.1788
16,000	216.66	10,275	0.1652
16,500	216.66	9,496	0.1527
17,000	216.66	8,775	0.1411
17,500	216.66	8,110	0.1304
18,000	216.66	7,495	0.1205
18,500	216.66	6,926	0.1114
19,000	216.66	6,401	0.1029
19,500	216.66	5,915	0.0951
20,000	216.66	5,467	0.0879
22,000	218.6	4,048	0.0645
24,000	220.6	2,972	0.0469
26,000	222.5	2,189	0.0343
28,000	224.5	1,616	0.0251
30,000	226.5	1,197	0.0184
40,000	250.4	287	0.0040
50,000	270.7	80	0.0010
60,000	255.7	22	0.0003
70,000	219.7	6	0.0001

Appendix B
Compressible-Flow Tables

Table B.1
Isentropic Flow of a Perfect Gas, $k = 1.4$

Ma	p/p_0	ρ/ρ_0	T/T_0	A/A^*	Ma	p/p_0	ρ/ρ_0	T/T_0	A/A^*
0.0	1.0	1.0	1.0	∞	0.74	0.6951	0.7712	0.9013	1.0681
0.02	0.9997	0.9998	0.9999	28.9421	0.76	0.6821	0.7609	0.8964	1.0570
0.04	0.9989	0.9992	0.9997	14.4815	0.78	0.6690	0.7505	0.8915	1.0471
0.06	0.9975	0.9982	0.9993	9.6659	0.8	0.6560	0.7400	0.8865	1.0382
0.08	0.9955	0.9968	0.9987	7.2616	0.82	0.6430	0.7295	0.8815	1.0305
0.1	0.9930	0.9950	0.9980	5.8218	0.84	0.6300	0.7189	0.8763	1.0237
0.12	0.9900	0.9928	0.9971	4.8643	0.86	0.6170	0.7083	0.8711	1.0179
0.14	0.9864	0.9903	0.9961	4.1824	0.88	0.6041	0.6977	0.8659	1.0129
0.16	0.9823	0.9873	0.9949	3.6727	0.9	0.5913	0.6870	0.8606	1.0089
0.18	0.9776	0.9840	0.9936	3.2779	0.92	0.5785	0.6764	0.8552	1.0056
0.2	0.9725	0.9803	0.9921	2.9635	0.94	0.5658	0.6658	0.8498	1.0031
0.22	0.9668	0.9762	0.9904	2.7076	0.96	0.5532	0.6551	0.8444	1.0014
0.24	0.9607	0.9718	0.9886	2.4956	0.98	0.5407	0.6445	0.8389	1.0003
0.26	0.9541	0.9670	0.9867	2.3173	1.0	0.5283	0.6339	0.8333	1.0000
0.28	0.9470	0.9619	0.9846	2.1656	1.02	0.5160	0.6234	0.8278	1.0003
0.3	0.9395	0.9564	0.9823	2.0351	1.04	0.5039	0.6129	0.8222	1.0013
0.32	0.9315	0.9506	0.9799	1.9219	1.06	0.4919	0.6024	0.8165	1.0029
0.34	0.9231	0.9445	0.9774	1.8229	1.08	0.4800	0.5920	0.8108	1.0051
0.36	0.9143	0.9380	0.9747	1.7358	1.1	0.4684	0.5817	0.8052	1.0079
0.38	0.9052	0.9313	0.9719	1.6587	1.12	0.4568	0.5714	0.7994	1.0113
0.4	0.8956	0.9243	0.9690	1.5901	1.14	0.4455	0.5612	0.7937	1.0153
0.42	0.8857	0.9170	0.9659	1.5289	1.16	0.4343	0.5511	0.7879	1.0198
0.44	0.8755	0.9094	0.9627	1.4740	1.18	0.4232	0.5411	0.7822	1.0248
0.46	0.8650	0.9016	0.9594	1.4246	1.2	0.4124	0.5311	0.7764	1.0304
0.48	0.8541	0.8935	0.9559	1.3801	1.22	0.4017	0.5213	0.7706	1.0366
0.5	0.8430	0.8852	0.9524	1.3398	1.24	0.3912	0.5115	0.7648	1.0432
0.52	0.8317	0.8766	0.9487	1.3034	1.26	0.3809	0.5019	0.7590	1.0504
0.54	0.8201	0.8679	0.9449	1.2703	1.28	0.3708	0.4923	0.7532	1.0581
0.56	0.8082	0.8589	0.9410	1.2403	1.3	0.3609	0.4829	0.7474	1.0663
0.58	0.7962	0.8498	0.9370	1.2130	1.32	0.3512	0.4736	0.7416	1.0750
0.6	0.7840	0.8405	0.9328	1.1882	1.34	0.3417	0.4644	0.7358	1.0842
0.62	0.7716	0.8310	0.9286	1.1656	1.36	0.3323	0.4553	0.7300	1.0940
0.64	0.7591	0.8213	0.9243	1.1451	1.38	0.3232	0.4463	0.7242	1.1042
0.66	0.7465	0.8115	0.9199	1.1265	1.4	0.3142	0.4374	0.7184	1.1149
0.68	0.7338	0.8016	0.9153	1.1097	1.42	0.3055	0.4287	0.7126	1.1262
0.7	0.7209	0.7916	0.9107	1.0944	1.44	0.2969	0.4201	0.7069	1.1379
0.72	0.7080	0.7814	0.9061	1.0806	1.46	0.2886	0.4116	0.7011	1.1501

Table B.1 (*Cont.*)

Ma	p/p_0	ρ/ρ_0	T/T_0	A/A^*	Ma	p/p_0	ρ/ρ_0	T/T_0	A/A^*
1.48	0.2804	0.4032	0.6954	1.1629	2.56	0.0533	0.1232	0.4328	2.7891
1.5	0.2724	0.3950	0.6897	1.1762	2.58	0.0517	0.1205	0.4289	2.8420
1.52	0.2646	0.3869	0.6840	1.1899	2.6	0.0501	0.1179	0.4252	2.8960
1.54	0.2570	0.3789	0.6783	1.2042	2.62	0.0486	0.1153	0.4214	2.9511
1.56	0.2496	0.3710	0.6726	1.2190	2.64	0.0471	0.1128	0.4177	3.0073
1.58	0.2423	0.3633	0.6670	1.2344	2.66	0.0457	0.1103	0.4141	3.0647
1.6	0.2353	0.3557	0.6614	1.2502	2.68	0.0443	0.1079	0.4104	3.1233
1.62	0.2284	0.3483	0.6558	1.2666	2.7	0.0430	0.1056	0.4068	3.1830
1.64	0.2217	0.3409	0.6502	1.2836	2.72	0.0417	0.1033	0.4033	3.2440
1.66	0.2151	0.3337	0.6447	1.3010	2.74	0.0404	0.1010	0.3998	3.3061
1.68	0.2088	0.3266	0.6392	1.3190	2.76	0.0392	0.0989	0.3963	3.3695
1.7	0.2026	0.3197	0.6337	1.3376	2.78	0.0380	0.0967	0.3928	3.4342
1.72	0.1966	0.3129	0.6283	1.3567	2.8	0.0368	0.0946	0.3894	3.5001
1.74	0.1907	0.3062	0.6229	1.3764	2.82	0.0357	0.0926	0.3860	3.5674
1.76	0.1850	0.2996	0.6175	1.3967	2.84	0.0347	0.0906	0.3827	3.6359
1.78	0.1794	0.2931	0.6121	1.4175	2.86	0.0336	0.0886	0.3794	3.7058
1.8	0.1740	0.2868	0.6068	1.4390	2.88	0.0326	0.0867	0.3761	3.7771
1.82	0.1688	0.2806	0.6015	1.4610	2.9	0.0317	0.0849	0.3729	3.8498
1.84	0.1637	0.2745	0.5963	1.4836	2.92	0.0307	0.0831	0.3696	3.9238
1.86	0.1587	0.2686	0.5910	1.5069	2.94	0.0298	0.0813	0.3665	3.9993
1.88	0.1539	0.2627	0.5859	1.5308	2.96	0.0289	0.0796	0.3633	4.0763
1.9	0.1492	0.2570	0.5807	1.5553	2.98	0.0281	0.0779	0.3602	4.1547
1.92	0.1447	0.2514	0.5756	1.5804	3.0	0.0272	0.0762	0.3571	4.2346
1.94	0.1403	0.2459	0.5705	1.6062	3.02	0.0264	0.0746	0.3541	4.3160
1.96	0.1360	0.2405	0.5655	1.6326	3.04	0.0256	0.0730	0.3511	4.3990
1.98	0.1318	0.2352	0.5605	1.6597	3.06	0.0249	0.0715	0.3481	4.4835
2.0	0.1278	0.2300	0.5556	1.6875	3.08	0.0242	0.0700	0.3452	4.5696
2.02	0.1239	0.2250	0.5506	1.7160	3.1	0.0234	0.0685	0.3422	4.6573
2.04	0.1201	0.2200	0.5458	1.7451	3.12	0.0228	0.0671	0.3393	4.7467
2.06	0.1164	0.2152	0.5409	1.7750	3.14	0.0221	0.0657	0.3365	4.8377
2.08	0.1128	0.2104	0.5361	1.8056	3.16	0.0215	0.0643	0.3337	4.9304
2.1	0.1094	0.2058	0.5313	1.8369	3.18	0.0208	0.0630	0.3309	5.0248
2.12	0.1060	0.2013	0.5266	1.8690	3.2	0.0202	0.0617	0.3281	5.1210
2.14	0.1027	0.1968	0.5219	1.9018	3.22	0.0196	0.0604	0.3253	5.2189
2.16	0.0996	0.1925	0.5173	1.9354	3.24	0.0191	0.0591	0.3226	5.3186
2.18	0.0965	0.1882	0.5127	1.9698	3.26	0.0185	0.0579	0.3199	5.4201
2.2	0.0935	0.1841	0.5081	2.0050	3.28	0.0180	0.0567	0.3173	5.5234
2.22	0.0906	0.1800	0.5036	2.0409	3.3	0.0175	0.0555	0.3147	5.6286
2.24	0.0878	0.1760	0.4991	2.0777	3.32	0.0170	0.0544	0.3121	5.7358
2.26	0.0851	0.1721	0.4947	2.1153	3.34	0.0165	0.0533	0.3095	5.8448
2.28	0.0825	0.1683	0.4903	2.1538	3.36	0.0160	0.0522	0.3069	5.9558
2.3	0.0800	0.1646	0.4859	2.1931	3.38	0.0156	0.0511	0.3044	6.0687
2.32	0.0775	0.1609	0.4816	2.2333	3.4	0.0151	0.0501	0.3019	6.1837
2.34	0.0751	0.1574	0.4773	2.2744	3.42	0.0147	0.0491	0.2995	6.3007
2.36	0.0728	0.1539	0.4731	2.3164	3.44	0.0143	0.0481	0.2970	6.4198
2.38	0.0706	0.1505	0.4688	2.3593	3.46	0.0139	0.0471	0.2946	6.5409
2.4	0.0684	0.1472	0.4647	2.4031	3.48	0.0135	0.0462	0.2922	6.6642
2.42	0.0663	0.1439	0.4606	2.4479	3.5	0.0131	0.0452	0.2899	6.7896
2.44	0.0643	0.1408	0.4565	2.4936	3.52	0.0127	0.0443	0.2875	6.9172
2.46	0.0623	0.1377	0.4524	2.5403	3.54	0.0124	0.0434	0.2852	7.0471
2.48	0.0604	0.1346	0.4484	2.5880	3.56	0.0120	0.0426	0.2829	7.1791
2.5	0.0585	0.1317	0.4444	2.6367	3.58	0.0117	0.0417	0.2806	7.3135
2.52	0.0567	0.1288	0.4405	2.6865	3.6	0.0114	0.0409	0.2784	7.4501
2.54	0.0550	0.1260	0.4366	2.7372	3.62	0.0111	0.0401	0.2762	7.5891

Table B.1 (*Cont.*)
Isentropic Flow
of a Perfect Gas,
$k = 1.4$

Ma	p/p_0	ρ/ρ_0	T/T_0	A/A^*		Ma	p/p_0	ρ/ρ_0	T/T_0	A/A^*
3.64	0.0108	0.0393	0.2740	7.7305		4.34	0.0042	0.0202	0.2098	14.4456
3.66	0.0105	0.0385	0.2718	7.8742		4.36	0.0041	0.0198	0.2083	14.6965
3.68	0.0102	0.0378	0.2697	8.0204		4.38	0.0040	0.0194	0.2067	14.9513
3.7	0.0099	0.0370	0.2675	8.1691		4.4	0.0039	0.0191	0.2053	15.2099
3.72	0.0096	0.0363	0.2654	8.3202		4.42	0.0038	0.0187	0.2038	15.4724
3.74	0.0094	0.0356	0.2633	8.4739		4.44	0.0037	0.0184	0.2023	15.7388
3.76	0.0091	0.0349	0.2613	8.6302		4.46	0.0036	0.0181	0.2009	16.0092
3.78	0.0089	0.0342	0.2592	8.7891		4.48	0.0035	0.0178	0.1994	16.2837
3.8	0.0086	0.0335	0.2572	8.9506		4.5	0.0035	0.0174	0.1980	16.5622
3.82	0.0084	0.0329	0.2552	9.1148		4.52	0.0034	0.0171	0.1966	16.8449
3.84	0.0082	0.0323	0.2532	9.2817		4.54	0.0033	0.0168	0.1952	17.1317
3.86	0.0080	0.0316	0.2513	9.4513		4.56	0.0032	0.0165	0.1938	17.4228
3.88	0.0077	0.0310	0.2493	9.6237		4.58	0.0031	0.0163	0.1925	17.7181
3.9	0.0075	0.0304	0.2474	9.7990		4.6	0.0031	0.0160	0.1911	18.0178
3.92	0.0073	0.0299	0.2455	9.9771		4.62	0.0030	0.0157	0.1898	18.3218
3.94	0.0071	0.0293	0.2436	10.1581		4.64	0.0029	0.0154	0.1885	18.6303
3.96	0.0069	0.0287	0.2418	10.3420		4.66	0.0028	0.0152	0.1872	18.9433
3.98	0.0068	0.0282	0.2399	10.5289		4.68	0.0028	0.0149	0.1859	19.2608
4.0	0.0066	0.0277	0.2381	10.7188		4.7	0.0027	0.0146	0.1846	19.5828
4.02	0.0064	0.0271	0.2363	10.9117		4.72	0.0026	0.0144	0.1833	19.9095
4.04	0.0062	0.0266	0.2345	11.1077		4.74	0.0026	0.0141	0.1820	20.2409
4.06	0.0061	0.0261	0.2327	11.3068		4.76	0.0025	0.0139	0.1808	20.5770
4.08	0.0059	0.0256	0.2310	11.5091		4.78	0.0025	0.0137	0.1795	20.9179
4.1	0.0058	0.0252	0.2293	11.7147		4.8	0.0024	0.0134	0.1783	21.2637
4.12	0.0056	0.0247	0.2275	11.9234		4.82	0.0023	0.0132	0.1771	21.6144
4.14	0.0055	0.0242	0.2258	12.1354		4.84	0.0023	0.0130	0.1759	21.9700
4.16	0.0053	0.0238	0.2242	12.3508		4.86	0.0022	0.0128	0.1747	22.3306
4.18	0.0052	0.0234	0.2225	12.5695		4.88	0.0022	0.0125	0.1735	22.6963
4.2	0.0051	0.0229	0.2208	12.7916		4.9	0.0021	0.0123	0.1724	23.0671
4.22	0.0049	0.0225	0.2192	13.0172		4.92	0.0021	0.0121	0.1712	23.4431
4.24	0.0048	0.0221	0.2176	13.2463		4.94	0.0020	0.0119	0.1700	23.8243
4.26	0.0047	0.0217	0.2160	13.4789		4.96	0.0020	0.0117	0.1689	24.2109
4.28	0.0046	0.0213	0.2144	13.7151		4.98	0.0019	0.0115	0.1678	24.6027
4.3	0.0044	0.0209	0.2129	13.9549		5.0	0.0019	0.0113	0.1667	25.0000
4.32	0.0043	0.0205	0.2113	14.1984						

Table B.2 Normal-Shock Relations
for a Perfect Gas, $k = 1.4$

Ma_{n1}	Ma_{n2}	p_2/p_1	$V_1/V_2 = \rho_2/\rho_1$	T_2/T_1	p_{02}/p_{01}	A_2^*/A_1^*
1.0	1.0000	1.0000	1.0000	1.0000	1.0000	1.0000
1.02	0.9805	1.0471	1.0334	1.0132	1.0000	1.0000
1.04	0.9620	1.0952	1.0671	1.0263	0.9999	1.0001
1.06	0.9444	1.1442	1.1009	1.0393	0.9998	1.0002
1.08	0.9277	1.1941	1.1349	1.0522	0.9994	1.0006
1.1	0.9118	1.2450	1.1691	1.0649	0.9989	1.0011
1.12	0.8966	1.2968	1.2034	1.0776	0.9982	1.0018
1.14	0.8820	1.3495	1.2378	1.0903	0.9973	1.0027
1.16	0.8682	1.4032	1.2723	1.1029	0.9961	1.0040
1.18	0.8549	1.4578	1.3069	1.1154	0.9946	1.0055
1.2	0.8422	1.5133	1.3416	1.1280	0.9928	1.0073
1.22	0.8300	1.5698	1.3764	1.1405	0.9907	1.0094
1.24	0.8183	1.6272	1.4112	1.1531	0.9884	1.0118

Table B.2 (*Cont.*)

Ma_{n1}	Ma_{n2}	p_2/p_1	$V_1/V_2 = \rho_2/\rho_1$	T_2/T_1	p_{02}/p_{01}	A_2^*/A_1^*
1.26	0.8071	1.6855	1.4460	1.1657	0.9857	1.0145
1.28	0.7963	1.7448	1.4808	1.1783	0.9827	1.0176
1.3	0.7860	1.8050	1.5157	1.1909	0.9794	1.0211
1.32	0.7760	1.8661	1.5505	1.2035	0.9758	1.0249
1.34	0.7664	1.9282	1.5854	1.2162	0.9718	1.0290
1.36	0.7572	1.9912	1.6202	1.2290	0.9676	1.0335
1.38	0.7483	2.0551	1.6549	1.2418	0.9630	1.0384
1.4	0.7397	2.1200	1.6897	1.2547	0.9582	1.0436
1.42	0.7314	2.1858	1.7243	1.2676	0.9531	1.0492
1.44	0.7235	2.2525	1.7589	1.2807	0.9476	1.0552
1.46	0.7157	2.3202	1.7934	1.2938	0.9420	1.0616
1.48	0.7083	2.3888	1.8278	1.3069	0.9360	1.0684
1.5	0.7011	2.4583	1.8621	1.3202	0.9298	1.0755
1.52	0.6941	2.5288	1.8963	1.3336	0.9233	1.0830
1.54	0.6874	2.6002	1.9303	1.3470	0.9166	1.0910
1.56	0.6809	2.6725	1.9643	1.3606	0.9097	1.0993
1.58	0.6746	2.7458	1.9981	1.3742	0.9026	1.1080
1.6	0.6684	2.8200	2.0317	1.3880	0.8952	1.1171
1.62	0.6625	2.8951	2.0653	1.4018	0.8877	1.1266
1.64	0.6568	2.9712	2.0986	1.4158	0.8799	1.1365
1.66	0.6512	3.0482	2.1318	1.4299	0.8720	1.1468
1.68	0.6458	3.1261	2.1649	1.4440	0.8639	1.1575
1.7	0.6405	3.2050	2.1977	1.4583	0.8557	1.1686
1.72	0.6355	3.2848	2.2304	1.4727	0.8474	1.1801
1.74	0.6305	3.3655	2.2629	1.4873	0.8389	1.1921
1.76	0.6257	3.4472	2.2952	1.5019	0.8302	1.2045
1.78	0.6210	3.5298	2.3273	1.5167	0.8215	1.2173
1.8	0.6165	3.6133	2.3592	1.5316	0.8127	1.2305
1.82	0.6121	3.6978	2.3909	1.5466	0.8038	1.2441
1.84	0.6078	3.7832	2.4224	1.5617	0.7948	1.2582
1.86	0.6036	3.8695	2.4537	1.5770	0.7857	1.2728
1.88	0.5996	3.9568	2.4848	1.5924	0.7765	1.2877
1.9	0.5956	4.0450	2.5157	1.6079	0.7674	1.3032
1.92	0.5918	4.1341	2.5463	1.6236	0.7581	1.3191
1.94	0.5880	4.2242	2.5767	1.6394	0.7488	1.3354
1.96	0.5844	4.3152	2.6069	1.6553	0.7395	1.3522
1.98	0.5808	4.4071	2.6369	1.6713	0.7302	1.3695
2.0	0.5774	4.5000	2.6667	1.6875	0.7209	1.3872
2.02	0.5740	4.5938	2.6962	1.7038	0.7115	1.4054
2.04	0.5707	4.6885	2.7255	1.7203	0.7022	1.4241
2.06	0.5675	4.7842	2.7545	1.7369	0.6928	1.4433
2.08	0.5643	4.8808	2.7833	1.7536	0.6835	1.4630
2.1	0.5613	4.9783	2.8119	1.7705	0.6742	1.4832
2.12	0.5583	5.0768	2.8402	1.7875	0.6649	1.5039
2.14	0.5554	5.1762	2.8683	1.8046	0.6557	1.5252
2.16	0.5525	5.2765	2.8962	1.8219	0.6464	1.5469
2.18	0.5498	5.3778	2.9238	1.8393	0.6373	1.5692
2.2	0.5471	5.4800	2.9512	1.8569	0.6281	1.5920
2.22	0.5444	5.5831	2.9784	1.8746	0.6191	1.6154
2.24	0.5418	5.6872	3.0053	1.8924	0.6100	1.6393
2.26	0.5393	5.7922	3.0319	1.9104	0.6011	1.6638
2.28	0.5368	5.8981	3.0584	1.9285	0.5921	1.6888
2.3	0.5344	6.0050	3.0845	1.9468	0.5833	1.7144
2.32	0.5321	6.1128	3.1105	1.9652	0.5745	1.7406

Table B.2 (*Cont.*) Normal-Shock Relations for a Perfect Gas, $k = 1.4$

Ma_{n1}	Ma_{n2}	p_2/p_1	$V_1/V_2 = \rho_2/\rho_1$	T_2/T_1	p_{02}/p_{01}	A_2^*/A_1^*
2.34	0.5297	6.2215	3.1362	1.9838	0.5658	1.7674
2.36	0.5275	6.3312	3.1617	2.0025	0.5572	1.7948
2.38	0.5253	6.4418	3.1869	2.0213	0.5486	1.8228
2.4	0.5231	6.5533	3.2119	2.0403	0.5401	1.8514
2.42	0.5210	6.6658	3.2367	2.0595	0.5317	1.8806
2.44	0.5189	6.7792	3.2612	2.0788	0.5234	1.9105
2.46	0.5169	6.8935	3.2855	2.0982	0.5152	1.9410
2.48	0.5149	7.0088	3.3095	2.1178	0.5071	1.9721
2.5	0.5130	7.1250	3.3333	2.1375	0.4990	2.0039
2.52	0.5111	7.2421	3.3569	2.1574	0.4911	2.0364
2.54	0.5092	7.3602	3.3803	2.1774	0.4832	2.0696
2.56	0.5074	7.4792	3.4034	2.1976	0.4754	2.1035
2.58	0.5056	7.5991	3.4263	2.2179	0.4677	2.1381
2.6	0.5039	7.7200	3.4490	2.2383	0.4601	2.1733
2.62	0.5022	7.8418	3.4714	2.2590	0.4526	2.2093
2.64	0.5005	7.9645	3.4937	2.2797	0.4452	2.2461
2.66	0.4988	8.0882	3.5157	2.3006	0.4379	2.2835
2.68	0.4972	8.2128	3.5374	2.3217	0.4307	2.3218
2.7	0.4956	8.3383	3.5590	2.3429	0.4236	2.3608
2.72	0.4941	8.4648	3.5803	2.3642	0.4166	2.4005
2.74	0.4926	8.5922	3.6015	2.3858	0.4097	2.4411
2.76	0.4911	8.7205	3.6224	2.4074	0.4028	2.4825
2.78	0.4896	8.8498	3.6431	2.4292	0.3961	2.5246
2.8	0.4882	8.9800	2.6636	2.4512	0.3895	2.5676
2.82	0.4868	9.1111	3.6838	2.4733	0.3829	2.6115
2.84	0.4854	9.2432	3.7039	2.4955	0.3765	2.6561
2.86	0.4840	9.3762	3.7238	2.5179	0.3701	2.7017
2.88	0.4827	9.5101	3.7434	2.5405	0.3639	2.7481
2.9	0.4814	9.6450	3.7629	2.5632	0.3577	2.7954
2.92	0.4801	9.7808	3.7821	2.5861	0.3517	2.8436
2.94	0.4788	9.9175	3.8012	2.6091	0.3457	2.8927
2.96	0.4776	10.0552	3.8200	2.6322	0.3398	2.9427
2.98	0.4764	10.1938	3.8387	2.6555	0.3340	2.9937
3.0	0.4752	10.3333	3.8571	2.6790	0.3283	3.0456
3.02	0.4740	10.4738	3.8754	2.7026	0.3227	3.0985
3.04	0.4729	10.6152	3.8935	2.7264	0.3172	3.1523
3.06	0.4717	10.7575	3.9114	2.7503	0.3118	3.2072
3.08	0.4706	10.9008	3.9291	2.7744	0.3065	3.2630
3.1	0.4695	11.0450	3.9466	2.7986	0.3012	3.3199
3.12	0.4685	11.1901	3.9639	2.8230	0.2960	3.3778
3.14	0.4674	11.3362	3.9811	2.8475	0.2910	3.4368
3.16	0.4664	11.4832	3.9981	2.8722	0.2860	3.4969
3.18	0.4654	11.6311	4.0149	2.8970	0.2811	3.5580
3.2	0.4643	11.7800	4.0315	2.9220	0.2762	3.6202
3.22	0.4634	11.9298	4.0479	2.9471	0.2715	3.6835
3.24	0.4624	12.0805	4.0642	2.9724	0.2668	3.7480
3.26	0.4614	12.2322	4.0803	2.9979	0.2622	3.8136
3.28	0.4605	12.3848	4.0963	3.0234	0.2577	3.8803
3.3	0.4596	12.5383	4.1120	3.0492	0.2533	3.9483
3.32	0.4587	12.6928	4.1276	3.0751	0.2489	4.0174
3.34	0.4578	12.8482	4.1431	3.1011	0.2446	4.0877
3.36	0.4569	13.0045	4.1583	3.1273	0.2404	4.1593
3.38	0.4560	13.1618	4.1734	3.1537	0.2363	4.2321
3.4	0.4552	13.3200	4.1884	3.1802	0.2322	4.3062

Table B.2 (*Cont.*)

Ma$_{n1}$	Ma$_{n2}$	p_2/p_1	$V_1/V_2 = \rho_2/\rho_1$	T_2/T_1	p_{02}/p_{01}	A_2^*/A_1^*
3.42	0.4544	13.4791	4.2032	3.2069	0.2282	4.3815
3.44	0.4535	13.6392	4.2178	3.2337	0.2243	4.4581
3.46	0.4527	13.8002	4.2323	3.2607	0.2205	4.5361
3.48	0.4519	13.9621	4.2467	3.2878	0.2167	4.6154
3.5	0.4512	14.1250	4.2609	3.3151	0.2129	4.6960
3.52	0.4504	14.2888	4.2749	3.3425	0.2093	4.7780
3.54	0.4496	14.4535	4.2888	3.3701	0.2057	4.8614
3.56	0.4489	14.6192	4.3026	3.3978	0.2022	4.9461
3.58	0.4481	14.7858	4.3162	3.4257	0.1987	5.0324
3.6	0.4474	14.9533	4.3296	3.4537	0.1953	5.1200
3.62	0.4467	15.1218	4.3429	3.4819	0.1920	5.2091
3.64	0.4460	15.2912	4.3561	3.5103	0.1887	5.2997
3.66	0.4453	15.4615	4.3692	3.5388	0.1855	5.3918
3.68	0.4446	15.6328	4.3821	3.5674	0.1823	5.4854
3.7	0.4439	15.8050	4.3949	3.5962	0.1792	5.5806
3.72	0.4433	15.9781	4.4075	3.6252	0.1761	5.6773
3.74	0.4426	16.1522	4.4200	3.6543	0.1731	5.7756
3.76	0.4420	16.3272	4.4324	3.6836	0.1702	5.8755
3.78	0.4414	16.5031	4.4447	3.7130	0.1673	5.9770
3.8	0.4407	16.6800	4.4568	3.7426	0.1645	6.0801
3.82	0.4401	16.8578	4.4688	3.7723	0.1617	6.1849
3.84	0.4395	17.0365	4.4807	3.8022	0.1589	6.2915
3.86	0.4389	17.2162	4.4924	3.8323	0.1563	6.3997
3.88	0.4383	17.3968	4.5041	3.8625	0.1536	6.5096
3.9	0.4377	17.5783	4.4156	3.8928	0.1510	6.6213
3.92	0.4372	17.7608	4.5270	3.9233	0.1485	6.7348
3.94	0.4366	17.9442	4.5383	3.9540	0.1460	6.8501
3.96	0.4360	18.1285	4.5494	3.9848	0.1435	6.9672
3.98	0.4355	18.3138	4.5605	4.0158	0.1411	7.0861
4.0	0.4350	18.5000	4.5714	4.0469	0.1388	7.2069
4.02	0.4344	18.6871	4.5823	4.0781	0.1364	7.3296
4.04	0.4339	18.8752	4.5930	4.1096	0.1342	7.4542
4.06	0.4334	19.0642	4.6036	4.1412	0.1319	7.5807
4.08	0.4329	19.2541	4.6141	4.1729	0.1297	7.7092
4.1	0.4324	19.4450	4.6245	4.2048	0.1276	7.8397
4.12	0.4319	19.6368	4.6348	4.2368	0.1254	7.9722
4.14	0.4314	19.8295	4.6450	4.2690	0.1234	8.1067
4.16	0.4309	20.0232	4.6550	4.3014	0.1213	8.2433
4.18	0.4304	20.2178	4.6650	4.3339	0.1193	8.3819
4.2	0.4299	20.4133	4.6749	4.3666	0.1173	8.5227
4.22	0.4295	20.6098	4.6847	4.3994	0.1154	8.6656
4.24	0.4290	20.8072	4.6944	4.4324	0.1135	8.8107
4.26	0.4286	21.0055	4.7040	4.4655	0.1116	8.9579
4.28	0.4281	21.2048	4.7135	4.4988	0.1098	9.1074
4.3	0.4277	21.4050	4.7229	4.5322	0.1080	9.2591
4.32	0.4272	21.6061	4.7322	4.5658	0.1062	9.4131
4.34	0.4268	21.8082	4.7414	4.5995	0.1045	9.5694
4.36	0.4264	22.0112	4.7505	4.6334	0.1028	9.7280
4.38	0.4260	22.2151	4.7595	4.6675	0.1011	9.8889
4.4	0.4255	22.4200	4.7685	4.7017	0.0995	10.0522
4.42	0.4251	22.6258	4.7773	4.7361	0.0979	10.2179
4.44	0.4247	22.8325	4.7861	4.7706	0.0963	10.3861
4.46	0.4243	23.0402	4.7948	4.8053	0.0947	10.5567
4.48	0.4239	23.2488	4.8034	4.8401	0.0932	10.7298

Table B.2 (*Cont.*) Normal-Shock Relations for a Perfect Gas, $k = 1.4$

Ma_{n1}	Ma_{n2}	p_2/p_1	$V_1/V_2 = \rho_2/\rho_1$	T_2/T_1	p_{02}/p_{01}	A_2^*/A_1^*
4.5	0.4236	23.4583	4.8119	4.8751	0.0917	10.9054
4.52	0.4232	23.6688	4.8203	4.9102	0.0902	11.0835
4.54	0.4228	23.8802	4.8287	4.9455	0.0888	11.2643
4.56	0.4224	24.0925	4.8369	4.9810	0.0874	11.4476
4.58	0.4220	24.3058	4.8451	5.0166	0.0860	11.6336
4.6	0.4217	24.5200	4.8532	5.0523	0.0846	11.8222
4.62	0.4213	24.7351	4.8612	5.0882	0.0832	12.0136
4.64	0.4210	24.9512	4.8692	5.1243	0.0819	12.2076
4.66	0.4206	25.1682	4.8771	5.1605	0.0806	12.4044
4.68	0.4203	25.3861	4.8849	5.1969	0.0793	12.6040
4.7	0.4199	25.6050	4.8926	5.2334	0.0781	12.8065
4.72	0.4196	25.8248	4.9002	5.2701	0.0769	13.0117
4.74	0.4192	26.0455	4.9078	5.3070	0.0756	13.2199
4.76	0.4189	26.2672	4.9153	5.3440	0.0745	13.4310
4.78	0.4186	26.4898	4.9227	5.3811	0.0733	13.6450
4.8	0.4183	26.7133	4.9301	5.4184	0.0721	13.8620
4.82	0.4179	26.9378	4.9374	5.4559	0.0710	14.0820
4.84	0.4176	27.1632	4.9446	5.4935	0.0699	14.3050
4.86	0.4173	27.3895	4.9518	5.5313	0.0688	14.5312
4.88	0.4170	27.6168	4.9589	5.5692	0.0677	14.7604
4.9	0.4167	27.8450	4.9659	5.6073	0.0667	14.9928
4.92	0.4164	28.0741	4.9728	5.6455	0.0657	15.2284
4.94	0.4161	28.3042	4.9797	5.6839	0.0647	15.4672
4.96	0.4158	28.5352	4.9865	5.7224	0.0637	15.7902
4.98	0.4155	28.7671	4.9933	5.7611	0.0627	15.9545
5.0	0.4152	29.0000	5.0000	5.8000	0.0617	16.2032

Table B.3 Adiabatic Frictional Flow in a Constant-Area Duct for $k = 1.4$

Ma	$\bar{f}L^*/D$	p/p^*	T/T^*	$\rho^*/\rho = V/V^*$	p_0/p_0^*
0.0	∞	∞	1.2000	0.0	∞
0.02	1778.4500	54.7701	1.1999	0.0219	28.9421
0.04	440.3520	27.3817	1.1996	0.0438	14.4815
0.06	193.0310	18.2508	1.1991	0.0657	9.6659
0.08	106.7180	13.6843	1.1985	0.0876	7.2616
0.1	66.9216	10.9435	1.1976	0.1094	5.8218
0.12	45.4080	9.1156	1.1966	0.1313	4.8643
0.14	32.5113	7.8093	1.1953	0.1531	4.1824
0.16	24.1978	6.8291	1.1939	0.1748	3.6727
0.18	18.5427	6.0662	1.1923	0.1965	3.2779
0.2	14.5333	5.4554	1.1905	0.2182	2.9635
0.22	11.5961	4.9554	1.1885	0.2398	2.7076
0.24	9.3865	4.5383	1.1863	0.2614	2.4956
0.26	7.6876	4.1851	1.1840	0.2829	2.3173
0.28	6.3572	3.8820	1.1815	0.3043	2.1656
0.3	5.2993	3.6191	1.1788	0.3257	2.0351
0.32	4.4467	3.3887	1.1759	0.3470	1.9219
0.34	3.7520	3.1853	1.1729	0.3682	1.8229
0.36	3.1801	3.0042	1.1697	0.3893	1.7358
0.38	2.7054	2.8420	1.1663	0.4104	1.6587
0.4	2.3085	2.6958	1.1628	0.4313	1.5901
0.42	1.9744	2.5634	1.1591	0.4522	1.5289

Table B.3 (*Cont.*)

Ma	$\bar{f}L^*/D$	p/p^*	T/T^*	$\rho^*/\rho = V/V^*$	p_0/p_0^*
0.44	1.6915	2.4428	1.1553	0.4729	1.4740
0.46	1.4509	2.3326	1.1513	0.4936	1.4246
0.48	1.2453	2.2313	1.1471	0.5141	1.3801
0.5	1.0691	2.1381	1.1429	0.5345	1.3398
0.52	0.9174	2.0519	1.1384	0.5548	1.3034
0.54	0.7866	1.9719	1.1339	0.5750	1.2703
0.56	0.6736	1.8975	1.1292	0.5951	1.2403
0.58	0.5757	1.8282	1.1244	0.6150	1.2130
0.6	0.4908	1.7634	1.1194	0.6348	1.1882
0.62	0.4172	1.7026	1.1143	0.6545	1.1656
0.64	0.3533	1.6456	1.1091	0.6740	1.1451
0.66	0.2979	1.5919	1.1038	0.6934	1.1265
0.68	0.2498	1.5413	1.0984	0.7127	1.1097
0.7	0.2081	1.4935	1.0929	0.7318	1.0944
0.72	0.1721	1.4482	1.0873	0.7508	1.0806
0.74	0.1411	1.4054	1.0815	0.7696	1.0681
0.76	0.1145	1.3647	1.0757	0.7883	1.0570
0.78	0.0917	1.3261	1.0698	0.8068	1.0471
0.8	0.0723	1.2893	1.0638	0.8251	1.0382
0.82	0.0559	1.2542	1.0578	0.8433	1.0305
0.84	0.0423	1.2208	1.0516	0.8614	1.0237
0.86	0.0310	1.1889	1.0454	0.8793	1.0179
0.88	0.0218	1.1583	1.0391	0.8970	1.0129
0.9	0.0145	1.1291	1.0327	0.9146	1.0089
0.92	0.0089	1.1011	1.0263	0.9320	1.0056
0.94	0.0048	1.0743	1.0198	0.9493	1.0031
0.96	0.0021	1.0485	1.0132	0.9663	1.0014
0.98	0.0005	1.0238	1.0066	0.9833	1.0003
1.0	0.0000	1.0000	1.0000	1.0000	1.0000
1.02	0.0005	0.9771	0.9933	1.0166	1.0003
1.04	0.0018	0.9551	0.9866	1.0330	1.0013
1.06	0.0038	0.9338	0.9798	1.0492	1.0029
1.08	0.0066	0.9133	0.9730	1.0653	1.0051
1.1	0.0099	0.8936	0.9662	1.0812	1.0079
1.12	0.0138	0.8745	0.9593	1.0970	1.0113
1.14	0.0182	0.8561	0.9524	1.1126	1.0153
1.16	0.0230	0.8383	0.9455	1.1280	1.0198
1.18	0.0281	0.8210	0.9386	1.1432	1.0248
1.2	0.0336	0.8044	0.9317	1.1583	1.0304
1.22	0.0394	0.7882	0.9247	1.1732	1.0366
1.24	0.0455	0.7726	0.9178	1.1879	1.0432
1.26	0.0517	0.7574	0.9108	1.2025	1.0504
1.28	0.0582	0.7427	0.9038	1.2169	1.0581
1.3	0.0648	0.7285	0.8969	1.2311	1.0663
1.32	0.0716	0.7147	0.8899	1.2452	1.0750
1.34	0.0785	0.7012	0.8829	1.2591	1.0842
1.36	0.0855	0.6882	0.8760	1.2729	1.0940
1.38	0.0926	0.6755	0.8690	1.2864	1.1042
1.4	0.0997	0.6632	0.8621	1.2999	1.1149
1.42	0.1069	0.6512	0.8551	1.3131	1.1262
1.44	0.1142	0.6396	0.8482	1.3262	1.1379
1.46	0.1215	0.6282	0.8413	1.3392	1.1501
1.48	0.1288	0.6172	0.8344	1.3520	1.1629
1.5	0.1361	0.6065	0.8276	1.3646	1.1762

Table B.3 (*Cont.*) Adiabatic Frictional Flow in a Constant-Area Duct for $k = 1.4$

Ma	$\bar{f}L^*/D$	p/p^*	T/T^*	$\rho^*/\rho = V/V^*$	p_0/p_0^*
1.52	0.1433	0.5960	0.8207	1.3770	1.1899
1.54	0.1506	0.5858	0.8139	1.3894	1.2042
1.56	0.1579	0.5759	0.8071	1.4015	1.2190
1.58	0.1651	0.5662	0.8004	1.4135	1.2344
1.6	0.1724	0.5568	0.7937	1.4254	1.2502
1.62	0.1795	0.5476	0.7869	1.4371	1.2666
1.64	0.1867	0.5386	0.7803	1.4487	1.2836
1.66	0.1938	0.5299	0.7736	1.4601	1.3010
1.68	0.2008	0.5213	0.7670	1.4713	1.3190
1.7	0.2078	0.5130	0.7605	1.4825	1.3376
1.72	0.2147	0.5048	0.7539	1.4935	1.3567
1.74	0.2216	0.4969	0.7474	1.5043	1.3764
1.76	0.2284	0.4891	0.7410	1.5150	1.3967
1.78	0.2352	0.4815	0.7345	1.5256	1.4175
1.8	0.2419	0.4741	0.7282	1.5360	1.4390
1.82	0.2485	0.4668	0.7218	1.5463	1.4610
1.84	0.2551	0.4597	0.7155	1.5564	1.4836
1.86	0.2616	0.4528	0.7093	1.5664	1.5069
1.88	0.2680	0.4460	0.7030	1.5763	1.5308
1.9	0.2743	0.4394	0.6969	1.5861	1.5553
1.92	0.2806	0.4329	0.6907	1.5957	1.5804
1.94	0.2868	0.4265	0.6847	1.6052	1.6062
1.96	0.2929	0.4203	0.6786	1.6146	1.6326
1.98	0.2990	0.4142	0.6726	1.6239	1.6597
2.0	0.3050	0.4082	0.6667	1.6330	1.6875
2.02	0.3109	0.4024	0.6608	1.6420	1.7160
2.04	0.3168	0.3967	0.6549	1.6509	1.7451
2.06	0.3225	0.3911	0.6491	1.6597	1.7750
2.08	0.3282	0.3856	0.6433	1.6683	1.8056
2.1	0.3339	0.3802	0.6376	1.6769	1.8369
2.12	0.3394	0.3750	0.6320	1.6853	1.8690
2.14	0.3449	0.3698	0.6263	1.6936	1.9018
2.16	0.3503	0.3648	0.6208	1.7018	1.9354
2.18	0.3556	0.3598	0.6152	1.7099	1.9698
2.2	0.3609	0.3549	0.6098	1.7179	2.0050
2.22	0.3661	0.3502	0.6043	1.7258	2.0409
2.24	0.3712	0.3455	0.5989	1.7336	2.0777
2.26	0.3763	0.3409	0.5936	1.7412	2.1153
2.28	0.3813	0.3364	0.5883	1.7488	2.1538
2.3	0.3862	0.3320	0.5831	1.7563	2.1931
2.32	0.3911	0.3277	0.5779	1.7637	2.2333
2.34	0.3959	0.3234	0.5728	1.7709	2.2744
2.36	0.4006	0.3193	0.5677	1.7781	2.3164
2.38	0.4053	0.3152	0.5626	1.7852	2.3593
2.4	0.4099	0.3111	0.5576	1.7922	2.4031
2.42	0.4144	0.3072	0.5527	1.7991	2.4479
2.44	0.4189	0.3033	0.5478	1.8059	2.4936
2.46	0.4233	0.2995	0.5429	1.8126	2.5403
2.48	0.4277	0.2958	0.5381	1.8192	2.5880
2.5	0.4320	0.2921	0.5333	1.8257	2.6367
2.52	0.4362	0.2885	0.5286	1.8322	2.6865
2.54	0.4404	0.2850	0.5239	1.8386	2.7372
2.56	0.4445	0.2815	0.5193	1.8448	2.7891
2.58	0.4486	0.2781	0.5147	1.8510	2.8420

Table B.3 (*Cont.*)

Ma	$\bar{f}L^*/D$	p/p^*	T/T^*	$\rho^*/\rho = V/V^*$	p_0/p_0^*
2.6	0.4526	0.2747	0.5102	1.8571	2.8960
2.62	0.4565	0.2714	0.5057	1.8632	2.9511
2.64	0.4604	0.2682	0.5013	1.8691	3.0073
2.66	0.4643	0.2650	0.4969	1.8750	3.0647
2.68	0.4681	0.2619	0.4925	1.8808	3.1233
2.7	0.4718	0.2588	0.4882	1.8865	3.1830
2.72	0.4755	0.2558	0.4839	1.8922	3.2440
2.74	0.4791	0.2528	0.4797	1.8978	3.3061
2.76	0.4827	0.2498	0.4755	1.9033	3.3695
2.78	0.4863	0.2470	0.4714	1.9087	3.4342
2.8	0.4898	0.2441	0.4673	1.9140	3.5001
2.82	0.4932	0.2414	0.4632	1.9193	3.5674
2.84	0.4966	0.2386	0.4592	1.9246	3.6359
2.86	0.5000	0.2359	0.4552	1.9297	3.7058
2.88	0.5033	0.2333	0.4513	1.9348	3.7771
2.9	0.5065	0.2307	0.4474	1.9398	3.8498
2.92	0.5097	0.2281	0.4436	1.9448	3.9238
2.94	0.5129	0.2256	0.4398	1.9497	3.9993
2.96	0.5160	0.2231	0.4360	1.9545	4.0763
2.98	0.5191	0.2206	0.4323	1.9593	4.1547
3.0	0.5222	0.2182	0.4286	1.9640	4.2346
3.02	0.5252	0.2158	0.4249	1.9686	4.3160
3.04	0.5281	0.2135	0.4213	1.9732	4.3989
3.06	0.5310	0.2112	0.4177	1.9777	4.4835
3.08	0.5339	0.2090	0.4142	1.9822	4.5696
3.1	0.5368	0.2067	0.4107	1.9866	4.6573
3.12	0.5396	0.2045	0.4072	1.9910	4.7467
3.14	0.5424	0.2024	0.4038	1.9953	4.8377
3.16	0.5451	0.2002	0.4004	1.9995	4.9304
3.18	0.5478	0.1981	0.3970	2.0037	5.0248
3.2	0.5504	0.1961	0.3937	2.0079	5.1210
3.22	0.5531	0.1940	0.3904	2.0120	5.2189
3.24	0.5557	0.1920	0.3872	2.0160	5.3186
3.26	0.5582	0.1901	0.3839	2.0200	5.4201
3.28	0.5607	0.1881	0.3807	2.0239	5.5234
3.3	0.5632	0.1862	0.3776	2.0278	5.6286
3.32	0.5657	0.1843	0.3745	2.0317	5.7358
3.34	0.5681	0.1825	0.3714	2.0355	5.8448
3.36	0.5705	0.1806	0.3683	2.0392	5.9558
3.38	0.5729	0.1788	0.3653	2.0429	6.0687
3.4	0.5752	0.1770	0.3623	2.0466	6.1837
3.42	0.5775	0.1753	0.3594	2.0502	6.3007
3.44	0.5798	0.1736	0.3564	2.0537	6.4198
3.46	0.5820	0.1718	0.3535	2.0573	6.5409
3.48	0.5842	0.1702	0.3507	2.0607	6.6642
3.5	0.5864	0.1685	0.3478	2.0642	6.7896
3.52	0.5886	0.1669	0.3450	2.0676	6.9172
3.54	0.5907	0.1653	0.3422	2.0709	7.0471
3.56	0.5928	0.1637	0.3395	2.0743	7.1791
3.58	0.5949	0.1621	0.3368	2.0775	7.3135
3.6	0.5970	0.1616	0.3341	2.0808	7.4501
3.62	0.5990	0.1590	0.3314	2.0840	7.5891
3.64	0.6010	0.1575	0.3288	2.0871	7.7305
3.66	0.6030	0.1560	0.3262	2.0903	7.8742

Table B.3 (*Cont.*) Adiabatic Frictional Flow in a Constant-Area Duct for $k = 1.4$

Ma	$\bar{f}L^*/D$	p/p^*	T/T^*	$\rho^*/\rho = V/V^*$	p_0/p_0^*
3.68	0.6049	0.1546	0.3236	2.0933	8.0204
3.7	0.6068	0.1531	0.3210	2.0964	8.1691
3.72	0.6087	0.1517	0.3185	2.0994	8.3202
3.74	0.6106	0.1503	0.3160	2.1024	8.4739
3.76	0.6125	0.1489	0.3135	2.1053	8.6302
3.78	0.6143	0.1475	0.3111	2.1082	8.7891
3.8	0.6161	0.1462	0.3086	2.1111	8.9506
3.82	0.6179	0.1449	0.3062	2.1140	9.1148
3.84	0.6197	0.1436	0.3039	2.1168	9.2817
3.86	0.6214	0.1423	0.3015	2.1195	9.4513
3.88	0.6231	0.1410	0.2992	2.1223	9.6237
3.9	0.6248	0.1397	0.2969	2.1250	9.7990
3.92	0.6265	0.1385	0.2946	2.1277	9.9771
3.94	0.6282	0.1372	0.2923	2.1303	10.1581
3.96	0.6298	0.1360	0.2901	2.1329	10.3420
3.98	0.6315	0.1348	0.2879	2.1355	10.5289
4.0	0.6331	0.1336	0.2857	2.1381	10.7188

Table B.4 Frictionless Duct Flow with Heat Transfer for $k = 1.4$

Ma	T_0/T_0^*	p/p^*	T/T^*	$\rho^*/\rho = V/V^*$	p_0/p_0^*
0.0	0.0	2.4000	0.0	0.0	1.2679
0.02	0.0019	2.3987	0.0023	0.0010	1.2675
0.04	0.0076	2.3946	0.0092	0.0038	1.2665
0.06	0.0171	2.3800	0.0205	0.0086	1.2647
0.08	0.0302	2.3787	0.0362	0.0152	1.2623
0.1	0.0468	2.3669	0.0560	0.0237	1.2591
0.12	0.0666	2.3526	0.0797	0.0339	1.2554
0.14	0.0895	2.3359	0.1069	0.0458	1.2510
0.16	0.1151	2.3170	0.1374	0.0593	1.2461
0.18	0.1432	2.2959	0.1708	0.0744	1.2406
0.2	0.1736	2.2727	0.2066	0.0909	1.2346
0.22	0.2057	2.2477	0.2445	0.1088	1.2281
0.24	0.2395	2.2209	0.2841	0.1279	1.2213
0.26	0.2745	2.1925	0.3250	0.1482	1.2140
0.28	0.3104	2.1626	0.3667	0.1696	1.2064
0.3	0.3469	2.1314	0.4089	0.1918	1.1985
0.32	0.3837	2.0991	0.4512	0.2149	1.1904
0.34	0.4206	2.0657	0.4933	0.2388	1.1822
0.36	0.4572	2.0314	0.5348	0.2633	1.1737
0.38	0.4935	1.9964	0.5755	0.2883	1.1652
0.4	0.5290	1.9608	0.6151	0.3137	1.1566
0.42	0.5638	1.9247	0.6535	0.3395	1.1480
0.44	0.5975	1.8882	0.6903	0.3656	1.1394
0.46	0.6301	1.8515	0.7254	0.3918	1.1308
0.48	0.6614	1.8147	0.7587	0.4181	1.1224
0.5	0.6914	1.7778	0.7901	0.4444	1.1141
0.52	0.7199	1.7409	0.8196	0.4708	1.1059
0.54	0.7470	1.7043	0.8469	0.4970	1.0979
0.56	0.7725	1.6678	0.8723	0.5230	1.0901
0.58	0.7965	1.6316	0.8955	0.5489	1.0826
0.6	0.8189	1.5957	0.9167	0.5745	1.0753

Table B.4 (*Cont.*)

Ma	T_0/T_0^*	p/p^*	T/T^*	$\rho^*/\rho = V/V^*$	p_0/p_0^*
0.62	0.8398	1.5603	0.9358	0.5998	1.0682
0.64	0.8592	1.5253	0.9530	0.6248	1.0615
0.66	0.8771	1.4908	0.9682	0.6494	1.0550
0.68	0.8935	1.4569	0.9814	0.6737	1.0489
0.7	0.9085	1.4235	0.9929	0.6975	1.0431
0.72	0.9221	1.3907	1.0026	0.7209	1.0376
0.74	0.9344	1.3585	1.0106	0.7439	1.0325
0.76	0.9455	1.3270	1.0171	0.7665	1.0278
0.78	0.9553	1.2961	1.0220	0.7885	1.0234
0.8	0.9639	1.2658	1.0255	0.8101	1.0193
0.82	0.9715	1.2362	1.0276	0.8313	1.0157
0.84	0.9781	1.2073	1.0285	0.8519	1.0124
0.86	0.9836	1.1791	1.0283	0.8721	1.0095
0.88	0.9883	1.1515	1.0269	0.8918	1.0070
0.9	0.9921	1.1246	1.0245	0.9110	1.0049
0.92	0.9951	1.0984	1.0212	0.9297	1.0031
0.94	0.9973	1.0728	1.0170	0.9480	1.0017
0.96	0.9988	1.0479	1.0121	0.9658	1.0008
0.98	0.9997	1.0236	1.0064	0.9831	1.0002
1.0	1.0000	1.0000	1.0000	1.0000	1.0000
1.02	0.9997	0.9770	0.9930	1.0164	1.0002
1.04	0.9989	0.9546	0.9855	1.0325	1.0008
1.06	0.9977	0.9327	0.9776	1.0480	1.0017
1.08	0.9960	0.9115	0.9691	1.0632	1.0031
1.1	0.9939	0.8909	0.9603	1.0780	1.0049
1.12	0.9915	0.8708	0.9512	1.0923	1.0070
1.14	0.9887	0.8512	0.9417	1.1063	1.0095
1.16	0.9856	0.8322	0.9320	1.1198	1.0124
1.18	0.9823	0.8137	0.9220	1.1330	1.0157
1.2	0.9787	0.7958	0.9118	1.1459	1.0194
1.22	0.9749	0.7783	0.9015	1.1584	1.0235
1.24	0.9709	0.7613	0.8911	1.1705	1.0279
1.26	0.9668	0.7447	0.8805	1.1823	1.0328
1.28	0.9624	0.7287	0.8699	1.1938	1.0380
1.3	0.9580	0.7130	0.8592	1.2050	1.0437
1.32	0.9534	0.6978	0.8484	1.2159	1.0497
1.34	0.9487	0.6830	0.8377	1.2264	1.0561
1.36	0.9440	0.6686	0.8269	1.2367	1.0629
1.38	0.9391	0.6546	0.8161	1.2467	1.0701
1.4	0.9343	0.6410	0.8054	1.2564	1.0777
1.42	0.9293	0.6278	0.7947	1.2659	1.0856
1.44	0.9243	0.6149	0.7840	1.2751	1.0940
1.46	0.9193	0.6024	0.7735	1.2840	1.1028
1.48	0.9143	0.5902	0.7629	1.2927	1.1120
1.5	0.9093	0.5783	0.7525	1.3012	1.1215
1.52	0.9042	0.5668	0.7422	1.3095	1.1315
1.54	0.8992	0.5555	0.7319	1.3175	1.1419
1.56	0.8942	0.5446	0.7217	1.3253	1.1527
1.58	0.8892	0.5339	0.7117	1.3329	1.1640
1.6	0.8842	0.5236	0.7017	1.3403	1.1756
1.62	0.8792	0.5135	0.6919	1.3475	1.1877
1.64	0.8743	0.5036	0.6822	1.3546	1.2002
1.66	0.8694	0.4940	0.6726	1.3614	1.2131
1.68	0.8645	0.4847	0.6631	1.3681	1.2264

Table B.4 (*Cont.*) Frictionless Duct Flow with Heat Transfer for $k = 1.4$

Ma	T_0/T_0^*	p/p^*	T/T^*	$\rho^*/\rho = V/V^*$	p_0/p_0^*
1.7	0.8597	0.4756	0.6538	1.3746	1.2402
1.72	0.8549	0.4668	0.6445	1.3809	1.2545
1.74	0.8502	0.4581	0.6355	1.3870	1.2692
1.76	0.8455	0.4497	0.6265	1.3931	1.2843
1.78	0.8409	0.4415	0.6176	1.3989	1.2999
1.8	0.8363	0.4335	0.6089	1.4046	1.3159
1.82	0.8317	0.4257	0.6004	1.4102	1.3324
1.84	0.8273	0.4181	0.5919	1.4156	1.3494
1.86	0.8228	0.4107	0.5836	1.4209	1.3669
1.88	0.8185	0.4035	0.5754	1.4261	1.3849
1.9	0.8141	0.3964	0.5673	1.4311	1.4033
1.92	0.8099	0.3895	0.5594	1.4360	1.4222
1.94	0.8057	0.3828	0.5516	1.4408	1.4417
1.96	0.8015	0.3763	0.5439	1.4455	1.4616
1.98	0.7974	0.3699	0.5364	1.4501	1.4821
2.0	0.7934	0.3636	0.5289	1.4545	1.5031
2.02	0.7894	0.3575	0.5216	1.4589	1.5246
2.04	0.7855	0.3516	0.5144	1.4632	1.5467
2.06	0.7816	0.3458	0.5074	1.4673	1.5693
2.08	0.7778	0.3401	0.5004	1.4714	1.5924
2.1	0.7741	0.3345	0.4936	1.4753	1.6162
2.12	0.7704	0.3291	0.4868	1.4792	1.6404
2.14	0.7667	0.3238	0.4802	1.4830	1.6653
2.16	0.7631	0.3186	0.4737	1.4867	1.6908
2.18	0.7596	0.3136	0.4673	1.4903	1.7168
2.2	0.7561	0.3086	0.4611	1.4938	1.7434
2.22	0.7527	0.3038	0.4549	1.4973	1.7707
2.24	0.7493	0.2991	0.4488	1.5007	1.7986
2.26	0.7460	0.2945	0.4428	1.5040	1.8271
2.28	0.7428	0.2899	0.4370	1.5072	1.8562
2.3	0.7395	0.2855	0.4312	1.5104	1.8860
2.32	0.7364	0.2812	0.4256	1.5134	1.9165
2.34	0.7333	0.2769	0.4200	1.5165	1.9476
2.36	0.7302	0.2728	0.4145	1.5194	1.9794
2.38	0.7272	0.2688	0.4091	1.5223	2.0119
2.4	0.7242	0.2648	0.4038	1.5252	2.0451
2.42	0.7213	0.2609	0.3986	1.5279	2.0789
2.44	0.7184	0.2571	0.3935	1.5306	2.1136
2.46	0.7156	0.2534	0.3885	1.5333	2.1489
2.48	0.7128	0.2497	0.3836	1.5359	2.1850
2.5	0.7101	0.2462	0.3787	1.5385	2.2218
2.52	0.7074	0.2427	0.3739	1.5410	2.2594
2.54	0.7047	0.2392	0.3692	1.5434	2.2978
2.56	0.7021	0.2359	0.3646	1.5458	2.3370
2.58	0.6995	0.2326	0.3601	1.5482	2.3770
2.6	0.6970	0.2294	0.3556	1.5505	2.4177
2.62	0.6945	0.2262	0.3512	1.5527	2.4593
2.64	0.6921	0.2231	0.3469	1.5549	2.5018
2.66	0.6896	0.2201	0.3427	1.5571	2.5451
2.68	0.6873	0.2171	0.3385	1.5592	2.5892
2.7	0.6849	0.2142	0.3344	1.5613	2.6343
2.72	0.6826	0.2113	0.3304	1.5634	2.6802
2.74	0.6804	0.2085	0.3264	1.5654	2.7270
2.76	0.6781	0.2058	0.3225	1.5673	2.7748

Table B.4 (*Cont.*)

Ma	T_0/T_0^*	p/p^*	T/T^*	$\rho^*/\rho = V/V^*$	p_0/p_0^*
2.78	0.6761	0.2030	0.3186	1.5693	2.8235
2.8	0.6738	0.2004	0.3149	1.5711	2.8731
2.82	0.6717	0.1978	0.3111	1.5730	2.9237
2.84	0.6696	0.1953	0.3075	1.5748	2.9752
2.86	0.6675	0.1927	0.3039	1.5766	3.0278
2.88	0.6655	0.1903	0.3004	1.5784	3.0813
2.9	0.6635	0.1879	0.2969	1.5801	3.1359
2.92	0.6615	0.1855	0.2934	1.5818	3.1914
2.94	0.6596	0.1832	0.2901	1.5834	3.2481
2.96	0.6577	0.1809	0.2868	1.5851	3.3058
2.98	0.6558	0.1787	0.2835	1.5867	3.3646
3.0	0.6540	0.1765	0.2803	1.5882	3.4245
3.02	0.6522	0.1743	0.2771	1.5898	3.4854
3.04	0.6504	0.1722	0.2740	1.5913	3.5476
3.06	0.6486	0.1701	0.2709	1.5928	3.6108
3.08	0.6469	0.1681	0.2679	1.5942	3.6752
3.1	0.6452	0.1660	0.2650	1.5957	3.7408
3.12	0.6435	0.1641	0.2620	1.5971	3.8076
3.14	0.6418	0.1621	0.2592	1.5985	3.8756
3.16	0.6402	0.1602	0.2563	1.5998	3.9449
3.18	0.6386	0.1583	0.2535	1.6012	4.0154
3.2	0.6370	0.1565	0.2508	1.6025	4.0871
3.22	0.6354	0.1547	0.2481	1.6038	4.1602
3.24	0.6339	0.1529	0.2454	1.6051	4.2345
3.26	0.6324	0.1511	0.2428	1.6063	4.3101
3.28	0.6309	0.1494	0.2402	1.6076	4.3871
3.3	0.6294	0.1477	0.2377	1.6088	4.4655
3.32	0.6280	0.1461	0.2352	1.6100	4.5452
3.34	0.6265	0.1444	0.2327	1.6111	4.6263
3.36	0.6251	0.1428	0.2303	1.6123	4.7089
3.38	0.6237	0.1412	0.2279	1.6134	4.7929
3.4	0.6224	0.1397	0.2255	1.6145	4.8783
3.42	0.6210	0.1381	0.2232	1.6156	4.9652
3.44	0.6197	0.1366	0.2209	1.6167	5.0536
3.46	0.6184	0.1351	0.2186	1.6178	5.1435
3.48	0.6171	0.1337	0.2164	1.6188	5.2350
3.5	0.6158	0.1322	0.2142	1.6198	5.3280
3.52	0.6145	0.1308	0.2120	1.6208	5.4226
3.54	0.6133	0.1294	0.2099	1.6218	5.5188
3.56	0.6121	0.1280	0.2078	1.6228	5.6167
3.58	0.6109	0.1267	0.2057	1.6238	5.7162
3.6	0.6097	0.1254	0.2037	1.6247	5.8173
3.62	0.6085	0.1241	0.2017	1.6257	5.9201
3.64	0.6074	0.1228	0.1997	1.6266	6.0247
3.66	0.6062	0.1215	0.1977	1.6275	6.1310
3.68	0.6051	0.1202	0.1958	1.6284	6.2390
3.7	0.6040	0.1190	0.1939	1.6293	6.3488
3.72	0.6029	0.1178	0.1920	1.6301	6.4605
3.74	0.6018	0.1166	0.1902	1.6310	6.5739
3.76	0.6008	0.1154	0.1884	1.6318	6.6893
3.78	0.5997	0.1143	0.1866	1.6327	6.8065
3.8	0.5987	0.1131	0.1848	1.6335	6.9256
3.82	0.5977	0.1120	0.1830	1.6343	7.0466
3.84	0.5967	0.1109	0.1813	1.6351	7.1696

Table B.4 (*Cont.*) Frictionless Duct Flow with Heat Transfer for $k = 1.4$

Ma	T_0/T_0^*	p/p^*	T/T^*	$\rho^*/\rho = V/V^*$	p_0/p_0^*
3.86	0.5957	0.1098	0.1796	1.6359	7.2945
3.88	0.5947	0.1087	0.1779	1.6366	7.4215
3.9	0.5937	0.1077	0.1763	1.6374	7.5505
3.92	0.5928	0.1066	0.1746	1.6381	7.6816
3.94	0.5918	0.1056	0.1730	1.6389	7.8147
3.96	0.5909	0.1046	0.1714	1.6396	7.9499
3.98	0.5900	0.1036	0.1699	1.6403	8.0873
4.0	0.5891	0.1026	0.1683	1.6410	8.2269

Table B.5 Prandtl-Meyer Supersonic Expansion Function for $k = 1.4$

Ma	ω, deg	Ma	ω, deg	Ma	ω, deg	Ma	ω, deg
1.00	0.0						
1.05	0.49	3.05	50.71	5.05	77.38	7.05	91.23
1.10	1.34	3.10	51.65	5.10	77.84	7.10	91.49
1.15	2.38	3.15	52.57	5.15	78.29	7.15	91.75
1.20	3.56	3.20	53.47	5.20	78.73	7.20	92.00
1.25	4.83	3.25	54.35	5.25	79.17	7.25	92.24
1.30	6.17	3.30	55.22	5.30	79.60	7.30	92.49
1.35	7.56	3.35	56.07	5.35	80.02	7.35	92.73
1.40	8.99	3.40	56.91	5.40	80.43	7.40	92.97
1.45	10.44	3.45	57.73	5.45	80.84	7.45	93.21
1.50	11.91	3.50	58.53	5.50	81.24	7.50	93.44
1.55	13.38	3.55	59.32	5.55	81.64	7.55	93.67
1.60	14.86	3.60	60.09	5.60	82.03	7.60	93.90
1.65	16.34	3.65	60.85	5.65	82.42	7.65	94.12
1.70	17.81	3.70	61.60	5.70	82.80	7.70	94.34
1.75	19.27	3.75	62.33	5.75	83.17	7.75	94.56
1.80	20.73	3.80	63.04	5.80	83.54	7.80	94.78
1.85	22.16	3.85	63.75	5.85	83.90	7.85	95.00
1.90	23.59	3.90	64.44	5.90	84.26	7.90	95.21
1.95	24.99	3.95	65.12	5.95	84.61	7.95	95.42
2.00	26.38	4.00	65.78	6.00	84.96	8.00	95.62
2.05	27.75	4.05	66.44	6.05	85.30	8.05	95.83
2.10	29.10	4.10	67.08	6.10	85.63	8.10	96.03
2.15	30.43	4.15	67.71	6.15	85.97	8.15	96.23
2.20	31.73	4.20	68.33	6.20	86.29	8.20	96.43
2.25	33.02	4.25	68.94	6.25	86.62	8.25	96.63
2.30	34.28	4.30	69.54	6.30	86.94	8.30	96.82
2.35	35.53	4.35	70.13	6.35	87.25	8.35	97.01
2.40	36.75	4.40	70.71	6.40	87.56	8.40	97.20
2.45	37.95	4.45	71.27	6.45	87.87	8.45	97.39
2.50	39.12	4.50	71.83	6.50	88.17	8.50	97.57
2.55	40.28	4.55	72.38	6.55	88.47	8.55	97.76
2.60	41.41	4.60	72.92	6.60	88.76	8.60	97.94
2.65	42.53	4.65	73.45	6.65	89.05	8.65	98.12
2.70	43.62	4.70	73.97	6.70	89.33	8.70	98.29
2.75	44.69	4.75	74.48	6.75	89.62	8.75	98.47
2.80	45.75	4.80	74.99	6.80	89.90	8.80	98.64
2.85	46.78	4.85	75.48	6.85	90.17	8.85	98.81
2.90	47.79	4.90	75.97	6.90	90.44	8.90	98.98
2.95	48.78	4.95	76.45	6.95	90.71	8.95	99.15
3.00	49.76	5.00	76.92	7.00	90.97	9.00	99.32

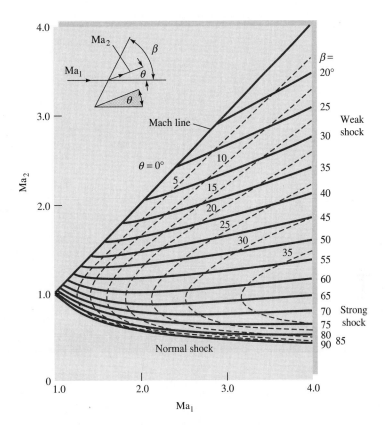

Fig. B.1 Mach number downstream of an oblique shock for $k = 1.4$.

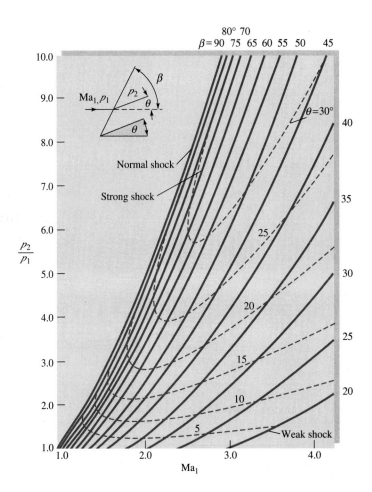

Fig. B.2 Pressure ratio downstream of an oblique shock for $k = 1.4$.

Appendix C
Films and Videotapes on Fluid Mechanics

A comprehensive collection of fluid mechanics films is held by the Engineering Societies Library, United Engineering Center, 345 East 47th Street, New York, NY 10017, phone (212) 705-7605, Fax (212) 486-1086. The original list of these films was published on pp. 151–155 of the June 1976 issue of the *Journal of Fluids Engineering*. Since then, new additions on fluid-mechanics topics have been rather disappointingly few.

The following 22 films, produced by the National Committee for Fluid Mechanics Films,[1] are available for rental from the Engineering Societies Library and can also be purchased, in VHS videotape form, from Encyclopaedia Britannica Educational Corporation, 310 South Michigan Ave., Chicago, IL 60604-9839.

1. The Fluid Dynamics of Drag (119 min in four parts)
2. Vorticity (44 min in two parts)
3. Flow Visualization (31 min)
4. Deformation of Continuous Media (38 min)
5. Pressure Fields and Fluid Acceleration (30 min)
6. Surface Tension in Fluid Mechanics (29 min)
7. Waves in Fluids (33 min)
8. Secondary Flow (30 min)
9. Boundary Layer Control (25 min)
10. Channel Flow of a Compressible Fluid (29 min)
11. Low Reynolds Number Flows (33 min)
12. Flow Instabilities (27 min)
13. Cavitation (27 min)
14. Fundamentals of Boundary Layers (24 min)
15. Turbulence (29 min)
16. Eulerian and Lagrangian Descriptions in Fluid Mechanics (27 min)
17. Rheological Behavior of Fluids (22 min)
18. Rotating Flows (29 min)
19. Stratified Flow (26 min)
20. Magnetohydrodynamics (27 min)
21. Rarefied Gas Dynamics (33 min)
22. Aerodynamic Generation of Sound (44 min)

[1] These films are very well described in the book *Illustrated Experiments in Fluid Mechanics*, M.I.T. Press, Cambridge, Mass., 1972.

University of Iowa, The Audiovisual Center, C4 Seashore Hall, Iowa City, IA 52240:

23. Introduction to the Study of Fluid Motion (25 min)
24. Fundamental Principles of Flow (23 min)
25. Fluid Motion in a Gravitational Field (24 min)
26. Characteristics of Laminar and Turbulent Flow (26 min)
27. Form, Drag, Lift, and Propulsion (24 min)
28. Effects of Fluid Compressibility (17 min)

American Institute of Aeronautics and Astronautics, 370 L'Enfant Promenade, S.W., Washington, DC 20024-2518:

29. America's Wings (29 min)

St. Anthony Falls Hydraulic Laboratory, Mississippi River at 3d Avenue S.E., Minneapolis, MN 55414:

30. Hydraulic Model Studies (20 min)
31. Some Phenomena of Open Channel Flow (33 min)
32. Flow in Culverts (20 min)
33. Spillway Design, Guayabo Dam, El Salvador (15 min)
34. Surface Waves (24 min)

U.S. Army Engineers Waterways Experiment Station, P.O. Box 631, Vicksburg, MS 39180:

35. Speaking of Models (20 min)

NASA Lewis Research Center, Photographic and Printing Branch, Mail Stop 5-2, 21000 Brookpark Road, Cleveland OH 44135:

36. Vorticity Amplification in Stagnation Flow about a Circular Cylinder (12 min)
37. Flow Visualization in Experimental Combustion Chambers (8 min)
38. Laser Doppler Velocimetry (13 min)
39. Spinning Water Waves in a Circular Pool (5 min)
40. Stability of Cylindrical Bubbles in a Vertical Pipe (9 min)
41. Visual Observations of Flow through a Radial-Bladed Centrifugal Impeller (22 min)
42. Some Visual Observations of Cavitation in Rotating Machinery (17 min)
43. Hydrodynamic Seals (14 min)
44. Compressor Flow Patterns Observed with a Hot-Wire Anemometer (11 min)
45. Smoke Study of Nozzle Secondary Flows in a Low-Speed Turbine (20 min)
46. Computer-Generated Flow-Visualization Motion Pictures (12 min)

The Shell Film Library is now closed. Many colleges own the following five color movies about compressible flow, which are highly recommended for students:

47. Approaching the Speed of Sound (27 min)
48. Transonic Flight (20 min)
49. Beyond the Speed of Sound (19 min)
50. Schlieren (20 min)
51. High Speed Flight (20 min)

Appendix D
Conversion Factors

During this period of transition there is a constant need for conversions between BG and SI units (see Table 1.2). Some additional conversions are given here. Conversion factors are given inside the front and back covers.

Length	Volume
1 ft = 12 in = 0.3048 m 1 mi = 5280 ft = 1609.344 m 1 nautical mile (nmi) = 6076 ft = 1852 m 1 yd = 3 ft	1 ft^3 = 0.028317 m^3 1 U.S. gal = 231 in^3 = 0.0037854 m^3 1 L = 0.001 m^3 = 0.035315 ft^3

Mass	Area
1 slug = 32.174 lbm = 14.594 kg 1 lbm = 0.4536 kg	1 ft^2 = 0.092903 m^2 1 mi^2 = 2.78784 E7 ft^2 = 2.59 E6 m^2 1 acre = 43,560 ft^2 = 4046.9 m^2

Velocity	Acceleration
1 ft/s = 0.3048 m/s 1 mi/h = 1.466666 ft/s = 0.44704 m/s 1 kn = 1 nmi/h = 1.6878 ft/s = 0.5144 m/s	1 ft/s^2 = 0.3048 m/s^2

Mass flow	Volume flow
1 slug/s = 14.594 kg/s 1 lbm/s = 0.4536 kg/s	1 gal/min = 0.002228 ft^3/s = 0.06309 L/s 1 × 10^6 gal/day = 1.5472 ft^3/s = 0.04381 m^3/s

Pressure	Force
1 lbf/ft^2 = 47.88 Pa 1 lbf/in^2 = 144 lbf/ft^2 = 6895 Pa 1 atm = 2116.2 lbf/ft^2 = 14.696 lbf/in^2 = 101,325 Pa	1 lbf = 4.448222 N = 16 oz 1 kgf = 2.2046 lbf = 9.80665 N 1 U.S. (short) ton = 2000 lbf

Energy	Power
1 ft · lbf = 1.35582 J 1 Btu = 252 cal = 1055.056 J = 778.17 ft · lbf	1 hp = 550 ft · lbf/s = 745.7 W 1 ft · lbf/s = 1.3558 W

Specific weight	Density
1 lbf/ft^3 = 157.09 N/m^3	1 slug/ft^3 = 515.38 kg/m^3 1 lbm/ft^3 = 16.0185 kg/m^3

Viscosity	Kinematic viscosity
1 slug/(ft · s) = 47.88 kg/(m · s) 1 poise (P) = 1 g/(cm · s) = 0.1 kg/(m · s)	1 ft²/h = 0.000025806 m²/s 1 stokes (St) = 1 cm²/s = 0.0001 m²/s

Temperature scale readings

$$T_F = \tfrac{9}{5}T_C + 32 \qquad T_C = \tfrac{5}{9}(T_F - 32) \qquad T_R = T_F + 459.69 \qquad T_K = T_C + 273.16$$

where subscripts F, C, R, and K refer to readings on the Fahrenheit, Celsius, Kelvin, and Rankine scales, respectively

Specific heat or gas constant*	Thermal conductivity*
1 ft · lbf/(slug · °R) = 0.16723 N · m/(kg · K) 1 Btu/(lb · °R) = 4186.8 J/(kg · K)	1 Btu/(h · ft · °R) = 1.7307 W/(m · K)

* Although the absolute (Kelvin) and Celsius temperature scales have different starting points, the intervals are the same size: 1 kelvin = 1 Celsius degree. The same holds true for the nonmetric absolute (Rankine) and Fahrenheit scales: 1 Rankine degree = 1 Fahrenheit degree. It is customary to express temperature differences in absolute-temperature units.

Appendix E
Equations of Motion in Cylindrical Coordinates

The equations of motion of an incompressible newtonian fluid with constant μ, k, and c_p are given here in cylindrical coordinates (r, θ, z), which are related to cartesian coordinates (x, y, z) as in Fig. 4.2:

$$x = r \cos \theta \qquad y = r \sin \theta \qquad z = z \tag{E.1}$$

The velocity components are v_r, v_θ, and v_z. The equations are:

Continuity:

$$\frac{1}{r}\frac{\partial}{\partial r}(rv_r) + \frac{1}{r}\frac{\partial}{\partial \theta}(v_\theta) + \frac{\partial}{\partial z}(v_z) = 0 \tag{E.2}$$

Convective time derivative:

$$\mathbf{V} \cdot \mathbf{\nabla} = v_r \frac{\partial}{\partial r} + \frac{1}{r} v_\theta \frac{\partial}{\partial \theta} + v_z \frac{\partial}{\partial z} \tag{E.3}$$

Laplacian operator:

$$\nabla^2 = \frac{1}{r}\frac{\partial}{\partial r}\left(r\frac{\partial}{\partial r}\right) + \frac{1}{r^2}\frac{\partial^2}{\partial \theta^2} + \frac{\partial^2}{\partial z^2} \tag{E.4}$$

The r-momentum equation:

$$\frac{\partial v_r}{\partial t} + (\mathbf{V} \cdot \mathbf{\nabla})v_r - \frac{1}{r}v_\theta^2 = -\frac{1}{\rho}\frac{\partial p}{\partial r} + g_r + \nu\left(\nabla^2 v_r - \frac{v_r}{r^2} - \frac{2}{r^2}\frac{\partial v_\theta}{\partial \theta}\right) \tag{E.5}$$

The θ-momentum equation:

$$\frac{\partial v_\theta}{\partial t} + (\mathbf{V} \cdot \mathbf{\nabla})v_\theta + \frac{1}{r}v_r v_\theta = -\frac{1}{\rho r}\frac{\partial p}{\partial \theta} + g_\theta + \nu\left(\nabla^2 v_\theta - \frac{v_\theta}{r^2} + \frac{2}{r^2}\frac{\partial v_r}{\partial \theta}\right) \tag{E.6}$$

The z-momentum equation:

$$\frac{\partial v_z}{\partial t} + (\mathbf{V} \cdot \mathbf{\nabla})v_z = -\frac{1}{\rho}\frac{\partial p}{\partial z} + g_z + \nu\nabla^2 v_z \tag{E.7}$$

The energy equation:

$$\rho c_p \left[\frac{\partial T}{\partial t} + (\mathbf{V} \cdot \nabla)T \right] = k\nabla^2 T + \mu[2(\epsilon_{rr}^2 + \epsilon_{\theta\theta}^2 + \epsilon_{zz}^2) + \epsilon_{\theta z}^2 + \epsilon_{rz}^2 + \epsilon_{r\theta}^2] \quad \text{(E.8)}$$

where

$$\epsilon_{rr} = \frac{\partial v_r}{\partial r} \qquad \epsilon_{\theta\theta} = \frac{1}{r}\left(\frac{\partial v_\theta}{\partial \theta} + v_r \right)$$

$$\epsilon_{zz} = \frac{\partial v_z}{\partial z} \qquad \epsilon_{\theta z} = \frac{1}{r}\frac{\partial v_z}{\partial \theta} + \frac{\partial v_\theta}{\partial z} \qquad \text{(E.9)}$$

$$\epsilon_{rz} = \frac{\partial v_r}{\partial z} + \frac{\partial v_z}{\partial r} \qquad \epsilon_{r\theta} = \frac{1}{r}\left(\frac{\partial v_r}{\partial \theta} - v_\theta \right) + \frac{\partial v_\theta}{\partial r}$$

Angular-velocity components:

$$\omega_r = \frac{1}{r}\frac{\partial v_z}{\partial \theta} - \frac{\partial v_\theta}{\partial z}$$

$$\omega_\theta = \frac{\partial v_r}{\partial z} - \frac{\partial v_z}{\partial r} \qquad \text{(E.10)}$$

$$\omega_z = \frac{1}{r}\frac{\partial}{\partial r}(rv_\theta) - \frac{1}{r}\frac{\partial v_r}{\partial \theta}$$

Index